# GEOMETRY FORMULAS

$A$ = area, $S$ = lateral surface area, $V$ = volume, $h$ = height, $B$ = area of base, $r$ = radius, $l$ = slant height, $C$ = circumference, $s$ = arc length

| Parallelogram | Triangle | Trapezoid | Circle | Sector |
|---|---|---|---|---|
| $A = bh$ | $A = \frac{1}{2}bh$ | $A = \frac{1}{2}(a+b)h$ | $A = \pi r^2,\ C = 2\pi r$ | $A = \frac{1}{2}r^2\theta,\ s = r\theta$ ($\theta$ in radians) |

| Right Circular Cylinder | Right Circular Cone | Any Cylinder or Prism with Parallel Bases | Sphere |
|---|---|---|---|
| $V = \pi r^2 h,\ S = 2\pi rh$ | $V = \frac{1}{3}\pi r^2 h,\ S = \pi rl$ | $V = Bh$ | $V = \frac{4}{3}\pi r^3,\ S = 4\pi r^2$ |

# ALGEBRA FORMULAS

| THE QUADRATIC FORMULA | THE BINOMIAL FORMULA |
|---|---|
| The solutions of the quadratic equation $ax^2 + bx + c = 0$ are $$x = \frac{-b \pm \sqrt{b^2 - 4ac}}{2a}$$ | $$(x+y)^n = x^n + nx^{n-1}y + \frac{n(n-1)}{1\cdot 2}x^{n-2}y^2 + \frac{n(n-1)(n-2)}{1\cdot 2\cdot 3}x^{n-3}y^3 + \cdots + nxy^{n-1} + y^n$$ $$(x-y)^n = x^n - nx^{n-1}y + \frac{n(n-1)}{1\cdot 2}x^{n-2}y^2 - \frac{n(n-1)(n-2)}{1\cdot 2\cdot 3}x^{n-3}y^3 + \cdots \pm nxy^{n-1} \mp y^n$$ |

# TABLE OF INTEGRALS

## BASIC FUNCTIONS

1. $\displaystyle\int u^n\, du = \frac{u^{n+1}}{n+1} + C$

2. $\displaystyle\int \frac{du}{u} = \ln|u| + C$

3. $\displaystyle\int e^u\, du = e^u + C$

4. $\displaystyle\int \sin u\, du = -\cos u + C$

5. $\displaystyle\int \cos u\, du = \sin u + C$

6. $\displaystyle\int \tan u\, du = \ln|\sec u| + C$

7. $\displaystyle\int \sin^{-1} u\, du = u\sin^{-1}u + \sqrt{1-u^2} + C$

8. $\displaystyle\int \cos^{-1} u\, du = u\cos^{-1}u - \sqrt{1-u^2} + C$

9. $\displaystyle\int \tan^{-1} u\, du = u\tan^{-1}u - \ln\sqrt{1+u^2} + C$

10. $\displaystyle\int a^u\, du = \frac{a^u}{\ln a} + C$

11. $\displaystyle\int \ln u\, du = u\ln u - u + C$

12. $\displaystyle\int \cot u\, du = \ln|\sin u| + C$

13. $\displaystyle\int \sec u\, du = \ln|\sec u + \tan u| + C$
$= \ln\left|\tan\left(\frac{1}{4}\pi + \frac{1}{2}u\right)\right| + C$

14. $\displaystyle\int \csc u\, du = \ln|\csc u - \cot u| + C$
$= \ln\left|\tan\frac{1}{2}u\right| + C$

15. $\displaystyle\int \cot^{-1} u\, du = u\cot^{-1}u + \ln\sqrt{1+u^2} + C$

16. $\displaystyle\int \sec^{-1} u\, du = u\sec^{-1}u - \ln|u + \sqrt{u^2-1}| + C$

17. $\displaystyle\int \csc^{-1} u\, du = u\csc^{-1}u + \ln|u + \sqrt{u^2-1}| + C$

## RECIPROCALS OF BASIC FUNCTIONS

18. $\int \dfrac{1}{1 \pm \sin u}\, du = \tan u \mp \sec u + C$

19. $\int \dfrac{1}{1 \pm \cos u}\, du = -\cot u \pm \csc u + C$

20. $\int \dfrac{1}{1 \pm \tan u}\, du = \frac{1}{2}(u \pm \ln |\cos u \pm \sin u|) + C$

21. $\int \dfrac{1}{\sin u \cos u}\, du = \ln |\tan u| + C$

22. $\int \dfrac{1}{1 \pm \cot u}\, du = \frac{1}{2}(u \mp \ln |\sin u \pm \cos u|) + C$

23. $\int \dfrac{1}{1 \pm \sec u}\, du = u + \cot u \mp \csc u + C$

24. $\int \dfrac{1}{1 \pm \csc u}\, du = u - \tan u \pm \sec u + C$

25. $\int \dfrac{1}{1 \pm e^u}\, du = u - \ln(1 \pm e^u) + C$

## POWERS OF TRIGONOMETRIC FUNCTIONS

26. $\int \sin^2 u\, du = \frac{1}{2}u - \frac{1}{4}\sin 2u + C$

27. $\int \cos^2 u\, du = \frac{1}{2}u + \frac{1}{4}\sin 2u + C$

28. $\int \tan^2 u\, du = \tan u - u + C$

29. $\int \sin^n u\, du = -\dfrac{1}{n}\sin^{n-1} u \cos u + \dfrac{n-1}{n}\int \sin^{n-2} u\, du$

30. $\int \cos^n u\, du = \dfrac{1}{n}\cos^{n-1} u \sin u + \dfrac{n-1}{n}\int \cos^{n-2} u\, du$

31. $\int \tan^n u\, du = \dfrac{1}{n-1}\tan^{n-1} u - \int \tan^{n-2} u\, du$

32. $\int \cot^2 u\, du = -\cot u - u + C$

33. $\int \sec^2 u\, du = \tan u + C$

34. $\int \csc^2 u\, du = -\cot u + C$

35. $\int \cot^n u\, du = -\dfrac{1}{n-1}\cot^{n-1} u - \int \cot^{n-2} u\, du$

36. $\int \sec^n u\, du = \dfrac{1}{n-1}\sec^{n-2} u \tan u + \dfrac{n-2}{n-1}\int \sec^{n-2} u\, du$

37. $\int \csc^n u\, du = -\dfrac{1}{n-1}\csc^{n-2} u \cot u + \dfrac{n-2}{n-1}\int \csc^{n-2} u\, du$

## PRODUCTS OF TRIGONOMETRIC FUNCTIONS

38. $\int \sin mu \sin nu\, du = -\dfrac{\sin(m+n)u}{2(m+n)} + \dfrac{\sin(m-n)u}{2(m-n)} + C$

39. $\int \cos mu \cos nu\, du = \dfrac{\sin(m+n)u}{2(m+n)} + \dfrac{\sin(m-n)u}{2(m-n)} + C$

40. $\int \sin mu \cos nu\, du = -\dfrac{\cos(m+n)u}{2(m+n)} - \dfrac{\cos(m-n)u}{2(m-n)} + C$

41. $\int \sin^m u \cos^n u\, du = -\dfrac{\sin^{m-1} u \cos^{n+1} u}{m+n} + \dfrac{m-1}{m+n}\int \sin^{m-2} u \cos^n u\, du$

$\qquad = \dfrac{\sin^{m+1} u \cos^{n-1} u}{m+n} + \dfrac{n-1}{m+n}\int \sin^m u \cos^{n-2} u\, du$

## PRODUCTS OF TRIGONOMETRIC AND EXPONENTIAL FUNCTIONS

42. $\int e^{au} \sin bu\, du = \dfrac{e^{au}}{a^2 + b^2}(a \sin bu - b \cos bu) + C$

43. $\int e^{au} \cos bu\, du = \dfrac{e^{au}}{a^2 + b^2}(a \cos bu + b \sin bu) + C$

## POWERS OF $u$ MULTIPLYING OR DIVIDING BASIC FUNCTIONS

44. $\int u \sin u\, du = \sin u - u \cos u + C$

45. $\int u \cos u\, du = \cos u + u \sin u + C$

46. $\int u^2 \sin u\, du = 2u \sin u + (2 - u^2) \cos u + C$

47. $\int u^2 \cos u\, du = 2u \cos u + (u^2 - 2) \sin u + C$

48. $\int u^n \sin u\, du = -u^n \cos u + n \int u^{n-1} \cos u\, du$

49. $\int u^n \cos u\, du = u^n \sin u - n \int u^{n-1} \sin u\, du$

50. $\int u^n \ln u\, du = \dfrac{u^{n+1}}{(n+1)^2}[(n+1)\ln u - 1] + C$

51. $\int u e^u\, du = e^u(u - 1) + C$

52. $\int u^n e^u\, du = u^n e^u - n \int u^{n-1} e^u\, du$

53. $\int u^n a^u\, du = \dfrac{u^n a^u}{\ln a} - \dfrac{n}{\ln a} \int u^{n-1} a^u\, du + C$

54. $\int \dfrac{e^u\, du}{u^n} = -\dfrac{e^u}{(n-1)u^{n-1}} + \dfrac{1}{n-1} \int \dfrac{e^u\, du}{u^{n-1}}$

55. $\int \dfrac{a^u\, du}{u^n} = -\dfrac{a^u}{(n-1)u^{n-1}} + \dfrac{\ln a}{n-1} \int \dfrac{a^u\, du}{u^{n-1}}$

56. $\int \dfrac{du}{u \ln u} = \ln |\ln u| + C$

## POLYNOMIALS MULTIPLYING BASIC FUNCTIONS

57. $\int p(u)e^{au}\, du = \dfrac{1}{a}p(u)e^{au} - \dfrac{1}{a^2}p'(u)e^{au} + \dfrac{1}{a^3}p''(u)e^{au} - \cdots$  [signs alternate: $+ - + - \cdots$]

58. $\int p(u) \sin au\, du = -\dfrac{1}{a}p(u) \cos au + \dfrac{1}{a^2}p'(u) \sin au + \dfrac{1}{a^3}p''(u) \cos au - \cdots$  [signs alternate in pairs after first term: $+ + - - + + - - \cdots$]

59. $\int p(u) \cos au\, du = \dfrac{1}{a}p(u) \sin au + \dfrac{1}{a^2}p'(u) \cos au - \dfrac{1}{a^3}p''(u) \sin au - \cdots$  [signs alternate in pairs: $+ + - - + + - - \cdots$]

Calculus provides a way of viewing and analyzing the physical world. As with all mathematics courses, calculus involves equations and formulas. However, if you successfully learn to use all the formulas and solve all of the problems in the text but do not master the underlying *ideas*, you will have missed the most important part of calculus. If you master these ideas, you will have a widely applicable tool that goes far beyond textbook exercises.

Before starting your studies, you may find it helpful to leaf through this text to get a general feeling for its different parts:

■ The opening page of each chapter gives you an overview of what that chapter is about, and the opening page of each section within a chapter gives you an overview of what that section is about. To help you locate specific information, sections are subdivided into topics that are marked with a box like this ■.

■ Each section ends with a set of exercises. The answers to most odd-numbered exercises appear in the back of the book. If you find that your answer to an exercise does not match that in the back of the book, do not assume immediately that yours is incorrect—there may be more than one way to express the answer. For example, if your answer is $\sqrt{2}/2$ and the text answer is $1/\sqrt{2}$, then both are correct since your answer can be obtained by "rationalizing" the text answer. In general, if your answer does not match that in the text, then your best first step is to look for an algebraic manipulation or a trigonometric identity that might help you determine if the two answers are equivalent. If the answer is in the form of a decimal approximation, then your answer might differ from that in the text because of a difference in the number of decimal places used in the computations.

■ The section exercises include regular exercises and four special categories: *Quick Check*, *Focus on Concepts*, *True/False*, and *Writing*.

• The *Quick Check* exercises are intended to give you quick feedback on whether you understand the key ideas in the section; they involve relatively little computation, and have answers provided at the end of the exercise set.

• The *Focus on Concepts* exercises, as their name suggests, key in on the main ideas in the section.

• *True/False* exercises focus on key ideas in a different way. You must decide whether the statement is true in *all possible circumstances*, in which case you would declare it to be "true," or whether there are some circumstances in which it is not true, in which case you would declare it to be "false." In each such exercise you are asked to "Explain your answer." You might do this by noting a theorem in the text that shows the statement to be true or

by finding a particular example in which the statement is not true.

• *Writing* exercises are intended to test your ability to explain mathematical ideas in words rather than relying solely on numbers and symbols. All exercises requiring writing should be answered in complete, correctly punctuated logical sentences—not with fragmented phrases and formulas.

■ Each chapter ends with two additional sets of exercises: *Chapter Review Exercises*, which, as the name suggests, is a select set of exercises that provide a review of the main concepts and techniques in the chapter, and *Making Connections*, in which exercises require you to draw on and combine various ideas developed throughout the chapter.

■ Your instructor may choose to incorporate technology in your calculus course. Exercises whose solution involves the use of some kind of technology are tagged with icons to alert you and your instructor. Those exercises tagged with the icon ⌐ require graphing technology—either a graphing calculator or a computer program that can graph equations. Those exercises tagged with the icon ⒸⓇ require a computer algebra system (CAS) such as *Mathematica*, *Maple*, or available on some graphing calculators.

■ At the end of the text you will find a set of four appendices covering various topics such as a detailed review of trigonometry and graphing techniques using technology. Inside the front and back covers of the text you will find endpapers that contain useful formulas.

■ The ideas in this text were created by real people with interesting personalities and backgrounds. Pictures and biographical sketches of many of these people appear throughout the book.

■ Notes in the margin are intended to clarify or comment on important points in the text.

## A Word of Encouragement

As you work your way through this text you will find some ideas that you understand immediately, some that you don't understand until you have read them several times, and others that you do not seem to understand, even after several readings. Do not become discouraged—some ideas are intrinsically difficult and take time to "percolate." You may well find that a hard idea becomes clear later when you least expect it.

## Web Sites for this Text

**www.antontextbooks.com**
**www.wiley.com/go/global/anton**

**www.wileyplus.com**

# WileyPLUS is a research-based online environment for effective teaching and learning.

*WileyPLUS* builds students' confidence because it takes the guesswork out of studying by providing students with a clear roadmap:

- what to do
- how to do it
- if they did it right

It offers interactive resources along with a complete digital textbook that help students learn more. With *WileyPLUS*, students take more initiative so you'll have greater impact on their achievement in the classroom and beyond.

# WILEY PLUS
www.wileyplus.com

# ALL THE HELP, RESOURCES, AND PERSONAL SUPPORT YOU AND YOUR STUDENTS NEED!
## www.wileyplus.com/resources

2-Minute Tutorials and all of the resources you and your students need to get started

Student support from an experienced student user

Collaborate with your colleagues, find a mentor, attend virtual and live events, and view resources
www.WhereFacultyConnect.com

Pre-loaded, ready-to-use assignments and presentations created by subject matter experts

Technical Support 24/7 FAQs, online chat, and phone support
www.wileyplus.com/support

Your WileyPLUS Account Manager, providing personal training and support

**10th**
EDITION

David Henderson/Getty Images

# CALCULUS

## MULTIVARIABLE

■ **HOWARD ANTON** *Drexel University*

■ **IRL BIVENS** *Davidson College*

■ **STEPHEN DAVIS** *Davidson College*

JOHN WILEY & SONS, INC.

WILEY

**Publisher:**  Laurie Rosatone
**Acquisitions Editor:**  David Dietz
**Project Editor:**  Ellen Keohane
**Marketing Manager:**  Debi Doyle
**Senior Product Designer:**  Tom Kulesa
**Operations Manager:**  Melissa Edwards
**Assistant Content Editor:**  Beth Pearson
**Media Assistant Editor:**  Courtney Welsh
**Media Specialist:**  Laura Abrams
**Editorial Assistant:**  Elizabeth Baird, Jacqueline Sinacori
**Full Service Production Management:**  Carol Sawyer/The Perfect Proof
**Senior Production Editor:**  Kerry Weinstein
**Senior Designer:**  Madelyn Lesure
**Photo Editor:**  Sheena Goldstein
**Freelance Illustration:**  Karen Hartpence
**Cover Photo:**  © David Henderson/Getty Images

This book was set in LaTeX by MPS Limited, and printed and bound by R.R. Donnelley/Jefferson City. The cover was printed by R.R. Donnelley.

This book is printed on acid-free paper.

Founded in 1807, John Wiley & Sons, Inc. has been a valued source of knowledge and understanding for more than 200 years, helping people around the world meet their needs and fulfill their aspirations. Our company is built on a foundation of principles that include responsibility to the communities we serve and where we live and work. In 2008, we launched a Corporate Citizenship Initiative, a global effort to address the environmental, social, economic, and ethical challenges we face in our business. Among the issues we are addressing are carbon impact, paper specifications and procurement, ethical conduct within our business and among our vendors, and community and charitable support. For more information, please visit our website: www.wiley.com/go/citizenship.

The paper in this book was manufactured by a mill whose forest management programs include sustained yield harvesting of its timberlands. Sustained yield harvesting principles ensure that the numbers of trees cut each year does not exceed the amount of new growth.

ISBN 978-1-119-93781-4

Printed in the United States of America

10 9 8 7 6 5 4 3 2 1

**About HOWARD ANTON**

Howard Anton obtained his B.A. from Lehigh University, his M.A. from the University of Illinois, and his Ph.D. from the Polytechnic University of Brooklyn, all in mathematics. In the early 1960s he worked for Burroughs Corporation and Avco Corporation at Cape Canaveral, Florida, where he was involved with the manned space program. In 1968 he joined the Mathematics Department at Drexel University, where he taught full time until 1983. Since that time he has been an Emeritus Professor at Drexel and has devoted the majority of his time to textbook writing and activities for mathematical associations. Dr. Anton was president of the EPADEL section of the Mathematical Association of America (MAA), served on the Board of Governors of that organization, and guided the creation of the student chapters of the MAA. He has published numerous research papers in functional analysis, approximation theory, and topology, as well as pedagogical papers. He is best known for his textbooks in mathematics, which are among the most widely used in the world. There are currently more than one hundred versions of his books, including translations into Spanish, Arabic, Portuguese, Italian, Indonesian, French, Japanese, Chinese, Hebrew, and German. His textbook in linear algebra has won both the Textbook Excellence Award and the McGuffey Award from the Textbook Author's Association. For relaxation, Dr. Anton enjoys traveling and photography.

**About IRL BIVENS**

Irl C. Bivens, recipient of the George Polya Award and the Merten M. Hasse Prize for Expository Writing in Mathematics, received his A.B. from Pfeiffer College and his Ph.D. from the University of North Carolina at Chapel Hill, both in mathematics. Since 1982, he has taught at Davidson College, where he currently holds the position of professor of mathematics. A typical academic year sees him teaching courses in calculus, topology, and geometry. Dr. Bivens also enjoys mathematical history, and his annual History of Mathematics seminar is a perennial favorite with Davidson mathematics majors. He has published numerous articles on undergraduate mathematics, as well as research papers in his specialty, differential geometry. He has served on the editorial boards of the MAA Problem Book series, the MAA Dolciani Mathematical Expositions series and *The College Mathematics Journal*. When he is not pursuing mathematics, Professor Bivens enjoys reading, juggling, swimming, and walking.

**About STEPHEN DAVIS**

Stephen L. Davis received his B.A. from Lindenwood College and his Ph.D. from Rutgers University in mathematics. Having previously taught at Rutgers University and Ohio State University, Dr. Davis came to Davidson College in 1981, where he is currently a professor of mathematics. He regularly teaches calculus, linear algebra, abstract algebra, and computer science. A sabbatical in 1995–1996 took him to Swarthmore College as a visiting associate professor. Professor Davis has published numerous articles on calculus reform and testing, as well as research papers on finite group theory, his specialty. Professor Davis has held several offices in the Southeastern section of the MAA, including chair and secretary-treasurer and has served on the MAA Board of Governors. He is currently a faculty consultant for the Educational Testing Service for the grading of the Advanced Placement Calculus Exam, webmaster for the North Carolina Association of Advanced Placement Mathematics Teachers, and is actively involved in nurturing mathematically talented high school students through leadership in the Charlotte Mathematics Club. For relaxation, he plays basketball, juggles, and travels. Professor Davis and his wife Elisabeth have three children, Laura, Anne, and James, all former calculus students.

*To*
my wife Pat and my children: Brian, David, and Lauren

*In Memory of*
my mother Shirley
my father Benjamin
my thesis advisor and inspiration, George Bachman
my benefactor in my time of need, Stephen Girard (1750–1831)
*—HA*


*To*
my son Robert
*—IB*


*To*
my wife Elisabeth
my children: Laura, Anne, and James
*—SD*

# PREFACE

This tenth edition of *Calculus* maintains those aspects of previous editions that have led to the series' success—we continue to strive for student comprehension without sacrificing mathematical accuracy, and the exercise sets are carefully constructed to avoid unhappy surprises that can derail a calculus class.

All of the changes to the tenth edition were carefully reviewed by outstanding teachers comprised of both users and nonusers of the previous edition. The charge of this committee was to ensure that all changes did not alter those aspects of the text that attracted users of the ninth edition and at the same time provide freshness to the new edition that would attract new users.

## NEW TO THIS EDITION

- Exercise sets have been modified to correspond more closely to questions in *WileyPLUS*. In addition, more *WileyPLUS* questions now correspond to specific exercises in the text.
- New applied exercises have been added to the book and existing applied exercises have been updated.
- Where appropriate, additional skill/practice exercises were added.

## OTHER FEATURES

**Flexibility**   This edition has a built-in flexibility that is designed to serve a broad spectrum of calculus philosophies—from traditional to "reform." Technology can be emphasized or not, and the order of many topics can be permuted freely to accommodate each instructor's specific needs.

**Rigor**   The challenge of writing a good calculus book is to strike the right balance between rigor and clarity. Our goal is to present precise mathematics to the fullest extent possible in an introductory treatment. Where clarity and rigor conflict, we choose clarity; however, we believe it to be important that the student understand the difference between a careful proof and an informal argument, so we have informed the reader when the arguments being presented are informal or motivational. Theory involving $\epsilon$-$\delta$ arguments appears in separate sections so that they can be covered or not, as preferred by the instructor.

**Rule of Four**   The "rule of four" refers to presenting concepts from the verbal, algebraic, visual, and numerical points of view. In keeping with current pedagogical philosophy, we used this approach whenever appropriate.

**Visualization**   This edition makes extensive use of modern computer graphics to clarify concepts and to develop the student's ability to visualize mathematical objects, particularly those in 3-space. For those students who are working with graphing technology, there are many exercises that are designed to develop the student's ability to generate and analyze mathematical curves and surfaces.

**Quick Check Exercises**    Each exercise set begins with approximately five exercises (answers included) that are designed to provide students with an immediate assessment of whether they have mastered key ideas from the section. They require a minimum of computation and are answered by filling in the blanks.

**Focus on Concepts Exercises**    Each exercise set contains a clearly identified group of problems that focus on the main ideas of the section.

**Technology Exercises**    Most sections include exercises that are designed to be solved using either a graphing calculator or a computer algebra system such as *Mathematica*, *Maple*, or the open source program *Sage*. These exercises are marked with an icon for easy identification.

**Applicability of Calculus**    One of the primary goals of this text is to link calculus to the real world and the student's own experience. This theme is carried through in the examples and exercises.

**Career Preparation**    This text is written at a mathematical level that will prepare students for a wide variety of careers that require a sound mathematics background, including engineering, the various sciences, and business.

**Trigonometry Review**    Deficiencies in trigonometry plague many students, so we have included a substantial trigonometry review in Appendix B.

**Appendix on Polynomial Equations**    Because many calculus students are weak in solving polynomial equations, we have included an appendix (Appendix C) that reviews the Factor Theorem, the Remainder Theorem, and procedures for finding rational roots.

**Principles of Integral Evaluation**    The traditional Techniques of Integration is entitled "Principles of Integral Evaluation" to reflect its more modern approach to the material. The chapter emphasizes general methods and the role of technology rather than specific tricks for evaluating complicated or obscure integrals.

**Historical Notes**    The biographies and historical notes have been a hallmark of this text from its first edition and have been maintained. All of the biographical materials have been distilled from standard sources with the goal of capturing and bringing to life for the student the personalities of history's greatest mathematicians.

**Margin Notes and Warnings**    These appear in the margins throughout the text to clarify or expand on the text exposition or to alert the reader to some pitfall.

# SUPPLEMENTS

The **Student Solutions Manual**, which is printed in two volumes, provides detailed solutions to the odd-numbered exercises in the text. The structure of the step-by-step solutions matches those of the worked examples in the textbook. The Student Solutions Manual is also provided in digital format to students in *WileyPLUS*.

Volume I (Single-Variable Calculus, Early Transcendentals) ISBN: 978-1-118-17381-7
Volume II (Multivariable Calculus) ISBN: 978-1-118-17383-1

**The Student Study Guide** is available for download from the book companion Web site at www.wiley.com/college/anton or at www.howardanton.com and to users of *WileyPLUS*.

The **Instructor's Solutions Manual** contains detailed solutions to all of the exercises in the text. The Instructor's Solutions Manual is also available in PDF format on the password-protected Instructor Companion Site at www.wiley.com/college/anton or at www.howardanton.com and in *WileyPLUS*.

Calculus, Early Transcendentals ISBN: 978-1-118-17378-7

The **Instructor's Manual** suggests time allocations and teaching plans for each section in the text. Most of the teaching plans contain a bulleted list of key points to emphasize. The discussion of each section concludes with a sample homework assignment. The Instructor's Manual is available in PDF format on the password-protected Instructor Companion Site at www.wiley.com/college/anton or at www.howardanton.com and in *WileyPLUS*.

The **Web Projects (Expanding the Calculus Horizon)** referenced in the text can also be downloaded from the companion Web sites and from *WileyPLUS*.

Instructors can also access the following materials from the book companion site or *WileyPLUS*:

- **Interactive Illustrations** can be used in the classroom or computer lab to present and explore key ideas graphically and dynamically. They are especially useful for display of three-dimensional graphs in multivariable calculus.

- The **Computerized Test Bank** features more than 4000 questions—mostly algorithmically generated—that allow for varied questions and numerical inputs.

- The **Printable Test Bank** features questions and answers for every section of the text.

- **PowerPoint lecture slides** cover the major concepts and themes of each section of the book. Personal-Response System questions ("Clicker Questions") appear at the end of each PowerPoint presentation and provide an easy way to gauge classroom understanding.

- **Additional calculus content** covers analytic geometry in calculus, mathematical modeling with differential equations and parametric equations, as well as an introduction to linear algebra.

## *WileyPLUS*

*WileyPLUS*, Wiley's digital-learning environment, is loaded with all of the supplements listed on the previous page, and also features the following:

- **Homework management tools**, which easily allow you to assign and grade algorithmic questions, as well as gauge student comprehension.

- **Algorithmic** questions with randomized numeric values and an answer-entry palette for symbolic notation are provided online though *WileyPLUS*. Students can click on "help" buttons for hints, link to the relevant section of the text, show their work or query their instructor using a white board, or see a step-by-step solution (depending on instructor-selecting settings).

- **Interactive Illustrations** can be used in the classroom or computer lab, or for student practice.

- **QuickStart** predesigned reading and homework assignments.  Use them as-is or customize them to fit the needs of your classroom.

- The **e-book**, which is an exact version of the print text but also features hyperlinks to questions, definitions, and supplements for quicker and easier support.

- **Guided Online (GO) Tutorial Exercises** that prompt students to build solutions step by step. Rather than simply grading an exercise answer as wrong, GO tutorial problems show students precisely where they are making a mistake.

- **Are You Ready?** quizzes gauge student mastery of chapter concepts and techniques and provide feedback on areas that require further attention.

- **Algebra and Trigonometry Refresher** quizzes provide students with an opportunity to brush up on the material necessary to master calculus, as well as to determine areas that require further review.

*WileyPLUS.* Learn more at www.wileyplus.com.

# ACKNOWLEDGMENTS

It has been our good fortune to have the advice and guidance of many talented people whose knowledge and skills have enhanced this book in many ways. For their valuable help we thank the following people.

## Reviewers of the Tenth Edition

Frederick Adkins, *Indiana University of Pennsylvania*
Gerardo Aladro, *Florida International University*
Mike Albanese, *Central Piedmont Community College*
Faiz Al-Rubaee, *University of North Florida*
Mahboub Baccouch, *University of Nebraska at Omaha*
Jim Brandt, *Southern Utah University*
Elizabeth Brown, *James Madison University*
Michael Brown, *San Diego Mesa College*
Christopher Butler, *Case Western Reserve University*
Nick Bykov, *San Joaquin Delta College*
Jamylle Carter, *Diablo Valley College*
Hongwei Chen, *Christopher Newport University*
David A. Clark, *Randolph-Macon College*
Dominic P. Clemence, *North Carolina Agricultural and Technical State University*
Michael Cohen, *Hofstra University*
Hugh Cornell, *Salt Lake Community College*

Kyle Costello, *Salt Lake Community College*
Walter Czarnec, *Framingham State University*
Michael Daniel, *Drexel University*
Judith Downey, *University of Nebraska, Omaha*
Artur Elezi, *American University*
David James Ellingson, *Napa Valley College*
Elaine B. Fitt, *Bucks County Community College*
Greg Gibson, *North Carolina Agricultural and Technical State University*
Yvonne A. Greenbaun, *Mercer County Community College*
Jerome I. Heaven, *Indiana Tech*
Kathryn Lesh, *Union College*
Eric Matsuoka, *Leeward Community College*
Ted Nirgiotis, *Diablo Valley College*
Mihaela Poplicher, *University of Cincinnati*
Adrian R. Ranic, *Erie Community College–North*
Thomas C. Redd, *North Carolina Agricultural and Technical State University*
R. A. Rock, *Daniel Webster College*

John Paul Roop, *North Carolina Agricultural and Technical State University*
Philippe Rukimbira, *Florida International University*
Dee Dee Shaulis, *University of Colorado at Boulder*
Michael D. Shaw, *Florida Institute of Technology*
Jennifer Siegel, *Broward College–Central Campus*
Thomas W. Simpson, *University of South Carolina Union*
Maria Siopsis, *Maryville College*
Mark A. Smith, *Miami University, Ohio*
Alan Taylor, *Union College*
Kathy Vranicar, *University of Nebraska, Omaha*
Anke Walz, *Kutztown University*
Zhi-Qiang Wang, *Utah State University*
Tom Wells, *Delta College*
Greg Wisloski, *Indiana University of Pennsylvania*

## Reviewers and Contributors to the Ninth Edition

Frederick Adkins, *Indiana University of Pennsylvania*
Bill Allen, *Reedley College-Clovis Center*
Jerry Allison, *Black Hawk College*
Seth Armstrong, *Southern Utah University*
Przemyslaw Bogacki, *Old Dominion University*
David Bradley, *University of Maine*
Wayne P. Britt, *Louisiana State University*
Dean Burbank, *Gulf Coast Community College*
Jason Cantarella, *University of Georgia*
Yanzhao Cao, *Florida A&M University*
Kristin Chatas, *Washtenaw Community College*

Michele Clement, *Louisiana State University*
Ray Collings, *Georgia Perimeter College*
David E. Dobbs, *University of Tennessee, Knoxville*
H. Edward Donley, *Indiana University of Pennsylvania*
T. J. Duda, *Columbus State Community College*
Jim Edmondson, *Santa Barbara City College*
Nancy Eschen, *Florida Community College, Jacksonville*
Reuben Farley, *Virginia Commonwealth University*
Michael Filaseta, *University of South Carolina*

Jose Flores, *University of South Dakota*
Mitch Francis, *Horace Mann*
Berit N. Givens, *California State Polytechnic University, Pomona*
Zhuang-dan Guan, *University of California, Riverside*
Jerome Heaven, *Indiana Tech*
Greg Henderson, *Hillsborough Community College*
Patricia Henry, *Drexel University*
Danrun Huang, *St. Cloud State University*
Alvaro Islas, *University of Central Florida*
Micah James, *University of Illinois*

Bin Jiang, *Portland State University*

Ronald Jorgensen, *Milwaukee School of Engineering*

Mohammad Kazemi, *University of North Carolina, Charlotte*

Raja Khoury, *Collin County Community College*

Przemo Kranz, *University of Mississippi*

Carole King Krueger, *The University of Texas at Arlington*

Steffen Lempp, *University of Wisconsin, Madison*

Thomas Leness, *Florida International University*

Kathryn Lesh, *Union College*

Wen-Xiu Ma, *University of South Florida*

Behailu Mammo, *Hofstra University*

Vania Mascioni, *Ball State University*

John McCuan, *Georgia Tech*

Daryl McGinnis, *Columbus State Community College*

Michael Mears, *Manatee Community College*

John G. Michaels, *SUNY Brockport*

Jason Miner, *Santa Barbara City College*

Darrell Minor, *Columbus State Community College*

Kathleen Miranda, *SUNY Old Westbury*

Carla Monticelli, *Camden County College*

Bryan Mosher, *University of Minnesota*

Ferdinand O. Orock, *Hudson County Community College*

Altay Ozgener, *Manatee Community College*

Chuang Peng, *Morehouse College*

Joni B. Pirnot, *Manatee Community College*

Elise Price, *Tarrant County College*

David Price, *Tarrant County College*

Holly Puterbaugh, *University of Vermont*

Hah Suey Quan, *Golden West College*

Joseph W. Rody, *Arizona State University*

Jan Rychtar, *University of North Carolina, Greensboro*

John T. Saccoman, *Seton Hall University*

Constance Schober, *University of Central Florida*

Kurt Sebastian, *United States Coast Guard*

Paul Seeburger, *Monroe Community College*

Charlotte Simmons, *University of Central Oklahoma*

Don Soash, *Hillsborough Community College*

Bradley Stetson, *Schoolcraft College*

Bryan Stewart, *Tarrant County College*

Walter E. Stone, Jr., *North Shore Community College*

Eleanor Storey, *Front Range Community College, Westminster Campus*

Stefania Tracogna, *Arizona State University*

Helene Tyler, *Manhattan College*

Pavlos Tzermias, *University of Tennessee, Knoxville*

Raja Varatharajah, *North Carolina Agricultural and Technical State University*

Francis J. Vasko, *Kutztown University*

David Voss, *Western Illinois University*

Jim Voss, *Front Range Community College*

Anke Walz, *Kutztown Community College*

Richard Watkins, *Tidewater Community College*

Xian Wu, *University of South Carolina*

Yvonne Yaz, *Milwaukee School of Engineering*

Richard A. Zang, *University of New Hampshire*

Xiao-Dong Zhang, *Florida Atlantic University*

Diane Zych, *Erie Community College*

We would also like to thank Celeste Hernandez and Roger Lipsett for their accuracy check of the tenth edition. Thanks also go to Tamas Wiandt for revising the solutions manuals, and Przemyslaw Bogacki for accuracy checking those solutions; Brian Camp and Lyle Smith for their revision of the Student Study Guide; Jim Hartman for his revision of the Instructor's Manual; Ann Ostberg for revising the PowerPoint slides; Beverly Fusfield for creating new GO Tutorials, and Mark McKibben for accuracy checking these new tutorials. We also appreciate the feedback we received from Mark Dunster, Cecelia Knoll, and Michael Rosenthal on selected *WileyPLUS* problems.

# CONTENTS

**WEB APPENDICES (online only)**

Available for download at www.wiley.com/college/anton or at www.howardanton.com and in *WileyPLUS*.

**A   GRAPHING FUNCTIONS USING CALCULATORS AND COMPUTER ALGEBRA SYSTEMS**

**B   TRIGONOMETRY REVIEW**

**C   SOLVING POLYNOMIAL EQUATIONS**

**D   SELECTED PROOFS**

**E   REAL NUMBERS, INTERVALS, AND INEQUALITIES**

**F   ABSOLUTE VALUE**

**G   COORDINATE PLANES, LINES, AND LINEAR FUNCTIONS**

**H   DISTANCE, CIRCLES, AND QUADRATIC EQUATIONS**

**I   EARLY PARAMETRIC EQUATIONS OPTION**

**J   MATHEMATICAL MODELS**

**WEB PROJECTS: Expanding the Calculus Horizon (online only)**

Available for download at www.wiley.com/college/anton or at www.howardanton.com and in *WileyPLUS*.

# THE ROOTS OF CALCULUS

Today's exciting applications of calculus have roots that can be traced to the work of the Greek mathematician Archimedes, but the actual discovery of the fundamental principles of calculus was made independently by Isaac Newton (English) and Gottfried Leibniz (German) in the late seventeenth century. The work of Newton and Leibniz was motivated by four major classes of scientific and mathematical problems of the time:

- Find the tangent line to a general curve at a given point.

- Find the area of a general region, the length of a general curve, and the volume of a general solid.

- Find the maximum or minimum value of a quantity—for example, the maximum and minimum distances of a planet from the Sun, or the maximum range attainable for a projectile by varying its angle of fire.

- Given a formula for the distance traveled by a body in any specified amount of time, find the velocity and acceleration of the body at any instant. Conversely, given a formula that specifies the acceleration of velocity at any instant, find the distance traveled by the body in a specified period of time.

Newton and Leibniz found a fundamental relationship between the problem of finding a tangent line to a curve and the problem of determining the area of a region. Their realization of this connection is considered to be the "discovery of calculus." Though Newton saw how these two problems are related ten years before Leibniz did, Leibniz published his work twenty years before Newton. This situation led to a stormy debate over who was the rightful discoverer of calculus. The debate engulfed Europe for half a century, with the scientists of the European continent supporting Leibniz and those from England supporting Newton. The conflict was extremely unfortunate because Newton's inferior notation badly hampered scientific development in England, and the Continent in turn lost the benefit of Newton's discoveries in astronomy and physics for nearly fifty years. In spite of it all, Newton and Leibniz were sincere admirers of each other's work.

[Image: Public domain image from http://commons.wikimedia.org/
wiki/File:Hw-newton.jpg. Image provided courtesy of the University
of Texas Libraries, The University of Texas at Austin.]

## ISAAC NEWTON (1642–1727)

Newton was born in the village of Woolsthorpe, England. His father died before he was born and his mother raised him on the family farm. As a youth he showed little evidence of his later brilliance, except for an unusual talent with mechanical devices—he apparently built a working water clock and a toy flour mill powered by a mouse. In 1661 he entered Trinity College in Cambridge with a deficiency in geometry. Fortunately, Newton caught the eye of Isaac Barrow, a gifted mathematician and teacher. Under Barrow's guidance Newton immersed himself in mathematics and science, but he graduated without any special distinction. Because the bubonic plague was spreading rapidly through London, Newton returned to his home in Woolsthorpe and stayed there during the years of 1665 and 1666. In those two momentous years the entire framework of modern science was miraculously created in Newton's mind. He discovered calculus, recognized the underlying principles of planetary motion and gravity, and determined that "white" sunlight was composed of all colors, red to violet. For whatever reasons he kept his discoveries to himself. In 1667 he returned to Cambridge to obtain his Master's degree and upon graduation became a teacher at Trinity. Then in 1669 Newton succeeded his teacher, Isaac Barrow, to the Lucasian chair of mathematics at Trinity, one of the most honored chairs of mathematics in the world.

Thereafter, brilliant discoveries flowed from Newton steadily. He formulated the law of gravitation and used it to explain the motion of the moon, the planets, and the tides; he formulated basic theories of light, thermodynamics, and hydrodynamics; and he devised and constructed the first modern reflecting telescope. Throughout his life Newton was hesitant to publish his major discoveries, revealing them only to a select circle of friends, perhaps because of a fear of criticism or controversy. In 1687, only after intense coaxing by the astronomer, Edmond Halley (discoverer of Halley's comet), did Newton publish his masterpiece, *Philosophiae Naturalis Principia Mathematica* (The Mathematical Principles of Natural Philosophy). This work is generally considered to be the most important and influential scientific book ever written. In it Newton explained the workings of the solar system and formulated the basic laws of motion, which to this day are fundamental in engineering and physics. However, not even the pleas of his friends could convince Newton to publish his discovery of calculus. Only after Leibniz published his results did Newton relent and publish his own work on calculus.

After twenty-five years as a professor, Newton suffered depression and a nervous break-down. He gave up research in 1695 to accept a position as warden and later master of the London mint. During the twenty-five years that he worked at the mint, he did virtually no scientific or mathematical work. He was knighted in 1705 and on his death was buried in Westminster Abbey with all the honors his country could bestow. It is interesting to note that Newton was a learned theologian who viewed the primary value of his work to be its support of the existence of God. Throughout his life he worked passionately to date biblical events by relating them to astronomical phenomena. He was so consumed with this passion that he spent years searching the Book of Daniel for clues to the end of the world and the geography of hell.

Newton described his brilliant accomplishments as follows: "I seem to have been only like a boy playing on the seashore and diverting myself in now and then finding a smoother pebble or prettier shell than ordinary, whilst the great ocean of truth lay all undiscovered before me."

---

[*Image: Public domain image from http://commons.wikimedia.org/wiki/ File:Gottfried_Wilhelm_von_ Leibniz.jpg*]

## GOTTFRIED WILHELM LEIBNIZ (1646–1716)

This gifted genius was one of the last people to have mastered most major fields of knowledge—an impossible accomplishment in our own era of specialization. He was an expert in law, religion, philosophy, literature, politics, geology, metaphysics, alchemy, history, and mathematics.

Leibniz was born in Leipzig, Germany. His father, a professor of moral philosophy at the University of Leipzig, died when Leibniz was six years old. The precocious boy then gained access to his father's library and began reading voraciously on a wide range of subjects, a habit that he maintained throughout his life. At age fifteen he entered the University of Leipzig as a law student and by the age of twenty received a doctorate from the University of Altdorf. Subsequently, Leibniz followed a career in law and international politics, serving as counsel to kings and princes. During his numerous foreign missions, Leibniz came in contact with outstanding mathematicians and scientists who stimulated his interest in mathematics—most notably, the physicist Christian Huygens. In mathematics Leibniz was self-taught, learning the subject by reading papers and journals. As a result of this fragmented mathematical education, Leibniz often rediscovered the results of others, and this helped to fuel the debate over the discovery of calculus.

Leibniz never married. He was moderate in his habits, quick-tempered but easily appeased, and charitable in his judgment of other people's work. In spite of his great achievements, Leibniz never received the honors showered on Newton, and he spent his final years as a lonely embittered man. At his funeral there was one mourner, his secretary. An eyewitness stated, "He was buried more like a robber than what he really was—an ornament of his country."

Craig Aurness/Corbis Images

# 11

# THREE-DIMENSIONAL SPACE; VECTORS

*To describe fully the motion of a boat, one must specify its speed and direction of motion at each instant. Speed and direction together describe a "vector" quantity. We will study vectors in this chapter.*

In this chapter we will discuss rectangular coordinate systems in three dimensions, and we will study the analytic geometry of lines, planes, and other basic surfaces. The second theme of this chapter is the study of vectors. These are the mathematical objects that physicists and engineers use to study forces, displacements, and velocities of objects moving on curved paths. More generally, vectors are used to represent all physical entities that involve both a magnitude and a direction for their complete description. We will introduce various algebraic operations on vectors, and we will apply these operations to problems involving force, work, and rotational tendencies in two and three dimensions. Finally, we will discuss cylindrical and spherical coordinate systems, which are appropriate in problems that involve various kinds of symmetries and also have specific applications in navigation and celestial mechanics.

## 11.1 RECTANGULAR COORDINATES IN 3-SPACE; SPHERES; CYLINDRICAL SURFACES

*In this section we will discuss coordinate systems in three-dimensional space and some basic facts about surfaces in three dimensions.*

### ▦ RECTANGULAR COORDINATE SYSTEMS

In the remainder of this text we will call three-dimensional space *3-space*, two-dimensional space (a plane) *2-space*, and one-dimensional space (a line) *1-space*. Just as points in 2-space can be placed in one-to-one correspondence with pairs of real numbers using two perpendicular coordinate lines, so points in 3-space can be placed in one-to-one correspondence with triples of real numbers by using three mutually perpendicular coordinate lines, called the *x-axis*, the *y-axis*, and the *z-axis*, positioned so that their origins coincide (Figure 11.1.1). The three coordinate axes form a three-dimensional *rectangular coordinate system* (or *Cartesian coordinate system*). The point of intersection of the coordinate axes is called the *origin* of the coordinate system.

Rectangular coordinate systems in 3-space fall into two categories: *left-handed* and *right-handed*. A right-handed system has the property that when the fingers of the right hand are cupped so that they curve from the positive *x*-axis toward the positive *y*-axis, the thumb points (roughly) in the direction of the positive *z*-axis (Figure 11.1.2). A similar

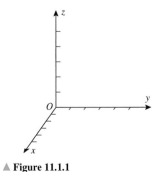

▲ **Figure 11.1.1**

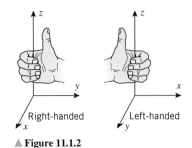

▲ **Figure 11.1.2**

property holds for a left-handed coordinate system (Figure 11.1.2). We will use only right-handed coordinate systems in this text.

The coordinate axes, taken in pairs, determine three ***coordinate planes***: the ***xy-plane***, the ***xz-plane***, and the ***yz-plane*** (Figure 11.1.3). To each point $P$ in 3-space we can assign a triple of real numbers by passing three planes through $P$ parallel to the coordinate planes and letting $a$, $b$, and $c$ be the coordinates of the intersections of those planes with the $x$-axis, $y$-axis, and $z$-axis, respectively (Figure 11.1.4). We call $a$, $b$, and $c$ the ***x-coordinate***, ***y-coordinate***, and ***z-coordinate*** of $P$, respectively, and we denote the point $P$ by $(a, b, c)$ or by $P(a, b, c)$. Figure 11.1.5 shows the points $(4, 5, 6)$ and $(-3, 2, -4)$.

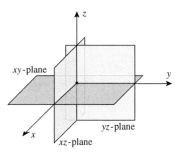

▲ **Figure 11.1.3**

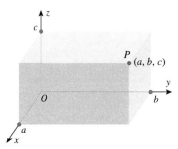

▲ **Figure 11.1.4**

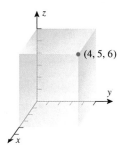

▲ **Figure 11.1.5**

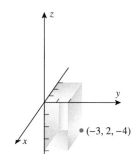

Just as the coordinate axes in a two-dimensional coordinate system divide 2-space into four quadrants, so the coordinate planes of a three-dimensional coordinate system divide 3-space into eight parts, called ***octants***. The set of points with three positive coordinates forms the ***first octant***; the remaining octants have no standard numbering.

You should be able to visualize the following facts about three-dimensional rectangular coordinate systems:

| REGION | DESCRIPTION |
|---|---|
| $xy$-plane | Consists of all points of the form $(x, y, 0)$ |
| $xz$-plane | Consists of all points of the form $(x, 0, z)$ |
| $yz$-plane | Consists of all points of the form $(0, y, z)$ |
| $x$-axis | Consists of all points of the form $(x, 0, 0)$ |
| $y$-axis | Consists of all points of the form $(0, y, 0)$ |
| $z$-axis | Consists of all points of the form $(0, 0, z)$ |

 **DISTANCE IN 3-SPACE; SPHERES**

Recall that in 2-space the distance $d$ between the points $P_1(x_1, y_1)$ and $P_2(x_2, y_2)$ is

$$d = \sqrt{(x_2 - x_1)^2 + (y_2 - y_1)^2} \tag{1}$$

The distance formula in 3-space has the same form, but it has a third term to account for the added dimension. (We will see that this is a common occurrence in extending formulas from 2-space to 3-space.) The distance between the points $P_1(x_1, y_1, z_1)$ and $P_2(x_2, y_2, z_2)$ is

$$d = \sqrt{(x_2 - x_1)^2 + (y_2 - y_1)^2 + (z_2 - z_1)^2} \tag{2}$$

We leave the proof of (2) as an exercise (Exercise 7).

▶ **Example 1**  Find the distance $d$ between the points $(2, 3, -1)$ and $(4, -1, 3)$.

*Solution.*  From Formula (2)

$$d = \sqrt{(4-2)^2 + (-1-3)^2 + (3+1)^2} = \sqrt{36} = 6 \quad \blacktriangleleft$$

In an $xy$-coordinate system, the set of points $(x, y)$ whose coordinates satisfy an equation in $x$ and $y$ is called the *graph* of the equation. Analogously, in an $xyz$-coordinate system, the set of points $(x, y, z)$ whose coordinates satisfy an equation in $x$, $y$, and $z$ is called the *graph* of the equation.

Recall that the standard equation of the circle in 2-space that has center $(x_0, y_0)$ and radius $r$ is

$$(x - x_0)^2 + (y - y_0)^2 = r^2 \tag{3}$$

This follows from distance formula (1) and the fact that the circle consists of all points in 2-space whose distance from $(x_0, y_0)$ is $r$. Analogously, the *standard equation of the sphere* in 3-space that has center $(x_0, y_0, z_0)$ and radius $r$ is

$$(x - x_0)^2 + (y - y_0)^2 + (z - z_0)^2 = r^2 \tag{4}$$

This follows from distance formula (2) and the fact that the sphere consists of all points in 3-space whose distance from $(x_0, y_0, z_0)$ is $r$. Note that (4) has the same form as the standard equation for the circle in 2-space, but with an additional term to account for the third coordinate. Some examples of the standard equation of the sphere are given in the following table:

| EQUATION | GRAPH |
|---|---|
| $(x-3)^2 + (y-2)^2 + (z-1)^2 = 9$ | Sphere with center $(3, 2, 1)$ and radius $3$ |
| $(x+1)^2 + y^2 + (z+4)^2 = 5$ | Sphere with center $(-1, 0, -4)$ and radius $\sqrt{5}$ |
| $x^2 + y^2 + z^2 = 1$ | Sphere with center $(0, 0, 0)$ and radius $1$ |

If the terms in (4) are expanded and like terms are collected, then the resulting equation has the form

$$x^2 + y^2 + z^2 + Gx + Hy + Iz + J = 0 \tag{5}$$

The following example shows how the center and radius of a sphere that is expressed in this form can be obtained by completing the squares.

▶ **Example 2**  Find the center and radius of the sphere

$$x^2 + y^2 + z^2 - 2x - 4y + 8z + 17 = 0$$

*Solution.*  We can put the equation in the form of (4) by completing the squares:

$$(x^2 - 2x) + (y^2 - 4y) + (z^2 + 8z) = -17$$
$$(x^2 - 2x + 1) + (y^2 - 4y + 4) + (z^2 + 8z + 16) = -17 + 21$$
$$(x - 1)^2 + (y - 2)^2 + (z + 4)^2 = 4$$

which is the equation of the sphere with center $(1, 2, -4)$ and radius $2$. ◀

In general, completing the squares in (5) produces an equation of the form

$$(x - x_0)^2 + (y - y_0)^2 + (z - z_0)^2 = k$$

If $k > 0$, then the graph of this equation is a sphere with center $(x_0, y_0, z_0)$ and radius $\sqrt{k}$. If $k = 0$, then the sphere has radius zero, so the graph is the single point $(x_0, y_0, z_0)$. If $k < 0$, the equation is not satisfied by any values of $x$, $y$, and $z$ (why?), so it has no graph.

> **11.1.1   THEOREM**   *An equation of the form*
>
> $$x^2 + y^2 + z^2 + Gx + Hy + Iz + J = 0$$
>
> *represents a sphere, a point, or has no graph.*

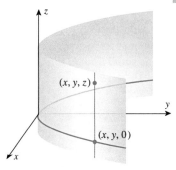

▲ **Figure 11.1.6**

### ■ CYLINDRICAL SURFACES

Although it is natural to graph equations in two variables in 2-space and equations in three variables in 3-space, it is also possible to graph equations in two variables in 3-space. For example, the graph of the equation $y = x^2$ in an $xy$-coordinate system is a parabola; however, there is nothing to prevent us from inquiring about its graph in an $xyz$-coordinate system. To obtain this graph we need only observe that the equation $y = x^2$ does not impose any restrictions on $z$. Thus, if we find values of $x$ and $y$ that satisfy this equation, then the coordinates of the point $(x, y, z)$ will also satisfy the equation for *arbitrary* values of $z$. Geometrically, the point $(x, y, z)$ lies on the vertical line through the point $(x, y, 0)$ in the $xy$-plane, which means that we can obtain the graph of $y = x^2$ in an $xyz$-coordinate system by first graphing the equation in the $xy$-plane and then translating that graph parallel to the $z$-axis to generate the entire graph (Figure 11.1.6).

The process of generating a surface by translating a plane curve parallel to some line is called *extrusion*, and surfaces that are generated by extrusion are called *cylindrical surfaces*. A familiar example is the surface of a right circular cylinder, which can be generated by translating a circle parallel to the axis of the cylinder. The following theorem provides basic information about graphing equations in two variables in 3-space:

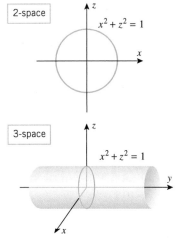

▲ **Figure 11.1.7**

> **11.1.2   THEOREM**   *An equation that contains only two of the variables $x$, $y$, and $z$ represents a cylindrical surface in an $xyz$-coordinate system. The surface can be obtained by graphing the equation in the coordinate plane of the two variables that appear in the equation and then translating that graph parallel to the axis of the missing variable.*

▶ **Example 3**   Sketch the graph of $x^2 + z^2 = 1$ in 3-space.

*Solution.*   Since $y$ does not appear in this equation, the graph is a cylindrical surface generated by extrusion parallel to the $y$-axis. In the $xz$-plane the graph of the equation $x^2 + z^2 = 1$ is a circle. Thus, in 3-space the graph is a right circular cylinder along the $y$-axis (Figure 11.1.7). ◀

▶ **Example 4**   Sketch the graph of $z = \sin y$ in 3-space.

*Solution.*   (See Figure 11.1.8.) ◀

In an $xy$-coordinate system, the graph of the equation $x = 1$ is a line parallel to the $y$-axis. What is the graph of this equation in an $xyz$-coordinate system?

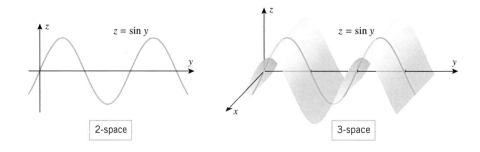

▶ **Figure 11.1.8**

✔ **QUICK CHECK EXERCISES 11.1**    *(See page 773 for answers.)*

1. The distance between the points $(1, -2, 0)$ and $(4, 0, 5)$ is _____.

2. The graph of $(x - 3)^2 + (y - 2)^2 + (z + 1)^2 = 16$ is a _____ of radius _____ centered at _____.

3. The shortest distance from the point $(4, 0, 5)$ to the sphere $(x - 1)^2 + (y + 2)^2 + z^2 = 36$ is _____.

4. Let $S$ be the graph of $x^2 + z^2 + 6z = 16$ in 3-space.
   (a) The intersection of $S$ with the $xz$-plane is a circle with center _____ and radius _____.
   (b) The intersection of $S$ with the $xy$-plane is two lines, $x =$ _____ and $x =$ _____.
   (c) The intersection of $S$ with the $yz$-plane is two lines, $z =$ _____ and $z =$ _____.

**EXERCISE SET 11.1**    ⌂ Graphing Utility

1. In each part, find the coordinates of the eight corners of the box.

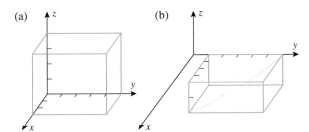

(a)     (b)

2. A cube of side 4 has its geometric center at the origin and its faces parallel to the coordinate planes. Sketch the cube and give the coordinates of the corners.

**FOCUS ON CONCEPTS**

3. Suppose that a box has its faces parallel to the coordinate planes and the points $(4, 2, -2)$ and $(-6, 1, 1)$ are endpoints of a diagonal. Sketch the box and give the coordinates of the remaining six corners.

4. Suppose that a box has its faces parallel to the coordinate planes and the points $(x_1, y_1, z_1)$ and $(x_2, y_2, z_2)$ are endpoints of a diagonal.
   (a) Find the coordinates of the remaining six corners.
   (b) Show that the midpoint of the line segment joining $(x_1, y_1, z_1)$ and $(x_2, y_2, z_2)$ is

   $$\left(\tfrac{1}{2}(x_1 + x_2), \tfrac{1}{2}(y_1 + y_2), \tfrac{1}{2}(z_1 + z_2)\right)$$

   *[Suggestion:* Apply Theorem H.2 in Web Appendix H to three appropriate edges of the box.]

5. Interpret the graph of $x = 1$ in the contexts of
   (a) a number line     (b) 2-space     (c) 3-space.

6. Consider the points $P(3, 1, 0)$ and $Q(1, 4, 4)$.
   (a) Sketch the triangle with vertices $P$, $Q$, and $(1, 4, 0)$. Without computing distances, explain why this triangle is a right triangle, and then apply the Theorem of Pythagoras twice to find the distance from $P$ to $Q$.
   (b) Repeat part (a) using the points $P$, $Q$, and $(3, 4, 0)$.
   (c) Repeat part (a) using the points $P$, $Q$, and $(1, 1, 4)$.

7. (a) Consider a box whose sides have lengths $a$, $b$, and $c$. Use the Theorem of Pythagoras to show that a diagonal of the box has length $d = \sqrt{a^2 + b^2 + c^2}$. *[Hint:* Use the Theorem of Pythagoras to find the length of a diagonal of the base and then again to find the length of a diagonal of the entire box.]
   (b) Use the result of part (a) to derive formula (2).

8. (a) Make a conjecture about the set of points in 3-space that are equidistant from the origin and the point $(1, 0, 0)$.
   (b) Confirm your conjecture in part (a) by using distance formula (2).

9. Find the center and radius of the sphere that has $(1, -2, 4)$ and $(3, 4, -12)$ as endpoints of a diameter. [See Exercise 4.]

10. Show that $(4, 5, 2)$, $(1, 7, 3)$, and $(2, 4, 5)$ are vertices of an equilateral triangle.

11. (a) Show that $(2, 1, 6)$, $(4, 7, 9)$, and $(8, 5, -6)$ are the vertices of a right triangle.
    (b) Which vertex is at the $90°$ angle?
    (c) Find the area of the triangle.

12. Find the distance from the point $(-5, 2, -3)$ to the
    (a) $xy$-plane    (b) $xz$-plane    (c) $yz$-plane
    (d) $x$-axis      (e) $y$-axis      (f) $z$-axis.

13. In each part, find the standard equation of the sphere that satisfies the stated conditions.
    (a) Center $(7, 1, 1)$; radius $= 4$.
    (b) Center $(1, 0, -1)$; diameter $= 8$.
    (c) Center $(-1, 3, 2)$ and passing through the origin.
    (d) A diameter has endpoints $(-1, 2, 1)$ and $(0, 2, 3)$.

14. Find equations of two spheres that are centered at the origin and are tangent to the sphere of radius 1 centered at $(3, -2, 4)$.

15. In each part, find an equation of the sphere with center $(2, -1, -3)$ and satisfying the given condition.
    (a) Tangent to the $xy$-plane
    (b) Tangent to the $xz$-plane
    (c) Tangent to the $yz$-plane

16. (a) Find an equation of the sphere that is inscribed in the cube that is centered at the point $(-2, 1, 3)$ and has sides of length 1 that are parallel to the coordinate planes.
    (b) Find an equation of the sphere that is circumscribed about the cube in part (a).     *(cont.)*

(c) Find an equation of the sphere that is inscribed in the cube determined by the planes $x = 6, x = 2, y = 5, y = 9, z = 0,$ and $z = 4$.

(d) Find an equation of the sphere that is circumscribed about the cube in part (c).

**17.** A sphere has center in the first octant and is tangent to each of the three coordinate planes. Show that the center of the sphere is at a point of the form $(r, r, r)$, where $r$ is the radius of the sphere.

**18.** A sphere has center in the first octant and is tangent to each of the three coordinate planes. The distance from the origin to the sphere is $3 - \sqrt{3}$ units. Find an equation for the sphere.

**19–22 True–False** Determine whether the statement is true or false. Explain your answer. ■

**19.** By definition, a "cylindrical surface" is a right circular cylinder whose axis is parallel to one of the coordinate axes.

**20.** The graph of $x^2 + y^2 = 1$ in 3-space is a circle of radius 1 centered at the origin.

**21.** If a point belongs to both the $xy$-plane and the $xz$-plane, then the point lies on the $x$-axis.

**22.** A sphere with center $P(x_0, y_0, z_0)$ and radius $r$ consists of all points $(x, y, z)$ that satisfy the inequality
$$(x - x_0)^2 + (y - y_0)^2 + (z - z_0)^2 \le r^2$$

**23–28** Describe the surface whose equation is given. ■

**23.** $x^2 + y^2 + z^2 + 10x + 4y + 2z - 19 = 0$

**24.** $x^2 + y^2 + z^2 - y = 0$

**25.** $2x^2 + 2y^2 + 2z^2 - 2x - 3y + 5z - 2 = 0$

**26.** $x^2 + y^2 + z^2 + 2x - 2y + 2z + 3 = 0$

**27.** $x^2 + y^2 + z^2 - 3x + 4y - 8z + 25 = 0$

**28.** $x^2 + y^2 + z^2 - 2x - 6y - 8z + 1 = 0$

**29.** In each part, sketch the portion of the surface that lies in the first octant.
(a) $y = x$         (b) $y = z$         (c) $x = z$

**30.** In each part, sketch the graph of the equation in 3-space.
(a) $x = 1$         (b) $y = 1$         (c) $z = 1$

**31.** In each part, sketch the graph of the equation in 3-space.
(a) $x^2 + y^2 = 25$   (b) $y^2 + z^2 = 25$   (c) $x^2 + z^2 = 25$

**32.** In each part, sketch the graph of the equation in 3-space.
(a) $x = y^2$         (b) $z = x^2$         (c) $y = z^2$

**33.** In each part, write an equation for the surface.
(a) The plane that contains the $x$-axis and the point $(0, 1, 2)$.
(b) The plane that contains the $y$-axis and the point $(1, 0, 2)$.
(c) The right circular cylinder that has radius 1 and is centered on the line parallel to the $z$-axis that passes through the point $(1, 1, 0)$.
(d) The right circular cylinder that has radius 1 and is centered on the line parallel to the $y$-axis that passes through the point $(1, 0, 1)$.

**34.** Find equations for the following right circular cylinders. Each cylinder has radius $a$ and is tangent to two coordinate planes.

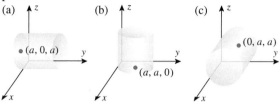

**35–44** Sketch the surface in 3-space. ■

**35.** $y = \sin x$

**36.** $y = e^x$

**37.** $z = 1 - y^2$

**38.** $z = \cos x$

**39.** $2x + z = 3$

**40.** $2x + 3y = 6$

**41.** $4x^2 + 9z^2 = 36$

**42.** $z = \sqrt{3 - x}$

**43.** $y^2 - 4z^2 = 4$

**44.** $yz = 1$

**45.** Use a graphing utility to generate the curve $y = x^3/(1 + x^2)$ in the $xy$-plane, and then use the graph to help sketch the surface $z = y^3/(1 + y^2)$ in 3-space.

**46.** Use a graphing utility to generate the curve $y = x/(1 + x^4)$ in the $xy$-plane, and then use the graph to help sketch the surface $z = y/(1 + y^4)$ in 3-space.

**47.** If a bug walks on the sphere
$$x^2 + y^2 + z^2 + 2x - 2y - 4z - 3 = 0$$
how close and how far can it get from the origin?

**48.** Describe the set of all points in 3-space whose coordinates satisfy the inequality $x^2 + y^2 + z^2 - 2x + 8z \le 8$.

**49.** Describe the set of all points in 3-space whose coordinates satisfy the inequality $y^2 + z^2 + 6y - 4z > 3$.

**50.** The distance between a point $P(x, y, z)$ and the point $A(1, -2, 0)$ is twice the distance between $P$ and the point $B(0, 1, 1)$. Show that the set of all such points is a sphere, and find the center and radius of the sphere.

**51.** As shown in the accompanying figure, a bowling ball of radius $R$ is placed inside a box just large enough to hold it, and it is secured for shipping by packing a Styrofoam sphere into each corner of the box. Find the radius of the largest Styrofoam sphere that can be used. [*Hint:* Take the origin of a Cartesian coordinate system at a corner of the box with the coordinate axes along the edges.]

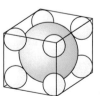

◀ **Figure Ex-51**

**52.** Consider the equation
$$x^2 + y^2 + z^2 + Gx + Hy + Iz + J = 0$$
and let $K = G^2 + H^2 + I^2 - 4J$.         *(cont.)*

(a) Prove that the equation represents a sphere if $K > 0$, a point if $K = 0$, and has no graph if $K < 0$.

(b) In the case where $K > 0$, find the center and radius of the sphere.

53. (a) The accompanying figure shows a surface of revolution that is generated by revolving the curve $y = f(x)$ in the $xy$-plane about the $x$-axis. Show that the equation of this surface is $y^2 + z^2 = [f(x)]^2$. [*Hint:* Each point on the curve traces a circle as it revolves about the $x$-axis.]

(b) Find an equation of the surface of revolution that is generated by revolving the curve $y = e^x$ in the $xy$-plane about the $x$-axis.

(c) Show that the ellipsoid $3x^2 + 4y^2 + 4z^2 = 16$ is a surface of revolution about the $x$-axis by finding a curve $y = f(x)$ in the $xy$-plane that generates it.

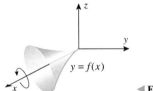

◀ Figure Ex-53

54. In each part, use the idea in Exercise 53(a) to derive a formula for the stated surface of revolution.

(a) The surface generated by revolving the curve $x = f(y)$ in the $xy$-plane about the $y$-axis.

(b) The surface generated by revolving the curve $y = f(z)$ in the $yz$-plane about the $z$-axis.

(c) The surface generated by revolving the curve $z = f(x)$ in the $xz$-plane about the $x$-axis.

55. Show that for all values of $\theta$ and $\phi$, the point

$$(a \sin \phi \cos \theta, a \sin \phi \sin \theta, a \cos \phi)$$

lies on the sphere $x^2 + y^2 + z^2 = a^2$.

56. **Writing** Explain how you might determine whether a set of points in 3-space is the graph of an equation involving at most two of the variables $x$, $y$, and $z$.

57. **Writing** Discuss what happens geometrically when equations in $x$, $y$, and $z$ are replaced by inequalities. For example, compare the graph of $x^2 + y^2 + z^2 = 1$ with the set of points that satisfy the inequality $x^2 + y^2 + z^2 \leq 1$.

✔ **QUICK CHECK ANSWERS 11.1**

1. $\sqrt{38}$    2. sphere; 4; $(3, 2, -1)$    3. $\sqrt{38} - 6$    4. (a) $(0, 0, -3)$; 5 (b) 4; $-4$ (c) 2; $-8$

## 11.2 VECTORS

*Many physical quantities such as area, length, mass, and temperature are completely described once the magnitude of the quantity is given. Such quantities are called "scalars." Other physical quantities, called "vectors," are not completely determined until both a magnitude and a direction are specified. For example, winds are usually described by giving their speed and direction, say 20 mi/h northeast. The wind speed and wind direction together form a vector quantity called the wind velocity. Other examples of vectors are force and displacement. In this section we will develop the basic mathematical properties of vectors.*

### ■ VECTORS IN PHYSICS AND ENGINEERING

A particle that moves along a line can move in only two directions, so its direction of motion can be described by taking one direction to be positive and the other negative. Thus, the *displacement* or *change in position* of the point can be described by a signed real number. For example, a displacement of 3 ($= +3$) describes a position change of 3 units in the positive direction, and a displacement of $-3$ describes a position change of 3 units in the negative direction. However, for a particle that moves in two dimensions or three dimensions, a plus or minus sign is no longer sufficient to specify the direction of motion—other methods are required. One method is to use an arrow, called a ***vector***, that points in the direction of motion and whose length represents the distance from the starting point to the ending point; this is called the ***displacement vector*** for the motion. For example, Figure 11.2.1$a$ shows the displacement vector of a particle that moves from point $A$ to point $B$ along a circuitous path. Note that the length of the arrow describes the

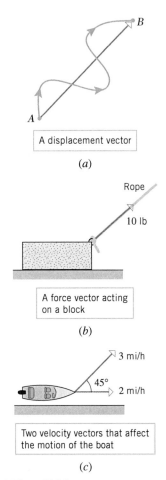

A displacement vector

*(a)*

A force vector acting on a block

*(b)*

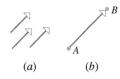

Two velocity vectors that affect the motion of the boat

*(c)*

▲ **Figure 11.2.1**

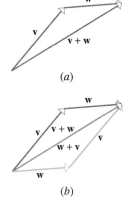

*(a)*          *(b)*

▲ **Figure 11.2.2**

*(a)*

*(b)*

▲ **Figure 11.2.3**

distance between the starting and ending points and not the actual distance traveled by the particle.

Arrows are not limited to describing displacements—they can be used to describe any physical quantity that involves both a magnitude and a direction. Two important examples are forces and velocities. For example, the arrow in Figure 11.2.1*b* represents a force vector of 10 lb acting in a specific direction on a block, and the arrows in Figure 11.2.1*c* show the velocity vector of a boat whose motor propels it parallel to the shore at 2 mi/h and the velocity vector of a 3 mi/h wind acting at an angle of 45° with the shoreline. Intuition suggests that the two velocity vectors will combine to produce some net velocity for the boat at an angle to the shoreline. Thus, our first objective in this section is to define mathematical operations on vectors that can be used to determine the combined effect of vectors.

### ■ VECTORS VIEWED GEOMETRICALLY

Vectors can be represented geometrically by arrows in 2-space or 3-space; the direction of the arrow specifies the direction of the vector, and the length of the arrow describes its magnitude. The tail of the arrow is called the ***initial point*** of the vector, and the tip of the arrow the ***terminal point***. We will denote vectors with lowercase boldface type such as **a**, **k**, **v**, **w**, and **x**. When discussing vectors, we will refer to real numbers as ***scalars***. Scalars will be denoted by lowercase italic type such as $a$, $k$, $v$, $w$, and $x$. Two vectors, **v** and **w**, are considered to be ***equal*** (also called ***equivalent***) if they have the same length and same direction, in which case we write **v** = **w**. Geometrically, two vectors are equal if they are translations of one another; thus, the three vectors in Figure 11.2.2*a* are equal, even though they are in different positions.

Because vectors are not affected by translation, the initial point of a vector **v** can be moved to any convenient point $A$ by making an appropriate translation. If the initial point of **v** is $A$ and the terminal point is $B$, then we write $\mathbf{v} = \overrightarrow{AB}$ when we want to emphasize the initial and terminal points (Figure 11.2.2*b*). If the initial and terminal points of a vector coincide, then the vector has length zero; we call this the ***zero vector*** and denote it by **0**. The zero vector does not have a specific direction, so we will agree that it can be assigned any convenient direction in a specific problem.

There are various algebraic operations that are performed on vectors, all of whose definitions originated in physics. We begin with vector addition.

---

**11.2.1**   **DEFINITION**   If **v** and **w** are vectors, then the ***sum*** **v** + **w** is the vector from the initial point of **v** to the terminal point of **w** when the vectors are positioned so the initial point of **w** is at the terminal point of **v** (Figure 11.2.3*a*).

---

In Figure 11.2.3*b* we have constructed two sums, **v** + **w** (from purple arrows) and **w** + **v** (from green arrows). It is evident that

$$\mathbf{v} + \mathbf{w} = \mathbf{w} + \mathbf{v}$$

and that the sum (gray arrow) coincides with the diagonal of the parallelogram determined by **v** and **w** when these vectors are positioned so they have the same initial point.

Since the initial and terminal points of **0** coincide, it follows that

$$\mathbf{0} + \mathbf{v} = \mathbf{v} + \mathbf{0} = \mathbf{v}$$

---

**11.2.2**   **DEFINITION**   If **v** is a nonzero vector and $k$ is a nonzero real number (a scalar), then the ***scalar multiple*** $k\mathbf{v}$ is defined to be the vector whose length is $|k|$ times the length of **v** and whose direction is the same as that of **v** if $k > 0$ and opposite to that of **v** if $k < 0$. We define $k\mathbf{v} = \mathbf{0}$ if $k = 0$ or $\mathbf{v} = \mathbf{0}$.

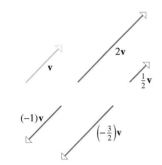

▲ Figure 11.2.4

Figure 11.2.4 shows the geometric relationship between a vector **v** and various scalar multiples of it. Observe that if $k$ and **v** are nonzero, then the vectors **v** and $k\mathbf{v}$ lie on the same line if their initial points coincide and lie on parallel or coincident lines if they do not. Thus, we say that **v** and $k\mathbf{v}$ are ***parallel vectors***. Observe also that the vector $(-1)\mathbf{v}$ has the same length as **v** but is oppositely directed. We call $(-1)\mathbf{v}$ the ***negative*** of **v** and denote it by $-\mathbf{v}$ (Figure 11.2.5). In particular, $-\mathbf{0} = (-1)\mathbf{0} = \mathbf{0}$.

Vector subtraction is defined in terms of addition and scalar multiplication by

$$\mathbf{v} - \mathbf{w} = \mathbf{v} + (-\mathbf{w})$$

The difference $\mathbf{v} - \mathbf{w}$ can be obtained geometrically by first constructing the vector $-\mathbf{w}$ and then adding **v** and $-\mathbf{w}$, say by the parallelogram method (Figure 11.2.6a). However, if **v** and **w** are positioned so their initial points coincide, then $\mathbf{v} - \mathbf{w}$ can be formed more directly, as shown in Figure 11.2.6b, by drawing the vector from the terminal point of **w** (the second term) to the terminal point of **v** (the first term). In the special case where $\mathbf{v} = \mathbf{w}$ the terminal points of the vectors coincide, so their difference is **0**; that is,

$$\mathbf{v} + (-\mathbf{v}) = \mathbf{v} - \mathbf{v} = \mathbf{0}$$

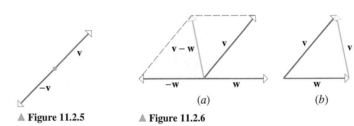

▲ Figure 11.2.5    ▲ Figure 11.2.6

### ■ VECTORS IN COORDINATE SYSTEMS

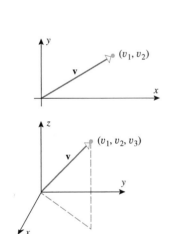

▲ Figure 11.2.7

Problems involving vectors are often best solved by introducing a rectangular coordinate system. If a vector **v** is positioned with its initial point at the origin of a rectangular coordinate system, then its terminal point will have coordinates of the form $(v_1, v_2)$ or $(v_1, v_2, v_3)$, depending on whether the vector is in 2-space or 3-space (Figure 11.2.7). We call these coordinates the ***components*** of **v**, and we write **v** in *component form* using the ***bracket notation***

$$\mathbf{v} = \langle v_1, v_2 \rangle \quad \text{or} \quad \mathbf{v} = \langle v_1, v_2, v_3 \rangle$$

2-space            3-space

In particular, the zero vectors in 2-space and 3-space are

$$\mathbf{0} = \langle 0, 0 \rangle \quad \text{and} \quad \mathbf{0} = \langle 0, 0, 0 \rangle$$

Note the difference in notation between a *point* $(v_1, v_2)$ and a *vector* $\langle v_1, v_2 \rangle$.

respectively.

Components provide a simple way of identifying equivalent vectors. For example, consider the vectors $\mathbf{v} = \langle v_1, v_2 \rangle$ and $\mathbf{w} = \langle w_1, w_2 \rangle$ in 2-space. If $\mathbf{v} = \mathbf{w}$, then the vectors have the same length and same direction, and this means that their terminal points coincide when their initial points are placed at the origin. It follows that $v_1 = w_1$ and $v_2 = w_2$, so we have shown that equivalent vectors have the same components. Conversely, if $v_1 = w_1$ and $v_2 = w_2$, then the terminal points of the vectors coincide when their initial points are placed at the origin. It follows that the vectors have the same length and same direction, so we have shown that vectors with the same components are equivalent. A similar argument holds for vectors in 3-space, so we have the following result.

11.2.3 THEOREM *Two vectors are equivalent if and only if their corresponding components are equal.*

For example,

$$\langle a, b, c \rangle = \langle 1, -4, 2 \rangle$$

if and only if $a = 1$, $b = -4$, and $c = 2$.

## ■ ARITHMETIC OPERATIONS ON VECTORS

The next theorem shows how to perform arithmetic operations on vectors using components.

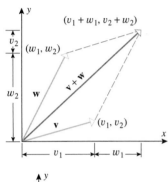

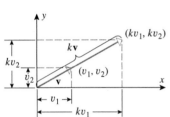

▲ Figure 11.2.8

11.2.4 THEOREM *If* $\mathbf{v} = \langle v_1, v_2 \rangle$ *and* $\mathbf{w} = \langle w_1, w_2 \rangle$ *are vectors in 2-space and $k$ is any scalar, then*

$$\mathbf{v} + \mathbf{w} = \langle v_1 + w_1, v_2 + w_2 \rangle \tag{1}$$
$$\mathbf{v} - \mathbf{w} = \langle v_1 - w_1, v_2 - w_2 \rangle \tag{2}$$
$$k\mathbf{v} = \langle kv_1, kv_2 \rangle \tag{3}$$

*Similarly, if* $\mathbf{v} = \langle v_1, v_2, v_3 \rangle$ *and* $\mathbf{w} = \langle w_1, w_2, w_3 \rangle$ *are vectors in 3-space and $k$ is any scalar, then*

$$\mathbf{v} + \mathbf{w} = \langle v_1 + w_1, v_2 + w_2, v_3 + w_3 \rangle \tag{4}$$
$$\mathbf{v} - \mathbf{w} = \langle v_1 - w_1, v_2 - w_2, v_3 - w_3 \rangle \tag{5}$$
$$k\mathbf{v} = \langle kv_1, kv_2, kv_3 \rangle \tag{6}$$

We will not prove this theorem. However, results (1) and (3) should be evident from Figure 11.2.8. Similar figures in 3-space can be used to motivate (4) and (6). Formulas (2) and (5) can be obtained by writing $\mathbf{v} + \mathbf{w} = \mathbf{v} + (-1)\mathbf{w}$.

▶ **Example 1** If $\mathbf{v} = \langle -2, 0, 1 \rangle$ and $\mathbf{w} = \langle 3, 5, -4 \rangle$, then

$$\mathbf{v} + \mathbf{w} = \langle -2, 0, 1 \rangle + \langle 3, 5, -4 \rangle = \langle 1, 5, -3 \rangle$$
$$3\mathbf{v} = \langle -6, 0, 3 \rangle$$
$$-\mathbf{w} = \langle -3, -5, 4 \rangle$$
$$\mathbf{w} - 2\mathbf{v} = \langle 3, 5, -4 \rangle - \langle -4, 0, 2 \rangle = \langle 7, 5, -6 \rangle \quad ◀$$

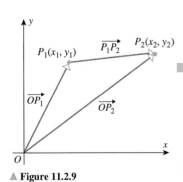

▲ Figure 11.2.9

## ■ VECTORS WITH INITIAL POINT NOT AT THE ORIGIN

Recall that we defined the components of a vector to be the coordinates of its terminal point when its initial point is at the origin. We will now consider the problem of finding the components of a vector whose initial point is not at the origin. To be specific, suppose that $P_1(x_1, y_1)$ and $P_2(x_2, y_2)$ are points in 2-space and we are interested in finding the components of the vector $\overrightarrow{P_1P_2}$. As illustrated in Figure 11.2.9, we can write this vector as

$$\overrightarrow{P_1P_2} = \overrightarrow{OP_2} - \overrightarrow{OP_1} = \langle x_2, y_2 \rangle - \langle x_1, y_1 \rangle = \langle x_2 - x_1, y_2 - y_1 \rangle$$

Thus, we have shown that the components of the vector $\overrightarrow{P_1P_2}$ can be obtained by subtracting the coordinates of its initial point from the coordinates of its terminal point. Similar computations hold in 3-space, so we have established the following result.

---

**11.2.5   THEOREM**   *If $\overrightarrow{P_1P_2}$ is a vector in 2-space with initial point $P_1(x_1, y_1)$ and terminal point $P_2(x_2, y_2)$, then*

$$\overrightarrow{P_1P_2} = \langle x_2 - x_1, y_2 - y_1 \rangle \tag{7}$$

*Similarly, if $\overrightarrow{P_1P_2}$ is a vector in 3-space with initial point $P_1(x_1, y_1, z_1)$ and terminal point $P_2(x_2, y_2, z_2)$, then*

$$\overrightarrow{P_1P_2} = \langle x_2 - x_1, y_2 - y_1, z_2 - z_1 \rangle \tag{8}$$

---

▶ **Example 2**   In 2-space the vector from $P_1(1, 3)$ to $P_2(4, -2)$ is

$$\overrightarrow{P_1P_2} = \langle 4 - 1, -2 - 3 \rangle = \langle 3, -5 \rangle$$

and in 3-space the vector from $A(0, -2, 5)$ to $B(3, 4, -1)$ is

$$\overrightarrow{AB} = \langle 3 - 0, 4 - (-2), -1 - 5 \rangle = \langle 3, 6, -6 \rangle ◀$$

■ **RULES OF VECTOR ARITHMETIC**

The following theorem shows that many of the familiar rules of ordinary arithmetic also hold for vector arithmetic.

---

It follows from part (*b*) of Theorem 11.2.6 that the expression

$$\mathbf{u} + \mathbf{v} + \mathbf{w}$$

is unambiguous since the same vector results no matter how the terms are grouped.

**11.2.6   THEOREM**   *For any vectors $\mathbf{u}$, $\mathbf{v}$, and $\mathbf{w}$ and any scalars $k$ and $l$, the following relationships hold:*

(*a*)  $\mathbf{u} + \mathbf{v} = \mathbf{v} + \mathbf{u}$

(*b*)  $(\mathbf{u} + \mathbf{v}) + \mathbf{w} = \mathbf{u} + (\mathbf{v} + \mathbf{w})$

(*c*)  $\mathbf{u} + \mathbf{0} = \mathbf{0} + \mathbf{u} = \mathbf{u}$

(*d*)  $\mathbf{u} + (-\mathbf{u}) = \mathbf{0}$

(*e*)  $k(l\mathbf{u}) = (kl)\mathbf{u}$

(*f*)  $k(\mathbf{u} + \mathbf{v}) = k\mathbf{u} + k\mathbf{v}$

(*g*)  $(k + l)\mathbf{u} = k\mathbf{u} + l\mathbf{u}$

(*h*)  $1\mathbf{u} = \mathbf{u}$

---

The results in this theorem can be proved either algebraically by using components or geometrically by treating the vectors as arrows. We will prove part (*b*) both ways and leave some of the remaining proofs as exercises.

Observe that in Figure 11.2.10 the vectors **u**, **v**, and **w** are positioned "tip to tail" and that

$$\mathbf{u} + \mathbf{v} + \mathbf{w}$$

is the vector from the initial point of **u** (the first term in the sum) to the terminal point of **w** (the last term in the sum). This "tip to tail" method of vector addition also works for four or more vectors (Figure 11.2.11).

**PROOF (*b*) (ALGEBRAIC IN 2-SPACE)**   Let $\mathbf{u} = \langle u_1, u_2 \rangle$, $\mathbf{v} = \langle v_1, v_2 \rangle$, and $\mathbf{w} = \langle w_1, w_2 \rangle$. Then

$$
\begin{aligned}
(\mathbf{u} + \mathbf{v}) + \mathbf{w} &= (\langle u_1, u_2 \rangle + \langle v_1, v_2 \rangle) + \langle w_1, w_2 \rangle \\
&= \langle u_1 + v_1, u_2 + v_2 \rangle + \langle w_1, w_2 \rangle \\
&= \langle (u_1 + v_1) + w_1, (u_2 + v_2) + w_2 \rangle \\
&= \langle u_1 + (v_1 + w_1), u_2 + (v_2 + w_2) \rangle \\
&= \langle u_1, u_2 \rangle + \langle v_1 + w_1, v_2 + w_2 \rangle \\
&= \mathbf{u} + (\mathbf{v} + \mathbf{w})
\end{aligned}
$$

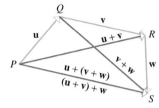

▲ Figure 11.2.10

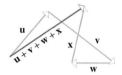

▲ Figure 11.2.11

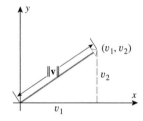

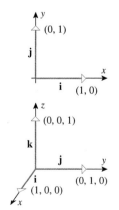

▲ Figure 11.2.12

**PROOF** (*b*) (GEOMETRIC)    Let **u**, **v**, and **w** be represented by $\overrightarrow{PQ}$, $\overrightarrow{QR}$, and $\overrightarrow{RS}$ as shown in Figure 11.2.10. Then

$$\mathbf{v} + \mathbf{w} = \overrightarrow{QS} \quad \text{and} \quad \mathbf{u} + (\mathbf{v} + \mathbf{w}) = \overrightarrow{PS}$$
$$\mathbf{u} + \mathbf{v} = \overrightarrow{PR} \quad \text{and} \quad (\mathbf{u} + \mathbf{v}) + \mathbf{w} = \overrightarrow{PS}$$

Therefore,

$$(\mathbf{u} + \mathbf{v}) + \mathbf{w} = \mathbf{u} + (\mathbf{v} + \mathbf{w}) \quad \blacksquare$$

■ **NORM OF A VECTOR**

The distance between the initial and terminal points of a vector **v** is called the ***length***, the ***norm***, or the ***magnitude*** of **v** and is denoted by $\|\mathbf{v}\|$. This distance does not change if the vector is translated, so for purposes of calculating the norm we can assume that the vector is positioned with its initial point at the origin (Figure 11.2.12). This makes it evident that the norm of a vector $\mathbf{v} = \langle v_1, v_2 \rangle$ in 2-space is given by

$$\|\mathbf{v}\| = \sqrt{v_1^2 + v_2^2} \tag{9}$$

and the norm of a vector $\mathbf{v} = \langle v_1, v_2, v_3 \rangle$ in 3-space is given by

$$\|\mathbf{v}\| = \sqrt{v_1^2 + v_2^2 + v_3^2} \tag{10}$$

▶ **Example 3**    Find the norms of $\mathbf{v} = \langle -2, 3 \rangle$, $10\mathbf{v} = \langle -20, 30 \rangle$, and $\mathbf{w} = \langle 2, 3, 6 \rangle$.

***Solution.***    From (9) and (10)

$$\|\mathbf{v}\| = \sqrt{(-2)^2 + 3^2} = \sqrt{13}$$
$$\|10\mathbf{v}\| = \sqrt{(-20)^2 + 30^2} = \sqrt{1300} = 10\sqrt{13}$$
$$\|\mathbf{w}\| = \sqrt{2^2 + 3^2 + 6^2} = \sqrt{49} = 7 \quad \blacktriangleleft$$

Note that $\|10\mathbf{v}\| = 10\|\mathbf{v}\|$ in Example 3. This is consistent with Definition 11.2.2, which stipulated that for any vector **v** and scalar $k$, the length of $k\mathbf{v}$ must be $|k|$ times the length of **v**; that is,

$$\|k\mathbf{v}\| = |k|\|\mathbf{v}\| \tag{11}$$

Thus, for example,

$$\|3\mathbf{v}\| = |3|\|\mathbf{v}\| = 3\|\mathbf{v}\|$$
$$\|-2\mathbf{v}\| = |-2|\|\mathbf{v}\| = 2\|\mathbf{v}\|$$
$$\|-1\mathbf{v}\| = |-1|\|\mathbf{v}\| = \|\mathbf{v}\|$$

This applies to vectors in 2-space and 3-space.

■ **UNIT VECTORS**

A vector of length 1 is called a ***unit vector***. In an *xy*-coordinate system the unit vectors along the *x*- and *y*-axes are denoted by **i** and **j**, respectively; and in an *xyz*-coordinate system the unit vectors along the *x*-, *y*-, and *z*-axes are denoted by **i**, **j**, and **k**, respectively (Figure 11.2.13). Thus,

$$\mathbf{i} = \langle 1, 0 \rangle, \quad \mathbf{j} = \langle 0, 1 \rangle \qquad \boxed{\text{In 2-space}}$$

$$\mathbf{i} = \langle 1, 0, 0 \rangle, \quad \mathbf{j} = \langle 0, 1, 0 \rangle, \quad \mathbf{k} = \langle 0, 0, 1 \rangle \qquad \boxed{\text{In 3-space}}$$

▲ Figure 11.2.13

Every vector in 2-space is expressible uniquely in terms of $\mathbf{i}$ and $\mathbf{j}$, and every vector in 3-space is expressible uniquely in terms of $\mathbf{i}$, $\mathbf{j}$, and $\mathbf{k}$ as follows:

$$\mathbf{v} = \langle v_1, v_2 \rangle = \langle v_1, 0 \rangle + \langle 0, v_2 \rangle = v_1 \langle 1, 0 \rangle + v_2 \langle 0, 1 \rangle = v_1\mathbf{i} + v_2\mathbf{j}$$

$$\mathbf{v} = \langle v_1, v_2, v_3 \rangle = v_1 \langle 1, 0, 0 \rangle + v_2 \langle 0, 1, 0 \rangle + v_3 \langle 0, 0, 1 \rangle = v_1\mathbf{i} + v_2\mathbf{j} + v_3\mathbf{k}$$

▶ **Example 4** The following table provides some examples of vector notation in 2-space and 3-space.

| 2-SPACE | 3-SPACE |
|---|---|
| $\langle 2, 3 \rangle = 2\mathbf{i} + 3\mathbf{j}$ | $\langle 2, -3, 4 \rangle = 2\mathbf{i} - 3\mathbf{j} + 4\mathbf{k}$ |
| $\langle -4, 0 \rangle = -4\mathbf{i} + 0\mathbf{j} = -4\mathbf{i}$ | $\langle 0, 3, 0 \rangle = 3\mathbf{j}$ |
| $\langle 0, 0 \rangle = 0\mathbf{i} + 0\mathbf{j} = \mathbf{0}$ | $\langle 0, 0, 0 \rangle = 0\mathbf{i} + 0\mathbf{j} + 0\mathbf{k} = \mathbf{0}$ |
| $(3\mathbf{i} + 2\mathbf{j}) + (4\mathbf{i} + \mathbf{j}) = 7\mathbf{i} + 3\mathbf{j}$ | $(3\mathbf{i} + 2\mathbf{j} - \mathbf{k}) - (4\mathbf{i} - \mathbf{j} + 2\mathbf{k}) = -\mathbf{i} + 3\mathbf{j} - 3\mathbf{k}$ |
| $5(6\mathbf{i} - 2\mathbf{j}) = 30\mathbf{i} - 10\mathbf{j}$ | $2(\mathbf{i} + \mathbf{j} - \mathbf{k}) + 4(\mathbf{i} - \mathbf{j}) = 6\mathbf{i} - 2\mathbf{j} - 2\mathbf{k}$ |
| $\|2\mathbf{i} - 3\mathbf{j}\| = \sqrt{2^2 + (-3)^2} = \sqrt{13}$ | $\|\mathbf{i} + 2\mathbf{j} - 3\mathbf{k}\| = \sqrt{1^2 + 2^2 + (-3)^2} = \sqrt{14}$ |
| $\|v_1\mathbf{i} + v_2\mathbf{j}\| = \sqrt{v_1^2 + v_2^2}$ | $\|\langle v_1, v_2, v_3 \rangle\| = \sqrt{v_1^2 + v_2^2 + v_3^2}$ |

◀

The two notations for vectors illustrated in Example 4 are completely interchangeable, the choice being a matter of convenience or personal preference.

■ **NORMALIZING A VECTOR**

A common problem in applications is to find a unit vector $\mathbf{u}$ that has the same direction as some given nonzero vector $\mathbf{v}$. This can be done by multiplying $\mathbf{v}$ by the reciprocal of its length; that is,

$$\mathbf{u} = \frac{1}{\|\mathbf{v}\|}\mathbf{v} = \frac{\mathbf{v}}{\|\mathbf{v}\|}$$

is a unit vector with the same direction as $\mathbf{v}$—the direction is the same because $k = 1/\|\mathbf{v}\|$ is a positive scalar, and the length is 1 because

$$\|\mathbf{u}\| = \|k\mathbf{v}\| = |k|\|\mathbf{v}\| = k\|\mathbf{v}\| = \frac{1}{\|\mathbf{v}\|}\|\mathbf{v}\| = 1$$

The process of multiplying a vector $\mathbf{v}$ by the reciprocal of its length to obtain a unit vector with the same direction is called ***normalizing*** $\mathbf{v}$.

**TECHNOLOGY MASTERY**

Many calculating utilities can perform vector operations, and some have built-in norm and normalization operations. If your calculator has these capabilities, use it to check the computations in Examples 1, 3, and 5.

▶ **Example 5** Find the unit vector that has the same direction as $\mathbf{v} = 2\mathbf{i} + 2\mathbf{j} - \mathbf{k}$.

*Solution.* The vector $\mathbf{v}$ has length

$$\|\mathbf{v}\| = \sqrt{2^2 + 2^2 + (-1)^2} = 3$$

so the unit vector $\mathbf{u}$ in the same direction as $\mathbf{v}$ is

$$\mathbf{u} = \tfrac{1}{3}\mathbf{v} = \tfrac{2}{3}\mathbf{i} + \tfrac{2}{3}\mathbf{j} - \tfrac{1}{3}\mathbf{k} \quad ◀$$

■ **VECTORS DETERMINED BY LENGTH AND ANGLE**

If $\mathbf{v}$ is a nonzero vector with its initial point at the origin of an $xy$-coordinate system, and if $\theta$ is the angle from the positive $x$-axis to the radial line through $\mathbf{v}$, then the $x$-component of $\mathbf{v}$ can be written as $\|\mathbf{v}\|\cos\theta$ and the $y$-component as $\|\mathbf{v}\|\sin\theta$ (Figure 11.2.14); and hence $\mathbf{v}$ can be expressed in trigonometric form as

$$\mathbf{v} = \|\mathbf{v}\|\langle\cos\theta, \sin\theta\rangle \quad \text{or} \quad \mathbf{v} = \|\mathbf{v}\|\cos\theta\mathbf{i} + \|\mathbf{v}\|\sin\theta\mathbf{j} \tag{12}$$

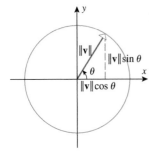

▲ **Figure 11.2.14**

In the special case of a unit vector **u** this simplifies to

$$\mathbf{u} = \langle \cos\theta, \sin\theta \rangle \quad \text{or} \quad \mathbf{u} = \cos\theta\,\mathbf{i} + \sin\theta\,\mathbf{j} \tag{13}$$

▶ **Example 6**

(a) Find the vector of length 2 that makes an angle of $\pi/4$ with the positive $x$-axis.

(b) Find the angle that the vector $\mathbf{v} = -\sqrt{3}\,\mathbf{i} + \mathbf{j}$ makes with the positive $x$-axis.

*Solution (a).*    From (12)

$$\mathbf{v} = 2\cos\frac{\pi}{4}\mathbf{i} + 2\sin\frac{\pi}{4}\mathbf{j} = \sqrt{2}\,\mathbf{i} + \sqrt{2}\,\mathbf{j}$$

*Solution (b).*    We will normalize **v**, then use (13) to find $\sin\theta$ and $\cos\theta$, and then use these values to find $\theta$. Normalizing **v** yields

$$\frac{\mathbf{v}}{\|\mathbf{v}\|} = \frac{-\sqrt{3}\,\mathbf{i} + \mathbf{j}}{\sqrt{(-\sqrt{3})^2 + 1^2}} = -\frac{\sqrt{3}}{2}\mathbf{i} + \frac{1}{2}\mathbf{j}$$

Thus, $\cos\theta = -\sqrt{3}/2$ and $\sin\theta = 1/2$, from which we conclude that $\theta = 5\pi/6$. ◀

■ **VECTORS DETERMINED BY LENGTH AND A VECTOR IN THE SAME DIRECTION**

It is a common problem in many applications that a direction in 2-space or 3-space is determined by some known unit vector **u**, and it is of interest to find the components of a vector **v** that has the same direction as **u** and some specified length $\|\mathbf{v}\|$. This can be done by expressing **v** as

$$\mathbf{v} = \|\mathbf{v}\|\mathbf{u} \qquad \boxed{\text{v is equal to its length times a unit vector in the same direction.}}$$

and then reading off the components of $\|\mathbf{v}\|\mathbf{u}$.

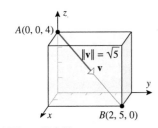

▲ **Figure 11.2.15**

▶ **Example 7**    Figure 11.2.15 shows a vector **v** of length $\sqrt{5}$ that extends along the line through $A$ and $B$. Find the components of **v**.

*Solution.*    First we will find the components of the vector $\overrightarrow{AB}$, then we will normalize this vector to obtain a unit vector in the direction of **v**, and then we will multiply this unit vector by $\|\mathbf{v}\|$ to obtain the vector **v**. The computations are as follows:

$$\overrightarrow{AB} = \langle 2, 5, 0 \rangle - \langle 0, 0, 4 \rangle = \langle 2, 5, -4 \rangle$$

$$\|\overrightarrow{AB}\| = \sqrt{2^2 + 5^2 + (-4)^2} = \sqrt{45} = 3\sqrt{5}$$

$$\frac{\overrightarrow{AB}}{\|\overrightarrow{AB}\|} = \left\langle \frac{2}{3\sqrt{5}}, \frac{5}{3\sqrt{5}}, -\frac{4}{3\sqrt{5}} \right\rangle$$

$$\mathbf{v} = \|\mathbf{v}\|\left( \frac{\overrightarrow{AB}}{\|\overrightarrow{AB}\|} \right) = \sqrt{5}\left\langle \frac{2}{3\sqrt{5}}, \frac{5}{3\sqrt{5}}, -\frac{4}{3\sqrt{5}} \right\rangle = \left\langle \frac{2}{3}, \frac{5}{3}, -\frac{4}{3} \right\rangle \quad ◀$$

■ **RESULTANT OF TWO CONCURRENT FORCES**

The effect that a force has on an object depends on the magnitude and direction of the force and the point at which it is applied. Thus, forces are regarded to be vector quantities and, indeed, the algebraic operations on vectors that we have defined in this section have their origin in the study of forces. For example, it is a fact of physics that if two forces $\mathbf{F}_1$ and

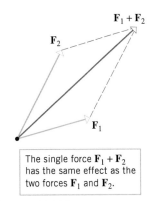

The single force $\mathbf{F}_1 + \mathbf{F}_2$ has the same effect as the two forces $\mathbf{F}_1$ and $\mathbf{F}_2$.

▲ **Figure 11.2.16**

$\mathbf{F}_2$ are applied at the same point on an object, then the two forces have the same effect on the object as the single force $\mathbf{F}_1 + \mathbf{F}_2$ applied at the point (Figure 11.2.16). Physicists and engineers call $\mathbf{F}_1 + \mathbf{F}_2$ the **resultant** of $\mathbf{F}_1$ and $\mathbf{F}_2$, and they say that the forces $\mathbf{F}_1$ and $\mathbf{F}_2$ are **concurrent** to indicate that they are applied at the same point.

In many applications, the magnitudes of two concurrent forces and the angle between them are known, and the problem is to find the magnitude and direction of the resultant. One approach to solving this problem is to use (12) to find the components of the concurrent forces, and then use (1) to find the components of the resultant. The next example illustrates this method.

▶ **Example 8**    Suppose that two forces are applied to an eye bracket, as shown in Figure 11.2.17. Find the magnitude of the resultant and the angle $\theta$ that it makes with the positive $x$-axis.

*Solution.*    Note that $\mathbf{F}_1$ makes an angle of $30°$ with the positive $x$-axis and $\mathbf{F}_2$ makes an angle of $30° + 40° = 70°$ with the positive $x$-axis. Since we are given that $\|\mathbf{F}_1\| = 200$ N and $\|\mathbf{F}_2\| = 300$ N, (12) yields

$$\mathbf{F}_1 = 200\langle \cos 30°, \sin 30° \rangle = \langle 100\sqrt{3}, 100 \rangle$$

and

$$\mathbf{F}_2 = 300\langle \cos 70°, \sin 70° \rangle = \langle 300 \cos 70°, 300 \sin 70° \rangle$$

Therefore, the resultant $\mathbf{F} = \mathbf{F}_1 + \mathbf{F}_2$ has component form

$$\mathbf{F} = \mathbf{F}_1 + \mathbf{F}_2 = \langle 100\sqrt{3} + 300 \cos 70°, 100 + 300 \sin 70° \rangle$$
$$= 100\langle \sqrt{3} + 3\cos 70°, 1 + 3\sin 70° \rangle \approx \langle 275.8, 381.9 \rangle$$

The magnitude of the resultant is then

$$\|\mathbf{F}\| = 100\sqrt{\left(\sqrt{3} + 3\cos 70°\right)^2 + \left(1 + 3\sin 70°\right)^2} \approx 471 \text{ N}$$

Let $\theta$ denote the angle $\mathbf{F}$ makes with the positive $x$-axis when the initial point of $\mathbf{F}$ is at the origin. Using (12) and equating the $x$-components of $\mathbf{F}$ yield

$$\|\mathbf{F}\|\cos\theta = 100\sqrt{3} + 300\cos 70° \quad \text{or} \quad \cos\theta = \frac{100\sqrt{3} + 300\cos 70°}{\|\mathbf{F}\|}$$

Since the terminal point of $\mathbf{F}$ is in the first quadrant, we have

$$\theta = \cos^{-1}\left(\frac{100\sqrt{3} + 300\cos 70°}{\|\mathbf{F}\|}\right) \approx 54.2°$$

(Figure 11.2.18). ◀

The resultant of three or more concurrent forces can be found by working in pairs. For example, the resultant of three forces can be found by finding the resultant of any two of the forces and then finding the resultant of that resultant with the third force.

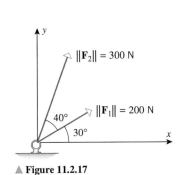

▲ **Figure 11.2.17**

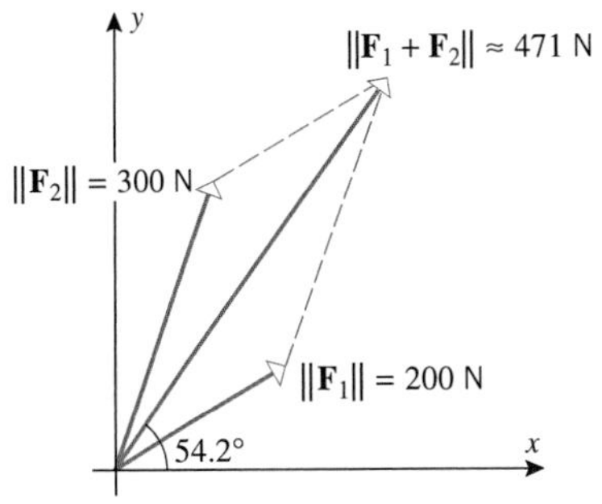

▲ **Figure 11.2.18**

## ✔ QUICK CHECK EXERCISES 11.2    *(See page 000 for answers.)*

**1.** If $\mathbf{v} = \langle 3, -1, 7 \rangle$ and $\mathbf{w} = \langle 4, 10, -5 \rangle$, then
   (a) $\|\mathbf{v}\| = $ _____    (b) $\mathbf{v} + \mathbf{w} = $ _____
   (c) $\mathbf{v} - \mathbf{w} = $ _____    (d) $2\mathbf{v} = $ _____.

**2.** The unit vector in the direction of $\mathbf{v} = \langle 3, -1, 7 \rangle$ is
   _____.

**3.** The unit vector in 2-space that makes an angle of $\pi/3$ with the positive $x$-axis is _____.

**4.** Consider points $A(3, 4, 0)$ and $B(0, 0, 5)$.
   (a) $\overrightarrow{AB} = $ _____
   (b) If $\mathbf{v}$ is a vector in the same direction as $\overrightarrow{AB}$ and the length of $\mathbf{v}$ is $\sqrt{2}$, then $\mathbf{v} = $ _____.

## EXERCISE SET 11.2     Graphing Utility

**1–4** Sketch the vectors with their initial points at the origin. ◾

**1.** (a) $\langle 2, 5 \rangle$    (b) $\langle -5, -4 \rangle$    (c) $\langle 2, 0 \rangle$
   (d) $-5\mathbf{i} + 3\mathbf{j}$    (e) $3\mathbf{i} - 2\mathbf{j}$    (f) $-6\mathbf{j}$

**2.** (a) $\langle -3, 7 \rangle$    (b) $\langle 6, -2 \rangle$    (c) $\langle 0, -8 \rangle$
   (d) $4\mathbf{i} + 2\mathbf{j}$    (e) $-2\mathbf{i} - \mathbf{j}$    (f) $4\mathbf{i}$

**3.** (a) $\langle 1, -2, 2 \rangle$    (b) $\langle 2, 2, -1 \rangle$
   (c) $-\mathbf{i} + 2\mathbf{j} + 3\mathbf{k}$    (d) $2\mathbf{i} + 3\mathbf{j} - \mathbf{k}$

**4.** (a) $\langle -1, 3, 2 \rangle$    (b) $\langle 3, 4, 2 \rangle$
   (c) $2\mathbf{j} - \mathbf{k}$    (d) $\mathbf{i} - \mathbf{j} + 2\mathbf{k}$

**5–6** Find the components of the vector, and sketch an equivalent vector with its initial point at the origin. ◾

**5.** (a)    (b)

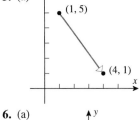 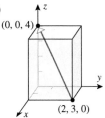

**6.** (a)    (b)

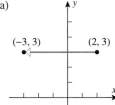 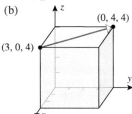

**7–8** Find the components of the vector $\overrightarrow{P_1 P_2}$. ◾

**7.** (a) $P_1(3, 5)$, $P_2(2, 8)$    (b) $P_1(7, -2)$, $P_2(0, 0)$
   (c) $P_1(5, -2, 1)$, $P_2(2, 4, 2)$

**8.** (a) $P_1(-6, -2)$, $P_2(-4, -1)$
   (b) $P_1(0, 0, 0)$, $P_2(-1, 6, 1)$
   (c) $P_1(4, 1, -3)$, $P_2(9, 1, -3)$

**9.** (a) Find the terminal point of $\mathbf{v} = 3\mathbf{i} - 2\mathbf{j}$ if the initial point is $(1, -2)$.
   (b) Find the initial point of $\mathbf{v} = \langle -3, 1, 2 \rangle$ if the terminal point is $(5, 0, -1)$.

**10.** (a) Find the terminal point of $\mathbf{v} = \langle 7, 6 \rangle$ if the initial point is $(2, -1)$.
   (b) Find the terminal point of $\mathbf{v} = \mathbf{i} + 2\mathbf{j} - 3\mathbf{k}$ if the initial point is $(-2, 1, 4)$.

**11–12** Perform the stated operations on the given vectors $\mathbf{u}$, $\mathbf{v}$, and $\mathbf{w}$. ◾

**11.** $\mathbf{u} = 3\mathbf{i} - \mathbf{k}$, $\mathbf{v} = \mathbf{i} - \mathbf{j} + 2\mathbf{k}$, $\mathbf{w} = 3\mathbf{j}$
   (a) $\mathbf{w} - \mathbf{v}$    (b) $6\mathbf{u} + 4\mathbf{w}$
   (c) $-\mathbf{v} - 2\mathbf{w}$    (d) $4(3\mathbf{u} + \mathbf{v})$
   (e) $-8(\mathbf{v} + \mathbf{w}) + 2\mathbf{u}$    (f) $3\mathbf{w} - (\mathbf{v} - \mathbf{w})$

**12.** $\mathbf{u} = \langle 2, -1, 3 \rangle$, $\mathbf{v} = \langle 4, 0, -2 \rangle$, $\mathbf{w} = \langle 1, 1, 3 \rangle$
   (a) $\mathbf{u} - \mathbf{w}$    (b) $7\mathbf{v} + 3\mathbf{w}$    (c) $-\mathbf{w} + \mathbf{v}$
   (d) $3(\mathbf{u} - 7\mathbf{v})$    (e) $-3\mathbf{v} - 8\mathbf{w}$    (f) $2\mathbf{v} - (\mathbf{u} + \mathbf{w})$

**13–14** Find the norm of $\mathbf{v}$. ◾

**13.** (a) $\mathbf{v} = \langle 1, -1 \rangle$    (b) $\mathbf{v} = -\mathbf{i} + 7\mathbf{j}$
   (c) $\mathbf{v} = \langle -1, 2, 4 \rangle$    (d) $\mathbf{v} = -3\mathbf{i} + 2\mathbf{j} + \mathbf{k}$

**14.** (a) $\mathbf{v} = \langle 3, 4 \rangle$    (b) $\mathbf{v} = \sqrt{2}\mathbf{i} - \sqrt{7}\mathbf{j}$
   (c) $\mathbf{v} = \langle 0, -3, 0 \rangle$    (d) $\mathbf{v} = \mathbf{i} + \mathbf{j} + \mathbf{k}$

**15.** Let $\mathbf{u} = \mathbf{i} - 3\mathbf{j} + 2\mathbf{k}$, $\mathbf{v} = \mathbf{i} + \mathbf{j}$, and $\mathbf{w} = 2\mathbf{i} + 2\mathbf{j} - 4\mathbf{k}$. Find
   (a) $\|\mathbf{u} + \mathbf{v}\|$    (b) $\|\mathbf{u}\| + \|\mathbf{v}\|$
   (c) $\|-2\mathbf{u}\| + 2\|\mathbf{v}\|$    (d) $\|3\mathbf{u} - 5\mathbf{v} + \mathbf{w}\|$
   (e) $\dfrac{1}{\|\mathbf{w}\|}\mathbf{w}$    (f) $\left\|\dfrac{1}{\|\mathbf{w}\|}\mathbf{w}\right\|$.

**16.** Is it possible to have $\|\mathbf{u} - \mathbf{v}\| = \|\mathbf{u} + \mathbf{v}\|$ if $\mathbf{u}$ and $\mathbf{v}$ are nonzero vectors? Justify your conclusion geometrically.

**17–20 True–False** Determine whether the statement is true or false. Explain your answer. ◾

**17.** The norm of the sum of two vectors is equal to the sum of the norms of the two vectors.

**18.** If two distinct vectors $\mathbf{v}$ and $\mathbf{w}$ are drawn with the same initial point, then a vector drawn between the terminal points of $\mathbf{v}$ and $\mathbf{w}$ will be either $\mathbf{v} - \mathbf{w}$ or $\mathbf{w} - \mathbf{v}$.

**19.** There are exactly two unit vectors that are parallel to a given nonzero vector.

**20.** Given a nonzero scalar $c$ and vectors **b** and **d**, the vector equation $c\mathbf{a} + \mathbf{b} = \mathbf{d}$ has a unique solution **a**.

**21–22** Find unit vectors that satisfy the stated conditions.

**21.** (a) Same direction as $-\mathbf{i} + 4\mathbf{j}$.
   (b) Oppositely directed to $6\mathbf{i} - 4\mathbf{j} + 2\mathbf{k}$.
   (c) Same direction as the vector from the point $A(-1, 0, 2)$ to the point $B(3, 1, 1)$.

**22.** (a) Oppositely directed to $3\mathbf{i} - 4\mathbf{j}$.
   (b) Same direction as $2\mathbf{i} - \mathbf{j} - 2\mathbf{k}$.
   (c) Same direction as the vector from the point $A(-3, 2)$ to the point $B(1, -1)$.

**23–24** Find the vectors that satisfy the stated conditions.

**23.** (a) Oppositely directed to $\mathbf{v} = \langle 3, -4 \rangle$ and half the length of **v**.
   (b) Length $\sqrt{17}$ and same direction as $\mathbf{v} = \langle 7, 0, -6 \rangle$.

**24.** (a) Same direction as $\mathbf{v} = -2\mathbf{i} + 3\mathbf{j}$ and three times the length of **v**.
   (b) Length 2 and oppositely directed to $\mathbf{v} = -3\mathbf{i} + 4\mathbf{j} + \mathbf{k}$.

**25.** In each part, find the component form of the vector **v** in 2-space that has the stated length and makes the stated angle $\theta$ with the positive $x$-axis.
   (a) $\|\mathbf{v}\| = 3$; $\theta = \pi/4$    (b) $\|\mathbf{v}\| = 2$; $\theta = 90°$
   (c) $\|\mathbf{v}\| = 5$; $\theta = 120°$    (d) $\|\mathbf{v}\| = 1$; $\theta = \pi$

**26.** Find the component forms of $\mathbf{v} + \mathbf{w}$ and $\mathbf{v} - \mathbf{w}$ in 2-space, given that $\|\mathbf{v}\| = 1$, $\|\mathbf{w}\| = 1$, **v** makes an angle of $\pi/6$ with the positive $x$-axis, and **w** makes an angle of $3\pi/4$ with the positive $x$-axis.

**27–28** Find the component form of $\mathbf{v} + \mathbf{w}$, given that **v** and **w** are unit vectors.

**27.**
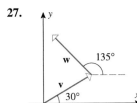

**28.**
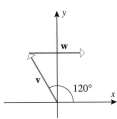

**29.** In each part, sketch the vector $\mathbf{u} + \mathbf{v} + \mathbf{w}$ and express it in component form.
   (a)
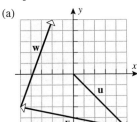
   (b)
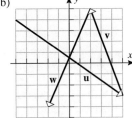

**30.** In each part of Exercise 29, sketch the vector $\mathbf{u} - \mathbf{v} + \mathbf{w}$ and express it in component form.

**31.** Let $\mathbf{u} = \langle 1, 3 \rangle$, $\mathbf{v} = \langle 2, 1 \rangle$, $\mathbf{w} = \langle 4, -1 \rangle$. Find the vector **x** that satisfies $2\mathbf{u} - \mathbf{v} + \mathbf{x} = 7\mathbf{x} + \mathbf{w}$.

**32.** Let $\mathbf{u} = \langle -1, 1 \rangle$, $\mathbf{v} = \langle 0, 1 \rangle$, and $\mathbf{w} = \langle 3, 4 \rangle$. Find the vector **x** that satisfies $\mathbf{u} - 2\mathbf{x} = \mathbf{x} - \mathbf{w} + 3\mathbf{v}$.

**33.** Find **u** and **v** if $\mathbf{u} + 2\mathbf{v} = 3\mathbf{i} - \mathbf{k}$ and $3\mathbf{u} - \mathbf{v} = \mathbf{i} + \mathbf{j} + \mathbf{k}$.

**34.** Find **u** and **v** if $\mathbf{u} + \mathbf{v} = \langle 2, -3 \rangle$ and $3\mathbf{u} + 2\mathbf{v} = \langle -1, 2 \rangle$.

**35.** Use vectors to find the lengths of the diagonals of the parallelogram that has $\mathbf{i} + \mathbf{j}$ and $\mathbf{i} - 2\mathbf{j}$ as adjacent sides.

**36.** Use vectors to find the fourth vertex of a parallelogram, three of whose vertices are $(0, 0)$, $(1, 3)$, and $(2, 4)$. [*Note:* There is more than one answer.]

**37.** (a) Given that $\|\mathbf{v}\| = 3$, find all values of $k$ such that $\|k\mathbf{v}\| = 5$.
   (b) Given that $k = -2$ and $\|k\mathbf{v}\| = 6$, find $\|\mathbf{v}\|$.

**38.** What do you know about $k$ and **v** if $\|k\mathbf{v}\| = 0$?

**39.** In each part, find two unit vectors in 2-space that satisfy the stated condition.
   (a) Parallel to the line $y = 3x + 2$
   (b) Parallel to the line $x + y = 4$
   (c) Perpendicular to the line $y = -5x + 1$

**40.** In each part, find two unit vectors in 3-space that satisfy the stated condition.
   (a) Perpendicular to the $xy$-plane
   (b) Perpendicular to the $xz$-plane
   (c) Perpendicular to the $yz$-plane

**FOCUS ON CONCEPTS**

**41.** Let $\mathbf{r} = \langle x, y \rangle$ be an arbitrary vector. In each part, describe the set of all points $(x, y)$ in 2-space that satisfy the stated condition.
   (a) $\|\mathbf{r}\| = 1$    (b) $\|\mathbf{r}\| \le 1$    (c) $\|\mathbf{r}\| > 1$

**42.** Let $\mathbf{r} = \langle x, y \rangle$ and $\mathbf{r}_0 = \langle x_0, y_0 \rangle$. In each part, describe the set of all points $(x, y)$ in 2-space that satisfy the stated condition.
   (a) $\|\mathbf{r} - \mathbf{r}_0\| = 1$    (b) $\|\mathbf{r} - \mathbf{r}_0\| \le 1$    (c) $\|\mathbf{r} - \mathbf{r}_0\| > 1$

**43.** Let $\mathbf{r} = \langle x, y, z \rangle$ be an arbitrary vector. In each part, describe the set of all points $(x, y, z)$ in 3-space that satisfy the stated condition.
   (a) $\|\mathbf{r}\| = 1$    (b) $\|\mathbf{r}\| \le 1$    (c) $\|\mathbf{r}\| > 1$

**44.** Let $\mathbf{r}_1 = \langle x_1, y_1 \rangle$, $\mathbf{r}_2 = \langle x_2, y_2 \rangle$, and $\mathbf{r} = \langle x, y \rangle$. Assuming that $k > \|\mathbf{r}_2 - \mathbf{r}_1\|$, describe the set of all points $(x, y)$ for which $\|\mathbf{r} - \mathbf{r}_1\| + \|\mathbf{r} - \mathbf{r}_2\| = k$.

**45–50** Find the magnitude of the resultant force and the angle that it makes with the positive $x$-axis.

**45.**
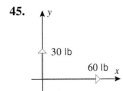

**46.**
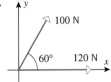

**47.** **48.**

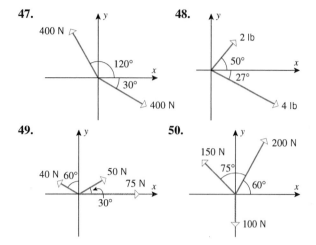

**49.** **50.**

**51–52** A particle is said to be in *static equilibrium* if the resultant of all forces applied to it is zero. In these exercises, find the force **F** that must be applied to the point to produce static equilibrium. Describe **F** by specifying its magnitude and the angle that it makes with the positive $x$-axis. ■

**51.** **52.**

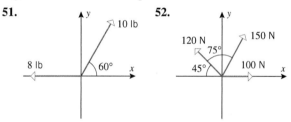

**53.** The accompanying figure shows a 250 lb traffic light supported by two flexible cables. The magnitudes of the forces that the cables apply to the eye ring are called the cable *tensions*. Find the tensions in the cables if the traffic light is in static equilibrium (defined above Exercise 51).

**54.** Find the tensions in the cables shown in the accompanying figure if the block is in static equilibrium (see Exercise 53).

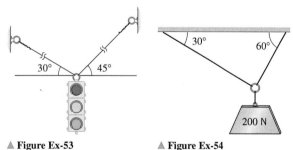

▲ Figure Ex-53          ▲ Figure Ex-54

**55.** A block weighing 300 lb is suspended by cables $A$ and $B$, as shown in the accompanying figure. Determine the forces that the block exerts along the cables.

**56.** A block weighing 100 N is suspended by cables $A$ and $B$, as shown in the accompanying figure.
(a) Use a graphing utility to graph the forces that the block exerts along cables $A$ and $B$ as functions of the "sag" $d$.

(b) Does increasing the sag increase or decrease the forces on the cables?
(c) How much sag is required if the cables cannot tolerate forces in excess of 150 N?

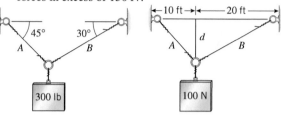

▲ Figure Ex-55          ▲ Figure Ex-56

**57.** A vector **w** is said to be a *linear combination* of the vectors $v_1$ and $v_2$ if **w** can be expressed as $w = c_1 v_1 + c_2 v_2$, where $c_1$ and $c_2$ are scalars.
(a) Find scalars $c_1$ and $c_2$ to express the vector $4\mathbf{j}$ as a linear combination of the vectors $\mathbf{v}_1 = 2\mathbf{i} - \mathbf{j}$ and $\mathbf{v}_2 = 4\mathbf{i} + 2\mathbf{j}$.
(b) Show that the vector $\langle 3, 5 \rangle$ cannot be expressed as a linear combination of the vectors $\mathbf{v}_1 = \langle 1, -3 \rangle$ and $\mathbf{v}_2 = \langle -2, 6 \rangle$.

**58.** A vector **w** is a *linear combination* of the vectors $v_1$, $v_2$, and $v_3$ if **w** can be expressed as $w = c_1 v_1 + c_2 v_2 + c_3 v_3$, where $c_1$, $c_2$, and $c_3$ are scalars.
(a) Find scalars $c_1$, $c_2$, and $c_3$ to express $\langle -1, 1, 5 \rangle$ as a linear combination of $\mathbf{v}_1 = \langle 1, 0, 1 \rangle$, $\mathbf{v}_2 = \langle 3, 2, 0 \rangle$, and $\mathbf{v}_3 = \langle 0, 1, 1 \rangle$.
(b) Show that the vector $2\mathbf{i} + \mathbf{j} - \mathbf{k}$ cannot be expressed as a linear combination of $\mathbf{v}_1 = \mathbf{i} - \mathbf{j}$, $\mathbf{v}_2 = 3\mathbf{i} + \mathbf{k}$, and $\mathbf{v}_3 = 4\mathbf{i} - \mathbf{j} + \mathbf{k}$.

**59.** Use a theorem from plane geometry to show that if **u** and **v** are vectors in 2-space or 3-space, then
$$\|u + v\| \le \|u\| + \|v\|$$
which is called the *triangle inequality for vectors*. Give some examples to illustrate this inequality.

**60.** Prove parts $(a)$, $(c)$, and $(e)$ of Theorem 11.2.6 algebraically in 2-space.

**61.** Prove parts $(d)$, $(g)$, and $(h)$ of Theorem 11.2.6 algebraically in 2-space.

**62.** Prove part $(f)$ of Theorem 11.2.6 geometrically.

**FOCUS ON CONCEPTS**

**63.** Use vectors to prove that the line segment joining the midpoints of two sides of a triangle is parallel to the third side and half as long.

**64.** Use vectors to prove that the midpoints of the sides of a quadrilateral are the vertices of a parallelogram.

**65.** Writing Do some research and then write a few paragraphs on the early history of the use of vectors in mathematics.

**66.** Writing Write a paragraph that discusses some of the similarities and differences between the rules of "vector arithmetic" and the rules of arithmetic of real numbers.

✔ **QUICK CHECK ANSWERS 11.2**

1. (a) $\sqrt{59}$ (b) $\langle 7, 9, 2 \rangle$ (c) $\langle -1, -11, 12 \rangle$ (d) $\langle 6, -2, 14 \rangle$ 2. $\dfrac{1}{\sqrt{59}}\mathbf{v} = \left\langle \dfrac{3}{\sqrt{59}}, -\dfrac{1}{\sqrt{59}}, \dfrac{7}{\sqrt{59}} \right\rangle$ 3. $\left\langle \dfrac{1}{2}, \dfrac{\sqrt{3}}{2} \right\rangle = \dfrac{1}{2}\mathbf{i} + \dfrac{\sqrt{3}}{2}\mathbf{j}$

4. (a) $\langle -3, -4, 5 \rangle$ (b) $\dfrac{1}{5}\overrightarrow{AB} = \left\langle -\dfrac{3}{5}, -\dfrac{4}{5}, 1 \right\rangle$

## 11.3 DOT PRODUCT; PROJECTIONS

*In the last section we defined three operations on vectors—addition, subtraction, and scalar multiplication. In scalar multiplication a vector is multiplied by a scalar and the result is a vector. In this section we will define a new kind of multiplication in which two vectors are multiplied to produce a scalar. This multiplication operation has many uses, some of which we will also discuss in this section.*

### DEFINITION OF THE DOT PRODUCT

> **11.3.1 DEFINITION** If $\mathbf{u} = \langle u_1, u_2 \rangle$ and $\mathbf{v} = \langle v_1, v_2 \rangle$ are vectors in 2-space, then the *dot product* of $\mathbf{u}$ and $\mathbf{v}$ is written as $\mathbf{u} \cdot \mathbf{v}$ and is defined as
>
> $$\mathbf{u} \cdot \mathbf{v} = u_1 v_1 + u_2 v_2$$
>
> Similarly, if $\mathbf{u} = \langle u_1, u_2, u_3 \rangle$ and $\mathbf{v} = \langle v_1, v_2, v_3 \rangle$ are vectors in 3-space, then their dot product is defined as
> $$\mathbf{u} \cdot \mathbf{v} = u_1 v_1 + u_2 v_2 + u_3 v_3$$

In words, the dot product of two vectors is formed by multiplying their corresponding components and adding the resulting products. Note that the dot product of two vectors is a scalar.

▶ **Example 1**

$$\langle 3, 5 \rangle \cdot \langle -1, 2 \rangle = 3(-1) + 5(2) = 7$$
$$\langle 2, 3 \rangle \cdot \langle -3, 2 \rangle = 2(-3) + 3(2) = 0$$
$$\langle 1, -3, 4 \rangle \cdot \langle 1, 5, 2 \rangle = 1(1) + (-3)(5) + 4(2) = -6$$

Here are the same computations expressed another way:

$$(3\mathbf{i} + 5\mathbf{j}) \cdot (-\mathbf{i} + 2\mathbf{j}) = 3(-1) + 5(2) = 7$$
$$(2\mathbf{i} + 3\mathbf{j}) \cdot (-3\mathbf{i} + 2\mathbf{j}) = 2(-3) + 3(2) = 0$$
$$(\mathbf{i} - 3\mathbf{j} + 4\mathbf{k}) \cdot (\mathbf{i} + 5\mathbf{j} + 2\mathbf{k}) = 1(1) + (-3)(5) + 4(2) = -6 ◀$$

**TECHNOLOGY MASTERY**

Many calculating utilities have a built-in dot product operation. If your calculating utility has this capability, use it to check the computations in Example 1.

### ALGEBRAIC PROPERTIES OF THE DOT PRODUCT

The following theorem provides some of the basic algebraic properties of the dot product.

> **11.3.2 THEOREM** *If $\mathbf{u}$, $\mathbf{v}$, and $\mathbf{w}$ are vectors in 2- or 3-space and $k$ is a scalar, then:*
>
> (*a*) $\mathbf{u} \cdot \mathbf{v} = \mathbf{v} \cdot \mathbf{u}$
>
> (*b*) $\mathbf{u} \cdot (\mathbf{v} + \mathbf{w}) = \mathbf{u} \cdot \mathbf{v} + \mathbf{u} \cdot \mathbf{w}$
>
> (*c*) $k(\mathbf{u} \cdot \mathbf{v}) = (k\mathbf{u}) \cdot \mathbf{v} = \mathbf{u} \cdot (k\mathbf{v})$
>
> (*d*) $\mathbf{v} \cdot \mathbf{v} = \|\mathbf{v}\|^2$
>
> (*e*) $\mathbf{0} \cdot \mathbf{v} = 0$

Note the difference between the two zeros that appear in part (e) of Theorem 11.3.2—the zero on the left side is the *zero vector* (boldface), whereas the zero on the right side is the *zero scalar* (lightface).

We will prove parts (*c*) and (*d*) for vectors in 3-space and leave some of the others as exercises.

PROOF (*c*)   Let $\mathbf{u} = \langle u_1, u_2, u_3 \rangle$ and $\mathbf{v} = \langle v_1, v_2, v_3 \rangle$. Then

$$k(\mathbf{u} \cdot \mathbf{v}) = k(u_1 v_1 + u_2 v_2 + u_3 v_3) = (ku_1)v_1 + (ku_2)v_2 + (ku_3)v_3 = (k\mathbf{u}) \cdot \mathbf{v}$$

Similarly, $k(\mathbf{u} \cdot \mathbf{v}) = \mathbf{u} \cdot (k\mathbf{v})$.

PROOF (*d*)   $\mathbf{v} \cdot \mathbf{v} = v_1 v_1 + v_2 v_2 + v_3 v_3 = v_1^2 + v_2^2 + v_3^2 = \|\mathbf{v}\|^2$.  ■

The following alternative form of the formula in part (*d*) of Theorem 11.3.2 provides a useful way of expressing the norm of a vector in terms of a dot product:

$$\|\mathbf{v}\| = \sqrt{\mathbf{v} \cdot \mathbf{v}} \tag{1}$$

### ■ ANGLE BETWEEN VECTORS

Suppose that $\mathbf{u}$ and $\mathbf{v}$ are nonzero vectors in 2-space or 3-space that are positioned so their initial points coincide. We define the **angle between u and v** to be the angle $\theta$ determined by the vectors that satisfies the condition $0 \leq \theta \leq \pi$ (Figure 11.3.1). In 2-space, $\theta$ is the smallest counterclockwise angle through which one of the vectors can be rotated until it aligns with the other.

The next theorem provides a way of calculating the angle between two vectors from their components.

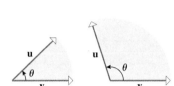

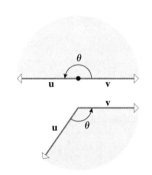

$\theta$ is the angle between $\mathbf{u}$ and $\mathbf{v}$.

▲ **Figure 11.3.1**

**11.3.3   THEOREM**   *If* $\mathbf{u}$ *and* $\mathbf{v}$ *are nonzero vectors in 2-space or 3-space, and if* $\theta$ *is the angle between them, then*

$$\cos\theta = \frac{\mathbf{u} \cdot \mathbf{v}}{\|\mathbf{u}\|\|\mathbf{v}\|} \tag{2}$$

PROOF   Suppose that the vectors $\mathbf{u}$, $\mathbf{v}$, and $\mathbf{v} - \mathbf{u}$ are positioned to form three sides of a triangle, as shown in Figure 11.3.2. It follows from the law of cosines that

$$\|\mathbf{v} - \mathbf{u}\|^2 = \|\mathbf{u}\|^2 + \|\mathbf{v}\|^2 - 2\|\mathbf{u}\|\|\mathbf{v}\|\cos\theta \tag{3}$$

Using the properties of the dot product in Theorem 11.3.2, we can rewrite the left side of this equation as

$$
\begin{aligned}
\|\mathbf{v} - \mathbf{u}\|^2 &= (\mathbf{v} - \mathbf{u}) \cdot (\mathbf{v} - \mathbf{u}) \\
&= (\mathbf{v} - \mathbf{u}) \cdot \mathbf{v} - (\mathbf{v} - \mathbf{u}) \cdot \mathbf{u} \\
&= \mathbf{v} \cdot \mathbf{v} - \mathbf{u} \cdot \mathbf{v} - \mathbf{v} \cdot \mathbf{u} + \mathbf{u} \cdot \mathbf{u} \\
&= \|\mathbf{v}\|^2 - 2\mathbf{u} \cdot \mathbf{v} + \|\mathbf{u}\|^2
\end{aligned}
$$

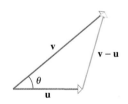

▲ **Figure 11.3.2**

Substituting this back into (3) yields

$$\|\mathbf{v}\|^2 - 2\mathbf{u} \cdot \mathbf{v} + \|\mathbf{u}\|^2 = \|\mathbf{u}\|^2 + \|\mathbf{v}\|^2 - 2\|\mathbf{u}\|\|\mathbf{v}\|\cos\theta$$

which we can simplify and rewrite as

$$\mathbf{u} \cdot \mathbf{v} = \|\mathbf{u}\|\|\mathbf{v}\|\cos\theta$$

Finally, dividing both sides of this equation by $\|\mathbf{u}\|\|\mathbf{v}\|$ yields (2).  ■

▶ **Example 2**   Find the angle between the vector $\mathbf{u} = \mathbf{i} - 2\mathbf{j} + 2\mathbf{k}$ and

(a) $\mathbf{v} = -3\mathbf{i} + 6\mathbf{j} + 2\mathbf{k}$     (b) $\mathbf{w} = 2\mathbf{i} + 7\mathbf{j} + 6\mathbf{k}$     (c) $\mathbf{z} = -3\mathbf{i} + 6\mathbf{j} - 6\mathbf{k}$

*Solution* (*a*).

$$\cos\theta = \frac{\mathbf{u} \cdot \mathbf{v}}{\|\mathbf{u}\|\|\mathbf{v}\|} = \frac{-11}{(3)(7)} = -\frac{11}{21}$$

Thus,

$$\theta = \cos^{-1}\left(-\tfrac{11}{21}\right) \approx 2.12 \text{ radians} \approx 121.6°$$

*Solution (b).*

$$\cos\theta = \frac{\mathbf{u} \cdot \mathbf{w}}{\|\mathbf{u}\|\|\mathbf{w}\|} = \frac{0}{\|\mathbf{u}\|\|\mathbf{w}\|} = 0$$

Thus, $\theta = \pi/2$, which means that the vectors are perpendicular.

*Solution (c).*

$$\cos\theta = \frac{\mathbf{u} \cdot \mathbf{z}}{\|\mathbf{u}\|\|\mathbf{z}\|} = \frac{-27}{(3)(9)} = -1$$

Thus, $\theta = \pi$, which means that the vectors are oppositely directed. (In retrospect, we could have seen this without computing $\theta$, since $\mathbf{z} = -3\mathbf{u}$.) ◄

### INTERPRETING THE SIGN OF THE DOT PRODUCT

It will often be convenient to express Formula (2) as

$$\mathbf{u} \cdot \mathbf{v} = \|\mathbf{u}\|\|\mathbf{v}\|\cos\theta \qquad (4)$$

which expresses the dot product of $\mathbf{u}$ and $\mathbf{v}$ in terms of the lengths of these vectors and the angle between them. Since $\mathbf{u}$ and $\mathbf{v}$ are assumed to be nonzero vectors, this version of the formula makes it clear that the sign of $\mathbf{u} \cdot \mathbf{v}$ is the same as the sign of $\cos\theta$. Thus, we can tell from the dot product whether the angle between two vectors is acute or obtuse or whether the vectors are perpendicular (Figure 11.3.3).

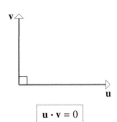

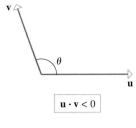

▲ **Figure 11.3.3**

**REMARK** The terms "perpendicular," "orthogonal," and "normal" are all commonly used to describe geometric objects that meet at right angles. For consistency, we will say that two vectors are *orthogonal*, a vector is *normal* to a plane, and two planes are *perpendicular*. Moreover, although the zero vector does not make a well-defined angle with other vectors, we will consider $\mathbf{0}$ to be orthogonal to *all* vectors. This convention allows us to say that $\mathbf{u}$ and $\mathbf{v}$ are orthogonal vectors if and only if $\mathbf{u} \cdot \mathbf{v} = 0$, and makes Formula (4) valid if $\mathbf{u}$ or $\mathbf{v}$ (or both) is zero.

### DIRECTION ANGLES

In an $xy$-coordinate system, the direction of a nonzero vector $\mathbf{v}$ is completely determined by the angles $\alpha$ and $\beta$ between $\mathbf{v}$ and the unit vectors $\mathbf{i}$ and $\mathbf{j}$ (Figure 11.3.4), and in an $xyz$-coordinate system the direction is completely determined by the angles $\alpha$, $\beta$, and $\gamma$ between $\mathbf{v}$ and the unit vectors $\mathbf{i}$, $\mathbf{j}$, and $\mathbf{k}$ (Figure 11.3.5). In both 2-space and 3-space the angles between a nonzero vector $\mathbf{v}$ and the vectors $\mathbf{i}$, $\mathbf{j}$, and $\mathbf{k}$ are called the *direction angles* of $\mathbf{v}$, and the cosines of those angles are called the *direction cosines* of $\mathbf{v}$. Formulas for the direction cosines of a vector can be obtained from Formula (2). For example, if $\mathbf{v} = v_1\mathbf{i} + v_2\mathbf{j} + v_3\mathbf{k}$, then

$$\cos\alpha = \frac{\mathbf{v} \cdot \mathbf{i}}{\|\mathbf{v}\|\|\mathbf{i}\|} = \frac{v_1}{\|\mathbf{v}\|}, \quad \cos\beta = \frac{\mathbf{v} \cdot \mathbf{j}}{\|\mathbf{v}\|\|\mathbf{j}\|} = \frac{v_2}{\|\mathbf{v}\|}, \quad \cos\gamma = \frac{\mathbf{v} \cdot \mathbf{k}}{\|\mathbf{v}\|\|\mathbf{k}\|} = \frac{v_3}{\|\mathbf{v}\|}$$

Thus, we have the following theorem.

▲ **Figure 11.3.4**

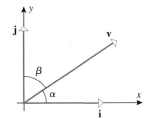

▲ **Figure 11.3.5**

**11.3.4 THEOREM** *The direction cosines of a nonzero vector* $\mathbf{v} = v_1\mathbf{i} + v_2\mathbf{j} + v_3\mathbf{k}$ *are*

$$\cos\alpha = \frac{v_1}{\|\mathbf{v}\|}, \quad \cos\beta = \frac{v_2}{\|\mathbf{v}\|}, \quad \cos\gamma = \frac{v_3}{\|\mathbf{v}\|}$$

The direction cosines of a vector $\mathbf{v} = v_1\mathbf{i} + v_2\mathbf{j} + v_3\mathbf{k}$ can be computed by normalizing $\mathbf{v}$ and reading off the components of $\mathbf{v}/\|\mathbf{v}\|$, since

$$\frac{\mathbf{v}}{\|\mathbf{v}\|} = \frac{v_1}{\|\mathbf{v}\|}\mathbf{i} + \frac{v_2}{\|\mathbf{v}\|}\mathbf{j} + \frac{v_3}{\|\mathbf{v}\|}\mathbf{k} = (\cos\alpha)\mathbf{i} + (\cos\beta)\mathbf{j} + (\cos\gamma)\mathbf{k}$$

We leave it as an exercise for you to show that the direction cosines of a vector satisfy the equation

$$\cos^2\alpha + \cos^2\beta + \cos^2\gamma = 1 \tag{5}$$

▶ **Example 3**   Find the direction cosines of the vector $\mathbf{v} = 2\mathbf{i} - 4\mathbf{j} + 4\mathbf{k}$, and approximate the direction angles to the nearest degree.

*Solution.*   First we will normalize the vector $\mathbf{v}$ and then read off the components. We have $\|\mathbf{v}\| = \sqrt{4 + 16 + 16} = 6$, so that $\mathbf{v}/\|\mathbf{v}\| = \frac{1}{3}\mathbf{i} - \frac{2}{3}\mathbf{j} + \frac{2}{3}\mathbf{k}$. Thus,

$$\cos\alpha = \tfrac{1}{3}, \quad \cos\beta = -\tfrac{2}{3}, \quad \cos\gamma = \tfrac{2}{3}$$

With the help of a calculating utility we obtain

$$\alpha = \cos^{-1}\left(\tfrac{1}{3}\right) \approx 71°, \quad \beta = \cos^{-1}\left(-\tfrac{2}{3}\right) \approx 132°, \quad \gamma = \cos^{-1}\left(\tfrac{2}{3}\right) \approx 48° \blacktriangleleft$$

▶ **Example 4**   Find the angle between a diagonal of a cube and one of its edges.

*Solution.*   Assume that the cube has side $a$, and introduce a coordinate system as shown in Figure 11.3.6. In this coordinate system the vector

$$\mathbf{d} = a\mathbf{i} + a\mathbf{j} + a\mathbf{k}$$

is a diagonal of the cube and the unit vectors $\mathbf{i}$, $\mathbf{j}$, and $\mathbf{k}$ run along the edges. By symmetry, the diagonal makes the same angle with each edge, so it is sufficient to find the angle between $\mathbf{d}$ and $\mathbf{i}$ (the direction angle $\alpha$). Thus,

$$\cos\alpha = \frac{\mathbf{d}\cdot\mathbf{i}}{\|\mathbf{d}\|\,\|\mathbf{i}\|} = \frac{a}{\|\mathbf{d}\|} = \frac{a}{\sqrt{3a^2}} = \frac{1}{\sqrt{3}}$$

and hence

$$\alpha = \cos^{-1}\left(\frac{1}{\sqrt{3}}\right) \approx 0.955 \text{ radian} \approx 54.7° \blacktriangleleft$$

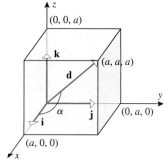

$z$
$(0, 0, a)$
$\mathbf{k}$
$(a, a, a)$
$\mathbf{d}$
$y$
$\alpha$   $\mathbf{j}$   $(0, a, 0)$
$\mathbf{i}$
$(a, 0, 0)$
$x$

▲ **Figure 11.3.6**

■ **DECOMPOSING VECTORS INTO ORTHOGONAL COMPONENTS**

In many applications it is desirable to "decompose" a vector into a sum of two orthogonal vectors with convenient specified directions. For example, Figure 11.3.7 shows a block on an inclined plane. The downward force $\mathbf{F}$ that gravity exerts on the block can be decomposed into the sum

$$\mathbf{F} = \mathbf{F}_1 + \mathbf{F}_2$$

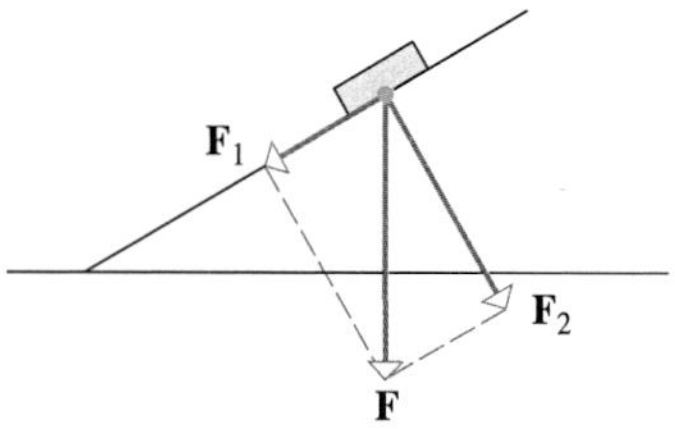

where the force $\mathbf{F}_1$ is parallel to the ramp and the force $\mathbf{F}_2$ is perpendicular to the ramp. The forces $\mathbf{F}_1$ and $\mathbf{F}_2$ are useful because $\mathbf{F}_1$ is the force that pulls the block *along* the ramp, and $\mathbf{F}_2$ is the force that the block exerts *against* the ramp.

Thus, our next objective is to develop a computational procedure for decomposing a vector into a sum of orthogonal vectors. For this purpose, suppose that $\mathbf{e}_1$ and $\mathbf{e}_2$ are two orthogonal *unit* vectors in 2-space, and suppose that we want to express a given vector $\mathbf{v}$ as a sum

$$\mathbf{v} = \mathbf{w}_1 + \mathbf{w}_2$$

$\mathbf{F}_1$
$\mathbf{F}_2$
$\mathbf{F}$

The force of gravity pulls the block against the ramp and down the ramp.

▲ **Figure 11.3.7**

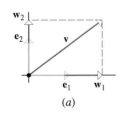

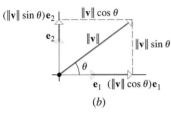

▲ **Figure 11.3.8**

so that $\mathbf{w}_1$ is a scalar multiple of $\mathbf{e}_1$ and $\mathbf{w}_2$ is a scalar multiple of $\mathbf{e}_2$ (Figure 11.3.8a). That is, we want to find scalars $k_1$ and $k_2$ such that

$$\mathbf{v} = k_1\mathbf{e}_1 + k_2\mathbf{e}_2 \tag{6}$$

We can find $k_1$ by taking the dot product of $\mathbf{v}$ with $\mathbf{e}_1$. This yields

$$\begin{aligned}
\mathbf{v} \cdot \mathbf{e}_1 &= (k_1\mathbf{e}_1 + k_2\mathbf{e}_2) \cdot \mathbf{e}_1 \\
&= k_1(\mathbf{e}_1 \cdot \mathbf{e}_1) + k_2(\mathbf{e}_2 \cdot \mathbf{e}_1) \\
&= k_1\|\mathbf{e}_1\|^2 + 0 = k_1
\end{aligned}$$

Similarly,

$$\mathbf{v} \cdot \mathbf{e}_2 = (k_1\mathbf{e}_1 + k_2\mathbf{e}_2) \cdot \mathbf{e}_2 = k_1(\mathbf{e}_1 \cdot \mathbf{e}_2) + k_2(\mathbf{e}_2 \cdot \mathbf{e}_2) = 0 + k_2\|\mathbf{e}_2\|^2 = k_2$$

Substituting these expressions for $k_1$ and $k_2$ in (6) yields

$$\mathbf{v} = (\mathbf{v} \cdot \mathbf{e}_1)\mathbf{e}_1 + (\mathbf{v} \cdot \mathbf{e}_2)\mathbf{e}_2 \tag{7}$$

In this formula we call $(\mathbf{v} \cdot \mathbf{e}_1)\mathbf{e}_1$ and $(\mathbf{v} \cdot \mathbf{e}_2)\mathbf{e}_2$ the ***vector components*** of $\mathbf{v}$ along $\mathbf{e}_1$ and $\mathbf{e}_2$, respectively; and we call $\mathbf{v} \cdot \mathbf{e}_1$ and $\mathbf{v} \cdot \mathbf{e}_2$ the ***scalar components*** of $\mathbf{v}$ along $\mathbf{e}_1$ and $\mathbf{e}_2$, respectively. If $\theta$ denotes the angle between $\mathbf{v}$ and $\mathbf{e}_1$, and the angle between $\mathbf{v}$ and $\mathbf{e}_2$ is $\pi/2$ or less, then the scalar components of $\mathbf{v}$ can be written in trigonometric form as

$$\mathbf{v} \cdot \mathbf{e}_1 = \|\mathbf{v}\|\cos\theta \quad \text{and} \quad \mathbf{v} \cdot \mathbf{e}_2 = \|\mathbf{v}\|\sin\theta \tag{8}$$

(Figure 11.3.8b). Moreover, the vector components of $\mathbf{v}$ can be expressed as

$$(\mathbf{v} \cdot \mathbf{e}_1)\mathbf{e}_1 = (\|\mathbf{v}\|\cos\theta)\mathbf{e}_1 \quad \text{and} \quad (\mathbf{v} \cdot \mathbf{e}_2)\mathbf{e}_2 = (\|\mathbf{v}\|\sin\theta)\mathbf{e}_2 \tag{9}$$

and the decomposition (6) can be expressed as

$$\mathbf{v} = (\|\mathbf{v}\|\cos\theta)\mathbf{e}_1 + (\|\mathbf{v}\|\sin\theta)\mathbf{e}_2 \tag{10}$$

provided the angle between $\mathbf{v}$ and $\mathbf{e}_2$ is at most $\pi/2$.

Note that the vector components of $\mathbf{v}$ along $\mathbf{e}_1$ and $\mathbf{e}_2$ are *vectors*, whereas the scalar components of $\mathbf{v}$ along $\mathbf{e}_1$ and $\mathbf{e}_2$ are *numbers*.

▶ **Example 5**    Let

$$\mathbf{v} = \langle 2, 3\rangle, \quad \mathbf{e}_1 = \left\langle \frac{1}{\sqrt{2}}, \frac{1}{\sqrt{2}} \right\rangle, \quad \text{and} \quad \mathbf{e}_2 = \left\langle -\frac{1}{\sqrt{2}}, \frac{1}{\sqrt{2}} \right\rangle$$

Find the scalar components of $\mathbf{v}$ along $\mathbf{e}_1$ and $\mathbf{e}_2$ and the vector components of $\mathbf{v}$ along $\mathbf{e}_1$ and $\mathbf{e}_2$.

*Solution.*    The scalar components of $\mathbf{v}$ along $\mathbf{e}_1$ and $\mathbf{e}_2$ are

$$\mathbf{v} \cdot \mathbf{e}_1 = 2\left(\frac{1}{\sqrt{2}}\right) + 3\left(\frac{1}{\sqrt{2}}\right) = \frac{5}{\sqrt{2}}$$

$$\mathbf{v} \cdot \mathbf{e}_2 = 2\left(-\frac{1}{\sqrt{2}}\right) + 3\left(\frac{1}{\sqrt{2}}\right) = \frac{1}{\sqrt{2}}$$

so the vector components are

$$(\mathbf{v} \cdot \mathbf{e}_1)\mathbf{e}_1 = \frac{5}{\sqrt{2}}\left\langle \frac{1}{\sqrt{2}}, \frac{1}{\sqrt{2}} \right\rangle = \left\langle \frac{5}{2}, \frac{5}{2} \right\rangle$$

$$(\mathbf{v} \cdot \mathbf{e}_2)\mathbf{e}_2 = \frac{1}{\sqrt{2}}\left\langle -\frac{1}{\sqrt{2}}, \frac{1}{\sqrt{2}} \right\rangle = \left\langle -\frac{1}{2}, \frac{1}{2} \right\rangle \quad ◀$$

Notice that in Example 5

$(\mathbf{v} \cdot \mathbf{e}_1)\mathbf{e}_1 + (\mathbf{v} \cdot \mathbf{e}_2)\mathbf{e}_2 = \langle 2, 3\rangle = \mathbf{v}$

as guaranteed by (7).

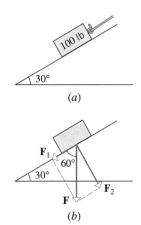

▲ **Figure 11.3.9**

▶ **Example 6**  A rope is attached to a 100 lb block on a ramp that is inclined at an angle of 30° with the ground (Figure 11.3.9a). How much force does the block exert against the ramp, and how much force must be applied to the rope in a direction parallel to the ramp to prevent the block from sliding down the ramp? (Assume that the ramp is smooth, that is, exerts no frictional forces.)

***Solution.***   Let **F** denote the downward force of gravity on the block (so $\|\mathbf{F}\| = 100$ lb), and let $\mathbf{F}_1$ and $\mathbf{F}_2$ be the vector components of **F** parallel and perpendicular to the ramp (as shown in Figure 11.3.9b). The lengths of $\mathbf{F}_1$ and $\mathbf{F}_2$ are

$$\|\mathbf{F}_1\| = \|\mathbf{F}\|\cos 60° = 100\left(\frac{1}{2}\right) = 50 \text{ lb}$$

$$\|\mathbf{F}_2\| = \|\mathbf{F}\|\sin 60° = 100\left(\frac{\sqrt{3}}{2}\right) \approx 86.6 \text{ lb}$$

Thus, the block exerts a force of approximately 86.6 lb against the ramp, and it requires a force of 50 lb to prevent the block from sliding down the ramp. ◀

### ORTHOGONAL PROJECTIONS

The vector components of **v** along $\mathbf{e}_1$ and $\mathbf{e}_2$ in (7) are also called the *orthogonal projections* of **v** on $\mathbf{e}_1$ and $\mathbf{e}_2$ and are commonly denoted by

$$\text{proj}_{\mathbf{e}_1}\mathbf{v} = (\mathbf{v} \cdot \mathbf{e}_1)\mathbf{e}_1 \quad \text{and} \quad \text{proj}_{\mathbf{e}_2}\mathbf{v} = (\mathbf{v} \cdot \mathbf{e}_2)\mathbf{e}_2$$

In general, if **e** is a unit vector, then we define the ***orthogonal projection of* v *on* e** to be

$$\text{proj}_{\mathbf{e}}\mathbf{v} = (\mathbf{v} \cdot \mathbf{e})\mathbf{e} \tag{11}$$

The orthogonal projection of **v** on an arbitrary nonzero vector **b** can be obtained by normalizing **b** and then applying Formula (11); that is,

$$\text{proj}_{\mathbf{b}}\mathbf{v} = \left(\mathbf{v} \cdot \frac{\mathbf{b}}{\|\mathbf{b}\|}\right)\left(\frac{\mathbf{b}}{\|\mathbf{b}\|}\right)$$

which can be rewritten as

$$\text{proj}_{\mathbf{b}}\mathbf{v} = \frac{\mathbf{v} \cdot \mathbf{b}}{\|\mathbf{b}\|^2}\mathbf{b} \tag{12}$$

Geometrically, if **b** and **v** have a common initial point, then $\text{proj}_{\mathbf{b}}\mathbf{v}$ is the vector that is determined when a perpendicular is dropped from the terminal point of **v** to the line through **b** (illustrated in Figure 11.3.10 in two cases).

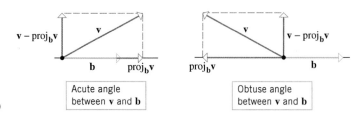

▶ **Figure 11.3.10**

Moreover, it is evident from Figure 11.3.10 that if we subtract $\text{proj}_{\mathbf{b}}\mathbf{v}$ from **v**, then the resulting vector

$$\mathbf{v} - \text{proj}_{\mathbf{b}}\mathbf{v}$$

will be orthogonal to **b**; we call this the ***vector component of* v *orthogonal to* b**.

Stated informally, the orthogonal projection $\text{proj}_{\mathbf{b}}\mathbf{v}$ is the "shadow" that $\mathbf{v}$ casts on the line through $\mathbf{b}$.

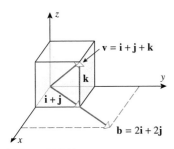

▲ **Figure 11.3.11**

▶ **Example 7**   Find the orthogonal projection of $\mathbf{v} = \mathbf{i} + \mathbf{j} + \mathbf{k}$ on $\mathbf{b} = 2\mathbf{i} + 2\mathbf{j}$, and then find the vector component of $\mathbf{v}$ orthogonal to $\mathbf{b}$.

*Solution.*   We have

$$\mathbf{v} \cdot \mathbf{b} = (\mathbf{i} + \mathbf{j} + \mathbf{k}) \cdot (2\mathbf{i} + 2\mathbf{j}) = 2 + 2 + 0 = 4$$

$$\|\mathbf{b}\|^2 = 2^2 + 2^2 = 8$$

Thus, the orthogonal projection of $\mathbf{v}$ on $\mathbf{b}$ is

$$\text{proj}_{\mathbf{b}}\mathbf{v} = \frac{\mathbf{v} \cdot \mathbf{b}}{\|\mathbf{b}\|^2}\mathbf{b} = \frac{4}{8}(2\mathbf{i} + 2\mathbf{j}) = \mathbf{i} + \mathbf{j}$$

and the vector component of $\mathbf{v}$ orthogonal to $\mathbf{b}$ is

$$\mathbf{v} - \text{proj}_{\mathbf{b}}\mathbf{v} = (\mathbf{i} + \mathbf{j} + \mathbf{k}) - (\mathbf{i} + \mathbf{j}) = \mathbf{k}$$

These results are consistent with Figure 11.3.11. ◀

### ▮ WORK

In Section 6.6 we discussed the work done by a constant force acting on an object that moves along a line. We defined the work $W$ done on the object by a constant force of magnitude $F$ acting in the direction of motion over a distance $d$ to be

$$W = Fd = \text{force} \times \text{distance} \tag{13}$$

If we let $\mathbf{F}$ denote a force vector of magnitude $\|\mathbf{F}\| = F$ *acting in the direction of motion,* then we can write (13) as
$$W = \|\mathbf{F}\|d$$

Furthermore, if we assume that the object moves along a line from point $P$ to point $Q$, then $d = \|\overrightarrow{PQ}\|$, so that the work can be expressed entirely in vector form as

$$W = \|\mathbf{F}\|\|\overrightarrow{PQ}\|$$

Note that in Formula (14) the quantity $\|\mathbf{F}\|\cos\theta$ is the scalar component of force along the displacement vector. Thus, in the case where $\cos\theta > 0$, a force of magnitude $\|\mathbf{F}\|$ acting at an angle $\theta$ does the same work as a force of magnitude $\|\mathbf{F}\|\cos\theta$ acting in the direction of motion.

(Figure 11.3.12*a*). The vector $\overrightarrow{PQ}$ is called the *displacement vector* for the object. In the case where a constant force $\mathbf{F}$ is not in the direction of motion, but rather makes an angle $\theta$ with the displacement vector, then we *define* the work $W$ done by $\mathbf{F}$ to be

$$W = (\|\mathbf{F}\|\cos\theta)\|\overrightarrow{PQ}\| = \mathbf{F} \cdot \overrightarrow{PQ} \tag{14}$$

(Figure 11.3.12*b*).

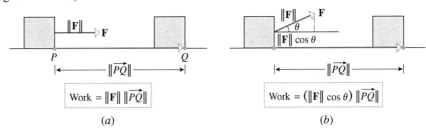

▲ **Figure 11.3.12**

It follows from Formula (14) that the work $W$ can be expressed as $W = (\|\mathbf{F}\|\cos\theta)\|\overrightarrow{PQ}\|$ or as $W = \mathbf{F} \cdot \overrightarrow{PQ}$. Although these two expressions are mathematically equivalent, in practice it may be more convenient to use one of them instead of the other.

### ▶ Example 8

(a) A wagon is pulled horizontally by exerting a constant force of 10 lb on the handle at an angle of 60° with the horizontal. How much work is done in moving the wagon 50 ft?

(b) A force of $\mathbf{F} = 3\mathbf{i} - \mathbf{j} + 2\mathbf{k}$ lb is applied to a point that moves on a line from $P(-1, 1, 2)$ to $Q(3, 0, -2)$. If distance is measured in feet, how much work is done?

*Solution (a).* With $\|\mathbf{F}\| = 10$, $\theta = 60°$, and $\|\overrightarrow{PQ}\| = 50$, it follows that the work done is

$$W = (\|\mathbf{F}\|\cos\theta)\|\overrightarrow{PQ}\| = 10 \cdot \frac{1}{2} \cdot 50 = 250 \text{ ft·lb}$$

*Solution (b).* Since $\overrightarrow{PQ} = (3 - (-1))\mathbf{i} + (0 - 1)\mathbf{j} + (-2 - 2)\mathbf{k} = 4\mathbf{i} - \mathbf{j} - 4\mathbf{k}$, the work done is

$$W = \mathbf{F} \cdot \overrightarrow{PQ} = (3\mathbf{i} - \mathbf{j} + 2\mathbf{k}) \cdot (4\mathbf{i} - \mathbf{j} - 4\mathbf{k}) = 12 + 1 - 8 = 5 \text{ ft·lb} \blacktriangleleft$$

## ✔QUICK CHECK EXERCISES 11.3   *(See page 794 for answers.)*

1. $\langle 3, 1, -2 \rangle \cdot \langle 6, 0, 5 \rangle = $ _____

2. Suppose that $\mathbf{u}$, $\mathbf{v}$, and $\mathbf{w}$ are vectors in 3-space such that $\|\mathbf{u}\| = 5$, $\mathbf{u} \cdot \mathbf{v} = 7$, and $\mathbf{u} \cdot \mathbf{w} = -3$.
   (a) $\mathbf{u} \cdot \mathbf{u} = $ _____    (b) $\mathbf{v} \cdot \mathbf{u} = $ _____
   (c) $\mathbf{u} \cdot (\mathbf{v} - \mathbf{w}) = $ _____    (d) $\mathbf{u} \cdot (2\mathbf{w}) = $ _____

3. For the vectors $\mathbf{u}$ and $\mathbf{v}$ in the preceding exercise, if the angle between $\mathbf{u}$ and $\mathbf{v}$ is $\pi/3$, then $\|\mathbf{v}\| = $ _____.

4. The direction cosines of $\langle 2, -1, 3 \rangle$ are $\cos\alpha = $ _____, $\cos\beta = $ _____, and $\cos\gamma = $ _____.

5. The orthogonal projection of $\mathbf{v} = 10\mathbf{i}$ on $\mathbf{b} = -3\mathbf{i} + \mathbf{j}$ is _____.

## EXERCISE SET 11.3   © CAS

1. In each part, find the dot product of the vectors and the cosine of the angle between them.
   (a) $\mathbf{u} = \mathbf{i} + 2\mathbf{j}$, $\mathbf{v} = 6\mathbf{i} - 8\mathbf{j}$
   (b) $\mathbf{u} = \langle -7, -3 \rangle$, $\mathbf{v} = \langle 0, 1 \rangle$
   (c) $\mathbf{u} = \mathbf{i} - 3\mathbf{j} + 7\mathbf{k}$, $\mathbf{v} = 8\mathbf{i} - 2\mathbf{j} - 2\mathbf{k}$
   (d) $\mathbf{u} = \langle -3, 1, 2 \rangle$, $\mathbf{v} = \langle 4, 2, -5 \rangle$

2. In each part use the given information to find $\mathbf{u} \cdot \mathbf{v}$.
   (a) $\|\mathbf{u}\| = 1$, $\|\mathbf{v}\| = 2$, the angle between $\mathbf{u}$ and $\mathbf{v}$ is $\pi/6$.
   (b) $\|\mathbf{u}\| = 2$, $\|\mathbf{v}\| = 3$, the angle between $\mathbf{u}$ and $\mathbf{v}$ is $135°$.

3. In each part, determine whether $\mathbf{u}$ and $\mathbf{v}$ make an acute angle, an obtuse angle, or are orthogonal.
   (a) $\mathbf{u} = 7\mathbf{i} + 3\mathbf{j} + 5\mathbf{k}$, $\mathbf{v} = -8\mathbf{i} + 4\mathbf{j} + 2\mathbf{k}$
   (b) $\mathbf{u} = 6\mathbf{i} + \mathbf{j} + 3\mathbf{k}$, $\mathbf{v} = 4\mathbf{i} - 6\mathbf{k}$
   (c) $\mathbf{u} = \langle 1, 1, 1 \rangle$, $\mathbf{v} = \langle -1, 0, 0 \rangle$
   (d) $\mathbf{u} = \langle 4, 1, 6 \rangle$, $\mathbf{v} = \langle -3, 0, 2 \rangle$

### FOCUS ON CONCEPTS

4. Does the triangle in 3-space with vertices $(-1, 2, 3)$, $(2, -2, 0)$, and $(3, 1, -4)$ have an obtuse angle? Justify your answer.

5. The accompanying figure shows eight vectors that are equally spaced around a circle of radius 1. Find the dot product of $\mathbf{v}_0$ with each of the other seven vectors.

6. The accompanying figure shows six vectors that are equally spaced around a circle of radius 5. Find the dot product of $\mathbf{v}_0$ with each of the other five vectors.

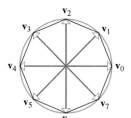
▲ Figure Ex-5

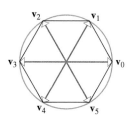
▲ Figure Ex-6

7. (a) Use vectors to show that $A(2, -1, 1)$, $B(3, 2, -1)$, and $C(7, 0, -2)$ are vertices of a right triangle. At which vertex is the right angle?
   (b) Use vectors to find the interior angles of the triangle with vertices $(-1, 0)$, $(2, -1)$, and $(1, 4)$. Express your answers to the nearest degree.

8. (a) Show that if $\mathbf{v} = a\mathbf{i} + b\mathbf{j}$ is a vector in 2-space, then the vectors
$$\mathbf{v}_1 = -b\mathbf{i} + a\mathbf{j} \quad \text{and} \quad \mathbf{v}_2 = b\mathbf{i} - a\mathbf{j}$$
   are both orthogonal to $\mathbf{v}$.
   (b) Use the result in part (a) to find two unit vectors that are orthogonal to the vector $\mathbf{v} = 3\mathbf{i} - 2\mathbf{j}$. Sketch the vectors $\mathbf{v}$, $\mathbf{v}_1$, and $\mathbf{v}_2$.

9. Explain why each of the following expressions makes no sense.
   (a) $\mathbf{u} \cdot (\mathbf{v} \cdot \mathbf{w})$    (b) $(\mathbf{u} \cdot \mathbf{v}) + \mathbf{w}$
   (c) $\|\mathbf{u} \cdot \mathbf{v}\|$    (d) $k \cdot (\mathbf{u} + \mathbf{v})$

**10.** Explain why each of the following expressions makes sense.

(a) $(\mathbf{u} \cdot \mathbf{v})\mathbf{w}$       (b) $(\mathbf{u} \cdot \mathbf{v})(\mathbf{v} \cdot \mathbf{w})$

(c) $\mathbf{u} \cdot \mathbf{v} + k$        (d) $(k\mathbf{u}) \cdot \mathbf{v}$

**11.** Verify parts (b) and (c) of Theorem 11.3.2 for the vectors $\mathbf{u} = 6\mathbf{i} - \mathbf{j} + 2\mathbf{k}$, $\mathbf{v} = 2\mathbf{i} + 7\mathbf{j} + 4\mathbf{k}$, $\mathbf{w} = \mathbf{i} + \mathbf{j} - 3\mathbf{k}$ and $k = -5$.

**12.** Let $\mathbf{u} = \langle 1, 2 \rangle$, $\mathbf{v} = \langle 4, -2 \rangle$, and $\mathbf{w} = \langle 6, 0 \rangle$. Find

(a) $\mathbf{u} \cdot (7\mathbf{v} + \mathbf{w})$       (b) $\|(\mathbf{u} \cdot \mathbf{w})\mathbf{w}\|$

(c) $\|\mathbf{u}\|(\mathbf{v} \cdot \mathbf{w})$       (d) $(\|\mathbf{u}\|\mathbf{v}) \cdot \mathbf{w}$.

**13.** Find $r$ so that the vector from the point $A(1, -1, 3)$ to the point $B(3, 0, 5)$ is orthogonal to the vector from $A$ to the point $P(r, r, r)$.

**14.** Find two unit vectors in 2-space that make an angle of $45°$ with $4\mathbf{i} + 3\mathbf{j}$.

**15–16** Find the direction cosines of $\mathbf{v}$ and confirm that they satisfy Equation (5). Then use the direction cosines to approximate the direction angles to the nearest degree. ■

**15.** (a) $\mathbf{v} = \mathbf{i} + \mathbf{j} - \mathbf{k}$       (b) $\mathbf{v} = 2\mathbf{i} - 2\mathbf{j} + \mathbf{k}$

**16.** (a) $\mathbf{v} = 3\mathbf{i} - 2\mathbf{j} - 6\mathbf{k}$       (b) $\mathbf{v} = 3\mathbf{i} - 4\mathbf{k}$

**FOCUS ON CONCEPTS**

**17.** Show that the direction cosines of a vector satisfy
$$\cos^2 \alpha + \cos^2 \beta + \cos^2 \gamma = 1$$

**18.** Let $\theta$ and $\lambda$ be the angles shown in the accompanying figure. Show that the direction cosines of $\mathbf{v}$ can be expressed as
$$\cos \alpha = \cos \lambda \cos \theta$$
$$\cos \beta = \cos \lambda \sin \theta$$
$$\cos \gamma = \sin \lambda$$

[*Hint:* Express $\mathbf{v}$ in component form and normalize.]

**19.** The accompanying figure shows a cube.

(a) Find the angle between the vectors $\mathbf{d}$ and $\mathbf{u}$ to the nearest degree.

(b) Make a conjecture about the angle between the vectors $\mathbf{d}$ and $\mathbf{v}$, and confirm your conjecture by computing the angle.

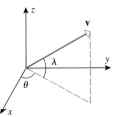
▲ **Figure Ex-18**

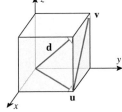
▲ **Figure Ex-19**

**20.** Show that two nonzero vectors $\mathbf{v}_1$ and $\mathbf{v}_2$ are orthogonal if and only if their direction cosines satisfy
$$\cos \alpha_1 \cos \alpha_2 + \cos \beta_1 \cos \beta_2 + \cos \gamma_1 \cos \gamma_2 = 0$$

**21.** Use the result in Exercise 18 to find the direction angles of the vector shown in the accompanying figure to the nearest degree.

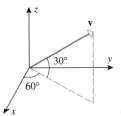
◀ **Figure Ex-21**

**22.** Find, to the nearest degree, the acute angle formed by two diagonals of a cube.

**23.** Find, to the nearest degree, the angles that a diagonal of a box with dimensions 10 cm by 15 cm by 25 cm makes with the edges of the box.

**24.** In each part, find the vector component of $\mathbf{v}$ along $\mathbf{b}$ and the vector component of $\mathbf{v}$ orthogonal to $\mathbf{b}$. Then sketch the vectors $\mathbf{v}$, $\text{proj}_{\mathbf{b}}\mathbf{v}$, and $\mathbf{v} - \text{proj}_{\mathbf{b}}\mathbf{v}$.

(a) $\mathbf{v} = 2\mathbf{i} - \mathbf{j}$, $\mathbf{b} = 3\mathbf{i} + 4\mathbf{j}$

(b) $\mathbf{v} = \langle 4, 5 \rangle$, $\mathbf{b} = \langle 1, -2 \rangle$

(c) $\mathbf{v} = -3\mathbf{i} - 2\mathbf{j}$, $\mathbf{b} = 2\mathbf{i} + \mathbf{j}$

**25.** In each part, find the vector component of $\mathbf{v}$ along $\mathbf{b}$ and the vector component of $\mathbf{v}$ orthogonal to $\mathbf{b}$.

(a) $\mathbf{v} = 2\mathbf{i} - \mathbf{j} + 3\mathbf{k}$, $\mathbf{b} = \mathbf{i} + 2\mathbf{j} + 2\mathbf{k}$

(b) $\mathbf{v} = \langle 4, -1, 7 \rangle$, $\mathbf{b} = \langle 2, 3, -6 \rangle$

**26–27** Express the vector $\mathbf{v}$ as the sum of a vector parallel to $\mathbf{b}$ and a vector orthogonal to $\mathbf{b}$. ■

**26.** (a) $\mathbf{v} = 2\mathbf{i} - 4\mathbf{j}$, $\mathbf{b} = \mathbf{i} + \mathbf{j}$

(b) $\mathbf{v} = 3\mathbf{i} + \mathbf{j} - 2\mathbf{k}$, $\mathbf{b} = 2\mathbf{i} - \mathbf{k}$

(c) $\mathbf{v} = 4\mathbf{i} - 2\mathbf{j} + 6\mathbf{k}$, $\mathbf{b} = -2\mathbf{i} + \mathbf{j} - 3\mathbf{k}$

**27.** (a) $\mathbf{v} = \langle -3, 5 \rangle$, $\mathbf{b} = \langle 1, 1 \rangle$

(b) $\mathbf{v} = \langle -2, 1, 6 \rangle$, $\mathbf{b} = \langle 0, -2, 1 \rangle$

(c) $\mathbf{v} = \langle 1, 4, 1 \rangle$, $\mathbf{b} = \langle 3, -2, 5 \rangle$

**28–31 True–False** Determine whether the statement is true or false. Explain your answer. ■

**28.** If $\mathbf{a} \cdot \mathbf{b} = \mathbf{a} \cdot \mathbf{c}$ and $\mathbf{a} \neq \mathbf{0}$, then $\mathbf{b} = \mathbf{c}$.

**29.** If $\mathbf{v}$ and $\mathbf{w}$ are nonzero orthogonal vectors, then $\mathbf{v} + \mathbf{w} \neq \mathbf{0}$.

**30.** If $\mathbf{u}$ is a unit vector that is parallel to a nonzero vector $\mathbf{v}$, then $\mathbf{u} \cdot \mathbf{v} = \pm\|\mathbf{v}\|$.

**31.** If $\mathbf{v}$ and $\mathbf{b}$ are nonzero vectors, then the orthogonal projection of $\mathbf{v}$ on $\mathbf{b}$ is a vector that is parallel to $\mathbf{b}$.

**32.** If $L$ is a line in 2-space or 3-space that passes through the points $A$ and $B$, then the distance from a point $P$ to the line $L$ is equal to the length of the component of the vector $\overrightarrow{AP}$ that is orthogonal to the vector $\overrightarrow{AB}$ (see the accompanying figure). Use this result to find the distance from the point $P(1, 0)$ to the line through $A(2, -3)$ and $B(5, 1)$.

◀ **Figure Ex-32**

33. Use the method of Exercise 32 to find the distance from the point $P(-3, 1, 2)$ to the line through $A(1, 1, 0)$ and $B(-2, 3, -4)$.

34. As shown in the accompanying figure, a child with mass 34 kg is seated on a smooth (frictionless) playground slide that is inclined at an angle of 27° with the horizontal. Estimate the force that the child exerts on the slide, and estimate how much force must be applied in the direction of **P** to prevent the child from sliding down the slide. Take the acceleration due to gravity to be 9.8 m/s².

35. For the child in Exercise 34, estimate how much force must be applied in the direction of **Q** (shown in the accompanying figure) to prevent the child from sliding down the slide?

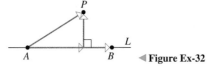

▲ **Figure Ex-34**          ▲ **Figure Ex-35**

36. Suppose that the slide in Exercise 34 is 4 m long. Estimate the work done by gravity if the child slides from the top of the slide to the bottom.

37. A box is dragged along the floor by a rope that applies a force of 50 lb at an angle of 60° with the floor. How much work is done in moving the box 15 ft?

38. Find the work done by a force $\mathbf{F} = -3\mathbf{j}$ pounds applied to a point that moves on a line from $(1, 3)$ to $(4, 7)$. Assume that distance is measured in feet.

39. A force of $\mathbf{F} = 4\mathbf{i} - 6\mathbf{j} + \mathbf{k}$ newtons is applied to a point that moves a distance of 15 meters in the direction of the vector $\mathbf{i} + \mathbf{j} + \mathbf{k}$. How much work is done?

40. A boat travels 100 meters due north while the wind exerts a force of 500 newtons toward the northeast. How much work does the wind do?

**FOCUS ON CONCEPTS**

41. Let **u** and **v** be adjacent sides of a parallelogram. Use vectors to prove that the diagonals of the parallelogram are perpendicular if the sides are equal in length.

42. Let **u** and **v** be adjacent sides of a parallelogram. Use vectors to prove that the parallelogram is a rectangle if the diagonals are equal in length.

43. Prove that
$$\|\mathbf{u} + \mathbf{v}\|^2 + \|\mathbf{u} - \mathbf{v}\|^2 = 2\|\mathbf{u}\|^2 + 2\|\mathbf{v}\|^2$$
and interpret the result geometrically by translating it into a theorem about parallelograms.

44. Prove: $\mathbf{u} \cdot \mathbf{v} = \frac{1}{4}\|\mathbf{u} + \mathbf{v}\|^2 - \frac{1}{4}\|\mathbf{u} - \mathbf{v}\|^2$.

45. Show that if $\mathbf{v}_1$, $\mathbf{v}_2$, and $\mathbf{v}_3$ are mutually orthogonal nonzero vectors in 3-space, and if a vector **v** in 3-space is expressed as
$$\mathbf{v} = c_1\mathbf{v}_1 + c_2\mathbf{v}_2 + c_3\mathbf{v}_3$$
then the scalars $c_1$, $c_2$, and $c_3$ are given by the formulas
$$c_i = (\mathbf{v} \cdot \mathbf{v}_i)/\|\mathbf{v}_i\|^2, \quad i = 1, 2, 3$$

46. Show that the three vectors
$$\mathbf{v}_1 = 3\mathbf{i} - \mathbf{j} + 2\mathbf{k}, \quad \mathbf{v}_2 = \mathbf{i} + \mathbf{j} - \mathbf{k}, \quad \mathbf{v}_3 = \mathbf{i} - 5\mathbf{j} - 4\mathbf{k}$$
are mutually orthogonal, and then use the result of Exercise 45 to find scalars $c_1$, $c_2$, and $c_3$ so that
$$c_1\mathbf{v}_1 + c_2\mathbf{v}_2 + c_3\mathbf{v}_3 = \mathbf{i} - \mathbf{j} + \mathbf{k}$$

47. For each $x$ in $(-\infty, +\infty)$, let $\mathbf{u}(x)$ be the vector from the origin to the point $P(x, y)$ on the curve $y = x^2 + 1$, and $\mathbf{v}(x)$ the vector from the origin to the point $Q(x, y)$ on the line $y = -x - 1$.
   (a) Use a CAS to find, to the nearest degree, the minimum angle between $\mathbf{u}(x)$ and $\mathbf{v}(x)$ for $x$ in $(-\infty, +\infty)$.
   (b) Determine whether there are any real values of $x$ for which $\mathbf{u}(x)$ and $\mathbf{v}(x)$ are orthogonal.

48. Let **u** be a unit vector in the $xy$-plane of an $xyz$-coordinate system, and let **v** be a unit vector in the $yz$-plane. Let $\theta_1$ be the angle between **u** and **i**, let $\theta_2$ be the angle between **v** and **k**, and let $\theta$ be the angle between **u** and **v**.
   (a) Show that $\cos\theta = \pm\sin\theta_1\sin\theta_2$.
   (b) Find $\theta$ if $\theta$ is acute and $\theta_1 = \theta_2 = 45°$.
   (c) Use a CAS to find, to the nearest degree, the maximum and minimum values of $\theta$ if $\theta$ is acute and $\theta_2 = 2\theta_1$.

49. Prove parts (b) and (e) of Theorem 11.3.2 for vectors in 3-space.

50. **Writing** Discuss some of the similarities and differences between the multiplication properties of real numbers and those of the dot product of vectors.

51. **Writing** Discuss the merits of the following claim: "Suppose an algebraic identity involves only the addition, subtraction, and multiplication of real numbers. If the numbers are replaced by vectors, and the multiplication is replaced by the dot product, then an identity involving vectors will result."

✔ **QUICK CHECK ANSWERS 11.3**

1. 8   2. (a) 25 (b) 7 (c) 10 (d) −6   3. $\frac{14}{5}$   4. $\dfrac{2}{\sqrt{14}}$; $-\dfrac{1}{\sqrt{14}}$; $\dfrac{3}{\sqrt{14}}$   5. $9\mathbf{i} - 3\mathbf{j}$

## 11.4  CROSS PRODUCT

*In many applications of vectors in mathematics, physics, and engineering, there is a need to find a vector that is orthogonal to two given vectors. In this section we will discuss a new type of vector multiplication that can be used for this purpose.*

### ◼ DETERMINANTS

Some of the concepts that we will develop in this section require basic ideas about **determinants**, which are functions that assign numerical values to square arrays of numbers. For example, if $a_1$, $a_2$, $b_1$, and $b_2$ are real numbers, then we define a **2 × 2 determinant** by

$$\begin{vmatrix} a_1 & a_2 \\ b_1 & b_2 \end{vmatrix} = a_1 b_2 - a_2 b_1 \tag{1}$$

The purpose of the arrows is to help you remember the formula—the determinant is the product of the entries on the rightward arrow minus the product of the entries on the leftward arrow. For example,

$$\begin{vmatrix} 3 & -2 \\ 4 & 5 \end{vmatrix} = (3)(5) - (-2)(4) = 15 + 8 = 23$$

A **3 × 3 determinant** is defined in terms of 2 × 2 determinants by

$$\begin{vmatrix} a_1 & a_2 & a_3 \\ b_1 & b_2 & b_3 \\ c_1 & c_2 & c_3 \end{vmatrix} = a_1 \begin{vmatrix} b_2 & b_3 \\ c_2 & c_3 \end{vmatrix} - a_2 \begin{vmatrix} b_1 & b_3 \\ c_1 & c_3 \end{vmatrix} + a_3 \begin{vmatrix} b_1 & b_2 \\ c_1 & c_2 \end{vmatrix} \tag{2}$$

The right side of this formula is easily remembered by noting that $a_1$, $a_2$, and $a_3$ are the entries in the first "row" of the left side, and the 2 × 2 determinants on the right side arise by deleting the first row and an appropriate column from the left side. The pattern is as follows:

$$\begin{vmatrix} a_1 & a_2 & a_3 \\ b_1 & b_2 & b_3 \\ c_1 & c_2 & c_3 \end{vmatrix} = a_1 \begin{vmatrix} a_1 & a_2 & a_3 \\ b_1 & b_2 & b_3 \\ c_1 & c_2 & c_3 \end{vmatrix} - a_2 \begin{vmatrix} a_1 & a_2 & a_3 \\ b_1 & b_2 & b_3 \\ c_1 & c_2 & c_3 \end{vmatrix} + a_3 \begin{vmatrix} a_1 & a_2 & a_3 \\ b_1 & b_2 & b_3 \\ c_1 & c_2 & c_3 \end{vmatrix}$$

For example,

$$\begin{vmatrix} 3 & -2 & -5 \\ 1 & 4 & -4 \\ 0 & 3 & 2 \end{vmatrix} = 3 \begin{vmatrix} 4 & -4 \\ 3 & 2 \end{vmatrix} - (-2) \begin{vmatrix} 1 & -4 \\ 0 & 2 \end{vmatrix} + (-5) \begin{vmatrix} 1 & 4 \\ 0 & 3 \end{vmatrix}$$

$$= 3(20) + 2(2) - 5(3) = 49$$

There are also definitions of 4 × 4 determinants, 5 × 5 determinants, and higher, but we will not need them in this text. Properties of determinants are studied in a branch of mathematics called **linear algebra**, but we will only need the two properties stated in the following theorem.

---

**11.4.1  THEOREM**

(a)  *If two rows in the array of a determinant are the same, then the value of the determinant is 0.*

(b)  *Interchanging two rows in the array of a determinant multiplies its value by −1.*

---

We will give the proofs of parts (*a*) and (*b*) for $2 \times 2$ determinants and leave the proofs for $3 \times 3$ determinants as exercises.

**PROOF (*a*)**

$$\begin{vmatrix} a_1 & a_2 \\ a_1 & a_2 \end{vmatrix} = a_1 a_2 - a_2 a_1 = 0$$

**PROOF (*b*)**

$$\begin{vmatrix} b_1 & b_2 \\ a_1 & a_2 \end{vmatrix} = b_1 a_2 - b_2 a_1 = -(a_1 b_2 - a_2 b_1) = -\begin{vmatrix} a_1 & a_2 \\ b_1 & b_2 \end{vmatrix} \quad \blacksquare$$

## ■ CROSS PRODUCT

We now turn to the main concept in this section.

---

**11.4.2 DEFINITION** If $\mathbf{u} = \langle u_1, u_2, u_3 \rangle$ and $\mathbf{v} = \langle v_1, v_2, v_3 \rangle$ are vectors in 3-space, then the ***cross product*** $\mathbf{u} \times \mathbf{v}$ is the vector defined by

$$\mathbf{u} \times \mathbf{v} = \begin{vmatrix} u_2 & u_3 \\ v_2 & v_3 \end{vmatrix} \mathbf{i} - \begin{vmatrix} u_1 & u_3 \\ v_1 & v_3 \end{vmatrix} \mathbf{j} + \begin{vmatrix} u_1 & u_2 \\ v_1 & v_2 \end{vmatrix} \mathbf{k} \tag{3}$$

or, equivalently,

$$\mathbf{u} \times \mathbf{v} = (u_2 v_3 - u_3 v_2)\mathbf{i} - (u_1 v_3 - u_3 v_1)\mathbf{j} + (u_1 v_2 - u_2 v_1)\mathbf{k} \tag{4}$$

---

Observe that the right side of Formula (3) has the same form as the right side of Formula (2), the difference being notation and the order of the factors in the three terms. Thus, we can rewrite (3) as

$$\mathbf{u} \times \mathbf{v} = \begin{vmatrix} \mathbf{i} & \mathbf{j} & \mathbf{k} \\ u_1 & u_2 & u_3 \\ v_1 & v_2 & v_3 \end{vmatrix} \tag{5}$$

However, this is just a mnemonic device and not a true determinant since the entries in a determinant are numbers, not vectors.

---

▶ **Example 1** Let $\mathbf{u} = \langle 1, 2, -2 \rangle$ and $\mathbf{v} = \langle 3, 0, 1 \rangle$. Find

$$\text{(a) } \mathbf{u} \times \mathbf{v} \qquad \text{(b) } \mathbf{v} \times \mathbf{u}$$

*Solution (a).*

$$\mathbf{u} \times \mathbf{v} = \begin{vmatrix} \mathbf{i} & \mathbf{j} & \mathbf{k} \\ 1 & 2 & -2 \\ 3 & 0 & 1 \end{vmatrix}$$

$$= \begin{vmatrix} 2 & -2 \\ 0 & 1 \end{vmatrix} \mathbf{i} - \begin{vmatrix} 1 & -2 \\ 3 & 1 \end{vmatrix} \mathbf{j} + \begin{vmatrix} 1 & 2 \\ 3 & 0 \end{vmatrix} \mathbf{k} = 2\mathbf{i} - 7\mathbf{j} - 6\mathbf{k}$$

*Solution (b).* We could use the method of part (a), but it is really not necessary to perform any computations. We need only observe that reversing $\mathbf{u}$ and $\mathbf{v}$ interchanges the second and third rows in (5), which in turn interchanges the rows in the arrays for the $2 \times 2$ determinants in (3). But interchanging the rows in the array of a $2 \times 2$ determinant reverses its sign, so the net effect of reversing the factors in a cross product is to reverse the signs of the components. Thus, by inspection

$$\mathbf{v} \times \mathbf{u} = -(\mathbf{u} \times \mathbf{v}) = -2\mathbf{i} + 7\mathbf{j} + 6\mathbf{k} \blacktriangleleft$$

▶ **Example 2** Show that $\mathbf{u} \times \mathbf{u} = \mathbf{0}$ for any vector $\mathbf{u}$ in 3-space.

*Solution.* We could let $\mathbf{u} = u_1\mathbf{i} + u_2\mathbf{j} + u_3\mathbf{k}$ and apply the method in part (a) of Example 1 to show that

$$\mathbf{u} \times \mathbf{u} = \begin{vmatrix} \mathbf{i} & \mathbf{j} & \mathbf{k} \\ u_1 & u_2 & u_3 \\ u_1 & u_2 & u_3 \end{vmatrix} = 0$$

However, the actual computations are unnecessary. We need only observe that if the two factors in a cross product are the same, then each $2 \times 2$ determinant in (3) is zero because its array has identical rows. Thus, $\mathbf{u} \times \mathbf{u} = \mathbf{0}$ by inspection. ◀

■ **ALGEBRAIC PROPERTIES OF THE CROSS PRODUCT**
Our next goal is to establish some of the basic algebraic properties of the cross product. As you read the discussion, keep in mind the essential differences between the cross product and the dot product:

- The cross product is defined only for vectors in 3-space, whereas the dot product is defined for vectors in 2-space and 3-space.
- The cross product of two vectors is a vector, whereas the dot product of two vectors is a scalar.

The main algebraic properties of the cross product are listed in the next theorem.

Whereas the order of the factors does not matter for ordinary multiplication, or for dot products, it does matter for cross products. Specifically, part (a) of Theorem 11.4.3 shows that reversing the order of the factors in a cross product reverses the direction of the resulting vector.

---

**11.4.3** THEOREM *If $\mathbf{u}$, $\mathbf{v}$, and $\mathbf{w}$ are any vectors in 3-space and $k$ is any scalar, then:*

(a) $\mathbf{u} \times \mathbf{v} = -(\mathbf{v} \times \mathbf{u})$

(b) $\mathbf{u} \times (\mathbf{v} + \mathbf{w}) = (\mathbf{u} \times \mathbf{v}) + (\mathbf{u} \times \mathbf{w})$

(c) $(\mathbf{u} + \mathbf{v}) \times \mathbf{w} = (\mathbf{u} \times \mathbf{w}) + (\mathbf{v} \times \mathbf{w})$

(d) $k(\mathbf{u} \times \mathbf{v}) = (k\mathbf{u}) \times \mathbf{v} = \mathbf{u} \times (k\mathbf{v})$

(e) $\mathbf{u} \times \mathbf{0} = \mathbf{0} \times \mathbf{u} = \mathbf{0}$

(f) $\mathbf{u} \times \mathbf{u} = \mathbf{0}$

---

Parts (a) and (f) were addressed in Examples 1 and 2. The other proofs are left as exercises.

The following cross products occur so frequently that it is helpful to be familiar with them:

$$\begin{array}{lll} \mathbf{i} \times \mathbf{j} = \mathbf{k} & \mathbf{j} \times \mathbf{k} = \mathbf{i} & \mathbf{k} \times \mathbf{i} = \mathbf{j} \\ \mathbf{j} \times \mathbf{i} = -\mathbf{k} & \mathbf{k} \times \mathbf{j} = -\mathbf{i} & \mathbf{i} \times \mathbf{k} = -\mathbf{j} \end{array} \tag{6}$$

These results are easy to obtain; for example,

$$\mathbf{i} \times \mathbf{j} = \begin{vmatrix} \mathbf{i} & \mathbf{j} & \mathbf{k} \\ 1 & 0 & 0 \\ 0 & 1 & 0 \end{vmatrix} = \begin{vmatrix} 0 & 0 \\ 1 & 0 \end{vmatrix}\mathbf{i} - \begin{vmatrix} 1 & 0 \\ 0 & 0 \end{vmatrix}\mathbf{j} + \begin{vmatrix} 1 & 0 \\ 0 & 1 \end{vmatrix}\mathbf{k} = \mathbf{k}$$

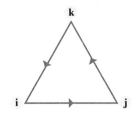

▲ Figure 11.4.1

However, rather than computing these cross products each time you need them, you can use the diagram in Figure 11.4.1. In this diagram, the cross product of two consecutive vectors in the counterclockwise direction is the next vector around, and the cross product of two consecutive vectors in the clockwise direction is the negative of the next vector around.

**WARNING**

We can write a product of three real numbers as $uvw$ since the associative law $u(vw) = (uv)w$ ensures that the same value for the product results no matter how the factors are grouped. However, the associative law *does not* hold for cross products. For example,

$$\mathbf{i} \times (\mathbf{j} \times \mathbf{j}) = \mathbf{i} \times \mathbf{0} = \mathbf{0} \quad \text{and} \quad (\mathbf{i} \times \mathbf{j}) \times \mathbf{j} = \mathbf{k} \times \mathbf{j} = -\mathbf{i}$$

so that $\mathbf{i} \times (\mathbf{j} \times \mathbf{j}) \neq (\mathbf{i} \times \mathbf{j}) \times \mathbf{j}$. Thus, we cannot write a cross product with three vectors as $\mathbf{u} \times \mathbf{v} \times \mathbf{w}$, since this expression is ambiguous without parentheses.

### ■ GEOMETRIC PROPERTIES OF THE CROSS PRODUCT

The following theorem shows that the cross product of two vectors is orthogonal to both factors. This property of the cross product will be used many times in the following sections.

---

**11.4.4** THEOREM *If* **u** *and* **v** *are vectors in 3-space, then:*

(*a*) $\mathbf{u} \cdot (\mathbf{u} \times \mathbf{v}) = 0$     (**u** × **v** *is orthogonal to* **u**)

(*b*) $\mathbf{v} \cdot (\mathbf{u} \times \mathbf{v}) = 0$     (**u** × **v** *is orthogonal to* **v**)

---

We will prove part (*a*). The proof of part (*b*) is similar.

**PROOF** (*a*) Let $\mathbf{u} = \langle u_1, u_2, u_3 \rangle$ and $\mathbf{v} = \langle v_1, v_2, v_3 \rangle$. Then from (4)

$$\mathbf{u} \times \mathbf{v} = \langle u_2 v_3 - u_3 v_2, u_3 v_1 - u_1 v_3, u_1 v_2 - u_2 v_1 \rangle \tag{7}$$

so that

$$\mathbf{u} \cdot (\mathbf{u} \times \mathbf{v}) = u_1(u_2 v_3 - u_3 v_2) + u_2(u_3 v_1 - u_1 v_3) + u_3(u_1 v_2 - u_2 v_1) = 0 \ \blacksquare$$

---

▶ **Example 3** Find a vector that is orthogonal to both of the vectors $\mathbf{u} = \langle 2, -1, 3 \rangle$ and $\mathbf{v} = \langle -7, 2, -1 \rangle$.

*Solution.* By Theorem 11.4.4, the vector **u** × **v** will be orthogonal to both **u** and **v**. We compute that

$$\mathbf{u} \times \mathbf{v} = \begin{vmatrix} \mathbf{i} & \mathbf{j} & \mathbf{k} \\ 2 & -1 & 3 \\ -7 & 2 & -1 \end{vmatrix}$$

Confirm that **u** × **v** in Example 3 is orthogonal to both **u** and **v** by computing **u** · (**u** × **v**) and **v** · (**u** × **v**).

$$= \begin{vmatrix} -1 & 3 \\ 2 & -1 \end{vmatrix}\mathbf{i} - \begin{vmatrix} 2 & 3 \\ -7 & -1 \end{vmatrix}\mathbf{j} + \begin{vmatrix} 2 & -1 \\ -7 & 2 \end{vmatrix}\mathbf{k} = -5\mathbf{i} - 19\mathbf{j} - 3\mathbf{k} \ ◀$$

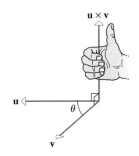

▲ **Figure 11.4.2**

It can be proved that if **u** and **v** are nonzero and nonparallel vectors, then the direction of **u** × **v** relative to **u** and **v** is determined by a right-hand rule;* that is, if the fingers of the right hand are cupped so they curl from **u** toward **v** in the direction of rotation that takes **u** into **v** in less than 180°, then the thumb will point (roughly) in the direction of **u** × **v** (Figure 11.4.2). For example, we stated in (6) that

$$\mathbf{i} \times \mathbf{j} = \mathbf{k}, \quad \mathbf{j} \times \mathbf{k} = \mathbf{i}, \quad \mathbf{k} \times \mathbf{i} = \mathbf{j}$$

all of which are consistent with the right-hand rule (verify).

The next theorem lists some more important geometric properties of the cross product.

---

**11.4.5** **THEOREM** *Let **u** and **v** be nonzero vectors in 3-space, and let θ be the angle between these vectors when they are positioned so their initial points coincide.*

(a) $\|\mathbf{u} \times \mathbf{v}\| = \|\mathbf{u}\| \|\mathbf{v}\| \sin \theta$

(b) *The area A of the parallelogram that has **u** and **v** as adjacent sides is*

$$A = \|\mathbf{u} \times \mathbf{v}\| \tag{8}$$

(c) $\mathbf{u} \times \mathbf{v} = \mathbf{0}$ *if and only if **u** and **v** are parallel vectors, that is, if and only if they are scalar multiples of one another.*

---

**PROOF** (*a*)

$$\|\mathbf{u}\| \|\mathbf{v}\| \sin \theta = \|\mathbf{u}\| \|\mathbf{v}\| \sqrt{1 - \cos^2 \theta}$$

$$= \|\mathbf{u}\| \|\mathbf{v}\| \sqrt{1 - \frac{(\mathbf{u} \cdot \mathbf{v})^2}{\|\mathbf{u}\|^2 \|\mathbf{v}\|^2}} \quad \boxed{\text{Theorem 11.3.3}}$$

$$= \sqrt{\|\mathbf{u}\|^2 \|\mathbf{v}\|^2 - (\mathbf{u} \cdot \mathbf{v})^2}$$

$$= \sqrt{(u_1^2 + u_2^2 + u_3^2)(v_1^2 + v_2^2 + v_3^2) - (u_1 v_1 + u_2 v_2 + u_3 v_3)^2}$$

$$= \sqrt{(u_2 v_3 - u_3 v_2)^2 + (u_1 v_3 - u_3 v_1)^2 + (u_1 v_2 - u_2 v_1)^2}$$

$$= \|\mathbf{u} \times \mathbf{v}\| \quad \boxed{\text{See Formula (4).}}$$

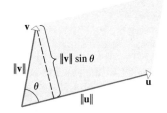

▲ **Figure 11.4.3**

**PROOF** (*b*)   Referring to Figure 11.4.3, the parallelogram that has **u** and **v** as adjacent sides can be viewed as having base $\|\mathbf{u}\|$ and altitude $\|\mathbf{v}\| \sin \theta$. Thus, its area $A$ is

$$A = (\text{base})(\text{altitude}) = \|\mathbf{u}\| \|\mathbf{v}\| \sin \theta = \|\mathbf{u} \times \mathbf{v}\|$$

**PROOF** (*c*)   Since **u** and **v** are assumed to be nonzero vectors, it follows from part (*a*) that $\mathbf{u} \times \mathbf{v} = \mathbf{0}$ if and only if $\sin \theta = 0$; this is true if and only if $\theta = 0$ or $\theta = \pi$ (since $0 \le \theta \le \pi$). Geometrically, this means that $\mathbf{u} \times \mathbf{v} = \mathbf{0}$ if and only if **u** and **v** are parallel vectors. ∎

---

▶ **Example 4**   Find the area of the triangle that is determined by the points $P_1(2, 2, 0)$, $P_2(-1, 0, 2)$, and $P_3(0, 4, 3)$.

---

*Recall that we agreed to consider only right-handed coordinate systems in this text. Had we used left-handed systems instead, a "left-hand rule" would apply here.

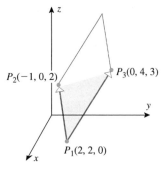

▲ **Figure 11.4.4**

*Solution.* The area $A$ of the triangle is half the area of the parallelogram determined by the vectors $\overrightarrow{P_1P_2}$ and $\overrightarrow{P_1P_3}$ (Figure 11.4.4). But $\overrightarrow{P_1P_2} = \langle -3, -2, 2 \rangle$ and $\overrightarrow{P_1P_3} = \langle -2, 2, 3 \rangle$, so

$$\overrightarrow{P_1P_2} \times \overrightarrow{P_1P_3} = \langle -10, 5, -10 \rangle$$

(verify), and consequently

$$A = \tfrac{1}{2} \| \overrightarrow{P_1P_2} \times \overrightarrow{P_1P_3} \| = \tfrac{15}{2} \ \blacktriangleleft$$

■ **SCALAR TRIPLE PRODUCTS**

If $\mathbf{u} = \langle u_1, u_2, u_3 \rangle$, $\mathbf{v} = \langle v_1, v_2, v_3 \rangle$, and $\mathbf{w} = \langle w_1, w_2, w_3 \rangle$ are vectors in 3-space, then the number

$$\mathbf{u} \cdot (\mathbf{v} \times \mathbf{w})$$

is called the *scalar triple product* of $\mathbf{u}$, $\mathbf{v}$, and $\mathbf{w}$. It is not necessary to compute the dot product and cross product to evaluate a scalar triple product—the value can be obtained directly from the formula

$$\mathbf{u} \cdot (\mathbf{v} \times \mathbf{w}) = \begin{vmatrix} u_1 & u_2 & u_3 \\ v_1 & v_2 & v_3 \\ w_1 & w_2 & w_3 \end{vmatrix} \tag{9}$$

the validity of which can be seen by writing

$$\mathbf{u} \cdot (\mathbf{v} \times \mathbf{w}) = \mathbf{u} \cdot \left( \begin{vmatrix} v_2 & v_3 \\ w_2 & w_3 \end{vmatrix} \mathbf{i} - \begin{vmatrix} v_1 & v_3 \\ w_1 & w_3 \end{vmatrix} \mathbf{j} + \begin{vmatrix} v_1 & v_2 \\ w_1 & w_2 \end{vmatrix} \mathbf{k} \right)$$

$$= u_1 \begin{vmatrix} v_2 & v_3 \\ w_2 & w_3 \end{vmatrix} - u_2 \begin{vmatrix} v_1 & v_3 \\ w_1 & w_3 \end{vmatrix} + u_3 \begin{vmatrix} v_1 & v_2 \\ w_1 & w_2 \end{vmatrix}$$

$$= \begin{vmatrix} u_1 & u_2 & u_3 \\ v_1 & v_2 & v_3 \\ w_1 & w_2 & w_3 \end{vmatrix}$$

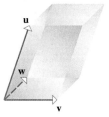

▲ **Figure 11.4.5**

It follows from Formula (10) that

$$\mathbf{u} \cdot (\mathbf{v} \times \mathbf{w}) = \pm V$$

The $+$ occurs when $\mathbf{u}$ makes an acute angle with $\mathbf{v} \times \mathbf{w}$ and the $-$ occurs when it makes an obtuse angle.

▶ **Example 5** Calculate the scalar triple product $\mathbf{u} \cdot (\mathbf{v} \times \mathbf{w})$ of the vectors

$$\mathbf{u} = 3\mathbf{i} - 2\mathbf{j} - 5\mathbf{k}, \quad \mathbf{v} = \mathbf{i} + 4\mathbf{j} - 4\mathbf{k}, \quad \mathbf{w} = 3\mathbf{j} + 2\mathbf{k}$$

*Solution.*

$$\mathbf{u} \cdot (\mathbf{v} \times \mathbf{w}) = \begin{vmatrix} 3 & -2 & -5 \\ 1 & 4 & -4 \\ 0 & 3 & 2 \end{vmatrix} = 49 \ \blacktriangleleft$$

■ **GEOMETRIC PROPERTIES OF THE SCALAR TRIPLE PRODUCT**

If $\mathbf{u}$, $\mathbf{v}$, and $\mathbf{w}$ are nonzero vectors in 3-space that are positioned so their initial points coincide, then these vectors form the adjacent sides of a parallelepiped (Figure 11.4.5). The following theorem establishes a relationship between the volume of this parallelepiped and the scalar triple product of the sides.

---

**11.4.6  THEOREM**  *Let $\mathbf{u}$, $\mathbf{v}$, and $\mathbf{w}$ be nonzero vectors in 3-space.*

*(a)   The volume $V$ of the parallelepiped that has $\mathbf{u}$, $\mathbf{v}$, and $\mathbf{w}$ as adjacent edges is*

$$V = |\mathbf{u} \cdot (\mathbf{v} \times \mathbf{w})| \tag{10}$$

*(b)   $\mathbf{u} \cdot (\mathbf{v} \times \mathbf{w}) = 0$ if and only if $\mathbf{u}$, $\mathbf{v}$, and $\mathbf{w}$ lie in the same plane.*

---

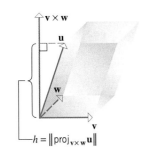

▲ **Figure 11.4.6**

**PROOF** (*a*)   Referring to Figure 11.4.6, let us regard the base of the parallelepiped with **u**, **v**, and **w** as adjacent sides to be the parallelogram determined by **v** and **w**. Thus, the area of the base is $\|\mathbf{v} \times \mathbf{w}\|$, and the altitude $h$ of the parallelepiped (shown in the figure) is the length of the orthogonal projection of **u** on the vector $\mathbf{v} \times \mathbf{w}$. Therefore, from Formula (12) of Section 11.3 we have

$$h = \|\text{proj}_{\mathbf{v} \times \mathbf{w}}\mathbf{u}\| = \frac{|\mathbf{u} \cdot (\mathbf{v} \times \mathbf{w})|}{\|\mathbf{v} \times \mathbf{w}\|^2}\|\mathbf{v} \times \mathbf{w}\| = \frac{|\mathbf{u} \cdot (\mathbf{v} \times \mathbf{w})|}{\|\mathbf{v} \times \mathbf{w}\|}$$

It now follows that the volume of the parallelepiped is

$$V = (\text{area of base})(\text{height}) = \|\mathbf{v} \times \mathbf{w}\|h = |\mathbf{u} \cdot (\mathbf{v} \times \mathbf{w})|$$

**PROOF** (*b*)   The vectors **u**, **v**, and **w** lie in the same plane if and only if the parallelepiped with these vectors as adjacent sides has volume zero (why?). Thus, from part (*a*) the vectors lie in the same plane if and only if $\mathbf{u} \cdot (\mathbf{v} \times \mathbf{w}) = 0$.  ■

### ALGEBRAIC PROPERTIES OF THE SCALAR TRIPLE PRODUCT

We observed earlier in this section that the expression $\mathbf{u} \times \mathbf{v} \times \mathbf{w}$ must be avoided because it is ambiguous without parentheses. However, the expression $\mathbf{u} \cdot \mathbf{v} \times \mathbf{w}$ is not ambiguous—it has to mean $\mathbf{u} \cdot (\mathbf{v} \times \mathbf{w})$ and not $(\mathbf{u} \cdot \mathbf{v}) \times \mathbf{w}$ because we cannot form the cross product of a scalar and a vector. Similarly, the expression $\mathbf{u} \times \mathbf{v} \cdot \mathbf{w}$ must mean $(\mathbf{u} \times \mathbf{v}) \cdot \mathbf{w}$ and not $\mathbf{u} \times (\mathbf{v} \cdot \mathbf{w})$. Thus, when you see an expression of the form $\mathbf{u} \cdot \mathbf{v} \times \mathbf{w}$ or $\mathbf{u} \times \mathbf{v} \cdot \mathbf{w}$, the cross product is formed first and the dot product second.

Since interchanging two rows of a determinant multiplies its value by $-1$, making two row interchanges in a determinant has no effect on its value. This being the case, it follows that

$$\mathbf{u} \cdot (\mathbf{v} \times \mathbf{w}) = \mathbf{w} \cdot (\mathbf{u} \times \mathbf{v}) = \mathbf{v} \cdot (\mathbf{w} \times \mathbf{u}) \qquad (11)$$

> A good way to remember Formula (11) is to observe that the second expression in the formula can be obtained from the first by leaving the dot, cross, and parentheses fixed, moving the first two vectors to the right, and bringing the third vector to the first position. The same procedure produces the third expression from the second and the first expression from the third (verify).

since the $3 \times 3$ determinants that are used to compute these scalar triple products can be obtained from one another by two row interchanges (verify).

Another useful formula can be obtained by rewriting the first equality in (11) as

$$\mathbf{u} \cdot (\mathbf{v} \times \mathbf{w}) = (\mathbf{u} \times \mathbf{v}) \cdot \mathbf{w}$$

and then omitting the superfluous parentheses to obtain

$$\mathbf{u} \cdot \mathbf{v} \times \mathbf{w} = \mathbf{u} \times \mathbf{v} \cdot \mathbf{w} \qquad (12)$$

In words, this formula states that the dot and cross in a scalar triple product can be interchanged (provided the factors are grouped appropriately).

### DOT AND CROSS PRODUCTS ARE COORDINATE INDEPENDENT

In Definitions 11.3.1 and 11.4.2 we defined the dot product and the cross product of two vectors in terms of the components of those vectors in a coordinate system. Thus, it is theoretically possible that changing the coordinate system might change $\mathbf{u} \cdot \mathbf{v}$ or $\mathbf{u} \times \mathbf{v}$, since the components of a vector depend on the coordinate system that is chosen. However, the relationships

$$\mathbf{u} \cdot \mathbf{v} = \|\mathbf{u}\|\|\mathbf{v}\|\cos\theta \qquad (13)$$

> This independence of a coordinate system is important in applications because it allows us to choose any convenient coordinate system for solving a problem with full confidence that the choice will not affect computations that involve dot products or cross products.

$$\|\mathbf{u} \times \mathbf{v}\| = \|\mathbf{u}\|\|\mathbf{v}\|\sin\theta \qquad (14)$$

that were obtained in Theorems 11.3.3 and 11.4.5 show that this is not the case. Formula (13) shows that the value of $\mathbf{u} \cdot \mathbf{v}$ depends only on the lengths of the vectors and the angle between them—not on the coordinate system. Similarly, Formula (14), in combination with the right-hand rule and Theorem 11.4.4, shows that $\mathbf{u} \times \mathbf{v}$ does not depend on the coordinate system (as long as it is right-handed).

World Perspectives/Getty Images

*Astronauts use tools that are designed to limit forces that would impart unintended rotational motion to a satellite.*

■ **MOMENTS AND ROTATIONAL MOTION IN 3-SPACE**

Cross products play an important role in describing rotational motion in 3-space. For example, suppose that an astronaut on a satellite repair mission in space applies a force **F** at a point $Q$ on the surface of a spherical satellite. If the force is directed along a line that passes through the center $P$ of the satellite, then Newton's Second Law of Motion implies that the force will accelerate the satellite in the direction of **F**. However, if the astronaut applies the same force at an angle $\theta$ with the vector $\overrightarrow{PQ}$, then **F** will tend to cause a rotation, as well as an acceleration in the direction of **F**. To see why this is so, let us resolve **F** into a sum of orthogonal components $\mathbf{F} = \mathbf{F}_1 + \mathbf{F}_2$, where $\mathbf{F}_1$ is the orthogonal projection of **F** on the vector $\overrightarrow{PQ}$ and $\mathbf{F}_2$ is the component of **F** orthogonal to $\overrightarrow{PQ}$ (Figure 11.4.7). Since the force $\mathbf{F}_1$ acts along the line through the center of the satellite, it contributes to the linear acceleration of the satellite but does not cause any rotation. However, the force $\mathbf{F}_2$ is tangent to the circle around the satellite in the plane of **F** and $\overrightarrow{PQ}$, so it causes the satellite to rotate about an axis that is perpendicular to that plane.

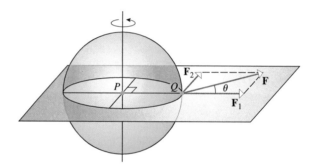

▶ **Figure 11.4.7**

You know from your own experience that the "tendency" for rotation about an axis depends both on the amount of force and how far from the axis it is applied. For example, it is easier to close a door by pushing on its outer edge than applying the same force close to the hinges. In fact, the tendency of rotation of the satellite can be measured by

$$\|\overrightarrow{PQ}\|\|\mathbf{F}_2\| \quad \boxed{\text{distance from the center} \times \text{magnitude of the force}} \tag{15}$$

However, $\|\mathbf{F}_2\| = \|\mathbf{F}\|\sin\theta$, so we can rewrite (15) as

$$\|\overrightarrow{PQ}\|\|\mathbf{F}\|\sin\theta = \|\overrightarrow{PQ} \times \mathbf{F}\|$$

This is called the **scalar moment** or **torque** of **F** about the point $P$. Scalar moments have units of force times distance—pound-feet or newton-meters, for example. The vector $\overrightarrow{PQ} \times \mathbf{F}$ is called the **vector moment** or **torque vector** of **F** about $P$.

Recalling that the direction of $\overrightarrow{PQ} \times \mathbf{F}$ is determined by the right-hand rule, it follows that the direction of rotation about $P$ that results by applying the force **F** at the point $Q$ is counterclockwise looking down the axis of $\overrightarrow{PQ} \times \mathbf{F}$ (Figure 11.4.7). Thus, the vector moment $\overrightarrow{PQ} \times \mathbf{F}$ captures the essential information about the rotational effect of the force—the magnitude of the cross product provides the scalar moment of the force, and the cross product vector itself provides the axis and direction of rotation.

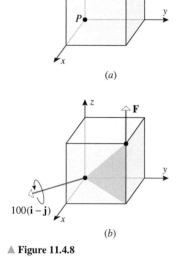

▲ **Figure 11.4.8**

▶ **Example 6** Figure 11.4.8*a* shows a force **F** of 100 N applied in the positive $z$-direction at the point $Q(1, 1, 1)$ of a cube whose sides have a length of 1 m. Assuming that the cube is free to rotate about the point $P(0, 0, 0)$ (the origin), find the scalar moment of the force about $P$, and describe the direction of rotation.

***Solution.*** The force vector is $\mathbf{F} = 100\mathbf{k}$, and the vector from $P$ to $Q$ is $\overrightarrow{PQ} = \mathbf{i} + \mathbf{j} + \mathbf{k}$, so the vector moment of $\mathbf{F}$ about $P$ is

$$\overrightarrow{PQ} \times \mathbf{F} = \begin{vmatrix} \mathbf{i} & \mathbf{j} & \mathbf{k} \\ 1 & 1 & 1 \\ 0 & 0 & 100 \end{vmatrix} = 100\mathbf{i} - 100\mathbf{j}$$

Thus, the scalar moment of $\mathbf{F}$ about $P$ is $\|100\mathbf{i} - 100\mathbf{j}\| = 100\sqrt{2} \approx 141$ N·m, and the direction of rotation is counterclockwise looking along the vector $100\mathbf{i} - 100\mathbf{j} = 100(\mathbf{i} - \mathbf{j})$ toward its initial point (Figure 11.4.8*b*). ◄

---

✔ **QUICK CHECK EXERCISES 11.4**    *(See page 805 for answers.)*

**1.** (a) $\begin{vmatrix} 3 & 2 \\ 4 & 5 \end{vmatrix} = $ _____    (b) $\begin{vmatrix} 3 & 2 & 1 \\ 3 & 2 & 1 \\ 5 & 5 & 5 \end{vmatrix} = $ _____

**2.** $\langle 1, 2, 0 \rangle \times \langle 3, 0, 4 \rangle = $ _____

**3.** Suppose that $\mathbf{u}$, $\mathbf{v}$, and $\mathbf{w}$ are vectors in 3-space such that $\mathbf{u} \times \mathbf{v} = \langle 2, 7, 3 \rangle$ and $\mathbf{u} \times \mathbf{w} = \langle -5, 4, 0 \rangle$.
(a) $\mathbf{u} \times \mathbf{u} = $ _____    (b) $\mathbf{v} \times \mathbf{u} = $ _____

(c) $\mathbf{u} \times (\mathbf{v} + \mathbf{w}) = $ _____
(d) $\mathbf{u} \times (2\mathbf{w}) = $ _____

**4.** Let $\mathbf{u} = \mathbf{i} - 5\mathbf{k}$, $\mathbf{v} = 2\mathbf{i} - 4\mathbf{j} + \mathbf{k}$, and $\mathbf{w} = 3\mathbf{i} - 2\mathbf{j} + 5\mathbf{k}$.
(a) $\mathbf{u} \cdot (\mathbf{v} \times \mathbf{w}) = $ _____
(b) The volume of the parallelepiped that has $\mathbf{u}$, $\mathbf{v}$, and $\mathbf{w}$ as adjacent edges is $V = $ _____.

---

**EXERCISE SET 11.4**    □ CAS

**1.** (a) Use a determinant to find the cross product

$$\mathbf{i} \times (\mathbf{i} + \mathbf{j} + \mathbf{k})$$

(b) Check your answer in part (a) by rewriting the cross product as

$$\mathbf{i} \times (\mathbf{i} + \mathbf{j} + \mathbf{k}) = (\mathbf{i} \times \mathbf{i}) + (\mathbf{i} \times \mathbf{j}) + (\mathbf{i} \times \mathbf{k})$$

and evaluating each term.

**2.** In each part, use the two methods in Exercise 1 to find
(a) $\mathbf{j} \times (\mathbf{i} + \mathbf{j} + \mathbf{k})$    (b) $\mathbf{k} \times (\mathbf{i} + \mathbf{j} + \mathbf{k})$.

**3–6** Find $\mathbf{u} \times \mathbf{v}$ and check that it is orthogonal to both $\mathbf{u}$ and $\mathbf{v}$. ▪

**3.** $\mathbf{u} = \langle 1, 2, -3 \rangle$, $\mathbf{v} = \langle -4, 1, 2 \rangle$

**4.** $\mathbf{u} = 3\mathbf{i} + 2\mathbf{j} - \mathbf{k}$, $\mathbf{v} = -\mathbf{i} - 3\mathbf{j} + \mathbf{k}$

**5.** $\mathbf{u} = \langle 0, 1, -2 \rangle$, $\mathbf{v} = \langle 3, 0, -4 \rangle$

**6.** $\mathbf{u} = 4\mathbf{i} + \mathbf{k}$, $\mathbf{v} = 2\mathbf{i} - \mathbf{j}$

**7.** Let $\mathbf{u} = \langle 2, -1, 3 \rangle$, $\mathbf{v} = \langle 0, 1, 7 \rangle$, and $\mathbf{w} = \langle 1, 4, 5 \rangle$. Find
(a) $\mathbf{u} \times (\mathbf{v} \times \mathbf{w})$    (b) $(\mathbf{u} \times \mathbf{v}) \times \mathbf{w}$
(c) $(\mathbf{u} \times \mathbf{v}) \times (\mathbf{v} \times \mathbf{w})$    (d) $(\mathbf{v} \times \mathbf{w}) \times (\mathbf{u} \times \mathbf{v})$.

□ **8.** Use a CAS or a calculating utility that can compute determinants or cross products to solve Exercise 7.

**9.** Find the direction cosines of $\mathbf{u} \times \mathbf{v}$ for the vectors $\mathbf{u}$ and $\mathbf{v}$ in the accompanying figure.

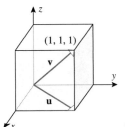

◄ **Figure Ex-9**

**10.** Find two unit vectors that are orthogonal to both

$$\mathbf{u} = -7\mathbf{i} + 3\mathbf{j} + \mathbf{k}, \quad \mathbf{v} = 2\mathbf{i} + 4\mathbf{k}$$

**11.** Find two unit vectors that are normal to the plane determined by the points $A(0, -2, 1)$, $B(1, -1, -2)$, and $C(-1, 1, 0)$.

**12.** Find two unit vectors that are parallel to the $yz$-plane and are orthogonal to the vector $3\mathbf{i} - \mathbf{j} + 2\mathbf{k}$.

**13–16 True–False** Determine whether the statement is true or false. Explain your answer. ▪

**13.** If the cross product of two nonzero vectors is the zero vector, then each of the two vectors is a scalar multiple of the other.

**14.** For any three vectors $\mathbf{a}$, $\mathbf{b}$, and $\mathbf{c}$, we have $\mathbf{a} \times (\mathbf{b} \times \mathbf{c}) = (\mathbf{a} \times \mathbf{b}) \times \mathbf{c}$.

**15.** If $\mathbf{v} \times \mathbf{u} = \mathbf{v} \times \mathbf{w}$ and if $\mathbf{v} \neq \mathbf{0}$, then $\mathbf{u} = \mathbf{w}$.

**16.** If $\mathbf{u} = a\mathbf{v} + b\mathbf{w}$, then $\mathbf{u} \cdot \mathbf{v} \times \mathbf{w} = 0$.

**17–18** Find the area of the parallelogram that has **u** and **v** as adjacent sides. ■

**17.** $\mathbf{u} = \mathbf{i} - \mathbf{j} + 2\mathbf{k}$, $\mathbf{v} = 3\mathbf{j} + \mathbf{k}$

**18.** $\mathbf{u} = 2\mathbf{i} + 3\mathbf{j}$, $\mathbf{v} = -\mathbf{i} + 2\mathbf{j} - 2\mathbf{k}$

**19–20** Find the area of the triangle with vertices $P$, $Q$, and $R$. ■

**19.** $P(1, 5, -2)$, $Q(0, 0, 0)$, $R(3, 5, 1)$

**20.** $P(2, 0, -3)$, $Q(1, 4, 5)$, $R(7, 2, 9)$

**21–24** Find $\mathbf{u} \cdot (\mathbf{v} \times \mathbf{w})$. ■

**21.** $\mathbf{u} = 2\mathbf{i} - 3\mathbf{j} + \mathbf{k}$, $\mathbf{v} = 4\mathbf{i} + \mathbf{j} - 3\mathbf{k}$, $\mathbf{w} = \mathbf{j} + 5\mathbf{k}$

**22.** $\mathbf{u} = \langle 1, -2, 2 \rangle$, $\mathbf{v} = \langle 0, 3, 2 \rangle$, $\mathbf{w} = \langle -4, 1, -3 \rangle$

**23.** $\mathbf{u} = \langle 2, 1, 0 \rangle$, $\mathbf{v} = \langle 1, -3, 1 \rangle$, $\mathbf{w} = \langle 4, 0, 1 \rangle$

**24.** $\mathbf{u} = \mathbf{i}$, $\mathbf{v} = \mathbf{i} + \mathbf{j}$, $\mathbf{w} = \mathbf{i} + \mathbf{j} + \mathbf{k}$

**25–26** Use a scalar triple product to find the volume of the parallelepiped that has **u**, **v**, and **w** as adjacent edges. ■

**25.** $\mathbf{u} = \langle 2, -6, 2 \rangle$, $\mathbf{v} = \langle 0, 4, -2 \rangle$, $\mathbf{w} = \langle 2, 2, -4 \rangle$

**26.** $\mathbf{u} = 3\mathbf{i} + \mathbf{j} + 2\mathbf{k}$, $\mathbf{v} = 4\mathbf{i} + 5\mathbf{j} + \mathbf{k}$, $\mathbf{w} = \mathbf{i} + 2\mathbf{j} + 4\mathbf{k}$

**27.** In each part, use a scalar triple product to determine whether the vectors lie in the same plane.
(a) $\mathbf{u} = \langle 1, -2, 1 \rangle$, $\mathbf{v} = \langle 3, 0, -2 \rangle$, $\mathbf{w} = \langle 5, -4, 0 \rangle$
(b) $\mathbf{u} = 5\mathbf{i} - 2\mathbf{j} + \mathbf{k}$, $\mathbf{v} = 4\mathbf{i} - \mathbf{j} + \mathbf{k}$, $\mathbf{w} = \mathbf{i} - \mathbf{j}$
(c) $\mathbf{u} = \langle 4, -8, 1 \rangle$, $\mathbf{v} = \langle 2, 1, -2 \rangle$, $\mathbf{w} = \langle 3, -4, 12 \rangle$

**28.** Suppose that $\mathbf{u} \cdot (\mathbf{v} \times \mathbf{w}) = 3$. Find
(a) $\mathbf{u} \cdot (\mathbf{w} \times \mathbf{v})$　　　(b) $(\mathbf{v} \times \mathbf{w}) \cdot \mathbf{u}$
(c) $\mathbf{w} \cdot (\mathbf{u} \times \mathbf{v})$　　　(d) $\mathbf{v} \cdot (\mathbf{u} \times \mathbf{w})$
(e) $(\mathbf{u} \times \mathbf{w}) \cdot \mathbf{v}$　　　(f) $\mathbf{v} \cdot (\mathbf{w} \times \mathbf{w})$.

**29.** Consider the parallelepiped with adjacent edges

$$\mathbf{u} = 3\mathbf{i} + 2\mathbf{j} + \mathbf{k}$$
$$\mathbf{v} = \mathbf{i} + \mathbf{j} + 2\mathbf{k}$$
$$\mathbf{w} = \mathbf{i} + 3\mathbf{j} + 3\mathbf{k}$$

(a) Find the volume.
(b) Find the area of the face determined by **u** and **w**.
(c) Find the angle between **u** and the plane containing the face determined by **v** and **w**.

**30.** Show that in 3-space the distance $d$ from a point $P$ to the line $L$ through points $A$ and $B$ can be expressed as

$$d = \frac{\| \overrightarrow{AP} \times \overrightarrow{AB} \|}{\| \overrightarrow{AB} \|}$$

**31.** Use the result in Exercise 30 to find the distance between the point $P$ and the line through the points $A$ and $B$.
(a) $P(-3, 1, 2)$, $A(1, 1, 0)$, $B(-2, 3, -4)$
(b) $P(4, 3)$, $A(2, 1)$, $B(0, 2)$

**32.** It is a theorem of solid geometry that the volume of a tetrahedron is $\frac{1}{3}$(area of base) · (height). Use this result to prove that the volume of a tetrahedron with adjacent edges given by the vectors **u**, **v**, and **w** is $\frac{1}{6} |\mathbf{u} \cdot (\mathbf{v} \times \mathbf{w})|$.

**33.** Use the result of Exercise 32 to find the volume of the tetrahedron with vertices

$$P(-1, 2, 0), \quad Q(2, 1, -3), \quad R(1, 0, 1), \quad S(3, -2, 3)$$

**34.** Let $\theta$ be the angle between the vectors $\mathbf{u} = 2\mathbf{i} + 3\mathbf{j} - 6\mathbf{k}$ and $\mathbf{v} = 2\mathbf{i} + 3\mathbf{j} + 6\mathbf{k}$.
(a) Use the dot product to find $\cos \theta$.
(b) Use the cross product to find $\sin \theta$.
(c) Confirm that $\sin^2 \theta + \cos^2 \theta = 1$.

---

**FOCUS ON CONCEPTS**

**35.** Let $A$, $B$, $C$, and $D$ be four distinct points in 3-space. If $\overrightarrow{AB} \times \overrightarrow{CD} \neq \mathbf{0}$ and $\overrightarrow{AC} \cdot (\overrightarrow{AB} \times \overrightarrow{CD}) = 0$, explain why the line through $A$ and $B$ must intersect the line through $C$ and $D$.

**36.** Let $A$, $B$, and $C$ be three distinct noncollinear points in 3-space. Describe the set of all points $P$ that satisfy the vector equation $\overrightarrow{AP} \cdot (\overrightarrow{AB} \times \overrightarrow{AC}) = 0$.

**37.** What can you say about the angle between nonzero vectors **u** and **v** if $\mathbf{u} \cdot \mathbf{v} = \| \mathbf{u} \times \mathbf{v} \|$?

**38.** Show that if **u** and **v** are vectors in 3-space, then

$$\| \mathbf{u} \times \mathbf{v} \|^2 = \| \mathbf{u} \|^2 \| \mathbf{v} \|^2 - (\mathbf{u} \cdot \mathbf{v})^2$$

[*Note:* This result is sometimes called *Lagrange's identity*.]

---

**39.** The accompanying figure shows a force **F** of 10 lb applied in the positive $y$-direction to the point $Q(1, 1, 1)$ of a cube whose sides have a length of 1 ft. In each part, find the scalar moment of **F** about the point $P$, and describe the direction of rotation, if any, if the cube is free to rotate about $P$.
(a) $P$ is the point $(0, 0, 0)$.　(b) $P$ is the point $(1, 0, 0)$.
(c) $P$ is the point $(1, 0, 1)$.

**40.** The accompanying figure shows a force **F** of 1000 N applied to the corner of a box.
(a) Find the scalar moment of **F** about the point $P$.
(b) Find the direction angles of the vector moment of **F** about the point $P$ to the nearest degree.

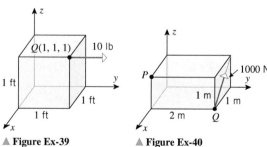

▲ **Figure Ex-39**　　　　▲ **Figure Ex-40**

**41.** As shown in the accompanying figure on the next page, a force of 200 N is applied at an angle of 18° to a point near the end of a monkey wrench. Find the scalar moment of the force about the center of the bolt. [*Note:* Treat this as a problem in two dimensions.]

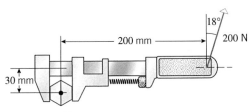

▲ **Figure Ex-41**

**42.** Prove parts (*b*) and (*c*) of Theorem 11.4.3.

**43.** Prove parts (*d*) and (*e*) of Theorem 11.4.3.

**44.** Prove part (*b*) of Theorem 11.4.1 for $3 \times 3$ determinants. [*Note:* Just give the proof for the first two rows.] Then use (*b*) to prove (*a*).

**FOCUS ON CONCEPTS**

**45.** Expressions of the form

$$\mathbf{u} \times (\mathbf{v} \times \mathbf{w}) \quad \text{and} \quad (\mathbf{u} \times \mathbf{v}) \times \mathbf{w}$$

are called *vector triple products*. It can be proved with some effort that

$$\mathbf{u} \times (\mathbf{v} \times \mathbf{w}) = (\mathbf{u} \cdot \mathbf{w})\mathbf{v} - (\mathbf{u} \cdot \mathbf{v})\mathbf{w}$$
$$(\mathbf{u} \times \mathbf{v}) \times \mathbf{w} = (\mathbf{w} \cdot \mathbf{u})\mathbf{v} - (\mathbf{w} \cdot \mathbf{v})\mathbf{u}$$

These expressions can be summarized with the following mnemonic rule:

vector triple product = (outer · remote)adjacent
$$\qquad\qquad\qquad - \text{(outer · adjacent)remote}$$

See if you can figure out what the expressions "outer," "remote," and "adjacent" mean in this rule, and then use the rule to find the two vector triple products of the vectors

$$\mathbf{u} = \mathbf{i} + 3\mathbf{j} - \mathbf{k}, \quad \mathbf{v} = \mathbf{i} + \mathbf{j} + 2\mathbf{k}, \quad \mathbf{w} = 3\mathbf{i} - \mathbf{j} + 2\mathbf{k}$$

**46.** (a) Use the result in Exercise 45 to show that $\mathbf{u} \times (\mathbf{v} \times \mathbf{w})$ lies in the same plane as $\mathbf{v}$ and $\mathbf{w}$, and $(\mathbf{u} \times \mathbf{v}) \times \mathbf{w}$ lies in the same plane as $\mathbf{u}$ and $\mathbf{v}$.

(b) Use a geometrical argument to justify the results in part (a).

**47.** In each part, use the result in Exercise 45 to prove the vector identity.

(a) $(\mathbf{a} \times \mathbf{b}) \times (\mathbf{c} \times \mathbf{d}) = (\mathbf{a} \times \mathbf{b} \cdot \mathbf{d})\mathbf{c} - (\mathbf{a} \times \mathbf{b} \cdot \mathbf{c})\mathbf{d}$

(b) $(\mathbf{a} \times \mathbf{b}) \times \mathbf{c} + (\mathbf{b} \times \mathbf{c}) \times \mathbf{a} + (\mathbf{c} \times \mathbf{a}) \times \mathbf{b} = 0$

**48.** Prove: If $\mathbf{a}, \mathbf{b}, \mathbf{c}$, and $\mathbf{d}$ lie in the same plane when positioned with a common initial point, then

$$(\mathbf{a} \times \mathbf{b}) \times (\mathbf{c} \times \mathbf{d}) = 0$$

**C 49.** Use a CAS to approximate the minimum area of a triangle if two of its vertices are $(2, -1, 0)$ and $(3, 2, 2)$ and its third vertex is on the curve $y = \ln x$ in the *xy*-plane.

**50.** If a force $\mathbf{F}$ is applied to an object at a point $Q$, then the line through $Q$ parallel to $\mathbf{F}$ is called the *line of action* of the force. We defined the vector moment of $\mathbf{F}$ about a point $P$ to be $\overrightarrow{PQ} \times \mathbf{F}$. Show that if $Q'$ is any point on the line of action of $\mathbf{F}$, then $\overrightarrow{PQ} \times \mathbf{F} = \overrightarrow{PQ'} \times \mathbf{F}$; that is, it is not essential to use the point of application to compute the vector moment—any point on the line of action will do. [*Hint:* Write $\overrightarrow{PQ'} = \overrightarrow{PQ} + \overrightarrow{QQ'}$ and use properties of the cross product.]

**51.** *Writing* Discuss some of the similarities and differences between the multiplication of real numbers and the cross product of vectors.

**52.** *Writing* In your own words, describe what it means to say that the cross-product operation is "coordinate independent," and state why this fact is significant.

**✔ QUICK CHECK ANSWERS 11.4**

**1.** (a) 7 (b) 0   **2.** $8\mathbf{i} - 4\mathbf{j} - 6\mathbf{k}$   **3.** (a) $\langle 0, 0, 0 \rangle$ (b) $\langle -2, -7, -3 \rangle$ (c) $\langle -3, 11, 3 \rangle$ (d) $\langle -10, 8, 0 \rangle$   **4.** (a) $-58$ (b) 58

---

## 11.5 PARAMETRIC EQUATIONS OF LINES

*In this section we will discuss parametric equations of lines in 2-space and 3-space. In 3-space, parametric equations of lines are especially important because they generally provide the most convenient form for representing lines algebraically.*

### ■ LINES DETERMINED BY A POINT AND A VECTOR

A line in 2-space or 3-space can be determined uniquely by specifying a point on the line and a nonzero vector parallel to the line (Figure 11.5.1). For example, consider a line $L$

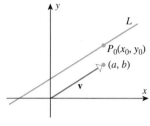

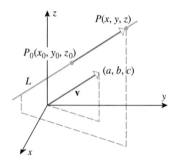

A unique line $L$ passes through $P_0$ and is parallel to $\mathbf{v}$.

▲ **Figure 11.5.1**

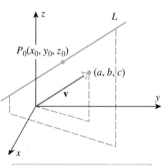

▲ **Figure 11.5.2**

in 3-space that passes through the point $P_0(x_0, y_0, z_0)$ and is parallel to the nonzero vector $\mathbf{v} = \langle a, b, c \rangle$. Then $L$ consists precisely of those points $P(x, y, z)$ for which the vector $\overrightarrow{P_0P}$ is parallel to $\mathbf{v}$ (Figure 11.5.2). In other words, the point $P(x, y, z)$ is on $L$ if and only if $\overrightarrow{P_0P}$ is a scalar multiple of $\mathbf{v}$, say

$$\overrightarrow{P_0P} = t\mathbf{v}$$

This equation can be written as

$$\langle x - x_0, y - y_0, z - z_0 \rangle = \langle ta, tb, tc \rangle$$

which implies that

$$x - x_0 = ta, \quad y - y_0 = tb, \quad z - z_0 = tc$$

Thus, $L$ can be described by the parametric equations

$$x = x_0 + at, \quad y = y_0 + bt, \quad z = z_0 + ct$$

A similar description applies to lines in 2-space. We summarize these descriptions in the following theorem.

---

**11.5.1** THEOREM

(a)  The line in 2-space that passes through the point $P_0(x_0, y_0)$ and is parallel to the nonzero vector $\mathbf{v} = \langle a, b \rangle = a\mathbf{i} + b\mathbf{j}$ has parametric equations

$$x = x_0 + at, \quad y = y_0 + bt \tag{1}$$

(b)  The line in 3-space that passes through the point $P_0(x_0, y_0, z_0)$ and is parallel to the nonzero vector $\mathbf{v} = \langle a, b, c \rangle = a\mathbf{i} + b\mathbf{j} + c\mathbf{k}$ has parametric equations

$$x = x_0 + at, \quad y = y_0 + bt, \quad z = z_0 + ct \tag{2}$$

---

**REMARK**  Although it is not stated explicitly, it is understood in Equations (1) and (2) that $-\infty < t < +\infty$, which reflects the fact that lines extend indefinitely.

---

▶ **Example 1**  Find parametric equations of the line

(a)  passing through $(4, 2)$ and parallel to $\mathbf{v} = \langle -1, 5 \rangle$;

(b)  passing through $(1, 2, -3)$ and parallel to $\mathbf{v} = 4\mathbf{i} + 5\mathbf{j} - 7\mathbf{k}$;

(c)  passing through the origin in 3-space and parallel to $\mathbf{v} = \langle 1, 1, 1 \rangle$.

*Solution (a).*  From (1) with $x_0 = 4$, $y_0 = 2$, $a = -1$, and $b = 5$ we obtain

$$x = 4 - t, \quad y = 2 + 5t$$

*Solution (b).*  From (2) we obtain

$$x = 1 + 4t, \quad y = 2 + 5t, \quad z = -3 - 7t$$

*Solution (c).*  From (2) with $x_0 = 0$, $y_0 = 0$, $z_0 = 0$, $a = 1$, $b = 1$, and $c = 1$ we obtain

$$x = t, \quad y = t, \quad z = t \quad \blacktriangleleft$$

▶ **Example 2**

(a) Find parametric equations of the line $L$ passing through the points $P_1(2, 4, -1)$ and $P_2(5, 0, 7)$.

(b) Where does the line intersect the $xy$-plane?

*Solution* (*a*). The vector $\overrightarrow{P_1P_2} = \langle 3, -4, 8 \rangle$ is parallel to $L$ and the point $P_1(2, 4, -1)$ lies on $L$, so it follows from (2) that $L$ has parametric equations

$$x = 2 + 3t, \quad y = 4 - 4t, \quad z = -1 + 8t \tag{3}$$

Had we used $P_2$ as the point on $L$ rather than $P_1$, we would have obtained the equations

$$x = 5 + 3t, \quad y = -4t, \quad z = 7 + 8t$$

Although these equations look different from those obtained using $P_1$, the two sets of equations are actually equivalent in that both generate $L$ as $t$ varies from $-\infty$ to $+\infty$. To see this, note that if $t_1$ gives a point

$$(x, y, z) = (2 + 3t_1, 4 - 4t_1, -1 + 8t_1)$$

on $L$ using the first set of equations, then $t_2 = t_1 - 1$ gives the *same* point

$$\begin{aligned}
(x, y, z) &= (5 + 3t_2, -4t_2, 7 + 8t_2) \\
&= (5 + 3(t_1 - 1), -4(t_1 - 1), 7 + 8(t_1 - 1)) \\
&= (2 + 3t_1, 4 - 4t_1, -1 + 8t_1)
\end{aligned}$$

on $L$ using the second set of equations. Conversely, if $t_2$ gives a point on $L$ using the second set of equations, then $t_1 = t_2 + 1$ gives the same point using the first set.

*Solution* (*b*). It follows from (3) in part (a) that the line intersects the $xy$-plane at the point where $z = -1 + 8t = 0$, that is, when $t = \frac{1}{8}$. Substituting this value of $t$ in (3) yields the point of intersection $(x, y, z) = \left(\frac{19}{8}, \frac{7}{2}, 0\right)$. ◀

▶ **Example 3** Let $L_1$ and $L_2$ be the lines

$$L_1: x = 1 + 4t, \quad y = 5 - 4t, \quad z = -1 + 5t$$
$$L_2: x = 2 + 8t, \quad y = 4 - 3t, \quad z = 5 + t$$

(a) Are the lines parallel?

(b) Do the lines intersect?

*Solution* (*a*). The line $L_1$ is parallel to the vector $4\mathbf{i} - 4\mathbf{j} + 5\mathbf{k}$, and the line $L_2$ is parallel to the vector $8\mathbf{i} - 3\mathbf{j} + \mathbf{k}$. These vectors are not parallel since neither is a scalar multiple of the other. Thus, the lines are not parallel.

*Solution* (*b*). For $L_1$ and $L_2$ to intersect at some point $(x_0, y_0, z_0)$ these coordinates would have to satisfy the equations of both lines. In other words, there would have to exist values $t_1$ and $t_2$ for the parameters such that

$$x_0 = 1 + 4t_1, \quad y_0 = 5 - 4t_1, \quad z_0 = -1 + 5t_1$$

and

$$x_0 = 2 + 8t_2, \quad y_0 = 4 - 3t_2, \quad z_0 = 5 + t_2$$

This leads to three conditions on $t_1$ and $t_2$,

$$1 + 4t_1 = 2 + 8t_2$$
$$5 - 4t_1 = 4 - 3t_2 \qquad\qquad (4)$$
$$-1 + 5t_1 = 5 + t_2$$

Thus, the lines intersect if there are values of $t_1$ and $t_2$ that satisfy all three equations, and the lines do not intersect if there are no such values. You should be familiar with methods for solving systems of two linear equations in two unknowns; however, this is a system of three linear equations in two unknowns. To determine whether this system has a solution we will solve the first two equations for $t_1$ and $t_2$ and then check whether these values satisfy the third equation.

We will solve the first two equations by the method of elimination. We can eliminate the unknown $t_1$ by adding the equations. This yields the equation

$$6 = 6 + 5t_2$$

from which we obtain $t_2 = 0$. We can now find $t_1$ by substituting this value of $t_2$ in either the first or second equation. This yields $t_1 = \frac{1}{4}$. However, the values $t_1 = \frac{1}{4}$ and $t_2 = 0$ do not satisfy the third equation in (4), so the lines do not intersect. ◄

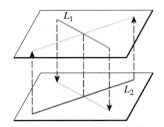

Parallel planes containing skew lines $L_1$ and $L_2$ can be determined by translating each line until it intersects the other.

▲ **Figure 11.5.3**

Two lines in 3-space that are not parallel and do not intersect (such as those in Example 3) are called *skew* lines. As illustrated in Figure 11.5.3, any two skew lines lie in parallel planes.

■ **LINE SEGMENTS**

Sometimes one is not interested in an entire line, but rather some *segment* of a line. Parametric equations of a line segment can be obtained by finding parametric equations for the entire line, and then restricting the parameter appropriately so that only the desired segment is generated.

▸ **Example 4**    Find parametric equations describing the line segment joining the points $P_1(2, 4, -1)$ and $P_2(5, 0, 7)$.

*Solution.*    From Example 2, the line through the points $P_1$ and $P_2$ has parametric equations $x = 2 + 3t$, $y = 4 - 4t$, $z = -1 + 8t$. With these equations, the point $P_1$ corresponds to $t = 0$ and $P_2$ to $t = 1$. Thus, the line segment that joins $P_1$ and $P_2$ is given by

$$x = 2 + 3t, \quad y = 4 - 4t, \quad z = -1 + 8t \qquad (0 \le t \le 1) ◄$$

■ **VECTOR EQUATIONS OF LINES**

We will now show how vector notation can be used to express the parametric equations of a line more compactly. Because two vectors are equal if and only if their components are equal, (1) and (2) can be written in vector form as

$$\langle x, y \rangle = \langle x_0 + at, y_0 + bt \rangle$$
$$\langle x, y, z \rangle = \langle x_0 + at, y_0 + bt, z_0 + ct \rangle$$

or, equivalently, as

$$\langle x, y \rangle = \langle x_0, y_0 \rangle + t \langle a, b \rangle \qquad\qquad (5)$$

$$\langle x, y, z \rangle = \langle x_0, y_0, z_0 \rangle + t \langle a, b, c \rangle \qquad\qquad (6)$$

For the equation in 2-space we define the vectors $\mathbf{r}$, $\mathbf{r}_0$, and $\mathbf{v}$ as

$$\mathbf{r} = \langle x, y \rangle, \quad \mathbf{r}_0 = \langle x_0, y_0 \rangle, \quad \mathbf{v} = \langle a, b \rangle \tag{7}$$

and for the equation in 3-space we define them as

$$\mathbf{r} = \langle x, y, z \rangle, \quad \mathbf{r}_0 = \langle x_0, y_0, z_0 \rangle, \quad \mathbf{v} = \langle a, b, c \rangle \tag{8}$$

Substituting (7) and (8) in (5) and (6), respectively, yields the equation

$$\mathbf{r} = \mathbf{r}_0 + t\mathbf{v} \tag{9}$$

in both cases. We call this the ***vector equation of a line*** in 2-space or 3-space. In this equation, $\mathbf{v}$ is a nonzero vector parallel to the line, and $\mathbf{r}_0$ is a vector whose components are the coordinates of a point on the line.

We can interpret Equation (9) geometrically by positioning the vectors $\mathbf{r}_0$ and $\mathbf{v}$ with their initial points at the origin and the vector $t\mathbf{v}$ with its initial point at $P_0$ (Figure 11.5.4). The vector $t\mathbf{v}$ is a scalar multiple of $\mathbf{v}$ and hence is parallel to $\mathbf{v}$ and $L$. Moreover, since the initial point of $t\mathbf{v}$ is at the point $P_0$ on $L$, this vector actually runs along $L$; hence, the vector $\mathbf{r} = \mathbf{r}_0 + t\mathbf{v}$ can be interpreted as the vector from the origin to a point on $L$. As the parameter $t$ varies from 0 to $+\infty$, the terminal point of $\mathbf{r}$ traces out the portion of $L$ that extends from $P_0$ in the direction of $\mathbf{v}$, and as $t$ varies from 0 to $-\infty$, the terminal point of $\mathbf{r}$ traces out the portion of $L$ that extends from $P_0$ in the direction that is opposite to $\mathbf{v}$. Thus, the entire line is traced as $t$ varies over the interval $(-\infty, +\infty)$, and it is traced in the direction of $\mathbf{v}$ as $t$ increases.

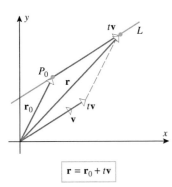

$$\mathbf{r} = \mathbf{r}_0 + t\mathbf{v}$$

▲ **Figure 11.5.4**

▶ **Example 5**    The equation

$$\langle x, y, z \rangle = \langle -1, 0, 2 \rangle + t\langle 1, 5, -4 \rangle$$

is of form (9) with

$$\mathbf{r}_0 = \langle -1, 0, 2 \rangle \quad \text{and} \quad \mathbf{v} = \langle 1, 5, -4 \rangle$$

Thus, the equation represents the line in 3-space that passes through the point $(-1, 0, 2)$ and is parallel to the vector $\langle 1, 5, -4 \rangle$. ◀

▶ **Example 6**    Find an equation of the line in 3-space that passes through the points $P_1(2, 4, -1)$ and $P_2(5, 0, 7)$.

***Solution.***    The vector

$$\overrightarrow{P_1P_2} = \langle 3, -4, 8 \rangle$$

is parallel to the line, so it can be used as $\mathbf{v}$ in (9). For $\mathbf{r}_0$ we can use either the vector from the origin to $P_1$ or the vector from the origin to $P_2$. Using the former yields

$$\mathbf{r}_0 = \langle 2, 4, -1 \rangle$$

Thus, a vector equation of the line through $P_1$ and $P_2$ is

$$\langle x, y, z \rangle = \langle 2, 4, -1 \rangle + t\langle 3, -4, 8 \rangle$$

If needed, we can express the line parametrically by equating corresponding components on the two sides of this vector equation, in which case we obtain the parametric equations in Example 2 (verify). ◀

✔**QUICK CHECK EXERCISES 11.5**   *(See page 812 for answers.)*

1. Let $L$ be the line through $(2, 5)$ and parallel to $\mathbf{v} = \langle 3, -1 \rangle$.
   (a) Parametric equations of $L$ are

   $$x = \underline{\hspace{1.5cm}} \qquad y = \underline{\hspace{1.5cm}}$$

   (b) A vector equation of $L$ is $\langle x, y \rangle = \underline{\hspace{1.5cm}}$.

2. Parametric equations for the line through $(5, 3, 7)$ and parallel to the line $x = 3 - t$, $y = 2$, $z = 8 + 4t$ are

   $$x = \underline{\hspace{1.5cm}}, \qquad y = \underline{\hspace{1.5cm}}, \qquad z = \underline{\hspace{1.5cm}}$$

3. Parametric equations for the line segment joining the points $(3, 0, 11)$ and $(2, 6, 7)$ are

   $$x = \underline{\hspace{1cm}}, \qquad y = \underline{\hspace{1cm}}, \qquad z = \underline{\hspace{1cm}} \quad (\underline{\hspace{1cm}})$$

4. The line through the points $(-3, 8, -4)$ and $(1, 0, 8)$ intersects the $yz$-plane at $\underline{\hspace{1.5cm}}$.

---

**EXERCISE SET 11.5**   ⌐ Graphing Utility   $\boxed{\text{C}}$ CAS

---

1. (a) Find parametric equations for the lines through the corner of the unit square shown in part (*a*) of the accompanying figure.
   (b) Find parametric equations for the lines through the corner of the unit cube shown in part (*b*) of the accompanying figure.

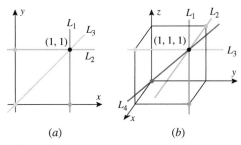

(*a*)                              (*b*)

▲ **Figure Ex-1**

2. (a) Find parametric equations for the line segments in the unit square in part (*a*) of the accompanying figure.
   (b) Find parametric equations for the line segments in the unit cube shown in part (*b*) of the accompanying figure.

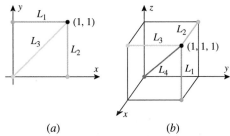

(*a*)                              (*b*)

▲ **Figure Ex-2**

**3–4** Find parametric equations for the line through $P_1$ and $P_2$ and also for the line segment joining those points. ■

3. (a) $P_1(3, -2)$, $P_2(5, 1)$    (b) $P_1(5, -2, 1)$, $P_2(2, 4, 2)$

4. (a) $P_1(0, 1)$, $P_2(-3, -4)$
   (b) $P_1(-1, 3, 5)$, $P_2(-1, 3, 2)$

**5–6** Find parametric equations for the line whose vector equation is given. ■

5. (a) $\langle x, y \rangle = \langle 2, -3 \rangle + t\langle 1, -4 \rangle$
   (b) $x\mathbf{i} + y\mathbf{j} + z\mathbf{k} = \mathbf{k} + t(\mathbf{i} - \mathbf{j} + \mathbf{k})$

6. (a) $x\mathbf{i} + y\mathbf{j} = (3\mathbf{i} - 4\mathbf{j}) + t(2\mathbf{i} + \mathbf{j})$
   (b) $\langle x, y, z \rangle = \langle -1, 0, 2 \rangle + t\langle -1, 3, 0 \rangle$

**7–8** Find a point $P$ on the line and a vector $\mathbf{v}$ parallel to the line by inspection. ■

7. (a) $x\mathbf{i} + y\mathbf{j} = (2\mathbf{i} - \mathbf{j}) + t(4\mathbf{i} - \mathbf{j})$
   (b) $\langle x, y, z \rangle = \langle -1, 2, 4 \rangle + t\langle 5, 7, -8 \rangle$

8. (a) $\langle x, y \rangle = \langle -1, 5 \rangle + t\langle 2, 3 \rangle$
   (b) $x\mathbf{i} + y\mathbf{j} + z\mathbf{k} = (\mathbf{i} + \mathbf{j} - 2\mathbf{k}) + t\mathbf{j}$

**9–10** Express the given parametric equations of a line using bracket notation and also using $\mathbf{i}, \mathbf{j}, \mathbf{k}$ notation. ■

9. (a) $x = -3 + t$, $y = 4 + 5t$
   (b) $x = 2 - t$, $y = -3 + 5t$, $z = t$

10. (a) $x = t$, $y = -2 + t$
    (b) $x = 1 + t$, $y = -7 + 3t$, $z = 4 - 5t$

**11–14 True–False** Determine whether the statement is true or false. Explain your answer. In these exercises $L_0$ and $L_1$ are lines in 3-space whose parametric equations are

$$L_0: x = x_0 + a_0 t, \quad y = y_0 + b_0 t, \quad z = z_0 + c_0 t$$
$$L_1: x = x_1 + a_1 t, \quad y = y_1 + b_1 t, \quad z = z_1 + c_1 t \quad ■$$

11. By definition, if $L_1$ and $L_2$ do not intersect, then $L_1$ and $L_2$ are parallel.

12. If $L_1$ and $L_2$ are parallel, then $\mathbf{v}_0 = \langle a_0, b_0, c_0 \rangle$ is a scalar multiple of $\mathbf{v}_1 = \langle a_1, b_1, c_1 \rangle$.

13. If $L_1$ and $L_2$ intersect at a point $(x, y, z)$, then there exists a single value of $t$ such that

$$L_0: x = x_0 + a_0 t, \quad y = y_0 + b_0 t, \quad z = z_0 + c_0 t$$
$$L_1: x = x_1 + a_1 t, \quad y = y_1 + b_1 t, \quad z = z_1 + c_1 t$$

are satisfied.

**14.** If $L_0$ passes through the origin, then the vectors $\langle a_0, b_0, c_0 \rangle$ and $\langle x_0, y_0, z_0 \rangle$ are parallel.

**15–22** Find parametric equations of the line that satisfies the stated conditions. ■

**15.** The line through $(-5, 2)$ that is parallel to $2\mathbf{i} - 3\mathbf{j}$.

**16.** The line through $(0, 3)$ that is parallel to the line $x = -5 + t$, $y = 1 - 2t$.

**17.** The line that is tangent to the circle $x^2 + y^2 = 25$ at the point $(3, -4)$.

**18.** The line that is tangent to the parabola $y = x^2$ at the point $(-2, 4)$.

**19.** The line through $(-1, 2, 4)$ that is parallel to $3\mathbf{i} - 4\mathbf{j} + \mathbf{k}$.

**20.** The line through $(2, -1, 5)$ that is parallel to $\langle -1, 2, 7 \rangle$.

**21.** The line through $(-2, 0, 5)$ that is parallel to the line given by $x = 1 + 2t$, $y = 4 - t$, $z = 6 + 2t$.

**22.** The line through the origin that is parallel to the line given by $x = t$, $y = -1 + t$, $z = 2$.

**23.** Where does the line $x = 1 + 3t$, $y = 2 - t$ intersect
(a) the $x$-axis          (b) the $y$-axis
(c) the parabola $y = x^2$?

**24.** Where does the line $\langle x, y \rangle = \langle 4t, 3t \rangle$ intersect the circle $x^2 + y^2 = 25$?

**25–26** Find the intersections of the lines with the $xy$-plane, the $xz$-plane, and the $yz$-plane. ■

**25.** $x = -2$, $y = 4 + 2t$, $z = -3 + t$

**26.** $x = -1 + 2t$, $y = 3 + t$, $z = 4 - t$

**27.** Where does the line $x = 1 + t$, $y = 3 - t$, $z = 2t$ intersect the cylinder $x^2 + y^2 = 16$?

**28.** Where does the line $x = 2 - t$, $y = 3t$, $z = -1 + 2t$ intersect the plane $2y + 3z = 6$?

**29–30** Show that the lines $L_1$ and $L_2$ intersect, and find their point of intersection. ■

**29.** $L_1 : x = 2 + t$, $y = 2 + 3t$, $z = 3 + t$
$L_2 : x = 2 + t$, $y = 3 + 4t$, $z = 4 + 2t$

**30.** $L_1 : x + 1 = 4t$, $y - 3 = t$, $z - 1 = 0$
$L_2 : x + 13 = 12t$, $y - 1 = 6t$, $z - 2 = 3t$

**31–32** Show that the lines $L_1$ and $L_2$ are skew. ■

**31.** $L_1 : x = 1 + 7t$, $y = 3 + t$, $z = 5 - 3t$
$L_2 : x = 4 - t$, $y = 6$, $z = 7 + 2t$

**32.** $L_1 : x = 2 + 8t$, $y = 6 - 8t$, $z = 10t$
$L_2 : x = 3 + 8t$, $y = 5 - 3t$, $z = 6 + t$

**33–34** Determine whether the lines $L_1$ and $L_2$ are parallel. ■

**33.** $L_1 : x = 3 - 2t$, $y = 4 + t$, $z = 6 - t$
$L_2 : x = 5 - 4t$, $y = -2 + 2t$, $z = 7 - 2t$

**34.** $L_1 : x = 5 + 3t$, $y = 4 - 2t$, $z = -2 + 3t$
$L_2 : x = -1 + 9t$, $y = 5 - 6t$, $z = 3 + 8t$

**35–36** Determine whether the points $P_1$, $P_2$, and $P_3$ lie on the same line. ■

**35.** $P_1(6, 9, 7)$, $P_2(9, 2, 0)$, $P_3(0, -5, -3)$

**36.** $P_1(1, 0, 1)$, $P_2(3, -4, -3)$, $P_3(4, -6, -5)$

**37–38** Show that the lines $L_1$ and $L_2$ are the same. ■

**37.** $L_1 : x = 3 - t$, $y = 1 + 2t$
$L_2 : x = -1 + 3t$, $y = 9 - 6t$

**38.** $L_1 : x = 1 + 3t$, $y = -2 + t$, $z = 2t$
$L_2 : x = 4 - 6t$, $y = -1 - 2t$, $z = 2 - 4t$

**FOCUS ON CONCEPTS**

**39.** Sketch the vectors $\mathbf{r}_0 = \langle -1, 2 \rangle$ and $\mathbf{v} = \langle 1, 1 \rangle$, and then sketch the six vectors $\mathbf{r}_0 \pm \mathbf{v}$, $\mathbf{r}_0 \pm 2\mathbf{v}$, $\mathbf{r}_0 \pm 3\mathbf{v}$. Draw the line $L : x = -1 + t$, $y = 2 + t$, and describe the relationship between $L$ and the vectors you sketched. What is the vector equation of $L$?

**40.** Sketch the vectors $\mathbf{r}_0 = \langle 0, 2, 1 \rangle$ and $\mathbf{v} = \langle 1, 0, 1 \rangle$, and then sketch the vectors $\mathbf{r}_0 + \mathbf{v}$, $\mathbf{r}_0 + 2\mathbf{v}$, and $\mathbf{r}_0 + 3\mathbf{v}$. Draw the line $L : x = t$, $y = 2$, $z = 1 + t$, and describe the relationship between $L$ and the vectors you sketched. What is the vector equation of $L$?

**41.** Sketch the vectors $\mathbf{r}_0 = \langle -2, 0 \rangle$ and $\mathbf{r}_1 = \langle 1, 3 \rangle$, and then sketch the vectors
$$\tfrac{1}{3}\mathbf{r}_0 + \tfrac{2}{3}\mathbf{r}_1, \quad \tfrac{1}{2}\mathbf{r}_0 + \tfrac{1}{2}\mathbf{r}_1, \quad \tfrac{2}{3}\mathbf{r}_0 + \tfrac{1}{3}\mathbf{r}_1$$
Draw the line segment $(1 - t)\mathbf{r}_0 + t\mathbf{r}_1$ $(0 \le t \le 1)$. If $n$ is a positive integer, what is the position of the point on this line segment corresponding to $t = 1/n$, relative to the points $(-2, 0)$ and $(1, 3)$?

**42.** Sketch the vectors $\mathbf{r}_0 = \langle 2, 0, 4 \rangle$ and $\mathbf{r}_1 = \langle 0, 4, 0 \rangle$, and then sketch the vectors
$$\tfrac{1}{4}\mathbf{r}_0 + \tfrac{3}{4}\mathbf{r}_1, \quad \tfrac{1}{2}\mathbf{r}_0 + \tfrac{1}{2}\mathbf{r}_1, \quad \tfrac{3}{4}\mathbf{r}_0 + \tfrac{1}{4}\mathbf{r}_1$$
Draw the line segment $(1 - t)\mathbf{r}_0 + t\mathbf{r}_1$ $(0 \le t \le 1)$. If $n$ is a positive integer, what is the position of the point on this line segment corresponding to $t = 1/n$, relative to the points $(2, 0, 4)$ and $(0, 4, 0)$?

**43–44** Describe the line segment represented by the vector equation. ■

**43.** $\langle x, y \rangle = \langle 1, 0 \rangle + t \langle -2, 3 \rangle$   $(0 \le t \le 2)$

**44.** $\langle x, y, z \rangle = \langle -2, 1, 4 \rangle + t \langle 3, 0, -1 \rangle$   $(0 \le t \le 3)$

**45.** Find the point on the line segment joining $P_1(3, 6)$ and $P_2(8, -4)$ that is $\tfrac{2}{5}$ of the way from $P_1$ to $P_2$.

**46.** Find the point on the line segment joining $P_1(1, 4, -3)$ and $P_2(1, 5, -1)$ that is $\tfrac{2}{3}$ of the way from $P_1$ to $P_2$.

**47–48** Use the method in Exercise 32 of Section 11.3 to find the distance from the point $P$ to the line $L$, and then check your answer using the method in Exercise 30 of Section 11.4. ■

**47.** $P(-2, 1, 1)$
$L : x = 3 - t$, $y = t$, $z = 1 + 2t$

**48.** $P(1, 4, -3)$
$L: x = 2 + t, \ y = -1 - t, \ z = 3t$

**49–50** Show that the lines $L_1$ and $L_2$ are parallel, and find the distance between them. ◼

**49.** $L_1: x = 2 - t, \ y = 2t, \ z = 1 + t$
$L_2: x = 1 + 2t, \ y = 3 - 4t, \ z = 5 - 2t$

**50.** $L_1: x = 2t, \ y = 3 + 4t, \ z = 2 - 6t$
$L_2: x = 1 + 3t, \ y = 6t, \ z = -9t$

**51.** (a) Find parametric equations for the line through the points $(x_0, y_0, z_0)$ and $(x_1, y_1, z_1)$.
(b) Find parametric equations for the line through the point $(x_1, y_1, z_1)$ and parallel to the line
$$x = x_0 + at, \quad y = y_0 + bt, \quad z = z_0 + ct$$

**52.** Let $L$ be the line that passes through the point $(x_0, y_0, z_0)$ and is parallel to the vector $\mathbf{v} = \langle a, b, c \rangle$, where $a$, $b$, and $c$ are nonzero. Show that a point $(x, y, z)$ lies on the line $L$ if and only if
$$\frac{x - x_0}{a} = \frac{y - y_0}{b} = \frac{z - z_0}{c}$$
These equations, which are called the ***symmetric equations*** of $L$, provide a nonparametric representation of $L$.

**53.** (a) Describe the line whose symmetric equations are
$$\frac{x - 1}{2} = \frac{y + 3}{4} = z - 5$$
(see Exercise 52).
(b) Find parametric equations for the line in part (a).

**54.** Consider the lines $L_1$ and $L_2$ whose symmetric equations are
$$L_1: \frac{x - 1}{2} = \frac{y + \frac{3}{2}}{1} = \frac{z + 1}{2}$$
$$L_2: \frac{x - 4}{-1} = \frac{y - 3}{-2} = \frac{z + 4}{2}$$
(see Exercise 52).
(a) Are $L_1$ and $L_2$ parallel? Perpendicular?
(b) Find parametric equations for $L_1$ and $L_2$.
(c) Do $L_1$ and $L_2$ intersect? If so, where?

**55.** Let $L_1$ and $L_2$ be the lines whose parametric equations are
$$L_1: x = 1 + 2t, \quad y = 2 - t, \quad z = 4 - 2t$$
$$L_2: x = 9 + t, \quad y = 5 + 3t, \quad z = -4 - t$$
(a) Show that $L_1$ and $L_2$ intersect at the point $(7, -1, -2)$.
(b) Find, to the nearest degree, the acute angle between $L_1$ and $L_2$ at their intersection.
(c) Find parametric equations for the line that is perpendicular to $L_1$ and $L_2$ and passes through their point of intersection.

**56.** Let $L_1$ and $L_2$ be the lines whose parametric equations are
$$L_1: x = 4t, \qquad y = 1 - 2t, \quad z = 2 + 2t$$
$$L_2: x = 1 + t, \quad y = 1 - t, \qquad z = -1 + 4t$$
(a) Show that $L_1$ and $L_2$ intersect at the point $(2, 0, 3)$.
(b) Find, to the nearest degree, the acute angle between $L_1$ and $L_2$ at their intersection.
(c) Find parametric equations for the line that is perpendicular to $L_1$ and $L_2$ and passes through their point of intersection.

**57–58** Find parametric equations of the line that contains the point $P$ and intersects the line $L$ at a right angle, and find the distance between $P$ and $L$. ◼

**57.** $P(0, 2, 1)$
$L: x = 2t, \ y = 1 - t, \ z = 2 + t$

**58.** $P(3, 1, -2)$
$L: x = -2 + 2t, \ y = 4 + 2t, \ z = 2 + t$

**59.** Two bugs are walking along lines in 3-space. At time $t$ bug 1 is at the point $(x, y, z)$ on the line
$$x = 4 - t, \quad y = 1 + 2t, \quad z = 2 + t$$
and at the same time $t$ bug 2 is at the point $(x, y, z)$ on the line
$$x = t, \quad y = 1 + t, \quad z = 1 + 2t$$
Assume that distance is in centimeters and that time is in minutes.
(a) Find the distance between the bugs at time $t = 0$.
(b) Use a graphing utility to graph the distance between the bugs as a function of time from $t = 0$ to $t = 5$.
(c) What does the graph tell you about the distance between the bugs?
(d) How close do the bugs get?

**60.** Suppose that the temperature $T$ at a point $(x, y, z)$ on the line $x = t, y = 1 + t, z = 3 - 2t$ is $T = 25x^2yz$. Use a CAS or a calculating utility with a root-finding capability to approximate the maximum temperature on that portion of the line that extends from the $xz$-plane to the $xy$-plane.

**61.** Writing Give some examples of geometric problems that can be solved using the parametric equations of a line, and describe their solution. For example, how would you find the points of intersection of a line and a sphere?

**62.** Writing Discuss how the vector equation of a line can be used to model the motion of a point that is moving with constant velocity in 3-space.

✔**QUICK CHECK ANSWERS 11.5**

**1.** (a) $2 + 3t; \ 5 - t$ (b) $\langle 2, 5 \rangle + t\langle 3, -1 \rangle$    **2.** $5 - t; \ 3; \ 7 + 4t$    **3.** $3 - t; \ 6t; \ 11 - 4t; \ 0 \le t \le 1$    **4.** $(0, 2, 5)$

## 11.6 PLANES IN 3-SPACE

*In this section we will use vectors to derive equations of planes in 3-space, and then we will use these equations to solve various geometric problems.*

### ▇ PLANES PARALLEL TO THE COORDINATE PLANES

The graph of the equation $x = a$ in an $xyz$-coordinate system consists of all points of the form $(a, y, z)$, where $y$ and $z$ are arbitrary. One such point is $(a, 0, 0)$, and all others are in the plane that passes through this point and is parallel to the $yz$-plane (Figure 11.6.1). Similarly, the graph of $y = b$ is the plane through $(0, b, 0)$ that is parallel to the $xz$-plane, and the graph of $z = c$ is the plane through $(0, 0, c)$ that is parallel to the $xy$-plane.

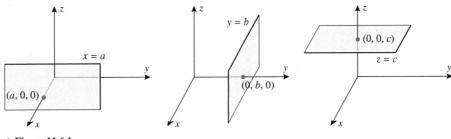

▲ **Figure 11.6.1**

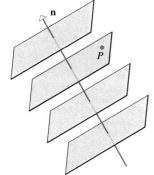

The colored plane is determined uniquely by the point $P$ and the vector **n** perpendicular to the plane.

▲ **Figure 11.6.2**

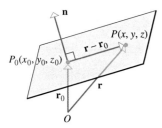

▲ **Figure 11.6.3**

### ▇ PLANES DETERMINED BY A POINT AND A NORMAL VECTOR

A plane in 3-space can be determined uniquely by specifying a point in the plane and a vector perpendicular to the plane (Figure 11.6.2). A vector perpendicular to a plane is called a ***normal*** to the plane.

Suppose that we want to find an equation of the plane passing through $P_0(x_0, y_0, z_0)$ and perpendicular to the vector $\mathbf{n} = \langle a, b, c \rangle$. Define the vectors $\mathbf{r}_0$ and $\mathbf{r}$ as

$$\mathbf{r}_0 = \langle x_0, y_0, z_0 \rangle \quad \text{and} \quad \mathbf{r} = \langle x, y, z \rangle$$

It should be evident from Figure 11.6.3 that the plane consists precisely of those points $P(x, y, z)$ for which the vector $\mathbf{r} - \mathbf{r}_0$ is orthogonal to $\mathbf{n}$; or, expressed as an equation,

$$\mathbf{n} \cdot (\mathbf{r} - \mathbf{r}_0) = 0 \tag{1}$$

If preferred, we can express this vector equation in terms of components as

$$\langle a, b, c \rangle \cdot \langle x - x_0, y - y_0, z - z_0 \rangle = 0 \tag{2}$$

from which we obtain

$$a(x - x_0) + b(y - y_0) + c(z - z_0) = 0 \tag{3}$$

This is called the ***point-normal form*** of the equation of a plane. Formulas (1) and (2) are vector versions of this formula.

What does Equation (1) represent if

$\mathbf{n} = \langle a, b \rangle$, $\mathbf{r}_0 = \langle x_0, y_0 \rangle$, $\mathbf{r} = \langle x, y \rangle$

are vectors in an $xy$-plane in 2-space? Draw a picture.

▶ **Example 1**    Find an equation of the plane passing through the point $(3, -1, 7)$ and perpendicular to the vector $\mathbf{n} = \langle 4, 2, -5 \rangle$.

***Solution.***    From (3), a point-normal form of the equation is

$$4(x - 3) + 2(y + 1) - 5(z - 7) = 0 \tag{4}$$

If preferred, this equation can be written in vector form as

$$\langle 4, 2, -5 \rangle \cdot \langle x - 3, y + 1, z - 7 \rangle = 0 \blacktriangleleft$$

Observe that if we multiply out the terms in (3) and simplify, we obtain an equation of the form

$$ax + by + cz + d = 0 \tag{5}$$

For example, Equation (4) in Example 1 can be rewritten as

$$4x + 2y - 5z + 25 = 0$$

The following theorem shows that every equation of form (5) represents a plane in 3-space.

---

**11.6.1    THEOREM**    *If $a$, $b$, $c$, and $d$ are constants, and $a$, $b$, and $c$ are not all zero, then the graph of the equation*

$$ax + by + cz + d = 0 \tag{6}$$

*is a plane that has the vector $\mathbf{n} = \langle a, b, c \rangle$ as a normal.*

---

**PROOF**    Since $a, b,$ and $c$ are not all zero, there is at least one point $(x_0, y_0, z_0)$ whose coordinates satisfy Equation (6). For example, if $a \neq 0$, then such a point is $(-d/a, 0, 0)$, and similarly if $b \neq 0$ or $c \neq 0$ (verify). Thus, let $(x_0, y_0, z_0)$ be any point whose coordinates satisfy (6); that is,

$$ax_0 + by_0 + cz_0 + d = 0$$

Subtracting this equation from (6) yields

$$a(x - x_0) + b(y - y_0) + c(z - z_0) = 0$$

which is the point-normal form of a plane with normal $\mathbf{n} = \langle a, b, c \rangle$. ∎

Equation (6) is called the ***general form*** of the equation of a plane.

---

▶ **Example 2**    Determine whether the planes

$$3x - 4y + 5z = 0 \quad \text{and} \quad -6x + 8y - 10z - 4 = 0$$

are parallel.

***Solution.***    It is clear geometrically that two planes are parallel if and only if their normals are parallel vectors. A normal to the first plane is

$$\mathbf{n}_1 = \langle 3, -4, 5 \rangle$$

and a normal to the second plane is

$$\mathbf{n}_2 = \langle -6, 8, -10 \rangle$$

Since $\mathbf{n}_2$ is a scalar multiple of $\mathbf{n}_1$, the normals are parallel, and hence so are the planes. ◀

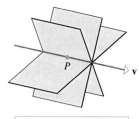

There are infinitely many planes containing $P$ and parallel to $\mathbf{v}$.

▲ **Figure 11.6.4**

We have seen that a unique plane is determined by a point in the plane and a nonzero vector normal to the plane. In contrast, a unique plane is not determined by a point in the plane and a nonzero vector *parallel* to the plane (Figure 11.6.4). However, a unique plane

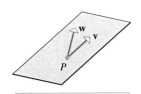

There is a unique plane through $P$ that is parallel to both $\mathbf{v}$ and $\mathbf{w}$.

▲ **Figure 11.6.5**

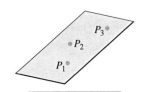

There is a unique plane through three noncollinear points.

▲ **Figure 11.6.6**

is determined by a point in the plane and two nonparallel vectors that are parallel to the plane (Figure 11.6.5). A unique plane is also determined by three noncollinear points that lie in the plane (Figure 11.6.6).

▶ **Example 3**  Find an equation of the plane through the points $P_1(1, 2, -1)$, $P_2(2, 3, 1)$, and $P_3(3, -1, 2)$.

***Solution.***  Since the points $P_1$, $P_2$, and $P_3$ lie in the plane, the vectors $\overrightarrow{P_1P_2} = \langle 1, 1, 2 \rangle$ and $\overrightarrow{P_1P_3} = \langle 2, -3, 3 \rangle$ are parallel to the plane. Therefore,

$$\overrightarrow{P_1P_2} \times \overrightarrow{P_1P_3} = \begin{vmatrix} \mathbf{i} & \mathbf{j} & \mathbf{k} \\ 1 & 1 & 2 \\ 2 & -3 & 3 \end{vmatrix} = 9\mathbf{i} + \mathbf{j} - 5\mathbf{k}$$

is normal to the plane, since it is orthogonal to both $\overrightarrow{P_1P_2}$ and $\overrightarrow{P_1P_3}$. By using this normal and the point $P_1(1, 2, -1)$ in the plane, we obtain the point-normal form

$$9(x - 1) + (y - 2) - 5(z + 1) = 0$$

which can be rewritten as

$$9x + y - 5z - 16 = 0 \quad ◀$$

▶ **Example 4**  Determine whether the line

$$x = 3 + 8t, \quad y = 4 + 5t, \quad z = -3 - t$$

is parallel to the plane $x - 3y + 5z = 12$.

***Solution.***  The vector $\mathbf{v} = \langle 8, 5, -1 \rangle$ is parallel to the line and the vector $\mathbf{n} = \langle 1, -3, 5 \rangle$ is normal to the plane. For the line and plane to be parallel, the vectors $\mathbf{v}$ and $\mathbf{n}$ must be orthogonal. But this is not so, since the dot product

$$\mathbf{v} \cdot \mathbf{n} = (8)(1) + (5)(-3) + (-1)(5) = -12$$

is nonzero. Thus, the line and plane are not parallel. ◀

▶ **Example 5**  Find the intersection of the line and plane in Example 4.

***Solution.***  If we let $(x_0, y_0, z_0)$ be the point of intersection, then the coordinates of this point satisfy both the equation of the plane and the parametric equations of the line. Thus,

$$x_0 - 3y_0 + 5z_0 = 12 \tag{7}$$

and for some value of $t$, say $t = t_0$,

$$x_0 = 3 + 8t_0, \quad y_0 = 4 + 5t_0, \quad z_0 = -3 - t_0 \tag{8}$$

Substituting (8) in (7) yields

$$(3 + 8t_0) - 3(4 + 5t_0) + 5(-3 - t_0) = 12$$

Solving for $t_0$ yields $t_0 = -3$ and on substituting this value in (8), we obtain

$$(x_0, y_0, z_0) = (-21, -11, 0) \quad ◀$$

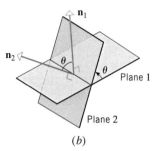

(a)

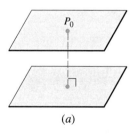

(b)

▲ **Figure 11.6.7**

### ▨ INTERSECTING PLANES

Two distinct intersecting planes determine two positive angles of intersection—an (acute) angle $\theta$ that satisfies the condition $0 \le \theta \le \pi/2$ and the supplement of that angle (Figure 11.6.7a). If $\mathbf{n}_1$ and $\mathbf{n}_2$ are normals to the planes, then depending on the directions of $\mathbf{n}_1$ and $\mathbf{n}_2$, the angle $\theta$ is either the angle between $\mathbf{n}_1$ and $\mathbf{n}_2$ or the angle between $\mathbf{n}_1$ and $-\mathbf{n}_2$ (Figure 11.6.7b). In both cases, Theorem 11.3.3 yields the following formula for the *acute angle $\theta$ between the planes*:

$$\cos\theta = \frac{|\mathbf{n}_1 \cdot \mathbf{n}_2|}{\|\mathbf{n}_1\|\,\|\mathbf{n}_2\|} \tag{9}$$

▶ **Example 6**    Find the acute angle of intersection between the two planes

$$2x - 4y + 4z = 6 \quad\text{and}\quad 6x + 2y - 3z = 4$$

**Solution.**    The given equations yield the normals $\mathbf{n}_1 = \langle 2, -4, 4\rangle$ and $\mathbf{n}_2 = \langle 6, 2, -3\rangle$. Thus, Formula (9) yields

$$\cos\theta = \frac{|\mathbf{n}_1 \cdot \mathbf{n}_2|}{\|\mathbf{n}_1\|\,\|\mathbf{n}_2\|} = \frac{|-8|}{\sqrt{36}\sqrt{49}} = \frac{4}{21}$$

from which we obtain

$$\theta = \cos^{-1}\left(\frac{4}{21}\right) \approx 79° \quad\blacktriangleleft$$

▶ **Example 7**    Find an equation for the line $L$ of intersection of the planes in Example 6.

**Solution.**    First compute $\mathbf{v} = \mathbf{n}_1 \times \mathbf{n}_2 = \langle 2, -4, 4\rangle \times \langle 6, 2, -3\rangle = \langle 4, 30, 28\rangle$. Since $\mathbf{v}$ is orthogonal to $\mathbf{n}_1$, it is parallel to the first plane, and since $\mathbf{v}$ is orthogonal to $\mathbf{n}_2$, it is parallel to the second plane. That is, $\mathbf{v}$ is parallel to $L$, the intersection of the two planes. To find a point on $L$ we observe that $L$ must intersect the $xy$-plane, $z = 0$, since $\mathbf{v} \cdot \langle 0, 0, 1\rangle = 28 \ne 0$. Substituting $z = 0$ in the equations of both planes yields

$$2x - 4y = 6$$
$$6x + 2y = 4$$

with solution $x = 1$, $y = -1$. Thus, $P(1, -1, 0)$ is a point on $L$. A vector equation for $L$ is

$$\langle x, y, z\rangle = \langle 1, -1, 0\rangle + t\langle 4, 30, 28\rangle \quad\blacktriangleleft$$

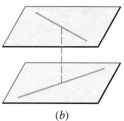

(a)

(b)

▲ **Figure 11.6.8**

### ▨ DISTANCE PROBLEMS INVOLVING PLANES

Next we will consider three basic distance problems in 3-space:

- Find the distance between a point and a plane.
- Find the distance between two parallel planes.
- Find the distance between two skew lines.

The three problems are related. If we can find the distance between a point and a plane, then we can find the distance between parallel planes by computing the distance between one of the planes and an arbitrary point $P_0$ in the other plane (Figure 11.6.8a). Moreover, we can find the distance between two skew lines by computing the distance between parallel planes containing them (Figure 11.6.8b).

> **11.6.2** **THEOREM** *The distance $D$ between a point $P_0(x_0, y_0, z_0)$ and the plane $ax + by + cz + d = 0$ is*
>
> $$D = \frac{|ax_0 + by_0 + cz_0 + d|}{\sqrt{a^2 + b^2 + c^2}} \qquad (10)$$

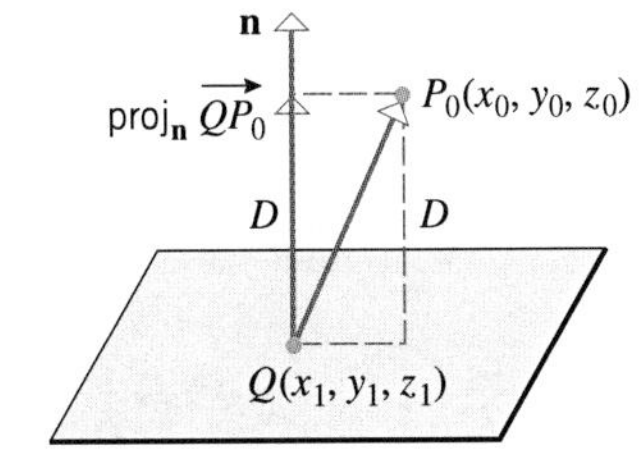

**PROOF** Let $Q(x_1, y_1, z_1)$ be any point in the plane, and position the normal $\mathbf{n} = \langle a, b, c \rangle$ so that its initial point is at $Q$. As illustrated in Figure 11.6.9, the distance $D$ is equal to the length of the orthogonal projection of $\overrightarrow{QP_0}$ on $\mathbf{n}$. Thus, from (12) of Section 11.3,

$$D = \|\text{proj}_{\mathbf{n}} \overrightarrow{QP_0}\| = \left\| \frac{\overrightarrow{QP_0} \cdot \mathbf{n}}{\|\mathbf{n}\|^2} \mathbf{n} \right\| = \frac{|\overrightarrow{QP_0} \cdot \mathbf{n}|}{\|\mathbf{n}\|^2} \|\mathbf{n}\| = \frac{|\overrightarrow{QP_0} \cdot \mathbf{n}|}{\|\mathbf{n}\|}$$

But

$$\overrightarrow{QP_0} = \langle x_0 - x_1, y_0 - y_1, z_0 - z_1 \rangle$$
$$\overrightarrow{QP_0} \cdot \mathbf{n} = a(x_0 - x_1) + b(y_0 - y_1) + c(z_0 - z_1)$$
$$\|\mathbf{n}\| = \sqrt{a^2 + b^2 + c^2}$$

Thus,

$$D = \frac{|a(x_0 - x_1) + b(y_0 - y_1) + c(z_0 - z_1)|}{\sqrt{a^2 + b^2 + c^2}} \qquad (11)$$

Since the point $Q(x_1, y_1, z_1)$ lies in the plane, its coordinates satisfy the equation of the plane; that is,

$$ax_1 + by_1 + cz_1 + d = 0$$

or

$$d = -ax_1 - by_1 - cz_1$$

Combining this expression with (11) yields (10). ∎

▲ **Figure 11.6.9**

There is an analog of Formula (10) in 2-space that can be used to compute the distance between a point and a line (see Exercise 52).

▶ **Example 8** Find the distance $D$ between the point $(1, -4, -3)$ and the plane

$$2x - 3y + 6z = -1$$

**Solution.** Formula (10) requires the plane be rewritten in the form $ax + by + cz + d = 0$. Thus, we rewrite the equation of the given plane as

$$2x - 3y + 6z + 1 = 0$$

from which we obtain $a = 2$, $b = -3$, $c = 6$, and $d = 1$. Substituting these values and the coordinates of the given point in (10), we obtain

$$D = \frac{|(2)(1) + (-3)(-4) + 6(-3) + 1|}{\sqrt{2^2 + (-3)^2 + 6^2}} = \frac{|-3|}{7} = \frac{3}{7} \blacktriangleleft$$

▶ **Example 9** The planes

$$x + 2y - 2z = 3 \quad \text{and} \quad 2x + 4y - 4z = 7$$

are parallel since their normals, $\langle 1, 2, -2 \rangle$ and $\langle 2, 4, -4 \rangle$, are parallel vectors. Find the distance between these planes.

***Solution.*** To find the distance $D$ between the planes, we can select an *arbitrary* point in one of the planes and compute its distance to the other plane. By setting $y = z = 0$ in the equation $x + 2y - 2z = 3$, we obtain the point $P_0(3, 0, 0)$ in this plane. From (10), the distance from $P_0$ to the plane $2x + 4y - 4z = 7$ is

$$D = \frac{|(2)(3) + 4(0) + (-4)(0) - 7|}{\sqrt{2^2 + 4^2 + (-4)^2}} = \frac{1}{6} \quad \blacktriangleleft$$

▶ **Example 10** It was shown in Example 3 of Section 11.5 that the lines

$$L_1: x = 1 + 4t, \quad y = 5 - 4t, \quad z = -1 + 5t$$
$$L_2: x = 2 + 8t, \quad y = 4 - 3t, \quad z = 5 + t$$

are skew. Find the distance between them.

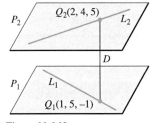

▲ **Figure 11.6.10**

***Solution.*** Let $P_1$ and $P_2$ denote parallel planes containing $L_1$ and $L_2$, respectively (Figure 11.6.10). To find the distance $D$ between $L_1$ and $L_2$, we will calculate the distance from a point in $P_1$ to the plane $P_2$. Since $L_1$ lies in plane $P_1$, we can find a point in $P_1$ by finding a point on the line $L_1$; we can do this by substituting any convenient value of $t$ in the parametric equations of $L_1$. The simplest choice is $t = 0$, which yields the point $Q_1(1, 5, -1)$.

The next step is to find an equation for the plane $P_2$. For this purpose, observe that the vector $\mathbf{u}_1 = \langle 4, -4, 5 \rangle$ is parallel to line $L_1$, and therefore also parallel to planes $P_1$ and $P_2$. Similarly, $\mathbf{u}_2 = \langle 8, -3, 1 \rangle$ is parallel to $L_2$ and hence parallel to $P_1$ and $P_2$. Therefore, the cross product

$$\mathbf{n} = \mathbf{u}_1 \times \mathbf{u}_2 = \begin{vmatrix} \mathbf{i} & \mathbf{j} & \mathbf{k} \\ 4 & -4 & 5 \\ 8 & -3 & 1 \end{vmatrix} = 11\mathbf{i} + 36\mathbf{j} + 20\mathbf{k}$$

is normal to both $P_1$ and $P_2$. Using this normal and the point $Q_2(2, 4, 5)$ found by setting $t = 0$ in the equations of $L_2$, we obtain an equation for $P_2$:

$$11(x - 2) + 36(y - 4) + 20(z - 5) = 0$$

or

$$11x + 36y + 20z - 266 = 0$$

The distance between $Q_1(1, 5, -1)$ and this plane is

$$D = \frac{|(11)(1) + (36)(5) + (20)(-1) - 266|}{\sqrt{11^2 + 36^2 + 20^2}} = \frac{95}{\sqrt{1817}}$$

which is also the distance between $L_1$ and $L_2$. ◀

---

✔**QUICK CHECK EXERCISES 11.6** (*See page 821 for answers.*)

1. The point-normal form of the equation of the plane through $(0, 3, 5)$ and perpendicular to $\langle -4, 1, 7 \rangle$ is _____.

2. A normal vector for the plane $4x - 2y + 7z - 11 = 0$ is _____.

3. A normal vector for the plane through the points $(2, 5, 1)$, $(3, 7, 0)$, and $(2, 5, 2)$ is _____.

4. The acute angle of intersection of the planes $x + y - 2z = 5$ and $3y - 4z = 6$ is _____.

5. The distance between the point $(9, 8, 3)$ and the plane $x + y - 2z = 5$ is _____.

**EXERCISE SET 11.6**

1. Find equations of the planes $P_1$, $P_2$, and $P_3$ that are parallel to the coordinate planes and pass through the corner $(3, 4, 5)$ of the box shown in the accompanying figure.

2. Find equations of the planes $P_1$, $P_2$, and $P_3$ that are parallel to the coordinate planes and pass through the corner $(x_0, y_0, z_0)$ of the box shown in the accompanying figure.

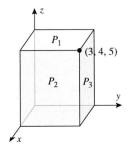

▲ Figure Ex-1

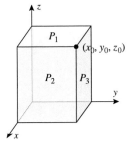

▲ Figure Ex-2

**3–6** Find an equation of the plane that passes through the point $P$ and has the vector $\mathbf{n}$ as a normal. ■

3. $P(2, 6, 1)$; $\mathbf{n} = \langle 1, 4, 2 \rangle$

4. $P(-1, -1, 2)$; $\mathbf{n} = \langle -1, 7, 6 \rangle$

5. $P(1, 0, 0)$; $\mathbf{n} = \langle 0, 0, 1 \rangle$

6. $P(0, 0, 0)$; $\mathbf{n} = \langle 2, -3, -4 \rangle$

**7–10** Find an equation of the plane indicated in the figure. ■

7.
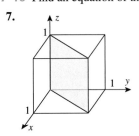

8.
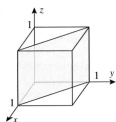

9.
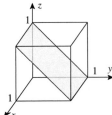

10.
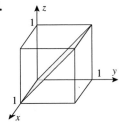

**11–12** Find an equation of the plane that passes through the given points. ■

11. $(-2, 1, 1)$, $(0, 2, 3)$, and $(1, 0, -1)$

12. $(3, 2, 1)$, $(2, 1, -1)$, and $(-1, 3, 2)$

**13–14** Determine whether the planes are parallel, perpendicular, or neither. ■

13. (a) $2x - 8y - 6z - 2 = 0$  (b) $3x - 2y + z = 1$
    $-x + 4y + 3z - 5 = 0$      $4x + 5y - 2z = 4$
    (c) $x - y + 3z - 2 = 0$
    $2x + z = 1$

14. (a) $3x - 2y + z = 4$    (b) $y = 4x - 2z + 3$
    $6x - 4y + 3z = 7$        $x = \frac{1}{4}y + \frac{1}{2}z$
    (c) $x + 4y + 7z = 3$
    $5x - 3y + z = 0$

**15–16** Determine whether the line and plane are parallel, perpendicular, or neither. ■

15. (a) $x = 4 + 2t$, $y = -t$, $z = -1 - 4t$;
    $3x + 2y + z - 7 = 0$
    (b) $x = t$, $y = 2t$, $z = 3t$;
    $x - y + 2z = 5$
    (c) $x = -1 + 2t$, $y = 4 + t$, $z = 1 - t$;
    $4x + 2y - 2z = 7$

16. (a) $x = 3 - t$, $y = 2 + t$, $z = 1 - 3t$;
    $2x + 2y - 5 = 0$
    (b) $x = 1 - 2t$, $y = t$, $z = -t$;
    $6x - 3y + 3z = 1$
    (c) $x = t$, $y = 1 - t$, $z = 2 + t$;
    $x + y + z = 1$

**17–18** Determine whether the line and plane intersect; if so, find the coordinates of the intersection. ■

17. (a) $x = t$, $y = t$, $z = t$;
    $3x - 2y + z - 5 = 0$
    (b) $x = 2 - t$, $y = 3 + t$, $z = t$;
    $2x + y + z = 1$

18. (a) $x = 3t$, $y = 5t$, $z = -t$;
    $2x - y + z + 1 = 0$
    (b) $x = 1 + t$, $y = -1 + 3t$, $z = 2 + 4t$;
    $x - y + 4z = 7$

**19–20** Find the acute angle of intersection of the planes to the nearest degree. ■

19. $x = 0$ and $2x - y + z - 4 = 0$

20. $x + 2y - 2z = 5$ and $6x - 3y + 2z = 8$

**21–24 True–False** Determine whether the statement is true or false. Explain your answer. ■

21. Every plane has exactly two unit normal vectors.

22. If a plane is parallel to one of the coordinate planes, then its normal vector is parallel to one of the three vectors $\mathbf{i}$, $\mathbf{j}$, or $\mathbf{k}$.

23. If two planes intersect in a line $L$, then $L$ is parallel to the cross product of the normals to the two planes.

**24.** If $a^2 + b^2 + c^2 = 1$, then the distance from $P(x_0, y_0, z_0)$ to the plane $ax + by + cz = 0$ is $|\langle a, b, c \rangle \cdot \langle x_0, y_0, z_0 \rangle|$.

**25–34** Find an equation of the plane that satisfies the stated conditions. ■

**25.** The plane through the origin that is parallel to the plane $4x - 2y + 7z + 12 = 0$.

**26.** The plane that contains the line $x = -2 + 3t$, $y = 4 + 2t$, $z = 3 - t$ and is perpendicular to the plane $x - 2y + z = 5$.

**27.** The plane through the point $(-1, 4, 2)$ that contains the line of intersection of the planes $4x - y + z - 2 = 0$ and $2x + y - 2z - 3 = 0$.

**28.** The plane through $(-1, 4, -3)$ that is perpendicular to the line $x - 2 = t$, $y + 3 = 2t$, $z = -t$.

**29.** The plane through $(1, 2, -1)$ that is perpendicular to the line of intersection of the planes $2x + y + z = 2$ and $x + 2y + z = 3$.

**30.** The plane through the points $P_1(-2, 1, 4)$, $P_2(1, 0, 3)$ that is perpendicular to the plane $4x - y + 3z = 2$.

**31.** The plane through $(-1, 2, -5)$ that is perpendicular to the planes $2x - y + z = 1$ and $x + y - 2z = 3$.

**32.** The plane that contains the point $(2, 0, 3)$ and the line $x = -1 + t$, $y = t$, $z = -4 + 2t$.

**33.** The plane whose points are equidistant from $(2, -1, 1)$ and $(3, 1, 5)$.

**34.** The plane that contains the line $x = 3t$, $y = 1 + t$, $z = 2t$ and is parallel to the intersection of the planes $y + z = -1$ and $2x - y + z = 0$.

**35.** Find parametric equations of the line through the point $(5, 0, -2)$ that is parallel to the planes $x - 4y + 2z = 0$ and $2x + 3y - z + 1 = 0$.

**36.** Let $L$ be the line $x = 3t + 1$, $y = -5t$, $z = t$.
(a) Show that $L$ lies in the plane $2x + y - z = 2$.
(b) Show that $L$ is parallel to the plane $x + y + 2z = 0$. Is the line above, below, or on this plane?

**37.** Show that the lines

$$x = -2 + t, \quad y = 3 + 2t, \quad z = 4 - t$$
$$x = 3 - t, \quad y = 4 - 2t, \quad z = t$$

are parallel and find an equation of the plane they determine.

**38.** Show that the lines

$$L_1: x + 1 = 4t, \quad y - 3 = t, \quad z - 1 = 0$$
$$L_2: x + 13 = 12t, \quad y - 1 = 6t, \quad z - 2 = 3t$$

intersect and find an equation of the plane they determine.

**39.** Do the points $(1, 0, -1)$, $(0, 2, 3)$, $(-2, 1, 1)$, and $(4, 2, 3)$ lie in the same plane? Justify your answer two different ways.

**40.** Show that if $a$, $b$, and $c$ are nonzero, then the plane whose intercepts with the coordinate axes are $x = a$,

$y = b$, and $z = c$ is given by the equation

$$\frac{x}{a} + \frac{y}{b} + \frac{z}{c} = 1$$

**41–42** Find parametric equations of the line of intersection of the planes. ■

**41.** $-2x + 3y + 7z + 2 = 0$ 　　**42.** $3x - 5y + 2z = 0$
$\phantom{41.}$ $x + 2y - 3z + 5 = 0$ 　　$\phantom{42.}$ $z = 0$

**43–44** Find the distance between the point and the plane. ■

**43.** $(1, -2, 3)$; $2x - 2y + z = 4$

**44.** $(0, 1, 5)$; $3x + 6y - 2z - 5 = 0$

**45–46** Find the distance between the given parallel planes. ■

**45.** $-2x + y + z = 0$ 　　　　**46.** $x + y + z = 1$
$\phantom{45.}$ $6x - 3y - 3z - 5 = 0$ 　　$\phantom{46.}$ $x + y + z = -1$

**47–48** Find the distance between the given skew lines. ■

**47.** $x = 1 + 7t$, $y = 3 + t$, $z = 5 - 3t$
$\phantom{47.}$ $x = 4 - t$, $y = 6$, $z = 7 + 2t$

**48.** $x = 3 - t$, $y = 4 + 4t$, $z = 1 + 2t$
$\phantom{48.}$ $x = t$, $y = 3$, $z = 2t$

**49.** Find an equation of the sphere with center $(2, 1, -3)$ that is tangent to the plane $x - 3y + 2z = 4$.

**50.** Locate the point of intersection of the plane $2x + y - z = 0$ and the line through $(3, 1, 0)$ that is perpendicular to the plane.

**51.** Show that the line $x = -1 + t$, $y = 3 + 2t$, $z = -t$ and the plane $2x - 2y - 2z + 3 = 0$ are parallel, and find the distance between them.

**52.** Formulas (1), (2), (3), (5), and (10), which apply to planes in 3-space, have analogs for lines in 2-space.
(a) Draw an analog of Figure 11.6.3 in 2-space to illustrate that the equation of the line that passes through the point $P(x_0, y_0)$ and is perpendicular to the vector $\mathbf{n} = \langle a, b \rangle$ can be expressed as

$$\mathbf{n} \cdot (\mathbf{r} - \mathbf{r}_0) = 0$$

where $\mathbf{r} = \langle x, y \rangle$ and $\mathbf{r}_0 = \langle x_0, y_0 \rangle$.
(b) Show that the vector equation in part (a) can be expressed as

$$a(x - x_0) + b(y - y_0) = 0$$

This is called the ***point-normal form of a line***.
(c) Using the proof of Theorem 11.6.1 as a guide, show that if $a$ and $b$ are not both zero, then the graph of the equation

$$ax + by + c = 0$$

is a line that has $\mathbf{n} = \langle a, b \rangle$ as a normal. *(cont.)*

(d) Using the proof of Theorem 11.6.2 as a guide, show that the distance $D$ between a point $P(x_0, y_0)$ and the line $ax + by + c = 0$ is

$$D = \frac{|ax_0 + by_0 + c|}{\sqrt{a^2 + b^2}}$$

(e) Use the formula in part (d) to find the distance between the point $P(-3, 5)$ and the line $y = -2x + 1$.

**53.** (a) Show that the distance $D$ between parallel planes

$$ax + by + cz + d_1 = 0$$
$$ax + by + cz + d_2 = 0$$

is

$$D = \frac{|d_1 - d_2|}{\sqrt{a^2 + b^2 + c^2}}$$

(b) Use the formula in part (a) to solve Exercise 45.

**54.** Writing Explain why any line in 3-space must lie in some vertical plane. Must any line in 3-space also lie in some horizontal plane?

**55.** Writing Given two planes, discuss the various possibilities for the set of points they have in common. Then consider the set of points that three planes can have in common.

## ✔ QUICK CHECK ANSWERS 11.6

1. $-4x + (y - 3) + 7(z - 5) = 0$    2. $\langle 4, -2, 7 \rangle$    3. $\langle 2, -1, 0 \rangle$    4. $\cos^{-1} \dfrac{11}{5\sqrt{6}} \approx 26°$    5. $\sqrt{6}$

## 11.7 QUADRIC SURFACES

*In this section we will study an important class of surfaces that are the three-dimensional analogs of the conic sections.*

### ■ TRACES OF SURFACES

Although the general shape of a curve in 2-space can be obtained by plotting points, this method is not usually helpful for surfaces in 3-space because too many points are required. It is more common to build up the shape of a surface with a network of **mesh lines**, which are curves obtained by cutting the surface with well-chosen planes. For example, Figure 11.7.1, which was generated by a CAS, shows the graph of $z = x^3 - 3xy^2$ rendered with a combination of mesh lines and colorization to produce the surface detail. This surface is called a "monkey saddle" because a monkey sitting astride the surface has a place for its two legs and tail.

The mesh line that results when a surface is cut by a plane is called the **trace** of the surface in the plane (Figure 11.7.2). One way to deduce the shape of a surface is by examining its traces in planes parallel to the coordinate planes. For example, consider the surface

$$z = x^2 + y^2 \tag{1}$$

To find its trace in the plane $z = k$, we substitute this value of $z$ into (1), which yields

$$x^2 + y^2 = k \qquad (z = k) \tag{2}$$

If $k < 0$, this equation has no real solutions, so there is no trace. However, if $k \geq 0$, then the graph of (2) is a circle of radius $\sqrt{k}$ centered at the point $(0, 0, k)$ on the $z$-axis (Figure 11.7.3a). Thus, for nonnegative values of $k$ the traces parallel to the $xy$-plane form a family of circles, centered on the $z$-axis, whose radii start at zero and increase with $k$. This suggests that the surface has the form shown in Figure 11.7.3b.

To obtain more detailed information about the shape of this surface, we can examine the traces of (1) in planes parallel to the $yz$-plane. Such planes have equations of the form $x = k$, so we substitute this in (1) to obtain

$$z = k^2 + y^2 \qquad (x = k)$$

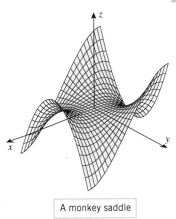

A monkey saddle

▲ **Figure 11.7.1**

The parenthetical part of Equation (2) is a reminder that the $z$-coordinate of each point in the trace is $z = k$. This needs to be stated explicitly because the variable $z$ does not appear in the equation $x^2 + y^2 = k$.

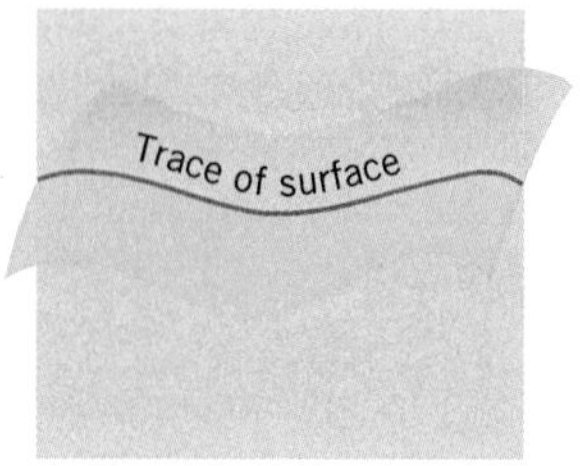

▲ Figure 11.7.2

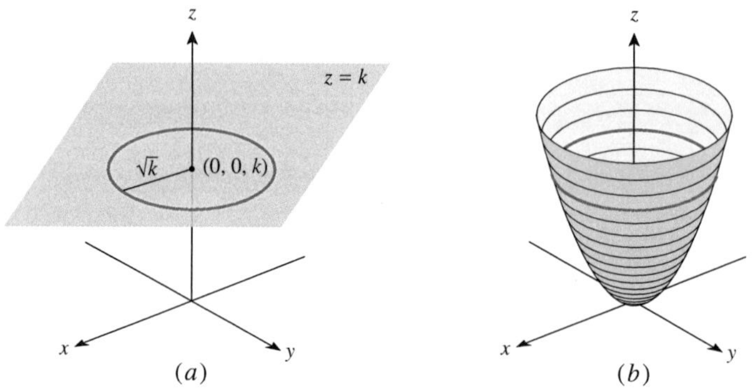

▲ Figure 11.7.3

which we can rewrite as

$$z - k^2 = y^2 \qquad (x = k) \tag{3}$$

For simplicity, let us start with the case where $k = 0$ (the trace in the $yz$-plane), in which case the trace has the equation

$$z = y^2 \qquad (x = 0)$$

You should be able to recognize that this is a parabola in the plane $x = 0$ that has its vertex at the origin, opens in the positive $z$-direction, and is symmetric about the $z$-axis (the blue parabola in Figure 11.7.4$a$). You should also be able to recognize that the $-k^2$ term in (3) has the effect of translating the parabola $z = y^2$ in the positive $z$-direction, so its new vertex in the plane $x = k$ is at the point $(k, 0, k^2)$. This is the red parabola in Figure 11.7.4$a$. Thus, the traces in planes parallel to the $yz$-plane form a family of parabolas whose vertices move upward as $k^2$ increases (Figure 11.7.4$b$). Similarly, the traces in planes parallel to the $xz$-plane have equations of the form

$$z - k^2 = x^2 \qquad (y = k)$$

which again is a family of parabolas whose vertices move upward as $k^2$ increases (Figure 11.7.4$c$).

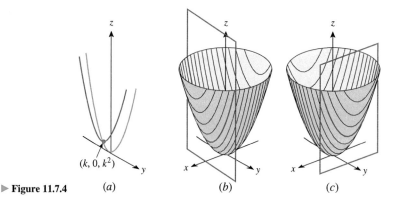

▶ Figure 11.7.4     ($a$)        ($b$)        ($c$)

### ▪ THE QUADRIC SURFACES

In the discussion of Formula (2) in Section 10.5 we noted that a second-degree equation

$$Ax^2 + Bxy + Cy^2 + Dx + Ey + F = 0$$

represents a conic section (possibly degenerate). The analog of this equation in an $xyz$-coordinate system is

$$Ax^2 + By^2 + Cz^2 + Dxy + Exz + Fyz + Gx + Hy + Iz + J = 0 \tag{4}$$

which is called a ***second-degree equation in x, y, and z***. The graphs of such equations are called ***quadric surfaces*** or sometimes ***quadrics***.

Six common types of quadric surfaces are shown in Table 11.7.1—*ellipsoids, hyperboloids of one sheet, hyperboloids of two sheets, elliptic cones, elliptic paraboloids,* and *hyperbolic paraboloids.* (The constants *a*, *b*, and *c* that appear in the equations in the table are assumed to be positive.) Observe that none of the quadric surfaces in the table have cross-product terms in their equations. This is because of their orientations relative

**Table 11.7.1**

| SURFACE | EQUATION | SURFACE | EQUATION |
|---------|----------|---------|----------|
| **ELLIPSOID** | $$\frac{x^2}{a^2} + \frac{y^2}{b^2} + \frac{z^2}{c^2} = 1$$ The traces in the coordinate planes are ellipses, as are the traces in those planes that are parallel to the coordinate planes and intersect the surface in more than one point. | **ELLIPTIC CONE** | $$z^2 = \frac{x^2}{a^2} + \frac{y^2}{b^2}$$ The trace in the *xy*-plane is a point (the origin), and the traces in planes parallel to the *xy*-plane are ellipses. The traces in the *yz*- and *xz*-planes are pairs of lines intersecting at the origin. The traces in planes parallel to these are hyperbolas. |
| **HYPERBOLOID OF ONE SHEET** | $$\frac{x^2}{a^2} + \frac{y^2}{b^2} - \frac{z^2}{c^2} = 1$$ The trace in the *xy*-plane is an ellipse, as are the traces in planes parallel to the *xy*-plane. The traces in the *yz*-plane and *xz*-plane are hyperbolas, as are the traces in those planes that are parallel to these and do not pass through the *x*- or *y*-intercepts. At these intercepts the traces are pairs of intersecting lines. | **ELLIPTIC PARABOLOID** | $$z = \frac{x^2}{a^2} + \frac{y^2}{b^2}$$ The trace in the *xy*-plane is a point (the origin), and the traces in planes parallel to and above the *xy*-plane are ellipses. The traces in the *yz*- and *xz*-planes are parabolas, as are the traces in planes parallel to these. |
| **HYPERBOLOID OF TWO SHEETS** | $$\frac{z^2}{c^2} - \frac{x^2}{a^2} - \frac{y^2}{b^2} = 1$$ There is no trace in the *xy*-plane. In planes parallel to the *xy*-plane that intersect the surface in more than one point the traces are ellipses. In the *yz*- and *xz*-planes, the traces are hyperbolas, as are the traces in those planes that are parallel to these. | **HYPERBOLIC PARABOLOID** | $$z = \frac{y^2}{b^2} - \frac{x^2}{a^2}$$ The trace in the *xy*-plane is a pair of lines intersecting at the origin. The traces in planes parallel to the *xy*-plane are hyperbolas. The hyperbolas above the *xy*-plane open in the *y*-direction, and those below in the *x*-direction. The traces in the *yz*- and *xz*-planes are parabolas, as are the traces in planes parallel to these. |

to the coordinate axes. Later in this section we will discuss other possible orientations that produce equations of the quadric surfaces with no cross-product terms. In the special case where the elliptic cross sections of an elliptic cone or an elliptic paraboloid are circles, the terms *circular cone* and *circular paraboloid* are used.

### ■ TECHNIQUES FOR GRAPHING QUADRIC SURFACES

Accurate graphs of quadric surfaces are best left for graphing utilities. However, the techniques that we will now discuss can be used to generate rough sketches of these surfaces that are useful for various purposes.

A rough sketch of an ellipsoid

$$\frac{x^2}{a^2} + \frac{y^2}{b^2} + \frac{z^2}{c^2} = 1 \qquad (a > 0, b > 0, c > 0) \tag{5}$$

can be obtained by first plotting the intersections with the coordinate axes, and then sketching the elliptical traces in the coordinate planes. Example 1 illustrates this technique.

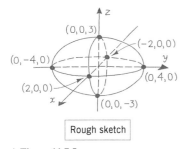

Rough sketch

▲ **Figure 11.7.5**

▶ **Example 1**    Sketch the ellipsoid

$$\frac{x^2}{4} + \frac{y^2}{16} + \frac{z^2}{9} = 1 \tag{6}$$

*Solution.*    The $x$-intercepts can be obtained by setting $y = 0$ and $z = 0$ in (6). This yields $x = \pm 2$. Similarly, the $y$-intercepts are $y = \pm 4$, and the $z$-intercepts are $z = \pm 3$. Sketching the elliptical traces in the coordinate planes yields the graph in Figure 11.7.5. ◀

A rough sketch of a hyperboloid of one sheet

$$\frac{x^2}{a^2} + \frac{y^2}{b^2} - \frac{z^2}{c^2} = 1 \qquad (a > 0, b > 0, c > 0) \tag{7}$$

can be obtained by first sketching the elliptical trace in the $xy$-plane, then the elliptical traces in the planes $z = \pm c$, and then the hyperbolic curves that join the endpoints of the axes of these ellipses. The next example illustrates this technique.

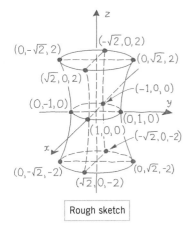

Rough sketch

▲ **Figure 11.7.6**

▶ **Example 2**    Sketch the graph of the hyperboloid of one sheet

$$x^2 + y^2 - \frac{z^2}{4} = 1 \tag{8}$$

*Solution.*    The trace in the $xy$-plane, obtained by setting $z = 0$ in (8), is

$$x^2 + y^2 = 1 \qquad (z = 0)$$

which is a circle of radius 1 centered on the $z$-axis. The traces in the planes $z = 2$ and $z = -2$, obtained by setting $z = \pm 2$ in (8), are given by

$$x^2 + y^2 = 2 \qquad (z = \pm 2)$$

which are circles of radius $\sqrt{2}$ centered on the $z$-axis. Joining these circles by the hyperbolic traces in the vertical coordinate planes yields the graph in Figure 11.7.6. ◀

A rough sketch of the hyperboloid of two sheets

$$\frac{z^2}{c^2} - \frac{x^2}{a^2} - \frac{y^2}{b^2} = 1 \qquad (a > 0, b > 0, c > 0) \tag{9}$$

can be obtained by first plotting the intersections with the $z$-axis, then sketching the elliptical traces in the planes $z = \pm 2c$, and then sketching the hyperbolic traces that connect the $z$-axis intersections and the endpoints of the axes of the ellipses. (It is not essential to use the planes $z = \pm 2c$, but these are good choices since they simplify the calculations slightly and have the right spacing for a good sketch.) The next example illustrates this technique.

▶ **Example 3** Sketch the graph of the hyperboloid of two sheets

$$z^2 - x^2 - \frac{y^2}{4} = 1 \tag{10}$$

*Solution.* The $z$-intercepts, obtained by setting $x = 0$ and $y = 0$ in (10), are $z = \pm 1$. The traces in the planes $z = 2$ and $z = -2$, obtained by setting $z = \pm 2$ in (10), are given by

$$\frac{x^2}{3} + \frac{y^2}{12} = 1 \qquad (z = \pm 2)$$

Sketching these ellipses and the hyperbolic traces in the vertical coordinate planes yields Figure 11.7.7. ◀

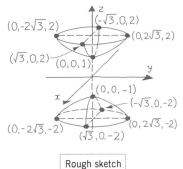

Rough sketch

▲ **Figure 11.7.7**

A rough sketch of the elliptic cone

$$z^2 = \frac{x^2}{a^2} + \frac{y^2}{b^2} \qquad (a > 0, b > 0) \tag{11}$$

can be obtained by first sketching the elliptical traces in the planes $z = \pm 1$ and then sketching the linear traces that connect the endpoints of the axes of the ellipses. The next example illustrates this technique.

▶ **Example 4** Sketch the graph of the elliptic cone

$$z^2 = x^2 + \frac{y^2}{4} \tag{12}$$

*Solution.* The traces of (12) in the planes $z = \pm 1$ are given by

$$x^2 + \frac{y^2}{4} = 1 \qquad (z = \pm 1)$$

Sketching these ellipses and the linear traces in the vertical coordinate planes yields the graph in Figure 11.7.8. ◀

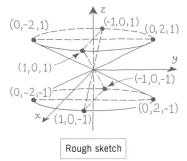

Rough sketch

▲ **Figure 11.7.8**

In the special cases of (11) and (13) where $a = b$, the traces parallel to the $xy$-plane are circles. In these cases, we call (11) a *circular cone* and (13) a *circular paraboloid*.

A rough sketch of the elliptic paraboloid

$$z = \frac{x^2}{a^2} + \frac{y^2}{b^2} \qquad (a > 0, b > 0) \tag{13}$$

can be obtained by first sketching the elliptical trace in the plane $z = 1$ and then sketching the parabolic traces in the vertical coordinate planes to connect the origin to the ends of the axes of the ellipse. The next example illustrates this technique.

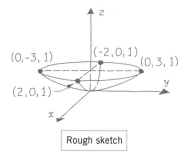

Rough sketch

▲ **Figure 11.7.9**

▶ **Example 5**  Sketch the graph of the elliptic paraboloid

$$z = \frac{x^2}{4} + \frac{y^2}{9} \tag{14}$$

*Solution.*  The trace of (14) in the plane $z = 1$ is

$$\frac{x^2}{4} + \frac{y^2}{9} = 1 \qquad (z = 1)$$

Sketching this ellipse and the parabolic traces in the vertical coordinate planes yields the graph in Figure 11.7.9. ◀

A rough sketch of the hyperbolic paraboloid

$$z = \frac{y^2}{b^2} - \frac{x^2}{a^2} \qquad (a > 0, b > 0) \tag{15}$$

can be obtained by first sketching the two parabolic traces that pass through the origin (one in the plane $x = 0$ and the other in the plane $y = 0$). After the parabolic traces are drawn, sketch the hyperbolic traces in the planes $z = \pm 1$ and then fill in any missing edges. The next example illustrates this technique.

▶ **Example 6**  Sketch the graph of the hyperbolic paraboloid

$$z = \frac{y^2}{4} - \frac{x^2}{9} \tag{16}$$

*Solution.*  Setting $x = 0$ in (16) yields

$$z = \frac{y^2}{4} \qquad (x = 0)$$

which is a parabola in the $yz$-plane with vertex at the origin and opening in the positive $z$-direction (since $z \geq 0$), and setting $y = 0$ yields

$$z = -\frac{x^2}{9} \qquad (y = 0)$$

which is a parabola in the $xz$-plane with vertex at the origin and opening in the negative $z$-direction.

The trace in the plane $z = 1$ is

$$\frac{y^2}{4} - \frac{x^2}{9} = 1 \qquad (z = 1)$$

which is a hyperbola that opens along a line parallel to the $y$-axis (verify), and the trace in the plane $z = -1$ is

$$\frac{x^2}{9} - \frac{y^2}{4} = 1 \qquad (z = -1)$$

which is a hyperbola that opens along a line parallel to the $x$-axis. Combining all of the above information leads to the sketch in Figure 11.7.10. ◀

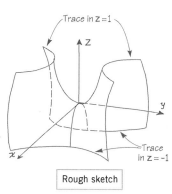

Rough sketch

▲ **Figure 11.7.10**

**REMARK**  The hyperbolic paraboloid in Figure 11.7.10 has an interesting behavior at the origin—the trace in the $xz$-plane has a relative maximum at $(0, 0, 0)$, and the trace in the $yz$-plane has a relative minimum at $(0, 0, 0)$. Thus, a bug walking on the surface may view the origin as a highest point if traveling along one path, or may view the origin as a lowest point if traveling along a different path. A point with this property is commonly called a *saddle point* or a *minimax point*.

Figure 11.7.11 shows two computer-generated views of the hyperbolic paraboloid in Example 6. The first view, which is much like our rough sketch in Figure 11.7.10, has cuts at the top and bottom that are hyperbolic traces parallel to the $xy$-plane. In the second view the top horizontal cut has been omitted; this helps to emphasize the parabolic traces parallel to the $xz$-plane.

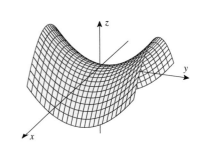

▶ **Figure 11.7.11**

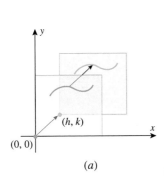

(a)

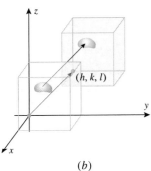

(b)

▲ **Figure 11.7.12**

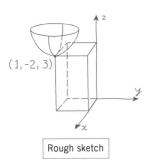

Rough sketch

▲ **Figure 11.7.13**

### TRANSLATIONS OF QUADRIC SURFACES

In Section 10.4 we saw that a conic in an $xy$-coordinate system can be translated by substituting $x - h$ for $x$ and $y - k$ for $y$ in its equation. To understand why this works, think of the $xy$-axes as fixed and think of the plane as a transparent sheet of plastic on which all graphs are drawn. When the coordinates of points are modified by substituting $(x - h, y - k)$ for $(x, y)$, the geometric effect is to translate the sheet of plastic (and hence all curves) so that the point on the plastic that was initially at $(0, 0)$ is moved to the point $(h, k)$ (see Figure 11.7.12a).

For the analog in three dimensions, think of the $xyz$-axes as fixed and think of 3-space as a transparent block of plastic in which all surfaces are embedded. When the coordinates of points are modified by substituting $(x - h, y - k, z - l)$ for $(x, y, z)$, the geometric effect is to translate the block of plastic (and hence all surfaces) so that the point in the plastic block that was initially at $(0, 0, 0)$ is moved to the point $(h, k, l)$ (see Figure 11.7.12b).

▶ **Example 7**  Describe the surface $z = (x - 1)^2 + (y + 2)^2 + 3$.

***Solution.***  The equation can be rewritten as

$$z - 3 = (x - 1)^2 + (y + 2)^2$$

This surface is the paraboloid that results by translating the paraboloid

$$z = x^2 + y^2$$

in Figure 11.7.3 so that the new "vertex" is at the point $(1, -2, 3)$. A rough sketch of this paraboloid is shown in Figure 11.7.13. ◀

▶ **Example 8**  Describe the surface

$$4x^2 + 4y^2 + z^2 + 8y - 4z = -4$$

***Solution.***  Completing the squares yields

$$4x^2 + 4(y + 1)^2 + (z - 2)^2 = -4 + 4 + 4$$

or

$$x^2 + (y + 1)^2 + \frac{(z - 2)^2}{4} = 1$$

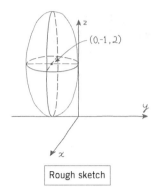

Rough sketch

▲ **Figure 11.7.14**

In Figure 11.7.14, the cross section in the yz-plane is shown tangent to both the y- and z-axes. Confirm that this is correct.

Thus, the surface is the ellipsoid that results when the ellipsoid

$$x^2 + y^2 + \frac{z^2}{4} = 1$$

is translated so that the new "center" is at the point $(0, -1, 2)$. A rough sketch of this ellipsoid is shown in Figure 11.7.14. ◄

■ **REFLECTIONS OF SURFACES IN 3-SPACE**

Recall that in an $xy$-coordinate system a point $(x, y)$ is reflected about the $x$-axis if $y$ is replaced by $-y$, and it is reflected about the $y$-axis if $x$ is replaced by $-x$. In an $xyz$-coordinate system, a point $(x, y, z)$ is reflected about the $xy$-plane if $z$ is replaced by $-z$, it is reflected about the $yz$-plane if $x$ is replaced by $-x$, and it is reflected about the $xz$-plane if $y$ is replaced by $-y$ (Figure 11.7.15). It follows that *replacing a variable by its negative in the equation of a surface causes that surface to be reflected about a coordinate plane.*

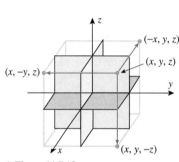

▲ **Figure 11.7.15**

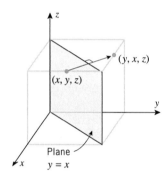

▲ **Figure 11.7.16**

Recall also that in an $xy$-coordinate system a point $(x, y)$ is reflected about the line $y = x$ if $x$ and $y$ are interchanged. However, in an $xyz$-coordinate system, interchanging $x$ and $y$ reflects the point $(x, y, z)$ about the plane $y = x$ (Figure 11.7.16). Similarly, interchanging $x$ and $z$ reflects the point about the plane $x = z$, and interchanging $y$ and $z$ reflects it about the plane $y = z$. Thus, it follows that *interchanging two variables in the equation of a surface reflects that surface about a plane that makes a 45° angle with two of the coordinate planes.*

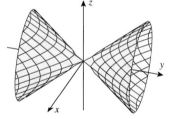

▲ **Figure 11.7.17**

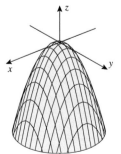

▲ **Figure 11.7.18**

► **Example 9**   Describe the surfaces

(a) $y^2 = x^2 + z^2$    (b) $z = -(x^2 + y^2)$

**Solution (a).**   The graph of the equation $y^2 = x^2 + z^2$ results from interchanging $y$ and $z$ in the equation $z^2 = x^2 + y^2$. Thus, the graph of the equation $y^2 = x^2 + z^2$ can be obtained by reflecting the graph of $z^2 = x^2 + y^2$ about the plane $y = z$. Since the graph of $z^2 = x^2 + y^2$ is a circular cone opening along the $z$-axis (see Table 11.7.1), it follows that the graph of $y^2 = x^2 + z^2$ is a circular cone opening along the $y$-axis (Figure 11.7.17).

**Solution (b).**   The graph of the equation $z = -(x^2 + y^2)$ can be written as $-z = x^2 + y^2$, which can be obtained by replacing $z$ with $-z$ in the equation $z = x^2 + y^2$. Since the graph of $z = x^2 + y^2$ is a circular paraboloid opening in the positive $z$-direction (see Table 11.7.1), it follows that the graph of $z = -(x^2 + y^2)$ is a circular paraboloid opening in the negative $z$-direction (Figure 11.7.18). ◄

### ■ A TECHNIQUE FOR IDENTIFYING QUADRIC SURFACES

The equations of the quadric surfaces in Table 11.7.1 have certain characteristics that make it possible to identify quadric surfaces that are derived from these equations by reflections. These identifying characteristics, which are shown in Table 11.7.2, are based on writing the equation of the quadric surface so that all of the variable terms are on the left side of the equation and there is a 1 or a 0 on the right side. These characteristics do not change when the surface is reflected about a coordinate plane or planes of the form $x = y$, $x = z$, or $y = z$, thereby making it possible to identify the reflected quadric surface from the form of its equation.

**Table 11.7.2**

IDENTIFYING A QUADRIC SURFACE FROM THE FORM OF ITS EQUATION

| EQUATION | $\dfrac{x^2}{a^2} + \dfrac{y^2}{b^2} + \dfrac{z^2}{c^2} = 1$ | $\dfrac{x^2}{a^2} + \dfrac{y^2}{b^2} - \dfrac{z^2}{c^2} = 1$ | $\dfrac{z^2}{c^2} - \dfrac{x^2}{a^2} - \dfrac{y^2}{b^2} = 1$ | $z^2 - \dfrac{x^2}{a^2} - \dfrac{y^2}{b^2} = 0$ | $z - \dfrac{x^2}{a^2} - \dfrac{y^2}{b^2} = 0$ | $z - \dfrac{y^2}{b^2} + \dfrac{x^2}{a^2} = 0$ |
|---|---|---|---|---|---|---|
| CHARACTERISTIC | No minus signs | One minus sign | Two minus signs | No linear terms | One linear term; two quadratic terms with the same sign | One linear term; two quadratic terms with opposite signs |
| CLASSIFICATION | Ellipsoid | Hyperboloid of one sheet | Hyperboloid of two sheets | Elliptic cone | Elliptic paraboloid | Hyperbolic paraboloid |

▶ **Example 10** Identify the surfaces

(a) $3x^2 - 4y^2 + 12z^2 + 12 = 0$     (b) $4x^2 - 4y + z^2 = 0$

***Solution (a).*** The equation can be rewritten as

$$\frac{y^2}{3} - \frac{x^2}{4} - z^2 = 1$$

This equation has a 1 on the right side and two negative terms on the left side, so its graph is a hyperboloid of two sheets.

***Solution (b).*** The equation has one linear term and two quadratic terms with the same sign, so its graph is an elliptic paraboloid. ◀

### ✔ QUICK CHECK EXERCISES 11.7     *(See page 832 for answers.)*

**1.** For the surface $4x^2 + y^2 + z^2 = 9$, classify the indicated trace as an ellipse, hyperbola, or parabola.
   (a) $x = 0$     (b) $y = 0$     (c) $z = 1$

**2.** For the surface $4x^2 + z^2 - y^2 = 9$, classify the indicated trace as an ellipse, hyperbola, or parabola.
   (a) $x = 0$     (b) $y = 0$     (c) $z = 1$

**3.** For the surface $4x^2 + y^2 - z = 0$, classify the indicated trace as an ellipse, hyperbola, or parabola.
   (a) $x = 0$     (b) $y = 0$     (c) $z = 1$

**4.** Classify each surface as an ellipsoid, hyperboloid of one sheet, hyperboloid of two sheets, elliptic cone, elliptic paraboloid, or hyperbolic paraboloid.
   (a) $\dfrac{x^2}{36} + \dfrac{y^2}{25} - z = 0$     (b) $\dfrac{x^2}{36} + \dfrac{y^2}{25} + z^2 = 1$

   (c) $\dfrac{x^2}{36} - \dfrac{y^2}{25} + z = 0$     (d) $\dfrac{x^2}{36} + \dfrac{y^2}{25} - z^2 = 1$

   (e) $\dfrac{x^2}{36} + \dfrac{y^2}{25} - z^2 = 0$     (f) $z^2 - \dfrac{x^2}{36} - \dfrac{y^2}{25} = 1$

**EXERCISE SET 11.7**

**1–2** Identify the quadric surface as an ellipsoid, hyperboloid of one sheet, hyperboloid of two sheets, elliptic cone, elliptic paraboloid, or hyperbolic paraboloid by matching the equation with one of the forms given in Table 11.7.1. State the values of $a$, $b$, and $c$ in each case. ■

**1.** (a) $z = \dfrac{x^2}{4} + \dfrac{y^2}{9}$     (b) $z = \dfrac{y^2}{25} - x^2$

(c) $x^2 + y^2 - z^2 = 16$     (d) $x^2 + y^2 - z^2 = 0$

(e) $4z = x^2 + 4y^2$     (f) $z^2 - x^2 - y^2 = 1$

**2.** (a) $6x^2 + 3y^2 + 4z^2 = 12$     (b) $y^2 - x^2 - z = 0$

(c) $9x^2 + y^2 - 9z^2 = 9$     (d) $4x^2 + y^2 - 4z^2 = -4$

(e) $2z - x^2 - 4y^2 = 0$     (f) $12z^2 - 3x^2 = 4y^2$

**3.** Find an equation for and sketch the surface that results when the circular paraboloid $z = x^2 + y^2$ is reflected about the plane

(a) $z = 0$     (b) $x = 0$     (c) $y = 0$

(d) $y = x$     (e) $x = z$     (f) $y = z$.

**4.** Find an equation for and sketch the surface that results when the hyperboloid of one sheet $x^2 + y^2 - z^2 = 1$ is reflected about the plane

(a) $z = 0$     (b) $x = 0$     (c) $y = 0$

(d) $y = x$     (e) $x = z$     (f) $y = z$.

**FOCUS ON CONCEPTS**

**5.** The given equations represent quadric surfaces whose orientations are different from those in Table 11.7.1. In each part, identify the quadric surface, and give a verbal description of its orientation (e.g., an elliptic cone opening along the $z$-axis or a hyperbolic paraboloid straddling the $y$-axis).

(a) $\dfrac{z^2}{c^2} - \dfrac{y^2}{b^2} + \dfrac{x^2}{a^2} = 1$     (b) $\dfrac{x^2}{a^2} - \dfrac{y^2}{b^2} - \dfrac{z^2}{c^2} = 1$

(c) $x = \dfrac{y^2}{b^2} + \dfrac{z^2}{c^2}$     (d) $x^2 = \dfrac{y^2}{b^2} + \dfrac{z^2}{c^2}$

(e) $y = \dfrac{z^2}{c^2} - \dfrac{x^2}{a^2}$     (f) $y = -\left(\dfrac{x^2}{a^2} + \dfrac{z^2}{c^2}\right)$

**6.** For each of the surfaces in Exercise 5, find the equation of the surface that results if the given surface is reflected about the $xz$-plane and that surface is then reflected about the plane $z = 0$.

**7–8** Find equations of the traces in the coordinate planes and sketch the traces in an $xyz$-coordinate system. [*Suggestion:* If you have trouble sketching a trace directly in three dimensions, start with a sketch in two dimensions by placing the coordinate plane in the plane of the paper, then transfer the sketch to three dimensions.] ■

**7.** (a) $\dfrac{x^2}{9} + \dfrac{y^2}{25} + \dfrac{z^2}{4} = 1$     (b) $z = x^2 + 4y^2$

(c) $\dfrac{x^2}{9} + \dfrac{y^2}{16} - \dfrac{z^2}{4} = 1$

**8.** (a) $y^2 + 9z^2 = x$     (b) $4x^2 - y^2 + 4z^2 = 4$

(c) $z^2 = x^2 + \dfrac{y^2}{4}$

**9–10** In these exercises, traces of the surfaces in the planes are conic sections. In each part, find an equation of the trace, and state whether it is an ellipse, a parabola, or a hyperbola. ■

**9.** (a) $4x^2 + y^2 + z^2 = 4$;  $y = 1$

(b) $4x^2 + y^2 + z^2 = 4$;  $x = \frac{1}{2}$

(c) $9x^2 - y^2 - z^2 = 16$;  $x = 2$

(d) $9x^2 - y^2 - z^2 = 16$;  $z = 2$

(e) $z = 9x^2 + 4y^2$;  $y = 2$

(f) $z = 9x^2 + 4y^2$;  $z = 4$

**10.** (a) $9x^2 - y^2 + 4z^2 = 9$;  $x = 2$

(b) $9x^2 - y^2 + 4z^2 = 9$;  $y = 4$

(c) $x^2 + 4y^2 - 9z^2 = 0$;  $y = 1$

(d) $x^2 + 4y^2 - 9z^2 = 0$;  $z = 1$

(e) $z = x^2 - 4y^2$;  $x = 1$

(f) $z = x^2 - 4y^2$;  $z = 4$

**11–14 True–False** Determine whether the statement is true or false. Explain your answer. ■

**11.** A quadric surface is the graph of a fourth-degree polynomial in $x$, $y$, and $z$.

**12.** Every ellipsoid will intersect the $z$-axis in exactly two points.

**13.** Every ellipsoid is a surface of revolution.

**14.** The hyperbolic paraboloid

$$z = \dfrac{y^2}{b^2} - \dfrac{x^2}{a^2}$$

intersects the $xy$-plane in a pair of intersecting lines.

**15–26** Identify and sketch the quadric surface. ■

**15.** $x^2 + \dfrac{y^2}{4} + \dfrac{z^2}{9} = 1$     **16.** $x^2 + 4y^2 + 9z^2 = 36$

**17.** $\dfrac{x^2}{4} + \dfrac{y^2}{9} - \dfrac{z^2}{16} = 1$     **18.** $x^2 + y^2 - z^2 = 9$

**19.** $4z^2 = x^2 + 4y^2$     **20.** $9x^2 + 4y^2 - 36z^2 = 0$

**21.** $9z^2 - 4y^2 - 9x^2 = 36$     **22.** $y^2 - \dfrac{x^2}{4} - \dfrac{z^2}{9} = 1$

**23.** $z = y^2 - x^2$     **24.** $16z = y^2 - x^2$

**25.** $4z = x^2 + 2y^2$     **26.** $z - 3x^2 - 3y^2 = 0$

**27–32** The given equation represents a quadric surface whose orientation is different from that in Table 11.7.1. Identify and sketch the surface. ■

**27.** $x^2 - 3y^2 - 3z^2 = 0$     **28.** $x - y^2 - 4z^2 = 0$

**29.** $2y^2 - x^2 + 2z^2 = 8$     **30.** $x^2 - 3y^2 - 3z^2 = 9$

**31.** $z = \dfrac{x^2}{4} - \dfrac{y^2}{9}$     **32.** $4x^2 - y^2 + 4z^2 = 16$

**33–36** Sketch the surface.

**33.** $z = \sqrt{x^2 + y^2}$

**34.** $z = \sqrt{1 - x^2 - y^2}$

**35.** $z = \sqrt{x^2 + y^2 - 1}$

**36.** $z = \sqrt{1 + x^2 + y^2}$

**37–40** Identify the surface and make a rough sketch that shows its position and orientation.

**37.** $z = (x + 2)^2 + (y - 3)^2 - 9$

**38.** $4x^2 - y^2 + 16(z - 2)^2 = 100$

**39.** $9x^2 + y^2 + 4z^2 - 18x + 2y + 16z = 10$

**40.** $z^2 = 4x^2 + y^2 + 8x - 2y + 4z$

**41–42** Use the ellipsoid $4x^2 + 9y^2 + 18z^2 = 72$ in these exercises.

**41.** (a) Find an equation of the elliptical trace in the plane $z = \sqrt{2}$.
  (b) Find the lengths of the major and minor axes of the ellipse in part (a).
  (c) Find the coordinates of the foci of the ellipse in part (a).
  (d) Describe the orientation of the focal axis of the ellipse in part (a) relative to the coordinate axes.

**42.** (a) Find an equation of the elliptical trace in the plane $x = 3$.
  (b) Find the lengths of the major and minor axes of the ellipse in part (a).
  (c) Find the coordinates of the foci of the ellipse in part (a).
  (d) Describe the orientation of the focal axis of the ellipse in part (a) relative to the coordinate axes.

**43–46** These exercises refer to the hyperbolic paraboloid $z = y^2 - x^2$.

**43.** (a) Find an equation of the hyperbolic trace in the plane $z = 4$.
  (b) Find the vertices of the hyperbola in part (a).
  (c) Find the foci of the hyperbola in part (a).
  (d) Describe the orientation of the focal axis of the hyperbola in part (a) relative to the coordinate axes.

**44.** (a) Find an equation of the hyperbolic trace in the plane $z = -4$.
  (b) Find the vertices of the hyperbola in part (a).
  (c) Find the foci of the hyperbola in part (a).
  (d) Describe the orientation of the focal axis of the hyperbola in part (a) relative to the coordinate axes.

**45.** (a) Find an equation of the parabolic trace in the plane $x = 2$.
  (b) Find the vertex of the parabola in part (a).
  (c) Find the focus of the parabola in part (a).
  (d) Describe the orientation of the focal axis of the parabola in part (a) relative to the coordinate axes.

**46.** (a) Find an equation of the parabolic trace in the plane $y = 2$.
  (b) Find the vertex of the parabola in part (a).
  (c) Find the focus of the parabola in part (a).

  (d) Describe the orientation of the focal axis of the parabola in part (a) relative to the coordinate axes.

**47–48** Sketch the region enclosed between the surfaces and describe their curve of intersection.

**47.** The paraboloids $z = x^2 + y^2$ and $z = 4 - x^2 - y^2$

**48.** The ellipsoid $2x^2 + 2y^2 + z^2 = 3$ and the paraboloid $z = x^2 + y^2$.

**49–50** Find an equation for the surface generated by revolving the curve about the $y$-axis.

**49.** $y = 4x^2$ $(z = 0)$

**50.** $y = 2x$ $(z = 0)$

**51.** Find an equation of the surface consisting of all points $P(x, y, z)$ that are equidistant from the point $(0, 0, 1)$ and the plane $z = -1$. Identify the surface.

**52.** Find an equation of the surface consisting of all points $P(x, y, z)$ that are twice as far from the plane $z = -1$ as from the point $(0, 0, 1)$. Identify the surface.

**53.** If a sphere
$$\frac{x^2}{a^2} + \frac{y^2}{a^2} + \frac{z^2}{a^2} = 1$$
of radius $a$ is compressed in the $z$-direction, then the resulting surface, called an *oblate spheroid*, has an equation of the form
$$\frac{x^2}{a^2} + \frac{y^2}{a^2} + \frac{z^2}{c^2} = 1$$
where $c < a$. Show that the oblate spheroid has a circular trace of radius $a$ in the $xy$-plane and an elliptical trace in the $xz$-plane with major axis of length $2a$ along the $x$-axis and minor axis of length $2c$ along the $z$-axis.

**54.** The Earth's rotation causes a flattening at the poles, so its shape is often modeled as an oblate spheroid rather than a sphere (see Exercise 53 for terminology). One of the models used by global positioning satellites is the *World Geodetic System of 1984* (WGS-84), which treats the Earth as an oblate spheroid whose equatorial radius is 6378.1370 km and whose polar radius (the distance from the Earth's center to the poles) is 6356.5231 km. Use the WGS-84 model to find an equation for the surface of the Earth relative to the coordinate system shown in the accompanying figure.

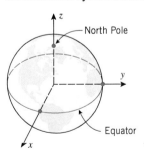

◀ **Figure Ex-54**

**55.** Use the method of slicing to show that the volume of the ellipsoid
$$\frac{x^2}{a^2} + \frac{y^2}{b^2} + \frac{z^2}{c^2} = 1$$
is $\frac{4}{3}\pi abc$.

**56. Writing** Discuss some of the connections between conic sections and traces of quadric surfaces.

**57. Writing** Give a sequence of steps for determining the type of quadric surface that is associated with a quadratic equation in $x$, $y$, and $z$.

✔**QUICK CHECK ANSWERS 11.7**

**1.** (a) ellipse (b) ellipse (c) ellipse   **2.** (a) hyperbola (b) ellipse (c) hyperbola   **3.** (a) parabola (b) parabola (c) ellipse
**4.** (a) elliptic paraboloid (b) ellipsoid (c) hyperbolic paraboloid (d) hyperboloid of one sheet (e) elliptic cone
(f) hyperboloid of two sheets

## 11.8 CYLINDRICAL AND SPHERICAL COORDINATES

*In this section we will discuss two new types of coordinate systems in 3-space that are often more useful than rectangular coordinate systems for studying surfaces with symmetries. These new coordinate systems also have important applications in navigation, astronomy, and the study of rotational motion about an axis.*

### CYLINDRICAL AND SPHERICAL COORDINATE SYSTEMS

Three coordinates are required to establish the location of a point in 3-space. We have already done this using rectangular coordinates. However, Figure 11.8.1 shows two other possibilities: part (*a*) of the figure shows the **rectangular coordinates** $(x, y, z)$ of a point $P$, part (*b*) shows the **cylindrical coordinates** $(r, \theta, z)$ of $P$, and part (*c*) shows the **spherical coordinates** $(\rho, \theta, \phi)$ of $P$. In a rectangular coordinate system the coordinates can be any real numbers, but in cylindrical and spherical coordinate systems there are restrictions on the allowable values of the coordinates (as indicated in Figure 11.8.1).

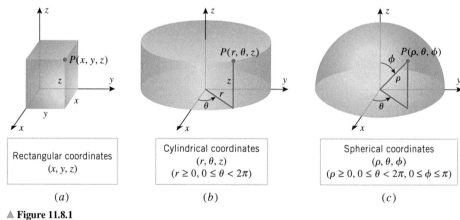

| Rectangular coordinates $(x, y, z)$ | Cylindrical coordinates $(r, \theta, z)$ $(r \geq 0, 0 \leq \theta < 2\pi)$ | Spherical coordinates $(\rho, \theta, \phi)$ $(\rho \geq 0, 0 \leq \theta < 2\pi, 0 \leq \phi \leq \pi)$ |
|---|---|---|
| (*a*) | (*b*) | (*c*) |

▲ **Figure 11.8.1**

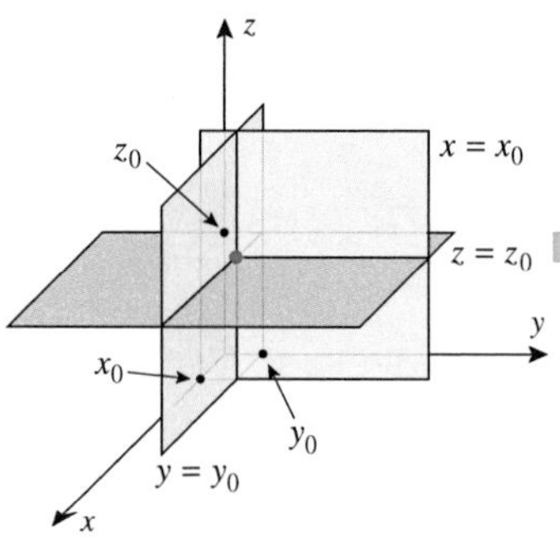

### CONSTANT SURFACES

In rectangular coordinates the surfaces represented by equations of the form

$$x = x_0, \quad y = y_0, \quad \text{and} \quad z = z_0$$

where $x_0$, $y_0$, and $z_0$ are constants, are planes parallel to the $yz$-plane, $xz$-plane, and $xy$-plane, respectively (Figure 11.8.2). In cylindrical coordinates the surfaces represented by equations of the form

$$r = r_0, \quad \theta = \theta_0, \quad \text{and} \quad z = z_0$$

▲ **Figure 11.8.2**

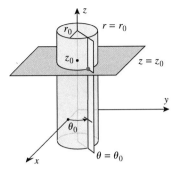

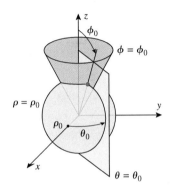

▲ **Figure 11.8.3**

▲ **Figure 11.8.4**

where $r_0$, $\theta_0$, and $z_0$ are constants, are shown in Figure 11.8.3:

- The surface $r = r_0$ is a right circular cylinder of radius $r_0$ centered on the $z$-axis.
- The surface $\theta = \theta_0$ is a half-plane attached along the $z$-axis and making an angle $\theta_0$ with the positive $x$-axis.
- The surface $z = z_0$ is a horizontal plane.

In spherical coordinates the surfaces represented by equations of the form

$$\rho = \rho_0, \quad \theta = \theta_0, \quad \text{and} \quad \phi = \phi_0$$

where $\rho_0$, $\theta_0$, and $\phi_0$ are constants, are shown in Figure 11.8.4:

- The surface $\rho = \rho_0$ consists of all points whose distance $\rho$ from the origin is $\rho_0$. Assuming $\rho_0$ to be nonnegative, this is a sphere of radius $\rho_0$ centered at the origin.
- As in cylindrical coordinates, the surface $\theta = \theta_0$ is a half-plane attached along the $z$-axis, making an angle of $\theta_0$ with the positive $x$-axis.
- The surface $\phi = \phi_0$ consists of all points from which a line segment to the origin makes an angle of $\phi_0$ with the positive $z$-axis. If $0 < \phi_0 < \pi/2$, this will be the nappe of a cone opening up, while if $\pi/2 < \phi_0 < \pi$, this will be the nappe of a cone opening down. (If $\phi_0 = \pi/2$, then the cone is flat, and the surface is the $xy$-plane.)

■ **CONVERTING COORDINATES**

Just as we needed to convert between rectangular and polar coordinates in 2-space, so we will need to be able to convert between rectangular, cylindrical, and spherical coordinates in 3-space. Table 11.8.1 provides formulas for making these conversions.

**Table 11.8.1**

CONVERSION FORMULAS FOR COORDINATE SYSTEMS

| CONVERSION | | FORMULAS | RESTRICTIONS |
|---|---|---|---|
| Cylindrical to rectangular | $(r, \theta, z) \rightarrow (x, y, z)$ | $x = r\cos\theta, \quad y = r\sin\theta, \quad z = z$ | |
| Rectangular to cylindrical | $(x, y, z) \rightarrow (r, \theta, z)$ | $r = \sqrt{x^2 + y^2}, \quad \tan\theta = y/x, \ z = z$ | $r \geq 0, \rho \geq 0$ |
| Spherical to cylindrical | $(\rho, \theta, \phi) \rightarrow (r, \theta, z)$ | $r = \rho\sin\phi, \quad \theta = \theta, \quad z = \rho\cos\phi$ | $0 \leq \theta < 2\pi$ |
| Cylindrical to spherical | $(r, \theta, z) \rightarrow (\rho, \theta, \phi)$ | $\rho = \sqrt{r^2 + z^2}, \quad \theta = \theta, \quad \tan\phi = r/z$ | $0 \leq \phi \leq \pi$ |
| Spherical to rectangular | $(\rho, \theta, \phi) \rightarrow (x, y, z)$ | $x = \rho\sin\phi\cos\theta, \quad y = \rho\sin\phi\sin\theta, \quad z = \rho\cos\phi$ | |
| Rectangular to spherical | $(x, y, z) \rightarrow (\rho, \theta, \phi)$ | $\rho = \sqrt{x^2 + y^2 + z^2}, \quad \tan\theta = y/x, \quad \cos\phi = z/\sqrt{x^2 + y^2 + z^2}$ | |

The diagrams in Figure 11.8.5 will help you to understand how the formulas in Table 11.8.1 are derived. For example, part (a) of the figure shows that in converting between rectangular coordinates $(x, y, z)$ and cylindrical coordinates $(r, \theta, z)$, we can interpret $(r, \theta)$ as polar coordinates of $(x, y)$. Thus, the polar-to-rectangular and rectangular-to-polar

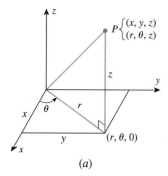

*(a)*

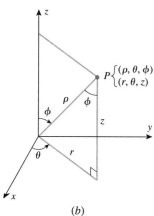

*(b)*

Comparison of coordinate systems

▲ **Figure 11.8.5**

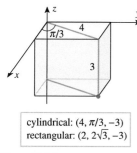

cylindrical: $(4, \pi/3, -3)$
rectangular: $(2, 2\sqrt{3}, -3)$

▲ **Figure 11.8.6**

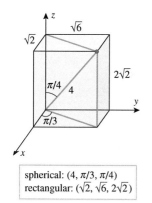

spherical: $(4, \pi/3, \pi/4)$
rectangular: $(\sqrt{2}, \sqrt{6}, 2\sqrt{2})$

▲ **Figure 11.8.7**

conversion formulas (1) and (2) of Section 10.2 provide the conversion formulas between rectangular and cylindrical coordinates in the table.

Part (*b*) of Figure 11.8.5 suggests that the spherical coordinates $(\rho, \theta, \phi)$ of a point $P$ can be converted to cylindrical coordinates $(r, \theta, z)$ by the conversion formulas

$$r = \rho \sin \phi, \quad \theta = \theta, \quad z = \rho \cos \phi \tag{1}$$

Moreover, since the cylindrical coordinates $(r, \theta, z)$ of $P$ can be converted to rectangular coordinates $(x, y, z)$ by the conversion formulas

$$x = r \cos \theta, \quad y = r \sin \theta, \quad z = z \tag{2}$$

we can obtain direct conversion formulas from spherical coordinates to rectangular coordinates by substituting (1) in (2). This yields

$$x = \rho \sin \phi \cos \theta, \quad y = \rho \sin \phi \sin \theta, \quad z = \rho \cos \phi \tag{3}$$

The other conversion formulas in Table 11.8.1 are left as exercises.

▶ **Example 1**

(a) Find the rectangular coordinates of the point with cylindrical coordinates

$$(r, \theta, z) = (4, \pi/3, -3)$$

(b) Find the rectangular coordinates of the point with spherical coordinates

$$(\rho, \theta, \phi) = (4, \pi/3, \pi/4)$$

*Solution (a).* Applying the cylindrical-to-rectangular conversion formulas in Table 11.8.1 yields

$$x = r \cos \theta = 4 \cos \frac{\pi}{3} = 2, \quad y = r \sin \theta = 4 \sin \frac{\pi}{3} = 2\sqrt{3}, \quad z = -3$$

Thus, the rectangular coordinates of the point are $(x, y, z) = (2, 2\sqrt{3}, -3)$ (Figure 11.8.6).

*Solution (b).* Applying the spherical-to-rectangular conversion formulas in Table 11.8.1 yields

$$x = \rho \sin \phi \cos \theta = 4 \sin \frac{\pi}{4} \cos \frac{\pi}{3} = \sqrt{2}$$

$$y = \rho \sin \phi \sin \theta = 4 \sin \frac{\pi}{4} \sin \frac{\pi}{3} = \sqrt{6}$$

$$z = \rho \cos \phi = 4 \cos \frac{\pi}{4} = 2\sqrt{2}$$

The rectangular coordinates of the point are $(x, y, z) = (\sqrt{2}, \sqrt{6}, 2\sqrt{2})$ (Figure 11.8.7). ◀

Since the interval $0 \le \theta < 2\pi$ covers two periods of the tangent function, the conversion formula $\tan \theta = y/x$ does not completely determine $\theta$. The following example shows how to deal with this ambiguity.

▶ **Example 2**   Find the spherical coordinates of the point that has rectangular coordinates

$$(x, y, z) = (4, -4, 4\sqrt{6})$$

How should $\theta$ be chosen if $x = 0$?
How should $\theta$ be chosen if $y = 0$?

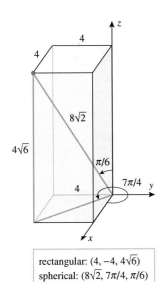

rectangular: $(4, -4, 4\sqrt{6})$
spherical: $(8\sqrt{2}, 7\pi/4, \pi/6)$

▲ **Figure 11.8.8**

*Solution.* From the rectangular-to-spherical conversion formulas in Table 11.8.1 we obtain

$$\rho = \sqrt{x^2 + y^2 + z^2} = \sqrt{16 + 16 + 96} = \sqrt{128} = 8\sqrt{2}$$

$$\tan\theta = \frac{y}{x} = -1$$

$$\cos\phi = \frac{z}{\sqrt{x^2 + y^2 + z^2}} = \frac{4\sqrt{6}}{8\sqrt{2}} = \frac{\sqrt{3}}{2}$$

From the restriction $0 \le \theta < 2\pi$ and the computed value of $\tan\theta$, the possibilities for $\theta$ are $\theta = 3\pi/4$ and $\theta = 7\pi/4$. However, the given point has a negative $y$-coordinate, so we must have $\theta = 7\pi/4$. Moreover, from the restriction $0 \le \phi \le \pi$ and the computed value of $\cos\phi$, the only possibility for $\phi$ is $\phi = \pi/6$. Thus, the spherical coordinates of the point are $(\rho, \theta, \phi) = (8\sqrt{2}, 7\pi/4, \pi/6)$ (Figure 11.8.8). ◄

■ **EQUATIONS OF SURFACES IN CYLINDRICAL AND SPHERICAL COORDINATES**

Surfaces of revolution about the $z$-axis of a rectangular coordinate system usually have simpler equations in cylindrical coordinates than in rectangular coordinates, and the equations of surfaces with symmetry about the origin are usually simpler in spherical coordinates than in rectangular coordinates. For example, consider the upper nappe of the circular cone whose equation in rectangular coordinates is

$$z = \sqrt{x^2 + y^2}$$

(Table 11.8.2). The corresponding equation in cylindrical coordinates can be obtained from the cylindrical-to-rectangular conversion formulas in Table 11.8.1. This yields

$$z = \sqrt{(r\cos\theta)^2 + (r\sin\theta)^2} = \sqrt{r^2} = |r| = r$$

so the equation of the cone in cylindrical coordinates is $z = r$. Going a step further, the equation of the cone in spherical coordinates can be obtained from the spherical-to-cylindrical conversion formulas from Table 11.8.1. This yields

$$\rho\cos\phi = \rho\sin\phi$$

which, if $\rho \ne 0$, can be rewritten as

$$\tan\phi = 1 \quad \text{or} \quad \phi = \frac{\pi}{4}$$

Geometrically, this tells us that the radial line from the origin to any point on the cone makes an angle of $\pi/4$ with the $z$-axis.

**Table 11.8.2**

| | CONE | CYLINDER | SPHERE | PARABOLOID | HYPERBOLOID |
|---|---|---|---|---|---|
| RECTANGULAR | $z = \sqrt{x^2 + y^2}$ | $x^2 + y^2 = 1$ | $x^2 + y^2 + z^2 = 1$ | $z = x^2 + y^2$ | $x^2 + y^2 - z^2 = 1$ |
| CYLINDRICAL | $z = r$ | $r = 1$ | $z^2 = 1 - r^2$ | $z = r^2$ | $z^2 = r^2 - 1$ |
| SPHERICAL | $\phi = \pi/4$ | $\rho = \csc\phi$ | $\rho = 1$ | $\rho = \cos\phi \csc^2\phi$ | $\rho^2 = -\sec 2\phi$ |

▶ **Example 3**   Find equations of the paraboloid $z = x^2 + y^2$ in cylindrical and spherical coordinates.

*Solution.*   The rectangular-to-cylindrical conversion formulas in Table 11.8.1 yield

$$z = r^2 \tag{4}$$

which is the equation in cylindrical coordinates. Now applying the spherical-to-cylindrical conversion formulas to (4) yields

$$\rho \cos \phi = \rho^2 \sin^2 \phi$$

which we can rewrite as

$$\rho = \cos \phi \csc^2 \phi$$

Alternatively, we could have obtained this equation directly from the equation in rectangular coordinates by applying the spherical-to-rectangular conversion formulas (verify). ◀

Verify the equations given in Table 11.8.2 for the cylinder and hyperboloid in cylindrical and spherical coordinates.

### SPHERICAL COORDINATES IN NAVIGATION

Spherical coordinates are related to longitude and latitude coordinates used in navigation. To see why this is so, let us construct a right-hand rectangular coordinate system with its origin at the center of the Earth, its positive $z$-axis passing through the North Pole, and its positive $x$-axis passing through the prime meridian (Figure 11.8.9). If we assume the Earth to be a sphere of radius $\rho = 4000$ miles, then each point on the Earth has spherical coordinates of the form $(4000, \theta, \phi)$, where $\phi$ and $\theta$ determine the latitude and longitude of the point. It is common to specify longitudes in degrees east or west of the prime meridian and latitudes in degrees north or south of the equator. However, the next example shows that it is a simple matter to determine $\phi$ and $\theta$ from such data.

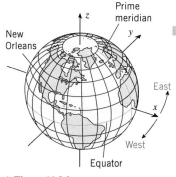

▲ **Figure 11.8.9**

Jon Arnold/Danita Delimont
*Modern navigation systems use multiple coordinate representations to calculate position.*

▶ **Example 4**   The city of New Orleans is located at 90° west longitude and 30° north latitude. Find its spherical and rectangular coordinates relative to the coordinate axes of Figure 11.8.9. (Assume that distance is in miles.)

*Solution.*   A longitude of 90° west corresponds to $\theta = 360° - 90° = 270°$ or $\theta = 3\pi/2$ radians; and a latitude of 30° north corresponds to $\phi = 90° - 30° = 60°$ or $\phi = \pi/3$ radians. Thus, the spherical coordinates $(\rho, \theta, \phi)$ of New Orleans are $(4000, 3\pi/2, \pi/3)$.

To find the rectangular coordinates we apply the spherical-to-rectangular conversion formulas in Table 11.8.1. This yields

$$x = 4000 \sin \frac{\pi}{3} \cos \frac{3\pi}{2} = 4000 \frac{\sqrt{3}}{2}(0) = 0 \text{ mi}$$

$$y = 4000 \sin \frac{\pi}{3} \sin \frac{3\pi}{2} = 4000 \frac{\sqrt{3}}{2}(-1) = -2000\sqrt{3} \text{ mi}$$

$$z = 4000 \cos \frac{\pi}{3} = 4000 \left(\frac{1}{2}\right) = 2000 \text{ mi} \blacktriangleleft$$

✔ **QUICK CHECK EXERCISES 11.8**    *(See page 838 for answers.)*

**1.** The conversion formulas from cylindrical coordinates $(r, \theta, z)$ to rectangular coordinates $(x, y, z)$ are

$$x = \underline{\qquad}, \quad y = \underline{\qquad}, \quad z = \underline{\qquad}$$

**2.** The conversion formulas from spherical coordinates $(\rho, \theta, \phi)$ to rectangular coordinates $(x, y, z)$ are

$$x = \underline{\qquad}, \quad y = \underline{\qquad}, \quad z = \underline{\qquad}$$

**3.** The conversion formulas from spherical coordinates $(\rho, \theta, \phi)$ to cylindrical coordinates $(r, \theta, z)$ are

$$r = \underline{\hspace{1cm}}, \quad \theta = \underline{\hspace{1cm}}, \quad z = \underline{\hspace{1cm}}$$

**4.** Let $P$ be the point in 3-space with rectangular coordinates $(\sqrt{2}, -\sqrt{2}, 2\sqrt{3})$.
   (a) Cylindrical coordinates for $P$ are $(r, \theta, z) = \underline{\hspace{1cm}}$.
   (b) Spherical coordinates for $P$ are $(\rho, \theta, \phi) = \underline{\hspace{1cm}}$.

**5.** Give an equation of a sphere of radius 5, centered at the origin, in
   (a) rectangular coordinates
   (b) cylindrical coordinates
   (c) spherical coordinates.

---

**EXERCISE SET 11.8**    ⌇ Graphing Utility    [c] CAS

---

**1–2** Convert from rectangular to cylindrical coordinates. ▨

**1.** (a) $(4\sqrt{3}, 4, -4)$      (b) $(-5, 5, 6)$
   (c) $(0, 2, 0)$           (d) $(4, -4\sqrt{3}, 6)$

**2.** (a) $(\sqrt{2}, -\sqrt{2}, 1)$     (b) $(0, 1, 1)$
   (c) $(-4, 4, -7)$       (d) $(2, -2, -2)$

**3–4** Convert from cylindrical to rectangular coordinates. ▨

**3.** (a) $(4, \pi/6, 3)$      (b) $(8, 3\pi/4, -2)$
   (c) $(5, 0, 4)$        (d) $(7, \pi, -9)$

**4.** (a) $(6, 5\pi/3, 7)$     (b) $(1, \pi/2, 0)$
   (c) $(3, \pi/2, 5)$      (d) $(4, \pi/2, -1)$

**5–6** Convert from rectangular to spherical coordinates. ▨

**5.** (a) $(1, \sqrt{3}, -2)$     (b) $(1, -1, \sqrt{2})$
   (c) $(0, 3\sqrt{3}, 3)$     (d) $(-5\sqrt{3}, 5, 0)$

**6.** (a) $(4, 4, 4\sqrt{6})$     (b) $(1, -\sqrt{3}, -2)$
   (c) $(2, 0, 0)$        (d) $(\sqrt{3}, 1, 2\sqrt{3})$

**7–8** Convert from spherical to rectangular coordinates. ▨

**7.** (a) $(5, \pi/6, \pi/4)$     (b) $(7, 0, \pi/2)$
   (c) $(1, \pi, 0)$         (d) $(2, 3\pi/2, \pi/2)$

**8.** (a) $(1, 2\pi/3, 3\pi/4)$    (b) $(3, 7\pi/4, 5\pi/6)$
   (c) $(8, \pi/6, \pi/4)$     (d) $(4, \pi/2, \pi/3)$

**9–10** Convert from cylindrical to spherical coordinates. ▨

**9.** (a) $(\sqrt{3}, \pi/6, 3)$     (b) $(1, \pi/4, -1)$
   (c) $(2, 3\pi/4, 0)$     (d) $(6, 1, -2\sqrt{3})$

**10.** (a) $(4, 5\pi/6, 4)$     (b) $(2, 0, -2)$
   (c) $(4, \pi/2, 3)$      (d) $(6, \pi, 2)$

**11–12** Convert from spherical to cylindrical coordinates. ▨

**11.** (a) $(5, \pi/4, 2\pi/3)$    (b) $(1, 7\pi/6, \pi)$
   (c) $(3, 0, 0)$         (d) $(4, \pi/6, \pi/2)$

**12.** (a) $(5, \pi/2, 0)$      (b) $(6, 0, 3\pi/4)$
   (c) $(\sqrt{2}, 3\pi/4, \pi)$   (d) $(5, 2\pi/3, 5\pi/6)$

**[c] 13.** Use a CAS or a programmable calculating utility to set up the conversion formulas in Table 11.8.1, and then use the CAS or calculating utility to solve the problems in Exercises 1, 3, 5, 7, 9, and 11.

**[c] 14.** Use a CAS or a programmable calculating utility to set up the conversion formulas in Table 11.8.1, and then use the CAS or calculating utility to solve the problems in Exercises 2, 4, 6, 8, 10, and 12.

**15–18 True–False** Determine whether the statement is true or false. Explain your answer. ▨

**15.** In cylindrical coordinates for a point, $r$ is the distance from the point to the $z$-axis.

**16.** In spherical coordinates for a point, $\rho$ is the distance from the point to the origin.

**17.** The graph of $\theta = \theta_0$ in cylindrical coordinates is the same as the graph of $\theta = \theta_0$ in spherical coordinates.

**18.** The graph of $r = f(\theta)$ in cylindrical coordinates can always be obtained by extrusion of the polar graph of $r = f(\theta)$ in the $xy$-plane.

**19–26** An equation is given in cylindrical coordinates. Express the equation in rectangular coordinates and sketch the graph. ▨

**19.** $r = 3$       **20.** $\theta = \pi/4$      **21.** $z = r^2$

**22.** $z = r \cos\theta$    **23.** $r = 4 \sin\theta$    **24.** $r = 2 \sec\theta$

**25.** $r^2 + z^2 = 1$    **26.** $r^2 \cos 2\theta = z$

**27–34** An equation is given in spherical coordinates. Express the equation in rectangular coordinates and sketch the graph. ▨

**27.** $\rho = 3$       **28.** $\theta = \pi/3$      **29.** $\phi = \pi/4$

**30.** $\rho = 2 \sec\phi$    **31.** $\rho = 4 \cos\phi$    **32.** $\rho \sin\phi = 1$

**33.** $\rho \sin\phi = 2 \cos\theta$        **34.** $\rho - 2 \sin\phi \cos\theta = 0$

**35–46** An equation of a surface is given in rectangular coordinates. Find an equation of the surface in (a) cylindrical coordinates and (b) spherical coordinates. ▨

**35.** $z = 3$               **36.** $y = 2$

**37.** $z = 3x^2 + 3y^2$     **38.** $z = \sqrt{3x^2 + 3y^2}$

**39.** $x^2 + y^2 = 4$       **40.** $x^2 + y^2 - 6y = 0$

**41.** $x^2 + y^2 + z^2 = 9$    **42.** $z^2 = x^2 - y^2$

**43.** $2x + 3y + 4z = 1$    **44.** $x^2 + y^2 - z^2 = 1$

**45.** $x^2 = 16 - z^2$      **46.** $x^2 + y^2 + z^2 = 2z$

**FOCUS ON CONCEPTS**

**47–50** Describe the region in 3-space that satisfies the given inequalities. ■

**47.** $r^2 \le z \le 4$

**48.** $0 \le r \le 2\sin\theta, \quad 0 \le z \le 3$

**49.** $1 \le \rho \le 3$

**50.** $0 \le \phi \le \pi/6, \quad 0 \le \rho \le 2$

**51.** St. Petersburg (Leningrad), Russia, is located at 30° east longitude and 60° north latitude. Find its spherical and rectangular coordinates relative to the coordinate axes of Figure 11.8.9. Take miles as the unit of distance and assume the Earth to be a sphere of radius 4000 miles.

**52.** (a) Show that the curve of intersection of the surfaces $z = \sin\theta$ and $r = a$ (cylindrical coordinates) is an ellipse.

(b) Sketch the surface $z = \sin\theta$ for $0 \le \theta \le \pi/2$.

**53.** The accompanying figure shows a right circular cylinder of radius 10 cm spinning at 3 revolutions per minute about the z-axis. At time $t = 0$ s, a bug at the point $(0, 10, 0)$ begins walking straight up the face of the cylinder at the rate of 0.5 cm/min.

(a) Find the cylindrical coordinates of the bug after 2 min.

(b) Find the rectangular coordinates of the bug after 2 min.

(c) Find the spherical coordinates of the bug after 2 min.

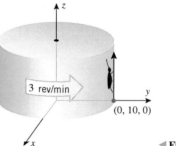

◀ Figure Ex-53

**54.** Referring to Exercise 53, use a graphing utility to graph the bug's distance from the origin as a function of time.

**55.** *Writing* Discuss some practical applications in which non-rectangular coordinate systems are useful.

**56.** *Writing* The terms "zenith" and "azimuth" are used in celestial navigation. How do these terms relate to spherical coordinates?

---

✔ **QUICK CHECK ANSWERS 11.8**

**1.** $r\cos\theta$; $r\sin\theta$; $z$   **2.** $\rho\sin\phi\cos\theta$; $\rho\sin\phi\sin\theta$; $\rho\cos\phi$   **3.** $\rho\sin\phi$; $\theta$; $\rho\cos\theta$
**4.** (a) $(2, 7\pi/4, 2\sqrt{3})$ (b) $(4, 7\pi/4, \pi/6)$   **5.** (a) $x^2 + y^2 + z^2 = 25$ (b) $r^2 + z^2 = 25$ (c) $\rho = 5$

---

## CHAPTER 11 REVIEW EXERCISES

**1.** (a) What is the difference between a vector and a scalar? Give a physical example of each.

(b) How can you determine whether or not two vectors are orthogonal?

(c) How can you determine whether or not two vectors are parallel?

(d) How can you determine whether or not three vectors with a common initial point lie in the same plane in 3-space?

**2.** (a) Sketch vectors **u** and **v** for which $\mathbf{u} + \mathbf{v}$ and $\mathbf{u} - \mathbf{v}$ are orthogonal.

(b) How can you use vectors to determine whether four points in 3-space lie in the same plane?

(c) If forces $\mathbf{F}_1 = \mathbf{i}$ and $\mathbf{F}_2 = \mathbf{j}$ are applied at a point in 2-space, what force would you apply at that point to cancel the combined effect of $\mathbf{F}_1$ and $\mathbf{F}_2$?

(d) Write an equation of the sphere with center $(1, -2, 2)$ that passes through the origin.

**3.** (a) Draw a picture that shows the direction angles $\alpha$, $\beta$, and $\gamma$ of a vector.

(b) What are the components of a unit vector in 2-space that makes an angle of 120° with the vector **i** (two answers)?

(c) How can you use vectors to determine whether a triangle with known vertices $P_1$, $P_2$, and $P_3$ has an obtuse angle?

(d) True or false: The cross product of orthogonal unit vectors is a unit vector. Explain your reasoning.

**4.** (a) Make a table that shows all possible cross products of the vectors **i**, **j**, and **k**.

(b) Give a geometric interpretation of $\|\mathbf{u} \times \mathbf{v}\|$.

(c) Give a geometric interpretation of $|\mathbf{u} \cdot (\mathbf{v} \times \mathbf{w})|$.

(d) Write an equation of the plane that passes through the origin and is perpendicular to the line $x = t$, $y = 2t$, $z = -t$.

**5.** In each part, find an equation of the sphere with center $(-3, 5, -4)$ and satisfying the given condition.

(a) Tangent to the xy-plane

(b) Tangent to the xz-plane

(c) Tangent to the yz-plane

**6.** Find the largest and smallest distances between the point $P(1, 1, 1)$ and the sphere

$$x^2 + y^2 + z^2 - 2y + 6z - 6 = 0$$

**7.** Given the points $P(3, 4)$, $Q(1, 1)$, and $R(5, 2)$, use vector methods to find the coordinates of the fourth vertex of the parallelogram whose adjacent sides are $\overrightarrow{PQ}$ and $\overrightarrow{QR}$.

**8.** Let $\mathbf{u} = \langle 3, 5, -1 \rangle$ and $\mathbf{v} = \langle 2, -2, 3 \rangle$. Find

(a) $2\mathbf{u} + 5\mathbf{v}$        (b) $\dfrac{1}{\|\mathbf{v}\|}\mathbf{v}$

(c) $\|\mathbf{u}\|$            (d) $\|\mathbf{u} - \mathbf{v}\|$.

**9.** Let $\mathbf{a} = c\mathbf{i} + \mathbf{j}$ and $\mathbf{b} = 4\mathbf{i} + 3\mathbf{j}$. Find $c$ so that

(a) $\mathbf{a}$ and $\mathbf{b}$ are orthogonal

(b) the angle between $\mathbf{a}$ and $\mathbf{b}$ is $\pi/4$

(c) the angle between $\mathbf{a}$ and $\mathbf{b}$ is $\pi/6$

(d) $\mathbf{a}$ and $\mathbf{b}$ are parallel.

**10.** Let $\mathbf{r}_0 = \langle x_0, y_0, z_0 \rangle$ and $\mathbf{r} = \langle x, y, z \rangle$. Describe the set of all points $(x, y, z)$ for which

(a) $\mathbf{r} \cdot \mathbf{r}_0 = 0$        (b) $(\mathbf{r} - \mathbf{r}_0) \cdot \mathbf{r}_0 = 0$.

**11.** Show that if $\mathbf{u}$ and $\mathbf{v}$ are unit vectors and $\theta$ is the angle between them, then $\|\mathbf{u} - \mathbf{v}\| = 2 \sin \frac{1}{2}\theta$.

**12.** Find the vector with length 5 and direction angles $\alpha = 60°$, $\beta = 120°$, $\gamma = 135°$.

**13.** Assuming that force is in pounds and distance is in feet, find the work done by a constant force $\mathbf{F} = 3\mathbf{i} - 4\mathbf{j} + \mathbf{k}$ acting on a particle that moves on a straight line from $P(5, 7, 0)$ to $Q(6, 6, 6)$.

**14.** Assuming that force is in newtons and distance is in meters, find the work done by the resultant of the constant forces $\mathbf{F}_1 = \mathbf{i} - 3\mathbf{j} + \mathbf{k}$ and $\mathbf{F}_2 = \mathbf{i} + 2\mathbf{j} + 2\mathbf{k}$ acting on a particle that moves on a straight line from $P(-1, -2, 3)$ to $Q(0, 2, 0)$.

**15.** (a) Find the area of the triangle with vertices $A(1, 0, 1)$, $B(0, 2, 3)$, and $C(2, 1, 0)$.

(b) Use the result in part (a) to find the length of the altitude from vertex $C$ to side $AB$.

**16.** True or false? Explain your reasoning.

(a) If $\mathbf{u} \cdot \mathbf{v} = 0$, then $\mathbf{u} = \mathbf{0}$ or $\mathbf{v} = \mathbf{0}$.

(b) If $\mathbf{u} \times \mathbf{v} = \mathbf{0}$, then $\mathbf{u} = \mathbf{0}$ or $\mathbf{v} = \mathbf{0}$.

(c) If $\mathbf{u} \cdot \mathbf{v} = 0$ and $\mathbf{u} \times \mathbf{v} = \mathbf{0}$, then $\mathbf{u} = \mathbf{0}$ or $\mathbf{v} = \mathbf{0}$.

**17.** Consider the points

$$A(1, -1, 2), \quad B(2, -3, 0), \quad C(-1, -2, 0), \quad D(2, 1, -1)$$

(a) Find the volume of the parallelepiped that has the vectors $\overrightarrow{AB}$, $\overrightarrow{AC}$, $\overrightarrow{AD}$ as adjacent edges.

(b) Find the distance from $D$ to the plane containing $A$, $B$, and $C$.

**18.** Suppose that a force $\mathbf{F}$ with a magnitude of 9 lb is applied to the lever–shaft assembly shown in the accompanying figure.

(a) Express the force $\mathbf{F}$ in component form.

(b) Find the vector moment of $\mathbf{F}$ about the origin.

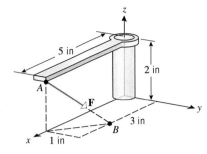

◀ **Figure Ex-18**

**19.** Let $P$ be the point $(4, 1, 2)$. Find parametric equations for the line through $P$ and parallel to the vector $\langle 1, -1, 0 \rangle$.

**20.** (a) Find parametric equations for the intersection of the planes $2x + y - z = 3$ and $x + 2y + z = 3$.

(b) Find the acute angle between the two planes.

**21.** Find an equation of the plane that is parallel to the plane $x + 5y - z + 8 = 0$ and contains the point $(1, 1, 4)$.

**22.** Find an equation of the plane through the point $(4, 3, 0)$ and parallel to the vectors $\mathbf{i} + \mathbf{k}$ and $2\mathbf{j} - \mathbf{k}$.

**23.** What condition must the constants satisfy for the planes

$$a_1 x + b_1 y + c_1 z = d_1 \quad \text{and} \quad a_2 x + b_2 y + c_2 z = d_2$$

to be perpendicular?

**24.** (a) List six common types of quadric surfaces, and describe their traces in planes parallel to the coordinate planes.

(b) Give the coordinates of the points that result when the point $(x, y, z)$ is reflected about the plane $y = x$, the plane $y = z$, and the plane $x = z$.

(c) Describe the intersection of the surfaces $r = 5$ and $z = 1$ in cylindrical coordinates.

(d) Describe the intersection of the surfaces $\phi = \pi/4$ and $\theta = 0$ in spherical coordinates.

**25.** In each part, identify the surface by completing the squares.

(a) $x^2 + 4y^2 - z^2 - 6x + 8y + 4z = 0$

(b) $x^2 + y^2 + z^2 + 6x - 4y + 12z = 0$

(c) $x^2 + y^2 - z^2 - 2x + 4y + 5 = 0$

**26.** In each part, express the equation in cylindrical and spherical coordinates.

(a) $x^2 + y^2 = z$        (b) $x^2 - y^2 - z^2 = 0$

**27.** In each part, express the equation in rectangular coordinates.

(a) $z = r^2 \cos 2\theta$        (b) $\rho^2 \sin \phi \cos \phi \cos \theta = 1$

**28–29** Sketch the solid in 3-space that is described in cylindrical coordinates by the stated inequalities. ◾

**28.** (a) $1 \leq r \leq 2$     (b) $2 \leq z \leq 3$     (c) $\pi/6 \leq \theta \leq \pi/3$

(d) $1 \leq r \leq 2$, $2 \leq z \leq 3$, and $\pi/6 \leq \theta \leq \pi/3$

**29.** (a) $r^2 + z^2 \leq 4$        (b) $r \leq 1$

(c) $r^2 + z^2 \leq 4$ and $r > 1$

**30–31** Sketch the solid in 3-space that is described in spherical coordinates by the stated inequalities. ◾

**30.** (a) $0 \leq \rho \leq 2$  (b) $0 \leq \phi \leq \pi/6$
(c) $0 \leq \rho \leq 2$ and $0 \leq \phi \leq \pi/6$

**31.** (a) $0 \leq \rho \leq 5$, $0 \leq \phi \leq \pi/2$, and $0 \leq \theta \leq \pi/2$
(b) $0 \leq \phi \leq \pi/3$ and $0 \leq \rho \leq 2 \sec \phi$
(c) $0 \leq \rho \leq 2$ and $\pi/6 \leq \phi \leq \pi/3$

**32.** Sketch the surface whose equation in spherical coordinates is $\rho = a(1 - \cos \phi)$. [*Hint:* The surface is shaped like a familiar fruit.]

## CHAPTER 11 MAKING CONNECTIONS

**1.** Define a "rotation operator" $R$ on vectors in the $xy$-plane by the formula

$$R(x\mathbf{i} + y\mathbf{j}) = -y\mathbf{i} + x\mathbf{j}$$

(a) Verify that $R$ rotates vectors $90°$ counterclockwise.

(b) Prove that $R$ has the following linearity properties:

$$R(c\mathbf{v}) = cR(\mathbf{v}) \quad \text{and} \quad R(\mathbf{v} + \mathbf{w}) = R(\mathbf{v}) + R(\mathbf{w})$$

**2.** (a) Given a triangle in the $xy$-plane, assign to each side of the triangle an outward normal vector whose length is the same as that of the corresponding side. Prove that the sum of the resulting three normal vectors is the zero vector.

(b) Extend the result of part (a) to a polygon of $n$ sides in the $xy$-plane. [*Hint:* Use the results of the preceding exercise.]

**3.** (a) Given a tetrahedron in 3-space, assign to each face of the tetrahedron an outward normal vector whose length is numerically the same as the area of the corresponding face. Prove that the sum of the resulting four normal vectors is the zero vector. [*Hint:* Use cross products.]

(b) Extend your result from part (a) to a pyramid with a four-sided base. [*Hint:* Divide the base into two triangles and use the result from part (a) on each of the two resulting tetrahedra.]

(c) Can you extend the results of parts (a) and (b) to other polyhedra?

**4.** Given a tetrahedron in 3-space, pick a vertex and label the three faces that meet at that vertex as $A$, $B$, and $C$. Let $a$, $b$, and $c$ denote the respective areas of those faces, and let $d$ denote the area of the fourth face of the tetrahedron. Let $\alpha$ denote the (internal) angle between faces $A$ and $B$, $\beta$ the angle between $B$ and $C$, and $\gamma$ the angle between $A$ and $C$.

(a) Prove that

$$d^2 = a^2 + b^2 + c^2 - 2ab \cos \alpha - 2bc \cos \beta - 2ac \cos \gamma$$

This result is sometimes referred to as the *law of cosines for a tetrahedron*. [*Hint:* Use the result in part (a) of the preceding exercise.]

(b) With the result in part (a) as motivation, state and prove a "Theorem of Pythagoras for a Tetrahedron."

**5.** Any circle that lies on a sphere can be realized as the intersection of the sphere and a plane. If the plane passes through the center of the sphere, then the circle is referred to as a *great circle*. Given two points on a sphere, the *great circle distance* between the two points is the length of the smallest arc of a great circle that contains both points. Assume that $\Sigma$ is a sphere of radius $\rho$ centered at the origin in 3-space. If points $P$ and $Q$ lie on $\Sigma$ and have spherical coordinates $(\rho, \theta_1, \phi_1)$ and $(\rho, \theta_2, \phi_2)$, respectively, prove that the great circle distance between $P$ and $Q$ is

$$\rho \cos^{-1}(\cos \phi_1 \cos \phi_2 + \cos(\theta_1 - \theta_2) \sin \phi_1 \sin \phi_2)$$

**6.** A ship at sea is at point $A$ that is $60°$ west longitude and $40°$ north latitude. The ship travels to point $B$ that is $40°$ west longitude and $20°$ north latitude. Assuming that the Earth is a sphere with radius 6370 kilometers, find the shortest distance the ship can travel in going from $A$ to $B$, given that the shortest distance between two points on a sphere is along the arc of the great circle joining the points. [*Suggestion:* Introduce an $xyz$-coordinate system as in Figure 11.8.9, and use the result of the preceding exercise.]

© Krystian Janczyński/iStockphoto

# 12

# VECTOR-VALUED FUNCTIONS

*The design of a roller coaster requires an understanding of the mathematical principles governing the motion of objects that move with varying speed and direction.*

In this chapter we will consider functions whose values are vectors. Such functions provide a unified way of studying parametric curves in 2-space and 3-space and are a basic tool for analyzing the motion of particles along curved paths. We will begin by developing the calculus of vector-valued functions—we will show how to differentiate and integrate such functions, and we will develop some of the basic properties of these operations. We will then apply these calculus tools to define three fundamental vectors that can be used to describe such basic characteristics of curves as curvature and twisting tendencies. Once this is done, we will develop the concepts of velocity and acceleration for such motion, and we will apply these concepts to explain various physical phenomena. Finally, we will use the calculus of vector-valued functions to develop basic principles of gravitational attraction and to derive Kepler's laws of planetary motion.

## 12.1 INTRODUCTION TO VECTOR-VALUED FUNCTIONS

*In Section 11.5 we discussed parametric equations of lines in 3-space. In this section we will discuss more general parametric curves in 3-space, and we will show how vector notation can be used to express parametric equations in 2-space and 3-space in a more compact form. This will lead us to consider a new kind of function—namely, functions that associate vectors with real numbers. Such functions have many important applications in physics and engineering.*

### PARAMETRIC CURVES IN 3-SPACE

Recall from Section 10.1 that if $f$ and $g$ are well-behaved functions, then the pair of parametric equations

$$x = f(t), \quad y = g(t) \tag{1}$$

generates a curve in 2-space that is traced in a specific direction as the parameter $t$ increases. We defined this direction to be the *orientation* of the curve or the *direction of increasing parameter*, and we called the curve together with its orientation the *graph* of the parametric equations or the *parametric curve* represented by the equations. Analogously, if $f$, $g$, and $h$ are three well-behaved functions, then the parametric equations

$$x = f(t), \quad y = g(t), \quad z = h(t) \tag{2}$$

generate a curve in 3-space that is traced in a specific direction as $t$ increases. As in 2-space, this direction is called the **orientation** or **direction of increasing parameter**, and

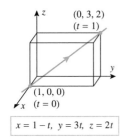

$$x = 1 - t, \quad y = 3t, \quad z = 2t$$

▲ **Figure 12.1.1**

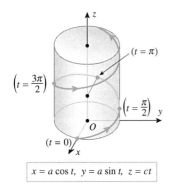

$$x = a \cos t, \quad y = a \sin t, \quad z = ct$$

▲ **Figure 12.1.2**

Ken Eward/Biografx/Photo Researchers, Inc.

The circular helix described in Example 2 occurs in nature. Above is a computer representation of the twin helix DNA molecule (deoxyribonucleic acid). This structure contains all the inherited instructions necessary for the development of a living organism.

**TECHNOLOGY MASTERY**

If you have a CAS, use it to generate the tricuspoid in Figure 12.1.3, and show that this parametric curve is oriented counterclockwise.

the curve together with its orientation is called the ***graph*** of the parametric equations or the ***parametric curve*** represented by the equations. If no restrictions are stated explicitly or are implied by the equations, then it will be understood that $t$ varies over the interval $(-\infty, +\infty)$.

▶ **Example 1**    The parametric equations

$$x = 1 - t, \quad y = 3t, \quad z = 2t$$

represent a line in 3-space that passes through the point $(1, 0, 0)$ and is parallel to the vector $\langle -1, 3, 2 \rangle$. Since $x$ decreases as $t$ increases, the line has the orientation shown in Figure 12.1.1. ◀

▶ **Example 2**    Describe the parametric curve represented by the equations

$$x = a \cos t, \quad y = a \sin t, \quad z = ct$$

where $a$ and $c$ are positive constants.

***Solution.***    As the parameter $t$ increases, the value of $z = ct$ also increases, so the point $(x, y, z)$ moves upward. However, as $t$ increases, the point $(x, y, z)$ also moves in a path directly over the circle

$$x = a \cos t, \quad y = a \sin t$$

in the $xy$-plane. The combination of these upward and circular motions produces a corkscrew-shaped curve that wraps around a right circular cylinder of radius $a$ centered on the $z$-axis (Figure 12.1.2). This curve is called a ***circular helix***. ◀

**■ PARAMETRIC CURVES GENERATED WITH TECHNOLOGY**

Except in the simplest cases, parametric curves can be difficult to visualize and draw without the help of a graphing utility. For example, the ***tricuspoid*** is the graph of the parametric equations

$$x = 2 \cos t + \cos 2t, \quad y = 2 \sin t - \sin 2t$$

Although it would be tedious to plot the tricuspoid by hand, a computer rendering is easy to obtain and reveals the significance of the name of the curve (Figure 12.1.3). However, note that the depiction of the tricuspoid in Figure 12.1.3 is incomplete, since the orientation of the curve is not indicated. This is often the case for curves that are generated with a graphing utility. (Some graphing utilities plot parametric curves slowly enough for the orientation to be discerned, or provide a feature for tracing the points along the curve in the direction of increasing parameter.)

Parametric curves in 3-space can be difficult to visualize correctly even with the help of a graphing utility. For example, Figure 12.1.4$a$ shows a parametric curve called a *torus knot* that was produced with a CAS. However, it is unclear from this computer-generated figure whether the points of overlap are intersections or whether one portion of the curve is in front of the other. To resolve the visualization problem, some graphing utilities provide the capability of enclosing the curve within a thin tube, as in Figure 12.1.4$b$. Such graphs are called ***tube plots***.

**■ PARAMETRIC EQUATIONS FOR INTERSECTIONS OF SURFACES**

Curves in 3-space often arise as intersections of surfaces. For example, Figure 12.1.5$a$ shows a portion of the intersection of the cylinders $z = x^3$ and $y = x^2$. One method for finding parametric equations for the curve of intersection is to choose one of the variables as the parameter and use the two equations to express the remaining two variables in terms

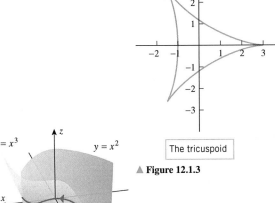

The tricuspoid

▲ **Figure 12.1.3**

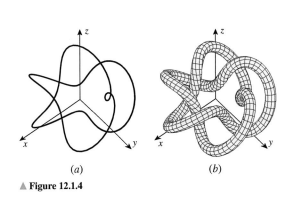

(a)                    (b)

▲ **Figure 12.1.4**

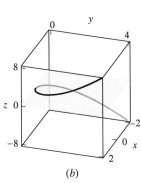

(a)

(b)

▲ **Figure 12.1.5**

of that parameter. In particular, if we choose $x = t$ as the parameter and substitute this into the equations $z = x^3$ and $y = x^2$, we obtain the parametric equations

$$x = t, \quad y = t^2, \quad z = t^3 \tag{3}$$

This curve is called a ***twisted cubic***. The portion of the twisted cubic shown in Figure 12.1.5a corresponds to $t \geq 0$; a computer-generated graph of the twisted cubic for positive and negative values of $t$ is shown in Figure 12.1.5b. Some other examples and techniques for finding intersections of surfaces are discussed in the exercises.

### ▓ VECTOR-VALUED FUNCTIONS

The twisted cubic defined by the equations in (3) is the set of points of the form $(t, t^2, t^3)$ for real values of $t$. If we view each of these points as a terminal point for a vector $\mathbf{r}$ whose initial point is at the origin,

$$\mathbf{r} = \langle x, y, z \rangle = \langle t, t^2, t^3 \rangle = t\mathbf{i} + t^2\mathbf{j} + t^3\mathbf{k}$$

then we obtain $\mathbf{r}$ as a function of the parameter $t$, that is, $\mathbf{r} = \mathbf{r}(t)$. Since this function produces a *vector*, we say that $\mathbf{r} = \mathbf{r}(t)$ defines $\mathbf{r}$ as a ***vector-valued function of a real variable***, or more simply, a ***vector-valued function***. The vectors that we will consider in this text are either in 2-space or 3-space, so we will say that a vector-valued function is in 2-space or in 3-space according to the kind of vectors that it produces.

If $\mathbf{r}(t)$ is a vector-valued function in 3-space, then for each allowable value of $t$ the vector $\mathbf{r} = \mathbf{r}(t)$ can be represented in terms of components as

$$\mathbf{r} = \mathbf{r}(t) = \langle x(t), y(t), z(t) \rangle = x(t)\mathbf{i} + y(t)\mathbf{j} + z(t)\mathbf{k} \tag{4}$$

The functions $x(t)$, $y(t)$, and $z(t)$ are called the ***component functions*** or the ***components*** of $\mathbf{r}(t)$.

Whereas a vector-valued function in 3-space, such as (4), has three components, a vector-valued function in 2-space has only two components and hence has the form

$$r(t) = \langle x(t), y(t) \rangle$$
$$= x(t)\mathbf{i} + y(t)\mathbf{j}$$

Find the vector-valued function in 2-space whose component functions are $x(t) = t$ and $y(t) = t^2$.

▶ **Example 3**    The component functions of

$$\mathbf{r}(t) = \langle t, t^2, t^3 \rangle = t\mathbf{i} + t^2\mathbf{j} + t^3\mathbf{k}$$

are

$$x(t) = t, \quad y(t) = t^2, \quad z(t) = t^3 \quad ◀$$

The ***domain*** of a vector-valued function $\mathbf{r}(t)$ is the set of allowable values for $t$. If $\mathbf{r}(t)$ is defined in terms of component functions and the domain is not specified explicitly, then it will be understood that the domain is the intersection of the natural domains of the component functions; this is called the ***natural domain*** of $\mathbf{r}(t)$.

▶ **Example 4**  Find the natural domain of
$$\mathbf{r}(t) = \langle \ln|t-1|, e^t, \sqrt{t} \rangle = (\ln|t-1|)\mathbf{i} + e^t\mathbf{j} + \sqrt{t}\mathbf{k}$$

*Solution.*  The natural domains of the component functions
$$x(t) = \ln|t-1|, \quad y(t) = e^t, \quad z(t) = \sqrt{t}$$
are
$$(-\infty, 1) \cup (1, +\infty), \quad (-\infty, +\infty), \quad [0, +\infty)$$
respectively. The intersection of these sets is
$$[0, 1) \cup (1, +\infty)$$
(verify), so the natural domain of $\mathbf{r}(t)$ consists of all values of $t$ such that
$$0 \le t < 1 \quad \text{or} \quad t > 1 \quad \blacktriangleleft$$

▨ **GRAPHS OF VECTOR-VALUED FUNCTIONS**
If $\mathbf{r}(t)$ is a vector-valued function in 2-space or 3-space, then we define the **graph** of $\mathbf{r}(t)$ to be the parametric curve described by the component functions for $\mathbf{r}(t)$. For example, if
$$\mathbf{r}(t) = \langle 1-t, 3t, 2t \rangle = (1-t)\mathbf{i} + 3t\mathbf{j} + 2t\mathbf{k} \tag{5}$$
then the graph of $\mathbf{r} = \mathbf{r}(t)$ is the graph of the parametric equations
$$x = 1-t, \quad y = 3t, \quad z = 2t$$
Thus, the graph of (5) is the line in Figure 12.1.1.

> Strictly speaking, we should write $(\cos t)\mathbf{i}$ and $(\sin t)\mathbf{j}$ rather than $\cos t\mathbf{i}$ and $\sin t\mathbf{j}$ for clarity. However, it is a common practice to omit the parentheses in such cases, since no misinterpretation is possible. Why?

▶ **Example 5**  Describe the graph of the vector-valued function
$$\mathbf{r}(t) = \langle \cos t, \sin t, t \rangle = \cos t\mathbf{i} + \sin t\mathbf{j} + t\mathbf{k}$$

*Solution.*  The corresponding parametric equations are
$$x = \cos t, \quad y = \sin t, \quad z = t$$
Thus, as we saw in Example 2, the graph is a circular helix wrapped around a cylinder of radius 1.  ◀

Up to now we have considered parametric curves to be paths traced by moving points. However, if a parametric curve is viewed as the graph of a vector-valued function, then we can also imagine the graph to be traced by the tip of a moving vector. For example, if the curve $C$ in 3-space is the graph of
$$\mathbf{r}(t) = x(t)\mathbf{i} + y(t)\mathbf{j} + z(t)\mathbf{k}$$
and if we position $\mathbf{r}(t)$ so its initial point is at the origin, then its terminal point will fall on the curve $C$ (as shown in Figure 12.1.6). Thus, when $\mathbf{r}(t)$ is positioned with its initial point at the origin, its terminal point will trace out the curve $C$ as the parameter $t$ varies, in which case we call $\mathbf{r}(t)$ the **radius vector** or the **position vector** for $C$. For simplicity, we will sometimes let the dependence on $t$ be understood and write $\mathbf{r}$ rather than $\mathbf{r}(t)$ for a radius vector.

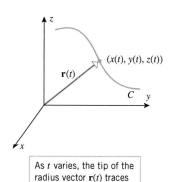

As $t$ varies, the tip of the radius vector $\mathbf{r}(t)$ traces out the curve $C$.

▲ **Figure 12.1.6**

▶ **Example 6**  Sketch the graph and a radius vector of

(a) $\mathbf{r}(t) = \cos t\mathbf{i} + \sin t\mathbf{j}, \quad 0 \le t \le 2\pi$

(b) $\mathbf{r}(t) = \cos t\mathbf{i} + \sin t\mathbf{j} + 2\mathbf{k}, \quad 0 \le t \le 2\pi$

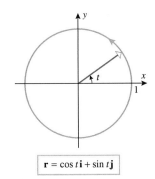

$$\mathbf{r} = \cos t\,\mathbf{i} + \sin t\,\mathbf{j}$$

▲ **Figure 12.1.7**

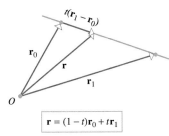

$$\mathbf{r} = \cos t\,\mathbf{i} + \sin t\,\mathbf{j} + 2\mathbf{k}$$

▲ **Figure 12.1.8**

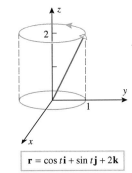

$$\mathbf{r} = (1 - t)\mathbf{r}_0 + t\mathbf{r}_1$$

▲ **Figure 12.1.9**

*Solution (a).* The corresponding parametric equations are

$$x = \cos t, \quad y = \sin t \qquad (0 \le t \le 2\pi)$$

so the graph is a circle of radius 1, centered at the origin, and oriented counterclockwise. The graph and a radius vector are shown in Figure 12.1.7.

*Solution (b).* The corresponding parametric equations are

$$x = \cos t, \quad y = \sin t, \quad z = 2 \qquad (0 \le t \le 2\pi)$$

From the third equation, the tip of the radius vector traces a curve in the plane $z = 2$, and from the first two equations, the curve is a circle of radius 1 centered at the point $(0, 0, 2)$ and traced counterclockwise looking down the $z$-axis. The graph and a radius vector are shown in Figure 12.1.8. ◄

■ **VECTOR FORM OF A LINE SEGMENT**

Recall from Formula (9) of Section 11.5 that if $\mathbf{r}_0$ is a vector in 2-space or 3-space with its initial point at the origin, then the line that passes through the terminal point of $\mathbf{r}_0$ and is parallel to the vector $\mathbf{v}$ can be expressed in vector form as

$$\mathbf{r} = \mathbf{r}_0 + t\mathbf{v}$$

In particular, if $\mathbf{r}_0$ and $\mathbf{r}_1$ are vectors in 2-space or 3-space with their initial points at the origin, then the line that passes through the terminal points of these vectors can be expressed in vector form as

$$\mathbf{r} = \mathbf{r}_0 + t(\mathbf{r}_1 - \mathbf{r}_0) \qquad \text{or} \qquad \mathbf{r} = (1 - t)\mathbf{r}_0 + t\mathbf{r}_1 \qquad (6\text{–}7)$$

as indicated in Figure 12.1.9.

It is common to call either (6) or (7) the *two-point vector form of a line* and to say, for simplicity, that the line passes through the *points* $\mathbf{r}_0$ and $\mathbf{r}_1$ (as opposed to saying that it passes through the *terminal points* of $\mathbf{r}_0$ and $\mathbf{r}_1$).

It is understood in (6) and (7) that $t$ varies from $-\infty$ to $+\infty$. However, if we restrict $t$ to vary over the interval $0 \le t \le 1$, then $\mathbf{r}$ will vary from $\mathbf{r}_0$ to $\mathbf{r}_1$. Thus, the equation

$$\mathbf{r} = (1 - t)\mathbf{r}_0 + t\mathbf{r}_1 \qquad (0 \le t \le 1) \qquad (8)$$

represents the line segment in 2-space or 3-space that is traced from $\mathbf{r}_0$ to $\mathbf{r}_1$.

✔ **QUICK CHECK EXERCISES 12.1**    *(See page 847 for answers.)*

1. (a) Express the parametric equations

$$x = \frac{1}{t}, \quad y = \sqrt{t}, \quad z = \sin^{-1} t$$

as a single vector equation of the form

$$\mathbf{r} = x(t)\mathbf{i} + y(t)\mathbf{j} + z(t)\mathbf{k}$$

   (b) The vector equation in part (a) defines $\mathbf{r} = \mathbf{r}(t)$ as a vector-valued function. The domain of $\mathbf{r}(t)$ is _____ and $\mathbf{r}\left(\frac{1}{2}\right) =$ _____.

2. Describe the graph of $\mathbf{r}(t) = \langle 1 + 2t, -1 + 3t \rangle$.

3. Describe the graph of $\mathbf{r}(t) = \sin^2 t\,\mathbf{i} + \cos^2 t\,\mathbf{j}$.

4. Find a vector equation for the curve of intersection of the surfaces $y = x^2$ and $z = y$ in terms of the parameter $x = t$.

**EXERCISE SET 12.1**    ∼ Graphing Utility

**1–4** Find the domain of $\mathbf{r}(t)$ and the value of $\mathbf{r}(t_0)$. ■

**1.** $\mathbf{r}(t) = \cos t\,\mathbf{i} - 3t\,\mathbf{j}; \ t_0 = \pi$

**2.** $\mathbf{r}(t) = \langle \sqrt{3t + 1}, t^2 \rangle; \ t_0 = 1$

**3.** $\mathbf{r}(t) = \cos \pi t\,\mathbf{i} - \ln t\,\mathbf{j} + \sqrt{t - 2}\,\mathbf{k}; \ t_0 = 3$

**4.** $\mathbf{r}(t) = \langle 2e^{-t}, \sin^{-1} t, \ln(1 - t) \rangle; \; t_0 = 0$

**5–6** Express the parametric equations as a single vector equation of the form

$$\mathbf{r} = x(t)\mathbf{i} + y(t)\mathbf{j} \quad \text{or} \quad \mathbf{r} = x(t)\mathbf{i} + y(t)\mathbf{j} + z(t)\mathbf{k} \quad \blacksquare$$

**5.** $x = 3 \cos t, \; y = t + \sin t$

**6.** $x = 2t, \; y = 2 \sin 3t, \; z = 5 \cos 3t$

**7–8** Find the parametric equations that correspond to the given vector equation. ■

**7.** $\mathbf{r} = 3t^2\mathbf{i} - 2\mathbf{j}$

**8.** $\mathbf{r} = (2t - 1)\mathbf{i} - 3\sqrt{t}\,\mathbf{j} + \sin 3t\mathbf{k}$

**9–14** Describe the graph of the equation. ■

**9.** $\mathbf{r} = (3 - 2t)\mathbf{i} + 5t\mathbf{j}$

**10.** $\mathbf{r} = 2 \sin 3t\mathbf{i} - 2 \cos 3t\mathbf{j}$

**11.** $\mathbf{r} = 2t\mathbf{i} - 3\mathbf{j} + (1 + 3t)\mathbf{k}$

**12.** $\mathbf{r} = 3\mathbf{i} + 2 \cos t\mathbf{j} + 2 \sin t\mathbf{k}$

**13.** $\mathbf{r} = 2 \cos t\mathbf{i} - 3 \sin t\mathbf{j} + \mathbf{k}$

**14.** $\mathbf{r} = -3\mathbf{i} + (1 - t^2)\mathbf{j} + t\mathbf{k}$

**15.** (a) Find the slope of the line in 2-space that is represented by the vector equation $\mathbf{r} = (1 - 2t)\mathbf{i} - (2 - 3t)\mathbf{j}$.
(b) Find the coordinates of the point where the line

$$\mathbf{r} = (2 + t)\mathbf{i} + (1 - 2t)\mathbf{j} + 3t\mathbf{k}$$

intersects the $xz$-plane.

**16.** (a) Find the $y$-intercept of the line in 2-space that is represented by the vector equation $\mathbf{r} = (3 + 2t)\mathbf{i} + 5t\mathbf{j}$.
(b) Find the coordinates of the point where the line

$$\mathbf{r} = t\mathbf{i} + (1 + 2t)\mathbf{j} - 3t\mathbf{k}$$

intersects the plane $3x - y - z = 2$.

**17–18** Sketch the line segment represented by each vector equation. ■

**17.** (a) $\mathbf{r} = (1 - t)\mathbf{i} + t\mathbf{j}; \; 0 \le t \le 1$
(b) $\mathbf{r} = (1 - t)(\mathbf{i} + \mathbf{j}) + t(\mathbf{i} - \mathbf{j}); \; 0 \le t \le 1$

**18.** (a) $\mathbf{r} = (1 - t)(\mathbf{i} + \mathbf{j}) + t\mathbf{k}; \; 0 \le t \le 1$
(b) $\mathbf{r} = (1 - t)(\mathbf{i} + \mathbf{j} + \mathbf{k}) + t(\mathbf{i} + \mathbf{j}); \; 0 \le t \le 1$

**19–20** Write a vector equation for the line segment from $P$ to $Q$. ■

**19.**
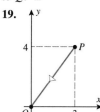

**20.**
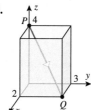

**21–30** Sketch the graph of $\mathbf{r}(t)$ and show the direction of increasing $t$. ■

**21.** $\mathbf{r}(t) = 2\mathbf{i} + t\mathbf{j}$

**22.** $\mathbf{r}(t) = \langle 3t - 4, 6t + 2 \rangle$

**23.** $\mathbf{r}(t) = (1 + \cos t)\mathbf{i} + (3 - \sin t)\mathbf{j}; \; 0 \le t \le 2\pi$

**24.** $\mathbf{r}(t) = \langle 2 \cos t, 5 \sin t \rangle; \; 0 \le t \le 2\pi$

**25.** $\mathbf{r}(t) = \cosh t\mathbf{i} + \sinh t\mathbf{j}$    **26.** $\mathbf{r}(t) = \sqrt{t}\mathbf{i} + (2t + 4)\mathbf{j}$

**27.** $\mathbf{r}(t) = 2 \cos t\mathbf{i} + 2 \sin t\mathbf{j} + t\mathbf{k}$

**28.** $\mathbf{r}(t) = 9 \cos t\mathbf{i} + 4 \sin t\mathbf{j} + t\mathbf{k}$

**29.** $\mathbf{r}(t) = t\mathbf{i} + t^2\mathbf{j} + 2\mathbf{k}$

**30.** $\mathbf{r}(t) = t\mathbf{i} + t\mathbf{j} + \sin t\mathbf{k}; \; 0 \le t \le 2\pi$

**31–34 True–False** Determine whether the statement is true or false. Explain your answer. ■

**31.** The natural domain of a vector-valued function is the union of the domains of its component functions.

**32.** If $\mathbf{r}(t) = \langle x(t), y(t) \rangle$ is a vector-valued function in 2-space, then the graph of $\mathbf{r}(t)$ is a surface in 3-space.

**33.** If $\mathbf{r}_0$ and $\mathbf{r}_1$ are vectors in 3-space, then the graph of the vector-valued function

$$\mathbf{r}(t) = (1 - t)\mathbf{r}_0 + t\mathbf{r}_1 \quad (0 \le t \le 1)$$

is the straight line segment joining the terminal points of $\mathbf{r}_0$ and $\mathbf{r}_1$.

**34.** The graph of $\mathbf{r}(t) = \langle 2 \cos t, 2 \sin t, t \rangle$ is a circular helix.

**35–36** Sketch the curve of intersection of the surfaces, and find parametric equations for the intersection in terms of parameter $x = t$. Check your work with a graphing utility by generating the parametric curve over the interval $-1 \le t \le 1$. ■

**35.** $z = x^2 + y^2, \; x - y = 0$

**36.** $y + x = 0, \; z = \sqrt{2 - x^2 - y^2}$

**37–38** Sketch the curve of intersection of the surfaces, and find a vector equation for the curve in terms of the parameter $x = t$. ■

**37.** $9x^2 + y^2 + 9z^2 = 81, \; y = x^2 \quad (z > 0)$

**38.** $y = x, \; x + y + z = 1$

**39.** Show that the graph of

$$\mathbf{r} = t \sin t\mathbf{i} + t \cos t\mathbf{j} + t^2\mathbf{k}$$

lies on the paraboloid $z = x^2 + y^2$.

**40.** Show that the graph of

$$\mathbf{r} = t\mathbf{i} + \frac{1 + t}{t}\mathbf{j} + \frac{1 - t^2}{t}\mathbf{k}, \quad t > 0$$

lies in the plane $x - y + z + 1 = 0$.

**FOCUS ON CONCEPTS**

**41.** Show that the graph of

$$\mathbf{r} = \sin t\mathbf{i} + 2 \cos t\mathbf{j} + \sqrt{3} \sin t\mathbf{k}$$

is a circle, and find its center and radius. [*Hint:* Show that the curve lies on both a sphere and a plane.]

**42.** Show that the graph of
$$\mathbf{r} = 3\cos t\mathbf{i} + 3\sin t\mathbf{j} + 3\sin t\mathbf{k}$$
is an ellipse, and find the lengths of the major and minor axes. [*Hint:* Show that the graph lies on both a circular cylinder and a plane and use the result in Exercise 44 of Section 10.4.]

**43.** For the helix $\mathbf{r} = a\cos t\mathbf{i} + a\sin t\mathbf{j} + ct\mathbf{k}$, find the value of $c$ ($c > 0$) so that the helix will make one complete turn in a distance of 3 units measured along the $z$-axis.

**44.** How many revolutions will the circular helix
$$\mathbf{r} = a\cos t\mathbf{i} + a\sin t\mathbf{j} + 0.2t\mathbf{k}$$
make in a distance of 10 units measured along the $z$-axis?

**45.** Show that the curve $\mathbf{r} = t\cos t\mathbf{i} + t\sin t\mathbf{j} + t\mathbf{k}$, $t \geq 0$, lies on the cone $z = \sqrt{x^2 + y^2}$. Describe the curve.

**46.** Describe the curve $\mathbf{r} = a\cos t\mathbf{i} + b\sin t\mathbf{j} + ct\mathbf{k}$, where $a$, $b$, and $c$ are positive constants such that $a \neq b$.

**47.** In each part, match the vector equation with one of the accompanying graphs, and explain your reasoning.
  (a) $\mathbf{r} = t\mathbf{i} - t\mathbf{j} + \sqrt{2 - t^2}\,\mathbf{k}$
  (b) $\mathbf{r} = \sin \pi t\mathbf{i} - t\mathbf{j} + t\mathbf{k}$
  (c) $\mathbf{r} = \sin t\mathbf{i} + \cos t\mathbf{j} + \sin 2t\mathbf{k}$
  (d) $\mathbf{r} = \frac{1}{2}t\mathbf{i} + \cos 3t\mathbf{j} + \sin 3t\mathbf{k}$

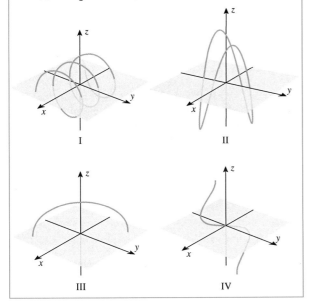

I    II

III    IV

**48.** Check your conclusions in Exercise 47 by generating the curves with a graphing utility. [*Note:* Your graphing utility may look at the curve from a different viewpoint. Read the documentation for your graphing utility to determine how to control the viewpoint, and see if you can generate a reasonable facsimile of the graphs shown in the figure by adjusting the viewpoint and choosing the interval of $t$-values appropriately.]

**49.** (a) Find parametric equations for the curve of intersection of the circular cylinder $x^2 + y^2 = 9$ and the parabolic cylinder $z = x^2$ in terms of a parameter $t$ for which $x = 3\cos t$.
  (b) Use a graphing utility to generate the curve of intersection in part (a).

**50.** (a) Sketch the graph of
$$\mathbf{r}(t) = \left\langle 2t, \frac{2}{1 + t^2}\right\rangle$$
  (b) Prove that the curve in part (a) is also the graph of the function
$$y = \frac{8}{4 + x^2}$$

  [The graphs of $y = a^3/(a^2 + x^2)$, where $a$ denotes a constant, were first studied by the French mathematician Pierre de Fermat, and later by the Italian mathematicians Guido Grandi and Maria Agnesi. Any such curve is now known as a "witch of Agnesi." There are a number of theories for the origin of this name. Some suggest there was a mistranslation by either Grandi or Agnesi of some less colorful Latin name into Italian. Others lay the blame on a translation into English of Agnesi's 1748 treatise, *Analytical Institutions*.]

**51.** Writing  Consider the curve $C$ of intersection of the cone $z = \sqrt{x^2 + y^2}$ and the plane $z = y + 2$. Sketch and identify the curve $C$, and describe a procedure for finding a vector-valued function $\mathbf{r}(t)$ whose graph is $C$.

**52.** Writing  Suppose that $\mathbf{r}_1(t)$ and $\mathbf{r}_2(t)$ are vector-valued functions in 2-space. Explain why solving the equation $\mathbf{r}_1(t) = \mathbf{r}_2(t)$ may not produce all of the points where the graphs of these functions intersect.

---

✔ **QUICK CHECK ANSWERS 12.1**

---

1. (a) $\mathbf{r} = \frac{1}{t}\mathbf{i} + \sqrt{t}\mathbf{j} + \sin^{-1} t\mathbf{k}$ (b) $0 < t \leq 1$; $2\mathbf{i} + \frac{\sqrt{2}}{2}\mathbf{j} + \frac{\pi}{6}\mathbf{k}$   2. The graph is a line through $(1, -1)$ with direction vector $2\mathbf{i} + 3\mathbf{j}$.   3. The graph is the line segment in the $xy$-plane from $(0, 1)$ to $(1, 0)$.   4. $\mathbf{r} = \langle t, t^2, t^2 \rangle$

## 12.2    CALCULUS OF VECTOR-VALUED FUNCTIONS

*In this section we will define limits, derivatives, and integrals of vector-valued functions and discuss their properties.*

### ■ LIMITS AND CONTINUITY

Our first goal in this section is to develop a notion of what it means for a vector-valued function $\mathbf{r}(t)$ in 2-space or 3-space to approach a limiting vector $\mathbf{L}$ as $t$ approaches a number $a$. That is, we want to define

$$\lim_{t \to a} \mathbf{r}(t) = \mathbf{L} \tag{1}$$

One way to motivate a reasonable definition of (1) is to position $\mathbf{r}(t)$ and $\mathbf{L}$ with their initial points at the origin and interpret this limit to mean that the terminal point of $\mathbf{r}(t)$ approaches the terminal point of $\mathbf{L}$ as $t$ approaches $a$ or, equivalently, that the vector $\mathbf{r}(t)$ approaches the vector $\mathbf{L}$ in both length and direction at $t$ approaches $a$ (Figure 12.2.1). Algebraically, this is equivalent to stating that

$$\lim_{t \to a} \|\mathbf{r}(t) - \mathbf{L}\| = 0 \tag{2}$$

(Figure 12.2.2). Thus, we make the following definition.

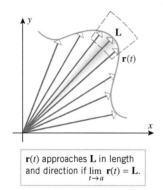

$\mathbf{r}(t)$ approaches $\mathbf{L}$ in length and direction if $\lim\limits_{t \to a} \mathbf{r}(t) = \mathbf{L}$.

▲ **Figure 12.2.1**

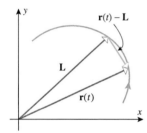

$\|\mathbf{r}(t) - \mathbf{L}\|$ is the distance between terminal points for vectors $\mathbf{r}(t)$ and $\mathbf{L}$ when positioned with the same initial points.

▲ **Figure 12.2.2**

---

Note that $\|\mathbf{r}(t) - \mathbf{L}\|$ is a real number for each value of $t$, so even though this expression involves a vector-valued function, the limit

$$\lim_{t \to a} \|\mathbf{r}(t) - \mathbf{L}\|$$

is an ordinary limit of a real-valued function.

---

> **12.2.1  DEFINITION**  Let $\mathbf{r}(t)$ be a vector-valued function that is defined for all $t$ in some open interval containing the number $a$, except that $\mathbf{r}(t)$ need not be defined at $a$. We will write
> $$\lim_{t \to a} \mathbf{r}(t) = \mathbf{L}$$
> if and only if
> $$\lim_{t \to a} \|\mathbf{r}(t) - \mathbf{L}\| = 0$$

It is clear intuitively that $\mathbf{r}(t)$ will approach a limiting vector $\mathbf{L}$ as $t$ approaches $a$ if and only if the component functions of $\mathbf{r}(t)$ approach the corresponding components of $\mathbf{L}$. This suggests the following theorem, whose formal proof is omitted.

> **12.2.2  THEOREM**
>
> (*a*)  *If* $\mathbf{r}(t) = \langle x(t), y(t) \rangle = x(t)\mathbf{i} + y(t)\mathbf{j}$, *then*
> $$\lim_{t \to a} \mathbf{r}(t) = \left\langle \lim_{t \to a} x(t), \lim_{t \to a} y(t) \right\rangle = \lim_{t \to a} x(t)\mathbf{i} + \lim_{t \to a} y(t)\mathbf{j}$$
> *provided the limits of the component functions exist. Conversely, the limits of the component functions exist provided* $\mathbf{r}(t)$ *approaches a limiting vector as* $t$ *approaches* $a$.
>
> (*b*)  *If* $\mathbf{r}(t) = \langle x(t), y(t), z(t) \rangle = x(t)\mathbf{i} + y(t)\mathbf{j} + z(t)\mathbf{k}$, *then*
> $$\lim_{t \to a} \mathbf{r}(t) = \left\langle \lim_{t \to a} x(t), \lim_{t \to a} y(t), \lim_{t \to a} z(t) \right\rangle$$
> $$= \lim_{t \to a} x(t)\mathbf{i} + \lim_{t \to a} y(t)\mathbf{j} + \lim_{t \to a} z(t)\mathbf{k}$$
> *provided the limits of the component functions exist. Conversely, the limits of the component functions exist provided* $\mathbf{r}(t)$ *approaches a limiting vector as* $t$ *approaches* $a$.

How would you define the one-sided limits

$$\lim_{t \to a^+} \mathbf{r}(t) \quad \text{and} \quad \lim_{t \to a^-} \mathbf{r}(t)?$$

Limits of vector-valued functions have many of the same properties as limits of real-valued functions. For example, assuming that the limits exist, the limit of a sum is the sum of the limits, the limit of a difference is the difference of the limits, and a constant scalar factor can be moved through a limit symbol.

▶ **Example 1**  Let $\mathbf{r}(t) = t^2\mathbf{i} + e^t\mathbf{j} - (2\cos \pi t)\mathbf{k}$. Then

$$\lim_{t \to 0} \mathbf{r}(t) = \left(\lim_{t \to 0} t^2\right)\mathbf{i} + \left(\lim_{t \to 0} e^t\right)\mathbf{j} - \left(\lim_{t \to 0} 2\cos \pi t\right)\mathbf{k} = \mathbf{j} - 2\mathbf{k}$$

Alternatively, using the angle bracket notation for vectors,

$$\lim_{t \to 0} \mathbf{r}(t) = \lim_{t \to 0}\langle t^2, e^t, -2\cos \pi t\rangle = \left\langle \lim_{t \to 0} t^2, \lim_{t \to 0} e^t, \lim_{t \to 0}(-2\cos \pi t)\right\rangle = \langle 0, 1, -2\rangle \ ◀$$

Motivated by the definition of continuity for real-valued functions, we define a vector-valued function $\mathbf{r}(t)$ to be **continuous** at $t = a$ if

$$\lim_{t \to a} \mathbf{r}(t) = \mathbf{r}(a) \tag{3}$$

That is, $\mathbf{r}(a)$ is defined, the limit of $\mathbf{r}(t)$ as $t \to a$ exists, and the two are equal. As in the case for real-valued functions, we say that $\mathbf{r}(t)$ is **continuous on an interval** $I$ if it is continuous at each point of $I$ [with the understanding that at an endpoint in $I$ the two-sided limit in (3) is replaced by the appropriate one-sided limit]. It follows from Theorem 12.2.2 that a vector-valued function is continuous at $t = a$ if and only if its component functions are continuous at $t = a$.

■ **DERIVATIVES**

The derivative of a vector-valued function is defined by a limit similar to that for the derivative of a real-valued function.

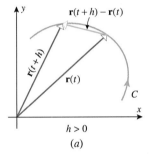

$\mathbf{r}(t+h) - \mathbf{r}(t)$

$\mathbf{r}(t+h)$

$\mathbf{r}(t)$

$C$

$h > 0$

(a)

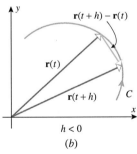

$\mathbf{r}(t+h) - \mathbf{r}(t)$

$\mathbf{r}(t)$

$\mathbf{r}(t+h)$

$C$

$h < 0$

(b)

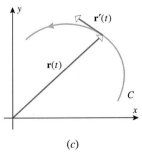

$\mathbf{r}'(t)$

$\mathbf{r}(t)$

$C$

(c)

▲ **Figure 12.2.3**

> **12.2.3  DEFINITION**  If $\mathbf{r}(t)$ is a vector-valued function, we define the **derivative of** $\mathbf{r}$ **with respect to** $t$ to be the vector-valued function $\mathbf{r}'$ given by
>
> $$\mathbf{r}'(t) = \lim_{h \to 0} \frac{\mathbf{r}(t+h) - \mathbf{r}(t)}{h} \tag{4}$$
>
> The domain of $\mathbf{r}'$ consists of all values of $t$ in the domain of $\mathbf{r}(t)$ for which the limit exists.

The function $\mathbf{r}(t)$ is **differentiable** at $t$ if the limit in (4) exists. All of the standard notations for derivatives continue to apply. For example, the derivative of $\mathbf{r}(t)$ can be expressed as

$$\frac{d}{dt}[\mathbf{r}(t)], \quad \frac{d\mathbf{r}}{dt}, \quad \mathbf{r}'(t), \quad \text{or} \quad \mathbf{r}'$$

It is important to keep in mind that $\mathbf{r}'(t)$ is a vector, not a number, and hence has a magnitude and a direction for each value of $t$ [except if $\mathbf{r}'(t) = \mathbf{0}$, in which case $\mathbf{r}'(t)$ has magnitude zero but no specific direction]. In the next section we will consider the significance of the magnitude of $\mathbf{r}'(t)$, but for now our goal is to obtain a geometric interpretation of the direction of $\mathbf{r}'(t)$. For this purpose, consider parts (a) and (b) of Figure 12.2.3. These illustrations show the graph $C$ of $\mathbf{r}(t)$ (with its orientation) and the vectors $\mathbf{r}(t)$, $\mathbf{r}(t+h)$, and $\mathbf{r}(t+h) - \mathbf{r}(t)$ for positive $h$ and for negative $h$. In both cases, the vector $\mathbf{r}(t+h) - \mathbf{r}(t)$ runs along the secant line joining the terminal points of $\mathbf{r}(t+h)$ and $\mathbf{r}(t)$, but with opposite directions in the two cases. In the case where $h$ is positive the vector $\mathbf{r}(t+h) - \mathbf{r}(t)$ points in the direction of increasing parameter, and in the case where $h$ is negative it points in the opposite direction. However, in the case where $h$ is negative the direction gets reversed when we multiply by $1/h$, so in both cases the vector

$$\frac{1}{h}[\mathbf{r}(t+h) - \mathbf{r}(t)] = \frac{\mathbf{r}(t+h) - \mathbf{r}(t)}{h}$$

points in the direction of increasing parameter and runs along the secant line. As $h \to 0$, the secant line approaches the tangent line at the terminal point of $\mathbf{r}(t)$, so we can conclude that the limit

$$\mathbf{r}'(t) = \lim_{h \to 0} \frac{\mathbf{r}(t+h) - \mathbf{r}(t)}{h}$$

(if it exists and is nonzero) is a vector that is tangent to the curve $C$ at the tip of $\mathbf{r}(t)$ and points in the direction of increasing parameter (Figure 12.2.3c).

We can summarize all of this as follows.

---

**12.2.4** GEOMETRIC INTERPRETATION OF THE DERIVATIVE  Suppose that $C$ is the graph of a vector-valued function $\mathbf{r}(t)$ in 2-space or 3-space and that $\mathbf{r}'(t)$ exists and is nonzero for a given value of $t$. If the vector $\mathbf{r}'(t)$ is positioned with its initial point at the terminal point of the radius vector $\mathbf{r}(t)$, then $\mathbf{r}'(t)$ is tangent to $C$ and points in the direction of increasing parameter.

---

Since limits of vector-valued functions can be computed componentwise, it seems reasonable that we should be able to compute derivatives in terms of component functions as well. This is the result of the next theorem.

---

**12.2.5** THEOREM  *If $\mathbf{r}(t)$ is a vector-valued function, then $\mathbf{r}$ is differentiable at $t$ if and only if each of its component functions is differentiable at $t$, in which case the component functions of $\mathbf{r}'(t)$ are the derivatives of the corresponding component functions of $\mathbf{r}(t)$.*

---

PROOF  For simplicity, we give the proof in 2-space; the proof in 3-space is identical, except for the additional component. Assume that $\mathbf{r}(t) = x(t)\mathbf{i} + y(t)\mathbf{j}$. Then

$$\mathbf{r}'(t) = \lim_{h \to 0} \frac{\mathbf{r}(t+h) - \mathbf{r}(t)}{h}$$

$$= \lim_{h \to 0} \frac{[x(t+h)\mathbf{i} + y(t+h)\mathbf{j}] - [x(t)\mathbf{i} + y(t)\mathbf{j}]}{h}$$

$$= \left( \lim_{h \to 0} \frac{x(t+h) - x(t)}{h} \right)\mathbf{i} + \left( \lim_{h \to 0} \frac{y(t+h) - y(t)}{h} \right)\mathbf{j}$$

$$= x'(t)\mathbf{i} + y'(t)\mathbf{j} \quad \blacksquare$$

---

▶ **Example 2**  Let $\mathbf{r}(t) = t^2\mathbf{i} + e^t\mathbf{j} - (2\cos \pi t)\mathbf{k}$. Then

$$\mathbf{r}'(t) = \frac{d}{dt}(t^2)\mathbf{i} + \frac{d}{dt}(e^t)\mathbf{j} - \frac{d}{dt}(2\cos \pi t)\mathbf{k}$$

$$= 2t\mathbf{i} + e^t\mathbf{j} + (2\pi \sin \pi t)\mathbf{k} \quad \blacktriangleleft$$

---

▨ **DERIVATIVE RULES**

Many of the rules for differentiating real-valued functions have analogs in the context of differentiating vector-valued functions. We state some of these in the following theorem.

**12.2.6    THEOREM (*Rules of Differentiation*)**  *Let* $\mathbf{r}(t)$, $\mathbf{r}_1(t)$, *and* $\mathbf{r}_2(t)$ *be differentiable vector-valued functions that are all in 2-space or all in 3-space, and let* $f(t)$ *be a differentiable real-valued function, $k$ a scalar, and $\mathbf{c}$ a constant vector (that is, a vector whose value does not depend on $t$). Then the following rules of differentiation hold:*

(a)  $\dfrac{d}{dt}[\mathbf{c}] = \mathbf{0}$

(b)  $\dfrac{d}{dt}[k\mathbf{r}(t)] = k\dfrac{d}{dt}[\mathbf{r}(t)]$

(c)  $\dfrac{d}{dt}[\mathbf{r}_1(t) + \mathbf{r}_2(t)] = \dfrac{d}{dt}[\mathbf{r}_1(t)] + \dfrac{d}{dt}[\mathbf{r}_2(t)]$

(d)  $\dfrac{d}{dt}[\mathbf{r}_1(t) - \mathbf{r}_2(t)] = \dfrac{d}{dt}[\mathbf{r}_1(t)] - \dfrac{d}{dt}[\mathbf{r}_2(t)]$

(e)  $\dfrac{d}{dt}[f(t)\mathbf{r}(t)] = f(t)\dfrac{d}{dt}[\mathbf{r}(t)] + \dfrac{d}{dt}[f(t)]\mathbf{r}(t)$

The proofs of most of these rules are immediate consequences of Definition 12.2.3, although the last rule can be seen more easily by application of the product rule for real-valued functions to the component functions. The proof of Theorem 12.2.6 is left as an exercise.

### ■ TANGENT LINES TO GRAPHS OF VECTOR-VALUED FUNCTIONS

Motivated by the discussion of the geometric interpretation of the derivative of a vector-valued function, we make the following definition.

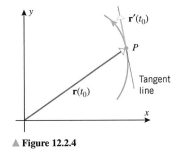

▲ **Figure 12.2.4**

**12.2.7    DEFINITION**   Let $P$ be a point on the graph of a vector-valued function $\mathbf{r}(t)$, and let $\mathbf{r}(t_0)$ be the radius vector from the origin to $P$ (Figure 12.2.4). If $\mathbf{r}'(t_0)$ exists and $\mathbf{r}'(t_0) \neq \mathbf{0}$, then we call $\mathbf{r}'(t_0)$ a ***tangent vector*** to the graph of $\mathbf{r}(t)$ at $\mathbf{r}(t_0)$, and we call the line through $P$ that is parallel to the tangent vector the ***tangent line*** to the graph of $\mathbf{r}(t)$ at $\mathbf{r}(t_0)$.

Let $\mathbf{r}_0 = \mathbf{r}(t_0)$ and $\mathbf{v}_0 = \mathbf{r}'(t_0)$. It follows from Formula (9) of Section 11.5 that the tangent line to the graph of $\mathbf{r}(t)$ at $\mathbf{r}_0$ is given by the vector equation

$$\mathbf{r} = \mathbf{r}_0 + t\mathbf{v}_0 \tag{5}$$

▶ **Example 3**   Find parametric equations of the tangent line to the circular helix

$$x = \cos t, \quad y = \sin t, \quad z = t$$

where $t = t_0$, and use that result to find parametric equations for the tangent line at the point where $t = \pi$.

***Solution.***   The vector equation of the helix is

$$\mathbf{r}(t) = \cos t\,\mathbf{i} + \sin t\,\mathbf{j} + t\mathbf{k}$$

so we have

$$\mathbf{r}_0 = \mathbf{r}(t_0) = \cos t_0 \mathbf{i} + \sin t_0 \mathbf{j} + t_0 \mathbf{k}$$

$$\mathbf{v}_0 = \mathbf{r}'(t_0) = (-\sin t_0)\mathbf{i} + \cos t_0 \mathbf{j} + \mathbf{k}$$

It follows from (5) that the vector equation of the tangent line at $t = t_0$ is

$$\mathbf{r} = \cos t_0 \mathbf{i} + \sin t_0 \mathbf{j} + t_0 \mathbf{k} + t[(-\sin t_0)\mathbf{i} + \cos t_0 \mathbf{j} + \mathbf{k}]$$

$$= (\cos t_0 - t \sin t_0)\mathbf{i} + (\sin t_0 + t \cos t_0)\mathbf{j} + (t_0 + t)\mathbf{k}$$

Thus, the parametric equations of the tangent line at $t = t_0$ are

$$x = \cos t_0 - t \sin t_0, \quad y = \sin t_0 + t \cos t_0, \quad z = t_0 + t$$

In particular, the tangent line at $t = \pi$ has parametric equations

$$x = -1, \quad y = -t, \quad z = \pi + t$$

The graph of the helix and this tangent line are shown in Figure 12.2.5. ◄

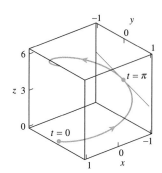

▲ **Figure 12.2.5**

▶ **Example 4**   Let

$$\mathbf{r}_1(t) = (\tan^{-1} t)\mathbf{i} + (\sin t)\mathbf{j} + t^2 \mathbf{k}$$

and

$$\mathbf{r}_2(t) = (t^2 - t)\mathbf{i} + (2t - 2)\mathbf{j} + (\ln t)\mathbf{k}$$

The graphs of $\mathbf{r}_1(t)$ and $\mathbf{r}_2(t)$ intersect at the origin. Find the degree measure of the acute angle between the tangent lines to the graphs of $\mathbf{r}_1(t)$ and $\mathbf{r}_2(t)$ at the origin.

*Solution.*   The graph of $\mathbf{r}_1(t)$ passes through the origin at $t = 0$, where its tangent vector is

$$\mathbf{r}_1'(0) = \left\langle \frac{1}{1 + t^2}, \cos t, 2t \right\rangle \Bigg|_{t=0} = \langle 1, 1, 0 \rangle$$

The graph of $\mathbf{r}_2(t)$ passes through the origin at $t = 1$ (verify), where its tangent vector is

$$\mathbf{r}_2'(1) = \left\langle 2t - 1, 2, \frac{1}{t} \right\rangle \Bigg|_{t=1} = \langle 1, 2, 1 \rangle$$

By Theorem 11.3.3, the angle $\theta$ between these two tangent vectors satisfies

$$\cos \theta = \frac{\langle 1, 1, 0 \rangle \cdot \langle 1, 2, 1 \rangle}{\|\langle 1, 1, 0 \rangle\| \, \|\langle 1, 2, 1 \rangle\|} = \frac{1 + 2 + 0}{\sqrt{2}\sqrt{6}} = \frac{3}{\sqrt{12}} = \frac{\sqrt{3}}{2}$$

It follows that $\theta = \pi/6$ radians, or $30°$. ◄

■ **DERIVATIVES OF DOT AND CROSS PRODUCTS**

The following rules, which are derived in the exercises, provide a method for differentiating dot products in 2-space and 3-space and cross products in 3-space.

Note that in (6) the order of the factors in each term on the right does not matter, but in (7) it does.

$$\frac{d}{dt}[\mathbf{r}_1(t) \cdot \mathbf{r}_2(t)] = \mathbf{r}_1(t) \cdot \frac{d\mathbf{r}_2}{dt} + \frac{d\mathbf{r}_1}{dt} \cdot \mathbf{r}_2(t) \tag{6}$$

$$\frac{d}{dt}[\mathbf{r}_1(t) \times \mathbf{r}_2(t)] = \mathbf{r}_1(t) \times \frac{d\mathbf{r}_2}{dt} + \frac{d\mathbf{r}_1}{dt} \times \mathbf{r}_2(t) \tag{7}$$

In plane geometry one learns that a tangent line to a circle is perpendicular to the radius at the point of tangency. Consequently, if a point moves along a circle in 2-space that is centered at the origin, then one would expect the radius vector and the tangent vector at any point on the circle to be orthogonal. This is the motivation for the following useful theorem, which is applicable in both 2-space and 3-space.

> **12.2.8 THEOREM** *If $\mathbf{r}(t)$ is a differentiable vector-valued function in 2-space or 3-space and $\|\mathbf{r}(t)\|$ is constant for all $t$, then*
>
> $$\mathbf{r}(t) \cdot \mathbf{r}'(t) = 0 \qquad (8)$$
>
> *that is, $\mathbf{r}(t)$ and $\mathbf{r}'(t)$ are orthogonal vectors for all $t$.*

**PROOF** It follows from (6) with $\mathbf{r}_1(t) = \mathbf{r}_2(t) = \mathbf{r}(t)$ that

$$\frac{d}{dt}[\mathbf{r}(t) \cdot \mathbf{r}(t)] = \mathbf{r}(t) \cdot \frac{d\mathbf{r}}{dt} + \frac{d\mathbf{r}}{dt} \cdot \mathbf{r}(t)$$

or, equivalently,

$$\frac{d}{dt}[\|\mathbf{r}(t)\|^2] = 2\mathbf{r}(t) \cdot \frac{d\mathbf{r}}{dt} \qquad (9)$$

But $\|\mathbf{r}(t)\|^2$ is constant, so its derivative is zero. Thus

$$2\mathbf{r}(t) \cdot \frac{d\mathbf{r}}{dt} = 0$$

from which (8) follows. ∎

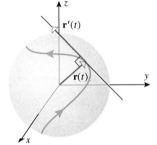

▲ Figure 12.2.6

▶ **Example 5** Just as a tangent line to a circle in 2-space is perpendicular to the radius at the point of tangency, so a tangent vector to a curve on the surface of a sphere in 3-space that is centered at the origin is orthogonal to the radius vector at the point of tangency (Figure 12.2.6). To see that this is so, suppose that the graph of $\mathbf{r}(t)$ lies on the surface of a sphere of positive radius $k$ centered at the origin. For each value of $t$ we have $\|\mathbf{r}(t)\| = k$, so by Theorem 12.2.8

$$\mathbf{r}(t) \cdot \mathbf{r}'(t) = 0$$

and hence the radius vector $\mathbf{r}(t)$ and the tangent vector $\mathbf{r}'(t)$ are orthogonal. ◀

## DEFINITE INTEGRALS OF VECTOR-VALUED FUNCTIONS

If $\mathbf{r}(t)$ is a vector-valued function that is continuous on the interval $a \le t \le b$, then we define the *definite integral* of $\mathbf{r}(t)$ over this interval as a limit of Riemann sums, just as in Definition 5.5.1, except here the integrand is a vector-valued function. Specifically, we define

$$\int_a^b \mathbf{r}(t)\,dt = \lim_{\max \Delta t_k \to 0} \sum_{k=1}^n \mathbf{r}(t_k^*)\Delta t_k \qquad (10)$$

It follows from (10) that the definite integral of $\mathbf{r}(t)$ over the interval $a \le t \le b$ can be expressed as a vector whose components are the definite integrals of the component functions of $\mathbf{r}(t)$. For example, if $\mathbf{r}(t) = x(t)\mathbf{i} + y(t)\mathbf{j}$, then

$$\int_a^b \mathbf{r}(t)\,dt = \lim_{\max \Delta t_k \to 0} \sum_{k=1}^n \mathbf{r}(t_k^*)\Delta t_k$$

$$= \lim_{\max \Delta t_k \to 0} \left[ \left( \sum_{k=1}^n x(t_k^*)\Delta t_k \right)\mathbf{i} + \left( \sum_{k=1}^n y(t_k^*)\Delta t_k \right)\mathbf{j} \right]$$

$$= \left( \lim_{\max \Delta t_k \to 0} \sum_{k=1}^n x(t_k^*)\Delta t_k \right)\mathbf{i} + \left( \lim_{\max \Delta t_k \to 0} \sum_{k=1}^n y(t_k^*)\Delta t_k \right)\mathbf{j}$$

$$= \left( \int_a^b x(t)\,dt \right)\mathbf{i} + \left( \int_a^b y(t)\,dt \right)\mathbf{j}$$

Rewrite Formulas (11) and (12) in bracket notation with

$$\mathbf{r}(t) = \langle x(t), y(t) \rangle$$

and

$$\mathbf{r}(t) = \langle x(t), y(t), z(t) \rangle$$

respectively.

In general, we have

$$\int_a^b \mathbf{r}(t)\,dt = \left( \int_a^b x(t)\,dt \right) \mathbf{i} + \left( \int_a^b y(t)\,dt \right) \mathbf{j} \qquad \boxed{\text{2-space}} \qquad (11)$$

$$\int_a^b \mathbf{r}(t)\,dt = \left( \int_a^b x(t)\,dt \right) \mathbf{i} + \left( \int_a^b y(t)\,dt \right) \mathbf{j} + \left( \int_a^b z(t)\,dt \right) \mathbf{k} \qquad \boxed{\text{3-space}} \qquad (12)$$

▶ **Example 6** Let $\mathbf{r}(t) = t^2 \mathbf{i} + e^t \mathbf{j} - (2\cos \pi t)\mathbf{k}$. Then

$$\int_0^1 \mathbf{r}(t)\,dt = \left( \int_0^1 t^2\,dt \right) \mathbf{i} + \left( \int_0^1 e^t\,dt \right) \mathbf{j} - \left( \int_0^1 2\cos \pi t\,dt \right) \mathbf{k}$$

$$= \frac{t^3}{3}\Bigg]_0^1 \mathbf{i} + e^t \Bigg]_0^1 \mathbf{j} - \frac{2}{\pi} \sin \pi t \Bigg]_0^1 \mathbf{k} = \frac{1}{3}\mathbf{i} + (e - 1)\mathbf{j} \blacktriangleleft$$

■ **RULES OF INTEGRATION**

As with differentiation, many of the rules for integrating real-valued functions have analogs for vector-valued functions.

> **12.2.9** THEOREM (*Rules of Integration*) *Let* $\mathbf{r}(t)$, $\mathbf{r}_1(t)$, *and* $\mathbf{r}_2(t)$ *be vector-valued functions in 2-space or 3-space that are continuous on the interval* $a \le t \le b$, *and let k be a scalar. Then the following rules of integration hold:*
>
> (a) $\displaystyle \int_a^b k\mathbf{r}(t)\,dt = k \int_a^b \mathbf{r}(t)\,dt$
>
> (b) $\displaystyle \int_a^b [\mathbf{r}_1(t) + \mathbf{r}_2(t)]\,dt = \int_a^b \mathbf{r}_1(t)\,dt + \int_a^b \mathbf{r}_2(t)\,dt$
>
> (c) $\displaystyle \int_a^b [\mathbf{r}_1(t) - \mathbf{r}_2(t)]\,dt = \int_a^b \mathbf{r}_1(t)\,dt - \int_a^b \mathbf{r}_2(t)\,dt$

We omit the proof.

■ **ANTIDERIVATIVES OF VECTOR-VALUED FUNCTIONS**

An *antiderivative* for a vector-valued function $\mathbf{r}(t)$ is a vector-valued function $\mathbf{R}(t)$ such that

$$\mathbf{R}'(t) = \mathbf{r}(t) \qquad (13)$$

As in Chapter 5, we express Equation (13) using integral notation as

$$\int \mathbf{r}(t)\,dt = \mathbf{R}(t) + \mathbf{C} \qquad (14)$$

where $\mathbf{C}$ represents an arbitrary constant *vector*.

Since differentiation of vector-valued functions can be performed componentwise, it follows that antidifferentiation can be done this way as well. This is illustrated in the next example.

▶ **Example 7**

$$\int (2t\mathbf{i} + 3t^2\mathbf{j})\, dt = \left(\int 2t\, dt\right)\mathbf{i} + \left(\int 3t^2\, dt\right)\mathbf{j}$$

$$= (t^2 + C_1)\mathbf{i} + (t^3 + C_2)\mathbf{j}$$

$$= (t^2\mathbf{i} + t^3\mathbf{j}) + (C_1\mathbf{i} + C_2\mathbf{j}) = (t^2\mathbf{i} + t^3\mathbf{j}) + \mathbf{C}$$

where $\mathbf{C} = C_1\mathbf{i} + C_2\mathbf{j}$ is an arbitrary vector constant of integration. ◀

Most of the familiar integration properties have vector counterparts. For example, vector differentiation and integration are inverse operations in the sense that

$$\frac{d}{dt}\left[\int \mathbf{r}(t)\, dt\right] = \mathbf{r}(t) \qquad \text{and} \qquad \int \mathbf{r}'(t)\, dt = \mathbf{r}(t) + \mathbf{C} \qquad (15\text{--}16)$$

Moreover, if $\mathbf{R}(t)$ is an antiderivative of $\mathbf{r}(t)$ on an interval containing $t = a$ and $t = b$, then we have the following vector form of the Fundamental Theorem of Calculus:

$$\int_a^b \mathbf{r}(t)\, dt = \mathbf{R}(t)\Big]_a^b = \mathbf{R}(b) - \mathbf{R}(a) \qquad (17)$$

▶ **Example 8**   Evaluate the definite integral $\displaystyle\int_0^2 (2t\mathbf{i} + 3t^2\mathbf{j})\, dt$.

*Solution.*   Integrating the components yields

$$\int_0^2 (2t\mathbf{i} + 3t^2\mathbf{j})\, dt = t^2\Big]_0^2 \mathbf{i} + t^3\Big]_0^2 \mathbf{j} = 4\mathbf{i} + 8\mathbf{j}$$

*Alternative Solution.*   The function $\mathbf{R}(t) = t^2\mathbf{i} + t^3\mathbf{j}$ is an antiderivative of the integrand since $\mathbf{R}'(t) = 2t\mathbf{i} + 3t^2\mathbf{j}$. Thus, it follows from (17) that

$$\int_0^2 (2t\mathbf{i} + 3t^2\mathbf{j})\, dt = \mathbf{R}(t)\Big]_0^2 = t^2\mathbf{i} + t^3\mathbf{j}\Big]_0^2 = (4\mathbf{i} + 8\mathbf{j}) - (0\mathbf{i} + 0\mathbf{j}) = 4\mathbf{i} + 8\mathbf{j} \blacktriangleleft$$

▶ **Example 9**   Find $\mathbf{r}(t)$ given that $\mathbf{r}'(t) = \langle 3, 2t\rangle$ and $\mathbf{r}(1) = \langle 2, 5\rangle$.

*Solution.*   Integrating $\mathbf{r}'(t)$ to obtain $\mathbf{r}(t)$ yields

$$\mathbf{r}(t) = \int \mathbf{r}'(t)\, dt = \int \langle 3, 2t\rangle\, dt = \langle 3t, t^2\rangle + \mathbf{C}$$

where $\mathbf{C}$ is a vector constant of integration. To find the value of $\mathbf{C}$ we substitute $t = 1$ and use the given value of $\mathbf{r}(1)$ to obtain

$$\mathbf{r}(1) = \langle 3, 1\rangle + \mathbf{C} = \langle 2, 5\rangle$$

so that $\mathbf{C} = \langle -1, 4\rangle$. Thus,

$$\mathbf{r}(t) = \langle 3t, t^2\rangle + \langle -1, 4\rangle = \langle 3t - 1, t^2 + 4\rangle \blacktriangleleft$$

✔ **QUICK CHECK EXERCISES 12.2** (*See page 858 for answers.*)

1. (a) $\lim\limits_{t \to 3} (t^2\mathbf{i} + 2t\mathbf{j}) = $ _____

   (b) $\lim\limits_{t \to \pi/4} \langle \cos t, \sin t \rangle = $ _____

2. Find $\mathbf{r}'(t)$.

   (a) $\mathbf{r}(t) = (4 + 5t)\mathbf{i} + (t - t^2)\mathbf{j}$

   (b) $\mathbf{r}(t) = \left\langle \dfrac{1}{t}, \tan t, e^{2t} \right\rangle$

3. Suppose that $\mathbf{r}_1(0) = \langle 3, 2, 1 \rangle$, $\mathbf{r}_2(0) = \langle 1, 2, 3 \rangle$, $\mathbf{r}_1'(0) = \langle 0, 0, 0 \rangle$, and $\mathbf{r}_2'(0) = \langle -6, -4, -2 \rangle$. Use this in-

formation to evaluate the derivative of each function at $t = 0$.

   (a) $\mathbf{r}(t) = 2\mathbf{r}_1(t) - \mathbf{r}_2(t)$

   (b) $\mathbf{r}(t) = \cos t \, \mathbf{r}_1(t) + e^{2t}\mathbf{r}_2(t)$

   (c) $\mathbf{r}(t) = \mathbf{r}_1(t) \times \mathbf{r}_2(t)$

   (d) $f(t) = \mathbf{r}_1(t) \cdot \mathbf{r}_2(t)$

4. (a) $\displaystyle\int_0^1 \langle 2t, t^2, \sin \pi t \rangle \, dt = $ _____

   (b) $\displaystyle\int (t\mathbf{i} - 3t^2\mathbf{j} + e^t\mathbf{k}) \, dt = $ _____

---

**EXERCISE SET 12.2** 〰 Graphing Utility

---

**1–4** Find the limit. ▪

1. $\lim\limits_{t \to +\infty} \left\langle \dfrac{t^2 + 1}{3t^2 + 2}, \dfrac{1}{t} \right\rangle$

2. $\lim\limits_{t \to 0^+} \left( \sqrt{t}\,\mathbf{i} + \dfrac{\sin t}{t}\mathbf{j} \right)$

3. $\lim\limits_{t \to 2} (t\mathbf{i} - 3\mathbf{j} + t^2\mathbf{k})$

4. $\lim\limits_{t \to 1} \left\langle \dfrac{3}{t^2}, \dfrac{\ln t}{t^2 - 1}, \sin 2t \right\rangle$

**5–6** Determine whether $\mathbf{r}(t)$ is continuous at $t = 0$. Explain your reasoning. ▪

5. (a) $\mathbf{r}(t) = 3 \sin t\,\mathbf{i} - 2t\mathbf{j}$
   (b) $\mathbf{r}(t) = t^2\mathbf{i} + \dfrac{1}{t}\mathbf{j} + t\mathbf{k}$

6. (a) $\mathbf{r}(t) = e^t\mathbf{i} + \mathbf{j} + \csc t\,\mathbf{k}$
   (b) $\mathbf{r}(t) = 5\mathbf{i} - \sqrt{3t + 1}\,\mathbf{j} + e^{2t}\mathbf{k}$

7. Sketch the circle $\mathbf{r}(t) = \cos t\,\mathbf{i} + \sin t\,\mathbf{j}$, and in each part draw the vector with its correct length.
   (a) $\mathbf{r}'(\pi/4)$　(b) $\mathbf{r}''(\pi)$　(c) $\mathbf{r}(2\pi) - \mathbf{r}(3\pi/2)$

8. Sketch the circle $\mathbf{r}(t) = \cos t\,\mathbf{i} - \sin t\,\mathbf{j}$, and in each part draw the vector with its correct length.
   (a) $\mathbf{r}'(\pi/4)$　(b) $\mathbf{r}''(\pi)$　(c) $\mathbf{r}(2\pi) - \mathbf{r}(3\pi/2)$

**9–10** Find $\mathbf{r}'(t)$. ▪

9. $\mathbf{r}(t) = 4\mathbf{i} - \cos t\,\mathbf{j}$

10. $\mathbf{r}(t) = (\tan^{-1} t)\mathbf{i} + t \cos t\,\mathbf{j} - \sqrt{t}\,\mathbf{k}$

**11–14** Find the vector $\mathbf{r}'(t_0)$; then sketch the graph of $\mathbf{r}(t)$ in 2-space and draw the tangent vector $\mathbf{r}'(t_0)$. ▪

11. $\mathbf{r}(t) = \langle t, t^2 \rangle$; $t_0 = 2$　12. $\mathbf{r}(t) = t^3\mathbf{i} + t^2\mathbf{j}$; $t_0 = 1$

13. $\mathbf{r}(t) = \sec t\,\mathbf{i} + \tan t\,\mathbf{j}$; $t_0 = 0$

14. $\mathbf{r}(t) = 2 \sin t\,\mathbf{i} + 3 \cos t\,\mathbf{j}$; $t_0 = \pi/6$

**15–16** Find the vector $\mathbf{r}'(t_0)$; then sketch the graph of $\mathbf{r}(t)$ in 3-space and draw the tangent vector $\mathbf{r}'(t_0)$. ▪

15. $\mathbf{r}(t) = 2 \sin t\,\mathbf{i} + \mathbf{j} + 2 \cos t\,\mathbf{k}$; $t_0 = \pi/2$

16. $\mathbf{r}(t) = \cos t\,\mathbf{i} + \sin t\,\mathbf{j} + t\mathbf{k}$; $t_0 = \pi/4$

〰 **17–18** Use a graphing utility to generate the graph of $\mathbf{r}(t)$ and the graph of the tangent line at $t_0$ on the same screen. ▪

17. $\mathbf{r}(t) = \sin \pi t\,\mathbf{i} + t^2\mathbf{j}$; $t_0 = \frac{1}{2}$

18. $\mathbf{r}(t) = 3 \sin t\,\mathbf{i} + 4 \cos t\,\mathbf{j}$; $t_0 = \pi/4$

**19–22** Find parametric equations of the line tangent to the graph of $\mathbf{r}(t)$ at the point where $t = t_0$. ▪

19. $\mathbf{r}(t) = t^2\mathbf{i} + (2 - \ln t)\mathbf{j}$; $t_0 = 1$

20. $\mathbf{r}(t) = e^{2t}\mathbf{i} - 2 \cos 3t\,\mathbf{j}$; $t_0 = 0$

21. $\mathbf{r}(t) = 2 \cos \pi t\,\mathbf{i} + 2 \sin \pi t\,\mathbf{j} + 3t\mathbf{k}$; $t_0 = \frac{1}{3}$

22. $\mathbf{r}(t) = \ln t\,\mathbf{i} + e^{-t}\mathbf{j} + t^3\mathbf{k}$; $t_0 = 2$

**23–26** Find a vector equation of the line tangent to the graph of $\mathbf{r}(t)$ at the point $P_0$ on the curve. ▪

23. $\mathbf{r}(t) = (2t - 1)\mathbf{i} + \sqrt{3t + 4}\,\mathbf{j}$; $P_0(-1, 2)$

24. $\mathbf{r}(t) = 4 \cos t\,\mathbf{i} - 3t\mathbf{j}$; $P_0(2, -\pi)$

25. $\mathbf{r}(t) = t^2\mathbf{i} - \dfrac{1}{t + 1}\mathbf{j} + (4 - t^2)\mathbf{k}$; $P_0(4, 1, 0)$

26. $\mathbf{r}(t) = \sin t\,\mathbf{i} + \cosh t\,\mathbf{j} + (\tan^{-1} t)\mathbf{k}$; $P_0(0, 1, 0)$

27. Let $\mathbf{r}(t) = \cos t\,\mathbf{i} + \sin t\,\mathbf{j} + \mathbf{k}$. Find
   (a) $\lim\limits_{t \to 0} (\mathbf{r}(t) - \mathbf{r}'(t))$　　(b) $\lim\limits_{t \to 0} (\mathbf{r}(t) \times \mathbf{r}'(t))$
   (c) $\lim\limits_{t \to 0} (\mathbf{r}(t) \cdot \mathbf{r}'(t))$.

28. Let $\mathbf{r}(t) = t\mathbf{i} + t^2\mathbf{j} + t^3\mathbf{k}$. Find
   $$\lim\limits_{t \to 1} \mathbf{r}(t) \cdot (\mathbf{r}'(t) \times \mathbf{r}''(t))$$

**29–30** Calculate
$$\dfrac{d}{dt}[\mathbf{r}_1(t) \cdot \mathbf{r}_2(t)] \quad \text{and} \quad \dfrac{d}{dt}[\mathbf{r}_1(t) \times \mathbf{r}_2(t)]$$
first by differentiating the product directly and then by applying Formulas (6) and (7). ▪

29. $\mathbf{r}_1(t) = 2t\mathbf{i} + 3t^2\mathbf{j} + t^3\mathbf{k}$, $\mathbf{r}_2(t) = t^4\mathbf{k}$

30. $\mathbf{r}_1(t) = \cos t\,\mathbf{i} + \sin t\,\mathbf{j} + t\mathbf{k}$, $\mathbf{r}_2(t) = \mathbf{i} + t\mathbf{k}$

**31–34** Evaluate the indefinite integral. ▪

**31.** $\displaystyle\int (3\mathbf{i} + 4t\mathbf{j})\, dt$

**32.** $\displaystyle\int \left(t^2\mathbf{i} - 2t\mathbf{j} + \frac{1}{t}\mathbf{k}\right) dt$

**33.** $\displaystyle\int \langle te^t, \ln t\rangle\, dt$

**34.** $\displaystyle\int \langle e^{-t}, e^t, 3t^2\rangle\, dt$

**35–40** Evaluate the definite integral. ■

**35.** $\displaystyle\int_0^{\pi/2} \langle \cos 2t, \sin 2t\rangle\, dt$

**36.** $\displaystyle\int_0^1 (t^2\mathbf{i} + t^3\mathbf{j})\, dt$

**37.** $\displaystyle\int_0^2 \|t\mathbf{i} + t^2\mathbf{j}\|\, dt$

**38.** $\displaystyle\int_{-3}^3 \langle (3-t)^{3/2}, (3+t)^{3/2}, 1\rangle\, dt$

**39.** $\displaystyle\int_1^9 (t^{1/2}\mathbf{i} + t^{-1/2}\mathbf{j})\, dt$

**40.** $\displaystyle\int_0^1 (e^{2t}\mathbf{i} + e^{-t}\mathbf{j} + t\mathbf{k})\, dt$

**41–44 True–False** Determine whether the statement is true or false. Explain your answer. ■

**41.** If a vector-valued function $\mathbf{r}(t)$ is continuous at $t = a$, then the limit
$$\lim_{h \to 0} \frac{\mathbf{r}(a+h) - \mathbf{r}(a)}{h}$$
exists.

**42.** If $\mathbf{r}(t)$ is a vector-valued function in 2-space and $\|\mathbf{r}(t)\|$ is constant, then $\mathbf{r}(t)$ and $\mathbf{r}'(t)$ are parallel vectors for all $t$.

**43.** If $\mathbf{r}(t)$ is a vector-valued function that is continuous on the interval $a \leq t \leq b$, then
$$\int_a^b \mathbf{r}(t)\, dt$$
is a vector.

**44.** If $\mathbf{r}(t)$ is a vector-valued function that is continuous on the interval $[a, b]$, then for $a < t < b$,
$$\frac{d}{dt}\left[\int_a^t \mathbf{r}(u)\, du\right] = \mathbf{r}(t)$$

**45–48** Solve the vector initial-value problem for $\mathbf{y}(t)$ by integrating and using the initial conditions to find the constants of integration. ■

**45.** $\mathbf{y}'(t) = 2t\mathbf{i} + 3t^2\mathbf{j}, \quad \mathbf{y}(0) = \mathbf{i} - \mathbf{j}$

**46.** $\mathbf{y}'(t) = \cos t\mathbf{i} + \sin t\mathbf{j}, \quad \mathbf{y}(0) = \mathbf{i} - \mathbf{j}$

**47.** $\mathbf{y}''(t) = \mathbf{i} + e^t\mathbf{j}, \quad \mathbf{y}(0) = 2\mathbf{i}, \quad \mathbf{y}'(0) = \mathbf{j}$

**48.** $\mathbf{y}''(t) = 12t^2\mathbf{i} - 2t\mathbf{j}, \quad \mathbf{y}(0) = 2\mathbf{i} - 4\mathbf{j}, \quad \mathbf{y}'(0) = \mathbf{0}$

**49.** (a) Find the points where the curve
$$\mathbf{r} = t\mathbf{i} + t^2\mathbf{j} - 3t\mathbf{k}$$
intersects the plane $2x - y + z = -2$.

(b) For the curve and plane in part (a), find, to the nearest degree, the acute angle that the tangent line to the curve makes with a line normal to the plane at each point of intersection.

**50.** Find where the tangent line to the curve
$$\mathbf{r} = e^{-2t}\mathbf{i} + \cos t\mathbf{j} + 3\sin t\mathbf{k}$$
at the point $(1, 1, 0)$ intersects the $yz$-plane.

**51–52** Show that the graphs of $\mathbf{r}_1(t)$ and $\mathbf{r}_2(t)$ intersect at the point $P$. Find, to the nearest degree, the acute angle between the tangent lines to the graphs of $\mathbf{r}_1(t)$ and $\mathbf{r}_2(t)$ at the point $P$. ■

**51.** $\mathbf{r}_1(t) = t^2\mathbf{i} + t\mathbf{j} + 3t^3\mathbf{k}$
$\mathbf{r}_2(t) = (t-1)\mathbf{i} + \frac{1}{4}t^2\mathbf{j} + (5-t)\mathbf{k}; \quad P(1, 1, 3)$

**52.** $\mathbf{r}_1(t) = 2e^{-t}\mathbf{i} + \cos t\mathbf{j} + (t^2 + 3)\mathbf{k}$
$\mathbf{r}_2(t) = (1-t)\mathbf{i} + t^2\mathbf{j} + (t^3 + 4)\mathbf{k}; \quad P(2, 1, 3)$

**FOCUS ON CONCEPTS**

**53.** Use Formula (7) to derive the differentiation formula
$$\frac{d}{dt}[\mathbf{r}(t) \times \mathbf{r}'(t)] = \mathbf{r}(t) \times \mathbf{r}''(t)$$

**54.** Let $\mathbf{u} = \mathbf{u}(t)$, $\mathbf{v} = \mathbf{v}(t)$, and $\mathbf{w} = \mathbf{w}(t)$ be differentiable vector-valued functions. Use Formulas (6) and (7) to show that
$$\frac{d}{dt}[\mathbf{u} \cdot (\mathbf{v} \times \mathbf{w})]$$
$$= \frac{d\mathbf{u}}{dt} \cdot [\mathbf{v} \times \mathbf{w}] + \mathbf{u} \cdot \left[\frac{d\mathbf{v}}{dt} \times \mathbf{w}\right] + \mathbf{u} \cdot \left[\mathbf{v} \times \frac{d\mathbf{w}}{dt}\right]$$

**55.** Let $u_1$, $u_2$, $u_3$, $v_1$, $v_2$, $v_3$, $w_1$, $w_2$, and $w_3$ be differentiable functions of $t$. Use Exercise 54 to show that
$$\frac{d}{dt}\begin{vmatrix} u_1 & u_2 & u_3 \\ v_1 & v_2 & v_3 \\ w_1 & w_2 & w_3 \end{vmatrix}$$
$$= \begin{vmatrix} u_1' & u_2' & u_3' \\ v_1 & v_2 & v_3 \\ w_1 & w_2 & w_3 \end{vmatrix} + \begin{vmatrix} u_1 & u_2 & u_3 \\ v_1' & v_2' & v_3' \\ w_1 & w_2 & w_3 \end{vmatrix} + \begin{vmatrix} u_1 & u_2 & u_3 \\ v_1 & v_2 & v_3 \\ w_1' & w_2' & w_3' \end{vmatrix}$$

**56.** Prove Theorem 12.2.6 for 2-space.

**57.** Derive Formulas (6) and (7) for 3-space.

**58.** Prove Theorem 12.2.9 for 2-space.

**59. Writing** Explain what it means for a vector-valued function $\mathbf{r}(t)$ to be differentiable, and discuss geometric interpretations of $\mathbf{r}'(t)$.

**60. Writing** Let $\mathbf{r}(t) = \langle t^2, t^3 + 1\rangle$ and define $\theta(t)$ to be the angle between $\mathbf{r}(t)$ and $\mathbf{r}'(t)$. The graph of $\theta = \theta(t)$ is shown in the accompanying figure. Interpret important features of this graph in terms of information about $\mathbf{r}(t)$ and $\mathbf{r}'(t)$. Accompany your discussion with a graph of $\mathbf{r}(t)$, highlighting particular instances of the vectors $\mathbf{r}(t)$ and $\mathbf{r}'(t)$.

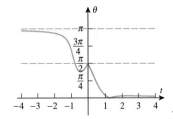

◀ **Figure Ex-60**

✔ **QUICK CHECK ANSWERS 12.2**

1. (a) $9\mathbf{i} + 6\mathbf{j}$ (b) $\left\langle \dfrac{\sqrt{2}}{2}, \dfrac{\sqrt{2}}{2} \right\rangle$   2. (a) $\mathbf{r}'(t) = 5\mathbf{i} + (1 - 2t)\mathbf{j}$ (b) $\mathbf{r}'(t) = \left\langle -\dfrac{1}{t^2}, \sec^2 t, 2e^{2t} \right\rangle$   3. (a) $\langle 6, 4, 2 \rangle$ (b) $\langle -4, 0, 4 \rangle$

(c) $\mathbf{0}$ (d) $-28$   4. (a) $\left\langle 1, \dfrac{1}{3}, \dfrac{2}{\pi} \right\rangle$ (b) $\dfrac{t^2}{2}\mathbf{i} - t^3\mathbf{j} + e^t\mathbf{k} + \mathbf{C}$

---

## 12.3 CHANGE OF PARAMETER; ARC LENGTH

*We observed in earlier sections that a curve in 2-space or 3-space can be represented parametrically in more than one way. For example, in Section 10.1 we gave two parametric representations of a circle—one in which the circle was traced clockwise and the other in which it was traced counterclockwise. Sometimes it will be desirable to change the parameter for a parametric curve to a different parameter that is better suited for the problem at hand. In this section we will investigate issues associated with changes of parameter, and we will show that arc length plays a special role in parametric representations of curves.*

■ **SMOOTH PARAMETRIZATIONS**

Graphs of vector-valued functions range from continuous and smooth to discontinuous and wildly erratic. In this text we will not be concerned with graphs of the latter type, so we will need to impose restrictions to eliminate the unwanted behavior. We will say that a curve represented by $\mathbf{r}(t)$ is *smoothly parametrized* by $\mathbf{r}(t)$, or that $\mathbf{r}(t)$ is a *smooth function* of $t$ if $\mathbf{r}'(t)$ is continuous and $\mathbf{r}'(t) \neq \mathbf{0}$ for any allowable value of $t$. Geometrically, this means that a smoothly parametrized curve can have no abrupt changes in direction as the parameter increases.

Mathematically, "smoothness" is a property of the *parametrization* and not of the curve itself. Exercise 38 gives an example of a curve that is well-behaved geometrically and has one parametrization that is smooth and another that is not.

▶ **Example 1**   Determine whether the following vector-valued functions are smooth.

(a) $\mathbf{r}(t) = a \cos t \mathbf{i} + a \sin t \mathbf{j} + ct\mathbf{k}$   $(a > 0, c > 0)$
(b) $\mathbf{r}(t) = t^2\mathbf{i} + t^3\mathbf{j}$

*Solution (a).*   We have

$$\mathbf{r}'(t) = -a \sin t \mathbf{i} + a \cos t \mathbf{j} + c\mathbf{k}$$

The components are continuous functions, and there is no value of $t$ for which all three of them are zero (verify), so $\mathbf{r}(t)$ is a smooth function. The graph of $\mathbf{r}(t)$ is the circular helix in Figure 12.1.2.

*Solution (b).*   We have
$$\mathbf{r}'(t) = 2t\mathbf{i} + 3t^2\mathbf{j}$$

Although the components are continuous functions, they are both equal to zero if $t = 0$, so $\mathbf{r}(t)$ is not a smooth function. The graph of $\mathbf{r}(t)$, which is shown in Figure 12.3.1, is a semicubical parabola traced in the upward direction (see Example 6 of Section 10.1). Observe that for values of $t$ slightly less than zero the angle between $\mathbf{r}'(t)$ and $\mathbf{i}$ is near $\pi$, and for values of $t$ slightly larger than zero the angle is near 0; hence there is a sudden reversal in the direction of the tangent vector as $t$ increases through $t = 0$ (see Exercise 44).   ◀

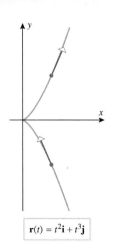

$\mathbf{r}(t) = t^2\mathbf{i} + t^3\mathbf{j}$

▲ **Figure 12.3.1**

■ ARC LENGTH FROM THE VECTOR VIEWPOINT

Recall from Theorem 10.1.1 that the arc length $L$ of a parametric curve

$$x = x(t), \quad y = y(t) \qquad (a \le t \le b) \tag{1}$$

is given by the formula

$$L = \int_a^b \sqrt{\left(\frac{dx}{dt}\right)^2 + \left(\frac{dy}{dt}\right)^2}\, dt \tag{2}$$

Analogously, the arc length $L$ of a parametric curve

$$x = x(t), \quad y = y(t), \quad z = z(t) \qquad (a \le t \le b) \tag{3}$$

in 3-space is given by the formula

$$L = \int_a^b \sqrt{\left(\frac{dx}{dt}\right)^2 + \left(\frac{dy}{dt}\right)^2 + \left(\frac{dz}{dt}\right)^2}\, dt \tag{4}$$

Formulas (2) and (4) have vector forms that we can obtain by letting

$$\mathbf{r}(t) = x(t)\mathbf{i} + y(t)\mathbf{j} \quad \text{or} \quad \mathbf{r}(t) = x(t)\mathbf{i} + y(t)\mathbf{j} + z(t)\mathbf{k}$$

$$\boxed{\text{2-space}} \qquad\qquad\qquad \boxed{\text{3-space}}$$

It follows that

$$\frac{d\mathbf{r}}{dt} = \frac{dx}{dt}\mathbf{i} + \frac{dy}{dt}\mathbf{j} \quad \text{or} \quad \frac{d\mathbf{r}}{dt} = \frac{dx}{dt}\mathbf{i} + \frac{dy}{dt}\mathbf{j} + \frac{dz}{dt}\mathbf{k}$$

$$\boxed{\text{2-space}} \qquad\qquad\qquad \boxed{\text{3-space}}$$

and hence

$$\left\|\frac{d\mathbf{r}}{dt}\right\| = \sqrt{\left(\frac{dx}{dt}\right)^2 + \left(\frac{dy}{dt}\right)^2} \quad \text{or} \quad \left\|\frac{d\mathbf{r}}{dt}\right\| = \sqrt{\left(\frac{dx}{dt}\right)^2 + \left(\frac{dy}{dt}\right)^2 + \left(\frac{dz}{dt}\right)^2}$$

$$\boxed{\text{2-space}} \qquad\qquad\qquad\qquad \boxed{\text{3-space}}$$

Substituting these expressions in (2) and (4) leads us to the following theorem.

---

**12.3.1   THEOREM**   *If C is the graph in 2-space or 3-space of a smooth vector-valued function* $\mathbf{r}(t)$, *then its arc length L from* $t = a$ *to* $t = b$ *is*

$$L = \int_a^b \left\|\frac{d\mathbf{r}}{dt}\right\| dt \tag{5}$$

---

▶ **Example 2**   Find the arc length of that portion of the circular helix

$$x = \cos t, \quad y = \sin t, \quad z = t$$

from $t = 0$ to $t = \pi$.

**Solution.**   Set $\mathbf{r}(t) = (\cos t)\mathbf{i} + (\sin t)\mathbf{j} + t\mathbf{k} = \langle \cos t, \sin t, t \rangle$. Then

$$\mathbf{r}'(t) = \langle -\sin t, \cos t, 1 \rangle \quad \text{and} \quad \|\mathbf{r}'(t)\| = \sqrt{(-\sin t)^2 + (\cos t)^2 + 1} = \sqrt{2}$$

From Theorem 12.3.1 the arc length of the helix is

$$L = \int_0^\pi \left\| \frac{d\mathbf{r}}{dt} \right\| dt = \int_0^\pi \sqrt{2}\, dt = \sqrt{2}\pi \blacktriangleleft$$

■ **ARC LENGTH AS A PARAMETER**

For many purposes the best parameter to use for representing a curve in 2-space or 3-space parametrically is the length of arc measured along the curve from some fixed reference point. This can be done as follows:

*Using Arc Length as a Parameter*

**Step 1.** Select an arbitrary point on the curve $C$ to serve as a *reference point*.

**Step 2.** Starting from the reference point, choose one direction along the curve to be the *positive direction* and the other to be the *negative direction*.

**Step 3.** If $P$ is a point on the curve, let $s$ be the "signed" arc length along $C$ from the reference point to $P$, where $s$ is positive if $P$ is in the positive direction from the reference point and $s$ is negative if $P$ is in the negative direction. Figure 12.3.2 illustrates this idea.

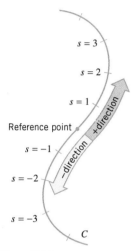

▲ **Figure 12.3.2**

By this procedure, a unique point $P$ on the curve is determined when a value for $s$ is given. For example, $s = 2$ determines the point that is 2 units along the curve in the positive direction from the reference point, and $s = -\frac{3}{2}$ determines the point that is $\frac{3}{2}$ units along the curve in the negative direction from the reference point.

Let us now treat $s$ as a variable. As the value of $s$ changes, the corresponding point $P$ moves along $C$ and the coordinates of $P$ become functions of $s$. Thus, in 2-space the coordinates of $P$ are $(x(s), y(s))$, and in 3-space they are $(x(s), y(s), z(s))$. Therefore, in 2-space or 3-space the curve $C$ is given by the parametric equations

$$x = x(s), \quad y = y(s) \quad \text{or} \quad x = x(s), \quad y = y(s), \quad z = z(s)$$

A parametric representation of a curve with arc length as the parameter is called an *arc length parametrization* of the curve. Note that a given curve will generally have infinitely many different arc length parametrizations, since the reference point and orientation can be chosen arbitrarily.

▶ **Example 3** Find the arc length parametrization of the circle $x^2 + y^2 = a^2$ with counterclockwise orientation and $(a, 0)$ as the reference point.

*Solution.* The circle with counterclockwise orientation can be represented by the parametric equations

$$x = a\cos t, \quad y = a\sin t \quad (0 \le t \le 2\pi) \tag{6}$$

in which $t$ can be interpreted as the angle in radian measure from the positive $x$-axis to the radius from the origin to the point $P(x, y)$ (Figure 12.3.3). If we take the positive direction for measuring the arc length to be counterclockwise, and we take $(a, 0)$ to be the reference point, then $s$ and $t$ are related by

$$s = at \quad \text{or} \quad t = s/a$$

Making this change of variable in (6) and noting that $s$ increases from 0 to $2\pi a$ as $t$ increases from 0 to $2\pi$ yields the following arc length parametrization of the circle:

$$x = a\cos(s/a), \quad y = a\sin(s/a) \quad (0 \le s \le 2\pi a) \blacktriangleleft$$

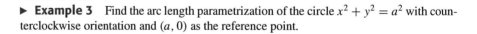

▲ **Figure 12.3.3**

### CHANGE OF PARAMETER

In many situations the solution of a problem can be simplified by choosing the parameter in a vector-valued function or a parametric curve in the right way. The two most common parameters for curves in 2-space or 3-space are time and arc length. However, there are other useful possibilities as well. For example, in analyzing the motion of a particle in 2-space, it is often desirable to parametrize its trajectory in terms of the angle $\phi$ between the tangent vector and the positive $x$-axis (Figure 12.3.4). Thus, our next objective is to develop methods for changing the parameter in a vector-valued function or parametric curve. This will allow us to move freely between different possible parametrizations.

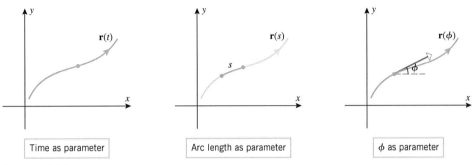

| Time as parameter | Arc length as parameter | $\phi$ as parameter |

▲ **Figure 12.3.4**

A *change of parameter* in a vector-valued function $\mathbf{r}(t)$ is a substitution $t = g(\tau)$ that produces a new vector-valued function $\mathbf{r}(g(\tau))$ having the same graph as $\mathbf{r}(t)$, but possibly traced differently as the parameter $\tau$ increases.

▶ **Example 4**   Find a change of parameter $t = g(\tau)$ for the circle

$$\mathbf{r}(t) = \cos t \mathbf{i} + \sin t \mathbf{j} \qquad (0 \le t \le 2\pi)$$

such that

(a)  the circle is traced counterclockwise as $\tau$ increases over the interval $[0, 1]$;

(b)  the circle is traced clockwise as $\tau$ increases over the interval $[0, 1]$.

*Solution (a).*   The given circle is traced counterclockwise as $t$ increases. Thus, if we choose $g$ to be an increasing function, then it will follow from the relationship $t = g(\tau)$ that $t$ increases when $\tau$ increases, thereby ensuring that the circle will be traced counterclockwise as $\tau$ increases. We also want to choose $g$ so that $t$ increases from 0 to $2\pi$ as $\tau$ increases from 0 to 1. A simple choice of $g$ that satisfies all of the required criteria is the linear function graphed in Figure 12.3.5a. The equation of this line is

$$t = g(\tau) = 2\pi\tau \tag{7}$$

which is the desired change of parameter. The resulting representation of the circle in terms of the parameter $\tau$ is

$$\mathbf{r}(g(\tau)) = \cos 2\pi\tau \mathbf{i} + \sin 2\pi\tau \mathbf{j} \qquad (0 \le \tau \le 1)$$

*Solution (b).*   To ensure that the circle is traced clockwise, we will choose $g$ to be a decreasing function such that $t$ decreases from $2\pi$ to 0 as $\tau$ increases from 0 to 1. A simple choice of $g$ that achieves this is the linear function

$$t = g(\tau) = 2\pi(1 - \tau) \tag{8}$$

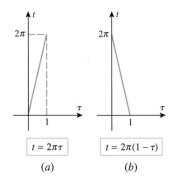

| $t = 2\pi\tau$ | $t = 2\pi(1 - \tau)$ |
| (a) | (b) |

▲ **Figure 12.3.5**

graphed in Figure 12.3.5b. The resulting representation of the circle in terms of the parameter $\tau$ is

$$\mathbf{r}(g(\tau)) = \cos(2\pi(1 - \tau))\mathbf{i} + \sin(2\pi(1 - \tau))\mathbf{j} \qquad (0 \leq \tau \leq 1)$$

which simplifies to (verify)

$$\mathbf{r}(g(\tau)) = \cos 2\pi\tau\,\mathbf{i} - \sin 2\pi\tau\,\mathbf{j} \qquad (0 \leq \tau \leq 1) \blacktriangleleft$$

When making a change of parameter $t = g(\tau)$ in a vector-valued function $\mathbf{r}(t)$, it will be important to ensure that the new vector-valued function $\mathbf{r}(g(\tau))$ is smooth if $\mathbf{r}(t)$ is smooth. To establish conditions under which this happens, we will need the following version of the chain rule for vector-valued functions. The proof is left as an exercise.

Strictly speaking, since $d\mathbf{r}/dt$ is a vector and $dt/d\tau$ is a scalar, Formula (9) should be written in the form

$$\frac{d\mathbf{r}}{d\tau} = \frac{dt}{d\tau}\frac{d\mathbf{r}}{dt}$$

(scalar first). However, reversing the order of the factors makes the formula easier to remember, and we will continue to do so.

**12.3.2** THEOREM (*Chain Rule*)   *Let $\mathbf{r}(t)$ be a vector-valued function in 2-space or 3-space that is differentiable with respect to $t$. If $t = g(\tau)$ is a change of parameter in which $g$ is differentiable with respect to $\tau$, then $\mathbf{r}(g(\tau))$ is differentiable with respect to $\tau$ and*

$$\frac{d\mathbf{r}}{d\tau} = \frac{d\mathbf{r}}{dt}\frac{dt}{d\tau} \tag{9}$$

A change of parameter $t = g(\tau)$ in which $\mathbf{r}(g(\tau))$ is smooth if $\mathbf{r}(t)$ is smooth is called a *smooth change of parameter*. It follows from (9) that $t = g(\tau)$ will be a smooth change of parameter if $dt/d\tau$ is continuous and $dt/d\tau \neq 0$ for all values of $\tau$, since these conditions imply that $d\mathbf{r}/d\tau$ is continuous and nonzero if $d\mathbf{r}/dt$ is continuous and nonzero. Smooth changes of parameter fall into two categories—those for which $dt/d\tau > 0$ for all $\tau$ (called *positive changes of parameter*) and those for which $dt/d\tau < 0$ for all $\tau$ (called *negative changes of parameter*). A positive change of parameter preserves the orientation of a parametric curve, and a negative change of parameter reverses it.

▶ **Example 5**   In Example 4 the change of parameter in Formula (7) is positive since $dt/d\tau = 2\pi > 0$, and the change of parameter given by Formula (8) is negative since $dt/d\tau = -2\pi < 0$. The positive change of parameter preserved the orientation of the circle, and the negative change of parameter reversed it. ◀

■ **FINDING ARC LENGTH PARAMETRIZATIONS**

Next we will consider the problem of finding an arc length parametrization of a vector-valued function that is expressed initially in terms of some other parameter $t$. The following theorem will provide a general method for doing this.

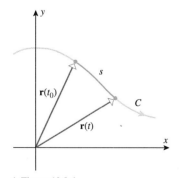

▲ **Figure 12.3.6**

**12.3.3** THEOREM   *Let $C$ be the graph of a smooth vector-valued function $\mathbf{r}(t)$ in 2-space or 3-space, and let $\mathbf{r}(t_0)$ be any point on $C$. Then the following formula defines a positive change of parameter from $t$ to $s$, where $s$ is an arc length parameter having $\mathbf{r}(t_0)$ as its reference point (Figure 12.3.6):*

$$s = \int_{t_0}^{t} \left\| \frac{d\mathbf{r}}{du} \right\| du \tag{10}$$

PROOF   From (5) with $u$ as the variable of integration instead of $t$, the integral represents the arc length of that portion of $C$ between $\mathbf{r}(t_0)$ and $\mathbf{r}(t)$ if $t > t_0$ and the negative of that arc length if $t < t_0$. Thus, $s$ is the arc length parameter with $\mathbf{r}(t_0)$ as its reference point and its positive direction in the direction of increasing $t$.   ■

When needed, Formula (10) can be expressed in component form as

$$s = \int_{t_0}^{t} \sqrt{\left(\frac{dx}{du}\right)^2 + \left(\frac{dy}{du}\right)^2}\, du \qquad \boxed{\text{2-space}} \qquad (11)$$

$$s = \int_{t_0}^{t} \sqrt{\left(\frac{dx}{du}\right)^2 + \left(\frac{dy}{du}\right)^2 + \left(\frac{dz}{du}\right)^2}\, du \qquad \boxed{\text{3-space}} \qquad (12)$$

▶ **Example 6**   Find the arc length parametrization of the circular helix

$$\mathbf{r} = \cos t\,\mathbf{i} + \sin t\,\mathbf{j} + t\mathbf{k} \qquad (13)$$

that has reference point $\mathbf{r}(0) = (1, 0, 0)$ and the same orientation as the given helix.

*Solution.*   Replacing $t$ by $u$ in $\mathbf{r}$ for integration purposes and taking $t_0 = 0$ in Formula (10), we obtain

$$\mathbf{r} = \cos u\,\mathbf{i} + \sin u\,\mathbf{j} + u\mathbf{k}$$

$$\frac{d\mathbf{r}}{du} = (-\sin u)\mathbf{i} + \cos u\,\mathbf{j} + \mathbf{k}$$

$$\left\|\frac{d\mathbf{r}}{du}\right\| = \sqrt{(-\sin u)^2 + \cos^2 u + 1} = \sqrt{2}$$

$$s = \int_{0}^{t} \left\|\frac{d\mathbf{r}}{du}\right\| du = \int_{0}^{t} \sqrt{2}\, du = \sqrt{2}\,u\Big]_{0}^{t} = \sqrt{2}\,t$$

Thus, $t = s/\sqrt{2}$, so (13) can be reparametrized in terms of $s$ as

$$\mathbf{r} = \cos\left(\frac{s}{\sqrt{2}}\right)\mathbf{i} + \sin\left(\frac{s}{\sqrt{2}}\right)\mathbf{j} + \frac{s}{\sqrt{2}}\mathbf{k}$$

We are guaranteed that this reparametrization preserves the orientation of the helix since Formula (10) produces a positive change of parameter.   ◀

▶ **Example 7**   A bug walks along the trunk of a tree following a path modeled by the circular helix in Example 6. The bug starts at the reference point $(1, 0, 0)$ and walks up the helix for a distance of 10 units. What are the bug's final coordinates?

*Solution.*   From Example 6, the arc length parametrization of the helix relative to the reference point $(1, 0, 0)$ is

$$\mathbf{r} = \cos\left(\frac{s}{\sqrt{2}}\right)\mathbf{i} + \sin\left(\frac{s}{\sqrt{2}}\right)\mathbf{j} + \frac{s}{\sqrt{2}}\mathbf{k}$$

or, expressed parametrically,

$$x = \cos\left(\frac{s}{\sqrt{2}}\right), \quad y = \sin\left(\frac{s}{\sqrt{2}}\right), \quad z = \frac{s}{\sqrt{2}}$$

Thus, at $s = 10$ the coordinates are

$$\left(\cos\left(\frac{10}{\sqrt{2}}\right), \sin\left(\frac{10}{\sqrt{2}}\right), \frac{10}{\sqrt{2}}\right) \approx (0.705, 0.709, 7.07) \blacktriangleleft$$

▶ **Example 8** Recall from Formula (9) of Section 11.5 that the equation

$$\mathbf{r} = \mathbf{r}_0 + t\mathbf{v} \tag{14}$$

is the vector form of the line that passes through the terminal point of $\mathbf{r}_0$ and is parallel to the vector $\mathbf{v}$. Find the arc length parametrization of the line that has reference point $\mathbf{r}_0$ and the same orientation as the given line.

*Solution.* Replacing $t$ by $u$ in (14) for integration purposes and taking $t_0 = 0$ in Formula (10), we obtain

$$\mathbf{r} = \mathbf{r}_0 + u\mathbf{v} \quad \text{and} \quad \frac{d\mathbf{r}}{du} = \mathbf{v} \quad \boxed{\text{Since } \mathbf{r}_0 \text{ is constant}}$$

It follows from this that

$$s = \int_0^t \left\| \frac{d\mathbf{r}}{du} \right\| du = \int_0^t \|\mathbf{v}\| \, du = \|\mathbf{v}\|u \Big]_0^t = t\|\mathbf{v}\|$$

This implies that $t = s/\|\mathbf{v}\|$, so (14) can be reparametrized in terms of $s$ as

> In words, Formula (15) tells us that the line represented by Equation (14) can be reparametrized in terms of arc length with $\mathbf{r}_0$ as the reference point by normalizing $\mathbf{v}$ and then replacing $t$ by $s$.

$$\mathbf{r} = \mathbf{r}_0 + s\left(\frac{\mathbf{v}}{\|\mathbf{v}\|}\right) \blacktriangleleft \tag{15}$$

▶ **Example 9** Find the arc length parametrization of the line

$$x = 2t + 1, \quad y = 3t - 2$$

that has the same orientation as the given line and uses $(1, -2)$ as the reference point.

*Solution.* The line passes through the point $(1, -2)$ and is parallel to $\mathbf{v} = 2\mathbf{i} + 3\mathbf{j}$. To find the arc length parametrization of the line, we need only rewrite the given equations using $\mathbf{v}/\|\mathbf{v}\|$ rather than $\mathbf{v}$ to determine the direction and replace $t$ by $s$. Since

$$\frac{\mathbf{v}}{\|\mathbf{v}\|} = \frac{2\mathbf{i} + 3\mathbf{j}}{\sqrt{13}} = \frac{2}{\sqrt{13}}\mathbf{i} + \frac{3}{\sqrt{13}}\mathbf{j}$$

it follows that the parametric equations for the line in terms of $s$ are

$$x = \frac{2}{\sqrt{13}}s + 1, \quad y = \frac{3}{\sqrt{13}}s - 2 \blacktriangleleft$$

■ **PROPERTIES OF ARC LENGTH PARAMETRIZATIONS**

Because arc length parameters for a curve $C$ are intimately related to the geometric characteristics of $C$, arc length parametrizations have properties that are not enjoyed by other parametrizations. For example, the following theorem shows that if a smooth curve is represented parametrically using an arc length parameter, then the tangent vectors all have length 1.

**12.3.4 THEOREM**

(a) *If C is the graph of a smooth vector-valued function* $\mathbf{r}(t)$ *in 2-space or 3-space, where t is a general parameter, and if s is the arc length parameter for C defined by Formula (10), then for every value of t the tangent vector has length*

$$\left\|\frac{d\mathbf{r}}{dt}\right\| = \frac{ds}{dt} \tag{16}$$

(b) *If C is the graph of a smooth vector-valued function* $\mathbf{r}(s)$ *in 2-space or 3-space, where s is an arc length parameter, then for every value of s the tangent vector to C has length*

$$\left\|\frac{d\mathbf{r}}{ds}\right\| = 1 \tag{17}$$

(c) *If C is the graph of a smooth vector-valued function* $\mathbf{r}(t)$ *in 2-space or 3-space, and if* $\|d\mathbf{r}/dt\| = 1$ *for every value of t, then for any value of* $t_0$ *in the domain of* $\mathbf{r}$, *the parameter* $s = t - t_0$ *is an arc length parameter that has its reference point at the point on C where* $t = t_0$.

**PROOF** (*a*)    This result follows by applying the Fundamental Theorem of Calculus (Theorem 5.6.3) to Formula (10).

**PROOF** (*b*)    Let $t = s$ in part (*a*).

**PROOF** (*c*)    It follows from Theorem 12.3.3 that the formula

$$s = \int_{t_0}^{t} \left\|\frac{d\mathbf{r}}{du}\right\| du$$

defines an arc length parameter for C with reference point $\mathbf{r}(0)$. However, $\|d\mathbf{r}/du\| = 1$ by hypothesis, so we can rewrite the formula for s as

$$s = \int_{t_0}^{t} du = u \Big]_{t_0}^{t} = t - t_0 \quad \blacksquare$$

The component forms of Formulas (16) and (17) will be of sufficient interest in later sections that we provide them here for reference:

$$\frac{ds}{dt} = \left\|\frac{d\mathbf{r}}{dt}\right\| = \sqrt{\left(\frac{dx}{dt}\right)^2 + \left(\frac{dy}{dt}\right)^2} \qquad \text{2-space} \tag{18}$$

$$\frac{ds}{dt} = \left\|\frac{d\mathbf{r}}{dt}\right\| = \sqrt{\left(\frac{dx}{dt}\right)^2 + \left(\frac{dy}{dt}\right)^2 + \left(\frac{dz}{dt}\right)^2} \qquad \text{3-space} \tag{19}$$

$$\left\|\frac{d\mathbf{r}}{ds}\right\| = \sqrt{\left(\frac{dx}{ds}\right)^2 + \left(\frac{dy}{ds}\right)^2} = 1 \qquad \text{2-space} \tag{20}$$

$$\left\|\frac{d\mathbf{r}}{ds}\right\| = \sqrt{\left(\frac{dx}{ds}\right)^2 + \left(\frac{dy}{ds}\right)^2 + \left(\frac{dz}{ds}\right)^2} = 1 \qquad \text{3-space} \tag{21}$$

Note that Formulas (18) and (19) do not involve $t_0$, and hence do not depend on where the reference point for s is chosen. This is to be expected since changing the reference point shifts s by a constant (the arc length between the two reference points), and this constant drops out on differentiating.

✔**QUICK CHECK EXERCISES 12.3**    *(See page 868 for answers.)*

---

**1.** If $\mathbf{r}(t)$ is a smooth vector-valued function, then the integral

$$\int_a^b \left\| \frac{d\mathbf{r}}{dt} \right\| dt$$

may be interpreted geometrically as the _____.

**2.** If $\mathbf{r}(s)$ is a smooth vector-valued function parametrized by arc length $s$, then

$$\left\| \frac{d\mathbf{r}}{ds} \right\| = \text{_____}$$

and the arc length of the graph of $\mathbf{r}$ over the interval $a \leq s \leq b$ is _____.

**3.** If $\mathbf{r}(t)$ is a smooth vector-valued function, then the arc length parameter $s$ having $\mathbf{r}(t_0)$ as the reference point may be defined by the integral

$$s = \int_{t_0}^t \text{_____}\, du$$

**4.** Suppose that $\mathbf{r}(t)$ is a smooth vector-valued function of $t$ with $\mathbf{r}'(1) = \langle \sqrt{3}, -\sqrt{3}, -1 \rangle$, and let $\mathbf{r}_1(t)$ be defined by the equation $\mathbf{r}_1(t) = \mathbf{r}(2 \cos t)$. Then $\mathbf{r}_1'(\pi/3) = $ _____.

---

**EXERCISE SET 12.3**

---

**1–4** Determine whether $\mathbf{r}(t)$ is a smooth function of the parameter $t$. ▪

**1.** $\mathbf{r}(t) = t^3 \mathbf{i} + (3t^2 - 2t)\mathbf{j} + t^2 \mathbf{k}$

**2.** $\mathbf{r}(t) = \cos t^2 \mathbf{i} + \sin t^2 \mathbf{j} + e^{-t} \mathbf{k}$

**3.** $\mathbf{r}(t) = te^{-t} \mathbf{i} + (t^2 - 2t)\mathbf{j} + \cos \pi t \mathbf{k}$

**4.** $\mathbf{r}(t) = \sin \pi t \mathbf{i} + (2t - \ln t)\mathbf{j} + (t^2 - t)\mathbf{k}$

**5–8** Find the arc length of the parametric curve. ▪

**5.** $x = \cos^3 t,\ y = \sin^3 t,\ z = 2;\ 0 \leq t \leq \pi/2$

**6.** $x = 3\cos t,\ y = 3\sin t,\ z = 4t;\ 0 \leq t \leq \pi$

**7.** $x = e^t,\ y = e^{-t},\ z = \sqrt{2}t;\ 0 \leq t \leq 1$

**8.** $x = \frac{1}{2}t,\ y = \frac{1}{3}(1-t)^{3/2},\ z = \frac{1}{3}(1+t)^{3/2};\ -1 \leq t \leq 1$

**9–12** Find the arc length of the graph of $\mathbf{r}(t)$. ▪

**9.** $\mathbf{r}(t) = t^3 \mathbf{i} + t\mathbf{j} + \frac{1}{2}\sqrt{6}t^2 \mathbf{k};\ 1 \leq t \leq 3$

**10.** $\mathbf{r}(t) = (4 + 3t)\mathbf{i} + (2 - 2t)\mathbf{j} + (5 + t)\mathbf{k};\ 3 \leq t \leq 4$

**11.** $\mathbf{r}(t) = 3\cos t \mathbf{i} + 3\sin t \mathbf{j} + t\mathbf{k};\ 0 \leq t \leq 2\pi$

**12.** $\mathbf{r}(t) = t^2 \mathbf{i} + (\cos t + t\sin t)\mathbf{j} + (\sin t - t\cos t)\mathbf{k};$ $0 \leq t \leq \pi$

**13–16** Calculate $d\mathbf{r}/d\tau$ by the chain rule, and then check your result by expressing $\mathbf{r}$ in terms of $\tau$ and differentiating. ▪

**13.** $\mathbf{r} = t\mathbf{i} + t^2 \mathbf{j};\ t = 4\tau + 1$

**14.** $\mathbf{r} = \langle 3\cos t, 3\sin t \rangle;\ t = \pi\tau$

**15.** $\mathbf{r} = e^t \mathbf{i} + 4e^{-t} \mathbf{j};\ t = \tau^2$

**16.** $\mathbf{r} = \mathbf{i} + 3t^{3/2}\mathbf{j} + t\mathbf{k};\ t = 1/\tau$

**17–20 True–False** Determine whether the statement is true or false. Explain your answer. ▪

**17.** If $\mathbf{r}(t)$ is a smooth vector-valued function in 2-space, then

$$\int_a^b \|\mathbf{r}'(t)\|\, dt$$

is a vector.

**18.** If the line $y = x$ is parametrized by the vector-valued function $\mathbf{r}(t)$, then $\mathbf{r}(t)$ is smooth.

**19.** If $\mathbf{r}(s)$ parametrizes the graph of $y = |x|$ in 2-space by arc length, then $\mathbf{r}(s)$ is smooth.

**20.** If a curve $C$ in the plane is parametrized by the smooth vector-valued function $\mathbf{r}(s)$, where $s$ is an arc length parameter, then

$$\int_{-1}^3 \|\mathbf{r}'(s)\|\, ds = 4$$

**21.** (a) Find the arc length parametrization of the line

$$x = t,\quad y = t$$

that has the same orientation as the given line and has reference point $(0, 0)$.

(b) Find the arc length parametrization of the line

$$x = t,\quad y = t,\quad z = t$$

that has the same orientation as the given line and has reference point $(0, 0, 0)$.

**22.** Find arc length parametrizations of the lines in Exercise 21 that have the stated reference points but are oriented opposite to the given lines.

**23.** (a) Find the arc length parametrization of the line

$$x = 1 + t,\quad y = 3 - 2t,\quad z = 4 + 2t$$

that has the same direction as the given line and has reference point $(1, 3, 4)$.

(b) Use the parametric equations obtained in part (a) to find the point on the line that is 25 units from the reference point in the direction of increasing parameter.

**24.** (a) Find the arc length parametrization of the line
$$x = -5 + 3t, \quad y = 2t, \quad z = 5 + t$$
that has the same direction as the given line and has reference point $(-5, 0, 5)$.

(b) Use the parametric equations obtained in part (a) to find the point on the line that is 10 units from the reference point in the direction of increasing parameter.

**25–30** Find an arc length parametrization of the curve that has the same orientation as the given curve and for which the reference point corresponds to $t = 0$. ■

**25.** $\mathbf{r}(t) = (3 + \cos t)\mathbf{i} + (2 + \sin t)\mathbf{j}; \ 0 \le t \le 2\pi$

**26.** $\mathbf{r}(t) = \cos^3 t\mathbf{i} + \sin^3 t\mathbf{j}; \ 0 \le t \le \pi/2$

**27.** $\mathbf{r}(t) = \frac{1}{3}t^3\mathbf{i} + \frac{1}{2}t^2\mathbf{j}; \ t \ge 0$

**28.** $\mathbf{r}(t) = (1 + t)^2\mathbf{i} + (1 + t)^3\mathbf{j}; \ 0 \le t \le 1$

**29.** $\mathbf{r}(t) = e^t \cos t\mathbf{i} + e^t \sin t\mathbf{j}; \ 0 \le t \le \pi/2$

**30.** $\mathbf{r}(t) = \sin e^t\mathbf{i} + \cos e^t\mathbf{j} + \sqrt{3}e^t\mathbf{k}; \ t \ge 0$

**31.** Show that the arc length of the circular helix $x = a \cos t$, $y = a \sin t$, $z = ct$ for $0 \le t \le t_0$ is $t_0\sqrt{a^2 + c^2}$.

**32.** Use the result in Exercise 31 to show the circular helix
$$\mathbf{r} = a \cos t\mathbf{i} + a \sin t\mathbf{j} + ct\mathbf{k}$$
can be expressed as
$$\mathbf{r} = \left(a \cos \frac{s}{w}\right)\mathbf{i} + \left(a \sin \frac{s}{w}\right)\mathbf{j} + \frac{cs}{w}\mathbf{k}$$
where $w = \sqrt{a^2 + c^2}$ and $s$ is an arc length parameter with reference point at $(a, 0, 0)$.

**33.** Find an arc length parametrization of the cycloid
$$x = at - a \sin t \qquad (0 \le t \le 2\pi)$$
$$y = a - a \cos t$$
with $(0, 0)$ as the reference point.

**34.** Show that in cylindrical coordinates a curve given by the parametric equations $r = r(t)$, $\theta = \theta(t)$, $z = z(t)$ for $a \le t \le b$ has arc length
$$L = \int_a^b \sqrt{\left(\frac{dr}{dt}\right)^2 + r^2\left(\frac{d\theta}{dt}\right)^2 + \left(\frac{dz}{dt}\right)^2}\, dt$$
[*Hint:* Use the relationships $x = r \cos \theta$, $y = r \sin \theta$.]

**35.** In each part, use the formula in Exercise 34 to find the arc length of the curve.

(a) $r = e^{2t}, \theta = t, z = e^{2t}; \ 0 \le t \le \ln 2$

(b) $r = t^2, \theta = \ln t, z = \frac{1}{3}t^3; \ 1 \le t \le 2$

**36.** Show that in spherical coordinates a curve given by the parametric equations $\rho = \rho(t)$, $\theta = \theta(t)$, $\phi = \phi(t)$ for $a \le t \le b$ has arc length
$$L = \int_a^b \sqrt{\left(\frac{d\rho}{dt}\right)^2 + \rho^2 \sin^2 \phi \left(\frac{d\theta}{dt}\right)^2 + \rho^2\left(\frac{d\phi}{dt}\right)^2}\, dt$$
[*Hint:* $x = \rho \sin \phi \cos \theta$, $y = \rho \sin \phi \sin \theta$, $z = \rho \cos \phi$.]

**37.** In each part, use the formula in Exercise 36 to find the arc length of the curve.

(a) $\rho = e^{-t}, \theta = 2t, \phi = \pi/4; \ 0 \le t \le 2$

(b) $\rho = 2t, \theta = \ln t, \phi = \pi/6; \ 1 \le t \le 5$

**FOCUS ON CONCEPTS**

**38.** (a) Sketch the graph of $\mathbf{r}(t) = t\mathbf{i} + t^2\mathbf{j}$. Show that $\mathbf{r}(t)$ is a smooth vector-valued function but the change of parameter $t = \tau^3$ produces a vector-valued function that is not smooth, yet has the same graph as $\mathbf{r}(t)$.

(b) Examine how the two vector-valued functions are traced, and see if you can explain what causes the problem.

**39.** Find a change of parameter $t = g(\tau)$ for the semicircle
$$\mathbf{r}(t) = \cos t\mathbf{i} + \sin t\mathbf{j} \quad (0 \le t \le \pi)$$
such that

(a) the semicircle is traced counterclockwise as $\tau$ varies over the interval $[0, 1]$

(b) the semicircle is traced clockwise as $\tau$ varies over the interval $[0, 1]$.

**40.** What change of parameter $t = g(\tau)$ would you make if you wanted to trace the graph of $\mathbf{r}(t)$ $(0 \le t \le 1)$ in the opposite direction with $\tau$ varying from 0 to 1?

**41.** As illustrated in the accompanying figure, copper cable with a diameter of $\frac{1}{2}$ inch is to be wrapped in a circular helix around a cylinder that has a 12-inch diameter. What length of cable (measured along its centerline) will make one complete turn around the cylinder in a distance of 20 inches (between centerlines) measured parallel to the axis of the cylinder?

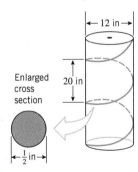

◀ **Figure Ex-41**

**42.** Let $\mathbf{r}(t) = \langle \cos t, \sin t, t^{3/2} \rangle$. Find

(a) $\|\mathbf{r}'(t)\|$    (b) $\dfrac{ds}{dt}$    (c) $\displaystyle\int_0^2 \|\mathbf{r}'(t)\|\, dt.$

**43.** Let $\mathbf{r}(t) = \ln t\mathbf{i} + 2t\mathbf{j} + t^2\mathbf{k}$. Find

(a) $\|\mathbf{r}'(t)\|$    (b) $\dfrac{ds}{dt}$    (c) $\displaystyle\int_1^3 \|\mathbf{r}'(t)\|\, dt.$

**44.** Let $\mathbf{r}(t) = t^2\mathbf{i} + t^3\mathbf{j}$ (see Figure 12.3.1). Let $\theta(t)$ be the angle between $\mathbf{r}'(t)$ and $\mathbf{i}$. Show that
$$\theta(t) \to \pi \text{ as } t \to 0^- \quad \text{and} \quad \theta(t) \to 0 \text{ as } t \to 0^+$$

**45.** Prove: If $\mathbf{r}(t)$ is a smoothly parametrized function, then the angles between $\mathbf{r}'(t)$ and the vectors $\mathbf{i}$, $\mathbf{j}$, and $\mathbf{k}$ are continuous functions of $t$.

**46.** Prove the vector form of the chain rule for 2-space (Theorem 12.3.2) by expressing $\mathbf{r}(t)$ in terms of components.

**47.** Writing   The triangle with vertices $(0, 0)$, $(1, 0)$, and $(0, 1)$ has three "corners." Discuss whether it is possible to have a smooth vector-valued function whose graph is this triangle. Also discuss whether it is possible to have a differentiable vector-valued function whose graph is this triangle.

✔ **QUICK CHECK ANSWERS 12.3**

1. arc length of the graph of $\mathbf{r}(t)$ from $t = a$ to $t = b$   2. $1$; $b - a$   3. $\left\| \dfrac{d\mathbf{r}}{du} \right\|$   4. $\langle -3, 3, \sqrt{3} \rangle$

---

## 12.4   UNIT TANGENT, NORMAL, AND BINORMAL VECTORS

*In this section we will discuss some of the fundamental geometric properties of vector-valued functions. Our work here will have important applications to the study of motion along a curved path in 2-space or 3-space and to the study of the geometric properties of curves and surfaces.*

### UNIT TANGENT VECTORS

Recall that if $C$ is the graph of a *smooth* vector-valued function $\mathbf{r}(t)$ in 2-space or 3-space, then the vector $\mathbf{r}'(t)$ is nonzero, tangent to $C$, and points in the direction of increasing parameter. Thus, by normalizing $\mathbf{r}'(t)$ we obtain a unit vector

As a general rule, we will position $\mathbf{T}(t)$ with its initial point at the terminal point of $\mathbf{r}(t)$, as in Figure 12.4.1. This will ensure that $\mathbf{T}(t)$ is actually tangent to the graph of $\mathbf{r}(t)$ and not simply parallel to the tangent line.

$$\mathbf{T}(t) = \frac{\mathbf{r}'(t)}{\|\mathbf{r}'(t)\|} \tag{1}$$

that is tangent to $C$ and points in the direction of increasing parameter. We call $\mathbf{T}(t)$ the ***unit tangent vector*** to $C$ at $t$.

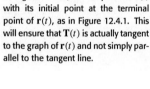

▶ **Example 1**   Find the unit tangent vector to the graph of $\mathbf{r}(t) = t^2\mathbf{i} + t^3\mathbf{j}$ at the point where $t = 2$.

*Solution.*   Since

$$\mathbf{r}'(t) = 2t\mathbf{i} + 3t^2\mathbf{j}$$

we obtain

$$\mathbf{T}(2) = \frac{\mathbf{r}'(2)}{\|\mathbf{r}'(2)\|} = \frac{4\mathbf{i} + 12\mathbf{j}}{\sqrt{160}} = \frac{4\mathbf{i} + 12\mathbf{j}}{4\sqrt{10}} = \frac{1}{\sqrt{10}}\mathbf{i} + \frac{3}{\sqrt{10}}\mathbf{j}$$

The graph of $\mathbf{r}(t)$ and the vector $\mathbf{T}(2)$ are shown in Figure 12.4.2. ◀

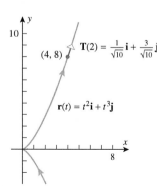

**▲ Figure 12.4.1**

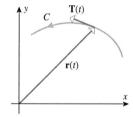

**▲ Figure 12.4.2**

### UNIT NORMAL VECTORS

Recall from Theorem 12.2.8 that if a vector-valued function $\mathbf{r}(t)$ has constant norm, then $\mathbf{r}(t)$ and $\mathbf{r}'(t)$ are orthogonal vectors. In particular, $\mathbf{T}(t)$ has constant norm 1, so $\mathbf{T}(t)$ and $\mathbf{T}'(t)$ are orthogonal vectors. This implies that $\mathbf{T}'(t)$ is perpendicular to the tangent line to $C$ at $t$, so we say that $\mathbf{T}'(t)$ is ***normal*** to $C$ at $t$. It follows that if $\mathbf{T}'(t) \neq \mathbf{0}$, and if we normalize $\mathbf{T}'(t)$, then we obtain a unit vector

$$\mathbf{N}(t) = \frac{\mathbf{T}'(t)}{\|\mathbf{T}'(t)\|} \tag{2}$$

that is normal to $C$ and points in the same direction as $\mathbf{T}'(t)$. We call $\mathbf{N}(t)$ the ***principal unit normal vector*** to $C$ at $t$, or more simply, the ***unit normal vector***. Observe that the unit normal vector is defined only at points where $\mathbf{T}'(t) \neq \mathbf{0}$. Unless stated otherwise, we will assume that this condition is satisfied. In particular, this *excludes* straight lines.

**REMARK** | In 2-space there are two unit vectors that are orthogonal to $\mathbf{T}(t)$, and in 3-space there are infinitely many such vectors (Figure 12.4.3). In both cases the principal unit normal is that particular normal that points in the direction of $\mathbf{T}'(t)$. After the next example we will show that for a nonlinear parametric curve in 2-space the principal unit normal is the one that points "inward" toward the concave side of the curve.

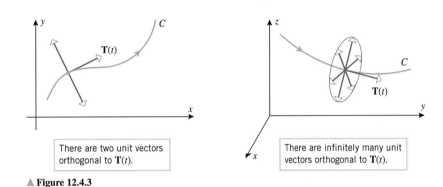

There are two unit vectors orthogonal to $\mathbf{T}(t)$.

There are infinitely many unit vectors orthogonal to $\mathbf{T}(t)$.

▲ **Figure 12.4.3**

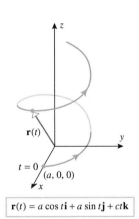

$$\mathbf{r}(t) = a\cos t\,\mathbf{i} + a\sin t\,\mathbf{j} + ct\mathbf{k}$$

▲ **Figure 12.4.4**

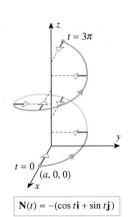

$$\mathbf{N}(t) = -(\cos t\,\mathbf{i} + \sin t\,\mathbf{j})$$

▲ **Figure 12.4.5**

▶ **Example 2** Find $\mathbf{T}(t)$ and $\mathbf{N}(t)$ for the circular helix

$$x = a\cos t, \quad y = a\sin t, \quad z = ct$$

where $a > 0$.

***Solution.*** The radius vector for the helix is

$$\mathbf{r}(t) = a\cos t\,\mathbf{i} + a\sin t\,\mathbf{j} + ct\mathbf{k}$$

(Figure 12.4.4). Thus,

$$\mathbf{r}'(t) = (-a\sin t)\mathbf{i} + a\cos t\,\mathbf{j} + c\mathbf{k}$$

$$\|\mathbf{r}'(t)\| = \sqrt{(-a\sin t)^2 + (a\cos t)^2 + c^2} = \sqrt{a^2 + c^2}$$

$$\mathbf{T}(t) = \frac{\mathbf{r}'(t)}{\|\mathbf{r}'(t)\|} = -\frac{a\sin t}{\sqrt{a^2 + c^2}}\mathbf{i} + \frac{a\cos t}{\sqrt{a^2 + c^2}}\mathbf{j} + \frac{c}{\sqrt{a^2 + c^2}}\mathbf{k}$$

$$\mathbf{T}'(t) = -\frac{a\cos t}{\sqrt{a^2 + c^2}}\mathbf{i} - \frac{a\sin t}{\sqrt{a^2 + c^2}}\mathbf{j}$$

$$\|\mathbf{T}'(t)\| = \sqrt{\left(-\frac{a\cos t}{\sqrt{a^2 + c^2}}\right)^2 + \left(-\frac{a\sin t}{\sqrt{a^2 + c^2}}\right)^2} = \sqrt{\frac{a^2}{a^2 + c^2}} = \frac{a}{\sqrt{a^2 + c^2}}$$

$$\mathbf{N}(t) = \frac{\mathbf{T}'(t)}{\|\mathbf{T}'(t)\|} = (-\cos t)\mathbf{i} - (\sin t)\mathbf{j} = -(\cos t\,\mathbf{i} + \sin t\,\mathbf{j})$$

Note that the $\mathbf{k}$ component of the principal unit normal $\mathbf{N}(t)$ is zero for every value of $t$, so this vector always lies in a horizontal plane, as illustrated in Figure 12.4.5. We leave it as an exercise to show that this vector actually always points toward the $z$-axis. ◀

### INWARD UNIT NORMAL VECTORS IN 2-SPACE

Our next objective is to show that for a nonlinear parametric curve $C$ in 2-space the unit normal vector always points toward the concave side of $C$. For this purpose, let $\phi(t)$ be the angle from the positive $x$-axis to $\mathbf{T}(t)$, and let $\mathbf{n}(t)$ be the unit vector that results when $\mathbf{T}(t)$ is rotated counterclockwise through an angle of $\pi/2$ (Figure 12.4.6). Since $\mathbf{T}(t)$ and $\mathbf{n}(t)$ are unit vectors, it follows from Formula (13) of Section 11.2 that these vectors can be expressed as

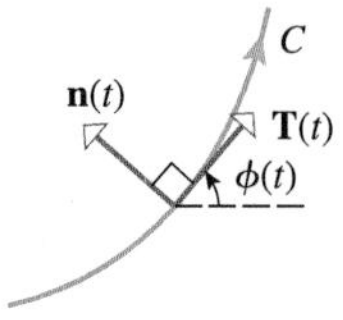

$$\mathbf{T}(t) = \cos\phi(t)\mathbf{i} + \sin\phi(t)\mathbf{j} \tag{3}$$

and

$$\mathbf{n}(t) = \cos[\phi(t) + \pi/2]\mathbf{i} + \sin[\phi(t) + \pi/2]\mathbf{j} = -\sin\phi(t)\mathbf{i} + \cos\phi(t)\mathbf{j} \tag{4}$$

Observe that on intervals where $\phi(t)$ is increasing the vector $\mathbf{n}(t)$ points *toward* the concave side of $C$, and on intervals where $\phi(t)$ is decreasing it points *away* from the concave side (Figure 12.4.7).

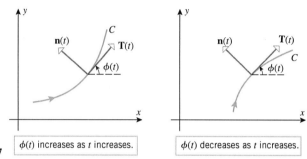

$\phi(t)$ increases as $t$ increases.          $\phi(t)$ decreases as $t$ increases.

▶ **Figure 12.4.7**

▲ **Figure 12.4.6**

Now let us differentiate $\mathbf{T}(t)$ by using Formula (3) and applying the chain rule. This yields

$$\frac{d\mathbf{T}}{dt} = \frac{d\mathbf{T}}{d\phi}\frac{d\phi}{dt} = [(-\sin\phi)\mathbf{i} + (\cos\phi)\mathbf{j}]\frac{d\phi}{dt}$$

and thus from (4)

$$\frac{d\mathbf{T}}{dt} = \mathbf{n}(t)\frac{d\phi}{dt} \tag{5}$$

But $d\phi/dt > 0$ on intervals where $\phi(t)$ is increasing and $d\phi/dt < 0$ on intervals where $\phi(t)$ is decreasing. Thus, it follows from (5) that $d\mathbf{T}/dt$ has the same direction as $\mathbf{n}(t)$ on intervals where $\phi(t)$ is increasing and the opposite direction on intervals where $\phi(t)$ is decreasing. Therefore, $\mathbf{T}'(t) = d\mathbf{T}/dt$ points "inward" toward the concave side of the curve in all cases, and hence so does $\mathbf{N}(t)$. For this reason, $\mathbf{N}(t)$ is also called the ***inward unit normal*** when applied to curves in 2-space.

### COMPUTING T AND N FOR CURVES PARAMETRIZED BY ARC LENGTH

In the case where $\mathbf{r}(s)$ is parametrized by arc length, the procedures for computing the unit tangent vector $\mathbf{T}(s)$ and the unit normal vector $\mathbf{N}(s)$ are simpler than in the general case. For example, we showed in Theorem 12.3.4 that if $s$ is an arc length parameter, then $\|\mathbf{r}'(s)\| = 1$. Thus, Formula (1) for the unit tangent vector simplifies to

$$\mathbf{T}(s) = \mathbf{r}'(s) \tag{6}$$

and consequently Formula (2) for the unit normal vector simplifies to

$$\mathbf{N}(s) = \frac{\mathbf{r}''(s)}{\|\mathbf{r}''(s)\|} \tag{7}$$

**WARNING**

Formulas (6) and (7) are only applicable when the curve is parametrized by an arc length parameter $s$. For other parametrizations Formulas (1) and (2) can be used.

▶ **Example 3** The circle of radius $a$ with counterclockwise orientation and centered at the origin can be represented by the vector-valued function

$$\mathbf{r} = a\cos t\,\mathbf{i} + a\sin t\,\mathbf{j} \qquad (0 \le t \le 2\pi) \qquad (8)$$

Parametrize this circle by arc length and find $\mathbf{T}(s)$ and $\mathbf{N}(s)$.

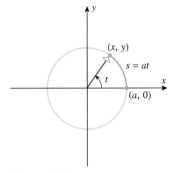

▲ **Figure 12.4.8**

*Solution.* In (8) we can interpret $t$ as the angle in radian measure from the positive $x$-axis to the radius vector (Figure 12.4.8). This angle subtends an arc of length $s = at$ on the circle, so we can reparametrize the circle in terms of $s$ by substituting $s/a$ for $t$ in (8). This yields

$$\mathbf{r}(s) = a\cos(s/a)\mathbf{i} + a\sin(s/a)\mathbf{j} \qquad (0 \le s \le 2\pi a)$$

To find $\mathbf{T}(s)$ and $\mathbf{N}(s)$ from Formulas (6) and (7), we must compute $\mathbf{r}'(s)$, $\mathbf{r}''(s)$, and $\|\mathbf{r}''(s)\|$. Doing so, we obtain

$$\mathbf{r}'(s) = -\sin(s/a)\mathbf{i} + \cos(s/a)\mathbf{j}$$

$$\mathbf{r}''(s) = -(1/a)\cos(s/a)\mathbf{i} - (1/a)\sin(s/a)\mathbf{j}$$

$$\|\mathbf{r}''(s)\| = \sqrt{(-1/a)^2\cos^2(s/a) + (-1/a)^2\sin^2(s/a)} = 1/a$$

Thus,

$$\mathbf{T}(s) = \mathbf{r}'(s) = -\sin(s/a)\mathbf{i} + \cos(s/a)\mathbf{j}$$

$$\mathbf{N}(s) = \mathbf{r}''(s)/\|\mathbf{r}''(s)\| = -\cos(s/a)\mathbf{i} - \sin(s/a)\mathbf{j}$$

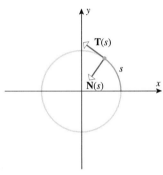

▲ **Figure 12.4.9**

so $\mathbf{N}(s)$ points toward the center of the circle for all $s$ (Figure 12.4.9). This makes sense geometrically and is also consistent with our earlier observation that in 2-space the unit normal vector is the inward normal. ◄

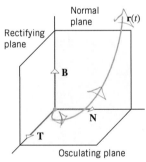

▲ **Figure 12.4.10**

■ **BINORMAL VECTORS IN 3-SPACE**
If $C$ is the graph of a vector-valued function $\mathbf{r}(t)$ in 3-space, then we define the ***binormal vector*** to $C$ at $t$ to be

$$\mathbf{B}(t) = \mathbf{T}(t) \times \mathbf{N}(t) \qquad (9)$$

It follows from properties of the cross product that $\mathbf{B}(t)$ is orthogonal to both $\mathbf{T}(t)$ and $\mathbf{N}(t)$ and is oriented relative to $\mathbf{T}(t)$ and $\mathbf{N}(t)$ by the right-hand rule. Moreover, $\mathbf{T}(t) \times \mathbf{N}(t)$ is a unit vector since

$$\|\mathbf{T}(t) \times \mathbf{N}(t)\| = \|\mathbf{T}(t)\|\|\mathbf{N}(t)\|\sin(\pi/2) = 1$$

Thus, $\{\mathbf{T}(t), \mathbf{N}(t), \mathbf{B}(t)\}$ is a set of three mutually orthogonal unit vectors.

Just as the vectors $\mathbf{i}$, $\mathbf{j}$, and $\mathbf{k}$ determine a right-handed coordinate system in 3-space, so do the vectors $\mathbf{T}(t)$, $\mathbf{N}(t)$, and $\mathbf{B}(t)$. At each point on a smooth parametric curve $C$ in 3-space, these vectors determine three mutually perpendicular planes that pass through the point—the **TB**-plane (called the ***rectifying plane***), the **TN**-plane (called the ***osculating plane***), and the **NB**-plane (called the ***normal plane***) (Figure 12.4.10). Moreover, one can show that a coordinate system determined by $\mathbf{T}(t)$, $\mathbf{N}(t)$, and $\mathbf{B}(t)$ is right-handed in the sense that each of these vectors is related to the other two by the right-hand rule (Figure 12.4.11):

$$\mathbf{B}(t) = \mathbf{T}(t) \times \mathbf{N}(t), \quad \mathbf{N}(t) = \mathbf{B}(t) \times \mathbf{T}(t), \quad \mathbf{T}(t) = \mathbf{N}(t) \times \mathbf{B}(t) \qquad (10)$$

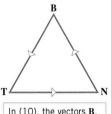

In (10), the vectors **B**, **N**, and **T** are each expressed as the cross product of the other two taken in the counterclockwise direction around the above triangle.

▲ **Figure 12.4.11**

The coordinate system determined by $\mathbf{T}(t)$, $\mathbf{N}(t)$, and $\mathbf{B}(t)$ is called the **TNB**-*frame* or sometimes the ***Frenet frame*** in honor of the French mathematician Jean Frédéric Frenet (1816–1900) who pioneered its application to the study of space curves. Typically, the $xyz$-coordinate system determined by the unit vectors $\mathbf{i}$, $\mathbf{j}$, and $\mathbf{k}$ remains fixed, whereas the **TNB**-frame changes as its origin moves along the curve $C$ (Figure 12.4.12).

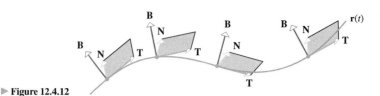

▶ **Figure 12.4.12**

Formula (9) expresses $\mathbf{B}(t)$ in terms of $\mathbf{T}(t)$ and $\mathbf{N}(t)$. Alternatively, the binormal $\mathbf{B}(t)$ can be expressed directly in terms of $\mathbf{r}(t)$ as

$$\mathbf{B}(t) = \frac{\mathbf{r}'(t) \times \mathbf{r}''(t)}{\|\mathbf{r}'(t) \times \mathbf{r}''(t)\|} \tag{11}$$

and in the case where the parameter is arc length it can be expressed in terms of $\mathbf{r}(s)$ as

$$\mathbf{B}(s) = \frac{\mathbf{r}'(s) \times \mathbf{r}''(s)}{\|\mathbf{r}''(s)\|} \tag{12}$$

We omit the proof.

---

✔ **QUICK CHECK EXERCISES 12.4**   (*See page 873 for answers.*)

**1.** If $C$ is the graph of a smooth vector-valued function $\mathbf{r}(t)$, then the unit tangent, unit normal, and binormal to $C$ at $t$ are defined, respectively, by

$$\mathbf{T}(t) = \underline{\hspace{1cm}}, \quad \mathbf{N}(t) = \underline{\hspace{1cm}}, \quad \mathbf{B}(t) = \underline{\hspace{1cm}}$$

**2.** If $C$ is the graph of a smooth vector-valued function $\mathbf{r}(s)$ parametrized by arc length, then the definitions of the unit tangent and unit normal to $C$ at $s$ simplify, respectively, to

$$\mathbf{T}(s) = \underline{\hspace{1cm}} \quad \text{and} \quad \mathbf{N}(s) = \underline{\hspace{1cm}}$$

**3.** If $C$ is the graph of a smooth vector-valued function $\mathbf{r}(t)$, then the unit binormal vector to $C$ at $t$ may be computed directly in terms of $\mathbf{r}'(t)$ and $\mathbf{r}''(t)$ by the formula $\mathbf{B}(t) = \underline{\hspace{1cm}}$. When $t = s$ is the arc length parameter, this formula simplifies to $\mathbf{B}(s) = \underline{\hspace{1cm}}$.

**4.** Suppose that $C$ is the graph of a smooth vector-valued function $\mathbf{r}(s)$ parametrized by arc length with $\mathbf{r}'(0) = \langle \frac{2}{3}, \frac{1}{3}, \frac{2}{3} \rangle$ and $\mathbf{r}''(0) = \langle -3, 12, -3 \rangle$. Then

$$\mathbf{T}(0) = \underline{\hspace{1cm}}, \quad \mathbf{N}(0) = \underline{\hspace{1cm}}, \quad \mathbf{B}(0) = \underline{\hspace{1cm}}$$

---

**EXERCISE SET 12.4**

**FOCUS ON CONCEPTS**

**1.** In each part, sketch the unit tangent and normal vectors at the points $P$, $Q$, and $R$, taking into account the orientation of the curve $C$.

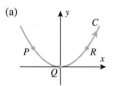

(a)   (b)

**2.** Make a rough sketch that shows the ellipse

$$\mathbf{r}(t) = 3 \cos t \mathbf{i} + 2 \sin t \mathbf{j}$$

for $0 \leq t \leq 2\pi$ and the unit tangent and normal vectors at the points $t = 0$, $t = \pi/4$, $t = \pi/2$, and $t = \pi$.

**3.** In the marginal note associated with Example 8 of Section 12.3, we observed that a line $\mathbf{r} = \mathbf{r}_0 + t\mathbf{v}$ can be parametrized in terms of an arc length parameter $s$ with reference point $\mathbf{r}_0$ by normalizing $\mathbf{v}$. Use this result to show that the tangent line to the graph of $\mathbf{r}(t)$ at the point $t_0$ can be expressed as

$$\mathbf{r} = \mathbf{r}(t_0) + s\mathbf{T}(t_0)$$

where $s$ is an arc length parameter with reference point $\mathbf{r}(t_0)$.

**4.** Use the result in Exercise 3 to show that the tangent line to the parabola

$$x = t, \quad y = t^2$$

at the point $(1, 1)$ can be expressed parametrically as

$$x = 1 + \frac{s}{\sqrt{5}}, \quad y = 1 + \frac{2s}{\sqrt{5}}$$

**5–12** Find $\mathbf{T}(t)$ and $\mathbf{N}(t)$ at the given point.

**5.** $\mathbf{r}(t) = (t^2 - 1)\mathbf{i} + t\mathbf{j}; \ t = 1$

**6.** $\mathbf{r}(t) = \frac{1}{2}t^2\mathbf{i} + \frac{1}{3}t^3\mathbf{j}; \ t = 1$

**7.** $\mathbf{r}(t) = 5\cos t\mathbf{i} + 5\sin t\mathbf{j}; \ t = \pi/3$

**8.** $\mathbf{r}(t) = \ln t\mathbf{i} + t\mathbf{j}; \ t = e$

**9.** $\mathbf{r}(t) = 4\cos t\mathbf{i} + 4\sin t\mathbf{j} + t\mathbf{k}; \ t = \pi/2$

**10.** $\mathbf{r}(t) = t\mathbf{i} + \frac{1}{2}t^2\mathbf{j} + \frac{1}{3}t^3\mathbf{k}; \ t = 0$

**11.** $x = e^t\cos t, \ y = e^t\sin t, z = e^t; \ t = 0$

**12.** $x = \cosh t, \ y = \sinh t, z = t; \ t = \ln 2$

**13–14** Use the result in Exercise 3 to find parametric equations for the tangent line to the graph of $\mathbf{r}(t)$ at $t_0$ in terms of an arc length parameter $s$.

**13.** $\mathbf{r}(t) = \sin t\mathbf{i} + \cos t\mathbf{j} + \frac{1}{2}t^2\mathbf{k}; \ t_0 = 0$

**14.** $\mathbf{r}(t) = t\mathbf{i} + t\mathbf{j} + \sqrt{9 - t^2}\mathbf{k}; \ t_0 = 1$

**15–18** Use the formula $\mathbf{B}(t) = \mathbf{T}(t) \times \mathbf{N}(t)$ to find $\mathbf{B}(t)$, and then check your answer by using Formula (11) to find $\mathbf{B}(t)$ directly from $\mathbf{r}(t)$.

**15.** $\mathbf{r}(t) = 3\sin t\mathbf{i} + 3\cos t\mathbf{j} + 4t\mathbf{k}$

**16.** $\mathbf{r}(t) = e^t\sin t\mathbf{i} + e^t\cos t\mathbf{j} + 3\mathbf{k}$

**17.** $\mathbf{r}(t) = (\sin t - t\cos t)\mathbf{i} + (\cos t + t\sin t)\mathbf{j} + \mathbf{k}$

**18.** $\mathbf{r}(t) = a\cos t\mathbf{i} + a\sin t\mathbf{j} + ct\mathbf{k} \quad (a \neq 0, c \neq 0)$

**19–20** Find $\mathbf{T}(t)$, $\mathbf{N}(t)$, and $\mathbf{B}(t)$ for the given value of $t$. Then find equations for the osculating, normal, and rectifying planes at the point that corresponds to that value of $t$.

**19.** $\mathbf{r}(t) = \cos t\mathbf{i} + \sin t\mathbf{j} + \mathbf{k}; \ t = \pi/4$

**20.** $\mathbf{r}(t) = e^t\mathbf{i} + e^t\cos t\mathbf{j} + e^t\sin t\mathbf{k}; \ t = 0$

**21–24 True–False** Determine whether the statement is true or false. Explain your answer.

**21.** If $C$ is the graph of a smooth vector-valued function $\mathbf{r}(t)$ in 2-space, then the unit tangent vector $\mathbf{T}(t)$ to $C$ is orthogonal to $\mathbf{r}(t)$ and points in the direction of increasing parameter.

**22.** If $C$ is the graph of a smooth vector-valued function $\mathbf{r}(t)$ in 2-space, then the angle measured in the counterclockwise direction from the unit tangent vector $\mathbf{T}(t)$ to the unit normal vector $\mathbf{N}(t)$ is $\pi/2$.

**23.** If the smooth vector-valued function $\mathbf{r}(s)$ is parametrized by arc length and $\mathbf{r}''(s)$ is defined, then $\mathbf{r}'(s)$ and $\mathbf{r}''(s)$ are orthogonal vectors.

**24.** The binormal vector $\mathbf{B}(t)$ to the graph of a vector-valued function $\mathbf{r}(t)$ in 3-space is the dot product of unit tangent and unit normal vectors, $\mathbf{T}(t)$ and $\mathbf{N}(t)$.

**25.** Writing Look up the definition of "osculating" in a dictionary and discuss why "osculating plane" is an appropriate term for the TN-plane.

**26.** Writing Discuss some of the advantages of parametrizing a curve by arc length.

✔ **QUICK CHECK ANSWERS 12.4**

**1.** $\dfrac{\mathbf{r}'(t)}{\|\mathbf{r}'(t)\|}$; $\dfrac{\mathbf{T}'(t)}{\|\mathbf{T}'(t)\|}$; $\mathbf{T}(t) \times \mathbf{N}(t)$ **2.** $\mathbf{r}'(s)$; $\dfrac{\mathbf{r}''(s)}{\|\mathbf{r}''(s)\|}$ **3.** $\dfrac{\mathbf{r}'(t) \times \mathbf{r}''(t)}{\|\mathbf{r}'(t) \times \mathbf{r}''(t)\|}$; $\dfrac{\mathbf{r}'(s) \times \mathbf{r}''(s)}{\|\mathbf{r}''(s)\|}$

**4.** $\left\langle \dfrac{2}{3}, \dfrac{1}{3}, \dfrac{2}{3} \right\rangle$; $\left\langle -\dfrac{1}{3\sqrt{2}}, \dfrac{4}{3\sqrt{2}}, -\dfrac{1}{3\sqrt{2}} \right\rangle$; $\left\langle -\dfrac{1}{\sqrt{2}}, 0, \dfrac{1}{\sqrt{2}} \right\rangle$

## 12.5 CURVATURE

*In this section we will consider the problem of obtaining a numerical measure of how sharply a curve in 2-space or 3-space bends. Our results will have applications in geometry and in the study of motion along a curved path.*

### DEFINITION OF CURVATURE

Suppose that $C$ is the graph of a smooth vector-valued function in 2-space or 3-space that is parametrized in terms of arc length. Figure 12.5.1 suggests that for a curve in 2-space the "sharpness" of the bend in $C$ is closely related to $d\mathbf{T}/ds$, which is the rate of change of the unit tangent vector $\mathbf{T}$ with respect to $s$. (Keep in mind that $\mathbf{T}$ has constant length, so only its direction changes.) If $C$ is a straight line (no bend), then the direction of $\mathbf{T}$ remains constant (Figure 12.5.1a); if $C$ bends slightly, then $\mathbf{T}$ undergoes a gradual change of direction (Figure 12.5.1b); and if $C$ bends sharply, then $\mathbf{T}$ undergoes a rapid change of direction (Figure 12.5.1c).

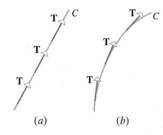

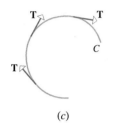

▲ Figure 12.5.1

The situation in 3-space is more complicated because bends in a curve are not limited to a single plane—they can occur in all directions, as illustrated by the complicated tube plot in Figure 12.1.4. To describe the bending characteristics of a curve in 3-space completely, one must take into account $d\mathbf{T}/ds$, $d\mathbf{N}/ds$, and $d\mathbf{B}/ds$. A complete study of this topic would take us too far afield, so we will limit our discussion to $d\mathbf{T}/ds$, which is the most important of these derivatives in applications.

---

**12.5.1 DEFINITION** If $C$ is a smooth curve in 2-space or 3-space that is parametrized by arc length, then the *curvature* of $C$, denoted by $\kappa = \kappa(s)$ ($\kappa$ = Greek "kappa"), is defined by

$$\kappa(s) = \left\| \frac{d\mathbf{T}}{ds} \right\| = \|\mathbf{r}''(s)\| \tag{1}$$

---

Observe that $\kappa(s)$ is a real-valued function of $s$, since it is the *length* of $d\mathbf{T}/ds$ that measures the curvature. In general, the curvature will vary from point to point along a curve; however, the following example shows that the curvature is constant for circles in 2-space, as you might expect.

---

▶ **Example 1** In Example 3 of Section 12.4 we showed that the circle of radius $a$, centered at the origin, can be parametrized in terms of arc length as

$$\mathbf{r}(s) = a \cos\left(\frac{s}{a}\right)\mathbf{i} + a \sin\left(\frac{s}{a}\right)\mathbf{j} \qquad (0 \le s \le 2\pi a)$$

Thus,

$$\mathbf{r}''(s) = -\frac{1}{a}\cos\left(\frac{s}{a}\right)\mathbf{i} - \frac{1}{a}\sin\left(\frac{s}{a}\right)\mathbf{j}$$

and hence from (1)

$$\kappa(s) = \|\mathbf{r}''(s)\| = \sqrt{\left[-\frac{1}{a}\cos\left(\frac{s}{a}\right)\right]^2 + \left[-\frac{1}{a}\sin\left(\frac{s}{a}\right)\right]^2} = \frac{1}{a}$$

so the circle has constant curvature $1/a$. ◀

The next example shows that lines have zero curvature, which is consistent with the fact that they do not bend.

---

▶ **Example 2** Recall from Formula (15) of Section 12.3 that a line in 2-space or 3-space can be parametrized in terms of arc length as

$$\mathbf{r} = \mathbf{r}_0 + s\mathbf{u}$$

where the terminal point of $\mathbf{r}_0$ is a point on the line and $\mathbf{u}$ is a unit vector parallel to the line. Since $\mathbf{u}$ and $\mathbf{r}_0$ are constant, their derivatives with respect to $s$ are zero, and hence

$$\mathbf{r}'(s) = \frac{d\mathbf{r}}{ds} = \frac{d}{ds}[\mathbf{r}_0 + s\mathbf{u}] = \mathbf{0} + \mathbf{u} = \mathbf{u}$$

$$\mathbf{r}''(s) = \frac{d\mathbf{r}'}{ds} = \frac{d}{ds}[\mathbf{u}] = \mathbf{0}$$

Thus,

$$\kappa(s) = \|\mathbf{r}''(s)\| = 0 \blacktriangleleft$$

### ■ FORMULAS FOR CURVATURE

Formula (1) is only applicable if the curve is parametrized in terms of arc length. The following theorem provides two formulas for curvature in terms of a general parameter $t$.

---

**12.5.2    THEOREM**    *If $\mathbf{r}(t)$ is a smooth vector-valued function in 2-space or 3-space, then for each value of t at which $\mathbf{T}'(t)$ and $\mathbf{r}''(t)$ exist, the curvature $\kappa$ can be expressed as*

$(a)$    $$\kappa(t) = \frac{\|\mathbf{T}'(t)\|}{\|\mathbf{r}'(t)\|} \tag{2}$$

$(b)$    $$\kappa(t) = \frac{\|\mathbf{r}'(t) \times \mathbf{r}''(t)\|}{\|\mathbf{r}'(t)\|^3} \tag{3}$$

---

**PROOF** $(a)$    It follows from Formula (1) and Formula (16) of Section 12.3 that

$$\kappa(t) = \left\| \frac{d\mathbf{T}}{ds} \right\| = \left\| \frac{d\mathbf{T}/dt}{ds/dt} \right\| = \left\| \frac{d\mathbf{T}/dt}{\|d\mathbf{r}/dt\|} \right\| = \frac{\|\mathbf{T}'(t)\|}{\|\mathbf{r}'(t)\|}$$

**PROOF** $(b)$    It follows from Formula (1) of Section 12.4 that

$$\mathbf{r}'(t) = \|\mathbf{r}'(t)\|\mathbf{T}(t) \tag{4}$$
$$\mathbf{r}''(t) = \|\mathbf{r}'(t)\|'\mathbf{T}(t) + \|\mathbf{r}'(t)\|\mathbf{T}'(t) \tag{5}$$

But from Formula (2) of Section 12.4 and part $(a)$ of this theorem we have

$$\mathbf{T}'(t) = \|\mathbf{T}'(t)\|\mathbf{N}(t) \quad \text{and} \quad \|\mathbf{T}'(t)\| = \kappa(t)\|\mathbf{r}'(t)\|$$

so

$$\mathbf{T}'(t) = \kappa(t)\|\mathbf{r}'(t)\|\mathbf{N}(t)$$

Substituting this into (5) yields

$$\mathbf{r}''(t) = \|\mathbf{r}'(t)\|'\mathbf{T}(t) + \kappa(t)\|\mathbf{r}'(t)\|^2\mathbf{N}(t) \tag{6}$$

Thus, from (4) and (6)

$$\mathbf{r}'(t) \times \mathbf{r}''(t) = \|\mathbf{r}'(t)\|\|\mathbf{r}'(t)\|'(\mathbf{T}(t) \times \mathbf{T}(t)) + \kappa(t)\|\mathbf{r}'(t)\|^3(\mathbf{T}(t) \times \mathbf{N}(t))$$

But the cross product of a vector with itself is zero, so this equation simplifies to

$$\mathbf{r}'(t) \times \mathbf{r}''(t) = \kappa(t)\|\mathbf{r}'(t)\|^3(\mathbf{T}(t) \times \mathbf{N}(t)) = \kappa(t)\|\mathbf{r}'(t)\|^3\mathbf{B}(t)$$

It follows from this equation and the fact that $\mathbf{B}(t)$ is a unit vector that

$$\|\mathbf{r}'(t) \times \mathbf{r}''(t)\| = \kappa(t)\|\mathbf{r}'(t)\|^3$$

Formula (3) now follows.  ■

**REMARK**    Formula (2) is useful if $\mathbf{T}(t)$ is known or is easy to obtain; however, Formula (3) will usually be easier to apply, since it involves only $\mathbf{r}(t)$ and its derivatives. We also note that cross products were defined only for vectors in 3-space, so to use Formula (3) in 2-space we must first write the 2-space function $\mathbf{r}(t) = x(t)\mathbf{i} + y(t)\mathbf{j}$ as the 3-space function $\mathbf{r}(t) = x(t)\mathbf{i} + y(t)\mathbf{j} + 0\mathbf{k}$ with a zero $\mathbf{k}$ component.

---

► **Example 3**    Find $\kappa(t)$ for the circular helix

$$x = a\cos t, \quad y = a\sin t, \quad z = ct$$

where $a > 0$.

*Solution.*    The radius vector for the helix is

$$\mathbf{r}(t) = a\cos t\mathbf{i} + a\sin t\mathbf{j} + ct\mathbf{k}$$

Thus,

$$\mathbf{r}'(t) = (-a\sin t)\mathbf{i} + a\cos t\mathbf{j} + c\mathbf{k}$$
$$\mathbf{r}''(t) = (-a\cos t)\mathbf{i} + (-a\sin t)\mathbf{j}$$

$$\mathbf{r}'(t) \times \mathbf{r}''(t) = \begin{vmatrix} \mathbf{i} & \mathbf{j} & \mathbf{k} \\ -a\sin t & a\cos t & c \\ -a\cos t & -a\sin t & 0 \end{vmatrix} = (ac\sin t)\mathbf{i} - (ac\cos t)\mathbf{j} + a^2\mathbf{k}$$

Therefore,

$$\|\mathbf{r}'(t)\| = \sqrt{(-a\sin t)^2 + (a\cos t)^2 + c^2} = \sqrt{a^2 + c^2}$$

and

$$\|\mathbf{r}'(t) \times \mathbf{r}''(t)\| = \sqrt{(ac\sin t)^2 + (-ac\cos t)^2 + a^4}$$
$$= \sqrt{a^2c^2 + a^4} = a\sqrt{a^2 + c^2}$$

so

$$\kappa(t) = \frac{\|\mathbf{r}'(t) \times \mathbf{r}''(t)\|}{\|\mathbf{r}'(t)\|^3} = \frac{a\sqrt{a^2 + c^2}}{\left(\sqrt{a^2 + c^2}\right)^3} = \frac{a}{a^2 + c^2}$$

Note that $\kappa$ does not depend on $t$, which tells us that the helix has constant curvature. ◄

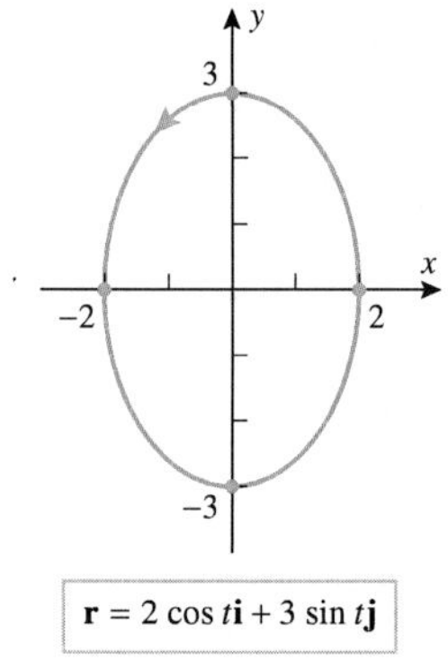

$$\mathbf{r} = 2\cos t\mathbf{i} + 3\sin t\mathbf{j}$$

▲ **Figure 12.5.2**

▶ **Example 4**    The graph of the vector equation

$$\mathbf{r} = 2\cos t\mathbf{i} + 3\sin t\mathbf{j} \quad (0 \leq t \leq 2\pi)$$

is the ellipse in Figure 12.5.2. Find the curvature of the ellipse at the endpoints of the major and minor axes, and use a graphing utility to generate the graph of $\kappa(t)$.

*Solution.*    To apply Formula (3), we must treat the ellipse as a curve in the *xy*-plane of an *xyz*-coordinate system by adding a zero **k** component and writing its equation as

$$\mathbf{r} = 2\cos t\mathbf{i} + 3\sin t\mathbf{j} + 0\mathbf{k}$$

It is not essential to write the zero **k** component explicitly as long as you assume it to be there when you calculate a cross product. Thus,

$$\mathbf{r}'(t) = (-2\sin t)\mathbf{i} + 3\cos t\mathbf{j}$$
$$\mathbf{r}''(t) = (-2\cos t)\mathbf{i} + (-3\sin t)\mathbf{j}$$

$$\mathbf{r}'(t) \times \mathbf{r}''(t) = \begin{vmatrix} \mathbf{i} & \mathbf{j} & \mathbf{k} \\ -2\sin t & 3\cos t & 0 \\ -2\cos t & -3\sin t & 0 \end{vmatrix} = [(6\sin^2 t) + (6\cos^2 t)]\mathbf{k} = 6\mathbf{k}$$

Therefore,

$$\|\mathbf{r}'(t)\| = \sqrt{(-2\sin t)^2 + (3\cos t)^2} = \sqrt{4\sin^2 t + 9\cos^2 t}$$
$$\|\mathbf{r}'(t) \times \mathbf{r}''(t)\| = 6$$

so

$$\kappa(t) = \frac{\|\mathbf{r}'(t) \times \mathbf{r}''(t)\|}{\|\mathbf{r}'(t)\|^3} = \frac{6}{[4\sin^2 t + 9\cos^2 t]^{3/2}} \tag{7}$$

The endpoints of the minor axis are $(2, 0)$ and $(-2, 0)$, which correspond to $t = 0$ and $t = \pi$, respectively. Substituting these values in (7) yields the same curvature at both points, namely,

$$\kappa = \kappa(0) = \kappa(\pi) = \frac{6}{9^{3/2}} = \frac{6}{27} = \frac{2}{9}$$

The endpoints of the major axis are $(0, 3)$ and $(0, -3)$, which correspond to $t = \pi/2$ and $t = 3\pi/2$, respectively; from (7) the curvature at these points is

$$\kappa = \kappa\left(\frac{\pi}{2}\right) = \kappa\left(\frac{3\pi}{2}\right) = \frac{6}{4^{3/2}} = \frac{3}{4}$$

Observe that the curvature is greater at the ends of the major axis than at the ends of the minor axis, as you might expect. Figure 12.5.3 shows the graph of $\kappa$ versus $t$. This graph illustrates clearly that the curvature is minimum at $t = 0$ (the right end of the minor axis), increases to a maximum at $t = \pi/2$ (the top of the major axis), decreases to a minimum again at $t = \pi$ (the left end of the minor axis), and continues cyclically in this manner. Figure 12.5.4 provides another way of picturing the curvature. ◄

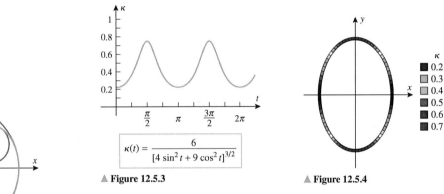

▲ Figure 12.5.3     ▲ Figure 12.5.4

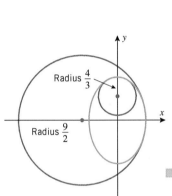

▲ Figure 12.5.5

### RADIUS OF CURVATURE

In the last example we found the curvature at the ends of the minor axis to be $\frac{2}{9}$ and the curvature at the ends of the major axis to be $\frac{3}{4}$. To obtain a better understanding of the meaning of these numbers, recall from Example 1 that a circle of radius $a$ has a constant curvature of $1/a$; thus, the curvature of the ellipse at the ends of the minor axis is the same as that of a circle of radius $\frac{9}{2}$, and the curvature at the ends of the major axis is the same as that of a circle of radius $\frac{4}{3}$ (Figure 12.5.5).

In general, if a curve $C$ in 2-space has nonzero curvature $\kappa$ at a point $P$, then the circle of radius $\rho = 1/\kappa$ sharing a common tangent with $C$ at $P$, and centered on the concave side of the curve at $P$, is called the *osculating circle* or *circle of curvature* at $P$ (Figure 12.5.6). The osculating circle and the curve $C$ not only touch at $P$ but they have equal curvatures at that point. In this sense, the osculating circle is the circle that best approximates the curve $C$ near $P$. The radius $\rho$ of the osculating circle at $P$ is called the *radius of curvature* at $P$, and the center of the circle is called the *center of curvature* at $P$ (Figure 12.5.6).

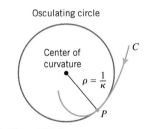

▲ Figure 12.5.6

### AN INTERPRETATION OF CURVATURE IN 2-SPACE

A useful geometric interpretation of curvature in 2-space can be obtained by considering the angle $\phi$ measured counterclockwise from the direction of the positive $x$-axis to the unit tangent vector $\mathbf{T}$ (Figure 12.5.7). By Formula (13) of Section 11.2, we can express $\mathbf{T}$ in terms of $\phi$ as

$$\mathbf{T}(\phi) = \cos\phi \, \mathbf{i} + \sin\phi \, \mathbf{j}$$

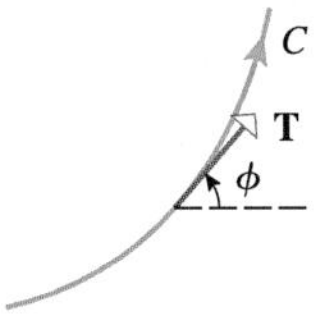

▲ Figure 12.5.7

Thus,

$$\frac{d\mathbf{T}}{d\phi} = (-\sin\phi)\mathbf{i} + \cos\phi\,\mathbf{j}$$

$$\frac{d\mathbf{T}}{ds} = \frac{d\mathbf{T}}{d\phi}\frac{d\phi}{ds}$$

from which we obtain

$$\kappa(s) = \left\|\frac{d\mathbf{T}}{ds}\right\| = \left|\frac{d\phi}{ds}\right|\left\|\frac{d\mathbf{T}}{d\phi}\right\| = \left|\frac{d\phi}{ds}\right|\sqrt{(-\sin\phi)^2 + \cos^2\phi} = \left|\frac{d\phi}{ds}\right|$$

In summary, we have shown that

$$\kappa(s) = \left|\frac{d\phi}{ds}\right| \tag{8}$$

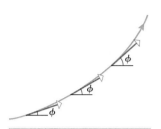

In 2-space, $\kappa(s)$ is the magnitude of the rate of change of $\phi$ with respect to $s$.

▲ **Figure 12.5.8**

which tells us that curvature in 2-space can be interpreted as the magnitude of the rate of change of $\phi$ with respect to $s$—the greater the curvature, the more rapidly $\phi$ changes with $s$ (Figure 12.5.8). In the case of a straight line, the angle $\phi$ is constant (Figure 12.5.9) and consequently $\kappa(s) = |d\phi/ds| = 0$, which is consistent with the fact that a straight line has zero curvature at every point.

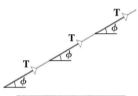

$\phi$ is constant, so the line has zero curvature.

▲ **Figure 12.5.9**

### ▮ FORMULA SUMMARY

We conclude this section with a summary of formulas for $\mathbf{T}$, $\mathbf{N}$, and $\mathbf{B}$. These formulas have either been derived in the text or are easily derivable from formulas we have already established.

$$\mathbf{T}(s) = \mathbf{r}'(s) \tag{9}$$

$$\mathbf{N}(s) = \frac{1}{\kappa(s)}\frac{d\mathbf{T}}{ds} = \frac{\mathbf{r}''(s)}{\|\mathbf{r}''(s)\|} = \frac{\mathbf{r}''(s)}{\kappa(s)} \tag{10}$$

$$\mathbf{B}(s) = \frac{\mathbf{r}'(s) \times \mathbf{r}''(s)}{\|\mathbf{r}''(s)\|} = \frac{\mathbf{r}'(s) \times \mathbf{r}''(s)}{\kappa(s)} \tag{11}$$

$$\mathbf{T}(t) = \frac{\mathbf{r}'(t)}{\|\mathbf{r}'(t)\|} \tag{12}$$

$$\mathbf{B}(t) = \frac{\mathbf{r}'(t) \times \mathbf{r}''(t)}{\|\mathbf{r}'(t) \times \mathbf{r}''(t)\|} \tag{13}$$

$$\mathbf{N}(t) = \mathbf{B}(t) \times \mathbf{T}(t) \tag{14}$$

---

### ✔ QUICK CHECK EXERCISES 12.5   (See page 881 for answers.)

1. If $C$ is a smooth curve parametrized by arc length, then the curvature is defined by $\kappa(s) = $ _____.

2. Let $\mathbf{r}(t)$ be a smooth vector-valued function with curvature $\kappa(t)$.
   (a) The curvature may be expressed in terms of $\mathbf{T}'(t)$ and $\mathbf{r}'(t)$ as $\kappa(t) = $ _____.
   (b) The curvature may be expressed directly in terms of $\mathbf{r}'(t)$ and $\mathbf{r}''(t)$ as $\kappa(t) = $ _____.

3. Suppose that $C$ is the graph of a smooth vector-valued function $\mathbf{r}(s) = \langle x(s), y(s) \rangle$ parametrized by arc length and that the unit tangent $\mathbf{T}(s) = \langle \cos\phi(s), \sin\phi(s) \rangle$. Then the curvature can be expressed in terms of $\phi(s)$ as $\kappa(s) = $ _____.

4. Suppose that $C$ is a smooth curve and that $x^2 + y^2 = 4$ is the osculating circle to $C$ at $P(1, \sqrt{3})$. Then the curvature of $C$ at $P$ is _____.

**EXERCISE SET 12.5**    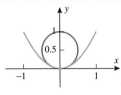 Graphing Utility    [c] CAS

**1–2** Use the osculating circle shown in the figure to estimate the curvature at the indicated point. ▨

**1.**          **2.**

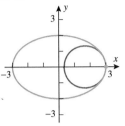

**3–4** For a plane curve $y = f(x)$ the curvature at $(x, f(x))$ is a function $\kappa(x)$. In these exercises the graphs of $f(x)$ and $\kappa(x)$ are shown. Determine which is which and explain your reasoning. ▨

**3.** (a)          (b)

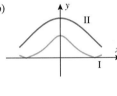

**4.** (a)          (b)

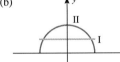

**5–12** Use Formula (3) to find $\kappa(t)$. ▨

**5.** $\mathbf{r}(t) = t^2\mathbf{i} + t^3\mathbf{j}$          **6.** $\mathbf{r}(t) = 4\cos t\mathbf{i} + \sin t\mathbf{j}$

**7.** $\mathbf{r}(t) = e^{3t}\mathbf{i} + e^{-t}\mathbf{j}$          **8.** $x = 1 - t^3, \ y = t - t^2$

**9.** $\mathbf{r}(t) = 4\cos t\mathbf{i} + 4\sin t\mathbf{j} + t\mathbf{k}$

**10.** $\mathbf{r}(t) = t\mathbf{i} + \frac{1}{2}t^2\mathbf{j} + \frac{1}{3}t^3\mathbf{k}$

**11.** $x = \cosh t, \ y = \sinh t, \ z = t$

**12.** $\mathbf{r}(t) = \mathbf{i} + t\mathbf{j} + t^2\mathbf{k}$

**13–16** Find the curvature and the radius of curvature at the stated point. ▨

**13.** $\mathbf{r}(t) = 3\cos t\mathbf{i} + 4\sin t\mathbf{j} + t\mathbf{k}; \ t = \pi/2$

**14.** $\mathbf{r}(t) = e^t\mathbf{i} + e^{-t}\mathbf{j} + t\mathbf{k}; \ t = 0$

**15.** $x = e^t \cos t, \ y = e^t \sin t, \ z = e^t; \ t = 0$

**16.** $x = \sin t, \ y = \cos t, \ z = \frac{1}{2}t^2; \ t = 0$

**17–18** Confirm that $s$ is an arc length parameter by showing that $\|d\mathbf{r}/ds\| = 1$, and then apply Formula (1) to find $\kappa(s)$. ▨

**17.** $\mathbf{r} = \sin\left(1 + \dfrac{s}{2}\right)\mathbf{i} + \cos\left(1 + \dfrac{s}{2}\right)\mathbf{j} + \sqrt{3}\left(1 + \dfrac{s}{2}\right)\mathbf{k}$

**18.** $\mathbf{r} = \left(1 - \frac{2}{3}s\right)^{3/2}\mathbf{i} + \left(\frac{2}{3}s\right)^{3/2}\mathbf{j} \quad \left(0 \le s \le \frac{3}{2}\right)$

**19–22 True–False** Determine whether the statement is true or false. Explain your answer. ▨

**19.** A circle of radius 2 has constant curvature $\frac{1}{2}$.

**20.** A vertical line in 2-space has undefined curvature.

**21.** If $\mathbf{r}(s)$ is parametrized by arc length, then the curvature of the graph of $\mathbf{r}(s)$ is the length of $\mathbf{r}'(s)$.

**22.** If $C$ is a curve in 2-space, then the osculating circle to $C$ at a point $P$ has radius equal to the curvature of $C$ at $P$.

**23.** (a) Use Formula (3) to show that in 2-space the curvature of a smooth parametric curve

$$x = x(t), \quad y = y(t)$$

is

$$\kappa(t) = \frac{|x'y'' - y'x''|}{(x'^2 + y'^2)^{3/2}}$$

where primes denote differentiation with respect to $t$.

(b) Use the result in part (a) to show that in 2-space the curvature of the plane curve given by $y = f(x)$ is

$$\kappa(x) = \frac{|d^2y/dx^2|}{[1 + (dy/dx)^2]^{3/2}}$$

[*Hint:* Express $y = f(x)$ parametrically with $x = t$ as the parameter.]

**24.** Use part (b) of Exercise 23 to show that the curvature of $y = f(x)$ can be expressed in terms of the angle of inclination of the tangent line as

$$\kappa(\phi) = \left|\frac{d^2y}{dx^2}\cos^3\phi\right|$$

[*Hint:* $\tan\phi = dy/dx$.]

**25–28** Use the result in Exercise 23(b) to find the curvature at the stated point. ▨

**25.** $y = \sin x; \ x = \pi/2$          **26.** $y = \tan x; \ x = \pi/4$

**27.** $y = e^{-x}; \ x = 1$          **28.** $y^2 - 4x^2 = 9; \ (2, 5)$

**29–32** Use the result in Exercise 23(a) to find the curvature at the stated point. ▨

**29.** $x = t^2, y = t^3; \ t = \frac{1}{2}$          **30.** $x = e^{3t}, y = e^{-t}; \ t = 0$

**31.** $x = t, y = 1/t; \ t = 1$

**32.** $x = 2\sin 2t, y = 3\sin t; \ t = \pi/2$

**33.** In each part, use the formulas in Exercise 23 to help find the radius of curvature at the stated points. Then sketch the graph together with the osculating circles at those points.

(a) $y = \cos x$ at $x = 0$ and $x = \pi$

(b) $x = 2\cos t, y = \sin t \ (0 \le t \le 2\pi)$ at $t = 0$ and $t = \pi/2$

**34.** Use the formula in Exercise 23(a) to find $\kappa(t)$ for the curve $x = e^{-t}\cos t, y = e^{-t}\sin t$. Then sketch the graph of $\kappa(t)$.

**35–36** Generate the graph of $y = f(x)$ using a graphing utility, and then make a conjecture about the shape of the graph of $y = \kappa(x)$. Check your conjecture by generating the graph of $y = \kappa(x)$. ■

**35.** $f(x) = xe^{-x}$   for $0 \le x \le 5$

**36.** $f(x) = x^3 - x$   for $-1 \le x \le 1$

**C 37.** (a) If you have a CAS, read the documentation on calculating higher-order derivatives. Then use the CAS and part (b) of Exercise 23 to find $\kappa(x)$ for $f(x) = x^4 - 2x^2$.
 (b) Use the CAS to generate the graphs of $f(x) = x^4 - 2x^2$ and $\kappa(x)$ on the same screen for $-2 \le x \le 2$.
 (c) Find the radius of curvature at each relative extremum.
 (d) Make a reasonably accurate hand-drawn sketch that shows the graph of $f(x) = x^4 - 2x^2$ and the osculating circles in their correct proportions at the relative extrema.

**C 38.** (a) Use a CAS to graph the parametric curve $x = t \cos t$, $y = t \sin t$ for $t \ge 0$.
 (b) Make a conjecture about the behavior of the curvature $\kappa(t)$ as $t \to +\infty$.
 (c) Use the CAS and part (a) of Exercise 23 to find $\kappa(t)$.
 (d) Check your conjecture by finding the limit of $\kappa(t)$ as $t \to +\infty$.

**39.** Use the formula in Exercise 23(a) to show that for a curve in polar coordinates described by $r = f(\theta)$ the curvature is

$$\kappa(\theta) = \frac{\left| r^2 + 2\left(\dfrac{dr}{d\theta}\right)^2 - r\dfrac{d^2r}{d\theta^2} \right|}{\left[ r^2 + \left(\dfrac{dr}{d\theta}\right)^2 \right]^{3/2}}$$

[*Hint:* Let $\theta$ be the parameter and use the relationships $x = r \cos\theta$, $y = r \sin\theta$.]

**40.** Use the result in Exercise 39 to show that a circle has constant curvature.

**41–44** Use the formula in Exercise 39 to find the curvature at the indicated point. ■

**41.** $r = 1 + \cos\theta$; $\theta = \pi/2$   **42.** $r = e^{2\theta}$; $\theta = 1$

**43.** $r = \sin 3\theta$; $\theta = 0$   **44.** $r = \theta$; $\theta = 1$

**45.** Find the radius of curvature of the parabola $y^2 = 4px$ at $(0, 0)$.

**46.** At what point(s) does $y = e^x$ have maximum curvature?

**47.** At what point(s) does $4x^2 + 9y^2 = 36$ have minimum radius of curvature?

**48.** Find the maximum and minimum values of the radius of curvature for the curve $x = \cos t$, $y = \sin t$, $z = \cos t$.

**49.** Use the formula in Exercise 39 to show that the curvature of the polar curve $r = e^{a\theta}$ is inversely proportional to $r$.

**C 50.** Use the formula in Exercise 39 and a CAS to show that the curvature of the lemniscate $r = \sqrt{a \cos 2\theta}$ is directly proportional to $r$.

**51.** (a) Use the result in Exercise 24 to show that for the parabola $y = x^2$ the curvature $\kappa(\phi)$ at points where the tangent line has an angle of inclination of $\phi$ is

$$\kappa(\phi) = |2 \cos^3 \phi|$$

 (b) Use the result in part (a) to find the radius of curvature of the parabola at the point on the parabola where the tangent line has slope 1.
 (c) Make a sketch with reasonably accurate proportions that shows the osculating circle at the point on the parabola where the tangent line has slope 1.

**52.** The *evolute* of a smooth parametric curve $C$ in 2-space is the curve formed from the centers of curvature of $C$. The accompanying figure shows the ellipse $x = 3 \cos t$, $y = 2 \sin t$ $(0 \le t \le 2\pi)$ and its evolute graphed together.
 (a) Which points on the evolute correspond to $t = 0$ and $t = \pi/2$?
 (b) In what direction is the evolute traced as $t$ increases from 0 to $2\pi$?
 (c) What does the evolute of a circle look like? Explain your reasoning.

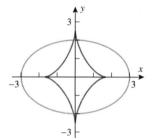

◀ **Figure Ex-52**

**53–57** These exercises are concerned with the problem of creating a single smooth curve by piecing together two separate smooth curves. If two smooth curves $C_1$ and $C_2$ are joined at a point $P$ to form a curve $C$, then we will say that $C_1$ and $C_2$ make a *smooth transition* at $P$ if the curvature of $C$ is continuous at $P$. ■

**53.** Show that the transition at $x = 0$ from the horizontal line $y = 0$ for $x \le 0$ to the parabola $y = x^2$ for $x > 0$ is not smooth, whereas the transition to $y = x^3$ for $x > 0$ is smooth.

**54.** (a) Sketch the graph of the curve defined piecewise by $y = x^2$ for $x < 0$, $y = x^4$ for $x \ge 0$.
 (b) Show that for the curve in part (a) the transition at $x = 0$ is not smooth.

**55.** The accompanying figure on the next page shows the arc of a circle of radius $r$ with center at $(0, r)$. Find the value of $a$ so that there is a smooth transition from the circle to the parabola $y = ax^2$ at the point where $x = 0$.

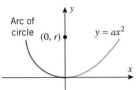

Figure Ex-55

**56.** Find $a, b,$ and $c$ so that there is a smooth transition at $x = 0$ from the curve $y = e^x$ for $x \le 0$ to the parabola $y = ax^2 + bx + c$ for $x > 0$. [*Hint:* The curvature is continuous at those points where $y''$ is continuous.]

**57.** Assume that $f$ is a function for which $f'''(x)$ is defined for all $x \le 0$. Explain why it is always possible to find numbers $a, b,$ and $c$ such that there is a smooth transition at $x = 0$ from the curve $y = f(x)$, $x \le 0$, to the parabola $y = ax^2 + bx + c$.

**58–61** Assume that $s$ is an arc length parameter for a smooth vector-valued function $\mathbf{r}(s)$ in 3-space and that $d\mathbf{T}/ds$ and $d\mathbf{N}/ds$ exist at each point on the curve. (This implies that $d\mathbf{B}/ds$ exists as well, since $\mathbf{B} = \mathbf{T} \times \mathbf{N}$.) ∎

**58.** Show that
$$\frac{d\mathbf{T}}{ds} = \kappa(s)\mathbf{N}(s)$$
and use this result to obtain the formulas in (10).

**59.** (a) Show that $d\mathbf{B}/ds$ is perpendicular to $\mathbf{B}(s)$.
 (b) Show that $d\mathbf{B}/ds$ is perpendicular to $\mathbf{T}(s)$. [*Hint:* Use the fact that $\mathbf{B}(s)$ is perpendicular to both $\mathbf{T}(s)$ and $\mathbf{N}(s)$, and differentiate $\mathbf{B} \cdot \mathbf{T}$ with respect to $s$.]
 (c) Use the results in parts (a) and (b) to show that $d\mathbf{B}/ds$ is a scalar multiple of $\mathbf{N}(s)$. The *negative* of this scalar is called the **torsion** of $\mathbf{r}(s)$ and is denoted by $\tau(s)$. Thus,
$$\frac{d\mathbf{B}}{ds} = -\tau(s)\mathbf{N}(s)$$
 (d) Show that $\tau(s) = 0$ for all $s$ if the graph of $\mathbf{r}(s)$ lies in a plane. [*Note:* For reasons that we cannot discuss here, the torsion is related to the "twisting" properties of the curve, and $\tau(s)$ is regarded as a numerical measure of the tendency for the curve to twist out of the osculating plane.]

**60.** Let $\kappa$ be the curvature of $C$ and $\tau$ the torsion (defined in Exercise 59). By differentiating $\mathbf{N} = \mathbf{B} \times \mathbf{T}$ with respect to $s$, show that $d\mathbf{N}/ds = -\kappa\mathbf{T} + \tau\mathbf{B}$.

**61.** The following derivatives, known as the **Frenet–Serret formulas**, are fundamental in the theory of curves in 3-space:
$$d\mathbf{T}/ds = \kappa\mathbf{N} \qquad \text{[Exercise 58]}$$
$$d\mathbf{N}/ds = -\kappa\mathbf{T} + \tau\mathbf{B} \qquad \text{[Exercise 60]}$$
$$d\mathbf{B}/ds = -\tau\mathbf{N} \qquad \text{[Exercise 59(c)]}$$

Use the first two Frenet–Serret formulas and the fact that $\mathbf{r}'(s) = \mathbf{T}$ if $\mathbf{r} = \mathbf{r}(s)$ to show that
$$\tau = \frac{[\mathbf{r}'(s) \times \mathbf{r}''(s)] \cdot \mathbf{r}'''(s)}{\|\mathbf{r}''(s)\|^2} \quad \text{and} \quad \mathbf{B} = \frac{\mathbf{r}'(s) \times \mathbf{r}''(s)}{\|\mathbf{r}''(s)\|}$$

**62.** (a) Use the chain rule and the first two Frenet–Serret formulas in Exercise 61 to show that
$$\mathbf{T}' = \kappa s'\mathbf{N} \quad \text{and} \quad \mathbf{N}' = -\kappa s'\mathbf{T} + \tau s'\mathbf{B}$$
 where primes denote differentiation with respect to $t$.
 (b) Show that Formulas (4) and (6) can be written in the form
$$\mathbf{r}'(t) = s'\mathbf{T} \quad \text{and} \quad \mathbf{r}''(t) = s''\mathbf{T} + \kappa(s')^2\mathbf{N}$$
 (c) Use the results in parts (a) and (b) to show that
$$\mathbf{r}'''(t) = [s''' - \kappa^2(s')^3]\mathbf{T}$$
$$+ [3\kappa s's'' + \kappa'(s')^2]\mathbf{N} + \kappa\tau(s')^3\mathbf{B}$$
 (d) Use the results in parts (b) and (c) to show that
$$\tau(t) = \frac{[\mathbf{r}'(t) \times \mathbf{r}''(t)] \cdot \mathbf{r}'''(t)}{\|\mathbf{r}'(t) \times \mathbf{r}''(t)\|^2}$$

**63–66** Use the formula in Exercise 62(d) to find the torsion $\tau = \tau(t)$. ∎

**63.** The twisted cubic $\mathbf{r}(t) = 2t\mathbf{i} + t^2\mathbf{j} + \frac{1}{3}t^3\mathbf{k}$

**64.** The circular helix $\mathbf{r}(t) = a\cos t\mathbf{i} + a\sin t\mathbf{j} + ct\mathbf{k}$

**65.** $\mathbf{r}(t) = e^t\mathbf{i} + e^{-t}\mathbf{j} + \sqrt{2}t\mathbf{k}$

**66.** $\mathbf{r}(t) = (t - \sin t)\mathbf{i} + (1 - \cos t)\mathbf{j} + t\mathbf{k}$

**67.** Writing One property of a twice-differentiable function $f(x)$ is that an inflection point on the graph is a point at which the tangent line crosses the graph of $f$. Consider the analogous issue in 2-space for an osculating circle to a curve $C$ at a point $P$: What does it mean for the osculating circle to cross (or not to cross) $C$ at $P$? Investigate this issue through some examples of your own and write a brief essay, with illustrations, supporting your conclusions.

**68.** Writing The accompanying figure is the graph of the radius of curvature versus $\theta$ in rectangular coordinates for the cardioid $r = 1 + \cos\theta$. In words, explain what the graph tells you about the cardioid.

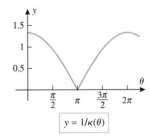

Figure Ex-68

## ✔ QUICK CHECK ANSWERS 12.5

**1.** $\left\|\dfrac{d\mathbf{T}}{ds}\right\| = \|\mathbf{r}''(s)\|$   **2.** (a) $\dfrac{\|\mathbf{T}'(t)\|}{\|\mathbf{r}'(t)\|}$   (b) $\dfrac{\|\mathbf{r}'(t) \times \mathbf{r}''(t)\|}{\|\mathbf{r}'(t)\|^3}$   **3.** $\left|\dfrac{d\phi}{ds}\right|$   **4.** $\dfrac{1}{2}$

## 12.6 MOTION ALONG A CURVE

*In earlier sections we considered the motion of a particle along a line. In that situation there are only two directions in which the particle can move—the positive direction or the negative direction. Motion in 2-space or 3-space is more complicated because there are infinitely many directions in which a particle can move. In this section we will show how vectors can be used to analyze motion along curves in 2-space or 3-space.*

### ■ VELOCITY, ACCELERATION, AND SPEED

Let us assume that the motion of a particle in 2-space or 3-space is described by a smooth vector-valued function $\mathbf{r}(t)$ in which the parameter $t$ denotes time; we will call this the *position function* or *trajectory* of the particle. As the particle moves along its trajectory, its direction of motion and its speed can vary from instant to instant. Thus, before we can undertake any analysis of such motion, we must have clear answers to the following questions:

- What is the direction of motion of the particle at an instant of time?
- What is the speed of the particle at an instant of time?

We will define the direction of motion at time $t$ to be the direction of the unit tangent vector $\mathbf{T}(t)$, and we will define the speed to be $ds/dt$—the instantaneous rate of change of the arc length traveled by the particle from an arbitrary reference point. Taking this a step further, we will combine the speed and the direction of motion to form the vector

$$\mathbf{v}(t) = \frac{ds}{dt}\mathbf{T}(t) \tag{1}$$

which we call the *velocity* of the particle at time $t$. Thus, at each instant of time the velocity vector $\mathbf{v}(t)$ points in the direction of motion and has a magnitude that is equal to the speed of the particle (Figure 12.6.1).

Recall that for motion along a coordinate line the velocity function is the derivative of the position function. The same is true for motion along a curve, since

$$\frac{d\mathbf{r}}{dt} = \frac{d\mathbf{r}}{ds}\frac{ds}{dt} = \frac{ds}{dt}\mathbf{T}(t) = \mathbf{v}(t)$$

For motion along a coordinate line the acceleration function was defined to be the derivative of the velocity function. The definition is the same for motion along a curve.

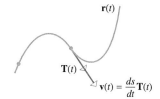

The length of the velocity vector is the speed of the particle, and the direction of the velocity vector is the direction of motion.

▲ **Figure 12.6.1**

**12.6.1 DEFINITION** If $\mathbf{r}(t)$ is the position function of a particle moving along a curve in 2-space or 3-space, then the *instantaneous velocity*, *instantaneous acceleration*, and *instantaneous speed* of the particle at time $t$ are defined by

$$\text{velocity} = \mathbf{v}(t) = \frac{d\mathbf{r}}{dt} \tag{2}$$

$$\text{acceleration} = \mathbf{a}(t) = \frac{d\mathbf{v}}{dt} = \frac{d^2\mathbf{r}}{dt^2} \tag{3}$$

$$\text{speed} = \|\mathbf{v}(t)\| = \frac{ds}{dt} \tag{4}$$

As shown in Table 12.6.1, the position, velocity, acceleration, and speed can also be expressed in component form.

**Table 12.6.1**

FORMULAS FOR POSITION, VELOCITY, ACCELERATION, AND SPEED

|  | 2-SPACE | 3-SPACE |
|---|---|---|
| **POSITION** | $\mathbf{r}(t) = x(t)\mathbf{i} + y(t)\mathbf{j}$ | $\mathbf{r}(t) = x(t)\mathbf{i} + y(t)\mathbf{j} + z(t)\mathbf{k}$ |
| **VELOCITY** | $\mathbf{v}(t) = \dfrac{dx}{dt}\mathbf{i} + \dfrac{dy}{dt}\mathbf{j}$ | $\mathbf{v}(t) = \dfrac{dx}{dt}\mathbf{i} + \dfrac{dy}{dt}\mathbf{j} + \dfrac{dz}{dt}\mathbf{k}$ |
| **ACCELERATION** | $\mathbf{a}(t) = \dfrac{d^2x}{dt^2}\mathbf{i} + \dfrac{d^2y}{dt^2}\mathbf{j}$ | $\mathbf{a}(t) = \dfrac{d^2x}{dt^2}\mathbf{i} + \dfrac{d^2y}{dt^2}\mathbf{j} + \dfrac{d^2z}{dt^2}\mathbf{k}$ |
| **SPEED** | $\|\mathbf{v}(t)\| = \sqrt{\left(\dfrac{dx}{dt}\right)^2 + \left(\dfrac{dy}{dt}\right)^2}$ | $\|\mathbf{v}(t)\| = \sqrt{\left(\dfrac{dx}{dt}\right)^2 + \left(\dfrac{dy}{dt}\right)^2 + \left(\dfrac{dz}{dt}\right)^2}$ |

▶ **Example 1**   A particle moves along a circular path in such a way that its $x$- and $y$-coordinates at time $t$ are
$$x = 2\cos t, \quad y = 2\sin t$$

(a) Find the instantaneous velocity and speed of the particle at time $t$.

(b) Sketch the path of the particle, and show the position and velocity vectors at time $t = \pi/4$ with the velocity vector drawn so that its initial point is at the tip of the position vector.

(c) Show that at each instant the acceleration vector is perpendicular to the velocity vector.

*Solution (a).*   At time $t$, the position vector is
$$\mathbf{r}(t) = 2\cos t\,\mathbf{i} + 2\sin t\,\mathbf{j}$$

so the instantaneous velocity and speed are
$$\mathbf{v}(t) = \frac{d\mathbf{r}}{dt} = -2\sin t\,\mathbf{i} + 2\cos t\,\mathbf{j}$$
$$\|\mathbf{v}(t)\| = \sqrt{(-2\sin t)^2 + (2\cos t)^2} = 2$$

*Solution (b).*   The graph of the parametric equations is a circle of radius 2 centered at the origin. At time $t = \pi/4$ the position and velocity vectors of the particle are
$$\mathbf{r}(\pi/4) = 2\cos(\pi/4)\mathbf{i} + 2\sin(\pi/4)\mathbf{j} = \sqrt{2}\mathbf{i} + \sqrt{2}\mathbf{j}$$
$$\mathbf{v}(\pi/4) = -2\sin(\pi/4)\mathbf{i} + 2\cos(\pi/4)\mathbf{j} = -\sqrt{2}\mathbf{i} + \sqrt{2}\mathbf{j}$$

These vectors and the circle are shown in Figure 12.6.2.

*Solution (c).*   At time $t$, the acceleration vector is
$$\mathbf{a}(t) = \frac{d\mathbf{v}}{dt} = -2\cos t\,\mathbf{i} - 2\sin t\,\mathbf{j}$$

One way of showing that $\mathbf{v}(t)$ and $\mathbf{a}(t)$ are perpendicular is to show that their dot product is zero (try it). However, it is easier to observe that $\mathbf{a}(t)$ is the negative of $\mathbf{r}(t)$, which implies that $\mathbf{v}(t)$ and $\mathbf{a}(t)$ are perpendicular, since at each point on a circle the radius and tangent line are perpendicular. ◀

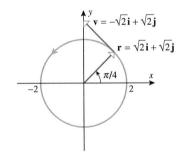

▲ Figure 12.6.2

How could you apply Theorem 12.2.8 to answer part (c) of Example 1?

Since $\mathbf{v}(t)$ can be obtained by differentiating $\mathbf{r}(t)$, and since $\mathbf{a}(t)$ can be obtained by differentiating $\mathbf{v}(t)$, it follows that $\mathbf{r}(t)$ can be obtained by integrating $\mathbf{v}(t)$, and $\mathbf{v}(t)$ can be obtained by integrating $\mathbf{a}(t)$. However, such integrations do not produce unique functions because constants of integration occur. Typically, initial conditions are required to determine these constants.

▶ **Example 2** A particle moves through 3-space in such a way that its velocity is

$$\mathbf{v}(t) = \mathbf{i} + t\mathbf{j} + t^2\mathbf{k}$$

Find the coordinates of the particle at time $t = 1$ given that the particle is at the point $(-1, 2, 4)$ at time $t = 0$.

*Solution.* Integrating the velocity function to obtain the position function yields

$$\mathbf{r}(t) = \int \mathbf{v}(t)\,dt = \int (\mathbf{i} + t\mathbf{j} + t^2\mathbf{k})\,dt = t\mathbf{i} + \frac{t^2}{2}\mathbf{j} + \frac{t^3}{3}\mathbf{k} + \mathbf{C} \qquad (5)$$

where $\mathbf{C}$ is a vector constant of integration. Since the coordinates of the particle at time $t = 0$ are $(-1, 2, 4)$, the position vector at time $t = 0$ is

$$\mathbf{r}(0) = -\mathbf{i} + 2\mathbf{j} + 4\mathbf{k} \qquad (6)$$

It follows on substituting $t = 0$ in (5) and equating the result with (6) that

$$\mathbf{C} = -\mathbf{i} + 2\mathbf{j} + 4\mathbf{k}$$

Substituting this value of $\mathbf{C}$ in (5) and simplifying yields

$$\mathbf{r}(t) = (t - 1)\mathbf{i} + \left(\frac{t^2}{2} + 2\right)\mathbf{j} + \left(\frac{t^3}{3} + 4\right)\mathbf{k}$$

Thus, at time $t = 1$ the position vector of the particle is

$$\mathbf{r}(1) = 0\mathbf{i} + \frac{5}{2}\mathbf{j} + \frac{13}{3}\mathbf{k}$$

so its coordinates at that instant are $\left(0, \frac{5}{2}, \frac{13}{3}\right)$. ◀

## DISPLACEMENT AND DISTANCE TRAVELED

If a particle travels along a curve $C$ in 2-space or 3-space, the **displacement** of the particle over the time interval $t_1 \leq t \leq t_2$ is commonly denoted by $\Delta\mathbf{r}$ and is defined as

$$\Delta\mathbf{r} = \mathbf{r}(t_2) - \mathbf{r}(t_1) \qquad (7)$$

(Figure 12.6.3). The displacement vector, which describes the change in position of the particle during the time interval, can be obtained by integrating the velocity function from $t_1$ to $t_2$:

$$\Delta\mathbf{r} = \int_{t_1}^{t_2} \mathbf{v}(t)\,dt = \int_{t_1}^{t_2} \frac{d\mathbf{r}}{dt}\,dt = \mathbf{r}(t)\Big]_{t_1}^{t_2} = \mathbf{r}(t_2) - \mathbf{r}(t_1) \qquad \boxed{\text{Displacement}} \qquad (8)$$

It follows from Theorem 12.3.1 that we can find the distance $s$ traveled by a particle over a time interval $t_1 \leq t \leq t_2$ by integrating the speed over that interval, since

$$s = \int_{t_1}^{t_2} \left\|\frac{d\mathbf{r}}{dt}\right\|\,dt = \int_{t_1}^{t_2} \|\mathbf{v}(t)\|\,dt \qquad \boxed{\text{Distance traveled}} \qquad (9)$$

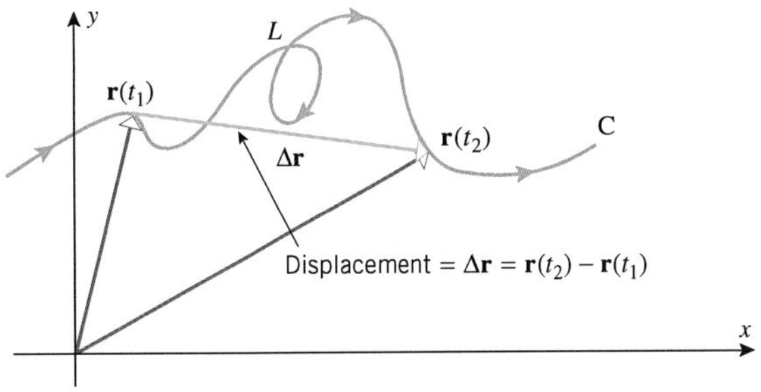

▶ **Figure 12.6.3**

▶ **Example 3**  Suppose that a particle moves along a circular helix in 3-space so that its position vector at time $t$ is

$$\mathbf{r}(t) = (4\cos \pi t)\mathbf{i} + (4\sin \pi t)\mathbf{j} + t\mathbf{k}$$

Find the distance traveled and the displacement of the particle during the time interval $1 \leq t \leq 5$.

*Solution.*  We have

$$\mathbf{v}(t) = \frac{d\mathbf{r}}{dt} = (-4\pi \sin \pi t)\mathbf{i} + (4\pi \cos \pi t)\mathbf{j} + \mathbf{k}$$

$$\|\mathbf{v}(t)\| = \sqrt{(-4\pi \sin \pi t)^2 + (4\pi \cos \pi t)^2 + 1} = \sqrt{16\pi^2 + 1}$$

Thus, it follows from (9) that the distance traveled by the particle from time $t = 1$ to $t = 5$ is

$$s = \int_1^5 \sqrt{16\pi^2 + 1}\, dt = 4\sqrt{16\pi^2 + 1}$$

Moreover, it follows from (8) that the displacement over the time interval is

$$\Delta \mathbf{r} = \mathbf{r}(5) - \mathbf{r}(1)$$
$$= (4\cos 5\pi \mathbf{i} + 4\sin 5\pi \mathbf{j} + 5\mathbf{k}) - (4\cos \pi \mathbf{i} + 4\sin \pi \mathbf{j} + \mathbf{k})$$
$$= (-4\mathbf{i} + 5\mathbf{k}) - (-4\mathbf{i} + \mathbf{k}) = 4\mathbf{k}$$

which tells us that the change in the position of the particle over the time interval was 4 units straight up. ◀

### NORMAL AND TANGENTIAL COMPONENTS OF ACCELERATION

You know from your experience as an automobile passenger that if a car speeds up rapidly, then your body is thrown back against the backrest of the seat. You also know that if the car rounds a turn in the road, then your body is thrown toward the outside of the curve—the greater the curvature in the road, the greater this effect. The explanation of these effects can be understood by resolving the velocity and acceleration components of the motion into vector components that are parallel to the unit tangent and unit normal vectors. The following theorem explains how to do this.

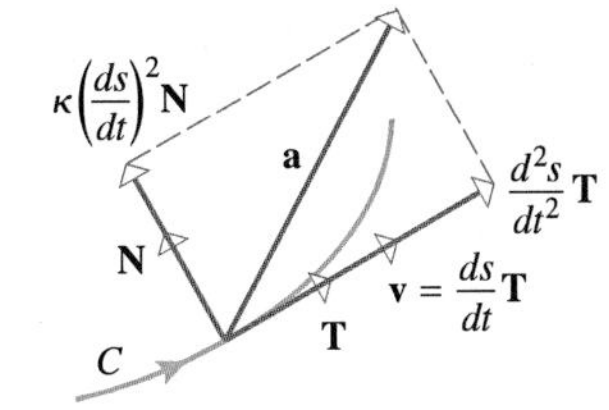

▲ **Figure 12.6.4**

**12.6.2  THEOREM**  *If a particle moves along a smooth curve C in 2-space or 3-space, then at each point on the curve velocity and acceleration vectors can be written as*

$$\mathbf{v} = \frac{ds}{dt}\mathbf{T} \qquad \mathbf{a} = \frac{d^2 s}{dt^2}\mathbf{T} + \kappa\left(\frac{ds}{dt}\right)^2 \mathbf{N} \qquad (10\text{--}11)$$

*where s is an arc length parameter for the curve, and* **T**, **N**, *and* $\kappa$ *denote the unit tangent vector, unit normal vector, and curvature at the point (Figure 12.6.4).*

PROOF   Formula (10) is just a restatement of (1). To obtain (11), we differentiate both sides of (10) with respect to $t$; this yields

$$\mathbf{a} = \frac{d}{dt}\left(\frac{ds}{dt}\mathbf{T}\right) = \frac{d^2 s}{dt^2}\mathbf{T} + \frac{ds}{dt}\frac{d\mathbf{T}}{dt}$$

$$= \frac{d^2 s}{dt^2}\mathbf{T} + \frac{ds}{dt}\frac{d\mathbf{T}}{ds}\frac{ds}{dt}$$

$$= \frac{d^2 s}{dt^2}\mathbf{T} + \left(\frac{ds}{dt}\right)^2 \frac{d\mathbf{T}}{ds}$$

$$= \frac{d^2 s}{dt^2}\mathbf{T} + \left(\frac{ds}{dt}\right)^2 \kappa\mathbf{N} \qquad \boxed{\text{Formula (10) of Section 12.5}}$$

from which (11) follows. ∎

The coefficients of $\mathbf{T}$ and $\mathbf{N}$ in (11) are commonly denoted by

$$a_T = \frac{d^2 s}{dt^2} \qquad a_N = \kappa\left(\frac{ds}{dt}\right)^2 \qquad (12\text{–}13)$$

in which case Formula (11) is expressed as

$$\mathbf{a} = a_T \mathbf{T} + a_N \mathbf{N} \qquad (14)$$

Formula (14) applies to motion in both 2-space and 3-space. What is interesting is that the 3-space formula does not involve the binormal vector $\mathbf{B}$, so the acceleration vector always lies in the plane of $\mathbf{T}$ and $\mathbf{N}$ (the osculating plane), even for highly twisting paths of motion (Figure 12.6.5).

In this formula the scalars $a_T$ and $a_N$ are called the *tangential scalar component of acceleration* and the *normal scalar component of acceleration*, and the vectors $a_T \mathbf{T}$ and $a_N \mathbf{N}$ are called the *tangential vector component of acceleration* and the *normal vector component of acceleration*.

The scalar components of acceleration explain the effect that you experience when a car speeds up rapidly or rounds a turn. The rapid increase in speed produces a large value for $d^2 s/dt^2$, which results in a large tangential scalar component of acceleration; and by Newton's second law this corresponds to a large tangential force on the car in the direction of motion. To understand the effect of rounding a turn, observe that the normal scalar component of acceleration has the curvature $\kappa$ and the square of the speed $ds/dt$ as factors. Thus, sharp turns or turns taken at high speed both correspond to large normal forces on the car.

Although Formulas (12) and (13) provide useful insight into the behavior of particles moving along curved paths, they are not always the best formulas for computations. The following theorem provides some more useful formulas that relate $a_T$, $a_N$, and $\kappa$ to the velocity $\mathbf{v}$ and acceleration $\mathbf{a}$.

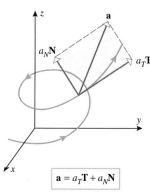

$$\mathbf{a} = a_T \mathbf{T} + a_N \mathbf{N}$$

▲ **Figure 12.6.5**

Theorem 12.6.3 applies to motion in 2-space and 3-space, but for motion in 2-space you will have to add a zero $\mathbf{k}$ component to $\mathbf{v}$ to calculate the cross product.

**12.6.3   THEOREM**   *If a particle moves along a smooth curve C in 2-space or 3-space, then at each point on the curve the velocity $\mathbf{v}$ and the acceleration $\mathbf{a}$ are related to $a_T$, $a_N$, and $\kappa$ by the formulas*

$$a_T = \frac{\mathbf{v} \cdot \mathbf{a}}{\|\mathbf{v}\|} \qquad a_N = \frac{\|\mathbf{v} \times \mathbf{a}\|}{\|\mathbf{v}\|} \qquad \kappa = \frac{\|\mathbf{v} \times \mathbf{a}\|}{\|\mathbf{v}\|^3} \qquad (15\text{–}17)$$

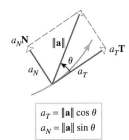

$a_T = \|\mathbf{a}\| \cos\theta$
$a_N = \|\mathbf{a}\| \sin\theta$

▲ **Figure 12.6.6**

PROOF   As illustrated in Figure 12.6.6, let $\theta$ be the angle between the vector $\mathbf{a}$ and the vector $a_T\mathbf{T}$. Thus,
$$a_T = \|\mathbf{a}\| \cos\theta \quad \text{and} \quad a_N = \|\mathbf{a}\| \sin\theta$$

from which we obtain
$$a_T = \|\mathbf{a}\| \cos\theta = \frac{\|\mathbf{v}\| \|\mathbf{a}\| \cos\theta}{\|\mathbf{v}\|} = \frac{\mathbf{v} \cdot \mathbf{a}}{\|\mathbf{v}\|}$$

$$a_N = \|\mathbf{a}\| \sin\theta = \frac{\|\mathbf{v}\| \|\mathbf{a}\| \sin\theta}{\|\mathbf{v}\|} = \frac{\|\mathbf{v} \times \mathbf{a}\|}{\|\mathbf{v}\|}$$

$$\kappa = \frac{a_N}{(ds/dt)^2} = \frac{a_N}{\|\mathbf{v}\|^2} = \frac{1}{\|\mathbf{v}\|^2} \frac{\|\mathbf{v} \times \mathbf{a}\|}{\|\mathbf{v}\|} = \frac{\|\mathbf{v} \times \mathbf{a}\|}{\|\mathbf{v}\|^3} \quad ■$$

Recall that for nonlinear smooth curves in 2-space the unit normal vector N is the inward normal (points toward the concave side of the curve). Explain why the same is true for $a_N\mathbf{N}$.

▶ **Example 4**   Suppose that a particle moves through 3-space so that its position vector at time $t$ is
$$\mathbf{r}(t) = t\mathbf{i} + t^2\mathbf{j} + t^3\mathbf{k}$$

(The path is the twisted cubic shown in Figure 12.1.5.)

(a) Find the scalar tangential and normal components of acceleration at time $t$.

(b) Find the scalar tangential and normal components of acceleration at time $t = 1$.

(c) Find the vector tangential and normal components of acceleration at time $t = 1$.

(d) Find the curvature of the path at the point where the particle is located at time $t = 1$.

*Solution (a).*   We have
$$\mathbf{v}(t) = \mathbf{r}'(t) = \mathbf{i} + 2t\mathbf{j} + 3t^2\mathbf{k}$$
$$\mathbf{a}(t) = \mathbf{v}'(t) = 2\mathbf{j} + 6t\mathbf{k}$$
$$\|\mathbf{v}(t)\| = \sqrt{1 + 4t^2 + 9t^4}$$
$$\mathbf{v}(t) \cdot \mathbf{a}(t) = 4t + 18t^3$$
$$\mathbf{v}(t) \times \mathbf{a}(t) = \begin{vmatrix} \mathbf{i} & \mathbf{j} & \mathbf{k} \\ 1 & 2t & 3t^2 \\ 0 & 2 & 6t \end{vmatrix} = 6t^2\mathbf{i} - 6t\mathbf{j} + 2\mathbf{k}$$

Thus, from (15) and (16)
$$a_T = \frac{\mathbf{v} \cdot \mathbf{a}}{\|\mathbf{v}\|} = \frac{4t + 18t^3}{\sqrt{1 + 4t^2 + 9t^4}}$$

$$a_N = \frac{\|\mathbf{v} \times \mathbf{a}\|}{\|\mathbf{v}\|} = \frac{\sqrt{36t^4 + 36t^2 + 4}}{\sqrt{1 + 4t^2 + 9t^4}} = 2\sqrt{\frac{9t^4 + 9t^2 + 1}{9t^4 + 4t^2 + 1}}$$

*Solution (b).*   At time $t = 1$, the components $a_T$ and $a_N$ in part (a) are
$$a_T = \frac{22}{\sqrt{14}} \approx 5.88 \quad \text{and} \quad a_N = 2\sqrt{\frac{19}{14}} \approx 2.33$$

*Solution (c).*   Since **T** and **v** have the same direction, **T** can be obtained by normalizing **v**, that is,
$$\mathbf{T}(t) = \frac{\mathbf{v}(t)}{\|\mathbf{v}(t)\|}$$

At time $t = 1$ we have

$$\mathbf{T}(1) = \frac{\mathbf{v}(1)}{\|\mathbf{v}(1)\|} = \frac{\mathbf{i} + 2\mathbf{j} + 3\mathbf{k}}{\|\mathbf{i} + 2\mathbf{j} + 3\mathbf{k}\|} = \frac{1}{\sqrt{14}}(\mathbf{i} + 2\mathbf{j} + 3\mathbf{k})$$

From this and part (b) we obtain the vector tangential component of acceleration:

$$a_T(1)\mathbf{T}(1) = \frac{22}{\sqrt{14}}\mathbf{T}(1) = \frac{11}{7}(\mathbf{i} + 2\mathbf{j} + 3\mathbf{k}) = \frac{11}{7}\mathbf{i} + \frac{22}{7}\mathbf{j} + \frac{33}{7}\mathbf{k}$$

To find the normal vector component of acceleration, we rewrite $\mathbf{a} = a_T\mathbf{T} + a_N\mathbf{N}$ as

$$a_N\mathbf{N} = \mathbf{a} - a_T\mathbf{T}$$

Thus, at time $t = 1$ the normal vector component of acceleration is

$$
\begin{aligned}
a_N(1)\mathbf{N}(1) &= \mathbf{a}(1) - a_T(1)\mathbf{T}(1) \\
&= (2\mathbf{j} + 6\mathbf{k}) - \left(\frac{11}{7}\mathbf{i} + \frac{22}{7}\mathbf{j} + \frac{33}{7}\mathbf{k}\right) \\
&= -\frac{11}{7}\mathbf{i} - \frac{8}{7}\mathbf{j} + \frac{9}{7}\mathbf{k}
\end{aligned}
$$

*Solution (d).* We will apply Formula (17) with $t = 1$. From part (a)

$$\|\mathbf{v}(1)\| = \sqrt{14} \quad \text{and} \quad \mathbf{v}(1) \times \mathbf{a}(1) = 6\mathbf{i} - 6\mathbf{j} + 2\mathbf{k}$$

Thus, at time $t = 1$

$$\kappa = \frac{\|\mathbf{v} \times \mathbf{a}\|}{\|\mathbf{v}\|^3} = \frac{\sqrt{76}}{(\sqrt{14})^3} = \frac{1}{14}\sqrt{\frac{38}{7}} \approx 0.17 \blacktriangleleft$$

In the case where $\|\mathbf{a}\|$ and $a_T$ are known, there is a useful alternative to Formula (16) for $a_N$ that does not require the calculation of a cross product. It follows algebraically from Formula (14) (see Exercise 51) or geometrically from Figure 12.6.6 and the Theorem of Pythagoras that

Confirm that the value of $a_N$ computed in Example 4 agrees with the value that results by applying Formula (18).

$$a_N = \sqrt{\|\mathbf{a}\|^2 - a_T^2} \tag{18}$$

### ▧ A MODEL OF PROJECTILE MOTION

Earlier in this text we examined various problems concerned with objects moving *vertically* in the Earth's gravitational field (see the subsection of Section 5.7 entitled Free-Fall Model and the subsection of Section 8.4 entitled A Model of Free-Fall Motion Retarded by Air Resistance). Now we will consider the motion of a projectile launched along a *curved* path in the Earth's gravitational field. For this purpose we will need the following *vector version* of Newton's Second Law of Motion (6.6.4)

$$\mathbf{F} = m\mathbf{a} \tag{19}$$

and we will need to make three modeling assumptions:

- The mass $m$ of the object is constant.
- The only force acting on the object after it is launched is the force of the Earth's gravity. (Thus, air resistance and the gravitational effect of other planets and celestial objects are ignored.)
- The object remains sufficiently close to the Earth that we can assume the force of gravity to be constant.

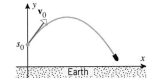

**▲ Figure 12.6.7**

Let us assume that at time $t = 0$ an object of mass $m$ is launched from a height of $s_0$ above the Earth with an initial velocity vector of $\mathbf{v}_0$. Furthermore, let us introduce an $xy$-coordinate system as shown in Figure 12.6.7. In this coordinate system the positive $y$-direction is up, the origin is at the surface of the Earth, and the initial location of the object is $(0, s_0)$. Our objective is to use basic principles of physics to derive the velocity function $\mathbf{v}(t)$ and the position function $\mathbf{r}(t)$ from the acceleration function $\mathbf{a}(t)$ of the object. Our starting point is the physical observation that the downward force $\mathbf{F}$ of the Earth's gravity on an object of mass $m$ is

$$\mathbf{F} = -mg\mathbf{j}$$

where $g$ is the acceleration due to gravity. It follows from this fact and Newton's second law (19) that

$$m\mathbf{a} = -mg\mathbf{j}$$

or on canceling $m$ from both sides

$$\mathbf{a} = -g\mathbf{j} \qquad (20)$$

Observe that this acceleration function does not involve $t$ and hence is constant. We can now obtain the velocity function $\mathbf{v}(t)$ by integrating this acceleration function and using the initial condition $\mathbf{v}(0) = \mathbf{v}_0$ to find the constant of integration. Integrating (20) with respect to $t$ and keeping in mind that $-g\mathbf{j}$ is constant yields

$$\mathbf{v}(t) = \int -g\mathbf{j}\, dt = -gt\mathbf{j} + \mathbf{c}_1$$

where $\mathbf{c}_1$ is a vector constant of integration. Substituting $t = 0$ in this equation and using the initial condition $\mathbf{v}(0) = \mathbf{v}_0$ yields $\mathbf{v}_0 = \mathbf{c}_1$. Thus, the velocity function of the object is

$$\mathbf{v}(t) = -gt\mathbf{j} + \mathbf{v}_0 \qquad (21)$$

To obtain the position function $\mathbf{r}(t)$ of the object, we will integrate the velocity function and use the known initial position of the object to find the constant of integration. For this purpose observe that the object has coordinates $(0, s_0)$ at time $t = 0$, so the position vector at that time is

$$\mathbf{r}(0) = 0\mathbf{i} + s_0\mathbf{j} = s_0\mathbf{j} \qquad (22)$$

This is the initial condition that we will need to find the constant of integration. Integrating (21) with respect to $t$ yields

$$\mathbf{r}(t) = \int (-gt\mathbf{j} + \mathbf{v}_0)\, dt = -\tfrac{1}{2}gt^2\mathbf{j} + t\mathbf{v}_0 + \mathbf{c}_2 \qquad (23)$$

where $\mathbf{c}_2$ is another vector constant of integration. Substituting $t = 0$ in (23) and using initial condition (22) yields

$$s_0\mathbf{j} = \mathbf{c}_2$$

so that (23) can be written as

$$\mathbf{r}(t) = \left(-\tfrac{1}{2}gt^2 + s_0\right)\mathbf{j} + t\mathbf{v}_0 \qquad (24)$$

This formula expresses the position function of the object in terms of its known initial position and velocity.

Observe that the mass $m$ does not appear in Formulas (21) and (24) and hence has no influence on the velocity or the trajectory of the object. This explains the famous observation of Galileo that two objects of different mass that are released from the same height reach the ground at the same time if air resistance is neglected.

**■ PARAMETRIC EQUATIONS OF PROJECTILE MOTION**
Formulas (21) and (24) can be used to obtain parametric equations for the position and velocity in terms of the initial speed of the object and the angle that the initial velocity vector makes with the positive $x$-axis. For this purpose, let $v_0 = \|\mathbf{v}_0\|$ be the initial speed, let $\alpha$ be the angle that the initial velocity vector $\mathbf{v}_0$ makes with the positive $x$-axis, let $v_x$ and $v_y$ be the horizontal and vertical scalar components of $\mathbf{v}(t)$ at time $t$, and let $x$ and $y$

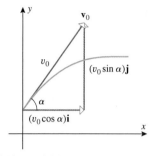

▲ Figure 12.6.8

be the horizontal and vertical components of $\mathbf{r}(t)$ at time $t$. As illustrated in Figure 12.6.8, the initial velocity vector can be expressed as

$$\mathbf{v}_0 = (v_0 \cos \alpha)\mathbf{i} + (v_0 \sin \alpha)\mathbf{j} \qquad (25)$$

Substituting this expression in (24) and combining like components yields (verify)

$$\mathbf{r}(t) = (v_0 \cos \alpha)t\mathbf{i} + \left(s_0 + (v_0 \sin \alpha)t - \tfrac{1}{2}gt^2\right)\mathbf{j} \qquad (26)$$

which is equivalent to the parametric equations

$$x = (v_0 \cos \alpha)t, \quad y = s_0 + (v_0 \sin \alpha)t - \tfrac{1}{2}gt^2 \qquad (27)$$

Similarly, substituting (25) in (21) and combining like components yields

$$\mathbf{v}(t) = (v_0 \cos \alpha)\mathbf{i} + (v_0 \sin \alpha - gt)\mathbf{j}$$

which is equivalent to the parametric equations

$$v_x = v_0 \cos \alpha, \quad v_y = v_0 \sin \alpha - gt \qquad (28)$$

The parameter $t$ can be eliminated in (27) by solving the first equation for $t$ and substituting in the second equation. We leave it for you to show that this yields

$$y = s_0 + (\tan \alpha)x - \left(\frac{g}{2v_0^2 \cos^2 \alpha}\right)x^2 \qquad (29)$$

which is the equation of a parabola, since the right side is a quadratic polynomial in $x$. Thus, we have shown that the trajectory of the projectile is a parabolic arc.

---

▶ **Example 5**   A shell, fired from a cannon, has a muzzle speed (the speed as it leaves the barrel) of 800 ft/s. The barrel makes an angle of 45° with the horizontal and, for simplicity, the barrel opening is assumed to be at ground level.

▲ Figure 12.6.9

(a) Find parametric equations for the shell's trajectory relative to the coordinate system in Figure 12.6.9.

(b) How high does the shell rise?

(c) How far does the shell travel horizontally?

(d) What is the speed of the shell at its point of impact with the ground?

*Solution (a).*   From (27) with $v_0 = 800$ ft/s, $\alpha = 45°$, $s_0 = 0$ ft (since the shell starts at ground level), and $g = 32$ ft/s$^2$, we obtain the parametric equations

$$x = (800 \cos 45°)t, \quad y = (800 \sin 45°)t - 16t^2 \qquad (t \geq 0)$$

which simplify to

$$x = 400\sqrt{2}t, \quad y = 400\sqrt{2}t - 16t^2 \qquad (t \geq 0) \qquad (30)$$

*Solution (b).*   The maximum height of the shell is the maximum value of $y$ in (30), which occurs when $dy/dt = 0$, that is, when

$$400\sqrt{2} - 32t = 0 \quad \text{or} \quad t = \frac{25\sqrt{2}}{2}$$

Substituting this value of $t$ in (30) yields

$$y = 5000 \text{ ft}$$

as the maximum height of the shell.

*Solution (c).*    The shell will hit the ground when $y = 0$. From (30), this occurs when

$$400\sqrt{2}t - 16t^2 = 0 \quad \text{or} \quad t(400\sqrt{2} - 16t) = 0$$

The solution $t = 0$ corresponds to the initial position of the shell and the solution $t = 25\sqrt{2}$ to the time of impact. Substituting the latter value in the equation for $x$ in (30) yields
$$x = 20{,}000 \text{ ft}$$

as the horizontal distance traveled by the shell.

*Solution (d).*    From (30), the position function of the shell is

$$\mathbf{r}(t) = 400\sqrt{2}t\mathbf{i} + (400\sqrt{2}t - 16t^2)\mathbf{j}$$

so that the velocity function is

$$\mathbf{v}(t) = \mathbf{r}'(t) = 400\sqrt{2}\mathbf{i} + (400\sqrt{2} - 32t)\mathbf{j}$$

From part (c), impact occurs when $t = 25\sqrt{2}$, so the velocity vector at this point is

$$\mathbf{v}(25\sqrt{2}) = 400\sqrt{2}\mathbf{i} + [400\sqrt{2} - 32(25\sqrt{2})]\mathbf{j} = 400\sqrt{2}\mathbf{i} - 400\sqrt{2}\mathbf{j}$$

Thus, the speed at impact is

$$\|\mathbf{v}(25\sqrt{2})\| = \sqrt{(400\sqrt{2})^2 + (-400\sqrt{2})^2} = 800 \text{ ft/s} \blacktriangleleft$$

---

The speed at impact and the muzzle speed of the shell in Example 5 are the same. Is this an expected result? Explain.

---

### ✔ QUICK CHECK EXERCISES 12.6    *(See page 895 for answers.)*

1. If $\mathbf{r}(t)$ is the position function of a particle, then the velocity, acceleration, and speed of the particle at time $t$ are given, respectively, by

$$\mathbf{v}(t) = \underline{\qquad}, \quad \mathbf{a}(t) = \underline{\qquad}, \quad \frac{ds}{dt} = \underline{\qquad}$$

2. If $\mathbf{r}(t)$ is the position function of a particle, then the displacement of the particle over the time interval $t_1 \leq t \leq t_2$ is _____, and the distance $s$ traveled by the particle during this time interval is given by the integral _____.

3. The tangential scalar component of acceleration is given by the formula _____, and the normal scalar component of acceleration is given by the formula _____.

4. The projectile motion model
$$\mathbf{r}(t) = \left(-\tfrac{1}{2}gt^2 + s_0\right)\mathbf{j} + t\mathbf{v}_0$$
describes the motion of an object with constant acceleration $\mathbf{a} = $ _____ and velocity function $\mathbf{v}(t) = $ _____. The initial position of the object is _____ and its initial velocity is _____.

---

**EXERCISE SET 12.6**    ⌇ Graphing Utility    [c] CAS

---

**1–4** In these exercises $\mathbf{r}(t)$ is the position vector of a particle moving in the plane. Find the velocity, acceleration, and speed at an arbitrary time $t$. Then sketch the path of the particle together with the velocity and acceleration vectors at the indicated time $t$. ▨

1. $\mathbf{r}(t) = 3\cos t\mathbf{i} + 3\sin t\mathbf{j}; \quad t = \pi/3$

2. $\mathbf{r}(t) = t\mathbf{i} + t^2\mathbf{j}; \quad t = 2$

3. $\mathbf{r}(t) = e^t\mathbf{i} + e^{-t}\mathbf{j}; \quad t = 0$

4. $\mathbf{r}(t) = (2 + 4t)\mathbf{i} + (1 - t)\mathbf{j}; \quad t = 1$

**5–8** Find the velocity, speed, and acceleration at the given time $t$ of a particle moving along the given curve. ▨

5. $\mathbf{r}(t) = t\mathbf{i} + \tfrac{1}{2}t^2\mathbf{j} + \tfrac{1}{3}t^3\mathbf{k}; \quad t = 1$

6. $x = 1 + 3t, \ y = 2 - 4t, \ z = 7 + t; \quad t = 2$

7. $x = 2\cos t, \ y = 2\sin t, \ z = t; \quad t = \pi/4$

8. $\mathbf{r}(t) = e^t\sin t\mathbf{i} + e^t\cos t\mathbf{j} + t\mathbf{k}; \quad t = \pi/2$

---

**FOCUS ON CONCEPTS**

9. As illustrated in the accompanying figure on the next page, suppose that the equations of motion of a particle moving along an elliptic path are $x = a\cos\omega t$, $y = b\sin\omega t$.
   (a) Show that the acceleration is directed toward the origin.    *(cont.)*

(b) Show that the magnitude of the acceleration is proportional to the distance from the particle to the origin.

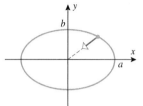

◀ **Figure Ex-9**

10. Suppose that a particle vibrates in such a way that its position function is $\mathbf{r}(t) = 16 \sin \pi t \mathbf{i} + 4 \cos 2\pi t \mathbf{j}$, where distance is in millimeters and $t$ is in seconds.
    (a) Find the velocity and acceleration at time $t = 1$ s.
    (b) Show that the particle moves along a parabolic curve.
    (c) Show that the particle moves back and forth along the curve.

11. What can you say about the trajectory of a particle that moves in 2-space or 3-space with zero acceleration? Justify your answer.

12. Recall from Theorem 12.2.8 that if $\mathbf{r}(t)$ is a vector-valued function in 2-space or 3-space, and if $\|\mathbf{r}(t)\|$ is constant for all $t$, then $\mathbf{r}(t) \cdot \mathbf{r}'(t) = 0$.
    (a) Translate this theorem into a statement about the motion of a particle in 2-space or 3-space.
    (b) Replace $\mathbf{r}(t)$ by $\mathbf{r}'(t)$ in the theorem, and translate the result into a statement about the motion of a particle in 2-space or 3-space.

13. Suppose that the position vector of a particle moving in the plane is $\mathbf{r} = 12\sqrt{t}\,\mathbf{i} + t^{3/2}\mathbf{j}$, $t > 0$. Find the minimum speed of the particle and its location when it has this speed.

14. Suppose that the motion of a particle is described by the position vector $\mathbf{r} = (t - t^2)\mathbf{i} - t^2\mathbf{j}$. Find the minimum speed of the particle and its location when it has this speed.

15. Suppose that the position function of a particle moving in 2-space is $\mathbf{r} = \sin 3t\mathbf{i} - 2\cos 3t\mathbf{j}$, $0 \le t \le 2\pi/3$.
    (a) Use a graphing utility to graph the speed of the particle versus time from $t = 0$ to $t = 2\pi/3$.
    (b) What are the maximum and minimum speeds of the particle?
    (c) Use the graph to estimate the time at which the maximum speed first occurs.
    (d) Find the exact time at which the maximum speed first occurs.

16. Suppose that the position function of a particle moving in 3-space is $\mathbf{r} = 3\cos 2t\mathbf{i} + \sin 2t\mathbf{j} + 4t\mathbf{k}$.
    (a) Use a graphing utility to graph the speed of the particle versus time from $t = 0$ to $t = \pi$.

(b) Use the graph to estimate the maximum and minimum speeds of the particle.
(c) Use the graph to estimate the time at which the maximum speed first occurs.
(d) Find the exact values of the maximum and minimum speeds and the exact time at which the maximum speed first occurs.

17–20 Use the given information to find the position and velocity vectors of the particle. ■

17. $\mathbf{a}(t) = -\cos t\mathbf{i} - \sin t\mathbf{j}$;  $\mathbf{v}(0) = \mathbf{i}$;  $\mathbf{r}(0) = \mathbf{j}$

18. $\mathbf{a}(t) = \mathbf{i} + e^{-t}\mathbf{j}$;  $\mathbf{v}(0) = 2\mathbf{i} + \mathbf{j}$;  $\mathbf{r}(0) = \mathbf{i} - \mathbf{j}$

19. $\mathbf{a}(t) = \sin t\mathbf{i} + \cos t\mathbf{j} + e^t\mathbf{k}$;  $\mathbf{v}(0) = \mathbf{k}$;  $\mathbf{r}(0) = -\mathbf{i} + \mathbf{k}$

20. $\mathbf{a}(t) = (t + 1)^{-2}\mathbf{j} - e^{-2t}\mathbf{k}$;  $\mathbf{v}(0) = 3\mathbf{i} - \mathbf{j}$;  $\mathbf{r}(0) = 2\mathbf{k}$

21. Find, to the nearest degree, the angle between $\mathbf{v}$ and $\mathbf{a}$ for $\mathbf{r} = t^3\mathbf{i} + t^2\mathbf{j}$ when $t = 1$.

22. Show that the angle between $\mathbf{v}$ and $\mathbf{a}$ is constant for the position vector $\mathbf{r} = e^t \cos t\mathbf{i} + e^t \sin t\mathbf{j}$. Find the angle.

23. (a) Suppose that at time $t = t_0$ an electron has a position vector of $\mathbf{r} = 3.5\mathbf{i} - 1.7\mathbf{j} + \mathbf{k}$, and at a later time $t = t_1$ it has a position vector of $\mathbf{r} = 4.2\mathbf{i} + \mathbf{j} - 2.4\mathbf{k}$. What is the displacement of the electron during the time interval from $t_0$ to $t_1$?
    (b) Suppose that during a certain time interval a proton has a displacement of $\Delta\mathbf{r} = 0.7\mathbf{i} + 2.9\mathbf{j} - 1.2\mathbf{k}$ and its final position vector is known to be $\mathbf{r} = 3.6\mathbf{k}$. What was the initial position vector of the proton?

24. Suppose that the position function of a particle moving along a circle in the $xy$-plane is $\mathbf{r} = 5\cos 2\pi t\mathbf{i} + 5\sin 2\pi t\mathbf{j}$.
    (a) Sketch some typical displacement vectors over the time interval from $t = 0$ to $t = 1$.
    (b) What is the distance traveled by the particle during the time interval?

25–28 Find the displacement and the distance traveled over the indicated time interval. ■

25. $\mathbf{r} = t^2\mathbf{i} + \frac{1}{3}t^3\mathbf{j}$;  $1 \le t \le 3$

26. $\mathbf{r} = (1 - 3\sin t)\mathbf{i} + 3\cos t\mathbf{j}$;  $0 \le t \le 3\pi/2$

27. $\mathbf{r} = e^t\mathbf{i} + e^{-t}\mathbf{j} + \sqrt{2}t\mathbf{k}$;  $0 \le t \le \ln 3$

28. $\mathbf{r} = \cos 2t\mathbf{i} + (1 - \cos 2t)\mathbf{j} + \left(3 + \frac{1}{2}\cos 2t\right)\mathbf{k}$;  $0 \le t \le \pi$

29–30 The position vectors $\mathbf{r}_1$ and $\mathbf{r}_2$ of two particles are given. Show that the particles move along the same path but the speed of the first is constant and the speed of the second is not. ■

29. $\mathbf{r}_1 = 2\cos 3t\mathbf{i} + 2\sin 3t\mathbf{j}$
    $\mathbf{r}_2 = 2\cos(t^2)\mathbf{i} + 2\sin(t^2)\mathbf{j}$   $(t \ge 0)$

30. $\mathbf{r}_1 = (3 + 2t)\mathbf{i} + t\mathbf{j} + (1 - t)\mathbf{k}$
    $\mathbf{r}_2 = (5 - 2t^3)\mathbf{i} + (1 - t^3)\mathbf{j} + t^3\mathbf{k}$

**31–36** The position function of a particle is given. Use Theorem 12.6.3 to find

(a) the scalar tangential and normal components of acceleration at the stated time $t$;

(b) the vector tangential and normal components of acceleration at the stated time $t$;

(c) the curvature of the path at the point where the particle is located at the stated time $t$. ▨

**31.** $\mathbf{r} = e^{-t}\mathbf{i} + e^{t}\mathbf{j}$;  $t = 0$

**32.** $\mathbf{r} = \cos(t^2)\mathbf{i} + \sin(t^2)\mathbf{j}$;  $t = \sqrt{\pi}/2$

**33.** $\mathbf{r} = (t^3 - 2t)\mathbf{i} + (t^2 - 4)\mathbf{j}$;  $t = 1$

**34.** $\mathbf{r} = e^{t}\cos t\,\mathbf{i} + e^{t}\sin t\,\mathbf{j}$;  $t = \pi/4$

**35.** $\mathbf{r} = e^{t}\mathbf{i} + e^{-2t}\mathbf{j} + t\mathbf{k}$;  $t = 0$

**36.** $\mathbf{r} = 3\sin t\,\mathbf{i} + 2\cos t\,\mathbf{j} - \sin 2t\,\mathbf{k}$;  $t = \pi/2$

**37–38** In these exercises $\mathbf{v}$ and $\mathbf{a}$ are given at a certain instant of time. Find $a_T$, $a_N$, $\mathbf{T}$, and $\mathbf{N}$ at this instant. ▨

**37.** $\mathbf{v} = -4\mathbf{j}$,  $\mathbf{a} = 2\mathbf{i} + 3\mathbf{j}$

**38.** $\mathbf{v} = 2\mathbf{i} + 2\mathbf{j} + \mathbf{k}$,  $\mathbf{a} = \mathbf{i} + 2\mathbf{k}$

**39–40** The speed $\|\mathbf{v}\|$ of a particle at an arbitrary time $t$ is given. Find the scalar tangential component of acceleration at the indicated time. ▨

**39.** $\|\mathbf{v}\| = \sqrt{t^2 + e^{-3t}}$;  $t = 0$

**40.** $\|\mathbf{v}\| = \sqrt{(4t - 1)^2 + \cos^2 \pi t}$;  $t = \frac{1}{4}$

**41.** The nuclear accelerator at the Enrico Fermi Laboratory is circular with a radius of 1 km. Find the scalar normal component of acceleration of a proton moving around the accelerator with a constant speed of $2.9 \times 10^5$ km/s.

**42.** Suppose that a particle moves with nonzero acceleration along the curve $y = f(x)$. Use part (b) of Exercise 23 in Section 12.5 to show that the acceleration vector is tangent to the curve at each point where $f''(x) = 0$.

**43–44** Use the given information and Exercise 23 of Section 12.5 to find the normal scalar component of acceleration as a function of $x$. ▨

**43.** A particle moves along the parabola $y = x^2$ with a constant speed of 3 units per second.

**44.** A particle moves along the curve $x = \ln y$ with a constant speed of 2 units per second.

**45–46** Use the given information to find the normal scalar component of acceleration at time $t = 1$. ▨

**45.** $\mathbf{a}(1) = \mathbf{i} + 2\mathbf{j} - 2\mathbf{k}$;  $a_T(1) = 3$

**46.** $\|\mathbf{a}(1)\| = 9$;  $a_T(1)\mathbf{T}(1) = 2\mathbf{i} - 2\mathbf{j} + \mathbf{k}$

**47–50 True–False** Determine whether the statement is true or false. Explain your answer. ▨

**47.** The velocity and unit tangent vectors for a moving particle are parallel.

**48.** If a particle moves along a smooth curve $C$ in 3-space, then at each point on $C$ the normal scalar component of acceleration for the particle is the product of the curvature of $C$ and speed of the particle at the point.

**49.** If a particle is moving along a smooth curve $C$ and passes through a point at which the curvature is zero, then the velocity and acceleration vectors have the same direction at that point.

**50.** The distance traveled by a particle over a time interval is the magnitude of the displacement vector for the particle during that time interval.

**51.** Derive Formula (18) from Formula (14).

**52.** An automobile travels at a constant speed around a curve whose radius of curvature is 1000 m. What is the maximum allowable speed if the maximum acceptable value for the normal scalar component of acceleration is 1.5 m/s$^2$?

**53.** If an automobile of mass $m$ rounds a curve, then its inward vector component of acceleration $a_N\mathbf{N}$ is caused by the frictional force $\mathbf{F}$ of the road. Thus, it follows from the vector form of Newton's second law [Equation (19)] that the frictional force and the normal scalar component of acceleration are related by the equation $\mathbf{F} = ma_N\mathbf{N}$. Thus,

$$\|\mathbf{F}\| = m\kappa\left(\frac{ds}{dt}\right)^2$$

Use this result to find the magnitude of the frictional force in newtons exerted by the road on a 500 kg go-cart driven at a speed of 10 km/h around a circular track of radius 15 m. [*Note:* 1 N = 1 kg·m/s$^2$.]

**54.** A shell is fired from ground level with a muzzle speed of 320 ft/s and elevation angle of 60°. Find

(a) parametric equations for the shell's trajectory

(b) the maximum height reached by the shell

(c) the horizontal distance traveled by the shell

(d) the speed of the shell at impact.

**55.** A rock is thrown downward from the top of a building, 168 ft high, at an angle of 60° with the horizontal. How far from the base of the building will the rock land if its initial speed is 80 ft/s?

**56.** Solve Exercise 55 assuming that the rock is thrown horizontally at a speed of 80 ft/s.

**57.** A shell is to be fired from ground level at an elevation angle of 30°. What should the muzzle speed be in order for the maximum height of the shell to be 2500 ft?

**58.** A shell, fired from ground level at an elevation angle of 45°, hits the ground 24,500 m away. Calculate the muzzle speed of the shell.

**59.** Find two elevation angles that will enable a shell, fired from ground level with a muzzle speed of 800 ft/s, to hit a ground-level target 10,000 ft away.

**60.** A ball rolls off a table 4 ft high while moving at a constant speed of 5 ft/s. *(cont.)*

(a) How long does it take for the ball to hit the floor after it leaves the table?

(b) At what speed does the ball hit the floor?

(c) If a ball were dropped from rest at table height just as the rolling ball leaves the table, which ball would hit the ground first? Justify your answer.

**61.** As illustrated in the accompanying figure, a fire hose sprays water with an initial velocity of 40 ft/s at an angle of 60° with the horizontal.

(a) Confirm that the water will clear corner point $A$.

(b) Confirm that the water will hit the roof.

(c) How far from corner point $A$ will the water hit the roof?

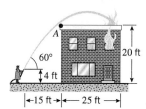

◀ **Figure Ex-61**

**62.** What is the minimum initial velocity that will allow the water in Exercise 61 to hit the roof?

**63.** As shown in the accompanying figure, water is sprayed from a hose with an initial velocity of 35 m/s at an angle of 45° with the horizontal.

(a) What is the radius of curvature of the stream at the point where it leaves the hose?

(b) What is the maximum height of the stream above the nozzle of the hose?

**64.** As illustrated in the accompanying figure, a train is traveling on a curved track. At a point where the train is traveling at a speed of 132 ft/s and the radius of curvature of the track is 3000 ft, the engineer hits the brakes to make the train slow down at a constant rate of 7.5 ft/s².

(a) Find the magnitude of the acceleration vector at the instant the engineer hits the brakes.

(b) Approximate the angle between the acceleration vector and the unit tangent vector $\mathbf{T}$ at the instant the engineer hits the brakes.

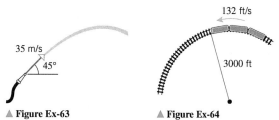

▲ **Figure Ex-63**       ▲ **Figure Ex-64**

**65.** A shell is fired from ground level at an elevation angle of $\alpha$ and a muzzle speed of $v_0$.

(a) Show that the maximum height reached by the shell is

$$\text{maximum height} = \frac{(v_0 \sin \alpha)^2}{2g}$$

(b) The *horizontal range* $R$ of the shell is the horizontal distance traveled when the shell returns to ground level. Show that $R = (v_0^2 \sin 2\alpha)/g$. For what elevation angle will the range be maximum? What is the maximum range?

**66.** A shell is fired from ground level with an elevation angle $\alpha$ and a muzzle speed of $v_0$. Find two angles that can be used to hit a target at ground level that is a distance of three-fourths the maximum range of the shell. Express your answer to the nearest tenth of a degree. [*Hint:* See Exercise 65(b).]

**67.** At time $t = 0$ a baseball that is 5 ft above the ground is hit with a bat. The ball leaves the bat with a speed of 80 ft/s at an angle of 30° above the horizontal.

(a) How long will it take for the baseball to hit the ground? Express your answer to the nearest hundredth of a second.

(b) Use the result in part (a) to find the horizontal distance traveled by the ball. Express your answer to the nearest tenth of a foot.

**68.** Repeat Exercise 67, assuming that the ball leaves the bat with a speed of 70 ft/s at an angle of 60° above the horizontal.

[c] **69.** At time $t = 0$ a skier leaves the end of a ski jump with a speed of $v_0$ ft/s at an angle $\alpha$ with the horizontal (see the accompanying figure). The skier lands 259 ft down the incline 2.9 s later.

(a) Approximate $v_0$ to the nearest ft/s and $\alpha$ to the nearest degree. [*Note:* Use $g = 32$ ft/s² as the acceleration due to gravity.]

(b) Use a CAS or a calculating utility with a numerical integration capability to approximate the distance traveled by the skier.

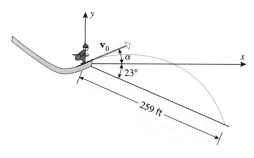

▲ **Figure Ex-69**

**70.** At time $t = 0$ a projectile is fired from a height $h$ above level ground at an elevation angle of $\alpha$ with a speed $v$. Let $R$ be the horizontal distance to the point where the projectile hits the ground.

(a) Show that $\alpha$ and $R$ must satisfy the equation

$$g(\sec^2 \alpha)R^2 - 2v^2(\tan \alpha)R - 2v^2 h = 0$$       *(cont.)*

(b) If $g, h$, and $v$ are constant, then the equation in part (a) defines $R$ implicitly as a function of $\alpha$. Let $R_0$ be the maximum value of $R$ and $\alpha_0$ the value of $\alpha$ when $R = R_0$. Use implicit differentiation to find $dR/d\alpha$ and show that
$$\tan \alpha_0 = \frac{v^2}{g R_0}$$
[*Hint:* Assume that $dR/d\alpha = 0$ when $R$ attains a maximum.]

(c) Use the results in parts (a) and (b) to show that
$$R_0 = \frac{v}{g} \sqrt{v^2 + 2gh}$$
and
$$\alpha_0 = \tan^{-1} \frac{v}{\sqrt{v^2 + 2gh}}$$

**71.** *Writing* Consider the various forces that a passenger in a car would sense while traveling over the crest of a hill or around a curve. Relate these sensations to the tangential and normal vector components of the acceleration vector for the car's motion. Discuss how speeding up or slowing down (e.g., doubling or halving the car's speed) affects these components.

**72.** *Writing* The formula
$$\mathbf{r}(t) = (v_0 \cos \alpha) t \mathbf{i} + (s_0 + (v_0 \sin \alpha) t - \tfrac{1}{2} g t^2) \mathbf{j}$$
models a position function for projectile motion [Formula (26)]. Identify the various quantities ($v_0$, $\alpha$, $s_0$, and $g$) in this formula and discuss how the formula is derived, including any assumptions that are made.

---

### ✔ QUICK CHECK ANSWERS 12.6

1. $\dfrac{d\mathbf{r}}{dt}$;  $\dfrac{d\mathbf{v}}{dt} = \dfrac{d^2\mathbf{r}}{dt^2}$;  $\|\mathbf{v}(t)\|$     2. $\mathbf{r}(t_2) - \mathbf{r}(t_1)$;  $\displaystyle\int_{t_1}^{t_2} \|\mathbf{v}(t)\| \, dt$     3. $\dfrac{d^2s}{dt^2}$;  $\kappa (ds/dt)^2$     4. $-g\mathbf{j}$;  $-gt\mathbf{j} + \mathbf{v}_0$;  $s_0\mathbf{j}$;  $\mathbf{v}_0$

---

## 12.7 KEPLER'S LAWS OF PLANETARY MOTION

*One of the great advances in the history of astronomy occurred in the early 1600s when Johannes Kepler\* deduced from empirical data that all planets in our solar system move in elliptical orbits with the Sun at a focus. Subsequently, Isaac Newton showed mathematically that such planetary motion is the consequence of an inverse-square law of gravitational attraction. In this section we will use the concepts developed in the preceding sections of this chapter to derive three basic laws of planetary motion, known as **Kepler's laws.***

---

### ▪ KEPLER'S LAWS

In Section 10.6 we stated the following laws of planetary motion that were published by Johannes Kepler in 1609 in his book known as *Astronomia Nova*.

© Science Photo Library/Photo Researchers, Inc.

*The planets in our solar system move in accordance with Kepler's three laws.*

**12.7.1    KEPLER'S LAWS**

- First law (*Law of Orbits*). Each planet moves in an elliptical orbit with the Sun at a focus.

- Second law (*Law of Areas*). Equal areas are swept out in equal times by the line from the Sun to a planet.

- Third law (*Law of Periods*). The square of a planet's period (the time it takes the planet to complete one orbit about the Sun) is proportional to the cube of the semimajor axis of its orbit.

---

\*See biography on p. 759.

### ■ CENTRAL FORCES

If a particle moves under the influence of a *single* force that is always directed toward a fixed point $O$, then the particle is said to be moving in a ***central force field***. The force is called a ***central force***, and the point $O$ is called the ***center of force***. For example, in the simplest model of planetary motion, it is assumed that the only force acting on a planet is the force of the Sun's gravity, directed toward the center of the Sun. This model, which produces Kepler's laws, ignores the forces that other celestial objects exert on the planet as well as the minor effect that the planet's gravity has on the Sun. Central force models are also used to study the motion of comets, asteroids, planetary moons, and artificial satellites. They also have important applications in electromagnetics. Our objective in this section is to develop some basic principles about central force fields and then use those results to derive Kepler's laws.

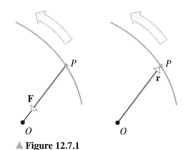

▲ Figure 12.7.1

Suppose that a particle $P$ of mass $m$ moves in a central force field due to a force $\mathbf{F}$ that is directed toward a fixed point $O$, and let $\mathbf{r} = \mathbf{r}(t)$ be the position vector from $O$ to $P$ (Figure 12.7.1). Let $\mathbf{v} = \mathbf{v}(t)$ and $\mathbf{a} = \mathbf{a}(t)$ be the velocity and acceleration functions of the particle, and assume that $\mathbf{F}$ and $\mathbf{a}$ are related by Newton's second law ($\mathbf{F} = m\mathbf{a}$).

Our first objective is to show that the particle $P$ moves in a plane containing the point $O$. For this purpose observe that $\mathbf{a}$ has the same direction as $\mathbf{F}$ by Newton's second law, and this implies that $\mathbf{a}$ and $\mathbf{r}$ are oppositely directed vectors. Thus, it follows from part $(c)$ of Theorem 11.4.5 that

$$\mathbf{r} \times \mathbf{a} = \mathbf{0}$$

Since the velocity and acceleration of the particle are given by $\mathbf{v} = d\mathbf{r}/dt$ and $\mathbf{a} = d\mathbf{v}/dt$, respectively, we have

$$\frac{d}{dt}(\mathbf{r} \times \mathbf{v}) = \mathbf{r} \times \frac{d\mathbf{v}}{dt} + \frac{d\mathbf{r}}{dt} \times \mathbf{v} = (\mathbf{r} \times \mathbf{a}) + (\mathbf{v} \times \mathbf{v}) = \mathbf{0} + \mathbf{0} = \mathbf{0} \qquad (1)$$

Integrating the left and right sides of this equation with respect to $t$ yields

$$\mathbf{r} \times \mathbf{v} = \mathbf{b} \qquad (2)$$

Astronomers call the plane containing the orbit of a planet the *ecliptic* of the planet.

where $\mathbf{b}$ is a constant (independent of $t$). However, $\mathbf{b}$ is orthogonal to both $\mathbf{r}$ and $\mathbf{v}$, so we can conclude that $\mathbf{r} = \mathbf{r}(t)$ and $\mathbf{v} = \mathbf{v}(t)$ lie in a fixed plane containing the point $O$.

### ■ NEWTON'S LAW OF UNIVERSAL GRAVITATION

Our next objective is to derive the position function of a particle moving under a central force in a polar coordinate system. For this purpose we will need the following result, known as ***Newton's Law of Universal Gravitation***.

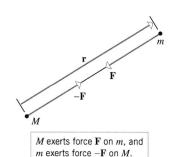

*M* exerts force **F** on *m*, and *m* exerts force −**F** on *M*.

▲ Figure 12.7.2

---

**12.7.2** NEWTON'S LAW OF UNIVERSAL GRAVITATION Every particle of matter in the Universe attracts every other particle of matter in the Universe with a force that is proportional to the product of their masses and inversely proportional to the square of the distance between them. Specifically, if a particle of mass $M$ and a particle of mass $m$ are at a distance $r$ from each other, then they attract each other with equal and opposite forces, $\mathbf{F}$ and $-\mathbf{F}$, of magnitude

$$\|\mathbf{F}\| = \frac{GMm}{r^2} \qquad (3)$$

where $G$ is a constant called the ***universal gravitational constant***.

---

To obtain a formula for the vector force $\mathbf{F}$ that mass $M$ exerts on mass $m$, we will let $\mathbf{r}$ be the radius vector from mass $M$ to mass $m$ (Figure 12.7.2). Thus, the distance $r$ between the masses is $\|\mathbf{r}\|$, and the force $\mathbf{F}$ can be expressed in terms of $\mathbf{r}$ as

$$\mathbf{F} = \|\mathbf{F}\| \left( -\frac{\mathbf{r}}{\|\mathbf{r}\|} \right) = \|\mathbf{F}\| \left( -\frac{\mathbf{r}}{r} \right)$$

which from (3) can be expressed as

$$\mathbf{F} = -\frac{GMm}{r^3}\mathbf{r} \tag{4}$$

We start by finding a formula for the acceleration function. To do this we use Formula (4) and Newton's second law to obtain

$$m\mathbf{a} = -\frac{GMm}{r^3}\mathbf{r}$$

from which we obtain

$$\mathbf{a} = -\frac{GM}{r^3}\mathbf{r} \tag{5}$$

Observe in Formula (5) that the acceleration $\mathbf{a}$ does not involve $m$. Thus, the mass of a planet has no effect on its acceleration.

To obtain a formula for the position function of the mass $m$, we will need to introduce a coordinate system and make some assumptions about the initial conditions:

- The distance $r$ from $m$ to $M$ is minimum at time $t = 0$.
- The mass $m$ has nonzero position and velocity vectors $\mathbf{r}_0$ and $\mathbf{v}_0$ at time $t = 0$.
- A polar coordinate system is introduced with its pole at mass $M$ and oriented so $\theta = 0$ at time $t = 0$.
- The vector $\mathbf{v}_0$ is perpendicular to the polar axis at time $t = 0$.

Moreover, to ensure that the polar angle $\theta$ increases with $t$, let us agree to observe this polar coordinate system looking toward the pole from the terminal point of the vector $\mathbf{b} = \mathbf{r}_0 \times \mathbf{v}_0$. We will also find it useful to superimpose an $xyz$-coordinate system on the polar coordinate system with the positive $z$-axis in the direction of $\mathbf{b}$ (Figure 12.7.3).

For computational purposes, it will be helpful to denote $\|\mathbf{r}_0\|$ by $r_0$ and $\|\mathbf{v}_0\|$ by $v_0$, in which case we can express the vectors $\mathbf{r}_0$ and $\mathbf{v}_0$ in $xyz$-coordinates as

$$\mathbf{r}_0 = r_0\mathbf{i} \quad \text{and} \quad \mathbf{v}_0 = v_0\mathbf{j}$$

and the vector $\mathbf{b}$ as

$$\mathbf{b} = \mathbf{r}_0 \times \mathbf{v}_0 = r_0\mathbf{i} \times v_0\mathbf{j} = r_0 v_0\mathbf{k} \tag{6}$$

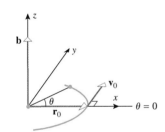

▲ Figure 12.7.3

(Figure 12.7.4). It will also be useful to introduce the unit vector

$$\mathbf{u} = \cos\theta\,\mathbf{i} + \sin\theta\,\mathbf{j} \tag{7}$$

which will allow us to express the polar form of the position vector $\mathbf{r}$ as

$$\mathbf{r} = r\cos\theta\,\mathbf{i} + r\sin\theta\,\mathbf{j} = r(\cos\theta\,\mathbf{i} + \sin\theta\,\mathbf{j}) = r\mathbf{u} \tag{8}$$

and to express the acceleration vector $\mathbf{a}$ in terms of $\mathbf{u}$ by rewriting (5) as

$$\mathbf{a} = -\frac{GM}{r^2}\mathbf{u} \tag{9}$$

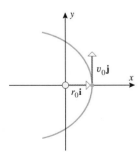

▲ Figure 12.7.4

We are now ready to derive the position function of the mass $m$ in polar coordinates. For this purpose, recall from (2) that the vector $\mathbf{b} = \mathbf{r} \times \mathbf{v}$ is constant, so it follows from (6) that the relationship

$$\mathbf{b} = \mathbf{r} \times \mathbf{v} = r_0 v_0\mathbf{k} \tag{10}$$

holds for *all* values of $t$. Now let us examine $\mathbf{b}$ from another point of view. It follows from (8) that

$$\mathbf{v} = \frac{d\mathbf{r}}{dt} = \frac{d}{dt}(r\mathbf{u}) = r\frac{d\mathbf{u}}{dt} + \frac{dr}{dt}\mathbf{u}$$

and hence

$$\mathbf{b} = \mathbf{r} \times \mathbf{v} = (r\mathbf{u}) \times \left( r\frac{d\mathbf{u}}{dt} + \frac{dr}{dt}\mathbf{u} \right) = r^2\mathbf{u} \times \frac{d\mathbf{u}}{dt} + r\frac{dr}{dt}\mathbf{u} \times \mathbf{u} = r^2\mathbf{u} \times \frac{d\mathbf{u}}{dt} \quad (11)$$

But (7) implies that
$$\frac{d\mathbf{u}}{dt} = \frac{d\mathbf{u}}{d\theta}\frac{d\theta}{dt} = (-\sin\theta\mathbf{i} + \cos\theta\mathbf{j})\frac{d\theta}{dt}$$

so

$$\mathbf{u} \times \frac{d\mathbf{u}}{dt} = \frac{d\theta}{dt}\mathbf{k} \quad (12)$$

Substituting (12) in (11) yields

$$\mathbf{b} = r^2\frac{d\theta}{dt}\mathbf{k} \quad (13)$$

Thus, it follows from (7), (9), and (13) that

$$\mathbf{a} \times \mathbf{b} = -\frac{GM}{r^2}(\cos\theta\mathbf{i} + \sin\theta\mathbf{j}) \times \left( r^2\frac{d\theta}{dt}\mathbf{k} \right)$$

$$= GM(-\sin\theta\mathbf{i} + \cos\theta\mathbf{j})\frac{d\theta}{dt} = GM\frac{d\mathbf{u}}{dt} \quad (14)$$

From this formula and the fact that $d\mathbf{b}/dt = \mathbf{0}$ (since $\mathbf{b}$ is constant), we obtain

$$\frac{d}{dt}(\mathbf{v} \times \mathbf{b}) = \mathbf{v} \times \frac{d\mathbf{b}}{dt} + \frac{d\mathbf{v}}{dt} \times \mathbf{b} = \mathbf{a} \times \mathbf{b} = GM\frac{d\mathbf{u}}{dt}$$

Integrating both sides of this equation with respect to $t$ yields

$$\mathbf{v} \times \mathbf{b} = GM\mathbf{u} + \mathbf{C} \quad (15)$$

where $\mathbf{C}$ is a vector constant of integration. This constant can be obtained by evaluating both sides of the equation at $t = 0$. We leave it as an exercise to show that

$$\mathbf{C} = (r_0 v_0^2 - GM)\mathbf{i} \quad (16)$$

from which it follows that

$$\mathbf{v} \times \mathbf{b} = GM\mathbf{u} + (r_0 v_0^2 - GM)\mathbf{i} \quad (17)$$

We can now obtain the position function by computing the scalar triple product $\mathbf{r} \cdot (\mathbf{v} \times \mathbf{b})$ in two ways. First we use (10) and property (11) of Section 11.4 to obtain

$$\mathbf{r} \cdot (\mathbf{v} \times \mathbf{b}) = (\mathbf{r} \times \mathbf{v}) \cdot \mathbf{b} = \mathbf{b} \cdot \mathbf{b} = r_0^2 v_0^2 \quad (18)$$

and next we use (17) to obtain

$$\mathbf{r} \cdot (\mathbf{v} \times \mathbf{b}) = \mathbf{r} \cdot (GM\mathbf{u}) + \mathbf{r} \cdot (r_0 v_0^2 - GM)\mathbf{i}$$

$$= \mathbf{r} \cdot \left( GM\frac{\mathbf{r}}{r} \right) + r\mathbf{u} \cdot (r_0 v_0^2 - GM)\mathbf{i}$$

$$= GMr + r(r_0 v_0^2 - GM)\cos\theta$$

If we now equate this to (18), we obtain

$$r_0^2 v_0^2 = GMr + r(r_0 v_0^2 - GM)\cos\theta$$

which when solved for $r$ gives

$$r = \frac{r_0^2 v_0^2}{GM + (r_0 v_0^2 - GM)\cos\theta} = \frac{\dfrac{r_0^2 v_0^2}{GM}}{1 + \left( \dfrac{r_0 v_0^2}{GM} - 1 \right)\cos\theta} \quad (19)$$

or more simply

$$r = \frac{k}{1 + e\cos\theta} \quad (20)$$

where

$$k = \frac{r_0^2 v_0^2}{GM} \quad \text{and} \quad e = \frac{r_0 v_0^2}{GM} - 1 \qquad (21\text{--}22)$$

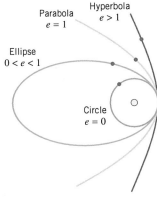

▲ **Figure 12.7.5**

We will leave it as an exercise to show that $e \geq 0$. Accepting this to be so, it follows by comparing (20) to Formula (3) of Section 10.6 that the trajectory is a conic section with eccentricity $e$, the focus at the pole, and $d = k/e$. Thus, depending on whether $e < 1$, $e = 1$, or $e > 1$, the trajectory will be, respectively, an ellipse, a parabola, or a hyperbola (Figure 12.7.5).

Note from Formula (22) that $e$ depends on $r_0$ and $v_0$, so the exact form of the trajectory is determined by the mass $M$ and the initial conditions. If the initial conditions are such that $e < 1$, then the mass $m$ becomes trapped in an elliptical orbit; otherwise the mass $m$ "escapes" and never returns to its initial position. Accordingly, the initial velocity that produces an eccentricity of $e = 1$ is called the **escape speed** and is denoted by $v_{\text{esc}}$. Thus, it follows from (22) that

$$v_{\text{esc}} = \sqrt{\frac{2GM}{r_0}} \qquad (23)$$

(verify).

■ **KEPLER'S FIRST AND SECOND LAWS**

It follows from our general discussion of central force fields that the planets have elliptical orbits with the Sun at the focus, which is Kepler's first law. To derive Kepler's second law, we begin by equating (10) and (13) to obtain

$$r^2 \frac{d\theta}{dt} = r_0 v_0 \qquad (24)$$

To prove that the radial line from the center of the Sun to the center of a planet sweeps out equal areas in equal times, let $r = f(\theta)$ denote the polar equation of the planet, and let $A$ denote the area swept out by the radial line as it varies from any fixed angle $\theta_0$ to an angle $\theta$. It follows from the area formula in 10.3.4 that $A$ can be expressed as

$$A = \int_{\theta_0}^{\theta} \frac{1}{2} [f(\phi)]^2 \, d\phi$$

where the dummy variable $\phi$ is introduced for the integration to reserve $\theta$ for the upper limit. It now follows from Part 2 of the Fundamental Theorem of Calculus and the chain rule that

$$\frac{dA}{dt} = \frac{dA}{d\theta} \frac{d\theta}{dt} = \frac{1}{2} [f(\theta)]^2 \frac{d\theta}{dt} = \frac{1}{2} r^2 \frac{d\theta}{dt}$$

Thus, it follows from (24) that

$$\frac{dA}{dt} = \frac{1}{2} r_0 v_0 \qquad (25)$$

which shows that $A$ changes at a constant rate. This implies that equal areas are swept out in equal times.

■ **KEPLER'S THIRD LAW**

To derive Kepler's third law, we let $a$ and $b$ be the semimajor and semiminor axes of the elliptical orbit, and we recall that the area of this ellipse is $\pi ab$. It follows by integrating (25) that in $t$ units of time the radial line will sweep out an area of $A = \frac{1}{2} r_0 v_0 t$. Thus, if $T$ denotes the time required for the planet to make one revolution around the Sun (the period), then the radial line will sweep out the area of the entire ellipse during that time and hence

$$\pi ab = \frac{1}{2} r_0 v_0 T$$

from which we obtain

$$T^2 = \frac{4\pi^2 a^2 b^2}{r_0^2 v_0^2} \tag{26}$$

However, it follows from Formula (1) of Section 10.6 and the relationship $c^2 = a^2 - b^2$ for an ellipse that

$$e = \frac{c}{a} = \frac{\sqrt{a^2 - b^2}}{a}$$

Thus, $b^2 = a^2(1 - e^2)$ and hence (26) can be written as

$$T^2 = \frac{4\pi^2 a^4 (1 - e^2)}{r_0^2 v_0^2} \tag{27}$$

But comparing Equation (20) to Equation (17) of Section 10.6 shows that

$$k = a(1 - e^2)$$

Finally, substituting this expression and (21) in (27) yields

$$T^2 = \frac{4\pi^2 a^3}{r_0^2 v_0^2} k = \frac{4\pi^2 a^3}{r_0^2 v_0^2} \frac{r_0^2 v_0^2}{GM} = \frac{4\pi^2}{GM} a^3 \tag{28}$$

Thus, we have proved that $T^2$ is proportional to $a^3$, which is Kepler's third law. When convenient, Formula (28) can also be expressed as

$$T = \frac{2\pi}{\sqrt{GM}} a^{3/2} \tag{29}$$

### ARTIFICIAL SATELLITES

Kepler's second and third laws and Formula (23) also apply to satellites that orbit a celestial body; we need only interpret $M$ to be the mass of the body exerting the force and $m$ to be the mass of the satellite. Values of $GM$ that are required in many of the formulas in this section have been determined experimentally for various attracting bodies (Table 12.7.1).

**Table 12.7.1**

| ATTRACTING BODY | INTERNATIONAL SYSTEM | BRITISH ENGINEERING SYSTEM |
|---|---|---|
| Earth | $GM = 3.99 \times 10^{14}$ m³/s² <br> $GM = 3.99 \times 10^{5}$ km³/s² | $GM = 1.41 \times 10^{16}$ ft³/s² <br> $GM = 1.24 \times 10^{12}$ mi³/h² |
| Sun | $GM = 1.33 \times 10^{20}$ m³/s² <br> $GM = 1.33 \times 10^{11}$ km³/s² | $GM = 4.69 \times 10^{21}$ ft³/s² <br> $GM = 4.13 \times 10^{17}$ mi³/h² |
| Moon | $GM = 4.90 \times 10^{12}$ m³/s² <br> $GM = 4.90 \times 10^{3}$ km³/s² | $GM = 1.73 \times 10^{14}$ ft³/s² <br> $GM = 1.53 \times 10^{10}$ mi³/h² |

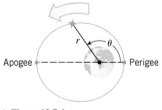

Apogee — Perigee

▲ **Figure 12.7.6**

   Recall that for orbits of planets around the Sun, the point at which the distance between the center of the planet and the center of the Sun is maximum is called the *aphelion* and the point at which it is minimum the *perihelion*. For satellites orbiting the Earth, the point at which the maximum distance occurs is called the ***apogee***, and the point at which the minimum distance occurs is called the ***perigee*** (Figure 12.7.6). The actual distances between the centers at apogee and perigee are called the ***apogee distance*** and the ***perigee distance***.

▶ **Example 1**   A geosynchronous orbit for a satellite is a circular orbit about the equator of the Earth in which the satellite stays fixed over a point on the equator. Use the fact that the Earth makes one revolution about its axis every 24 hours to find the altitude in miles of a communications satellite in geosynchronous orbit. Assume the Earth to be a sphere of radius 4000 mi.

*Solution.*    To remain fixed over a point on the equator, the satellite must have a period of $T = 24$ h. It follows from (28) or (29) and the Earth value of $GM = 1.24 \times 10^{12}$ mi$^3$/h$^2$ from Table 12.7.1 that

$$a = \sqrt[3]{\frac{GMT^2}{4\pi^2}} = \sqrt[3]{\frac{(1.24 \times 10^{12})(24)^2}{4\pi^2}} \approx 26{,}250 \text{ mi}$$

and hence the altitude $h$ of the satellite is

$$h \approx 26{,}250 - 4000 = 22{,}250 \text{ mi} \blacktriangleleft$$

## ✔ QUICK CHECK EXERCISES 12.7    *(See page 902 for answers.)*

1. Let $G$ denote the universal gravitational constant and let $M$ and $m$ denote masses a distance $r$ apart.
   (a) According to Newton's Law of Universal Gravitation, $M$ and $m$ attract each other with a force of magnitude
   _____.
   (b) If $\mathbf{r}$ is the radius vector from $M$ to $m$, then the force of attraction that mass $M$ exerts on mass $m$ is _____.

2. Suppose that a mass $m$ is in an orbit about a mass $M$ and that $r_0$ is the minimum distance from $m$ to $M$. If $G$ is the universal gravitational constant, then the "escape" speed of $m$ is _____.

3. For a planet in an elliptical orbit about the Sun, the square of the planet's period is proportional to what power of the semimajor axis of its orbit?

4. Suppose that a mass $m$ is in an orbit about a mass $M$ and that $r_0$ is the minimum distance from $m$ to $M$. If $v_0$ is the speed of mass $m$ when it is a distance $r_0$ from $M$, and if $G$ denotes the universal gravitational constant, then the eccentricity of the orbit is _____.

## EXERCISE SET 12.7

1–14 In exercises that require numerical values, use Table 12.7.1 and the following values, where needed:

> radius of Earth = 4000 mi = 6440 km
> radius of Moon = 1080 mi = 1740 km
> 1 year (Earth year) = 365 days

1. (a) Obtain the value of $C$ given in Formula (16) by setting $t = 0$ in (15).
   (b) Use Formulas (7), (17), and (22) to show that
   $$\mathbf{v} \times \mathbf{b} = GM[(e + \cos\theta)\mathbf{i} + \sin\theta\,\mathbf{j}]$$
   (c) Show that $\|\mathbf{v} \times \mathbf{b}\| = \|\mathbf{v}\|\|\mathbf{b}\|$.
   (d) Use the results in parts (b) and (c) to show that the speed of a particle in an elliptical orbit is
   $$v = \frac{v_0}{1+e}\sqrt{e^2 + 2e\cos\theta + 1}$$
   (e) Suppose that a particle is in an elliptical orbit. Use part (d) to conclude that the distance from the particle to the center of force is a minimum if and only if the speed of the particle is a maximum. Similarly,

argue that the distance from the particle to the center of force is a maximum if and only if the speed of the particle is a minimum.

2. Use the result in Exercise 1(d) to show that when a particle in an elliptical orbit with eccentricity $e$ reaches an end of the minor axis, its speed is
$$v = v_0\sqrt{\frac{1-e}{1+e}}$$

3. Use the result in Exercise 1(d) to show that for a particle in an elliptical orbit with eccentricity $e$, the maximum and minimum speeds are related by
$$v_{max} = v_{min}\frac{1+e}{1-e}$$

4. Use Formula (22) and the result in Exercise 1(d) to show that the speed $v$ of a particle in a circular orbit of radius $r_0$ is constant and is given by
$$v = \sqrt{\frac{GM}{r_0}}$$

**5.** Suppose that a particle is in an elliptical orbit in a central force field in which the center of force is at a focus, and let $\mathbf{r} = \mathbf{r}(t)$ and $\mathbf{v} = \mathbf{v}(t)$ be the position and velocity functions of the particle, respectively. Let $r_{min}$ and $r_{max}$ denote the minimum and maximum distances from the particle to the center of force, and let $v_{min}$ and $v_{max}$ denote the minimum and maximum speeds of the particle.

   (a) Review the discussion of ellipses in polar coordinates in Section 10.6, and show that if the ellipse has eccentricity $e$ and semimajor axis $a$, then $r_{min} = a(1 - e)$ and $r_{max} = a(1 + e)$.

   (b) Explain why $r_{min}$ and $r_{max}$ occur at points at which $\mathbf{r}$ and $\mathbf{v}$ are orthogonal. [*Hint:* First argue that the extreme values of $\|\mathbf{r}\|$ occur at critical points of the function $\|\mathbf{r}\|^2 = \mathbf{r} \cdot \mathbf{r}$.]

   (c) Explain why $v_{min}$ and $v_{max}$ occur at points at which $\mathbf{r}$ and $\mathbf{v}$ are orthogonal. [*Hint:* First argue that the extreme values of $\|\mathbf{v}\|$ occur at critical points of the function $\|\mathbf{v}\|^2 = \mathbf{v} \cdot \mathbf{v}$. Then use Equation (5).]

   (d) Use Equation (2) and parts (b) and (c) to conclude that $r_{max}v_{min} = r_{min}v_{max}$.

**6.** Use the results in parts (a) and (d) of Exercise 5 to give a derivation of the equation in Exercise 3.

**7.** Use the result in Exercise 4 to find the speed in km/s of a satellite in a circular orbit that is 200 km above the surface of the Earth.

**8.** Use the result in Exercise 4 to find the speed in mi/h of a communications satellite that is in geosynchronous orbit around the Earth (see Example 1).

**9.** Find the escape speed in km/s for a space probe in a circular orbit that is 300 km above the surface of the Earth.

**10.** The universal gravitational constant is approximately

$$G = 6.67 \times 10^{-11} \text{ m}^3/\text{kg·s}^2$$

and the semimajor axis of the Earth's orbit is approximately

$$a = 149.6 \times 10^6 \text{ km}$$

Estimate the mass of the Sun in kg.

**11.** (a) The eccentricity of the Moon's orbit around the Earth is 0.055, and its semimajor axis is $a = 238,900$ mi. Find the maximum and minimum distances between the surface of the Earth and the surface of the Moon.

   (b) Find the period of the Moon's orbit in days.

**12.** (a) *Vanguard 1* was launched in March 1958 with perigee and apogee altitudes above the Earth of 649 km and 4340 km, respectively. Find the length of the semimajor axis of its orbit.

   (b) Use the result in part (a) of Exercise 16 in Section 10.6 to find the eccentricity of its orbit.

   (c) Find the period of *Vanguard 1* in minutes.

**13.** (a) Suppose that a space probe is in a circular orbit at an altitude of 180 mi above the surface of the Earth. Use the result in Exercise 4 to find its speed.

   (b) During a very short period of time, a thruster rocket on the space probe is fired to increase the speed of the probe by 600 mi/h in its direction of motion. Find the eccentricity of the resulting elliptical orbit, and use the result in part (a) of Exercise 5 to find the apogee altitude.

**14.** Show that the quantity $e$ defined by Formula (22) is non-negative. [*Hint:* The polar axis was chosen so that $r$ is minimum when $\theta = 0$.]

✔ **QUICK CHECK ANSWERS 12.7**

1. (a) $\dfrac{GMm}{r^2}$ (b) $-\dfrac{GMm}{r^3}\mathbf{r}$  2. $\sqrt{\dfrac{2GM}{r_0}}$  3. 3  4. $e = \dfrac{r_0 v_0^2}{GM} - 1$

## CHAPTER 12 REVIEW EXERCISES

**1.** In words, what is meant by the graph of a vector-valued function?

**2–5** Describe the graph of the equation. ■

**2.** $\mathbf{r} = (2 - 3t)\mathbf{i} - 4t\mathbf{j}$      **3.** $\mathbf{r} = 3\sin 2t\mathbf{i} + 3\cos 2t\mathbf{j}$

**4.** $\mathbf{r} = 3\cos t\mathbf{i} + 2\sin t\mathbf{j} - \mathbf{k}$   **5.** $\mathbf{r} = -2\mathbf{i} + t\mathbf{j} + (t^2 - 1)\mathbf{k}$

**6.** Describe the graph of the vector-valued function.

   (a) $\mathbf{r} = \mathbf{r}_0 + t(\mathbf{r}_1 - \mathbf{r}_0)$

   (b) $\mathbf{r} = \mathbf{r}_0 + t(\mathbf{r}_1 - \mathbf{r}_0)$   $(0 \leq t \leq 1)$

   (c) $\mathbf{r} = \mathbf{r}_0 + t\mathbf{r}'(t_0)$

**7.** Show that the graph of $\mathbf{r}(t) = t\sin\pi t\mathbf{i} + t\mathbf{j} + t\cos\pi t\mathbf{k}$ lies on the surface of a cone, and sketch the cone.

**8.** Find parametric equations for the intersection of the surfaces

$$y = x^2 \quad \text{and} \quad 2x^2 + y^2 + 6z^2 = 24$$

and sketch the intersection.

**9.** In words, give a geometric description of the statement $\displaystyle\lim_{t \to a} \mathbf{r}(t) = \mathbf{L}$.

**10.** Evaluate $\lim\limits_{t \to 0} \left( e^{-t}\mathbf{i} + \dfrac{1 - \cos t}{t}\mathbf{j} + t^2\mathbf{k} \right)$.

**11.** Find parametric equations of the line tangent to the graph of
$$\mathbf{r}(t) = (t + \cos 2t)\mathbf{i} - (t^2 + t)\mathbf{j} + \sin t\mathbf{k}$$
at the point where $t = 0$.

**12.** Suppose that $\mathbf{r}_1(t)$ and $\mathbf{r}_2(t)$ are smooth vector-valued functions such that $\mathbf{r}_1(0) = \langle -1, 1, 2 \rangle$, $\mathbf{r}_2(0) = \langle 1, 2, 1 \rangle$, $\mathbf{r}_1'(0) = \langle 1, 0, 1 \rangle$, and $\mathbf{r}_2'(0) = \langle 4, 0, 2 \rangle$. Use this information to evaluate the derivative at $t = 0$ of each function.
  (a) $\mathbf{r}(t) = 3\mathbf{r}_1(t) + 2\mathbf{r}_2(t)$   (b) $\mathbf{r}(t) = [\ln(t+1)]\mathbf{r}_1(t)$
  (c) $\mathbf{r}(t) = \mathbf{r}_1(t) \times \mathbf{r}_2(t)$   (d) $f(t) = \mathbf{r}_1(t) \cdot \mathbf{r}_2(t)$

**13.** Evaluate $\displaystyle\int (\cos t\mathbf{i} + \sin t\mathbf{j})\, dt$.

**14.** Evaluate $\displaystyle\int_0^{\pi/3} \langle \cos 3t, -\sin 3t \rangle\, dt$.

**15.** Solve the vector initial-value problem
$$\mathbf{y}'(t) = t^2\mathbf{i} + 2t\mathbf{j}, \quad \mathbf{y}(0) = \mathbf{i} + \mathbf{j}$$

**16.** Solve the vector initial-value problem
$$\frac{d\mathbf{r}}{dt} = \mathbf{r}, \quad \mathbf{r}(0) = \mathbf{r}_0$$
for the unknown vector-valued function $\mathbf{r}(t)$.

**17.** Find the arc length of the graph of
$$\mathbf{r}(t) = e^{\sqrt{2}t}\mathbf{i} + e^{-\sqrt{2}t}\mathbf{j} + 2t\mathbf{k} \quad (0 \le t \le \sqrt{2}\ln 2)$$

**18.** Suppose that $\mathbf{r}(t)$ is a smooth vector-valued function of $t$ with $\mathbf{r}'(0) = 3\mathbf{i} - \mathbf{j} + \mathbf{k}$ and that $\mathbf{r}_1(t) = \mathbf{r}(2 - e^{t \ln 2})$. Find $\mathbf{r}_1'(1)$.

**19.** Find the arc length parametrization of the line through $P(-1, 4, 3)$ and $Q(0, 2, 5)$ that has reference point $P$ and orients the line in the direction from $P$ to $Q$.

**20.** Find an arc length parametrization of the curve
$$\mathbf{r}(t) = \langle e^t \cos t, -e^t \sin t \rangle \quad (0 \le t \le \pi/2)$$
which has the same orientation and has $\mathbf{r}(0)$ as the reference point.

**21.** Suppose that $\mathbf{r}(t)$ is a smooth vector-valued function. State the definitions of $\mathbf{T}(t)$, $\mathbf{N}(t)$, and $\mathbf{B}(t)$.

**22.** Find $\mathbf{T}(0)$, $\mathbf{N}(0)$, and $\mathbf{B}(0)$ for the curve
$$\mathbf{r}(t) = \left\langle 2\cos t, 2\cos t + \frac{3}{\sqrt{5}}\sin t, \cos t - \frac{6}{\sqrt{5}}\sin t \right\rangle$$

**23.** State the definition of "curvature" and explain what it means geometrically.

**24.** Suppose that $\mathbf{r}(t)$ is a smooth curve with $\mathbf{r}'(0) = \mathbf{i}$ and $\mathbf{r}''(0) = \mathbf{i} + 2\mathbf{j}$. Find the curvature at $t = 0$.

**25–28** Find the curvature of the curve at the stated point. ■

**25.** $\mathbf{r}(t) = 2\cos t\mathbf{i} + 3\sin t\mathbf{j} - t\mathbf{k}$; $t = \pi/2$

**26.** $\mathbf{r}(t) = \langle 2t, e^{2t}, e^{-2t} \rangle$; $t = 0$

**27.** $y = \cos x$; $x = \pi/2$   **28.** $y = \ln x$; $x = 1$

**29.** Suppose that $\mathbf{r}(t)$ is the position function of a particle moving in 2-space or 3-space. In each part, explain what the given quantity represents physically.
  (a) $\left\| \dfrac{d\mathbf{r}}{dt} \right\|$   (b) $\displaystyle\int_{t_0}^{t_1} \left\| \dfrac{d\mathbf{r}}{dt} \right\| dt$   (c) $\| \mathbf{r}(t) \|$

**30.** (a) What does Theorem 12.2.8 tell you about the velocity vector of a particle that moves over a sphere?
  (b) What does Theorem 12.2.8 tell you about the acceleration vector of a particle that moves with constant speed?
  (c) Show that the particle with position function
$$\mathbf{r}(t) = \sqrt{1 - \tfrac{1}{4}\cos^2 t}\, \cos t\mathbf{i} + \sqrt{1 - \tfrac{1}{4}\cos^2 t}\, \sin t\mathbf{j} + \tfrac{1}{2}\cos t\mathbf{k}$$
  moves over a sphere.

**31.** As illustrated in the accompanying figure, suppose that a particle moves counterclockwise around a circle of radius $R$ centered at the origin at a constant rate of $\omega$ radians per second. This is called *uniform circular motion*. If we assume that the particle is at the point $(R, 0)$ at time $t = 0$, then its position function will be
$$\mathbf{r}(t) = R\cos \omega t\mathbf{i} + R\sin \omega t\mathbf{j}$$
  (a) Show that the velocity vector $\mathbf{v}(t)$ is always tangent to the circle and that the particle has constant speed $v$ given by
$$v = R\omega$$
  (b) Show that the acceleration vector $\mathbf{a}(t)$ is always directed toward the center of the circle and has constant magnitude $a$ given by
$$a = R\omega^2$$
  (c) Show that the time $T$ required for the particle to make one complete revolution is
$$T = \frac{2\pi}{\omega} = \frac{2\pi R}{v}$$

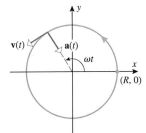

◄ **Figure Ex-31**

**32.** If a particle of mass $m$ has uniform circular motion (see Exercise 31), then the acceleration vector $\mathbf{a}(t)$ is called the *centripetal acceleration*. According to Newton's second law, this acceleration must be produced by some force $\mathbf{F}(t)$, called the *centripetal force*, that is related to $\mathbf{a}(t)$ by the equation $\mathbf{F}(t) = m\mathbf{a}(t)$. If this force is not present, then the particle cannot undergo uniform circular motion. *(cont.)*

(a) Show that the direction of the centripetal force varies with time but that it has constant magnitude $F$ given by

$$F = \frac{mv^2}{R}$$

(b) An astronaut with a mass of $m = 60$ kg orbits the Earth at an altitude of $h = 3200$ km with a constant speed of $v = 6.43$ km/s. Find her centripetal acceleration assuming that the radius of the Earth is 6440 km.

(c) What centripetal gravitational force in newtons does the Earth exert on the astronaut?

**33.** At time $t = 0$ a particle at the origin of an $xyz$-coordinate system has a velocity vector of $\mathbf{v}_0 = \mathbf{i} + 2\mathbf{j} - \mathbf{k}$. The acceleration function of the particle is $\mathbf{a}(t) = 2t^2\mathbf{i} + \mathbf{j} + \cos 2t\mathbf{k}$.
(a) Find the position function of the particle.
(b) Find the speed of the particle at time $t = 1$.

**34.** Let $\mathbf{v} = \mathbf{v}(t)$ and $\mathbf{a} = \mathbf{a}(t)$ be the velocity and acceleration vectors for a particle moving in 2-space or 3-space. Show that the rate of change of its speed can be expressed as

$$\frac{d}{dt}(\|\mathbf{v}\|) = \frac{1}{\|\mathbf{v}\|}(\mathbf{v} \cdot \mathbf{a})$$

**35.** Use Formula (23) in Section 12.7 and refer to Table 12.7.1 to find the escape speed (in km/s) for a space probe 600 km above the surface of the Earth.

**36.** As illustrated in the accompanying figure, the polar coordinates of a rocket are tracked by radar from a point that is $b$ units from the launching pad. Show that the speed $v$ of the rocket can be expressed in terms $b$, $\theta$, and $d\theta/dt$ as

$$v = b \sec^2 \theta \frac{d\theta}{dt}$$

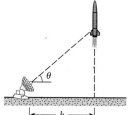

◀ **Figure Ex-36**

**37.** A player throws a ball with an initial speed of 60 ft/s at an unknown angle $\alpha$ with the horizontal from a point that is 4 ft above the floor of a gymnasium. Given that the ceiling of the gymnasium is 25 ft high, determine the maximum height $h$ at which the ball can hit a wall that is 60 ft away (see the accompanying figure).

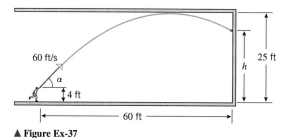

▲ **Figure Ex-37**

## CHAPTER 12 MAKING CONNECTIONS  [C] CAS

**1.** (a) Use the formulas

$$\mathbf{N}(t) = \mathbf{B}(t) \times \mathbf{T}(t)$$
$$\mathbf{T}(t) = \mathbf{r}'(t)/\|\mathbf{r}'(t)\|$$

and

$$\mathbf{B}(t) = \frac{\mathbf{r}'(t) \times \mathbf{r}''(t)}{\|\mathbf{r}'(t) \times \mathbf{r}''(t)\|}$$

to show that $\mathbf{N}(t)$ can be expressed in terms of $\mathbf{r}(t)$ as

$$\mathbf{N}(t) = \frac{\mathbf{r}'(t) \times \mathbf{r}''(t)}{\|\mathbf{r}'(t) \times \mathbf{r}''(t)\|} \times \frac{\mathbf{r}'(t)}{\|\mathbf{r}'(t)\|}$$

(b) Use properties of cross products to show that the formula in part (a) can be expressed as

$$\mathbf{N}(t) = \frac{(\mathbf{r}'(t) \times \mathbf{r}''(t)) \times \mathbf{r}'(t)}{\|(\mathbf{r}'(t) \times \mathbf{r}''(t)) \times \mathbf{r}'(t)\|}$$

(c) Use the result in part (b) to find $\mathbf{N}(t)$ at the given point.
(i) $\mathbf{r}(t) = (t^2 - 1)\mathbf{i} + t\mathbf{j}$; $t = 1$
(ii) $\mathbf{r}(t) = 4\cos t\mathbf{i} + 4\sin t\mathbf{j} + t\mathbf{k}$; $t = \pi/2$

**2.** (a) Use the result in Exercise 1(b) and Exercise 45 of Section 11.4 to show that $\mathbf{N}(t)$ can be expressed directly in terms of $\mathbf{r}(t)$ as

$$\mathbf{N}(t) = \frac{\mathbf{u}(t)}{\|\mathbf{u}(t)\|}$$

where

$$\mathbf{u}(t) = \|\mathbf{r}'(t)\|^2\mathbf{r}''(t) - (\mathbf{r}'(t) \cdot \mathbf{r}''(t))\mathbf{r}'(t)$$

(b) Use the result in part (a) to find $\mathbf{N}(t)$.
(i) $\mathbf{r}(t) = \sin t\mathbf{i} + \cos t\mathbf{j} + t\mathbf{k}$
(ii) $\mathbf{r}(t) = t\mathbf{i} + t^2\mathbf{j} + t^3\mathbf{k}$

**3.** In Making Connections Exercise 1 of Chapter 10 we defined the Cornu spiral parametrically as

$$x = \int_0^t \cos\left(\frac{\pi u^2}{2}\right) du, \quad y = \int_0^t \sin\left(\frac{\pi u^2}{2}\right) du$$

This curve, which is graphed in the accompanying figure, is used in highway design to create a gradual transition from a straight road (zero curvature) to an exit ramp with positive curvature. *(cont.)*

(a) Express the Cornu spiral as a vector-valued function $\mathbf{r}(t)$, and then use Theorem 12.3.4 to show that $s = t$ is the arc length parameter with reference point $(0, 0)$.

(b) Replace $t$ by $s$ and use Formula (1) of Section 12.5 to show that $\kappa(s) = \pi|s|$. [*Note:* If $s \geq 0$, then the curvature $\kappa(s) = \pi s$ increases from 0 at a constant rate with respect to $s$. This makes the spiral ideal for joining a curved road to a straight road.]

(c) What happens to the curvature of the Cornu spiral as $s \to +\infty$? In words, explain why this is consistent with the graph.

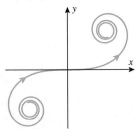

◀ **Figure Ex-3**

[C] **4.** In 1975, German engineer Werner Stengel pioneered the use of Cornu spirals (see Exercise 3) in the design of loops for roller coasters with the *Revolution* at Six Flags Magic Mountain in California. For this design, the top of the loop is a circular arc, joined at either end to Cornu spirals that ease the transitions to horizontal track. The accompanying figure illustrates this design when the circular arc (in red) is a semicircle, quarter-circle, or a single point, respectively. Suppose that a roller-coaster loop is designed to be 45 feet across at its widest point. For each case in Figure Ex-4, find the vertical distance between the level of the horizontal track and the top of the loop. Use the numerical integration capability of your CAS to estimate integrals, as necessary.

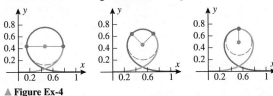

▲ **Figure Ex-4**

**5.** Use the results in Exercise 61 of Section 12.5 and the results in Exercise 32 of Section 12.3 to show that for the circular helix
$$\mathbf{r} = a \cos t\,\mathbf{i} + a \sin t\,\mathbf{j} + ct\,\mathbf{k}$$
with $a > 0$, the torsion and the binormal vector are
$$\tau = \frac{c}{w^2}$$

and
$$\mathbf{B} = \left(\frac{c}{w} \sin \frac{s}{w}\right)\mathbf{i} - \left(\frac{c}{w} \cos \frac{s}{w}\right)\mathbf{j} + \left(\frac{a}{w}\right)\mathbf{k}$$

where $w = \sqrt{a^2 + c^2}$ and $s$ has reference point $(a, 0, 0)$.

**6.** Suppose that the position function of a point moving in the $xy$-plane is
$$\mathbf{r} = x(t)\mathbf{i} + y(t)\mathbf{j}$$

This equation can be expressed in polar coordinates by making the substitution
$$x(t) = r(t) \cos \theta(t), \quad y(t) = r(t) \sin \theta(t)$$

This yields
$$\mathbf{r} = r(t) \cos \theta(t)\mathbf{i} + r(t) \sin \theta(t)\mathbf{j}$$

which can be expressed as
$$\mathbf{r} = r(t)\mathbf{e}_r(t)$$

where $\mathbf{e}_r(t) = \cos \theta(t)\mathbf{i} + \sin \theta(t)\mathbf{j}$.

(a) Show that $\mathbf{e}_r(t)$ is a unit vector in the same direction as the radius vector $\mathbf{r}$ if $r(t) > 0$. Also, show that $\mathbf{e}_\theta(t) = -\sin \theta(t)\mathbf{i} + \cos \theta(t)\mathbf{j}$ is the unit vector that results when $\mathbf{e}_r(t)$ is rotated counterclockwise through an angle of $\pi/2$. The vector $\mathbf{e}_r(t)$ is called the ***radial unit vector*** and the vector $\mathbf{e}_\theta(t)$ is called the ***transverse unit vector*** (see the accompanying figure).

(b) Show that the velocity function $\mathbf{v} = \mathbf{v}(t)$ can be expressed in terms of radial and transverse components as
$$\mathbf{v} = \frac{dr}{dt}\mathbf{e}_r + r\frac{d\theta}{dt}\mathbf{e}_\theta$$

(c) Show that the acceleration function $\mathbf{a} = \mathbf{a}(t)$ can be expressed in terms of radial and transverse components as
$$\mathbf{a} = \left[\frac{d^2r}{dt^2} - r\left(\frac{d\theta}{dt}\right)^2\right]\mathbf{e}_r + \left[r\frac{d^2\theta}{dt^2} + 2\frac{dr}{dt}\frac{d\theta}{dt}\right]\mathbf{e}_\theta$$

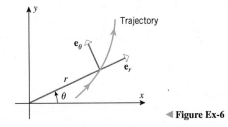

◀ **Figure Ex-6**

## EXPANDING THE CALCULUS HORIZON

For a practical application of projectile motion in a whimsical setting, see the module entitled **Blammo the Human Cannonball** at:

www.wiley.com/college/anton

# 13

# PARTIAL DERIVATIVES

© Science Photo Library/Photo Researchers, Inc.

*Three-dimensional surfaces have high points and low points that are analogous to the peaks and valleys of a mountain range. In this chapter we will use derivatives to locate these points and to study other features of such surfaces.*

In this chapter we will extend many of the basic concepts of calculus to functions of two or more variables, commonly called functions of several variables. We will begin by discussing limits and continuity for functions of two and three variables, then we will define derivatives of such functions, and then we will use these derivatives to study tangent planes, rates of change, slopes of surfaces, and maximization and minimization problems. Although many of the basic ideas that we developed for functions of one variable will carry over in a natural way, functions of several variables are intrinsically more complicated than functions of one variable, so we will need to develop new tools and new ideas to deal with such functions.

## 13.1 FUNCTIONS OF TWO OR MORE VARIABLES

*In previous sections we studied real-valued functions of a real variable and vector-valued functions of a real variable. In this section we will consider real-valued functions of two or more real variables.*

### ■ NOTATION AND TERMINOLOGY

There are many familiar formulas in which a given variable depends on two or more other variables. For example, the area $A$ of a triangle depends on the base length $b$ and height $h$ by the formula $A = \frac{1}{2}bh$; the volume $V$ of a rectangular box depends on the length $l$, the width $w$, and the height $h$ by the formula $V = lwh$; and the arithmetic average $\bar{x}$ of $n$ real numbers, $x_1, x_2, \ldots, x_n$, depends on those numbers by the formula

$$\bar{x} = \frac{1}{n}(x_1 + x_2 + \cdots + x_n)$$

Thus, we say that

$A$ is a function of the two variables $b$ and $h$;

$V$ is a function of the three variables $l$, $w$, and $h$;

$\bar{x}$ is a function of the $n$ variables $x_1, x_2, \ldots, x_n$.

The terminology and notation for functions of two or more variables is similar to that for functions of one variable. For example, the expression

$$z = f(x, y)$$

means that $z$ is a function of $x$ and $y$ in the sense that a unique value of the dependent variable $z$ is determined by specifying values for the independent variables $x$ and $y$. Similarly,

$$w = f(x, y, z)$$

expresses $w$ as a function of $x$, $y$, and $z$, and

$$u = f(x_1, x_2, \ldots, x_n)$$

expresses $u$ as a function of $x_1, x_2, \ldots, x_n$.

As with functions of one variable, the independent variables of a function of two or more variables may be restricted to lie in some set $D$, which we call the **domain** of $f$. Sometimes the domain will be determined by physical restrictions on the variables. If the function is defined by a formula and if there are no physical restrictions or other restrictions stated explicitly, then it is understood that the domain consists of all points for which the formula yields a real value for the dependent variable. We call this the **natural domain** of the function. The following definitions summarize this discussion.

By extension, one can define the notion of "$n$-dimensional space" in which a "point" is a sequence of $n$ real numbers $(x_1, x_2, \ldots, x_n)$, and a function of $n$ real variables is a rule that assigns a unique real number $f(x_1, x_2, \ldots, x_n)$ to each point in some set in this space.

---

**13.1.1 DEFINITION** A **function $f$ of two variables**, $x$ and $y$, is a rule that assigns a unique real number $f(x, y)$ to each point $(x, y)$ in some set $D$ in the $xy$-plane.

---

**13.1.2 DEFINITION** A **function $f$ of three variables**, $x$, $y$, and $z$, is a rule that assigns a unique real number $f(x, y, z)$ to each point $(x, y, z)$ in some set $D$ in three-dimensional space.

---

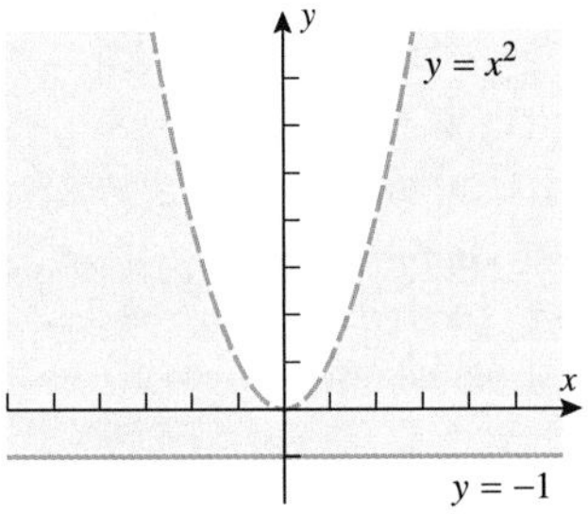

The solid boundary line is included in the domain, while the dashed boundary is not included in the domain.

▲ **Figure 13.1.1**

▶ **Example 1** Let $f(x, y) = \sqrt{y + 1} + \ln(x^2 - y)$. Find $f(e, 0)$ and sketch the natural domain of $f$.

**Solution.** By substitution,

$$f(e, 0) = \sqrt{0 + 1} + \ln(e^2 - 0) = \sqrt{1} + \ln(e^2) = 1 + 2 = 3$$

To find the natural domain of $f$, we note that $\sqrt{y + 1}$ is defined only when $y \geq -1$, while $\ln(x^2 - y)$ is defined only when $0 < x^2 - y$ or $y < x^2$. Thus, the natural domain of $f$ consists of all points in the $xy$-plane for which $-1 \leq y < x^2$. To sketch the natural domain, we first sketch the parabola $y = x^2$ as a "dashed" curve and the line $y = -1$ as a solid curve. The natural domain of $f$ is then the region lying above or on the line $y = -1$ and below the parabola $y = x^2$ (Figure 13.1.1). ◀

▶ **Example 2** Let

$$f(x, y, z) = \sqrt{1 - x^2 - y^2 - z^2}$$

Find $f\left(0, \frac{1}{2}, -\frac{1}{2}\right)$ and the natural domain of $f$.

**Solution.** By substitution,

$$f\left(0, \tfrac{1}{2}, -\tfrac{1}{2}\right) = \sqrt{1 - (0)^2 - \left(\tfrac{1}{2}\right)^2 - \left(-\tfrac{1}{2}\right)^2} = \sqrt{\tfrac{1}{2}}$$

Because of the square root sign, we must have $0 \leq 1 - x^2 - y^2 - z^2$ in order to have a real value for $f(x, y, z)$. Rewriting this inequality in the form

$$x^2 + y^2 + z^2 \leq 1$$

we see that the natural domain of $f$ consists of all points on or within the sphere

$$x^2 + y^2 + z^2 = 1 \blacktriangleleft$$

## ■ FUNCTIONS DESCRIBED BY TABLES

The wind chill index is that temperature (in °F) which would produce the same sensation on exposed skin at a wind speed of 3 mi/h as the temperature and wind speed combination in current weather conditions.

Sometimes it is either desirable or necessary to represent a function of two variables in table form, rather than as an explicit formula. For example, the U.S. National Weather Service uses the formula

$$W = 35.74 + 0.6215T + (0.4275T - 35.75)v^{0.16} \tag{1}$$

to model the wind chill index $W$ (in °F) as a function of the temperature $T$ (in °F) and the wind speed $v$ (in mi/h) for wind speeds greater than 3 mi/h. This formula is sufficiently complex that it is difficult to get an intuitive feel for the relationship between the variables. One can get a clearer sense of the relationship by selecting sample values of $T$ and $v$ and constructing a table, such as Table 13.1.1, in which we have rounded the values of $W$ to the nearest integer. For example, if the temperature is 30°F and the wind speed is 5 mi/h, it feels as if the temperature is 25°F. If the wind speed increases to 15 mi/h, the temperature then feels as if it has dropped to 19°F. Note that in this case, an increase in wind speed of 10 mi/h causes a 6°F decrease in the wind chill index. To estimate wind chill values not displayed in the table, we can use *linear interpolation*. For example, suppose that the temperature is 30°F and the wind speed is 7 mi/h. A reasonable estimate for the drop in the wind chill index from its value when the wind speed is 5 mi/h would be $\frac{2}{10} \cdot 6°F = 1.2°F$. (Why?) The resulting estimate in wind chill would then be $25° - 1.2° = 23.8°F$.

In some cases, tables for functions of two variables arise directly from experimental data, in which case one must either work directly with the table or else use some technique to construct a formula that models the data in the table. Such modeling techniques are developed in statistics and numerical analysis texts.

**Table 13.1.1**

TEMPERATURE $T$ (°F)

| WIND SPEED $v$ (mi/h) | 20 | 25 | 30 | 35 |
|---|---|---|---|---|
| 5 | 13 | 19 | 25 | 31 |
| 15 | 6 | 13 | 19 | 25 |
| 25 | 3 | 9 | 16 | 23 |
| 35 | 0 | 7 | 14 | 21 |
| 45 | −2 | 5 | 12 | 19 |

## ■ GRAPHS OF FUNCTIONS OF TWO VARIABLES

Recall that for a function $f$ of one variable, the graph of $f(x)$ in the $xy$-plane was defined to be the graph of the equation $y = f(x)$. Similarly, if $f$ is a function of two variables, we define the **graph** of $f(x, y)$ in $xyz$-space to be the graph of the equation $z = f(x, y)$. In general, such a graph will be a surface in 3-space.

▶ **Example 3** In each part, describe the graph of the function in an $xyz$-coordinate system.

(a) $f(x, y) = 1 - x - \frac{1}{2}y$ (b) $f(x, y) = \sqrt{1 - x^2 - y^2}$

(c) $f(x, y) = -\sqrt{x^2 + y^2}$

*Solution (a).* By definition, the graph of the given function is the graph of the equation

$$z = 1 - x - \frac{1}{2}y$$

which is a plane. A triangular portion of the plane can be sketched by plotting the intersections with the coordinate axes and joining them with line segments (Figure 13.1.2a).

*Solution (b).* By definition, the graph of the given function is the graph of the equation

$$z = \sqrt{1 - x^2 - y^2} \tag{2}$$

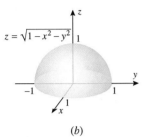

(a)

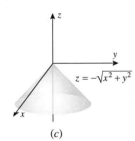

(b)

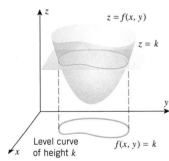

(c)

▲ **Figure 13.1.2**

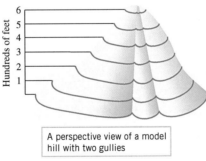

Level curve
of height $k$          $f(x, y) = k$

▲ **Figure 13.1.4**

After squaring both sides, this can be rewritten as

$$x^2 + y^2 + z^2 = 1$$

which represents a sphere of radius 1, centered at the origin. Since (2) imposes the added condition that $z \geq 0$, the graph is just the upper hemisphere (Figure 13.1.2b).

**Solution (c).**    The graph of the given function is the graph of the equation

$$z = -\sqrt{x^2 + y^2} \tag{3}$$

After squaring, we obtain          $z^2 = x^2 + y^2$

which is the equation of a circular cone (see Table 11.7.1). Since (3) imposes the condition that $z \leq 0$, the graph is just the lower nappe of the cone (Figure 13.1.2c). ◄

■ **LEVEL CURVES**

We are all familiar with the topographic (or contour) maps in which a three-dimensional landscape, such as a mountain range, is represented by two-dimensional contour lines or curves of constant elevation. Consider, for example, the model hill and its contour map shown in Figure 13.1.3. The contour map is constructed by passing planes of constant elevation through the hill, projecting the resulting contours onto a flat surface, and labeling the contours with their elevations. In Figure 13.1.3, note how the two gullies appear as indentations in the contour lines and how the curves are close together on the contour map where the hill has a steep slope and become more widely spaced where the slope is gradual.

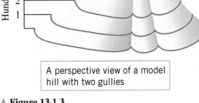

A perspective view of a model hill with two gullies

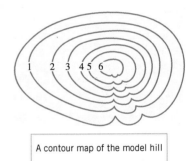

A contour map of the model hill

▲ **Figure 13.1.3**

Contour maps are also useful for studying functions of two variables. If the surface $z = f(x, y)$ is cut by the horizontal plane $z = k$, then at all points on the intersection we have $f(x, y) = k$. The projection of this intersection onto the $xy$-plane is called the ***level curve of height k*** or the ***level curve with constant k*** (Figure 13.1.4). A set of level curves for $z = f(x, y)$ is called a ***contour plot*** or ***contour map*** of $f$.

▶ **Example 4**    The graph of the function $f(x, y) = y^2 - x^2$ in $xyz$-space is the hyperbolic paraboloid (saddle surface) shown in Figure 13.1.5a. The level curves have equations of the form $y^2 - x^2 = k$. For $k > 0$ these curves are hyperbolas opening along lines parallel to the $y$-axis; for $k < 0$ they are hyperbolas opening along lines parallel to the $x$-axis; and for $k = 0$ the level curve consists of the intersecting lines $y + x = 0$ and $y - x = 0$ (Figure 13.1.5b). ◄

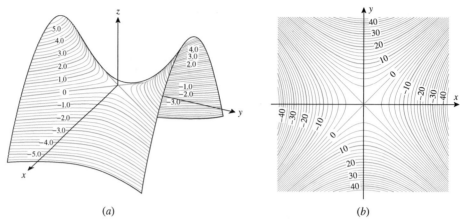

(a)

(b)

▲ **Figure 13.1.5**

▶ **Example 5** Sketch the contour plot of $f(x, y) = 4x^2 + y^2$ using level curves of height $k = 0, 1, 2, 3, 4, 5$.

*Solution.* The graph of the surface $z = 4x^2 + y^2$ is the paraboloid shown in the left part of Figure 13.1.6, so we can reasonably expect the contour plot to be a family of ellipses centered at the origin. The level curve of height $k$ has the equation $4x^2 + y^2 = k$. If $k = 0$, then the graph is the single point $(0, 0)$. For $k > 0$ we can rewrite the equation as

$$\frac{x^2}{k/4} + \frac{y^2}{k} = 1$$

which represents a family of ellipses with $x$-intercepts $\pm\sqrt{k}/2$ and $y$-intercepts $\pm\sqrt{k}$. The contour plot for the specified values of $k$ is shown in the right part of Figure 13.1.6. ◀

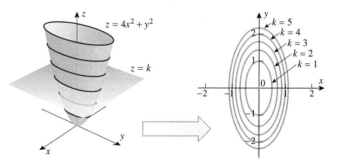

▶ **Figure 13.1.6**

In the last two examples we used a formula for $f(x, y)$ to find the contour plot of $f$. Conversely, if we are given a contour plot of some function, then we can use the plot to estimate values of the function.

▶ **Example 6** Let $f(r, L)$ be the monthly payment on a 5-year car loan as a function of the interest rate $r$ and the loan amount $L$. Figure 13.1.7 is a contour plot of $f(r, L)$. Use this plot in each part.

(a) Estimate the monthly payment on a loan of $3000 at an interest rate of 7%.

(b) Estimate the monthly payment on a loan of $5000 at an interest rate of 3%.

(c) Estimate the loan amount if the monthly payment is $80 and the interest rate is 3%.

*Solution (a).* Since the point $(7, 3000)$ appears to lie on the contour labeled 60, we estimate the monthly payment to be $60.

*Solution (b).* Since the point $(3, 5000)$ appears to be midway between the contours labeled 80 and 100, we estimate the monthly payment to be $90.

*Solution (c).* The vertical line $x = 3$ intersects the contour labeled 80 at a point whose $L$ coordinate appears to be 4500. Hence, we estimate the loan amount to be $4500. ◄

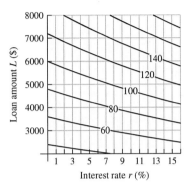

▶ **Figure 13.1.7**

## CONTOUR PLOTS USING TECHNOLOGY

Except in the simplest cases, contour plots can be difficult to produce without the help of a graphing utility. Figure 13.1.8 illustrates how graphing technology can be used to display level curves. Figure 13.1.8a shows the graph of $f(x, y) = |\sin x \sin y|$ plotted over the domain $0 \leq x \leq 2\pi, 0 \leq y \leq 2\pi$, and Figure 13.1.8b displays curves of constant elevation on the graph of $f$. The projections of these curves into the $xy$-plane are contours of $f$. Figure 13.1.8c illustrates how the use of color can enhance the display of these contours.

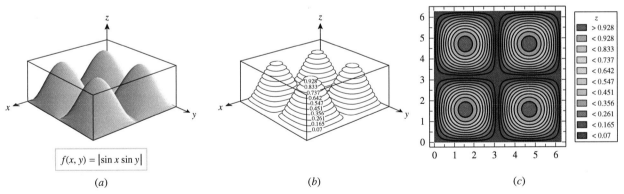

▶ **Figure 13.1.8**

## LEVEL SURFACES

The term "level surface" is standard but confusing, since a level surface need *not* be level in the sense of being horizontal—it is simply a surface on which all values of $f$ are the same.

Observe that the graph of $y = f(x)$ is a curve in 2-space, and the graph of $z = f(x, y)$ is a surface in 3-space, so the number of dimensions required for these graphs is one greater than the number of independent variables. Accordingly, there is no "direct" way to graph a function of three variables since four dimensions are required. However, if $k$ is a constant, then the graph of the equation $f(x, y, z) = k$ will generally be a surface in 3-space (e.g., the graph of $x^2 + y^2 + z^2 = 1$ is a sphere), which we call the *level surface with constant k*. Some geometric insight into the behavior of the function $f$ can sometimes be obtained by graphing these level surfaces for various values of $k$.

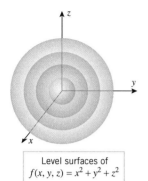

Level surfaces of
$f(x, y, z) = x^2 + y^2 + z^2$

► **Figure 13.1.9**

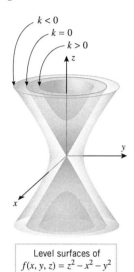

Level surfaces of
$f(x, y, z) = z^2 - x^2 - y^2$

► **Figure 13.1.10**

**TECHNOLOGY MASTERY**

If you have a graphing utility that can generate surfaces in 3-space, read the documentation and try to duplicate some of the surfaces in Figures 13.1.11 and 13.1.12 and Table 13.1.2.

► **Example 7**    Describe the level surfaces of

(a) $f(x, y, z) = x^2 + y^2 + z^2$      (b) $f(x, y, z) = z^2 - x^2 - y^2$

*Solution (a).*    The level surfaces have equations of the form

$$x^2 + y^2 + z^2 = k$$

For $k > 0$ the graph of this equation is a sphere of radius $\sqrt{k}$, centered at the origin; for $k = 0$ the graph is the single point $(0, 0, 0)$; and for $k < 0$ there is no level surface (Figure 13.1.9).

*Solution (b).*    The level surfaces have equations of the form

$$z^2 - x^2 - y^2 = k$$

As discussed in Section 11.7, this equation represents a cone if $k = 0$, a hyperboloid of two sheets if $k > 0$, and a hyperboloid of one sheet if $k < 0$ (Figure 13.1.10). ◄

■ **GRAPHING FUNCTIONS OF TWO VARIABLES USING TECHNOLOGY**

Generating surfaces with a graphing utility is more complicated than generating plane curves because there are more factors that must be taken into account. We can only touch on the ideas here, so if you want to use a graphing utility, its documentation will be your main source of information.

Graphing utilities can only show a portion of $xyz$-space in a viewing screen, so the first step in graphing a surface is to determine which portion of $xyz$-space you want to display. This region is called the *viewing box* or *viewing window*. For example, Figure 13.1.11 shows the effect of graphing the paraboloid $z = x^2 + y^2$ in three different viewing windows. However, within a fixed viewing box, the appearance of the surface is also affected by the *viewpoint*, that is, the direction from which the surface is viewed, and the distance from the viewer to the surface. For example, Figure 13.1.12 shows the graph of the paraboloid $z = x^2 + y^2$ from three different viewpoints using the first viewing box in Figure 13.1.11.

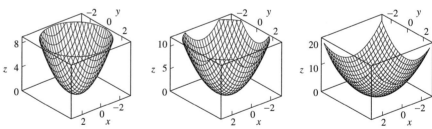

► **Figure 13.1.11**  Varying the viewing box.

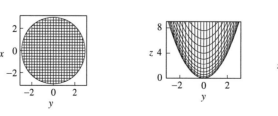

► **Figure 13.1.12**  Varying the viewpoint.

Table 13.1.2 shows six surfaces in 3-space along with their associated contour plots. Note that the mesh lines on the surface are traces in vertical planes, whereas the level curves correspond to traces in horizontal planes.

**Table 13.1.2**

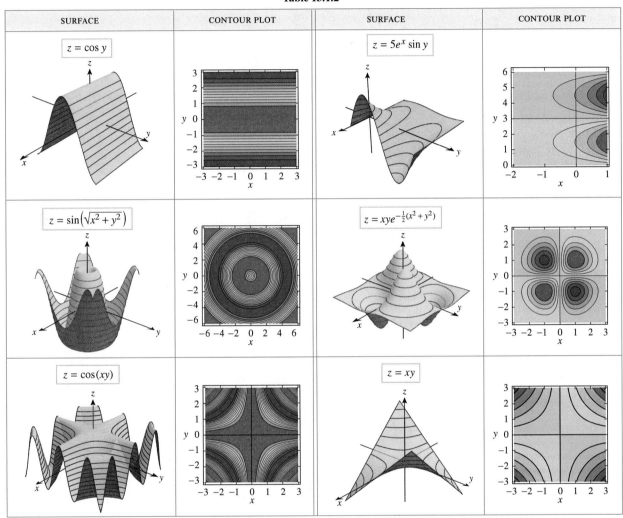

---

✔ **QUICK CHECK EXERCISES 13.1**    (See page 917 for answers.)

**1.** The domain of $f(x, y) = \ln xy$ is _____ and the domain of $g(x, y) = \ln x + \ln y$ is _____.

**2.** Let $f(x, y) = \dfrac{x - y}{x + y + 1}$.
   (a) $f(2, 1) = $ _____    (b) $f(1, 2) = $ _____
   (c) $f(a, a) = $ _____    (d) $f(y + 1, y) = $ _____

**3.** Let $f(x, y) = e^{x+y}$.
   (a) For what values of $k$ will the graph of the level curve $f(x, y) = k$ be nonempty?

   (b) Describe the level curves $f(x, y) = k$ for the values of $k$ obtained in part (a).

**4.** Let $f(x, y, z) = \dfrac{1}{x^2 + y^2 + z^2 + 1}$.
   (a) For what values of $k$ will the graph of the level surface $f(x, y, z) = k$ be nonempty?
   (b) Describe the level surfaces $f(x, y, z) = k$ for the values of $k$ obtained in part (a).

**EXERCISE SET 13.1** ☒ Graphing Utility  ☐© CAS

**1–8** These exercises are concerned with functions of two variables. ☒

1. Let $f(x, y) = x^2 y + 1$. Find
   (a) $f(2, 1)$    (b) $f(1, 2)$    (c) $f(0, 0)$
   (d) $f(1, -3)$    (e) $f(3a, a)$    (f) $f(ab, a - b)$.

2. Let $f(x, y) = x + \sqrt[3]{xy}$. Find
   (a) $f(t, t^2)$    (b) $f(x, x^2)$    (c) $f(2y^2, 4y)$.

3. Let $f(x, y) = xy + 3$. Find
   (a) $f(x + y, x - y)$    (b) $f(xy, 3x^2 y^3)$.

4. Let $g(x) = x \sin x$. Find
   (a) $g(x/y)$    (b) $g(xy)$    (c) $g(x - y)$.

5. Find $F(g(x), h(y))$ if $F(x, y) = xe^{xy}$, $g(x) = x^3$, and $h(y) = 3y + 1$.

6. Find $g(u(x, y), v(x, y))$ if $g(x, y) = y \sin(x^2 y)$, $u(x, y) = x^2 y^3$, and $v(x, y) = \pi xy$.

7. Let $f(x, y) = x + 3x^2 y^2$, $x(t) = t^2$, and $y(t) = t^3$. Find
   (a) $f(x(t), y(t))$    (b) $f(x(0), y(0))$
   (c) $f(x(2), y(2))$.

8. Let $g(x, y) = ye^{-3x}$, $x(t) = \ln(t^2 + 1)$, and $y(t) = \sqrt{t}$. Find $g(x(t), y(t))$.

**9–10** Suppose that the concentration $C$ in mg/L of medication in a patient's bloodstream is modeled by the function $C(x, t) = 0.2x(e^{-0.2t} - e^{-t})$, where $x$ is the dosage of the medication in mg and $t$ is the number of hours since the beginning of administration of the medication. ☒

9. (a) Estimate the value of $C(25, 3)$ to two decimal places. Include appropriate units and interpret your answer in a physical context.
   (b) If the dosage is 100 mg, give a formula for the concentration as a function of time $t$.
   (c) Give a formula that describes the concentration after 1 hour in terms of the dosage $x$.

☒ 10. (a) Suppose that the medication in the bloodstream reaches an effective level after a half hour. Estimate how much longer the medication remains effective.
   (b) Suppose the dosage is 100 mg. Estimate the maximum concentration in the bloodstream.

**11–14** Refer to Table 13.1.1 to estimate the given quantity. ☒

11. The wind chill index when
    (a) the temperature is 25°F and the wind speed is 7 mi/h
    (b) the temperature is 28°F and the wind speed is 5 mi/h.

12. The wind chill index when
    (a) the temperature is 35°F and the wind speed is 14 mi/h
    (b) the temperature is 32°F and the wind speed is 15 mi/h.

13. The temperature when
    (a) the wind chill index is 16°F and the wind speed is 25 mi/h

(b) the wind chill index is 6°F and the wind speed is 25 mi/h.

14. The wind speed when
    (a) the wind chill index is 7°F and the temperature is 25°F
    (b) the wind chill index is 15°F and the temperature is 30°F.

15. One method for determining relative humidity is to wet the bulb of a thermometer, whirl it through the air, and then compare the thermometer reading with the actual air temperature. If the relative humidity is less than 100%, the reading on the thermometer will be less than the temperature of the air. This difference in temperature is known as the *wet-bulb depression*. The accompanying table gives the relative humidity as a function of the air temperature and the wet-bulb depression. Use the table to complete parts (a)–(c).
    (a) What is the relative humidity if the air temperature is 20°C and the wet-bulb thermometer reads 16°C?
    (b) Estimate the relative humidity if the air temperature is 25°C and the wet-bulb depression is 3.5°C.
    (c) Estimate the relative humidity if the air temperature is 22°C and the wet-bulb depression is 5°C.

AIR TEMPERATURE (°C)

| | | 15 | 20 | 25 | 30 |
|---|---|---|---|---|---|
| WET-BULB DEPRESSION (°C) | 3 | 71 | 74 | 77 | 79 |
| | 4 | 62 | 66 | 70 | 73 |
| | 5 | 53 | 59 | 63 | 67 |

▶ **Table Ex-15**

16. Use the table in Exercise 15 to complete parts (a)–(c).
    (a) What is the wet-bulb depression if the air temperature is 30°C and the relative humidity is 73%?
    (b) Estimate the relative humidity if the air temperature is 15°C and the wet-bulb depression is 4.25°C.
    (c) Estimate the relative humidity if the air temperature is 26°C and the wet-bulb depression is 3°C.

**17–20** These exercises involve functions of three variables. ☒

17. Let $f(x, y, z) = xy^2 z^3 + 3$. Find
    (a) $f(2, 1, 2)$    (b) $f(-3, 2, 1)$
    (c) $f(0, 0, 0)$    (d) $f(a, a, a)$
    (e) $f(t, t^2, -t)$    (f) $f(a + b, a - b, b)$.

18. Let $f(x, y, z) = zxy + x$. Find
    (a) $f(x + y, x - y, x^2)$    (b) $f(xy, y/x, xz)$.

19. Find $F(f(x), g(y), h(z))$ if $F(x, y, z) = ye^{xyz}$, $f(x) = x^2$, $g(y) = y + 1$, and $h(z) = z^2$.

20. Find $g(u(x, y, z), v(x, y, z), w(x, y, z))$ if $g(x, y, z) = z \sin xy$, $u(x, y, z) = x^2 z^3$, $v(x, y, z) = \pi xyz$, and $w(x, y, z) = xy/z$.

**21–22** These exercises are concerned with functions of four or more variables.

**21.** (a) Let $f(x, y, z, t) = x^2 y^3 \sqrt{z + t}$.
   Find $f(\sqrt{5}, 2, \pi, 3\pi)$.

(b) Let $f(x_1, x_2, \ldots, x_n) = \displaystyle\sum_{k=1}^{n} k x_k$.
   Find $f(1, 1, \ldots, 1)$.

**22.** (a) Let $f(u, v, \lambda, \phi) = e^{u+v} \cos \lambda \tan \phi$.
   Find $f(-2, 2, 0, \pi/4)$.

(b) Let $f(x_1, x_2, \ldots, x_n) = x_1^2 + x_2^2 + \cdots + x_n^2$.
   Find $f(1, 2, \ldots, n)$.

**23–26** Sketch the domain of $f$. Use solid lines for portions of the boundary included in the domain and dashed lines for portions not included.

**23.** $f(x, y) = \ln(1 - x^2 - y^2)$   **24.** $f(x, y) = \sqrt{x^2 + y^2 - 4}$

**25.** $f(x, y) = \dfrac{1}{x - y^2}$   **26.** $f(x, y) = \ln xy$

**27–28** Describe the domain of $f$ in words.

**27.** (a) $f(x, y) = x e^{-\sqrt{y+2}}$
   (b) $f(x, y, z) = \sqrt{25 - x^2 - y^2 - z^2}$
   (c) $f(x, y, z) = e^{xyz}$

**28.** (a) $f(x, y) = \dfrac{\sqrt{4 - x^2}}{y^2 + 3}$   (b) $f(x, y) = \ln(y - 2x)$
   (c) $f(x, y, z) = \dfrac{xyz}{x + y + z}$

**29–32 True–False** Determine whether the statement is true or false. Explain your answer.

**29.** If the domain of $f(x, y)$ is the $xy$-plane, then the domain of $f(\sin^{-1} t, \sqrt{t})$ is the interval $[0, 1]$.

**30.** If $f(x, y) = y/x$, then a contour $f(x, y) = m$ is the straight line $y = mx$.

**31.** The natural domain of $f(x, y, z) = \sqrt{1 - x^2 - y^2}$ is a disk of radius 1 centered at the origin in the $xy$-plane.

**32.** Every level surface of $f(x, y, z) = x + 2y + 3z$ is a plane.

**33–42** Sketch the graph of $f$.

**33.** $f(x, y) = 3$   **34.** $f(x, y) = \sqrt{9 - x^2 - y^2}$

**35.** $f(x, y) = \sqrt{x^2 + y^2}$   **36.** $f(x, y) = x^2 + y^2$

**37.** $f(x, y) = x^2 - y^2$   **38.** $f(x, y) = 4 - x^2 - y^2$

**39.** $f(x, y) = \sqrt{x^2 + y^2 + 1}$   **40.** $f(x, y) = \sqrt{x^2 + y^2 - 1}$

**41.** $f(x, y) = y + 1$   **42.** $f(x, y) = x^2$

**43–44** In each part, select the term that best describes the level curves of the function $f$. Choose from the terms lines, circles, noncircular ellipses, parabolas, or hyperbolas.

**43.** (a) $f(x, y) = 5x^2 - 5y^2$   (b) $f(x, y) = y - 4x^2$
   (c) $f(x, y) = x^2 + 3y^2$   (d) $f(x, y) = 3x^2$

**44.** (a) $f(x, y) = x^2 - 2xy + y^2$   (b) $f(x, y) = 2x^2 + 2y^2$
   (c) $f(x, y) = x^2 - 2x - y^2$   (d) $f(x, y) = 2y^2 - x$

**45–46** Refer to Figure 13.1.7 in each part.

**45.** Suppose that \$6000 is borrowed at an interest rate of 11%.
   (a) Estimate the monthly payment on the loan.
   (b) If the interest rate drops to 9%, estimate how much more can be borrowed without increasing the monthly payment.

**46.** Suppose that \$3000 is borrowed at an interest rate of 4%.
   (a) Estimate the monthly payment on the loan.
   (b) If the interest rate increases to 7%, estimate how much less would need to be borrowed so as not to increase the monthly payment.

**FOCUS ON CONCEPTS**

**47.** In each part, match the contour plot with one of the functions

$$f(x, y) = \sqrt{x^2 + y^2}, \quad f(x, y) = x^2 + y^2,$$
$$f(x, y) = 1 - x^2 - y^2$$

by inspection, and explain your reasoning. Larger values of $z$ are indicated by lighter colors in the contour plot, and the concentric contours correspond to equally spaced values of $z$.

(a)    (b)    (c)

**48.** In each part, match the contour plot with one of the surfaces in the accompanying figure by inspection, and explain your reasoning. The larger the value of $z$, the lighter the color in the contour plot.

(a) 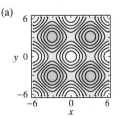   (b)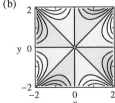

(c) 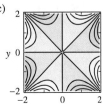   (d)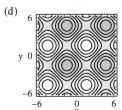

(I)     (II)

(III)     (IV)

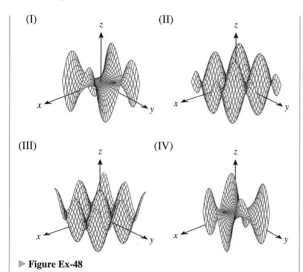

▶ **Figure Ex-48**

**49.** In each part, the questions refer to the contour map in the accompanying figure.
   (a) Is $A$ or $B$ the higher point? Explain your reasoning.
   (b) Is the slope steeper at point $A$ or at point $B$? Explain your reasoning.
   (c) Starting at $A$ and moving so that $y$ remains constant and $x$ increases, will the elevation begin to increase or decrease?
   (d) Starting at $B$ and moving so that $y$ remains constant and $x$ increases, will the elevation begin to increase or decrease?
   (e) Starting at $A$ and moving so that $x$ remains constant and $y$ decreases, will the elevation begin to increase or decrease?
   (f) Starting at $B$ and moving so that $x$ remains constant and $y$ decreases, will the elevation begin to increase or decrease?

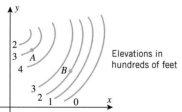

Elevations in hundreds of feet

◀ **Figure Ex-49**

**50.** A curve connecting points of equal atmospheric pressure on a weather map is called an **isobar**. On a typical weather map the isobars refer to pressure at mean sea level and are given in units of **millibars** (mb). Mathematically, isobars are level curves for the pressure function $p(x, y)$ defined at the geographic points $(x, y)$ represented on the map. Tightly packed isobars correspond to steep slopes on the graph of the pressure function, and these are usually associated with strong winds—the steeper the slope, the greater the speed of the wind.

(a) Referring to the accompanying weather map, is the wind speed greater in Medicine Hat, Alberta or in Chicago? Explain your reasoning.
(b) Estimate the average rate of change in atmospheric pressure (in mb/mi) from Medicine Hat to Chicago, given that the distance between the two cities is approximately 1400 mi.

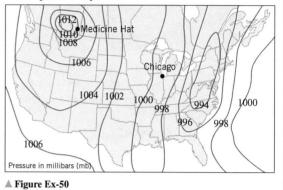

Pressure in millibars (mb)

▲ **Figure Ex-50**

**51–56** Sketch the level curve $z = k$ for the specified values of $k$. ■

**51.** $z = x^2 + y^2$; $k = 0, 1, 2, 3, 4$

**52.** $z = y/x$; $k = -2, -1, 0, 1, 2$

**53.** $z = x^2 + y$; $k = -2, -1, 0, 1, 2$

**54.** $z = x^2 + 9y^2$; $k = 0, 1, 2, 3, 4$

**55.** $z = x^2 - y^2$; $k = -2, -1, 0, 1, 2$

**56.** $z = y \csc x$; $k = -2, -1, 0, 1, 2$

**57–60** Sketch the level surface $f(x, y, z) = k$. ■

**57.** $f(x, y, z) = 4x^2 + y^2 + 4z^2$; $k = 16$

**58.** $f(x, y, z) = x^2 + y^2 - z^2$; $k = 0$

**59.** $f(x, y, z) = z - x^2 - y^2 + 4$; $k = 7$

**60.** $f(x, y, z) = 4x - 2y + z$; $k = 1$

**61–64** Describe the level surfaces in words. ■

**61.** $f(x, y, z) = (x - 2)^2 + y^2 + z^2$

**62.** $f(x, y, z) = 3x - y + 2z$    **63.** $f(x, y, z) = x^2 + z^2$

**64.** $f(x, y, z) = z - x^2 - y^2$

**65.** Let $f(x, y) = x^2 - 2x^3 + 3xy$. Find an equation of the level curve that passes through the point
   (a) $(-1, 1)$     (b) $(0, 0)$     (c) $(2, -1)$.

**66.** Let $f(x, y) = ye^x$. Find an equation of the level curve that passes through the point
   (a) $(\ln 2, 1)$     (b) $(0, 3)$     (c) $(1, -2)$.

**67.** Let $f(x, y, z) = x^2 + y^2 - z$. Find an equation of the level surface that passes through the point
   (a) $(1, -2, 0)$     (b) $(1, 0, 3)$     (c) $(0, 0, 0)$.

**68.** Let $f(x, y, z) = xyz + 3$. Find an equation of the level surface that passes through the point
   (a) $(1, 0, 2)$     (b) $(-2, 4, 1)$     (c) $(0, 0, 0)$.

**69.** If $T(x, y)$ is the temperature at a point $(x, y)$ on a thin metal plate in the $xy$-plane, then the level curves of $T$ are called *isothermal curves*. All points on such a curve are at the same temperature. Suppose that a plate occupies the first quadrant and $T(x, y) = xy$.
   (a) Sketch the isothermal curves on which $T = 1$, $T = 2$, and $T = 3$.
   (b) An ant, initially at $(1, 4)$, wants to walk on the plate so that the temperature along its path remains constant. What path should the ant take and what is the temperature along that path?

**70.** If $V(x, y)$ is the voltage or potential at a point $(x, y)$ in the $xy$-plane, then the level curves of $V$ are called *equipotential curves*. Along such a curve, the voltage remains constant. Given that
$$V(x, y) = \frac{8}{\sqrt{16 + x^2 + y^2}}$$
sketch the equipotential curves at which $V = 2.0$, $V = 1.0$, and $V = 0.5$.

**71.** Let $f(x, y) = x^2 + y^3$.
   (a) Use a graphing utility to generate the level curve that passes through the point $(2, -1)$.
   (b) Generate the level curve of height 1.

**72.** Let $f(x, y) = 2\sqrt{xy}$.
   (a) Use a graphing utility to generate the level curve that passes through the point $(2, 2)$.
   (b) Generate the level curve of height 8.

**c 73.** Let $f(x, y) = xe^{-(x^2+y^2)}$.
   (a) Use a CAS to generate the graph of $f$ for $-2 \le x \le 2$ and $-2 \le y \le 2$.

   (b) Generate a contour plot for the surface, and confirm visually that it is consistent with the surface obtained in part (a).
   (c) Read the appropriate documentation and explore the effect of generating the graph of $f$ from various viewpoints.

**c 74.** Let $f(x, y) = \frac{1}{10}e^x \sin y$.
   (a) Use a CAS to generate the graph of $f$ for $0 \le x \le 4$ and $0 \le y \le 2\pi$.
   (b) Generate a contour plot for the surface, and confirm visually that it is consistent with the surface obtained in part (a).
   (c) Read the appropriate documentation and explore the effect of generating the graph of $f$ from various viewpoints.

**75.** In each part, describe in words how the graph of $g$ is related to the graph of $f$.
   (a) $g(x, y) = f(x - 1, y)$    (b) $g(x, y) = 1 + f(x, y)$
   (c) $g(x, y) = -f(x, y + 1)$

**76.** (a) Sketch the graph of $f(x, y) = e^{-(x^2+y^2)}$.
   (b) Describe in words how the graph of the function $g(x, y) = e^{-a(x^2+y^2)}$ is related to the graph of $f$ for positive values of $a$.

**77.** Writing  Find a few practical examples of functions of two and three variables, and discuss how physical considerations affect their domains.

**78.** Writing  Describe two different ways in which a function $f(x, y)$ can be represented geometrically. Discuss some of the advantages and disadvantages of each representation.

✔ **QUICK CHECK ANSWERS 13.1**

1. points $(x, y)$ in the first or third quadrants;  points $(x, y)$ in the first quadrant    2. (a) $\frac{1}{4}$ (b) $-\frac{1}{4}$ (c) 0 (d) $1/(2y + 2)$
3. (a) $k > 0$ (b) the lines $x + y = \ln k$    4. (a) $0 < k \le 1$ (b) spheres of radius $\sqrt{(1 - k)/k}$ for $0 < k < 1$, the single point $(0, 0, 0)$ for $k = 1$

## 13.2 LIMITS AND CONTINUITY

*In this section we will introduce the notions of limit and continuity for functions of two or more variables. We will not go into great detail—our objective is to develop the basic concepts accurately and to obtain results needed in later sections. A more extensive study of these topics is usually given in advanced calculus.*

### LIMITS ALONG CURVES

For a function of one variable there are two one-sided limits at a point $x_0$, namely,

$$\lim_{x \to x_0^+} f(x) \quad \text{and} \quad \lim_{x \to x_0^-} f(x)$$

reflecting the fact that there are only two directions from which $x$ can approach $x_0$, the right or the left. For functions of two or three variables the situation is more complicated

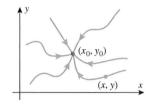

▶ **Figure 13.2.1**

In words, Formulas (1) and (2) state that a limit of a function $f$ along a parametric curve can be obtained by substituting the parametric equations for the curve into the formula for the function and then computing the limit of the resulting function of one variable at the appropriate point.

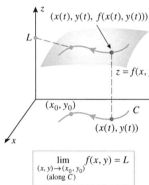

$$\lim_{\substack{(x, y) \to (x_0, y_0) \\ (\text{along } C)}} f(x, y) = L$$

▶ **Figure 13.2.2**

because there are infinitely many different curves along which one point can approach another (Figure 13.2.1). Our first objective in this section is to define the limit of $f(x, y)$ as $(x, y)$ approaches a point $(x_0, y_0)$ along a curve $C$ (and similarly for functions of three variables).

If $C$ is a smooth parametric curve in 2-space or 3-space that is represented by the equations

$$x = x(t), \quad y = y(t) \quad \text{or} \quad x = x(t), \quad y = y(t), \quad z = z(t)$$

and if $x_0 = x(t_0)$, $y_0 = y(t_0)$, and $z_0 = z(t_0)$, then the limits

$$\lim_{\substack{(x, y) \to (x_0, y_0) \\ (\text{along } C)}} f(x, y) \quad \text{and} \quad \lim_{\substack{(x, y, z) \to (x_0, y_0, z_0) \\ (\text{along } C)}} f(x, y, z)$$

are defined by

$$\lim_{\substack{(x, y) \to (x_0, y_0) \\ (\text{along } C)}} f(x, y) = \lim_{t \to t_0} f(x(t), y(t)) \tag{1}$$

$$\lim_{\substack{(x, y, z) \to (x_0, y_0, z_0) \\ (\text{along } C)}} f(x, y, z) = \lim_{t \to t_0} f(x(t), y(t), z(t)) \tag{2}$$

In these formulas the limit of the function of $t$ must be treated as a one-sided limit if $(x_0, y_0)$ or $(x_0, y_0, z_0)$ is an endpoint of $C$.

A geometric interpretation of the limit along a curve for a function of two variables is shown in Figure 13.2.2: As the point $(x(t), y(t))$ moves along the curve $C$ in the $xy$-plane toward $(x_0, y_0)$, the point $(x(t), y(t), f(x(t), y(t)))$ moves directly above it along the graph of $z = f(x, y)$ with $f(x(t), y(t))$ approaching the limiting value $L$. In the figure we followed a common practice of omitting the zero $z$-coordinate for points in the $xy$-plane.

▶ **Example 1** Figure 13.2.3a shows a computer-generated graph of the function

$$f(x, y) = -\frac{xy}{x^2 + y^2}$$

The graph reveals that the surface has a ridge above the line $y = -x$, which is to be expected since $f(x, y)$ has a constant value of $\frac{1}{2}$ for $y = -x$, except at $(0, 0)$ where $f$ is undefined (verify). Moreover, the graph suggests that the limit of $f(x, y)$ as $(x, y) \to (0, 0)$ along a line through the origin varies with the direction of the line. Find this limit along

(a) the $x$-axis  (b) the $y$-axis  (c) the line $y = x$

(d) the line $y = -x$  (e) the parabola $y = x^2$

**Solution (a).** The $x$-axis has parametric equations $x = t$, $y = 0$, with $(0, 0)$ corresponding to $t = 0$, so

$$\lim_{\substack{(x, y) \to (0, 0) \\ (\text{along } y = 0)}} f(x, y) = \lim_{t \to 0} f(t, 0) = \lim_{t \to 0} \left(-\frac{0}{t^2}\right) = \lim_{t \to 0} 0 = 0$$

which is consistent with Figure 13.2.3b.

**Solution (b).** The $y$-axis has parametric equations $x = 0$, $y = t$, with $(0, 0)$ corresponding to $t = 0$, so

$$\lim_{\substack{(x, y) \to (0, 0) \\ (\text{along } x = 0)}} f(x, y) = \lim_{t \to 0} f(0, t) = \lim_{t \to 0} \left(-\frac{0}{t^2}\right) = \lim_{t \to 0} 0 = 0$$

which is consistent with Figure 13.2.3b.

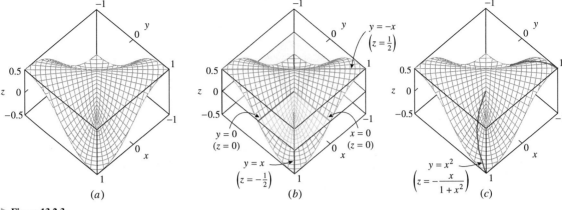

► **Figure 13.2.3**

**Solution (c).** The line $y = x$ has parametric equations $x = t$, $y = t$, with $(0, 0)$ corresponding to $t = 0$, so

$$\lim_{\substack{(x, y) \to (0, 0) \\ (\text{along } y = x)}} f(x, y) = \lim_{t \to 0} f(t, t) = \lim_{t \to 0} \left( -\frac{t^2}{2t^2} \right) = \lim_{t \to 0} \left( -\frac{1}{2} \right) = -\frac{1}{2}$$

which is consistent with Figure 13.2.3b.

**Solution (d).** The line $y = -x$ has parametric equations $x = t$, $y = -t$, with $(0, 0)$ corresponding to $t = 0$, so

$$\lim_{\substack{(x, y) \to (0, 0) \\ (\text{along } y = -x)}} f(x, y) = \lim_{t \to 0} f(t, -t) = \lim_{t \to 0} \frac{t^2}{2t^2} = \lim_{t \to 0} \frac{1}{2} = \frac{1}{2}$$

which is consistent with Figure 13.2.3b.

For uniformity, we have chosen the same parameter $t$ in each part of Example 1. We could have used $x$ or $y$ as the parameter, according to the context. For example, part (b) could be computed using

$$\lim_{y \to 0} f(0, y)$$

and part (e) could be computed using

$$\lim_{x \to 0} f(x, x^2)$$

**Solution (e).** The parabola $y = x^2$ has parametric equations $x = t$, $y = t^2$, with $(0, 0)$ corresponding to $t = 0$, so

$$\lim_{\substack{(x, y) \to (0, 0) \\ (\text{along } y = x^2)}} f(x, y) = \lim_{t \to 0} f(t, t^2) = \lim_{t \to 0} \left( -\frac{t^3}{t^2 + t^4} \right) = \lim_{t \to 0} \left( -\frac{t}{1 + t^2} \right) = 0$$

This is consistent with Figure 13.2.3c, which shows the parametric curve

$$x = t, \quad y = t^2, \quad z = -\frac{t}{1 + t^2}$$

superimposed on the surface. ◄

■ **OPEN AND CLOSED SETS**

Although limits along specific curves are useful for many purposes, they do not always tell the complete story about the limiting behavior of a function at a point; what is required is a limit concept that accounts for the behavior of the function in an *entire vicinity* of a point, not just along smooth curves passing through the point. For this purpose, we start by introducing some terminology.

Let $C$ be a circle in 2-space that is centered at $(x_0, y_0)$ and has positive radius $\delta$. The set of points that are enclosed by the circle, but do not lie on the circle, is called the **open disk** of radius $\delta$ centered at $(x_0, y_0)$, and the set of points that lie on the circle together with those enclosed by the circle is called the **closed disk** of radius $\delta$ centered at $(x_0, y_0)$

A closed disk includes all of the points on its bounding circle.

An open disk contains none of the points on its bounding circle.

▶ **Figure 13.2.4**

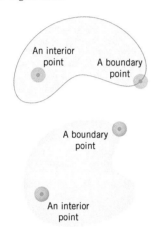

An interior point

A boundary point

A boundary point

An interior point

▶ **Figure 13.2.5**

(Figure 13.2.4). Analogously, if $S$ is a sphere in 3-space that is centered at $(x_0, y_0, z_0)$ and has positive radius $\delta$, then the set of points that are enclosed by the sphere, but do not lie on the sphere, is called the ***open ball*** of radius $\delta$ centered at $(x_0, y_0, z_0)$, and the set of points that lie on the sphere together with those enclosed by the sphere is called the ***closed ball*** of radius $\delta$ centered at $(x_0, y_0, z_0)$. Disks and balls are the two-dimensional and three-dimensional analogs of intervals on a line.

The notions of "open" and "closed" can be extended to more general sets in 2-space and 3-space. If $D$ is a set of points in 2-space, then a point $(x_0, y_0)$ is called an ***interior point*** of $D$ if there is *some* open disk centered at $(x_0, y_0)$ that contains only points of $D$, and $(x_0, y_0)$ is called a ***boundary point*** of $D$ if *every* open disk centered at $(x_0, y_0)$ contains both points in $D$ and points not in $D$. The same terminology applies to sets in 3-space, but in that case the definitions use balls rather than disks (Figure 13.2.5).

For a set $D$ in either 2-space or 3-space, the set of all interior points is called the ***interior*** of $D$ and the set of all boundary points is called the ***boundary*** of $D$. Moreover, just as for disks, we say that $D$ is ***closed*** if it contains all of its boundary points and ***open*** if it contains *none* of its boundary points. The set of all points in 2-space and the set of all points in 3-space have no boundary points (why?), so by agreement they are regarded to be both open and closed.

### GENERAL LIMITS OF FUNCTIONS OF TWO VARIABLES

The statement

$$\lim_{(x,y) \to (x_0, y_0)} f(x, y) = L$$

is intended to convey the idea that the value of $f(x, y)$ can be made as close as we like to the number $L$ by restricting the point $(x, y)$ to be sufficiently close to (but different from) the point $(x_0, y_0)$. This idea has a formal expression in the following definition and is illustrated in Figure 13.2.6.

When convenient, (3) can also be written as

$$\lim_{\substack{x \to x_0 \\ y \to y_0}} f(x, y) = L$$

or as

$$f(x, y) \to L \quad \text{as} \quad (x, y) \to (x_0, y_0)$$

---

**13.2.1 DEFINITION** Let $f$ be a function of two variables, and assume that $f$ is defined at all points of some open disk centered at $(x_0, y_0)$, except possibly at $(x_0, y_0)$. We will write

$$\lim_{(x,y) \to (x_0, y_0)} f(x, y) = L \tag{3}$$

if given any number $\epsilon > 0$, we can find a number $\delta > 0$ such that $f(x, y)$ satisfies

$$|f(x, y) - L| < \epsilon$$

whenever the distance between $(x, y)$ and $(x_0, y_0)$ satisfies

$$0 < \sqrt{(x - x_0)^2 + (y - y_0)^2} < \delta$$

---

Another illustration of Definition 13.2.1 is shown in the "arrow diagram" of Figure 13.2.7. As in Figure 13.2.6, this figure is intended to convey the idea that the values of $f(x, y)$ can be forced within $\epsilon$ units of $L$ on the $z$-axis by restricting $(x, y)$ to lie within $\delta$ units of $(x_0, y_0)$ in the $xy$-plane. We used a white dot at $(x_0, y_0)$ to suggest that the epsilon condition need not hold at this point.

We note without proof that the standard properties of limits hold for limits along curves and for general limits of functions of two variables, so that computations involving such limits can be performed in the usual way.

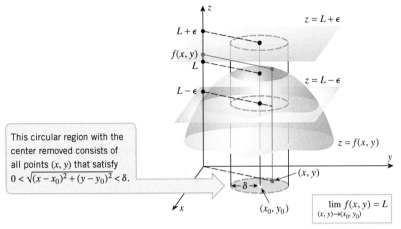

In Figure 13.2.6, the condition

$$|f(x, y) - L| < \epsilon$$

is satisfied at each point $(x, y)$ within the circular region. However, the fact that this condition is satisfied at the center of the circular region is not relevant to the limit.

This circular region with the center removed consists of all points $(x, y)$ that satisfy $0 < \sqrt{(x - x_0)^2 + (y - y_0)^2} < \delta$.

$$\lim_{(x,y)\to(x_0, y_0)} f(x, y) = L$$

▶ **Figure 13.2.6**

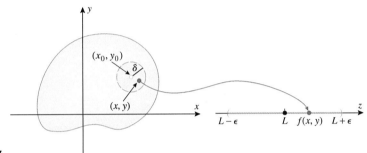

▶ **Figure 13.2.7**

▶ **Example 2**

$$\lim_{(x,y)\to(1,4)} [5x^3 y^2 - 9] = \lim_{(x,y)\to(1,4)} [5x^3 y^2] - \lim_{(x,y)\to(1,4)} 9$$

$$= 5 \left[ \lim_{(x,y)\to(1,4)} x \right]^3 \left[ \lim_{(x,y)\to(1,4)} y \right]^2 - 9$$

$$= 5(1)^3 (4)^2 - 9 = 71 \;\blacktriangleleft$$

### ▪ RELATIONSHIPS BETWEEN GENERAL LIMITS AND LIMITS ALONG SMOOTH CURVES

Stated informally, if $f(x, y)$ has limit $L$ as $(x, y)$ approaches $(x_0, y_0)$, then the value of $f(x, y)$ gets closer and closer to $L$ as the distance between $(x, y)$ and $(x_0, y_0)$ approaches zero. Since this statement imposes no restrictions on the direction in which $(x, y)$ approaches $(x_0, y_0)$, it is plausible that the function $f(x, y)$ will also have the limit $L$ as $(x, y)$ approaches $(x_0, y_0)$ along *any* smooth curve $C$. This is the implication of the following theorem, which we state without proof.

**WARNING**

In general, one cannot show that

$$\lim_{(x,y)\to(x_0, y_0)} f(x, y) = L$$

by showing that this limit holds along a specific curve, or even some specific family of curves. The problem is there may be some other curve along which the limit does not exist or has a value different from $L$ (see Exercise 34, for example).

**13.2.2 THEOREM**

(a) If $f(x, y) \to L$ as $(x, y) \to (x_0, y_0)$, then $f(x, y) \to L$ as $(x, y) \to (x_0, y_0)$ along any smooth curve.

(b) If the limit of $f(x, y)$ fails to exist as $(x, y) \to (x_0, y_0)$ along some smooth curve, or if $f(x, y)$ has different limits as $(x, y) \to (x_0, y_0)$ along two different smooth curves, then the limit of $f(x, y)$ does not exist as $(x, y) \to (x_0, y_0)$.

▶ **Example 3** The limit

$$\lim_{(x,y)\to(0,0)} -\frac{xy}{x^2+y^2}$$

does not exist because in Example 1 we found two different smooth curves along which this limit had different values. Specifically,

$$\lim_{\substack{(x,\,y)\to(0,\,0)\\ (\text{along } x\,=\,0)}} -\frac{xy}{x^2+y^2} = 0 \quad \text{and} \quad \lim_{\substack{(x,\,y)\to(0,\,0)\\ (\text{along } y\,=\,x)}} -\frac{xy}{x^2+y^2} = -\frac{1}{2} \quad ◀$$

■ **CONTINUITY**

Stated informally, a function of one variable is continuous if its graph is an unbroken curve without jumps or holes. To extend this idea to functions of two variables, imagine that the graph of $z = f(x, y)$ is formed from a thin sheet of clay that has been molded into peaks and valleys. We will regard $f$ as being continuous if the clay surface has no tears or holes. The functions graphed in Figure 13.2.8 fail to be continuous because of their behavior at $(0, 0)$.

The precise definition of continuity at a point for functions of two variables is similar to that for functions of one variable—we require the limit of the function and the value of the function to be the same at the point.

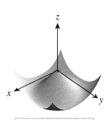

Hole at the origin

Infinite at the origin

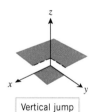

Vertical jump at the origin

▲ **Figure 13.2.8**

> **13.2.3** **DEFINITION** A function $f(x, y)$ is said to be **continuous at** $(x_0, y_0)$ if $f(x_0, y_0)$ is defined and if
>
> $$\lim_{(x,y)\to(x_0,y_0)} f(x, y) = f(x_0, y_0)$$
>
> In addition, if $f$ is continuous at every point in an open set $D$, then we say that $f$ is **continuous on** $D$, and if $f$ is continuous at every point in the $xy$-plane, then we say that $f$ is **continuous everywhere**.

The following theorem, which we state without proof, illustrates some of the ways in which continuous functions can be combined to produce new continuous functions.

> **13.2.4** **THEOREM**
>
> (a) If $g(x)$ is continuous at $x_0$ and $h(y)$ is continuous at $y_0$, then $f(x, y) = g(x)h(y)$ is continuous at $(x_0, y_0)$.
>
> (b) If $h(x, y)$ is continuous at $(x_0, y_0)$ and $g(u)$ is continuous at $u = h(x_0, y_0)$, then the composition $f(x, y) = g(h(x, y))$ is continuous at $(x_0, y_0)$.
>
> (c) If $f(x, y)$ is continuous at $(x_0, y_0)$, and if $x(t)$ and $y(t)$ are continuous at $t_0$ with $x(t_0) = x_0$ and $y(t_0) = y_0$, then the composition $f(x(t), y(t))$ is continuous at $t_0$.

▶ **Example 4** Use Theorem 13.2.4 to show that the functions $f(x, y) = 3x^2y^5$ and $f(x, y) = \sin(3x^2y^5)$ are continuous everywhere.

*Solution.* The polynomials $g(x) = 3x^2$ and $h(y) = y^5$ are continuous at every real number, and therefore by part ($a$) of Theorem 13.2.4, the function $f(x, y) = 3x^2y^5$ is continuous at every point $(x, y)$ in the $xy$-plane. Since $3x^2y^5$ is continuous at every point in the $xy$-plane and $\sin u$ is continuous at every real number $u$, it follows from part ($b$) of Theorem 13.2.4 that the composition $f(x, y) = \sin(3x^2y^5)$ is continuous everywhere. ◀

Theorem 13.2.4 is one of a whole class of theorems about continuity of functions in two or more variables. The content of these theorems can be summarized informally with three basic principles:

### Recognizing Continuous Functions

- A composition of continuous functions is continuous.
- A sum, difference, or product of continuous functions is continuous.
- A quotient of continuous functions is continuous, except where the denominator is zero.

By using these principles and Theorem 13.2.4, you should be able to confirm that the following functions are all continuous everywhere:

$$xe^{xy} + y^{2/3}, \quad \cosh(xy^3) - |xy|, \quad \frac{xy}{1 + x^2 + y^2}$$

▶ **Example 5** Evaluate $\displaystyle\lim_{(x,y) \to (-1,2)} \frac{xy}{x^2 + y^2}$.

**Solution.** Since $f(x, y) = xy/(x^2 + y^2)$ is continuous at $(-1, 2)$ (why?), it follows from the definition of continuity for functions of two variables that

$$\lim_{(x,y) \to (-1,2)} \frac{xy}{x^2 + y^2} = \frac{(-1)(2)}{(-1)^2 + (2)^2} = -\frac{2}{5} \quad ◀$$

▶ **Example 6** Since the function

$$f(x, y) = \frac{x^3 y^2}{1 - xy}$$

is a quotient of continuous functions, it is continuous except where $1 - xy = 0$. Thus, $f(x, y)$ is continuous everywhere except on the hyperbola $xy = 1$. ◀

### ■ LIMITS AT DISCONTINUITIES

Sometimes it is easy to recognize when a limit does not exist. For example, it is evident that

$$\lim_{(x,y) \to (0,0)} \frac{1}{x^2 + y^2} = +\infty$$

which implies that the values of the function approach $+\infty$ as $(x, y) \to (0, 0)$ along any smooth curve (Figure 13.2.9). However, it is not evident whether the limit

$$\lim_{(x,y) \to (0,0)} (x^2 + y^2) \ln(x^2 + y^2)$$

exists because it is an indeterminate form of type $0 \cdot \infty$. Although L'Hôpital's rule cannot be applied directly, the following example illustrates a method for finding this limit by converting to polar coordinates.

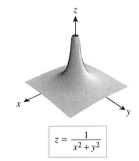

$$z = \frac{1}{x^2 + y^2}$$

▲ Figure 13.2.9

▶ **Example 7** Find $\displaystyle\lim_{(x,y) \to (0,0)} (x^2 + y^2) \ln(x^2 + y^2)$.

**Solution.** Let $(r, \theta)$ be polar coordinates of the point $(x, y)$ with $r \geq 0$. Then we have

$$x = r \cos\theta, \quad y = r \sin\theta, \quad r^2 = x^2 + y^2$$

Moreover, since $r \geq 0$ we have $r = \sqrt{x^2 + y^2}$, so that $r \to 0^+$ if and only if $(x, y) \to (0, 0)$. Thus, we can rewrite the given limit as

$$\lim_{(x,y) \to (0,0)} (x^2 + y^2) \ln(x^2 + y^2) = \lim_{r \to 0^+} r^2 \ln r^2$$

$$= \lim_{r \to 0^+} \frac{2 \ln r}{1/r^2} \qquad \boxed{\text{This converts the limit to an indeterminate form of type } \infty/\infty.}$$

$$= \lim_{r \to 0^+} \frac{2/r}{-2/r^3} \qquad \boxed{\text{L'Hôpital's rule}}$$

$$= \lim_{r \to 0^+} (-r^2) = 0 \quad \blacktriangleleft$$

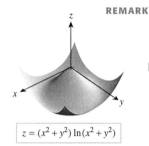

$z = (x^2 + y^2)\ln(x^2 + y^2)$

▲ **Figure 13.2.10**

**REMARK** | The graph of $f(x, y) = (x^2 + y^2)\ln(x^2 + y^2)$ in Example 7 is a surface with a hole (sometimes called a *puncture*) at the origin (Figure 13.2.10). We can remove this discontinuity by *defining* $f(0, 0)$ to be 0. (See Exercises 39 and 40, which also deal with the notion of a "removable" discontinuity.)

### ■ CONTINUITY AT BOUNDARY POINTS

Recall that in our study of continuity for functions of one variable, we first defined continuity at a point, then continuity on an open interval, and then, by using one-sided limits, we extended the notion of continuity to include the boundary points of the interval. Similarly, for functions of two variables one can extend the notion of continuity of $f(x, y)$ to the boundary of its domain by modifying Definition 13.2.1 appropriately so that $(x, y)$ is restricted to approach $(x_0, y_0)$ through points lying wholly in the domain of $f$. We will omit the details.

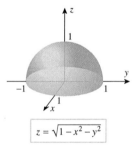

$z = \sqrt{1 - x^2 - y^2}$

▲ **Figure 13.2.11**

▶ **Example 8** The graph of the function $f(x, y) = \sqrt{1 - x^2 - y^2}$ is the upper hemisphere shown in Figure 13.2.11, and the natural domain of $f$ is the closed unit disk

$$x^2 + y^2 \leq 1$$

The graph of $f$ has no tears or holes, so it passes our "intuitive test" of continuity. In this case the continuity at a point $(x_0, y_0)$ on the boundary reflects the fact that

$$\lim_{(x,y) \to (x_0,y_0)} \sqrt{1 - x^2 - y^2} = \sqrt{1 - x_0^2 - y_0^2} = 0$$

when $(x, y)$ is restricted to points on the closed unit disk $x^2 + y^2 \leq 1$. It follows that $f$ is continuous on its domain. ◀

### ■ EXTENSIONS TO THREE VARIABLES

All of the results in this section can be extended to functions of three or more variables. For example, the distance between the points $(x, y, z)$ and $(x_0, y_0, z_0)$ in 3-space is

$$\sqrt{(x - x_0)^2 + (y - y_0)^2 + (z - z_0)^2}$$

so the natural extension of Definition 13.2.1 to 3-space is as follows:

---

**13.2.5 DEFINITION** Let $f$ be a function of three variables, and assume that $f$ is defined at all points within a ball centered at $(x_0, y_0, z_0)$, except possibly at $(x_0, y_0, z_0)$. We will write

$$\lim_{(x,y,z) \to (x_0,y_0,z_0)} f(x, y, z) = L \tag{4}$$

if given any number $\epsilon > 0$, we can find a number $\delta > 0$ such that $f(x, y, z)$ satisfies

$$|f(x, y, z) - L| < \epsilon$$

whenever the distance between $(x, y, z)$ and $(x_0, y_0, z_0)$ satisfies

$$0 < \sqrt{(x - x_0)^2 + (y - y_0)^2 + (z - z_0)^2} < \delta$$

---

As with functions of one and two variables, we define a function $f(x, y, z)$ of three variables to be continuous at a point $(x_0, y_0, z_0)$ if the limit of the function and the value of the function are the same at this point; that is,

$$\lim_{(x,y,z) \to (x_0, y_0, z_0)} f(x, y, z) = f(x_0, y_0, z_0)$$

Although we will omit the details, the properties of limits and continuity that we discussed for functions of two variables, including the notion of continuity at boundary points, carry over to functions of three variables.

## ✔ QUICK CHECK EXERCISES 13.2    (See page 927 for answers.)

**1.** Let
$$f(x, y) = \frac{x^2 - y^2}{x^2 + y^2}$$

Determine the limit of $f(x, y)$ as $(x, y)$ approaches $(0, 0)$ along the curve $C$.
(a) $C: x = 0$        (b) $C: y = 0$
(c) $C: y = x$        (d) $C: y = x^2$

**2.** (a) $\displaystyle\lim_{(x,y) \to (3,2)} x \cos \pi y =$ _____

(b) $\displaystyle\lim_{(x,y) \to (0,1)} e^{xy^2} =$ _____

(c) $\displaystyle\lim_{(x,y) \to (0,0)} (x^2 + y^2) \sin\left(\frac{1}{x^2 + y^2}\right) =$ _____

**3.** A function $f(x, y)$ is continuous at $(x_0, y_0)$ provided $f(x_0, y_0)$ exists and provided $f(x, y)$ has limit _____ as $(x, y)$ approaches _____.

**4.** Determine all values of the constant $a$ such that the function $f(x, y) = \sqrt{x^2 - ay^2 + 1}$ is continuous everywhere.

## EXERCISE SET 13.2

**1–6** Use limit laws and continuity properties to evaluate the limit. ▪

**1.** $\displaystyle\lim_{(x,y) \to (1,3)} (4xy^2 - x)$

**2.** $\displaystyle\lim_{(x,y) \to (0,0)} \frac{4x - y}{\sin y - 1}$

**3.** $\displaystyle\lim_{(x,y) \to (-1,2)} \frac{xy^3}{x + y}$

**4.** $\displaystyle\lim_{(x,y) \to (1,-3)} e^{2x - y^2}$

**5.** $\displaystyle\lim_{(x,y) \to (0,0)} \ln(1 + x^2 y^3)$

**6.** $\displaystyle\lim_{(x,y) \to (4,-2)} x \sqrt[3]{y^3 + 2x}$

**7–8** Show that the limit does not exist by considering the limits as $(x, y) \to (0, 0)$ along the coordinate axes. ▪

**7.** (a) $\displaystyle\lim_{(x,y) \to (0,0)} \frac{3}{x^2 + 2y^2}$

(b) $\displaystyle\lim_{(x,y) \to (0,0)} \frac{x + y}{2x^2 + y^2}$

**8.** (a) $\displaystyle\lim_{(x,y) \to (0,0)} \frac{x - y}{x^2 + y^2}$

(b) $\displaystyle\lim_{(x,y) \to (0,0)} \frac{\cos xy}{x^2 + y^2}$

**9–12** Evaluate the limit using the substitution $z = x^2 + y^2$ and observing that $z \to 0^+$ if and only if $(x, y) \to (0, 0)$. ▪

**9.** $\displaystyle\lim_{(x,y) \to (0,0)} \frac{\sin(x^2 + y^2)}{x^2 + y^2}$

**10.** $\displaystyle\lim_{(x,y) \to (0,0)} \frac{1 - \cos(x^2 + y^2)}{x^2 + y^2}$

**11.** $\displaystyle\lim_{(x,y) \to (0,0)} e^{-1/(x^2 + y^2)}$

**12.** $\displaystyle\lim_{(x,y) \to (0,0)} \frac{e^{-1/\sqrt{x^2 + y^2}}}{\sqrt{x^2 + y^2}}$

**13–22** Determine whether the limit exists. If so, find its value. ▪

**13.** $\displaystyle\lim_{(x,y) \to (0,0)} \frac{x^4 - y^4}{x^2 + y^2}$

**14.** $\displaystyle\lim_{(x,y) \to (0,0)} \frac{x^4 - 16y^4}{x^2 + 4y^2}$

**15.** $\displaystyle\lim_{(x,y) \to (0,0)} \frac{xy}{3x^2 + 2y^2}$

**16.** $\displaystyle\lim_{(x,y) \to (0,0)} \frac{1 - x^2 - y^2}{x^2 + y^2}$

**17.** $\displaystyle\lim_{(x,y,z) \to (2,-1,2)} \frac{xz^2}{\sqrt{x^2 + y^2 + z^2}}$

**18.** $\displaystyle\lim_{(x,y,z) \to (2,0,-1)} \ln(2x + y - z)$

**19.** $\displaystyle\lim_{(x,y,z) \to (0,0,0)} \frac{\sin(x^2 + y^2 + z^2)}{\sqrt{x^2 + y^2 + z^2}}$

**20.** $\displaystyle\lim_{(x,y,z) \to (0,0,0)} \frac{\sin \sqrt{x^2 + y^2 + z^2}}{x^2 + y^2 + z^2}$

**21.** $\displaystyle\lim_{(x,y,z) \to (0,0,0)} \frac{e^{\sqrt{x^2 + y^2 + z^2}}}{\sqrt{x^2 + y^2 + z^2}}$

**22.** $\displaystyle\lim_{(x,y,z) \to (0,0,0)} \tan^{-1}\left[\frac{1}{x^2 + y^2 + z^2}\right]$

**23–26** Evaluate the limits by converting to polar coordinates, as in Example 7. ▪

**23.** $\displaystyle\lim_{(x,y) \to (0,0)} \sqrt{x^2 + y^2} \ln(x^2 + y^2)$

**24.** $\displaystyle\lim_{(x,y) \to (0,0)} y \ln(x^2 + y^2)$

**25.** $\displaystyle\lim_{(x,y) \to (0,0)} \frac{x^2 y^2}{\sqrt{x^2 + y^2}}$

**26.** $\displaystyle\lim_{(x,y) \to (0,0)} \frac{xy}{\sqrt{x^2 + 2y^2}}$

**27–28** Evaluate the limits by converting to spherical coordinates $(\rho, \theta, \phi)$ and by observing that $\rho \to 0^+$ if and only if $(x, y, z) \to (0, 0, 0)$. ▪

**27.** $\displaystyle\lim_{(x,y,z) \to (0,0,0)} \frac{xyz}{x^2 + y^2 + z^2}$

**28.** $\displaystyle\lim_{(x,y,z)\to(0,0,0)}\frac{\sin x \sin y}{\sqrt{x^2+2y^2+3z^2}}$

**29–32 True–False** Determine whether the statement is true or false. Explain your answer. ■

**29.** If $D$ is an open set in 2-space or in 3-space, then every point in $D$ is an interior point of $D$.

**30.** If $f(x,y)\to L$ as $(x,y)$ approaches $(0,0)$ along the $x$-axis, and if $f(x,y)\to L$ as $(x,y)$ approaches $(0,0)$ along the $y$-axis, then $\lim_{(x,y)\to(0,0)} f(x,y)=L$.

**31.** If $f$ and $g$ are functions of two variables such that $f+g$ and $fg$ are both continuous, then $f$ and $g$ are themselves continuous.

**32.** If $\lim_{x\to 0^+} f(x)=L\neq 0$, then
$$\lim_{(x,y)\to(0,0)}\frac{x^2+y^2}{f(x^2+y^2)}=0$$

**FOCUS ON CONCEPTS**

**33.** The accompanying figure shows a portion of the graph of
$$f(x,y)=\frac{x^2 y}{x^4+y^2}$$

(a) Based on the graph in the figure, does $f(x,y)$ have a limit as $(x,y)\to(0,0)$? Explain your reasoning.

(b) Show that $f(x,y)\to 0$ as $(x,y)\to(0,0)$ along any line $y=mx$. Does this imply that $f(x,y)\to 0$ as $(x,y)\to(0,0)$? Explain.

(c) Show that $f(x,y)\to\frac{1}{2}$ as $(x,y)\to(0,0)$ along the parabola $y=x^2$, and confirm visually that this is consistent with the graph of $f(x,y)$.

(d) Based on parts (b) and (c), does $f(x,y)$ have a limit as $(x,y)\to(0,0)$? Is this consistent with your answer to part (a)?

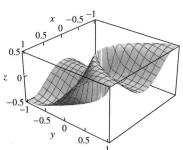

◀ **Figure Ex-33**

**34.** (a) Show that the value of
$$\frac{x^3 y}{2x^6+y^2}$$
approaches 0 as $(x,y)\to(0,0)$ along any straight line $y=mx$, or along any parabola $y=kx^2$.

(b) Show that
$$\lim_{(x,y)\to(0,0)}\frac{x^3 y}{2x^6+y^2}$$
does not exist by letting $(x,y)\to(0,0)$ along the curve $y=x^3$.

**35.** (a) Show that the value of
$$\frac{xyz}{x^2+y^4+z^4}$$
approaches 0 as $(x,y,z)\to(0,0,0)$ along any line $x=at$, $y=bt$, $z=ct$.

(b) Show that the limit
$$\lim_{(x,y,z)\to(0,0,0)}\frac{xyz}{x^2+y^4+z^4}$$
does not exist by letting $(x,y,z)\to(0,0,0)$ along the curve $x=t^2$, $y=t$, $z=t$.

**36.** Find $\displaystyle\lim_{(x,y)\to(0,1)}\tan^{-1}\left[\frac{x^2+1}{x^2+(y-1)^2}\right]$.

**37.** Find $\displaystyle\lim_{(x,y)\to(0,1)}\tan^{-1}\left[\frac{x^2-1}{x^2+(y-1)^2}\right]$.

**38.** Let $f(x,y)=\begin{cases}\dfrac{\sin(x^2+y^2)}{x^2+y^2}, & (x,y)\neq(0,0)\\[2mm] 1, & (x,y)=(0,0).\end{cases}$
Show that $f$ is continuous at $(0,0)$.

**39–40** A function $f(x,y)$ is said to have a **removable discontinuity** at $(x_0,y_0)$ if $\lim_{(x,y)\to(x_0,y_0)} f(x,y)$ exists but $f$ is not continuous at $(x_0,y_0)$, either because $f$ is not defined at $(x_0,y_0)$ or because $f(x_0,y_0)$ differs from the value of the limit. Determine whether $f(x,y)$ has a removable discontinuity at $(0,0)$. ■

**39.** $f(x,y)=\dfrac{x^2}{x^2+y^2}$

**40.** $f(x)=\begin{cases}x^2+7y^2, & \text{if } (x,y)\neq(0,0)\\ -4, & \text{if } (x,y)=(0,0)\end{cases}$

**41–48** Sketch the largest region on which the function $f$ is continuous. ■

**41.** $f(x,y)=y\ln(1+x)$     **42.** $f(x,y)=\sqrt{x-y}$

**43.** $f(x,y)=\dfrac{x^2 y}{\sqrt{25-x^2-y^2}}$

**44.** $f(x,y)=\ln(2x-y+1)$

**45.** $f(x,y)=\dfrac{y}{11x^2+3}$

**46.** $f(x,y)=e^{1-xy}$     **47.** $f(x,y)=\sin^{-1}(xy)$

**48.** $f(x,y)=\tan^{-1}(y-x)$

**49–52** Describe the largest region on which the function $f$ is continuous. ■

**49.** $f(x,y,z)=3x^2 e^{yz}\cos(xyz)$

**50.** $f(x,y,z)=\ln(4-x^2-y^2-z^2)$

**51.** $f(x,y,z)=\dfrac{y+1}{x^2+z^2-1}$

**52.** $f(x,y,z)=\sin\sqrt{x^2+y^2+3z^2}$

**53. Writing** Describe the procedure you would use to determine whether or not the limit

$$\lim_{(x,y)\to(x_0,y_0)} f(x,y)$$

exists.

**54. Writing** In your own words, state the geometric interpretations of $\epsilon$ and $\delta$ in the definition of

$$\lim_{(x,y)\to(x_0,y_0)} f(x,y) = L$$

given in Definition 13.2.1.

✔ **QUICK CHECK ANSWERS 13.2**

1. (a) $-1$ (b) $1$ (c) $0$ (d) $1$   2. (a) $3$ (b) $1$ (c) $0$   3. $f(x_0, y_0)$; $(x_0, y_0)$   4. $a \le 0$

## 13.3 PARTIAL DERIVATIVES

*In this section we will develop the mathematical tools for studying rates of change that involve two or more independent variables.*

### PARTIAL DERIVATIVES OF FUNCTIONS OF TWO VARIABLES

If $z = f(x, y)$, then one can inquire how the value of $z$ changes if $y$ is held fixed and $x$ is allowed to vary, or if $x$ is held fixed and $y$ is allowed to vary. For example, the ideal gas law in physics states that under appropriate conditions the pressure exerted by a gas is a function of the volume of the gas and its temperature. Thus, a physicist studying gases might be interested in the rate of change of the pressure if the volume is held fixed and the temperature is allowed to vary, or if the temperature is held fixed and the volume is allowed to vary. We now define a derivative that describes such rates of change.

Suppose that $(x_0, y_0)$ is a point in the domain of a function $f(x, y)$. If we fix $y = y_0$, then $f(x, y_0)$ is a function of the variable $x$ alone. The value of the derivative

$$\frac{d}{dx}[f(x, y_0)]$$

at $x_0$ then gives us a measure of the instantaneous rate of change of $f$ with respect to $x$ at the point $(x_0, y_0)$. Similarly, the value of the derivative

$$\frac{d}{dy}[f(x_0, y)]$$

at $y_0$ gives us a measure of the instantaneous rate of change of $f$ with respect to $y$ at the point $(x_0, y_0)$. These derivatives are so basic to the study of differential calculus of multivariable functions that they have their own name and notation.

**13.3.1 DEFINITION** If $z = f(x, y)$ and $(x_0, y_0)$ is a point in the domain of $f$, then the ***partial derivative of f with respect to x*** at $(x_0, y_0)$ [also called the ***partial derivative of z with respect to x*** at $(x_0, y_0)$] is the derivative at $x_0$ of the function that results when $y = y_0$ is held fixed and $x$ is allowed to vary. This partial derivative is denoted by $f_x(x_0, y_0)$ and is given by

$$f_x(x_0, y_0) = \frac{d}{dx}[f(x, y_0)]\Big|_{x=x_0} = \lim_{\Delta x \to 0} \frac{f(x_0 + \Delta x, y_0) - f(x_0, y_0)}{\Delta x} \tag{1}$$

The limits in (1) and (2) show the relationship between partial derivatives and derivatives of functions of one variable. In practice, our usual method for computing partial derivatives is to hold one variable fixed and then differentiate the resulting function using the derivative rules for functions of one variable.

Similarly, the ***partial derivative of f with respect to y*** at $(x_0, y_0)$ [also called the ***partial derivative of z with respect to y*** at $(x_0, y_0)$] is the derivative at $y_0$ of the function that results when $x = x_0$ is held fixed and $y$ is allowed to vary. This partial derivative is denoted by $f_y(x_0, y_0)$ and is given by

$$f_y(x_0, y_0) = \frac{d}{dy}[f(x_0, y)]\Big|_{y=y_0} = \lim_{\Delta y \to 0} \frac{f(x_0, y_0 + \Delta y) - f(x_0, y_0)}{\Delta y} \tag{2}$$

▶ **Example 1** Find $f_x(1, 3)$ and $f_y(1, 3)$ for the function $f(x, y) = 2x^3y^2 + 2y + 4x$.

*Solution.* Since

$$f_x(x, 3) = \frac{d}{dx}[f(x, 3)] = \frac{d}{dx}[18x^3 + 4x + 6] = 54x^2 + 4$$

we have $f_x(1, 3) = 54 + 4 = 58$. Also, since

$$f_y(1, y) = \frac{d}{dy}[f(1, y)] = \frac{d}{dy}[2y^2 + 2y + 4] = 4y + 2$$

we have $f_y(1, 3) = 4(3) + 2 = 14$. ◄

■ **THE PARTIAL DERIVATIVE FUNCTIONS**

Formulas (1) and (2) define the partial derivatives of a function at a specific point $(x_0, y_0)$. However, often it will be desirable to omit the subscripts and think of the partial derivatives as functions of the variables $x$ and $y$. These functions are

$$f_x(x, y) = \lim_{\Delta x \to 0} \frac{f(x + \Delta x, y) - f(x, y)}{\Delta x} \qquad f_y(x, y) = \lim_{\Delta y \to 0} \frac{f(x, y + \Delta y) - f(x, y)}{\Delta y}$$

The following example gives an alternative way of performing the computations in Example 1.

▶ **Example 2** Find $f_x(x, y)$ and $f_y(x, y)$ for $f(x, y) = 2x^3y^2 + 2y + 4x$, and use those partial derivatives to compute $f_x(1, 3)$ and $f_y(1, 3)$.

*Solution.* Keeping $y$ fixed and differentiating with respect to $x$ yields

$$f_x(x, y) = \frac{d}{dx}[2x^3y^2 + 2y + 4x] = 6x^2y^2 + 4$$

and keeping $x$ fixed and differentiating with respect to $y$ yields

$$f_y(x, y) = \frac{d}{dy}[2x^3y^2 + 2y + 4x] = 4x^3y + 2$$

Thus,

$$f_x(1, 3) = 6(1^2)(3^2) + 4 = 58 \quad \text{and} \quad f_y(1, 3) = 4(1^3)3 + 2 = 14$$

which agree with the results in Example 1. ◄

**TECHNOLOGY MASTERY**

Computer algebra systems have specific commands for calculating partial derivatives. If you have a CAS, use it to find the partial derivatives $f_x(x, y)$ and $f_y(x, y)$ in Example 2.

■ **PARTIAL DERIVATIVE NOTATION**

If $z = f(x, y)$, then the partial derivatives $f_x$ and $f_y$ are also denoted by the symbols

The symbol $\partial$ is called a partial derivative sign. It is derived from the Cyrillic alphabet.

$$\frac{\partial f}{\partial x}, \quad \frac{\partial z}{\partial x} \quad \text{and} \quad \frac{\partial f}{\partial y}, \quad \frac{\partial z}{\partial y}$$

Some typical notations for the partial derivatives of $z = f(x, y)$ at a point $(x_0, y_0)$ are

$$\left.\frac{\partial f}{\partial x}\right|_{x=x_0, y=y_0}, \quad \left.\frac{\partial z}{\partial x}\right|_{(x_0, y_0)}, \quad \left.\frac{\partial f}{\partial x}\right|_{(x_0, y_0)}, \quad \frac{\partial f}{\partial x}(x_0, y_0), \quad \frac{\partial z}{\partial x}(x_0, y_0)$$

▶ **Example 3**   Find $\partial z/\partial x$ and $\partial z/\partial y$ if $z = x^4 \sin(xy^3)$.

*Solution.*

$$\frac{\partial z}{\partial x} = \frac{\partial}{\partial x}[x^4 \sin(xy^3)] = x^4 \frac{\partial}{\partial x}[\sin(xy^3)] + \sin(xy^3) \cdot \frac{\partial}{\partial x}(x^4)$$

$$= x^4 \cos(xy^3) \cdot y^3 + \sin(xy^3) \cdot 4x^3 = x^4 y^3 \cos(xy^3) + 4x^3 \sin(xy^3)$$

$$\frac{\partial z}{\partial y} = \frac{\partial}{\partial y}[x^4 \sin(xy^3)] = x^4 \frac{\partial}{\partial y}[\sin(xy^3)] + \sin(xy^3) \cdot \frac{\partial}{\partial y}(x^4)$$

$$= x^4 \cos(xy^3) \cdot 3xy^2 + \sin(xy^3) \cdot 0 = 3x^5 y^2 \cos(xy^3) \quad \blacktriangleleft$$

### ■ PARTIAL DERIVATIVES VIEWED AS RATES OF CHANGE AND SLOPES

Recall that if $y = f(x)$, then the value of $f'(x_0)$ can be interpreted either as the rate of change of $y$ with respect to $x$ at $x_0$ or as the slope of the tangent line to the graph of $f$ at $x_0$. Partial derivatives have analogous interpretations. To see that this is so, suppose that $C_1$ is the intersection of the surface $z = f(x, y)$ with the plane $y = y_0$ and that $C_2$ is its intersection with the plane $x = x_0$ (Figure 13.3.1). Thus, $f_x(x, y_0)$ can be interpreted as the rate of change of $z$ with respect to $x$ along the curve $C_1$, and $f_y(x_0, y)$ can be interpreted as the rate of change of $z$ with respect to $y$ along the curve $C_2$. In particular, $f_x(x_0, y_0)$ is the rate of change of $z$ with respect to $x$ along the curve $C_1$ at the point $(x_0, y_0)$, and $f_y(x_0, y_0)$ is the rate of change of $z$ with respect to $y$ along the curve $C_2$ at the point $(x_0, y_0)$.

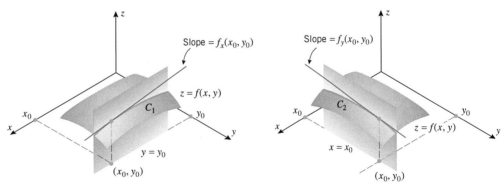

▲ **Figure 13.3.1**

In an applied problem, the interpretations of $f_x(x_0, y_0)$ and $f_y(x_0, y_0)$ must be accompanied by the proper units. See Example 4.

▶ **Example 4**   Recall that the wind chill temperature index is given by the formula

$$W = 35.74 + 0.6215T + (0.4275T - 35.75)v^{0.16}$$

Compute the partial derivative of $W$ with respect to $v$ at the point $(T, v) = (25, 10)$ and interpret this partial derivative as a rate of change.

*Solution.*   Holding $T$ fixed and differentiating with respect to $v$ yields

$$\frac{\partial W}{\partial v}(T, v) = 0 + 0 + (0.4275T - 35.75)(0.16)v^{0.16-1} = (0.4275T - 35.75)(0.16)v^{-0.84}$$

Since $W$ is in degrees Fahrenheit and $v$ is in miles per hour, a rate of change of $W$ with respect to $v$ will have units °F/(mi/h) (which may also be written as °F·h/mi). Substituting

Confirm the conclusion of Example 4 by calculating

$$\frac{W(25, 10 + \Delta v) - W(25, 10)}{\Delta v}$$

for values of $\Delta v$ near 0.

$T = 25$ and $v = 10$ gives

$$\frac{\partial W}{\partial v}(25, 10) = (-4.01)10^{-0.84} \approx -0.58 \; \frac{°F}{mi/h}$$

as the instantaneous rate of change of $W$ with respect to $v$ at $(T, v) = (25, 10)$. We conclude that if the air temperature is a constant $25°F$ and the wind speed changes by a small amount from an initial speed of 10 mi/h, then the ratio of the change in the wind chill index to the change in wind speed should be about $-0.58°F/(mi/h)$. ◄

Geometrically, $f_x(x_0, y_0)$ can be viewed as the slope of the tangent line to the curve $C_1$ at the point $(x_0, y_0)$, and $f_y(x_0, y_0)$ can be viewed as the slope of the tangent line to the curve $C_2$ at the point $(x_0, y_0)$ (Figure 13.3.1). We will call $f_x(x_0, y_0)$ the *slope of the surface in the x-direction* at $(x_0, y_0)$ and $f_y(x_0, y_0)$ the *slope of the surface in the y-direction* at $(x_0, y_0)$.

▶ **Example 5** Let $f(x, y) = x^2 y + 5y^3$.

(a) Find the slope of the surface $z = f(x, y)$ in the $x$-direction at the point $(1, -2)$.

(b) Find the slope of the surface $z = f(x, y)$ in the $y$-direction at the point $(1, -2)$.

*Solution (a).* Differentiating $f$ with respect to $x$ with $y$ held fixed yields

$$f_x(x, y) = 2xy$$

Thus, the slope in the $x$-direction is $f_x(1, -2) = -4$; that is, $z$ is decreasing at the rate of 4 units per unit increase in $x$.

*Solution (b).* Differentiating $f$ with respect to $y$ with $x$ held fixed yields

$$f_y(x, y) = x^2 + 15y^2$$

Thus, the slope in the $y$-direction is $f_y(1, -2) = 61$; that is, $z$ is increasing at the rate of 61 units per unit increase in $y$. ◄

■ **ESTIMATING PARTIAL DERIVATIVES FROM TABULAR DATA**

For functions that are presented in tabular form, we can estimate partial derivatives by using adjacent entries within the table.

▶ **Example 6** Use the values of the wind chill index function $W(T, v)$ displayed in Table 13.3.1 to estimate the partial derivative of $W$ with respect to $v$ at $(T, v) = (25, 10)$. Compare this estimate with the value of the partial derivative obtained in Example 4.

**Table 13.3.1**

TEMPERATURE $T$ (°F)

| WIND SPEED $v$ (mi/h) | 20 | 25 | 30 | 35 |
|---|---|---|---|---|
| 5 | 13 | 19 | 25 | 31 |
| 10 | 9 | 15 | 21 | 27 |
| 15 | 6 | 13 | 19 | 25 |
| 20 | 4 | 11 | 17 | 24 |

*Solution.* Since

$$\frac{\partial W}{\partial v}(25, 10) = \lim_{\Delta v \to 0} \frac{W(25, 10 + \Delta v) - W(25, 10)}{\Delta v} = \lim_{\Delta v \to 0} \frac{W(25, 10 + \Delta v) - 15}{\Delta v}$$

we can approximate the partial derivative by

$$\frac{\partial W}{\partial v}(25, 10) \approx \frac{W(25, 10 + \Delta v) - 15}{\Delta v}$$

With $\Delta v = 5$ this approximation is

$$\frac{\partial W}{\partial v}(25, 10) \approx \frac{W(25, 10 + 5) - 15}{5} = \frac{W(25, 15) - 15}{5} = \frac{13 - 15}{5} = -\frac{2}{5} \; \frac{°F}{mi/h}$$

and with $\Delta v = -5$ this approximation is

$$\frac{\partial W}{\partial v}(25, 10) \approx \frac{W(25, 10 - 5) - 15}{-5} = \frac{W(25, 5) - 15}{-5} = \frac{19 - 15}{-5} = -\frac{4}{5} \frac{°F}{mi/h}$$

We will take the average, $-\frac{3}{5} = -0.6°F/(mi/h)$, of these two approximations as our estimate of $(\partial W/\partial v)(25, 10)$. This is close to the value

$$\frac{\partial W}{\partial v}(25, 10) = (-4.01)10^{-0.84} \approx -0.58 \frac{°F}{mi/h}$$

found in Example 4. ◄

## ▇ IMPLICIT PARTIAL DIFFERENTIATION

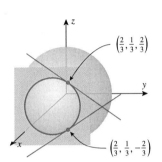

**▲ Figure 13.3.2**

▶ **Example 7**   Find the slope of the sphere $x^2 + y^2 + z^2 = 1$ in the $y$-direction at the points $\left(\frac{2}{3}, \frac{1}{3}, \frac{2}{3}\right)$ and $\left(\frac{2}{3}, \frac{1}{3}, -\frac{2}{3}\right)$ (Figure 13.3.2).

*Solution.*   The point $\left(\frac{2}{3}, \frac{1}{3}, \frac{2}{3}\right)$ lies on the upper hemisphere $z = \sqrt{1 - x^2 - y^2}$, and the point $\left(\frac{2}{3}, \frac{1}{3}, -\frac{2}{3}\right)$ lies on the lower hemisphere $z = -\sqrt{1 - x^2 - y^2}$. We could find the slopes by differentiating each expression for $z$ separately with respect to $y$ and then evaluating the derivatives at $x = \frac{2}{3}$ and $y = \frac{1}{3}$. However, it is more efficient to differentiate the given equation

$$x^2 + y^2 + z^2 = 1$$

implicitly with respect to $y$, since this will give us both slopes with one differentiation. To perform the implicit differentiation, we view $z$ as a function of $x$ and $y$ and differentiate both sides with respect to $y$, taking $x$ to be fixed. The computations are as follows:

$$\frac{\partial}{\partial y}[x^2 + y^2 + z^2] = \frac{\partial}{\partial y}[1]$$

$$0 + 2y + 2z\frac{\partial z}{\partial y} = 0$$

$$\frac{\partial z}{\partial y} = -\frac{y}{z}$$

Substituting the $y$- and $z$-coordinates of the points $\left(\frac{2}{3}, \frac{1}{3}, \frac{2}{3}\right)$ and $\left(\frac{2}{3}, \frac{1}{3}, -\frac{2}{3}\right)$ in this expression, we find that the slope at the point $\left(\frac{2}{3}, \frac{1}{3}, \frac{2}{3}\right)$ is $-\frac{1}{2}$ and the slope at $\left(\frac{2}{3}, \frac{1}{3}, -\frac{2}{3}\right)$ is $\frac{1}{2}$. ◄

Check the results in Example 7 by differentiating the functions

$$z = \sqrt{1 - x^2 - y^2}$$

and

$$z = -\sqrt{1 - x^2 - y^2}$$

directly.

▶ **Example 8**   Suppose that $D = \sqrt{x^2 + y^2}$ is the length of the diagonal of a rectangle whose sides have lengths $x$ and $y$ that are allowed to vary. Find a formula for the rate of change of $D$ with respect to $x$ if $x$ varies with $y$ held constant, and use this formula to find the rate of change of $D$ with respect to $x$ at the point where $x = 3$ and $y = 4$.

*Solution.*   Differentiating both sides of the equation $D^2 = x^2 + y^2$ with respect to $x$ yields

$$2D\frac{\partial D}{\partial x} = 2x \quad \text{and thus} \quad D\frac{\partial D}{\partial x} = x$$

Since $D = 5$ when $x = 3$ and $y = 4$, it follows that

$$5\frac{\partial D}{\partial x}\bigg|_{x=3, y=4} = 3 \quad \text{or} \quad \frac{\partial D}{\partial x}\bigg|_{x=3, y=4} = \frac{3}{5}$$

Thus, $D$ is increasing at a rate of $\frac{3}{5}$ unit per unit increase in $x$ at the point $(3, 4)$. ◄

■ **PARTIAL DERIVATIVES AND CONTINUITY**

In contrast to the case of functions of a single variable, the existence of partial derivatives for a multivariable function does not guarantee the continuity of the function. This fact is shown in the following example.

▶ **Example 9** Let

$$f(x, y) = \begin{cases} -\dfrac{xy}{x^2 + y^2}, & (x, y) \neq (0, 0) \\ 0, & (x, y) = (0, 0) \end{cases} \tag{3}$$

(a) Show that $f_x(x, y)$ and $f_y(x, y)$ exist at all points $(x, y)$.

(b) Explain why $f$ is not continuous at $(0, 0)$.

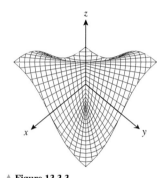

▲ **Figure 13.3.3**

*Solution (a).* Figure 13.3.3 shows the graph of $f$. Note that $f$ is similar to the function considered in Example 1 of Section 13.2, except that here we have assigned $f$ a value of 0 at $(0, 0)$. Except at this point, the partial derivatives of $f$ are

$$f_x(x, y) = -\frac{(x^2 + y^2)y - xy(2x)}{(x^2 + y^2)^2} = \frac{x^2y - y^3}{(x^2 + y^2)^2} \tag{4}$$

$$f_y(x, y) = -\frac{(x^2 + y^2)x - xy(2y)}{(x^2 + y^2)^2} = \frac{xy^2 - x^3}{(x^2 + y^2)^2} \tag{5}$$

It is not evident from Formula (3) whether $f$ has partial derivatives at $(0, 0)$, and if so, what the values of those derivatives are. To answer that question we will have to use the definitions of the partial derivatives (Definition 13.3.1). Applying Formulas (1) and (2) to (3) we obtain

$$f_x(0, 0) = \lim_{\Delta x \to 0} \frac{f(\Delta x, 0) - f(0, 0)}{\Delta x} = \lim_{\Delta x \to 0} \frac{0 - 0}{\Delta x} = 0$$

$$f_y(0, 0) = \lim_{\Delta y \to 0} \frac{f(0, \Delta y) - f(0, 0)}{\Delta y} = \lim_{\Delta y \to 0} \frac{0 - 0}{\Delta y} = 0$$

This shows that $f$ has partial derivatives at $(0, 0)$ and the values of both partial derivatives are 0 at that point.

*Solution (b).* We saw in Example 3 of Section 13.2 that

$$\lim_{(x,y) \to (0,0)} -\frac{xy}{x^2 + y^2}$$

does not exist. Thus, $f$ is not continuous at $(0, 0)$. ◀

We will study the relationship between the continuity of a function and the properties of its partial derivatives in the next section.

■ **PARTIAL DERIVATIVES OF FUNCTIONS WITH MORE THAN TWO VARIABLES**

For a function $f(x, y, z)$ of three variables, there are three *partial derivatives*:

$$f_x(x, y, z), \quad f_y(x, y, z), \quad f_z(x, y, z)$$

The partial derivative $f_x$ is calculated by holding $y$ and $z$ constant and differentiating with respect to $x$. For $f_y$ the variables $x$ and $z$ are held constant, and for $f_z$ the variables $x$ and $y$ are held constant. If a dependent variable

$$w = f(x, y, z)$$

is used, then the three partial derivatives of $f$ can be denoted by

$$\frac{\partial w}{\partial x}, \quad \frac{\partial w}{\partial y}, \quad \text{and} \quad \frac{\partial w}{\partial z}$$

▶ **Example 10** If $f(x, y, z) = x^3 y^2 z^4 + 2xy + z$, then

$$f_x(x, y, z) = 3x^2 y^2 z^4 + 2y$$
$$f_y(x, y, z) = 2x^3 y z^4 + 2x$$
$$f_z(x, y, z) = 4x^3 y^2 z^3 + 1$$
$$f_z(-1, 1, 2) = 4(-1)^3 (1)^2 (2)^3 + 1 = -31 \quad ◀$$

▶ **Example 11** If $f(\rho, \theta, \phi) = \rho^2 \cos \phi \sin \theta$, then

$$f_\rho(\rho, \theta, \phi) = 2\rho \cos \phi \sin \theta$$
$$f_\theta(\rho, \theta, \phi) = \rho^2 \cos \phi \cos \theta$$
$$f_\phi(\rho, \theta, \phi) = -\rho^2 \sin \phi \sin \theta \quad ◀$$

In general, if $f(v_1, v_2, \ldots, v_n)$ is a function of $n$ variables, there are $n$ partial derivatives of $f$, each of which is obtained by holding $n - 1$ of the variables fixed and differentiating the function $f$ with respect to the remaining variable. If $w = f(v_1, v_2, \ldots, v_n)$, then these partial derivatives are denoted by

$$\frac{\partial w}{\partial v_1}, \frac{\partial w}{\partial v_2}, \ldots, \frac{\partial w}{\partial v_n}$$

where $\partial w / \partial v_i$ is obtained by holding all variables except $v_i$ fixed and differentiating with respect to $v_i$.

### HIGHER-ORDER PARTIAL DERIVATIVES

Suppose that $f$ is a function of two variables $x$ and $y$. Since the partial derivatives $\partial f / \partial x$ and $\partial f / \partial y$ are also functions of $x$ and $y$, these functions may themselves have partial derivatives. This gives rise to four possible *second-order* partial derivatives of $f$, which are defined by

$$\frac{\partial^2 f}{\partial x^2} = \frac{\partial}{\partial x}\left(\frac{\partial f}{\partial x}\right) = f_{xx} \qquad\qquad \frac{\partial^2 f}{\partial y^2} = \frac{\partial}{\partial y}\left(\frac{\partial f}{\partial y}\right) = f_{yy}$$

| Differentiate twice with respect to $x$. | | Differentiate twice with respect to $y$. |

$$\frac{\partial^2 f}{\partial y \partial x} = \frac{\partial}{\partial y}\left(\frac{\partial f}{\partial x}\right) = f_{xy} \qquad\qquad \frac{\partial^2 f}{\partial x \partial y} = \frac{\partial}{\partial x}\left(\frac{\partial f}{\partial y}\right) = f_{yx}$$

| Differentiate first with respect to $x$ and then with respect to $y$. | | Differentiate first with respect to $y$ and then with respect to $x$. |

The last two cases are called the *mixed second-order partial derivatives* or the *mixed second partials*. Also, the derivatives $\partial f / \partial x$ and $\partial f / \partial y$ are often called the *first-order partial derivatives* when it is necessary to distinguish them from higher-order partial derivatives. Similar conventions apply to the second-order partial derivatives of a function of three variables.

**WARNING** Observe that the two notations for the mixed second partials have opposite conventions for the order of differentiation. In the "$\partial$" notation the derivatives are taken right to left, and in the "subscript" notation they are taken left to right. The conventions are logical if you insert parentheses:

$$\frac{\partial^2 f}{\partial y \partial x} = \frac{\partial}{\partial y}\left(\frac{\partial f}{\partial x}\right)$$   | Right to left. Differentiate inside the parentheses first. |    $f_{xy} = (f_x)_y$   | Left to right. Differentiate inside the parentheses first. |

---

▶ **Example 12**   Find the second-order partial derivatives of $f(x, y) = x^2 y^3 + x^4 y$.

*Solution.*   We have

$$\frac{\partial f}{\partial x} = 2xy^3 + 4x^3 y \quad \text{and} \quad \frac{\partial f}{\partial y} = 3x^2 y^2 + x^4$$

so that

$$\frac{\partial^2 f}{\partial x^2} = \frac{\partial}{\partial x}\left(\frac{\partial f}{\partial x}\right) = \frac{\partial}{\partial x}(2xy^3 + 4x^3 y) = 2y^3 + 12x^2 y$$

$$\frac{\partial^2 f}{\partial y^2} = \frac{\partial}{\partial y}\left(\frac{\partial f}{\partial y}\right) = \frac{\partial}{\partial y}(3x^2 y^2 + x^4) = 6x^2 y$$

$$\frac{\partial^2 f}{\partial x \partial y} = \frac{\partial}{\partial x}\left(\frac{\partial f}{\partial y}\right) = \frac{\partial}{\partial x}(3x^2 y^2 + x^4) = 6xy^2 + 4x^3$$

$$\frac{\partial^2 f}{\partial y \partial x} = \frac{\partial}{\partial y}\left(\frac{\partial f}{\partial x}\right) = \frac{\partial}{\partial y}(2xy^3 + 4x^3 y) = 6xy^2 + 4x^3 \quad ◀$$

Third-order, fourth-order, and higher-order partial derivatives can be obtained by successive differentiation. Some possibilities are

$$\frac{\partial^3 f}{\partial x^3} = \frac{\partial}{\partial x}\left(\frac{\partial^2 f}{\partial x^2}\right) = f_{xxx} \qquad \frac{\partial^4 f}{\partial y^4} = \frac{\partial}{\partial y}\left(\frac{\partial^3 f}{\partial y^3}\right) = f_{yyyy}$$

$$\frac{\partial^3 f}{\partial y^2 \partial x} = \frac{\partial}{\partial y}\left(\frac{\partial^2 f}{\partial y \partial x}\right) = f_{xyy} \qquad \frac{\partial^4 f}{\partial y^2 \partial x^2} = \frac{\partial}{\partial y}\left(\frac{\partial^3 f}{\partial y \partial x^2}\right) = f_{xxyy}$$

---

▶ **Example 13**   Let $f(x, y) = y^2 e^x + y$. Find $f_{xyy}$.

*Solution.*

$$f_{xyy} = \frac{\partial^3 f}{\partial y^2 \partial x} = \frac{\partial^2}{\partial y^2}\left(\frac{\partial f}{\partial x}\right) = \frac{\partial^2}{\partial y^2}(y^2 e^x) = \frac{\partial}{\partial y}(2ye^x) = 2e^x \quad ◀$$

▨ **EQUALITY OF MIXED PARTIALS**

For a function $f(x, y)$ it might be expected that there would be four distinct second-order partial derivatives: $f_{xx}$, $f_{xy}$, $f_{yx}$, and $f_{yy}$. However, observe that the mixed second-order partial derivatives in Example 12 are equal. The following theorem (proved in Appendix D) explains why this is so.

If $f$ is a function of three variables, then the analog of Theorem 13.3.2 holds for each pair of mixed second-order partials if we replace "open disk" by "open ball." How many second-order partials does $f(x, y, z)$ have?

---

**13.3.2**   **THEOREM**   *Let $f$ be a function of two variables. If $f_{xy}$ and $f_{yx}$ are continuous on some open disk, then $f_{xy} = f_{yx}$ on that disk.*

It follows from this theorem that if $f_{xy}(x, y)$ and $f_{yx}(x, y)$ are continuous everywhere, then $f_{xy}(x, y) = f_{yx}(x, y)$ for all values of $x$ and $y$. Since polynomials are continuous everywhere, this explains why the mixed second-order partials in Example 12 are equal.

### ■ THE WAVE EQUATION

Consider a string of length $L$ that is stretched taut between $x = 0$ and $x = L$ on an $x$-axis, and suppose that the string is set into vibratory motion by "plucking" it at time $t = 0$ (Figure 13.3.4a). The displacement of a point on the string depends both on its coordinate $x$ and the elapsed time $t$, and hence is described by a function $u(x, t)$ of two variables. For a fixed value $t$, the function $u(x, t)$ depends on $x$ alone, and the graph of $u$ versus $x$ describes the shape of the string—think of it as a "snapshot" of the string at time $t$ (Figure 13.3.4b). It follows that at a fixed time $t$, the partial derivative $\partial u/\partial x$ represents the slope of the string at $x$, and the sign of the second partial derivative $\partial^2 u/\partial x^2$ tells us whether the string is concave up or concave down at $x$ (Figure 13.3.4c).

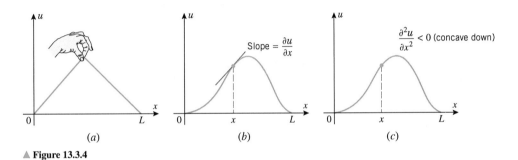

$$\text{Slope} = \frac{\partial u}{\partial x}$$

$$\frac{\partial^2 u}{\partial x^2} < 0 \text{ (concave down)}$$

(a)  (b)  (c)

▲ **Figure 13.3.4**

© vndrpttn/iStockphoto

*The vibration of a plucked string is governed by the wave equation.*

For a fixed value of $x$, the function $u(x, t)$ depends on $t$ alone, and the graph of $u$ versus $t$ is the position versus time curve of the point on the string with coordinate $x$. Thus, for a fixed value of $x$, the partial derivative $\partial u/\partial t$ is the velocity of the point with coordinate $x$, and $\partial^2 u/\partial t^2$ is the acceleration of that point.

It can be proved that under appropriate conditions the function $u(x, t)$ satisfies an equation of the form

$$\frac{\partial^2 u}{\partial t^2} = c^2 \frac{\partial^2 u}{\partial x^2} \tag{6}$$

where $c$ is a positive constant that depends on the physical characteristics of the string. This equation, which is called the ***one-dimensional wave equation***, involves partial derivatives of the unknown function $u(x, t)$ and hence is classified as a ***partial differential equation***. Techniques for solving partial differential equations are studied in advanced courses and will not be discussed in this text.

▶ **Example 14** Show that the function $u(x, t) = \sin(x - ct)$ is a solution of Equation (6).

*Solution.* We have

$$\frac{\partial u}{\partial x} = \cos(x - ct), \qquad \frac{\partial^2 u}{\partial x^2} = -\sin(x - ct)$$

$$\frac{\partial u}{\partial t} = -c \cos(x - ct), \qquad \frac{\partial^2 u}{\partial t^2} = -c^2 \sin(x - ct)$$

Thus, $u(x, t)$ satisfies (6). ◀

✔ **QUICK CHECK EXERCISES 13.3**    *(See page 940 for answers.)*

1. Let $f(x, y) = x \sin xy$.   Then $f_x(x, y) =$ _____ and $f_y(x, y) =$ _____.

2. The slope of the surface $z = xy^2$ in the $x$-direction at the point $(2, 3)$ is _____, and the slope of this surface in the $y$-direction at the point $(2, 3)$ is _____.

3. The volume $V$ of a right circular cone of radius $r$ and height $h$ is given by $V = \frac{1}{3}\pi r^2 h$.

(a) Find a formula for the instantaneous rate of change of $V$ with respect to $r$ if $r$ changes and $h$ remains constant.

(b) Find a formula for the instantaneous rate of change of $V$ with respect to $h$ if $h$ changes and $r$ remains constant.

4. Find all second-order partial derivatives for the function $f(x, y) = x^2 y^3$.

**EXERCISE SET 13.3**    ⊠ Graphing Utility

1. Let $f(x, y) = 3x^3 y^2$. Find
   (a) $f_x(x, y)$      (b) $f_y(x, y)$      (c) $f_x(1, y)$
   (d) $f_x(x, 1)$      (e) $f_y(1, y)$      (f) $f_y(x, 1)$
   (g) $f_x(1, 2)$      (h) $f_y(1, 2)$.

2. Let $z = e^{2x} \sin y$. Find
   (a) $\partial z/\partial x$      (b) $\partial z/\partial y$      (c) $\partial z/\partial x|_{(0,y)}$
   (d) $\partial z/\partial x|_{(x,0)}$   (e) $\partial z/\partial y|_{(0,y)}$   (f) $\partial z/\partial y|_{(x,0)}$
   (g) $\partial z/\partial x|_{(\ln 2,0)}$   (h) $\partial z/\partial y|_{(\ln 2,0)}$.

**3–10** Evaluate the indicated partial derivatives. ∎

3. $z = 9x^2 y - 3x^5 y$; $\dfrac{\partial z}{\partial x}, \dfrac{\partial z}{\partial y}$

4. $f(x, y) = 10x^2 y^4 - 6xy^2 + 10x^2$; $f_x(x, y), f_y(x, y)$

5. $z = (x^2 + 5x - 2y)^8$; $\dfrac{\partial z}{\partial x}, \dfrac{\partial z}{\partial y}$

6. $f(x, y) = \dfrac{1}{xy^2 - x^2 y}$; $f_x(x, y), f_y(x, y)$

7. $\dfrac{\partial}{\partial p}(e^{-7p/q}), \dfrac{\partial}{\partial q}(e^{-7p/q})$

8. $\dfrac{\partial}{\partial x}(xe^{\sqrt{15xy}}), \dfrac{\partial}{\partial y}(xe^{\sqrt{15xy}})$

9. $z = \sin(5x^3 y + 7xy^2)$; $\dfrac{\partial z}{\partial x}, \dfrac{\partial z}{\partial y}$

10. $f(x, y) = \cos(2xy^2 - 3x^2 y^2)$; $f_x(x, y), f_y(x, y)$

11. Let $f(x, y) = \sqrt{3x + 2y}$.
    (a) Find the slope of the surface $z = f(x, y)$ in the $x$-direction at the point $(4, 2)$.
    (b) Find the slope of the surface $z = f(x, y)$ in the $y$-direction at the point $(4, 2)$.

12. Let $f(x, y) = xe^{-y} + 5y$.
    (a) Find the slope of the surface $z = f(x, y)$ in the $x$-direction at the point $(3, 0)$.
    (b) Find the slope of the surface $z = f(x, y)$ in the $y$-direction at the point $(3, 0)$.

13. Let $z = \sin(y^2 - 4x)$.
    (a) Find the rate of change of $z$ with respect to $x$ at the point $(2, 1)$ with $y$ held fixed.
    (b) Find the rate of change of $z$ with respect to $y$ at the point $(2, 1)$ with $x$ held fixed.

14. Let $z = (x + y)^{-1}$.
    (a) Find the rate of change of $z$ with respect to $x$ at the point $(-2, 4)$ with $y$ held fixed.
    (b) Find the rate of change of $z$ with respect to $y$ at the point $(-2, 4)$ with $x$ held fixed.

**FOCUS ON CONCEPTS**

15. Use the information in the accompanying figure to find the values of the first-order partial derivatives of $f$ at the point $(1, 2)$.

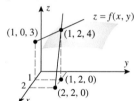

◀ **Figure Ex-15**

16. The accompanying figure shows a contour plot for an unspecified function $f(x, y)$. Make a conjecture about the signs of the partial derivatives $f_x(x_0, y_0)$ and $f_y(x_0, y_0)$, and explain your reasoning.

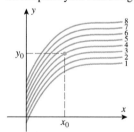

◀ **Figure Ex-16**

17. Suppose that Nolan throws a baseball to Ryan and that the baseball leaves Nolan's hand at the same height at which it is caught by Ryan. It we ignore air resistance, the horizontal range $r$ of the baseball is a function of the initial speed $v$ of the ball when it leaves Nolan's hand and the angle $\theta$ above the horizontal at which it is thrown. Use the accompanying table and the method of Example 6 to estimate
    (a) the partial derivative of $r$ with respect to $v$ when $v = 80$ ft/s and $\theta = 40°$

(b) the partial derivative of $r$ with respect to $\theta$ when $v = 80$ ft/s and $\theta = 40°$.

SPEED $v$ (ft/s)

| | 75 | 80 | 85 | 90 |
|---|---|---|---|---|
| 35 | 165 | 188 | 212 | 238 |
| 40 | 173 | 197 | 222 | 249 |
| 45 | 176 | 200 | 226 | 253 |
| 50 | 173 | 197 | 222 | 249 |

ANGLE $\theta$ (degrees)

◀ **Table Ex-17**

**18.** Use the table in Exercise 17 and the method of Example 6 to estimate
   (a) the partial derivative of $r$ with respect to $v$ when $v = 85$ ft/s and $\theta = 45°$
   (b) the partial derivative of $r$ with respect to $\theta$ when $v = 85$ ft/s and $\theta = 45°$.

**19.** The accompanying figure shows the graphs of an unspecified function $f(x, y)$ and its partial derivatives $f_x(x, y)$ and $f_y(x, y)$. Determine which is which, and explain your reasoning.

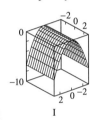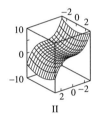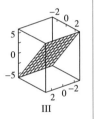

I                      II                      III

▲ **Figure Ex-19**

**20.** What can you say about the signs of $\partial z/\partial x$, $\partial^2 z/\partial x^2$, $\partial z/\partial y$, and $\partial^2 z/\partial y^2$ at the point $P$ in the accompanying figure? Explain your reasoning.

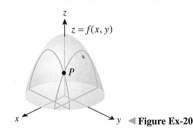

◀ **Figure Ex-20**

**21–24 True–False** Determine whether the statement is true or false. Explain your answer. ▪

**21.** If the line $y = 2$ is a contour of $f(x, y)$ through $(4, 2)$, then $f_x(4, 2) = 0$.

**22.** If the plane $x = 3$ intersects the surface $z = f(x, y)$ in a curve that passes through $(3, 4, 16)$ and satisfies $z = y^2$, then $f_y(3, 4) = 8$.

**23.** If the graph of $z = f(x, y)$ is a plane in 3-space, then both $f_x$ and $f_y$ are constant functions.

**24.** There exists a polynomial $f(x, y)$ that satisfies the equations $f_x(x, y) = 3x^2 + y^2 + 2y$ and $f_y(x, y) = 2xy + 2y$.

**25–30** Find $\partial z/\partial x$ and $\partial z/\partial y$. ▪

**25.** $z = 4e^{x^2 y^3}$
**26.** $z = \cos(x^5 y^4)$
**27.** $z = x^3 \ln(1 + xy^{-3/5})$
**28.** $z = e^{xy} \sin 4y^2$
**29.** $z = \dfrac{xy}{x^2 + y^2}$
**30.** $z = \dfrac{x^2 y^3}{\sqrt{x + y}}$

**31–36** Find $f_x(x, y)$ and $f_y(x, y)$. ▪

**31.** $f(x, y) = \sqrt{3x^5 y - 7x^3 y}$
**32.** $f(x, y) = \dfrac{x + y}{x - y}$
**33.** $f(x, y) = y^{-3/2} \tan^{-1}(x/y)$
**34.** $f(x, y) = x^3 e^{-y} + y^3 \sec \sqrt{x}$
**35.** $f(x, y) = (y^2 \tan x)^{-4/3}$
**36.** $f(x, y) = \cosh(\sqrt{x}) \sinh^2(xy^2)$

**37–40** Evaluate the indicated partial derivatives. ▪

**37.** $f(x, y) = 9 - x^2 - 7y^3$; $f_x(3, 1)$, $f_y(3, 1)$
**38.** $f(x, y) = x^2 y e^{xy}$; $\partial f/\partial x(1, 1)$, $\partial f/\partial y(1, 1)$
**39.** $z = \sqrt{x^2 + 4y^2}$; $\partial z/\partial x(1, 2)$, $\partial z/\partial y(1, 2)$
**40.** $w = x^2 \cos xy$; $\partial w/\partial x \left(\frac{1}{2}, \pi\right)$, $\partial w/\partial y \left(\frac{1}{2}, \pi\right)$
**41.** Let $f(x, y, z) = x^2 y^4 z^3 + xy + z^2 + 1$. Find
   (a) $f_x(x, y, z)$   (b) $f_y(x, y, z)$   (c) $f_z(x, y, z)$
   (d) $f_x(1, y, z)$   (e) $f_y(1, 2, z)$   (f) $f_z(1, 2, 3)$.
**42.** Let $w = x^2 y \cos z$. Find
   (a) $\partial w/\partial x(x, y, z)$   (b) $\partial w/\partial y(x, y, z)$
   (c) $\partial w/\partial z(x, y, z)$   (d) $\partial w/\partial x(2, y, z)$
   (e) $\partial w/\partial y(2, 1, z)$   (f) $\partial w/\partial z(2, 1, 0)$.

**43–46** Find $f_x$, $f_y$, and $f_z$. ▪

**43.** $f(x, y, z) = z \ln(x^2 y \cos z)$
**44.** $f(x, y, z) = y^{-3/2} \sec\left(\dfrac{xz}{y}\right)$
**45.** $f(x, y, z) = \tan^{-1}\left(\dfrac{1}{xy^2 z^3}\right)$
**46.** $f(x, y, z) = \cosh(\sqrt{z}) \sinh^2(x^2 yz)$

**47–50** Find $\partial w/\partial x$, $\partial w/\partial y$, and $\partial w/\partial z$. ▪

**47.** $w = y e^z \sin xz$
**48.** $w = \dfrac{x^2 - y^2}{y^2 + z^2}$
**49.** $w = \sqrt{x^2 + y^2 + z^2}$
**50.** $w = y^3 e^{2x+3z}$
**51.** Let $f(x, y, z) = y^2 e^{xz}$. Find
   (a) $\partial f/\partial x|_{(1,1,1)}$   (b) $\partial f/\partial y|_{(1,1,1)}$   (c) $\partial f/\partial z|_{(1,1,1)}$.
**52.** Let $w = \sqrt{x^2 + 4y^2 - z^2}$. Find
   (a) $\partial w/\partial x|_{(2,1,-1)}$   (b) $\partial w/\partial y|_{(2,1,-1)}$
   (c) $\partial w/\partial z|_{(2,1,-1)}$.
**53.** Let $f(x, y) = e^x \cos y$. Use a graphing utility to graph the functions $f_x(0, y)$ and $f_y(x, \pi/2)$.
**54.** Let $f(x, y) = e^x \sin y$. Use a graphing utility to graph the functions $f_x(0, y)$ and $f_y(x, 0)$.

**55.** A point moves along the intersection of the elliptic paraboloid $z = x^2 + 3y^2$ and the plane $y = 1$. At what rate is $z$ changing with respect to $x$ when the point is at $(2, 1, 7)$?

**56.** A point moves along the intersection of the elliptic paraboloid $z = x^2 + 3y^2$ and the plane $x = 2$. At what rate is $z$ changing with respect to $y$ when the point is at $(2, 1, 7)$?

**57.** A point moves along the intersection of the plane $y = 3$ and the surface $z = \sqrt{29 - x^2 - y^2}$. At what rate is $z$ changing with respect to $x$ when the point is at $(4, 3, 2)$?

**58.** Find the slope of the tangent line at $(-1, 1, 5)$ to the curve of intersection of the surface $z = x^2 + 4y^2$ and
(a) the plane $x = -1$    (b) the plane $y = 1$.

**59.** The volume $V$ of a right circular cylinder is given by the formula $V = \pi r^2 h$, where $r$ is the radius and $h$ is the height.
(a) Find a formula for the instantaneous rate of change of $V$ with respect to $r$ if $r$ changes and $h$ remains constant.
(b) Find a formula for the instantaneous rate of change of $V$ with respect to $h$ if $h$ changes and $r$ remains constant.
(c) Suppose that $h$ has a constant value of 4 in, but $r$ varies. Find the rate of change of $V$ with respect to $r$ at the point where $r = 6$ in.
(d) Suppose that $r$ has a constant value of 8 in, but $h$ varies. Find the instantaneous rate of change of $V$ with respect to $h$ at the point where $h = 10$ in.

**60.** The volume $V$ of a right circular cone is given by
$$V = \frac{\pi}{24} d^2 \sqrt{4s^2 - d^2}$$
where $s$ is the slant height and $d$ is the diameter of the base.
(a) Find a formula for the instantaneous rate of change of $V$ with respect to $s$ if $d$ remains constant.
(b) Find a formula for the instantaneous rate of change of $V$ with respect to $d$ if $s$ remains constant.
(c) Suppose that $d$ has a constant value of 16 cm, but $s$ varies. Find the rate of change of $V$ with respect to $s$ when $s = 10$ cm.
(d) Suppose that $s$ has a constant value of 10 cm, but $d$ varies. Find the rate of change of $V$ with respect to $d$ when $d = 16$ cm.

**61.** According to the ideal gas law, the pressure, temperature, and volume of a gas are related by $P = kT/V$, where $k$ is a constant of proportionality. Suppose that $V$ is measured in cubic inches (in$^3$), $T$ is measured in kelvins (K), and that for a certain gas the constant of proportionality is $k = 10$ in·lb/K.
(a) Find the instantaneous rate of change of pressure with respect to temperature if the temperature is 80 K and the volume remains fixed at 50 in$^3$.
(b) Find the instantaneous rate of change of volume with respect to pressure if the volume is 50 in$^3$ and the temperature remains fixed at 80 K.

**62.** The temperature at a point $(x, y)$ on a metal plate in the $xy$-plane is $T(x, y) = x^3 + 2y^2 + x$ degrees Celsius. Assume that distance is measured in centimeters and find the rate at which temperature changes with respect to distance if we start at the point $(1, 2)$ and move
(a) to the right and parallel to the $x$-axis
(b) upward and parallel to the $y$-axis.

**63.** The length, width, and height of a rectangular box are $l = 5$, $w = 2$, and $h = 3$, respectively.
(a) Find the instantaneous rate of change of the volume of the box with respect to the length if $w$ and $h$ are held constant.
(b) Find the instantaneous rate of change of the volume of the box with respect to the width if $l$ and $h$ are held constant.
(c) Find the instantaneous rate of change of the volume of the box with respect to the height if $l$ and $w$ are held constant.

**64.** The area $A$ of a triangle is given by $A = \frac{1}{2}ab \sin \theta$, where $a$ and $b$ are the lengths of two sides and $\theta$ is the angle between these sides. Suppose that $a = 5$, $b = 10$, and $\theta = \pi/3$.
(a) Find the rate at which $A$ changes with respect to $a$ if $b$ and $\theta$ are held constant.
(b) Find the rate at which $A$ changes with respect to $\theta$ if $a$ and $b$ are held constant.
(c) Find the rate at which $b$ changes with respect to $a$ if $A$ and $\theta$ are held constant.

**65.** The volume of a right circular cone of radius $r$ and height $h$ is $V = \frac{1}{3}\pi r^2 h$. Show that if the height remains constant while the radius changes, then the volume satisfies
$$\frac{\partial V}{\partial r} = \frac{2V}{r}$$

**66.** Find parametric equations for the tangent line at $(1, 3, 3)$ to the curve of intersection of the surface $z = x^2 y$ and
(a) the plane $x = 1$    (b) the plane $y = 3$.

**67.** (a) By differentiating implicitly, find the slope of the hyperboloid $x^2 + y^2 - z^2 = 1$ in the $x$-direction at the points $(3, 4, 2\sqrt{6})$ and $(3, 4, -2\sqrt{6})$.
(b) Check the results in part (a) by solving for $z$ and differentiating the resulting functions directly.

**68.** (a) By differentiating implicitly, find the slope of the hyperboloid $x^2 + y^2 - z^2 = 1$ in the $y$-direction at the points $(3, 4, 2\sqrt{6})$ and $(3, 4, -2\sqrt{6})$.
(b) Check the results in part (a) by solving for $z$ and differentiating the resulting functions directly.

**69–72** Calculate $\partial z/\partial x$ and $\partial z/\partial y$ using implicit differentiation. Leave your answers in terms of $x$, $y$, and $z$. ▨

**69.** $(x^2 + y^2 + z^2)^{3/2} = 1$    **70.** $\ln(2x^2 + y - z^3) = x$

**71.** $x^2 + z \sin xyz = 0$    **72.** $e^{xy} \sinh z - z^2 x + 1 = 0$

**73–76** Find $\partial w/\partial x$, $\partial w/\partial y$, and $\partial w/\partial z$ using implicit differentiation. Leave your answers in terms of $x$, $y$, $z$, and $w$. ▨

**73.** $(x^2 + y^2 + z^2 + w^2)^{3/2} = 4$

**74.** $\ln(2x^2 + y - z^3 + 3w) = z$

**75.** $w^2 + w \sin xyz = 1$

**76.** $e^{xy} \sinh w - z^2 w + 1 = 0$

**77–80** Find $f_x$ and $f_y$.

**77.** $f(x, y) = \int_y^x e^{t^2} \, dt$      **78.** $f(x, y) = \int_1^{xy} e^{t^2} \, dt$

**79.** $f(x, y) = \int_0^{x^2 y^3} \sin t^3 \, dt$    **80.** $f(x, y) = \int_{x+y}^{x-y} \sin t^3 \, dt$

**81.** Let $z = \sqrt{x} \cos y$. Find
(a) $\partial^2 z / \partial x^2$          (b) $\partial^2 z / \partial y^2$
(c) $\partial^2 z / \partial x \partial y$       (d) $\partial^2 z / \partial y \partial x$.

**82.** Let $f(x, y) = 4x^2 - 2y + 7x^4 y^5$. Find
(a) $f_{xx}$    (b) $f_{yy}$    (c) $f_{xy}$    (d) $f_{yx}$.

**83.** Let $f(x, y) = \sin(3x^2 + 6y^2)$. Find
(a) $f_{xx}$    (b) $f_{yy}$    (c) $f_{xy}$    (d) $f_{yx}$.

**84.** Let $f(x, y) = xe^{2y}$. Find
(a) $f_{xx}$    (b) $f_{yy}$    (c) $f_{xy}$    (d) $f_{yx}$.

**85–92** Confirm that the mixed second-order partial derivatives of $f$ are the same.

**85.** $f(x, y) = 4x^2 - 8xy^4 + 7y^5 - 3$

**86.** $f(x, y) = \sqrt{x^2 + y^2}$    **87.** $f(x, y) = e^x \cos y$

**88.** $f(x, y) = e^{x-y^2}$      **89.** $f(x, y) = \ln(4x - 5y)$

**90.** $f(x, y) = \ln(x^2 + y^2)$

**91.** $f(x, y) = (x - y)/(x + y)$

**92.** $f(x, y) = (x^2 - y^2)/(x^2 + y^2)$

**93.** Express the following derivatives in "$\partial$" notation.
(a) $f_{xxx}$    (b) $f_{xyy}$    (c) $f_{yyxx}$    (d) $f_{xyyy}$

**94.** Express the derivatives in "subscript" notation.
(a) $\dfrac{\partial^3 f}{\partial y^2 \partial x}$   (b) $\dfrac{\partial^4 f}{\partial x^4}$   (c) $\dfrac{\partial^4 f}{\partial y^2 \partial x^2}$   (d) $\dfrac{\partial^5 f}{\partial x^2 \partial y^3}$

**95.** Given $f(x, y) = x^3 y^5 - 2x^2 y + x$, find
(a) $f_{xxy}$    (b) $f_{yxy}$    (c) $f_{yyy}$.

**96.** Given $z = (2x - y)^5$, find
(a) $\dfrac{\partial^3 z}{\partial y \partial x \partial y}$   (b) $\dfrac{\partial^3 z}{\partial x^2 \partial y}$   (c) $\dfrac{\partial^4 z}{\partial x^2 \partial y^2}$.

**97.** Given $f(x, y) = y^3 e^{-5x}$, find
(a) $f_{xyy}(0, 1)$    (b) $f_{xxx}(0, 1)$    (c) $f_{yyxx}(0, 1)$.

**98.** Given $w = e^y \cos x$, find
(a) $\dfrac{\partial^3 w}{\partial y^2 \partial x}\bigg|_{(\pi/4, 0)}$   (b) $\dfrac{\partial^3 w}{\partial x^2 \partial y}\bigg|_{(\pi/4, 0)}$

**99.** Let $f(x, y, z) = x^3 y^5 z^7 + xy^2 + y^3 z$. Find
(a) $f_{xy}$    (b) $f_{yz}$    (c) $f_{xz}$    (d) $f_{zz}$
(e) $f_{zyy}$    (f) $f_{xxy}$    (g) $f_{zyx}$    (h) $f_{xxyz}$.

**100.** Let $w = (4x - 3y + 2z)^5$. Find
(a) $\dfrac{\partial^2 w}{\partial x \partial z}$   (b) $\dfrac{\partial^3 w}{\partial x \partial y \partial z}$   (c) $\dfrac{\partial^4 w}{\partial z^2 \partial y \partial x}$.

**101.** Show that the function satisfies *Laplace's equation*
$$\frac{\partial^2 z}{\partial x^2} + \frac{\partial^2 z}{\partial y^2} = 0$$
(a) $z = x^2 - y^2 + 2xy$
(b) $z = e^x \sin y + e^y \cos x$
(c) $z = \ln(x^2 + y^2) + 2\tan^{-1}(y/x)$

**102.** Show that the function satisfies the *heat equation*
$$\frac{\partial z}{\partial t} = c^2 \frac{\partial^2 z}{\partial x^2} \quad (c > 0, \text{ constant})$$
(a) $z = e^{-t} \sin(x/c)$      (b) $z = e^{-t} \cos(x/c)$

**103.** Show that the function $u(x, t) = \sin c\omega t \sin \omega x$ satisfies the wave equation [Equation (6)] for all real values of $\omega$.

**104.** In each part, show that $u(x, y)$ and $v(x, y)$ satisfy the *Cauchy–Riemann equations*
$$\frac{\partial u}{\partial x} = \frac{\partial v}{\partial y} \quad \text{and} \quad \frac{\partial u}{\partial y} = -\frac{\partial v}{\partial x}$$
(a) $u = x^2 - y^2$,        $v = 2xy$
(b) $u = e^x \cos y$,      $v = e^x \sin y$
(c) $u = \ln(x^2 + y^2)$,   $v = 2\tan^{-1}(y/x)$

**105.** Show that if $u(x, y)$ and $v(x, y)$ each have equal mixed second partials, and if $u$ and $v$ satisfy the Cauchy–Riemann equations (Exercise 104), then $u$, $v$, and $u + v$ satisfy Laplace's equation (Exercise 101).

**106.** When two resistors having resistances $R_1$ ohms and $R_2$ ohms are connected in parallel, their combined resistance $R$ in ohms is $R = R_1 R_2 / (R_1 + R_2)$. Show that
$$\frac{\partial^2 R}{\partial R_1^2} \frac{\partial^2 R}{\partial R_2^2} = \frac{4R^2}{(R_1 + R_2)^4}$$

**107–110** Find the indicated partial derivatives.

**107.** $f(v, w, x, y) = 4v^2 w^3 x^4 y^5$;
$\partial f / \partial v, \ \partial f / \partial w, \ \partial f / \partial x, \ \partial f / \partial y$

**108.** $w = r \cos st + e^u \sin ur$;
$\partial w / \partial r, \ \partial w / \partial s, \ \partial w / \partial t, \ \partial w / \partial u$

**109.** $f(v_1, v_2, v_3, v_4) = \dfrac{v_1^2 - v_2^2}{v_3^2 + v_4^2}$;
$\partial f / \partial v_1, \ \partial f / \partial v_2, \ \partial f / \partial v_3, \ \partial f / \partial v_4$

**110.** $V = xe^{2x-y} + we^{zw} + yw$;
$\partial V / \partial x, \ \partial V / \partial y, \ \partial V / \partial z, \ \partial V / \partial w$

**111.** Let $u(w, x, y, z) = xe^{yw} \sin^2 z$. Find
(a) $\dfrac{\partial u}{\partial x}(0, 0, 1, \pi)$    (b) $\dfrac{\partial u}{\partial y}(0, 0, 1, \pi)$
(c) $\dfrac{\partial u}{\partial w}(0, 0, 1, \pi)$    (d) $\dfrac{\partial u}{\partial z}(0, 0, 1, \pi)$
(e) $\dfrac{\partial^4 u}{\partial x \partial y \partial w \partial z}$    (f) $\dfrac{\partial^4 u}{\partial w \partial z \partial y^2}$.

**112.** Let $f(v, w, x, y) = 2v^{1/2} w^4 x^{1/2} y^{2/3}$. Find $f_v(1, -2, 4, 8)$, $f_w(1, -2, 4, 8)$, $f_x(1, -2, 4, 8)$, and $f_y(1, -2, 4, 8)$.

**113–114** Find $\partial w / \partial x_i$ for $i = 1, 2, \dots, n$. ■

**113.** $w = \cos(x_1 + 2x_2 + \cdots + nx_n)$

**114.** $w = \left( \displaystyle\sum_{k=1}^{n} x_k \right)^{1/n}$

**115–116** Describe the largest set on which Theorem 13.3.2 can be used to prove that $f_{xy}$ and $f_{yx}$ are equal on that set. Then confirm by direct computation that $f_{xy} = f_{yx}$ on the given set.

**115.** (a) $f(x, y) = 4x^3 y + 3x^2 y$    (b) $f(x, y) = x^3 / y$

**116.** (a) $f(x, y) = \sqrt{x^2 + y^2 - 1}$
    (b) $f(x, y) = \sin(x^2 + y^3)$

**117.** Let $f(x, y) = 2x^2 - 3xy + y^2$. Find $f_x(2, -1)$ and $f_y(2, -1)$ by evaluating the limits in Definition 13.3.1. Then check your work by calculating the derivative in the usual way.

**118.** Let $f(x, y) = (x^2 + y^2)^{2/3}$. Show that

$$f_x(x, y) = \begin{cases} \dfrac{4x}{3(x^2 + y^2)^{1/3}}, & (x, y) \neq (0, 0) \\ 0, & (x, y) = (0, 0) \end{cases}$$

*Source:* This problem, due to Don Cohen, appeared in *Mathematics and Computer Education*, Vol. 25, No. 2, 1991, p. 179.

**119.** Let $f(x, y) = (x^3 + y^3)^{1/3}$.
 (a) Show that $f_y(0, 0) = 1$.
 (b) At what points, if any, does $f_y(x, y)$ fail to exist?

**120.** Writing Explain how one might use the graph of the equation $z = f(x, y)$ to determine the signs of $f_x(x_0, y_0)$ and $f_y(x_0, y_0)$ by inspection.

**121.** Writing Explain how one might use the graphs of some appropriate contours of $z = f(x, y)$ to determine the signs of $f_x(x_0, y_0)$ and $f_y(x_0, y_0)$ by inspection.

✔ **QUICK CHECK ANSWERS 13.3**

1. $\sin xy + xy \cos xy$; $x^2 \cos xy$    2. 9; 12    3. (a) $\frac{2}{3}\pi r h$ (b) $\frac{1}{3}\pi r^2 s$
4. $f_{xx}(x, y) = 2y^3$, $f_{yy}(x, y) = 6x^2 y$, $f_{xy}(x, y) = f_{yx}(x, y) = 6xy^2$

---

## 13.4  DIFFERENTIABILITY, DIFFERENTIALS, AND LOCAL LINEARITY

*In this section we will extend the notion of differentiability to functions of two or three variables. Our definition of differentiability will be based on the idea that a function is differentiable at a point provided it can be very closely approximated by a linear function near that point. In the process, we will expand the concept of a "differential" to functions of more than one variable and define the "local linear approximation" of a function.*

---

### ■ DIFFERENTIABILITY

Recall that a function $f$ of one variable is called differentiable at $x_0$ if it has a derivative at $x_0$, that is, if the limit

$$f'(x_0) = \lim_{\Delta x \to 0} \frac{f(x_0 + \Delta x) - f(x_0)}{\Delta x} \tag{1}$$

exists. As a consequence of (1) a differentiable function enjoys a number of other important properties:

- The graph of $y = f(x)$ has a nonvertical tangent line at the point $(x_0, f(x_0))$;
- $f$ may be closely approximated by a linear function near $x_0$ (Section 3.5);
- $f$ is continuous at $x_0$.

Our primary objective in this section is to extend the notion of differentiability to functions of two or three variables in such a way that the natural analogs of these properties hold. For example, if a function $f(x, y)$ of two variables is differentiable at a point $(x_0, y_0)$, we want it to be the case that

- the surface $z = f(x, y)$ has a nonvertical tangent plane at the point $(x_0, y_0, f(x_0, y_0))$ (Figure 13.4.1);
- the values of $f$ at points near $(x_0, y_0)$ can be very closely approximated by the values of a linear function;
- $f$ is continuous at $(x_0, y_0)$.

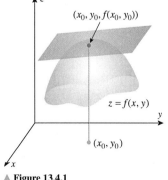

▲ **Figure 13.4.1**

One could reasonably conjecture that a function $f$ of two or three variables should be called differentiable at a point if all the first-order partial derivatives of the function exist at that point. Unfortunately, this condition is not strong enough to guarantee that the properties above hold. For instance, we saw in Example 9 of Section 13.3 that the mere existence of both first-order partial derivatives for a function is not sufficient to guarantee the continuity of the function. To determine what else we should include in our definition, it will be helpful to reexamine one of the consequences of differentiability for a *single-variable* function $f(x)$. Suppose that $f(x)$ is differentiable at $x = x_0$ and let

$$\Delta f = f(x_0 + \Delta x) - f(x_0)$$

denote the change in $f$ that corresponds to the change $\Delta x$ in $x$ from $x_0$ to $x_0 + \Delta x$. We saw in Section 3.5 that

$$\Delta f \approx f'(x_0)\Delta x$$

provided $\Delta x$ is close to 0. In fact, for $\Delta x$ close to 0 the error $\Delta f - f'(x_0)\Delta x$ in this approximation will have magnitude much smaller than that of $\Delta x$ because

$$\lim_{\Delta x \to 0} \frac{\Delta f - f'(x_0)\Delta x}{\Delta x} = \lim_{\Delta x \to 0} \left( \frac{f(x_0 + \Delta x) - f(x_0)}{\Delta x} - f'(x_0) \right) = f'(x_0) - f'(x_0) = 0$$

Since the magnitude of $\Delta x$ is just the distance between the points $x_0$ and $x_0 + \Delta x$, we see that when the two points are close together, the magnitude of the error in the approximation will be much smaller than the distance between the two points (Figure 13.4.2). The extension of this idea to functions of two or three variables is the "extra ingredient" needed in our definition of differentiability for multivariable functions.

For a function $f(x, y)$, the symbol $\Delta f$, called the ***increment*** of $f$, denotes the change in the value of $f(x, y)$ that results when $(x, y)$ varies from some initial position $(x_0, y_0)$ to some new position $(x_0 + \Delta x, y_0 + \Delta y)$; thus

$$\Delta f = f(x_0 + \Delta x, y_0 + \Delta y) - f(x_0, y_0) \tag{2}$$

(see Figure 13.4.3). [If a dependent variable $z = f(x, y)$ is used, then we will sometimes write $\Delta z$ rather than $\Delta f$.] Let us assume that both $f_x(x_0, y_0)$ and $f_y(x_0, y_0)$ exist and (by analogy with the one-variable case) make the approximation

$$\Delta f \approx f_x(x_0, y_0)\Delta x + f_y(x_0, y_0)\Delta y \tag{3}$$

For $\Delta x$ and $\Delta y$ close to 0, we would like the error

$$\Delta f - f_x(x_0, y_0)\Delta x - f_y(x_0, y_0)\Delta y$$

in this approximation to be much smaller than the distance $\sqrt{(\Delta x)^2 + (\Delta y)^2}$ between $(x_0, y_0)$ and $(x_0 + \Delta x, y_0 + \Delta y)$. We can guarantee this by requiring that

$$\lim_{(\Delta x, \Delta y) \to (0,0)} \frac{\Delta f - f_x(x_0, y_0)\Delta x - f_y(x_0, y_0)\Delta y}{\sqrt{(\Delta x)^2 + (\Delta y)^2}} = 0$$

> Show that if $f(x, y)$ is a linear function, then (3) becomes an equality.

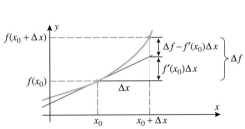

▲ **Figure 13.4.2**

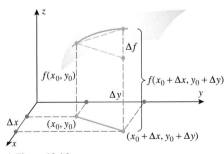

▲ **Figure 13.4.3**

Based on these ideas, we can now give our definition of differentiability for functions of two variables.

---

**13.4.1** DEFINITION    A function $f$ of two variables is said to be **differentiable** at $(x_0, y_0)$ provided $f_x(x_0, y_0)$ and $f_y(x_0, y_0)$ both exist and

$$\lim_{(\Delta x, \Delta y) \to (0,0)} \frac{\Delta f - f_x(x_0, y_0)\Delta x - f_y(x_0, y_0)\Delta y}{\sqrt{(\Delta x)^2 + (\Delta y)^2}} = 0 \tag{4}$$

---

As with the one-variable case, verification of differentiability using this definition involves the computation of a limit.

---

▶ **Example 1**    Use Definition 13.4.1 to prove that $f(x, y) = x^2 + y^2$ is differentiable at $(0, 0)$.

**Solution.**    The increment is

$$\Delta f = f(0 + \Delta x, 0 + \Delta y) - f(0, 0) = (\Delta x)^2 + (\Delta y)^2$$

Since $f_x(x, y) = 2x$ and $f_y(x, y) = 2y$, we have $f_x(0, 0) = f_y(0, 0) = 0$, and (4) becomes

$$\lim_{(\Delta x, \Delta y) \to (0,0)} \frac{(\Delta x)^2 + (\Delta y)^2}{\sqrt{(\Delta x)^2 + (\Delta y)^2}} = \lim_{(\Delta x, \Delta y) \to (0,0)} \sqrt{(\Delta x)^2 + (\Delta y)^2} = 0$$

Therefore, $f$ is differentiable at $(0, 0)$.    ◀

---

We now derive an important consequence of limit (4). Define a function

$$\epsilon = \epsilon(\Delta x, \Delta y) = \frac{\Delta f - f_x(x_0, y_0)\Delta x - f_y(x_0, y_0)\Delta y}{\sqrt{(\Delta x)^2 + (\Delta y)^2}} \quad \text{for } (\Delta x, \Delta y) \neq (0, 0)$$

and define $\epsilon(0, 0)$ to be 0. Equation (4) then implies that

$$\lim_{(\Delta x, \Delta y) \to (0,0)} \epsilon(\Delta x, \Delta y) = 0$$

Furthermore, it immediately follows from the definition of $\epsilon$ that

$$\Delta f = f_x(x_0, y_0)\Delta x + f_y(x_0, y_0)\Delta y + \epsilon\sqrt{(\Delta x)^2 + (\Delta y)^2} \tag{5}$$

In other words, if $f$ is differentiable at $(x_0, y_0)$, then $\Delta f$ may be expressed as shown in (5), where $\epsilon \to 0$ as $(\Delta x, \Delta y) \to (0, 0)$ and where $\epsilon = 0$ if $(\Delta x, \Delta y) = (0, 0)$.

For functions of three variables we have an analogous definition of differentiability in terms of the increment

$$\Delta f = f(x_0 + \Delta x, y_0 + \Delta y, z_0 + \Delta z) - f(x_0, y_0, z_0)$$

---

**13.4.2** DEFINITION    A function $f$ of three variables is said to be **differentiable** at $(x_0, y_0, z_0)$ provided $f_x(x_0, y_0, z_0)$, $f_y(x_0, y_0, z_0)$, and $f_z(x_0, y_0, z_0)$ exist and

$$\lim_{(\Delta x, \Delta y, \Delta z) \to (0,0,0)} \frac{\Delta f - f_x(x_0, y_0, z_0)\Delta x - f_y(x_0, y_0, z_0)\Delta y - f_z(x_0, y_0, z_0)\Delta z}{\sqrt{(\Delta x)^2 + (\Delta y)^2 + (\Delta z)^2}} = 0 \tag{6}$$

---

In a manner similar to the two-variable case, we can express the limit (6) in terms of a function $\epsilon(\Delta x, \Delta y, \Delta z)$ that vanishes at $(\Delta x, \Delta y, \Delta z) = (0, 0, 0)$ and is continuous there. The details are left as an exercise for the reader.

If a function $f$ of two variables is differentiable at each point of a region $R$ in the $xy$-plane, then we say that $f$ is **differentiable on R**; and if $f$ is differentiable at every point in the $xy$-plane, then we say that $f$ is **differentiable everywhere**. For a function $f$ of three variables we have corresponding conventions.

■ **DIFFERENTIABILITY AND CONTINUITY**

Recall that we want a function to be continuous at every point at which it is differentiable. The next result shows this to be the case.

---

**13.4.3 THEOREM** *If a function is differentiable at a point, then it is continuous at that point.*

---

**PROOF** We will give the proof for $f(x, y)$, a function of two variables, since that will reveal the essential ideas. Assume that $f$ is differentiable at $(x_0, y_0)$. To prove that $f$ is continuous at $(x_0, y_0)$ we must show that

$$\lim_{(x,y) \to (x_0,y_0)} f(x, y) = f(x_0, y_0)$$

which, on letting $x = x_0 + \Delta x$ and $y = y_0 + \Delta y$, is equivalent to

$$\lim_{(\Delta x,\Delta y) \to (0,0)} f(x_0 + \Delta x, y_0 + \Delta y) = f(x_0, y_0)$$

By Equation (2) this is equivalent to

$$\lim_{(\Delta x,\Delta y) \to (0,0)} \Delta f = 0$$

However, from Equation (5)

The converse of Theorem 13.4.3 is false. For example, the function

$$f(x, y) = \sqrt{x^2 + y^2}$$

is continuous at $(0, 0)$ but is not differentiable at $(0, 0)$. Why not?

$$\lim_{(\Delta x,\Delta y) \to (0,0)} \Delta f = \lim_{(\Delta x,\Delta y) \to (0,0)} \left[ f_x(x_0, y_0)\Delta x + f_y(x_0, y_0)\Delta y \right.$$
$$\left. + \epsilon(\Delta x, \Delta y)\sqrt{(\Delta x)^2 + (\Delta y)^2} \right]$$
$$= 0 + 0 + 0 \cdot 0 = 0 \ ■$$

It can be difficult to verify that a function is differentiable at a point directly from the definition. The next theorem, whose proof is usually studied in more advanced courses, provides simple conditions for a function to be differentiable at a point.

---

**13.4.4 THEOREM** *If all first-order partial derivatives of $f$ exist and are continuous at a point, then $f$ is differentiable at that point.*

---

For example, consider the function

$$f(x, y, z) = x + yz$$

Since $f_x(x, y, z) = 1$, $f_y(x, y, z) = z$, and $f_z(x, y, z) = y$ are defined and continuous everywhere, we conclude from Theorem 13.4.4 that $f$ is differentiable everywhere.

### ■ DIFFERENTIALS

As with the one-variable case, the approximations

$$\Delta f \approx f_x(x_0, y_0)\Delta x + f_y(x_0, y_0)\Delta y$$

for a function of two variables and the approximation

$$\Delta f \approx f_x(x_0, y_0, z_0)\Delta x + f_y(x_0, y_0, z_0)\Delta y + f_z(x_0, y_0, z_0)\Delta z \tag{7}$$

for a function of three variables have a convenient formulation in the language of differentials. If $z = f(x, y)$ is differentiable at a point $(x_0, y_0)$, we let

$$dz = f_x(x_0, y_0)\,dx + f_y(x_0, y_0)\,dy \tag{8}$$

denote a new function with dependent variable $dz$ and independent variables $dx$ and $dy$. We refer to this function (also denoted $df$) as the ***total differential of z*** at $(x_0, y_0)$ or as the ***total differential of f*** at $(x_0, y_0)$. Similarly, for a function $w = f(x, y, z)$ of three variables we have the ***total differential of w*** at $(x_0, y_0, z_0)$,

$$dw = f_x(x_0, y_0, z_0)\,dx + f_y(x_0, y_0, z_0)\,dy + f_z(x_0, y_0, z_0)\,dz \tag{9}$$

which is also referred to as the ***total differential of f*** at $(x_0, y_0, z_0)$. It is common practice to omit the subscripts and write Equations (8) and (9) as

$$dz = f_x(x, y)\,dx + f_y(x, y)\,dy \tag{10}$$

and

$$dw = f_x(x, y, z)\,dx + f_y(x, y, z)\,dy + f_z(x, y, z)\,dz \tag{11}$$

In the two-variable case, the approximation

$$\Delta f \approx f_x(x_0, y_0)\Delta x + f_y(x_0, y_0)\Delta y$$

can be written in the form

$$\Delta f \approx df \tag{12}$$

for $dx = \Delta x$ and $dy = \Delta y$. Equivalently, we can write approximation (12) as

$$\Delta z \approx dz \tag{13}$$

In other words, we can estimate the change $\Delta z$ in $z$ by the value of the differential $dz$ where $dx$ is the change in $x$ and $dy$ is the change in $y$. Furthermore, it follows from (4) that if $\Delta x$ and $\Delta y$ are close to 0, then the magnitude of the error in approximation (13) will be much smaller than the distance $\sqrt{(\Delta x)^2 + (\Delta y)^2}$ between $(x_0, y_0)$ and $(x_0 + \Delta x, y_0 + \Delta y)$.

---

▶ **Example 2** Use (13) to approximate the change in $z = xy^2$ from its value at $(0.5, 1.0)$ to its value at $(0.503, 1.004)$. Compare the magnitude of the error in this approximation with the distance between the points $(0.5, 1.0)$ and $(0.503, 1.004)$.

*Solution.* For $z = xy^2$ we have $dz = y^2\,dx + 2xy\,dy$. Evaluating this differential at $(x, y) = (0.5, 1.0), dx = \Delta x = 0.503 - 0.5 = 0.003$, and $dy = \Delta y = 1.004 - 1.0 = 0.004$ yields

$$dz = 1.0^2(0.003) + 2(0.5)(1.0)(0.004) = 0.007$$

Since $z = 0.5$ at $(x, y) = (0.5, 1.0)$ and $z = 0.507032048$ at $(x, y) = (0.503, 1.004)$, we have

$$\Delta z = 0.507032048 - 0.5 = 0.007032048$$

and the error in approximating $\Delta z$ by $dz$ has magnitude

$$|dz - \Delta z| = |0.007 - 0.007032048| = 0.000032048$$

Since the distance between $(0.5, 1.0)$ and $(0.503, 1.004) = (0.5 + \Delta x, 1.0 + \Delta y)$ is

$$\sqrt{(\Delta x)^2 + (\Delta y)^2} = \sqrt{(0.003)^2 + (0.004)^2} = \sqrt{0.000025} = 0.005$$

we have

$$\frac{|dz - \Delta z|}{\sqrt{(\Delta x)^2 + (\Delta y)^2}} = \frac{0.000032048}{0.005} = 0.0064096 < \frac{1}{150}$$

Thus, the magnitude of the error in our approximation is less than $\frac{1}{150}$ of the distance between the two points. ◄

With the appropriate changes in notation, the preceding analysis can be extended to functions of three or more variables.

▶ **Example 3**   The length, width, and height of a rectangular box are measured with an error of at most 5%. Use a total differential to estimate the maximum percentage error that results if these quantities are used to calculate the diagonal of the box.

*Solution.*   The diagonal $D$ of a box with length $x$, width $y$, and height $z$ is given by

$$D = \sqrt{x^2 + y^2 + z^2}$$

Let $x_0$, $y_0$, $z_0$, and $D_0 = \sqrt{x_0^2 + y_0^2 + z_0^2}$ denote the actual values of the length, width, height, and diagonal of the box. The total differential $dD$ of $D$ at $(x_0, y_0, z_0)$ is given by

$$dD = \frac{x_0}{\sqrt{x_0^2 + y_0^2 + z_0^2}} dx + \frac{y_0}{\sqrt{x_0^2 + y_0^2 + z_0^2}} dy + \frac{z_0}{\sqrt{x_0^2 + y_0^2 + z_0^2}} dz$$

If $x$, $y$, $z$, and $D = \sqrt{x^2 + y^2 + z^2}$ are the measured and computed values of the length, width, height, and diagonal, respectively, then

$$\Delta x = x - x_0, \quad \Delta y = y - y_0, \quad \Delta z = z - z_0$$

and

$$\left|\frac{\Delta x}{x_0}\right| \le 0.05, \quad \left|\frac{\Delta y}{y_0}\right| \le 0.05, \quad \left|\frac{\Delta z}{z_0}\right| \le 0.05$$

We are seeking an estimate for the maximum size of $\Delta D / D_0$. With the aid of Equation (11) we have

$$\frac{\Delta D}{D_0} \approx \frac{dD}{D_0} = \frac{1}{x_0^2 + y_0^2 + z_0^2}[x_0 \Delta x + y_0 \Delta y + z_0 \Delta z]$$

$$= \frac{1}{x_0^2 + y_0^2 + z_0^2}\left[x_0^2 \frac{\Delta x}{x_0} + y_0^2 \frac{\Delta y}{y_0} + z_0^2 \frac{\Delta z}{z_0}\right]$$

Since

$$\left|\frac{dD}{D_0}\right| = \frac{1}{x_0^2 + y_0^2 + z_0^2}\left|x_0^2 \frac{\Delta x}{x_0} + y_0^2 \frac{\Delta y}{y_0} + z_0^2 \frac{\Delta z}{z_0}\right|$$

$$\le \frac{1}{x_0^2 + y_0^2 + z_0^2}\left(x_0^2 \left|\frac{\Delta x}{x_0}\right| + y_0^2 \left|\frac{\Delta y}{y_0}\right| + z_0^2 \left|\frac{\Delta z}{z_0}\right|\right)$$

$$\le \frac{1}{x_0^2 + y_0^2 + z_0^2}\left(x_0^2(0.05) + y_0^2(0.05) + z_0^2(0.05)\right) = 0.05$$

we estimate the maximum percentage error in $D$ to be 5%. ◄

### ■ LOCAL LINEAR APPROXIMATIONS

We now show that if a function $f$ is differentiable at a point, then it can be very closely approximated by a linear function near that point. For example, suppose that $f(x, y)$ is differentiable at the point $(x_0, y_0)$. Then approximation (3) can be written in the form

$$f(x_0 + \Delta x, y_0 + \Delta y) \approx f(x_0, y_0) + f_x(x_0, y_0)\Delta x + f_y(x_0, y_0)\Delta y$$

If we let $x = x_0 + \Delta x$ and $y = x_0 + \Delta y$, this approximation becomes

$$f(x, y) \approx f(x_0, y_0) + f_x(x_0, y_0)(x - x_0) + f_y(x_0, y_0)(y - y_0) \tag{14}$$

Show that if $f(x, y)$ is a linear function, then (14) becomes an equality.

which yields a linear approximation of $f(x, y)$. Since the error in this approximation is equal to the error in approximation (3), we conclude that for $(x, y)$ close to $(x_0, y_0)$, the error in (14) will be much smaller than the distance between these two points. When $f(x, y)$ is differentiable at $(x_0, y_0)$ we get

Explain why the error in approximation (14) is the same as the error in approximation (3).

$$L(x, y) = f(x_0, y_0) + f_x(x_0, y_0)(x - x_0) + f_y(x_0, y_0)(y - y_0) \tag{15}$$

and refer to $L(x, y)$ as the **local linear approximation to $f$ at $(x_0, y_0)$**.

▶ **Example 4** Let $L(x, y)$ denote the local linear approximation to $f(x, y) = \sqrt{x^2 + y^2}$ at the point $(3, 4)$. Compare the error in approximating

$$f(3.04, 3.98) = \sqrt{(3.04)^2 + (3.98)^2}$$

by $L(3.04, 3.98)$ with the distance between the points $(3, 4)$ and $(3.04, 3.98)$.

*Solution.* We have

$$f_x(x, y) = \frac{x}{\sqrt{x^2 + y^2}} \quad \text{and} \quad f_y(x, y) = \frac{y}{\sqrt{x^2 + y^2}}$$

with $f_x(3, 4) = \frac{3}{5}$ and $f_y(3, 4) = \frac{4}{5}$. Therefore, the local linear approximation to $f$ at $(3, 4)$ is given by

$$L(x, y) = 5 + \tfrac{3}{5}(x - 3) + \tfrac{4}{5}(y - 4)$$

Consequently,

$$f(3.04, 3.98) \approx L(3.04, 3.98) = 5 + \tfrac{3}{5}(0.04) + \tfrac{4}{5}(-0.02) = 5.008$$

Since

$$f(3.04, 3.98) = \sqrt{(3.04)^2 + (3.98)^2} \approx 5.00819$$

the error in the approximation is about $5.00819 - 5.008 = 0.00019$. This is less than $\frac{1}{200}$ of the distance

$$\sqrt{(3.04 - 3)^2 + (3.98 - 4)^2} \approx 0.045$$

between the points $(3, 4)$ and $(3.04, 3.98)$. ◀

For a function $f(x, y, z)$ that is differentiable at $(x_0, y_0, z_0)$, the local linear approximation is

$$\begin{aligned} L(x, y, z) = {} & f(x_0, y_0, z_0) + f_x(x_0, y_0, z_0)(x - x_0) \\ & + f_y(x_0, y_0, z_0)(y - y_0) + f_z(x_0, y_0, z_0)(z - z_0) \end{aligned} \tag{16}$$

We have formulated our definitions in this section in such a way that continuity and local linearity are consequences of differentiability. In Section 13.7 we will show that if a function $f(x, y)$ is differentiable at a point $(x_0, y_0)$, then the graph of $L(x, y)$ is a nonvertical tangent plane to the graph of $f$ at the point $(x_0, y_0, f(x_0, y_0))$.

✔ **QUICK CHECK EXERCISES 13.4**   (See page 949 for answers.)

1. Assume that $f(x, y)$ is differentiable at $(x_0, y_0)$ and let $\Delta f$ denote the change in $f$ from its value at $(x_0, y_0)$ to its value at $(x_0 + \Delta x, y_0 + \Delta y)$.
   (a) $\Delta f \approx$ _____
   (b) The limit that guarantees the error in the approximation in part (a) is very small when both $\Delta x$ and $\Delta y$ are close to 0 is _____.

2. Compute the differential of each function.
   (a) $z = xe^{y^2}$   (b) $w = x \sin(yz)$

3. If $f$ is differentiable at $(x_0, y_0)$, then the local linear approximation to $f$ at $(x_0, y_0)$ is $L(x) =$ _____.

4. Assume that $f(1, -2) = 4$ and $f(x, y)$ is differentiable at $(1, -2)$ with $f_x(1, -2) = 2$ and $f_y(1, -2) = -3$. Estimate the value of $f(0.9, -1.950)$.

## EXERCISE SET 13.4

**FOCUS ON CONCEPTS**

1. Suppose that a function $f(x, y)$ is differentiable at the point $(3, 4)$ with $f_x(3, 4) = 2$ and $f_y(3, 4) = -1$. If $f(3, 4) = 5$, estimate the value of $f(3.01, 3.98)$.

2. Suppose that a function $f(x, y)$ is differentiable at the point $(-1, 2)$ with $f_x(-1, 2) = 1$ and $f_y(-1, 2) = 3$. If $f(-1, 2) = 2$, estimate the value of $f(-0.99, 2.02)$.

3. Suppose that a function $f(x, y, z)$ is differentiable at the point $(1, 2, 3)$ with $f_x(1, 2, 3) = 1$, $f_y(1, 2, 3) = 2$, and $f_z(1, 2, 3) = 3$. If $f(1, 2, 3) = 4$, estimate the value of $f(1.01, 2.02, 3.03)$.

4. Suppose that a function $f(x, y, z)$ is differentiable at the point $(2, 1, -2)$, $f_x(2, 1, -2) = -1$, $f_y(2, 1, -2) = 1$, and $f_z(2, 1, -2) = -2$. If $f(2, 1, -2) = 0$, estimate the value of $f(1.98, 0.99, -1.97)$.

5. Use Definitions 13.4.1 and 13.4.2 to prove that a constant function of two or three variables is differentiable everywhere.

6. Use Definitions 13.4.1 and 13.4.2 to prove that a linear function of two or three variables is differentiable everywhere.

7. Use Definition 13.4.2 to prove that
   $$f(x, y, z) = x^2 + y^2 + z^2$$
   is differentiable at $(0, 0, 0)$.

8. Use Definition 13.4.2 to determine all values of $r$ such that $f(x, y, z) = (x^2 + y^2 + z^2)^r$ is differentiable at $(0, 0, 0)$.

**9–20** Compute the differential $dz$ or $dw$ of the function. ▨

9. $z = 7x - 2y$   10. $z = e^{xy}$   11. $z = x^3 y^2$

12. $z = 5x^2 y^5 - 2x + 4y + 7$

13. $z = \tan^{-1} xy$   14. $z = e^{-3x} \cos 6y$

15. $w = 8x - 3y + 4z$   16. $w = e^{xyz}$

17. $w = x^3 y^2 z$

18. $w = 4x^2 y^3 z^7 - 3xy + z + 5$

19. $w = \tan^{-1}(xyz)$   20. $w = \sqrt{x} + \sqrt{y} + \sqrt{z}$

**21–26** Use a total differential to approximate the change in the values of $f$ from $P$ to $Q$. Compare your estimate with the actual change in $f$. ▨

21. $f(x, y) = x^2 + 2xy - 4x$;  $P(1, 2)$, $Q(1.01, 2.04)$

22. $f(x, y) = x^{1/3} y^{1/2}$;  $P(8, 9)$, $Q(7.78, 9.03)$

23. $f(x, y) = \dfrac{x + y}{xy}$;  $P(-1, -2)$, $Q(-1.02, -2.04)$

24. $f(x, y) = \ln \sqrt{1 + xy}$;  $P(0, 2)$, $Q(-0.09, 1.98)$

25. $f(x, y, z) = 2xy^2 z^3$;  $P(1, -1, 2)$, $Q(0.99, -1.02, 2.02)$

26. $f(x, y, z) = \dfrac{xyz}{x + y + z}$;  $P(-1, -2, 4)$,
    $Q(-1.04, -1.98, 3.97)$

**27–30 True–False** Determine whether the statement is true or false. Explain your answer. ▨

27. By definition, a function $f(x, y)$ is differentiable at $(x_0, y_0)$ provided both $f_x(x_0, y_0)$ and $f_y(x_0, y_0)$ are defined.

28. For any point $(x_0, y_0)$ in the domain of a function $f(x, y)$, we have
    $$\lim_{(\Delta x, \Delta y) \to (0,0)} \Delta f = 0$$
    where
    $$\Delta f = f(x_0 + \Delta x, y_0 + \Delta y) - f(x_0, y_0)$$

29. If $f_x$ and $f_y$ are both continuous at $(x_0, y_0)$, then so is $f$.

30. The graph of a local linear approximation to a function $f(x, y)$ is a plane.

**31.** In the accompanying figure a rectangle with initial length $x_0$ and initial width $y_0$ has been enlarged, resulting in a rectangle with length $x_0 + \Delta x$ and width $y_0 + \Delta y$. What portion of the figure represents the increase in the area of the rectangle? What portion of the figure represents an approximation of the increase in area by a total differential?

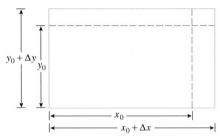

▲ **Figure Ex-31**

**32.** The volume $V$ of a right circular cone of radius $r$ and height $h$ is given by $V = \frac{1}{3}\pi r^2 h$. Suppose that the height decreases from 20 in to 19.95 in and the radius increases from 4 in to 4.05 in. Compare the change in volume of the cone with an approximation of this change using a total differential.

**33–40** (a) Find the local linear approximation $L$ to the specified function $f$ at the designated point $P$. (b) Compare the error in approximating $f$ by $L$ at the specified point $Q$ with the distance between $P$ and $Q$.

**33.** $f(x, y) = \dfrac{1}{\sqrt{x^2 + y^2}}$;   $P(4, 3)$, $Q(3.92, 3.01)$

**34.** $f(x, y) = x^{0.5}y^{0.3}$;   $P(1, 1)$, $Q(1.05, 0.97)$

**35.** $f(x, y) = x \sin y$;   $P(0, 0)$, $Q(0.003, 0.004)$

**36.** $f(x, y) = \ln xy$;   $P(1, 2)$, $Q(1.01, 2.02)$

**37.** $f(x, y, z) = xyz$;   $P(1, 2, 3)$, $Q(1.001, 2.002, 3.003)$

**38.** $f(x, y, z) = \dfrac{x + y}{y + z}$;   $P(-1, 1, 1)$, $Q(-0.99, 0.99, 1.01)$

**39.** $f(x, y, z) = xe^{yz}$;   $P(1, -1, -1)$, $Q(0.99, -1.01, -0.99)$

**40.** $f(x, y, z) = \ln(x + yz)$;   $P(2, 1, -1)$, $Q(2.02, 0.97, -1.01)$

**41.** In each part, confirm that the stated formula is the local linear approximation at $(0, 0)$.

(a) $e^x \sin y \approx y$   (b) $\dfrac{2x + 1}{y + 1} \approx 1 + 2x - y$

**42.** Show that the local linear approximation of the function $f(x, y) = x^\alpha y^\beta$ at $(1, 1)$ is

$$x^\alpha y^\beta \approx 1 + \alpha(x - 1) + \beta(y - 1)$$

**43.** In each part, confirm that the stated formula is the local linear approximation at $(1, 1, 1)$.

(a) $xyz + 2 \approx x + y + z$   (b) $\dfrac{4x}{y + z} \approx 2x - y - z + 2$

**44.** Based on Exercise 42, what would you conjecture is the local linear approximation to $x^\alpha y^\beta z^\gamma$ at $(1, 1, 1)$? Verify your conjecture by finding this local linear approximation.

**45.** Suppose that a function $f(x, y)$ is differentiable at the point $(1, 1)$ with $f_x(1, 1) = 2$ and $f(1, 1) = 3$. Let $L(x, y)$ denote the local linear approximation of $f$ at $(1, 1)$. If $L(1.1, 0.9) = 3.15$, find the value of $f_y(1, 1)$.

**46.** Suppose that a function $f(x, y)$ is differentiable at the point $(0, -1)$ with $f_y(0, -1) = -2$ and $f(0, -1) = 3$. Let $L(x, y)$ denote the local linear approximation of $f$ at $(0, -1)$. If $L(0.1, -1.1) = 3.3$, find the value of $f_x(0, -1)$.

**47.** Suppose that a function $f(x, y, z)$ is differentiable at the point $(3, 2, 1)$ and $L(x, y, z) = x - y + 2z - 2$ is the local linear approximation to $f$ at $(3, 2, 1)$. Find $f(3, 2, 1)$, $f_x(3, 2, 1)$, $f_y(3, 2, 1)$, and $f_z(3, 2, 1)$.

**48.** Suppose that a function $f(x, y, z)$ is differentiable at the point $(0, -1, -2)$ and $L(x, y, z) = x + 2y + 3z + 4$ is the local linear approximation to $f$ at $(0, -1, -2)$. Find $f(0, -1, -2)$, $f_x(0, -1, -2)$, $f_y(0, -1, -2)$, and $f_z(0, -1, -2)$.

**49–52** A function $f$ is given along with a local linear approximation $L$ to $f$ at a point $P$. Use the information given to determine point $P$.

**49.** $f(x, y) = x^2 + y^2$;  $L(x, y) = 2y - 2x - 2$

**50.** $f(x, y) = x^2 y$;  $L(x, y) = 4y - 4x + 8$

**51.** $f(x, y, z) = xy + z^2$;  $L(x, y, z) = y + 2z - 1$

**52.** $f(x, y, z) = xyz$;  $L(x, y, z) = x - y - z - 2$

**53.** The length and width of a rectangle are measured with errors of at most 3% and 5%, respectively. Use differentials to approximate the maximum percentage error in the calculated area.

**54.** The radius and height of a right circular cone are measured with errors of at most 1% and 4%, respectively. Use differentials to approximate the maximum percentage error in the calculated volume.

**55.** The length and width of a rectangle are measured with errors of at most $r$%, where $r$ is small. Use differentials to approximate the maximum percentage error in the calculated length of the diagonal.

**56.** The legs of a right triangle are measured to be 3 cm and 4 cm, with a maximum error of 0.05 cm in each measurement. Use differentials to approximate the maximum possible error in the calculated value of (a) the hypotenuse and (b) the area of the triangle.

**57.** The period $T$ of a simple pendulum with small oscillations is calculated from the formula $T = 2\pi\sqrt{L/g}$, where $L$ is the length of the pendulum and $g$ is the acceleration due to gravity. Suppose that measured values of $L$ and $g$ have errors of at most 0.5% and 0.1%, respectively. Use differentials to approximate the maximum percentage error in the calculated value of $T$.

**58.** According to the ideal gas law, the pressure, temperature, and volume of a confined gas are related by $P = kT/V$, where $k$ is a constant. Use differentials to approximate the percentage change in pressure if the temperature of a gas is increased 3% and the volume is increased 5%.

**59.** Suppose that certain measured quantities $x$ and $y$ have errors of at most $r\%$ and $s\%$, respectively. For each of the following formulas in $x$ and $y$, use differentials to approximate the maximum possible error in the calculated result.
(a) $xy$   (b) $x/y$   (c) $x^2 y^3$   (d) $x^3 \sqrt{y}$

**60.** The total resistance $R$ of three resistances $R_1$, $R_2$, and $R_3$, connected in parallel, is given by
$$\frac{1}{R} = \frac{1}{R_1} + \frac{1}{R_2} + \frac{1}{R_3}$$
Suppose that $R_1$, $R_2$, and $R_3$ are measured to be 100 ohms, 200 ohms, and 500 ohms, respectively, with a maximum error of 10% in each. Use differentials to approximate the maximum percentage error in the calculated value of $R$.

**61.** The area of a triangle is to be computed from the formula $A = \frac{1}{2}ab \sin \theta$, where $a$ and $b$ are the lengths of two sides and $\theta$ is the included angle. Suppose that $a$, $b$, and $\theta$ are measured to be 40 ft, 50 ft, and 30°, respectively. Use differentials to approximate the maximum error in the calculated value of $A$ if the maximum errors in $a$, $b$, and $\theta$ are $\frac{1}{2}$ ft, $\frac{1}{4}$ ft, and 2°, respectively.

**62.** The length, width, and height of a rectangular box are measured with errors of at most $r\%$ (where $r$ is small). Use differentials to approximate the maximum percentage error in the computed value of the volume.

**63.** Use Theorem 13.4.4 to prove that $f(x, y) = x^2 \sin y$ is differentiable everywhere.

**64.** Use Theorem 13.4.4 to prove that $f(x, y, z) = xy \sin z$ is differentiable everywhere.

**65.** Suppose that $f(x, y)$ is differentiable at the point $(x_0, y_0)$ and let $z_0 = f(x_0, y_0)$. Prove that $g(x, y, z) = z - f(x, y)$ is differentiable at $(x_0, y_0, z_0)$.

**66.** Suppose that $\Delta f$ satisfies an equation in the form of (5), where $\epsilon(\Delta x, \Delta y)$ is continuous at $(\Delta x, \Delta y) = (0, 0)$ with $\epsilon(0, 0) = 0$. Prove that $f$ is differentiable at $(x_0, y_0)$.

**67.** Writing Discuss the similarities and differences between the definition of "differentiability" for a function of a single variable and the definition of "differentiability" for a function of two variables.

**68.** Writing Discuss the use of differentials in the approximation of increments and in the estimation of errors.

✔ **QUICK CHECK ANSWERS 13.4**

**1.** (a) $f_x(x_0, y_0)\Delta x + f_y(x_0, y_0)\Delta y$   (b) $\displaystyle\lim_{(\Delta x, \Delta y) \to (0,0)} \frac{\Delta f - f_x(x_0, y_0)\Delta x - f_y(x_0, y_0)\Delta y}{\sqrt{(\Delta x)^2 + (\Delta y)^2}} = 0$   **2.** (a) $dz = e^{y^2} dx + 2xye^{y^2} dy$

(b) $dw = \sin(yz)\, dx + xz\cos(yz)\, dy + xy\cos(yz)\, dz$   **3.** $f(x_0, y_0) + f_x(x_0, y_0)(x - x_0) + f_y(x_0, y_0)(y - y_0)$   **4.** 3.65

## 13.5  THE CHAIN RULE

*In this section we will derive versions of the chain rule for functions of two or three variables. These new versions will allow us to generate useful relationships among the derivatives and partial derivatives of various functions.*

### ▨ CHAIN RULES FOR DERIVATIVES

If $y$ is a differentiable function of $x$ and $x$ is a differentiable function of $t$, then the chain rule for functions of one variable states that, under composition, $y$ becomes a differentiable function of $t$ with
$$\frac{dy}{dt} = \frac{dy}{dx}\frac{dx}{dt}$$

We will now derive a version of the chain rule for functions of two variables.

Assume that $z = f(x, y)$ is a function of $x$ and $y$, and suppose that $x$ and $y$ are in turn functions of a single variable $t$, say
$$x = x(t), \quad y = y(t)$$

The composition $z = f(x(t), y(t))$ then expresses $z$ as a function of the single variable $t$. Thus, we can ask for the derivative $dz/dt$ and we can inquire about its relationship to the derivatives $\partial z/\partial x$, $\partial z/\partial y$, $dx/dt$, and $dy/dt$. Letting $\Delta x$, $\Delta y$, and $\Delta z$ denote the changes in $x$, $y$, and $z$, respectively, that correspond to a change of $\Delta t$ in $t$, we have

$$\frac{dz}{dt} = \lim_{\Delta t \to 0} \frac{\Delta z}{\Delta t}, \quad \frac{dx}{dt} = \lim_{\Delta t \to 0} \frac{\Delta x}{\Delta t}, \quad \text{and} \quad \frac{dy}{dt} = \lim_{\Delta t \to 0} \frac{\Delta y}{\Delta t}$$

It follows from (3) of Section 13.4 that

$$\Delta z \approx \frac{\partial z}{\partial x} \Delta x + \frac{\partial z}{\partial y} \Delta y \tag{1}$$

where the partial derivatives are evaluated at $(x(t), y(t))$. Dividing both sides of (1) by $\Delta t$ yields

$$\frac{\Delta z}{\Delta t} \approx \frac{\partial z}{\partial x} \frac{\Delta x}{\Delta t} + \frac{\partial z}{\partial y} \frac{\Delta y}{\Delta t} \tag{2}$$

Similarly, we can produce the analog of (2) for functions of three variables as follows: assume that $w = f(x, y, z)$ is a function of $x$, $y$, and $z$, and suppose that $x$, $y$, and $z$ are functions of a single variable $t$. As above we define $\Delta w$, $\Delta x$, $\Delta y$, and $\Delta z$ to be the changes in $w$, $x$, $y$, and $z$ that correspond to a change of $\Delta t$ in $t$. Then (7) in Section 13.4 implies that

$$\Delta w \approx \frac{\partial w}{\partial x} \Delta x + \frac{\partial w}{\partial y} \Delta y + \frac{\partial w}{\partial z} \Delta z \tag{3}$$

and dividing both sides of (3) by $\Delta t$ yields

$$\frac{\Delta w}{\Delta t} \approx \frac{\partial w}{\partial x} \frac{\Delta x}{\Delta t} + \frac{\partial w}{\partial y} \frac{\Delta y}{\Delta t} + \frac{\partial w}{\partial z} \frac{\Delta z}{\Delta t} \tag{4}$$

Taking the limit as $\Delta t \to 0$ of both sides of (2) and (4) suggests the following results. (A complete proof of the two-variable case can be found in Appendix D.)

---

**13.5.1 THEOREM (Chain Rules for Derivatives)** *If $x = x(t)$ and $y = y(t)$ are differentiable at $t$, and if $z = f(x, y)$ is differentiable at the point $(x, y) = (x(t), y(t))$, then $z = f(x(t), y(t))$ is differentiable at $t$ and*

$$\frac{dz}{dt} = \frac{\partial z}{\partial x} \frac{dx}{dt} + \frac{\partial z}{\partial y} \frac{dy}{dt} \tag{5}$$

*where the ordinary derivatives are evaluated at $t$ and the partial derivatives are evaluated at $(x, y)$.*

*If each of the functions $x = x(t)$, $y = y(t)$, and $z = z(t)$ is differentiable at $t$, and if $w = f(x, y, z)$ is differentiable at the point $(x, y, z) = (x(t), y(t), z(t))$, then the function $w = f(x(t), y(t), z(t))$ is differentiable at $t$ and*

$$\frac{dw}{dt} = \frac{\partial w}{\partial x} \frac{dx}{dt} + \frac{\partial w}{\partial y} \frac{dy}{dt} + \frac{\partial w}{\partial z} \frac{dz}{dt} \tag{6}$$

*where the ordinary derivatives are evaluated at $t$ and the partial derivatives are evaluated at $(x, y, z)$.*

---

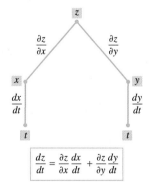

$$\frac{dz}{dt} = \frac{\partial z}{\partial x} \frac{dx}{dt} + \frac{\partial z}{\partial y} \frac{dy}{dt}$$

▲ **Figure 13.5.1**

Formula (5) can be represented schematically by a "tree diagram" that is constructed as follows (Figure 13.5.1). Starting with $z$ at the top of the tree and moving downward, join each variable by lines (or branches) to those variables on which it depends *directly*. Thus, $z$ is joined to $x$ and $y$ and these in turn are joined to $t$. Next, label each branch with a derivative whose "numerator" contains the variable at the top end of that branch and whose "denominator" contains the variable at the bottom end of that branch. This completes the "tree." To find the formula for $dz/dt$, follow the two paths through the tree that start with $z$ and end with $t$. Each such path corresponds to a term in Formula (5).

*Create a tree diagram for Formula (6).*

▶ **Example 1**  Suppose that

$$z = x^2 y, \quad x = t^2, \quad y = t^3$$

Use the chain rule to find $dz/dt$, and check the result by expressing $z$ as a function of $t$ and differentiating directly.

*Solution.*  By the chain rule [Formula (5)],

$$\frac{dz}{dt} = \frac{\partial z}{\partial x}\frac{dx}{dt} + \frac{\partial z}{\partial y}\frac{dy}{dt} = (2xy)(2t) + (x^2)(3t^2)$$

$$= (2t^5)(2t) + (t^4)(3t^2) = 7t^6$$

Alternatively, we can express $z$ directly as a function of $t$,

$$z = x^2 y = (t^2)^2(t^3) = t^7$$

and then differentiate to obtain $dz/dt = 7t^6$. However, this procedure may not always be convenient. ◀

▶ **Example 2**  Suppose that

$$w = \sqrt{x^2 + y^2 + z^2}, \quad x = \cos\theta, \quad y = \sin\theta, \quad z = \tan\theta$$

Use the chain rule to find $dw/d\theta$ when $\theta = \pi/4$.

*Solution.*  From Formula (6) with $\theta$ in the place of $t$, we obtain

$$\frac{dw}{d\theta} = \frac{\partial w}{\partial x}\frac{dx}{d\theta} + \frac{\partial w}{\partial y}\frac{dy}{d\theta} + \frac{\partial w}{\partial z}\frac{dz}{d\theta}$$

$$= \frac{1}{2}(x^2 + y^2 + z^2)^{-1/2}(2x)(-\sin\theta) + \frac{1}{2}(x^2 + y^2 + z^2)^{-1/2}(2y)(\cos\theta)$$

$$+ \frac{1}{2}(x^2 + y^2 + z^2)^{-1/2}(2z)(\sec^2\theta)$$

When $\theta = \pi/4$, we have

$$x = \cos\frac{\pi}{4} = \frac{1}{\sqrt{2}}, \quad y = \sin\frac{\pi}{4} = \frac{1}{\sqrt{2}}, \quad z = \tan\frac{\pi}{4} = 1$$

*Confirm the result of Example 2 by expressing $w$ directly as a function of $\theta$.*

Substituting $x = 1/\sqrt{2}, y = 1/\sqrt{2}, z = 1, \theta = \pi/4$ in the formula for $dw/d\theta$ yields

$$\frac{dw}{d\theta}\bigg|_{\theta=\pi/4} = \frac{1}{2}\left(\frac{1}{\sqrt{2}}\right)(\sqrt{2})\left(-\frac{1}{\sqrt{2}}\right) + \frac{1}{2}\left(\frac{1}{\sqrt{2}}\right)(\sqrt{2})\left(\frac{1}{\sqrt{2}}\right) + \frac{1}{2}\left(\frac{1}{\sqrt{2}}\right)(2)(2)$$

$$= \sqrt{2} \blacktriangleleft$$

REMARK | There are many variations in derivative notations, each of which gives the chain rule a different look. If $z = f(x, y)$, where $x$ and $y$ are functions of $t$, then some possibilities are

$$\frac{dz}{dt} = f_x \frac{dx}{dt} + f_y \frac{dy}{dt}$$

$$\frac{df}{dt} = \frac{\partial f}{\partial x}\frac{dx}{dt} + \frac{\partial f}{\partial y}\frac{dy}{dt}$$

$$\frac{df}{dt} = f_x x'(t) + f_y y'(t)$$

## CHAIN RULES FOR PARTIAL DERIVATIVES

In Formula (5) the variables $x$ and $y$ are each functions of a single variable $t$. We now consider the case where $x$ and $y$ are each functions of two variables. Let $z = f(x, y)$ and suppose that $x$ and $y$ are functions of $u$ and $v$, say

$$x = x(u, v), \quad y = y(u, v)$$

The composition $z = f(x(u, v), y(u, v))$ expresses $z$ as a function of the two variables $u$ and $v$. Thus, we can ask for the partial derivatives $\partial z / \partial u$ and $\partial z / \partial v$; and we can inquire about the relationship between these derivatives and the derivatives $\partial z / \partial x$, $\partial z / \partial y$, $\partial x / \partial u$, $\partial x / \partial v$, $\partial y / \partial u$, and $\partial y / \partial v$.

Similarly, if $w = f(x, y, z)$ and $x$, $y$, and $z$ are each functions of $u$ and $v$, then the composition $w = f(x(u, v), y(u, v), z(u, v))$ expresses $w$ as a function of $u$ and $v$. Thus we can also ask for the derivatives $\partial w / \partial u$ and $\partial w / \partial v$; and we can investigate the relationship between these derivatives, the partial derivatives $\partial w / \partial x$, $\partial w / \partial y$, and $\partial w / \partial z$, and the partial derivatives of $x$, $y$, and $z$ with respect to $u$ and $v$.

---

**13.5.2  THEOREM** (*Chain Rules for Partial Derivatives*)  *If $x = x(u, v)$ and $y = y(u, v)$ have first-order partial derivatives at the point $(u, v)$, and if $z = f(x, y)$ is differentiable at the point $(x, y) = (x(u, v), y(u, v))$, then $z = f(x(u, v), y(u, v))$ has first-order partial derivatives at the point $(u, v)$ given by*

$$\frac{\partial z}{\partial u} = \frac{\partial z}{\partial x}\frac{\partial x}{\partial u} + \frac{\partial z}{\partial y}\frac{\partial y}{\partial u} \quad \text{and} \quad \frac{\partial z}{\partial v} = \frac{\partial z}{\partial x}\frac{\partial x}{\partial v} + \frac{\partial z}{\partial y}\frac{\partial y}{\partial v} \tag{7–8}$$

*If each function $x = x(u, v)$, $y = y(u, v)$, and $z = z(u, v)$ has first-order partial derivatives at the point $(u, v)$, and if the function $w = f(x, y, z)$ is differentiable at the point $(x, y, z) = (x(u, v), y(u, v), z(u, v))$, then $w = f(x(u, v), y(u, v), z(u, v))$ has first-order partial derivatives at the point $(u, v)$ given by*

$$\frac{\partial w}{\partial u} = \frac{\partial w}{\partial x}\frac{\partial x}{\partial u} + \frac{\partial w}{\partial y}\frac{\partial y}{\partial u} + \frac{\partial w}{\partial z}\frac{\partial z}{\partial u} \quad \text{and} \quad \frac{\partial w}{\partial v} = \frac{\partial w}{\partial x}\frac{\partial x}{\partial v} + \frac{\partial w}{\partial y}\frac{\partial y}{\partial v} + \frac{\partial w}{\partial z}\frac{\partial z}{\partial v}$$

$$\tag{9–10}$$

---

PROOF  We will prove Formula (7); the other formulas are derived similarly. If $v$ is held fixed, then $x = x(u, v)$ and $y = y(u, v)$ become functions of $u$ alone. Thus, we are back to the case of Theorem 13.5.1. If we apply that theorem with $u$ in place of $t$, and if we use $\partial$ rather than $d$ to indicate that the variable $v$ is fixed, we obtain

$$\frac{\partial z}{\partial u} = \frac{\partial z}{\partial x}\frac{\partial x}{\partial u} + \frac{\partial z}{\partial y}\frac{\partial y}{\partial u} \quad \blacksquare$$

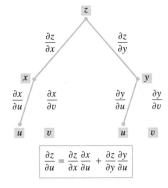

$$\frac{\partial z}{\partial u} = \frac{\partial z}{\partial x}\frac{\partial x}{\partial u} + \frac{\partial z}{\partial y}\frac{\partial y}{\partial u}$$

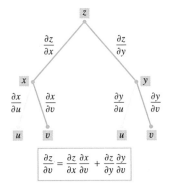

$$\frac{\partial z}{\partial v} = \frac{\partial z}{\partial x}\frac{\partial x}{\partial v} + \frac{\partial z}{\partial y}\frac{\partial y}{\partial v}$$

▲ **Figure 13.5.2**

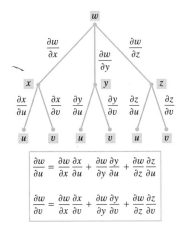

$$\frac{\partial w}{\partial u} = \frac{\partial w}{\partial x}\frac{\partial x}{\partial u} + \frac{\partial w}{\partial y}\frac{\partial y}{\partial u} + \frac{\partial w}{\partial z}\frac{\partial z}{\partial u}$$

$$\frac{\partial w}{\partial v} = \frac{\partial w}{\partial x}\frac{\partial x}{\partial v} + \frac{\partial w}{\partial y}\frac{\partial y}{\partial v} + \frac{\partial w}{\partial z}\frac{\partial z}{\partial v}$$

▲ **Figure 13.5.3**

Figures 13.5.2 and 13.5.3 show tree diagrams for the formulas in Theorem 13.5.2. As illustrated in Figure 13.5.2, the formula for $\partial z/\partial u$ can be obtained by tracing all paths through the tree that start with $z$ and end with $u$, and the formula for $\partial z/\partial v$ can be obtained by tracing all paths through the tree that start with $z$ and end with $v$. Figure 13.5.3 displays analogous results for $\partial w/\partial u$ and $\partial w/\partial v$.

▶ **Example 3**  Given that

$$z = e^{xy}, \quad x = 2u + v, \quad y = u/v$$

find $\partial z/\partial u$ and $\partial z/\partial v$ using the chain rule.

*Solution.*

$$\frac{\partial z}{\partial u} = \frac{\partial z}{\partial x}\frac{\partial x}{\partial u} + \frac{\partial z}{\partial y}\frac{\partial y}{\partial u} = (ye^{xy})(2) + (xe^{xy})\left(\frac{1}{v}\right) = \left[2y + \frac{x}{v}\right]e^{xy}$$

$$= \left[\frac{2u}{v} + \frac{2u+v}{v}\right]e^{(2u+v)(u/v)} = \left[\frac{4u}{v} + 1\right]e^{(2u+v)(u/v)}$$

$$\frac{\partial z}{\partial v} = \frac{\partial z}{\partial x}\frac{\partial x}{\partial v} + \frac{\partial z}{\partial y}\frac{\partial y}{\partial v} = (ye^{xy})(1) + (xe^{xy})\left(-\frac{u}{v^2}\right)$$

$$= \left[y - x\left(\frac{u}{v^2}\right)\right]e^{xy} = \left[\frac{u}{v} - (2u+v)\left(\frac{u}{v^2}\right)\right]e^{(2u+v)(u/v)}$$

$$= -\frac{2u^2}{v^2}e^{(2u+v)(u/v)} \quad ◀$$

▶ **Example 4**  Suppose that

$$w = e^{xyz}, \quad x = 3u + v, \quad y = 3u - v, \quad z = u^2v$$

Use appropriate forms of the chain rule to find $\partial w/\partial u$ and $\partial w/\partial v$.

*Solution.*  From the tree diagram and corresponding formulas in Figure 13.5.3 we obtain

$$\frac{\partial w}{\partial u} = yze^{xyz}(3) + xze^{xyz}(3) + xye^{xyz}(2uv) = e^{xyz}(3yz + 3xz + 2xyuv)$$

and

$$\frac{\partial w}{\partial v} = yze^{xyz}(1) + xze^{xyz}(-1) + xye^{xyz}(u^2) = e^{xyz}(yz - xz + xyu^2)$$

If desired, we can express $\partial w/\partial u$ and $\partial w/\partial v$ in terms of $u$ and $v$ alone by replacing $x$, $y$, and $z$ by their expressions in terms of $u$ and $v$.  ◀

■ **OTHER VERSIONS OF THE CHAIN RULE**
Although we will not prove it, the chain rule extends to functions $w = f(v_1, v_2, \ldots, v_n)$ of $n$ variables. For example, if each $v_i$ is a function of $t$, $i = 1, 2, \ldots, n$, the relevant formula is

$$\frac{dw}{dt} = \frac{\partial w}{\partial v_1}\frac{dv_1}{dt} + \frac{\partial w}{\partial v_2}\frac{dv_2}{dt} + \cdots + \frac{\partial w}{\partial v_n}\frac{dv_n}{dt} \tag{11}$$

Note that (11) is a natural extension of Formulas (5) and (6) in Theorem 13.5.1.

There are infinitely many variations of the chain rule, depending on the number of variables and the choice of independent and dependent variables. A good working procedure is to use tree diagrams to derive new versions of the chain rule as needed.

▶ **Example 5**    Suppose that $w = x^2 + y^2 - z^2$ and

$$x = \rho \sin\phi \cos\theta, \quad y = \rho \sin\phi \sin\theta, \quad z = \rho \cos\phi$$

Use appropriate forms of the chain rule to find $\partial w/\partial \rho$ and $\partial w/\partial \theta$.

*Solution.*    From the tree diagram and corresponding formulas in Figure 13.5.4 we obtain

$$\frac{\partial w}{\partial \rho} = 2x \sin\phi \cos\theta + 2y \sin\phi \sin\theta - 2z \cos\phi$$
$$= 2\rho \sin^2\phi \cos^2\theta + 2\rho \sin^2\phi \sin^2\theta - 2\rho \cos^2\phi$$
$$= 2\rho \sin^2\phi (\cos^2\theta + \sin^2\theta) - 2\rho \cos^2\phi$$
$$= 2\rho (\sin^2\phi - \cos^2\phi)$$
$$= -2\rho \cos 2\phi$$

$$\frac{\partial w}{\partial \theta} = (2x)(-\rho \sin\phi \sin\theta) + (2y)\rho \sin\phi \cos\theta$$
$$= -2\rho^2 \sin^2\phi \sin\theta \cos\theta + 2\rho^2 \sin^2\phi \sin\theta \cos\theta$$
$$= 0$$

This result is explained by the fact that $w$ does not vary with $\theta$. You can see this directly by expressing the variables $x$, $y$, and $z$ in terms of $\rho$, $\phi$, and $\theta$ in the formula for $w$. (Verify that $w = -\rho^2 \cos 2\phi$.) ◀

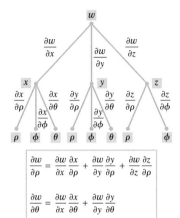

▲ **Figure 13.5.4**

▶ **Example 6**    Suppose that

$$w = xy + yz, \quad y = \sin x, \quad z = e^x$$

Use an appropriate form of the chain rule to find $dw/dx$.

*Solution.*    From the tree diagram and corresponding formulas in Figure 13.5.5 we obtain

$$\frac{dw}{dx} = y + (x + z)\cos x + ye^x$$
$$= \sin x + (x + e^x)\cos x + e^x \sin x$$

This result can also be obtained by first expressing $w$ explicitly in terms of $x$ as

$$w = x \sin x + e^x \sin x$$

and then differentiating with respect to $x$; however, such direct substitution is not always possible. ◀

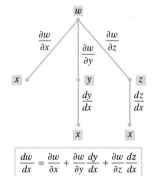

▲ **Figure 13.5.5**

WARNING | The symbol $\partial z$, unlike the differential $dz$, has no meaning of its own. For example, if we were to "cancel" partial symbols in the chain-rule formula

$$\frac{\partial z}{\partial u} = \frac{\partial z}{\partial x}\frac{\partial x}{\partial u} + \frac{\partial z}{\partial y}\frac{\partial y}{\partial u}$$

we would obtain

$$\frac{\partial z}{\partial u} = \frac{\partial z}{\partial u} + \frac{\partial z}{\partial u}$$

which is false in cases where $\partial z/\partial u \neq 0$.

One of the principal uses of the chain rule for functions of a *single* variable was to compute formulas for the derivatives of compositions of functions. Theorems 13.5.1 and 13.5.2 are important not so much for the computation of formulas but because they allow us to express *relationships* among various derivatives. As an illustration, we revisit the topic of implicit differentiation.

### ■ IMPLICIT DIFFERENTIATION

Consider the special case where $z = f(x, y)$ is a function of $x$ and $y$ and $y$ is a differentiable function of $x$. Equation (5) then becomes

$$\frac{dz}{dx} = \frac{\partial f}{\partial x}\frac{dx}{dx} + \frac{\partial f}{\partial y}\frac{dy}{dx} = \frac{\partial f}{\partial x} + \frac{\partial f}{\partial y}\frac{dy}{dx} \tag{12}$$

This result can be used to find derivatives of functions that are defined implicitly. For example, suppose that the equation

$$f(x, y) = c \tag{13}$$

defines $y$ implicitly as a differentiable function of $x$ and we are interested in finding $dy/dx$. Differentiating both sides of (13) with respect to $x$ and applying (12) yields

$$\frac{\partial f}{\partial x} + \frac{\partial f}{\partial y}\frac{dy}{dx} = 0$$

Thus, if $\partial f/\partial y \neq 0$, we obtain

$$\frac{dy}{dx} = -\frac{\partial f/\partial x}{\partial f/\partial y}$$

In summary, we have the following result.

---

Show that the function $y = x$ is defined implicitly by the equation

$$x^2 - 2xy + y^2 = 0$$

but that Theorem 13.5.3 is not applicable for finding $dy/dx$.

---

**13.5.3** THEOREM *If the equation $f(x, y) = c$ defines $y$ implicitly as a differentiable function of $x$, and if $\partial f/\partial y \neq 0$, then*

$$\frac{dy}{dx} = -\frac{\partial f/\partial x}{\partial f/\partial y} \tag{14}$$

---

▶ **Example 7** Given that

$$x^3 + y^2 x - 3 = 0$$

find $dy/dx$ using (14), and check the result using implicit differentiation.

**Solution.** By (14) with $f(x, y) = x^3 + y^2 x - 3$,

$$\frac{dy}{dx} = -\frac{\partial f/\partial x}{\partial f/\partial y} = -\frac{3x^2 + y^2}{2yx}$$

Alternatively, differentiating implicitly yields

$$3x^2 + y^2 + x\left(2y\frac{dy}{dx}\right) - 0 = 0 \quad \text{or} \quad \frac{dy}{dx} = -\frac{3x^2 + y^2}{2yx}$$

which agrees with the result obtained by (14). ◀

The chain rule also applies to implicit partial differentiation. Consider the case where $w = f(x, y, z)$ is a function of $x$, $y$, and $z$ and $z$ is a differentiable function of $x$ and $y$. It follows from Theorem 13.5.2 that

$$\frac{\partial w}{\partial x} = \frac{\partial f}{\partial x} + \frac{\partial f}{\partial z}\frac{\partial z}{\partial x} \tag{15}$$

If the equation

$$f(x, y, z) = c \qquad (16)$$

defines $z$ implicitly as a differentiable function of $x$ and $y$, then taking the partial derivative of each side of (16) with respect to $x$ and applying (15) gives

$$\frac{\partial f}{\partial x} + \frac{\partial f}{\partial z}\frac{\partial z}{\partial x} = 0$$

If $\partial f / \partial z \neq 0$, then

$$\frac{\partial z}{\partial x} = -\frac{\partial f / \partial x}{\partial f / \partial z}$$

A similar result holds for $\partial z / \partial y$.

---

**13.5.4**   **THEOREM**   *If the equation $f(x, y, z) = c$ defines $z$ implicitly as a differentiable function of $x$ and $y$, and if $\partial f / \partial z \neq 0$, then*

$$\frac{\partial z}{\partial x} = -\frac{\partial f / \partial x}{\partial f / \partial z} \qquad and \qquad \frac{\partial z}{\partial y} = -\frac{\partial f / \partial y}{\partial f / \partial z}$$

---

▶ **Example 8**   Consider the sphere $x^2 + y^2 + z^2 = 1$. Find $\partial z / \partial x$ and $\partial z / \partial y$ at the point $\left(\frac{2}{3}, \frac{1}{3}, \frac{2}{3}\right)$.

*Solution.*   By Theorem 13.5.4 with $f(x, y, z) = x^2 + y^2 + z^2$,

Note the similarity between the expression for $\partial z / \partial y$ found in Example 8 and that found in Example 7 of Section 13.3.

$$\frac{\partial z}{\partial x} = -\frac{\partial f / \partial x}{\partial f / \partial z} = -\frac{2x}{2z} = -\frac{x}{z} \quad \text{and} \quad \frac{\partial z}{\partial y} = -\frac{\partial f / \partial y}{\partial f / \partial z} = -\frac{2y}{2z} = -\frac{y}{z}$$

At the point $\left(\frac{2}{3}, \frac{1}{3}, \frac{2}{3}\right)$, evaluating these derivatives gives $\partial z / \partial x = -1$ and $\partial z / \partial y = -\frac{1}{2}$. ◀

✔ **QUICK CHECK EXERCISES 13.5**   *(See page 959 for answers.)*

1. Suppose that $z = xy^2$ and $x$ and $y$ are differentiable functions of $t$ with $x = 1$, $y = -1$, $dx/dt = -2$, and $dy/dt = 3$ when $t = -1$. Then $dz/dt = $ _____ when $t = -1$.

2. Suppose that $C$ is the graph of the equation $f(x, y) = 1$ and that this equation defines $y$ implicitly as a differentiable function of $x$. If the point $(2, 1)$ belongs to $C$ with $f_x(2, 1) = 3$ and $f_y(2, 1) = -1$, then the tangent line to $C$ at the point $(2, 1)$ has slope _____.

3. A rectangle is growing in such a way that when its length is 5 ft and its width is 2 ft, the length is increasing at a rate

of 3 ft/s and its width is increasing at a rate of 4 ft/s. At this instant the area of the rectangle is growing at a rate of _____.

4. Suppose that $z = x/y$, where $x$ and $y$ are differentiable functions of $u$ and $v$ such that $x = 3$, $y = 1$, $\partial x/\partial u = 4$, $\partial x/\partial v = -2$, $\partial y/\partial u = 1$, and $\partial y/\partial v = -1$ when $u = 2$ and $v = 1$. When $u = 2$ and $v = 1$, $\partial z/\partial u = $ _____ and $\partial z/\partial v = $ _____.

---

**EXERCISE SET 13.5**

---

**1–6** Use an appropriate form of the chain rule to find $dz/dt$. ▪

1. $z = 3x^2y^3$; $x = t^4$, $y = t^2$

2. $z = \ln(2x^2 + y)$; $x = \sqrt{t}$, $y = t^{2/3}$

3. $z = 3\cos x - \sin xy$; $x = 1/t$, $y = 3t$

4. $z = \sqrt{1 + x - 2xy^4}$; $x = \ln t$, $y = t$

5. $z = e^{1-xy}$; $x = t^{1/3}$, $y = t^3$

6. $z = \cosh^2 xy;\ x = t/2,\ y = e^t$

7–10 Use an appropriate form of the chain rule to find $dw/dt$.

7. $w = 5x^2y^3z^4;\ x = t^2,\ y = t^3,\ z = t^5$

8. $w = \ln(3x^2 - 2y + 4z^3);\ x = t^{1/2},\ y = t^{2/3},\ z = t^{-2}$

9. $w = 5\cos xy - \sin xz;\ x = 1/t,\ y = t,\ z = t^3$

10. $w = \sqrt{1 + x - 2yz^4x};\ x = \ln t,\ y = t,\ z = 4t$

---

**FOCUS ON CONCEPTS**

11. Suppose that
$$w = x^3y^2z^4;\quad x = t^2,\quad y = t+2,\quad z = 2t^4$$
Find the rate of change of $w$ with respect to $t$ at $t = 1$ by using the chain rule, and then check your work by expressing $w$ as a function of $t$ and differentiating.

12. Suppose that
$$w = x\sin yz^2;\quad x = \cos t,\quad y = t^2,\quad z = e^t$$
Find the rate of change of $w$ with respect to $t$ at $t = 0$ by using the chain rule, and then check your work by expressing $w$ as a function of $t$ and differentiating.

13. Suppose that $z = f(x, y)$ is differentiable at the point $(4, 8)$ with $f_x(4, 8) = 3$ and $f_y(4, 8) = -1$. If $x = t^2$ and $y = t^3$, find $dz/dt$ when $t = 2$.

14. Suppose that $w = f(x, y, z)$ is differentiable at the point $(1, 0, 2)$ with $f_x(1, 0, 2) = 1$, $f_y(1, 0, 2) = 2$, and $f_z(1, 0, 2) = 3$. If $x = t$, $y = \sin(\pi t)$, and $z = t^2 + 1$, find $dw/dt$ when $t = 1$.

15. Explain how the product rule for functions of a single variable may be viewed as a consequence of the chain rule applied to a particular function of two variables.

16. A student attempts to differentiate the function $x^x$ using the power rule, mistakenly getting $x \cdot x^{x-1}$. A second student attempts to differentiate $x^x$ by treating it as an exponential function, mistakenly getting $(\ln x)x^x$. Use the chain rule to explain why the correct derivative is the sum of these two incorrect results.

---

17–22 Use appropriate forms of the chain rule to find $\partial z/\partial u$ and $\partial z/\partial v$.

17. $z = 8x^2y - 2x + 3y;\ x = uv,\ y = u - v$

18. $z = x^2 - y\tan x;\ x = u/v,\ y = u^2v^2$

19. $z = x/y;\ x = 2\cos u,\ y = 3\sin v$

20. $z = 3x - 2y;\ x = u + v\ln u,\ y = u^2 - v\ln v$

21. $z = e^{x^2y};\ x = \sqrt{uv},\ y = 1/v$

22. $z = \cos x\sin y;\ x = u - v,\ y = u^2 + v^2$

---

23–30 Use appropriate forms of the chain rule to find the derivatives.

23. Let $T = x^2y - xy^3 + 2$; $x = r\cos\theta$, $y = r\sin\theta$. Find $\partial T/\partial r$ and $\partial T/\partial\theta$.

24. Let $R = e^{2s-t^2}$; $s = 3\phi, t = \phi^{1/2}$. Find $dR/d\phi$.

25. Let $t = u/v$; $u = x^2 - y^2$, $v = 4xy^3$. Find $\partial t/\partial x$ and $\partial t/\partial y$.

26. Let $w = rs/(r^2 + s^2)$; $r = uv$, $s = u - 2v$. Find $\partial w/\partial u$ and $\partial w/\partial v$.

27. Let $z = \ln(x^2 + 1)$, where $x = r\cos\theta$. Find $\partial z/\partial r$ and $\partial z/\partial\theta$.

28. Let $u = rs^2\ln t, r = x^2, s = 4y + 1, t = xy^3$. Find $\partial u/\partial x$ and $\partial u/\partial y$.

29. Let $w = 4x^2 + 4y^2 + z^2, x = \rho\sin\phi\cos\theta$, $y = \rho\sin\phi\sin\theta$, $z = \rho\cos\phi$. Find $\partial w/\partial\rho$, $\partial w/\partial\phi$, and $\partial w/\partial\theta$.

30. Let $w = 3xy^2z^3, y = 3x^2 + 2, z = \sqrt{x - 1}$. Find $dw/dx$.

31. Use a chain rule to find the value of $\left.\dfrac{dw}{ds}\right|_{s=1/4}$ if
$$w = r^2 - r\tan\theta; r = \sqrt{s}, \theta = \pi s.$$

32. Use a chain rule to find the values of
$$\left.\frac{\partial f}{\partial u}\right|_{u=1,v=-2} \quad\text{and}\quad \left.\frac{\partial f}{\partial v}\right|_{u=1,v=-2}$$
if $f(x, y) = x^2y^2 - x + 2y; x = \sqrt{u}, y = uv^3$.

33. Use a chain rule to find the values of
$$\left.\frac{\partial z}{\partial r}\right|_{r=2,\theta=\pi/6} \quad\text{and}\quad \left.\frac{\partial z}{\partial\theta}\right|_{r=2,\theta=\pi/6}$$
if $z = xye^{x/y}; x = r\cos\theta, y = r\sin\theta$.

34. Use a chain rule to find $\left.\dfrac{dz}{dt}\right|_{t=3}$ if $z = x^2y; x = t^2, y = t + 7$.

35. Let $a$ and $b$ denote two sides of a triangle and let $\theta$ denote the included angle. Suppose that $a$, $b$, and $\theta$ vary with time in such a way that the area of the triangle remains constant. At a certain instant $a = 5$ cm, $b = 4$ cm, and $\theta = \pi/6$ radians, and at that instant both $a$ and $b$ are increasing at a rate of 3 cm/s. Estimate the rate at which $\theta$ is changing at that instant.

36. The voltage, $V$ (in volts), across a circuit is given by Ohm's law: $V = IR$, where $I$ is the current (in amperes) flowing through the circuit and $R$ is the resistance (in ohms). If two circuits with resistances $R_1$ and $R_2$ are connected in parallel, then their combined resistance, $R$, is given by
$$\frac{1}{R} = \frac{1}{R_1} + \frac{1}{R_2}$$
Suppose that the current is 3 amperes and is increasing at $10^{-2}$ ampere/s, $R_1$ is 2 ohms and is increasing at 0.4 ohm/s, and $R_2$ is 5 ohms and is decreasing at 0.7 ohm/s. Estimate the rate at which the voltage is changing.

---

37–40 True–False Determine whether the statement is true or false. Explain your answer.

37. The symbols $\partial z$ and $\partial x$ are defined in such a way that the partial derivative $\partial z/\partial x$ can be interpreted as a ratio.

**38.** If $z$ is a differentiable function of $x_1$, $x_2$, and $x_3$, and if $x_i$ is a differentiable function of $t$ for $i = 1, 2, 3$, then $z$ is a differentiable function of $t$ and

$$\frac{dz}{dt} = \sum_{i=1}^{3} \frac{\partial z}{\partial x_i} \frac{dx_i}{dt}$$

**39.** If $z$ is a differentiable function of $x$ and $y$, and if $x$ and $y$ are twice differentiable functions of $t$, then $z$ is a twice differentiable function of $t$ and

$$\frac{d^2 z}{dt^2} = \frac{\partial z}{\partial x} \frac{d^2 x}{dt^2} + \frac{\partial z}{\partial y} \frac{d^2 y}{dt^2}$$

**40.** If $f(x, y)$ is a differentiable function of $x$ and $y$, and if the line $y = x$ is a contour of $f$, then $f_y(t, t) = -f_x(t, t)$ for all real numbers $t$.

**41–44** Use Theorem 13.5.3 to find $dy/dx$ and check your result using implicit differentiation. ■

**41.** $x^2 y^3 + \cos y = 0$     **42.** $x^3 - 3xy^2 + y^3 = 5$

**43.** $e^{xy} + ye^y = 1$     **44.** $x - \sqrt{xy} + 3y = 4$

**45–48** Find $\partial z/\partial x$ and $\partial z/\partial y$ by implicit differentiation, and confirm that the results obtained agree with those predicted by the formulas in Theorem 13.5.4. ■

**45.** $x^2 - 3yz^2 + xyz - 2 = 0$     **46.** $\ln(1 + z) + xy^2 + z = 1$

**47.** $ye^x - 5 \sin 3z = 3z$

**48.** $e^{xy} \cos yz - e^{yz} \sin xz + 2 = 0$

**49. (a)** Suppose that $z = f(u)$ and $u = g(x, y)$. Draw a tree diagram, and use it to construct chain rules that express $\partial z/\partial x$ and $\partial z/\partial y$ in terms of $dz/du$, $\partial u/\partial x$, and $\partial u/\partial y$.

**(b)** Show that

$$\frac{\partial^2 z}{\partial x^2} = \frac{dz}{du} \frac{\partial^2 u}{\partial x^2} + \frac{d^2 z}{du^2} \left( \frac{\partial u}{\partial x} \right)^2$$

$$\frac{\partial^2 z}{\partial y^2} = \frac{dz}{du} \frac{\partial^2 u}{\partial y^2} + \frac{d^2 z}{du^2} \left( \frac{\partial u}{\partial y} \right)^2$$

$$\frac{\partial^2 z}{\partial y \partial x} = \frac{dz}{du} \frac{\partial^2 u}{\partial y \partial x} + \frac{d^2 z}{du^2} \frac{\partial u}{\partial x} \frac{\partial u}{\partial y}$$

**50. (a)** Let $z = f(x^2 - y^2)$. Use the result in Exercise 49(a) to show that

$$y \frac{\partial z}{\partial x} + x \frac{\partial z}{\partial y} = 0$$

**(b)** Let $z = f(xy)$. Use the result in Exercise 49(a) to show that

$$x \frac{\partial z}{\partial x} - y \frac{\partial z}{\partial y} = 0$$

**(c)** Confirm the result in part (a) in the case where $z = \sin(x^2 - y^2)$.

**(d)** Confirm the result in part (b) in the case where $z = e^{xy}$.

**51.** Let $f$ be a differentiable function of one variable, and let $z = f(x + 2y)$. Show that

$$2 \frac{\partial z}{\partial x} - \frac{\partial z}{\partial y} = 0$$

**52.** Let $f$ be a differentiable function of one variable, and let $z = f(x^2 + y^2)$. Show that

$$y \frac{\partial z}{\partial x} - x \frac{\partial z}{\partial y} = 0$$

**53.** Let $f$ be a differentiable function of one variable, and let $w = f(u)$, where $u = x + 2y + 3z$. Show that

$$\frac{\partial w}{\partial x} + \frac{\partial w}{\partial y} + \frac{\partial w}{\partial z} = 6 \frac{dw}{du}$$

**54.** Let $f$ be a differentiable function of one variable, and let $w = f(\rho)$, where $\rho = (x^2 + y^2 + z^2)^{1/2}$. Show that

$$\left( \frac{\partial w}{\partial x} \right)^2 + \left( \frac{\partial w}{\partial y} \right)^2 + \left( \frac{\partial w}{\partial z} \right)^2 = \left( \frac{dw}{d\rho} \right)^2$$

**55.** Let $z = f(x - y, y - x)$. Show that $\partial z/\partial x + \partial z/\partial y = 0$.

**56.** Let $f$ be a differentiable function of three variables and suppose that $w = f(x - y, y - z, z - x)$. Show that

$$\frac{\partial w}{\partial x} + \frac{\partial w}{\partial y} + \frac{\partial w}{\partial z} = 0$$

**57.** Suppose that the equation $z = f(x, y)$ is expressed in the polar form $z = g(r, \theta)$ by making the substitution $x = r \cos \theta$ and $y = r \sin \theta$.

**(a)** View $r$ and $\theta$ as functions of $x$ and $y$ and use implicit differentiation to show that

$$\frac{\partial r}{\partial x} = \cos \theta \quad \text{and} \quad \frac{\partial \theta}{\partial x} = -\frac{\sin \theta}{r}$$

**(b)** View $r$ and $\theta$ as functions of $x$ and $y$ and use implicit differentiation to show that

$$\frac{\partial r}{\partial y} = \sin \theta \quad \text{and} \quad \frac{\partial \theta}{\partial y} = \frac{\cos \theta}{r}$$

**(c)** Use the results in parts (a) and (b) to show that

$$\frac{\partial z}{\partial x} = \frac{\partial z}{\partial r} \cos \theta - \frac{1}{r} \frac{\partial z}{\partial \theta} \sin \theta$$

$$\frac{\partial z}{\partial y} = \frac{\partial z}{\partial r} \sin \theta + \frac{1}{r} \frac{\partial z}{\partial \theta} \cos \theta$$

**(d)** Use the result in part (c) to show that

$$\left( \frac{\partial z}{\partial x} \right)^2 + \left( \frac{\partial z}{\partial y} \right)^2 = \left( \frac{\partial z}{\partial r} \right)^2 + \frac{1}{r^2} \left( \frac{\partial z}{\partial \theta} \right)^2$$

**(e)** Use the result in part (c) to show that if $z = f(x, y)$ satisfies Laplace's equation

$$\frac{\partial^2 z}{\partial x^2} + \frac{\partial^2 z}{\partial y^2} = 0$$

then $z = g(r, \theta)$ satisfies the equation

$$\frac{\partial^2 z}{\partial r^2} + \frac{1}{r^2} \frac{\partial^2 z}{\partial \theta^2} + \frac{1}{r} \frac{\partial z}{\partial r} = 0$$

and conversely. The latter equation is called the ***polar form of Laplace's equation***.

**58.** Show that the function

$$z = \tan^{-1} \frac{2xy}{x^2 - y^2}$$

satisfies Laplace's equation; then make the substitution $x = r \cos \theta$, $y = r \sin \theta$, and show that the resulting function of $r$ and $\theta$ satisfies the polar form of Laplace's equation given in part (e) of Exercise 57.

**59.** (a) Show that if $u(x, y)$ and $v(x, y)$ satisfy the Cauchy–Riemann equations (Exercise 104, Section 13.3), and if $x = r \cos\theta$ and $y = r \sin\theta$, then
$$\frac{\partial u}{\partial r} = \frac{1}{r}\frac{\partial v}{\partial \theta} \quad \text{and} \quad \frac{\partial v}{\partial r} = -\frac{1}{r}\frac{\partial u}{\partial \theta}$$
This is called the **polar form of the Cauchy–Riemann equations**.

(b) Show that the functions
$$u = \ln(x^2 + y^2), \quad v = 2\tan^{-1}(y/x)$$
satisfy the Cauchy–Riemann equations; then make the substitution $x = r \cos\theta$, $y = r \sin\theta$, and show that the resulting functions of $r$ and $\theta$ satisfy the polar form of the Cauchy–Riemann equations.

**60.** Recall from Formula (6) of Section 13.3 that under appropriate conditions a plucked string satisfies the wave equation
$$\frac{\partial^2 u}{\partial t^2} = c^2 \frac{\partial^2 u}{\partial x^2}$$
where $c$ is a positive constant.

(a) Show that a function of the form $u(x, t) = f(x + ct)$ satisfies the wave equation.

(b) Show that a function of the form $u(x, t) = g(x - ct)$ satisfies the wave equation.

(c) Show that a function of the form
$$u(x, t) = f(x + ct) + g(x - ct)$$
satisfies the wave equation.

(d) It can be proved that every solution of the wave equation is expressible in the form stated in part (c). Confirm that $u(x, t) = \sin t \sin x$ satisfies the wave equation in which $c = 1$, and then use appropriate trigonometric identities to express this function in the form $f(x + t) + g(x - t)$.

**61.** Let $f$ be a differentiable function of three variables, and let $w = f(x, y, z)$, $x = \rho \sin\phi \cos\theta$, $y = \rho \sin\phi \sin\theta$, and $z = \rho \cos\phi$. Express $\partial w/\partial\rho$, $\partial w/\partial\phi$, and $\partial w/\partial\theta$ in terms of $\partial w/\partial x$, $\partial w/\partial y$, and $\partial w/\partial z$.

**62.** Let $w = f(x, y, z)$ be differentiable, where $z = g(x, y)$. Taking $x$ and $y$ as the independent variables, express each of the following in terms of $\partial f/\partial x$, $\partial f/\partial y$, $\partial f/\partial z$, $\partial z/\partial x$, and $\partial z/\partial y$.

(a) $\partial w/\partial x$        (b) $\partial w/\partial y$

**63.** Let $w = \ln(e^r + e^s + e^t + e^u)$. Show that
$$w_{rstu} = -6e^{r+s+t+u-4w}$$
[*Hint:* Take advantage of the relationship $e^w = e^r + e^s + e^t + e^u$.]

**64.** Suppose that $w$ is a differentiable function of $x_1$, $x_2$, and $x_3$, and
$$x_1 = a_1 y_1 + b_1 y_2$$
$$x_2 = a_2 y_1 + b_2 y_2$$
$$x_3 = a_3 y_1 + b_3 y_2$$
where the $a$'s and $b$'s are constants. Express $\partial w/\partial y_1$ and $\partial w/\partial y_2$ in terms of $\partial w/\partial x_1$, $\partial w/\partial x_2$, and $\partial w/\partial x_3$.

**65.** (a) Let $w$ be a differentiable function of $x_1$, $x_2$, $x_3$, and $x_4$, and let each $x_i$ be a differentiable function of $t$. Find a chain-rule formula for $dw/dt$.

(b) Let $w$ be a differentiable function of $x_1$, $x_2$, $x_3$, and $x_4$, and let each $x_i$ be a differentiable function of $v_1$, $v_2$, and $v_3$. Find chain-rule formulas for $\partial w/\partial v_1$, $\partial w/\partial v_2$, and $\partial w/\partial v_3$.

**66.** Let $w = (x_1^2 + x_2^2 + \cdots + x_n^2)^k$, where $n \geq 2$. For what values of $k$ does
$$\frac{\partial^2 w}{\partial x_1^2} + \frac{\partial^2 w}{\partial x_2^2} + \cdots + \frac{\partial^2 w}{\partial x_n^2} = 0$$
hold?

**67.** Derive the identity
$$\frac{d}{dx}\int_{h(x)}^{g(x)} f(t)\, dt = f(g(x))g'(x) - f(h(x))h'(x)$$
by letting $u = g(x)$ and $v = h(x)$ and then differentiating the function
$$F(u, v) = \int_v^u f(t)\, dt$$
with respect to $x$.

**68.** Prove: If $f$, $f_x$, and $f_y$ are continuous on a circular region containing $A(x_0, y_0)$ and $B(x_1, y_1)$, then there is a point $(x^*, y^*)$ on the line segment joining $A$ and $B$ such that
$$f(x_1, y_1) - f(x_0, y_0)$$
$$= f_x(x^*, y^*)(x_1 - x_0) + f_y(x^*, y^*)(y_1 - y_0)$$
This result is the two-dimensional version of the Mean-Value Theorem. [*Hint:* Express the line segment joining $A$ and $B$ in parametric form and use the Mean-Value Theorem for functions of one variable.]

**69.** Prove: If $f_x(x, y) = 0$ and $f_y(x, y) = 0$ throughout a circular region, then $f(x, y)$ is constant on that region. [*Hint:* Use the result of Exercise 68.]

**70.** Writing   Use differentials to give an informal justification for the chain rules for derivatives.

**71.** Writing   Compare the use of the formula
$$\frac{dy}{dx} = -\frac{\partial f/\partial x}{\partial f/\partial y}$$
with the process of implicit differentiation.

✔ **QUICK CHECK ANSWERS 13.5**

1. $-8$    2. 3    3. $26 \text{ ft}^2/s$    4. 1; 1

## 13.6   DIRECTIONAL DERIVATIVES AND GRADIENTS

*The partial derivatives $f_x(x, y)$ and $f_y(x, y)$ represent the rates of change of $f(x, y)$ in directions parallel to the x- and y-axes. In this section we will investigate rates of change of $f(x, y)$ in other directions.*

### ■ DIRECTIONAL DERIVATIVES

In this section we extend the concept of a *partial* derivative to the more general notion of a *directional* derivative. We have seen that the partial derivatives of a function give the instantaneous rates of change of that function in directions parallel to the coordinate axes. Directional derivatives allow us to compute the rates of change of a function with respect to distance in *any* direction.

Suppose that we wish to compute the instantaneous rate of change of a function $f(x, y)$ with respect to distance from a point $(x_0, y_0)$ in some direction. Since there are infinitely many different directions from $(x_0, y_0)$ in which we could move, we need a convenient method for describing a specific direction starting at $(x_0, y_0)$. One way to do this is to use a unit vector

$$\mathbf{u} = u_1\mathbf{i} + u_2\mathbf{j}$$

that has its initial point at $(x_0, y_0)$ and points in the desired direction (Figure 13.6.1). This vector determines a line $l$ in the $xy$-plane that can be expressed parametrically as

$$x = x_0 + su_1, \quad y = y_0 + su_2 \tag{1}$$

Since $u$ is a unit vector, $s$ is the arc length parameter that has its reference point at $(x_0, y_0)$ and has positive values in the direction of $\mathbf{u}$. For $s = 0$, the point $(x, y)$ is at the reference point $(x_0, y_0)$, and as $s$ increases, the point $(x, y)$ moves along $l$ in the direction of $\mathbf{u}$. On the line $l$ the variable $z = f(x_0 + su_1, y_0 + su_2)$ is a function of the parameter $s$. The value of the derivative $dz/ds$ at $s = 0$ then gives an instantaneous rate of change of $f(x, y)$ with respect to distance from $(x_0, y_0)$ in the direction of $\mathbf{u}$.

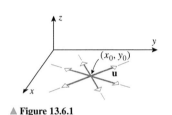

▲ **Figure 13.6.1**

> **13.6.1   DEFINITION**   If $f(x, y)$ is a function of $x$ and $y$, and if $\mathbf{u} = u_1\mathbf{i} + u_2\mathbf{j}$ is a unit vector, then the ***directional derivative of f in the direction of*** $\mathbf{u}$ at $(x_0, y_0)$ is denoted by $D_\mathbf{u} f(x_0, y_0)$ and is defined by
>
> $$D_\mathbf{u} f(x_0, y_0) = \frac{d}{ds}\left[f(x_0 + su_1, y_0 + su_2)\right]_{s=0} \tag{2}$$
>
> provided this derivative exists.

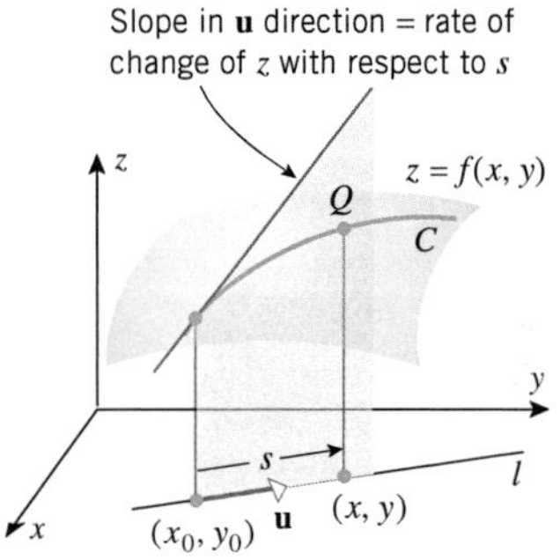

Slope in **u** direction = rate of change of *z* with respect to *s*

▲ **Figure 13.6.2**

Geometrically, $D_\mathbf{u} f(x_0, y_0)$ can be interpreted as the ***slope of the surface $z = f(x, y)$ in the direction of*** $\mathbf{u}$ at the point $(x_0, y_0, f(x_0, y_0))$ (Figure 13.6.2). Usually the value of $D_\mathbf{u} f(x_0, y_0)$ will depend on both the point $(x_0, y_0)$ and the direction $\mathbf{u}$. Thus, at a fixed point the slope of the surface may vary with the direction (Figure 13.6.3). Analytically, the directional derivative represents the ***instantaneous rate of change of $f(x, y)$ with respect to distance in the direction of*** $\mathbf{u}$ at the point $(x_0, y_0)$.

▶ **Example 1**   Let $f(x, y) = xy$. Find and interpret $D_\mathbf{u} f(1, 2)$ for the unit vector

$$\mathbf{u} = \frac{\sqrt{3}}{2}\mathbf{i} + \frac{1}{2}\mathbf{j}$$

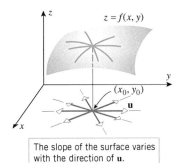

The slope of the surface varies with the direction of **u**.

▲ **Figure 13.6.3**

***Solution.***    It follows from Equation (2) that

$$D_{\mathbf{u}} f(1, 2) = \frac{d}{ds} \left[ f\left( 1 + \frac{\sqrt{3}s}{2}, 2 + \frac{s}{2} \right) \right]_{s=0}$$

Since

$$f\left( 1 + \frac{\sqrt{3}s}{2}, 2 + \frac{s}{2} \right) = \left( 1 + \frac{\sqrt{3}s}{2} \right)\left( 2 + \frac{s}{2} \right) = \frac{\sqrt{3}}{4}s^2 + \left( \frac{1}{2} + \sqrt{3} \right)s + 2$$

we have

$$D_{\mathbf{u}} f(1, 2) = \frac{d}{ds} \left[ \frac{\sqrt{3}}{4}s^2 + \left( \frac{1}{2} + \sqrt{3} \right)s + 2 \right]_{s=0}$$

$$= \left[ \frac{\sqrt{3}}{2}s + \frac{1}{2} + \sqrt{3} \right]_{s=0} = \frac{1}{2} + \sqrt{3}$$

Since $\frac{1}{2} + \sqrt{3} \approx 2.23$, we conclude that if we move a small distance from the point $(1, 2)$ in the direction of **u**, the function $f(x, y) = xy$ will increase by about 2.23 times the distance moved. ◄

The definition of a directional derivative for a function $f(x, y, z)$ of three variables is similar to Definition 13.6.1.

---

**13.6.2    DEFINITION**    If $\mathbf{u} = u_1\mathbf{i} + u_2\mathbf{j} + u_3\mathbf{k}$ is a unit vector, and if $f(x, y, z)$ is a function of $x$, $y$, and $z$, then the ***directional derivative of $f$ in the direction of*** **u** at $(x_0, y_0, z_0)$ is denoted by $D_{\mathbf{u}} f(x_0, y_0, z_0)$ and is defined by

$$D_{\mathbf{u}} f(x_0, y_0, z_0) = \frac{d}{ds} \left[ f(x_0 + su_1, y_0 + su_2, z_0 + su_3) \right]_{s=0} \tag{3}$$

provided this derivative exists.

---

Although Equation (3) does not have a convenient geometric interpretation, we can still interpret directional derivatives for functions of three variables in terms of instantaneous rates of change in a specified direction.

For a function that is differentiable at a point, directional derivatives exist in every direction from the point and can be computed directly in terms of the first-order partial derivatives of the function.

---

**13.6.3    THEOREM**

(a)    *If $f(x, y)$ is differentiable at $(x_0, y_0)$, and if $\mathbf{u} = u_1\mathbf{i} + u_2\mathbf{j}$ is a unit vector, then the directional derivative $D_{\mathbf{u}} f(x_0, y_0)$ exists and is given by*

$$D_{\mathbf{u}} f(x_0, y_0) = f_x(x_0, y_0)u_1 + f_y(x_0, y_0)u_2 \tag{4}$$

(b)    *If $f(x, y, z)$ is differentiable at $(x_0, y_0, z_0)$, and if $\mathbf{u} = u_1\mathbf{i} + u_2\mathbf{j} + u_3\mathbf{k}$ is a unit vector, then the directional derivative $D_{\mathbf{u}} f(x_0, y_0, z_0)$ exists and is given by*

$$D_{\mathbf{u}} f(x_0, y_0, z_0) = f_x(x_0, y_0, z_0)u_1 + f_y(x_0, y_0, z_0)u_2 + f_z(x_0, y_0, z_0)u_3 \tag{5}$$

---

PROOF We will give the proof of part (*a*); the proof of part (*b*) is similar and will be omitted. The function $z = f(x_0 + su_1, y_0 + su_2)$ is the composition of the function $z = f(x, y)$ with the functions

$$x = x(s) = x_0 + su_1 \quad \text{and} \quad y = y(s) = y_0 + su_2$$

As such, the chain rule in Formula (5) of Section 13.5 immediately gives

$$D_{\mathbf{u}} f(x_0, y_0) = \frac{d}{ds} \left[ f(x_0 + su_1, y_0 + su_2) \right]_{s=0}$$

$$= \frac{dz}{ds} \Bigg|_{s=0} = f_x(x_0, y_0)u_1 + f_y(x_0, y_0)u_2 \quad \blacksquare$$

We can use Theorem 13.6.3 to confirm the result of Example 1. For $f(x, y) = xy$ we have $f_x(1, 2) = 2$ and $f_y(1, 2) = 1$ (verify). With

$$\mathbf{u} = \frac{\sqrt{3}}{2}\mathbf{i} + \frac{1}{2}\mathbf{j}$$

Equation (4) becomes

$$D_{\mathbf{u}} f(1, 2) = 2\left(\frac{\sqrt{3}}{2}\right) + \frac{1}{2} = \sqrt{3} + \frac{1}{2}$$

which agrees with our solution in Example 1.

Recall from Formula (13) of Section 11.2 that a unit vector $\mathbf{u}$ in the $xy$-plane can be expressed as

$$\mathbf{u} = \cos\phi\,\mathbf{i} + \sin\phi\,\mathbf{j} \tag{6}$$

where $\phi$ is the angle from the positive $x$-axis to $\mathbf{u}$. Thus, Formula (4) can also be expressed as

$$D_{\mathbf{u}} f(x_0, y_0) = f_x(x_0, y_0) \cos\phi + f_y(x_0, y_0) \sin\phi \tag{7}$$

▶ **Example 2** Find the directional derivative of $f(x, y) = e^{xy}$ at $(-2, 0)$ in the direction of the unit vector that makes an angle of $\pi/3$ with the positive $x$-axis.

*Solution.* The partial derivatives of $f$ are

$$f_x(x, y) = ye^{xy}, \quad f_y(x, y) = xe^{xy}$$

$$f_x(-2, 0) = 0, \quad f_y(-2, 0) = -2$$

The unit vector $\mathbf{u}$ that makes an angle of $\pi/3$ with the positive $x$-axis is

$$\mathbf{u} = \cos(\pi/3)\mathbf{i} + \sin(\pi/3)\mathbf{j} = \frac{1}{2}\mathbf{i} + \frac{\sqrt{3}}{2}\mathbf{j}$$

Thus, from (7)

$$D_{\mathbf{u}} f(-2, 0) = f_x(-2, 0) \cos(\pi/3) + f_y(-2, 0) \sin(\pi/3)$$

$$= 0(1/2) + (-2)(\sqrt{3}/2) = -\sqrt{3} \quad \blacktriangleleft$$

Note that in Example 3 we used a *unit vector* to specify the direction of the directional derivative. This is required in order to apply either Formula (4) or Formula (5).

▶ **Example 3** Find the directional derivative of $f(x, y, z) = x^2 y - yz^3 + z$ at the point $(1, -2, 0)$ in the direction of the vector $\mathbf{a} = 2\mathbf{i} + \mathbf{j} - 2\mathbf{k}$.

*Solution.*  The partial derivatives of $f$ are

$$f_x(x, y, z) = 2xy, \quad f_y(x, y, z) = x^2 - z^3, \quad f_z(x, y, z) = -3yz^2 + 1$$

$$f_x(1, -2, 0) = -4, \quad f_y(1, -2, 0) = 1, \quad f_z(1, -2, 0) = 1$$

Since **a** is not a unit vector, we normalize it, getting

$$\mathbf{u} = \frac{\mathbf{a}}{\|\mathbf{a}\|} = \frac{1}{\sqrt{9}}(2\mathbf{i} + \mathbf{j} - 2\mathbf{k}) = \frac{2}{3}\mathbf{i} + \frac{1}{3}\mathbf{j} - \frac{2}{3}\mathbf{k}$$

Formula (5) then yields

$$D_{\mathbf{u}} f(1, -2, 0) = (-4)\left(\frac{2}{3}\right) + \frac{1}{3} - \frac{2}{3} = -3 \blacktriangleleft$$

### ▧ THE GRADIENT

Formula (4) can be expressed in the form of a dot product as

$$D_{\mathbf{u}} f(x_0, y_0) = (f_x(x_0, y_0)\mathbf{i} + f_y(x_0, y_0)\mathbf{j}) \cdot (u_1\mathbf{i} + u_2\mathbf{j})$$
$$= (f_x(x_0, y_0)\mathbf{i} + f_y(x_0, y_0)\mathbf{j}) \cdot \mathbf{u}$$

Similarly, Formula (5) can be expressed as

$$D_{\mathbf{u}} f(x_0, y_0, z_0) = (f_x(x_0, y_0, z_0)\mathbf{i} + f_y(x_0, y_0, z_0)\mathbf{j} + f_z(x_0, y_0, z_0)\mathbf{k}) \cdot \mathbf{u}$$

In both cases the directional derivative is obtained by dotting the direction vector **u** with a new vector constructed from the first-order partial derivatives of $f$.

---

**13.6.4**  **DEFINITION**

(a)  If $f$ is a function of $x$ and $y$, then the ***gradient of f*** is defined by

$$\nabla f(x, y) = f_x(x, y)\mathbf{i} + f_y(x, y)\mathbf{j} \tag{8}$$

(b)  If $f$ is a function of $x$, $y$, and $z$, then the ***gradient of f*** is defined by

$$\nabla f(x, y, z) = f_x(x, y, z)\mathbf{i} + f_y(x, y, z)\mathbf{j} + f_z(x, y, z)\mathbf{k} \tag{9}$$

---

Remember that $\nabla f$ is not a product of $\nabla$ and $f$. Think of $\nabla$ as an "operator" that acts on a function $f$ to produce the gradient $\nabla f$.

The symbol $\nabla$ (read "del") is an inverted delta. (It is sometimes called a "nabla" because of its similarity in form to an ancient Hebrew ten-stringed harp of that name.)

Formulas (4) and (5) can now be written as

$$D_{\mathbf{u}} f(x_0, y_0) = \nabla f(x_0, y_0) \cdot \mathbf{u} \tag{10}$$

and

$$D_{\mathbf{u}} f(x_0, y_0, z_0) = \nabla f(x_0, y_0, z_0) \cdot \mathbf{u} \tag{11}$$

respectively.  For example, using Formula (11) our solution to Example 3 would take the form

$$D_{\mathbf{u}} f(1, -2, 0) = \nabla f(1, -2, 0) \cdot \mathbf{u} = (-4\mathbf{i} + \mathbf{j} + \mathbf{k}) \cdot \left(\tfrac{2}{3}\mathbf{i} + \tfrac{1}{3}\mathbf{j} - \tfrac{2}{3}\mathbf{k}\right)$$
$$= (-4)\left(\tfrac{2}{3}\right) + \tfrac{1}{3} - \tfrac{2}{3} = -3$$

Formula (10) can be interpreted to mean that the slope of the surface $z = f(x, y)$ at the point $(x_0, y_0)$ in the direction of **u** is the dot product of the gradient with **u** (Figure 13.6.4).

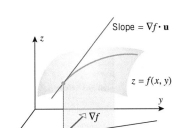

Slope = $\nabla f \cdot \mathbf{u}$

$z = f(x, y)$

$\nabla f$

$(x, y)$

**▲ Figure 13.6.4**

### PROPERTIES OF THE GRADIENT

The gradient is not merely a notational device to simplify the formula for the directional derivative; we will see that the length and direction of the gradient $\nabla f$ provide important information about the function $f$ and the surface $z = f(x, y)$. For example, suppose that $\nabla f(x, y) \neq \mathbf{0}$, and let us use Formula (4) of Section 11.3 to rewrite (10) as

$$D_{\mathbf{u}} f(x, y) = \nabla f(x, y) \cdot \mathbf{u} = \|\nabla f(x, y)\| \|\mathbf{u}\| \cos \theta = \|\nabla f(x, y)\| \cos \theta \qquad (12)$$

where $\theta$ is the angle between $\nabla f(x, y)$ and $\mathbf{u}$. Equation (12) tells us that the maximum value of $D_{\mathbf{u}} f$ at the point $(x, y)$ is $\|\nabla f(x, y)\|$, and this maximum occurs when $\theta = 0$, that is, when $\mathbf{u}$ is in the direction of $\nabla f(x, y)$. Geometrically, this means:

*At $(x, y)$, the surface $z = f(x, y)$ has its maximum slope in the direction of the gradient, and the maximum slope is $\|\nabla f(x, y)\|$.*

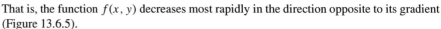

That is, the function $f(x, y)$ increases most rapidly in the direction of its gradient (Figure 13.6.5).

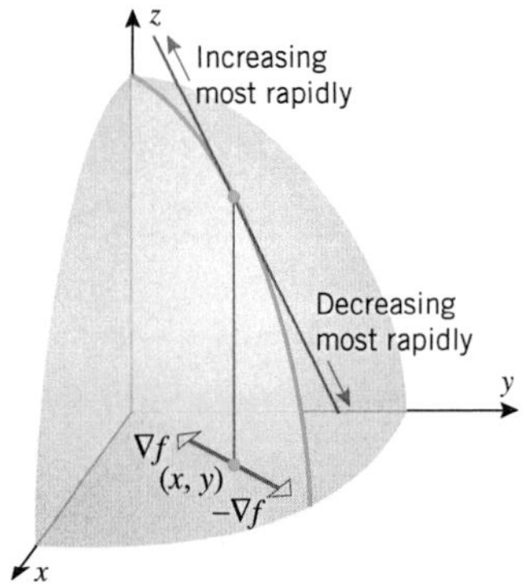

Similarly, (12) tells us that the minimum value of $D_{\mathbf{u}} f$ at the point $(x, y)$ is $-\|\nabla f(x, y)\|$, and this minimum occurs when $\theta = \pi$, that is, when $\mathbf{u}$ is oppositely directed to $\nabla f(x, y)$. Geometrically, this means:

*At $(x, y)$, the surface $z = f(x, y)$ has its minimum slope in the direction that is opposite to the gradient, and the minimum slope is $-\|\nabla f(x, y)\|$.*

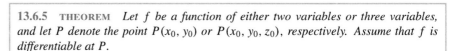

That is, the function $f(x, y)$ decreases most rapidly in the direction opposite to its gradient (Figure 13.6.5).

Finally, in the case where $\nabla f(x, y) = \mathbf{0}$, it follows from (12) that $D_{\mathbf{u}} f(x, y) = 0$ in all directions at the point $(x, y)$. This typically occurs where the surface $z = f(x, y)$ has a "relative maximum," a "relative minimum," or a saddle point.

A similar analysis applies to functions of three variables. As a consequence, we have the following result.

---

**13.6.5** **THEOREM** *Let $f$ be a function of either two variables or three variables, and let $P$ denote the point $P(x_0, y_0)$ or $P(x_0, y_0, z_0)$, respectively. Assume that $f$ is differentiable at $P$.*

*(a) If $\nabla f = \mathbf{0}$ at $P$, then all directional derivatives of $f$ at $P$ are zero.*

*(b) If $\nabla f \neq \mathbf{0}$ at $P$, then among all possible directional derivatives of $f$ at $P$, the derivative in the direction of $\nabla f$ at $P$ has the largest value. The value of this largest directional derivative is $\|\nabla f\|$ at $P$.*

*(c) If $\nabla f \neq \mathbf{0}$ at $P$, then among all possible directional derivatives of $f$ at $P$, the derivative in the direction opposite to that of $\nabla f$ at $P$ has the smallest value. The value of this smallest directional derivative is $-\|\nabla f\|$ at $P$.*

---

▶ **Example 4** Let $f(x, y) = x^2 e^y$. Find the maximum value of a directional derivative at $(-2, 0)$, and find the unit vector in the direction in which the maximum value occurs.

▲ **Figure 13.6.5**

*Solution.*   Since

$$\nabla f(x, y) = f_x(x, y)\mathbf{i} + f_y(x, y)\mathbf{j} = 2xe^y\mathbf{i} + x^2 e^y\mathbf{j}$$

the gradient of $f$ at $(-2, 0)$ is

$$\nabla f(-2, 0) = -4\mathbf{i} + 4\mathbf{j}$$

By Theorem 13.6.5, the maximum value of the directional derivative is

$$\|\nabla f(-2, 0)\| = \sqrt{(-4)^2 + 4^2} = \sqrt{32} = 4\sqrt{2}$$

This maximum occurs in the direction of $\nabla f(-2, 0)$. The unit vector in this direction is

$$\mathbf{u} = \frac{\nabla f(-2, 0)}{\|\nabla f(-2, 0)\|} = \frac{1}{4\sqrt{2}}(-4\mathbf{i} + 4\mathbf{j}) = -\frac{1}{\sqrt{2}}\mathbf{i} + \frac{1}{\sqrt{2}}\mathbf{j} \blacktriangleleft$$

> What would be the minimum value of
> a directional derivative of
>
> $$f(x, y) = x^2 e^y$$
>
> at $(-2, 0)$?

### GRADIENTS ARE NORMAL TO LEVEL CURVES

We have seen that the gradient points in the direction in which a function increases most rapidly. For a function $f(x, y)$ of two variables, we will now consider how this direction of maximum rate of increase can be determined from a contour map of the function. Suppose that $(x_0, y_0)$ is a point on a level curve $f(x, y) = c$ of $f$, and assume that this curve can be smoothly parametrized as

$$x = x(s), \quad y = y(s) \tag{13}$$

where $s$ is an arc length parameter. Recall from Formula (6) of Section 12.4 that the unit tangent vector to (13) is

$$\mathbf{T} = \mathbf{T}(s) = \left(\frac{dx}{ds}\right)\mathbf{i} + \left(\frac{dy}{ds}\right)\mathbf{j}$$

Since $\mathbf{T}$ gives a direction along which $f$ is nearly constant, we would expect the instantaneous rate of change of $f$ with respect to distance in the direction of $\mathbf{T}$ to be 0. That is, we would expect that

$$D_{\mathbf{T}}f(x, y) = \nabla f(x, y) \cdot \mathbf{T}(s) = 0$$

To show this to be the case, we differentiate both sides of the equation $f(x, y) = c$ with respect to $s$. Assuming that $f$ is differentiable at $(x, y)$, we can use the chain rule to obtain

$$\frac{\partial f}{\partial x}\frac{dx}{ds} + \frac{\partial f}{\partial y}\frac{dy}{ds} = 0$$

which we can rewrite as

$$\left(\frac{\partial f}{\partial x}\mathbf{i} + \frac{\partial f}{\partial y}\mathbf{j}\right) \cdot \left(\frac{dx}{ds}\mathbf{i} + \frac{dy}{ds}\mathbf{j}\right) = 0$$

or, alternatively, as

$$\nabla f(x, y) \cdot \mathbf{T} = 0$$

Therefore, if $\nabla f(x, y) \neq \mathbf{0}$, then $\nabla f(x, y)$ should be normal to the level curve $f(x, y) = c$ at any point $(x, y)$ on the curve.

It is proved in advanced courses that if $f(x, y)$ has continuous first-order partial derivatives, and if $\nabla f(x_0, y_0) \neq \mathbf{0}$, then near $(x_0, y_0)$ the graph of $f(x, y) = c$ is indeed a smooth curve through $(x_0, y_0)$. Furthermore, we also know from Theorem 13.4.4 that $f$ will be differentiable at $(x_0, y_0)$. We therefore have the following result.

> Show that the level curves for
>
> $$f(x, y) = x^2 + y^2$$
>
> are circles and verify Theorem 13.6.6 at
> $(x_0, y_0) = (3, 4)$.

> **13.6.6   THEOREM**   *Assume that $f(x, y)$ has continuous first-order partial derivatives in an open disk centered at $(x_0, y_0)$ and that $\nabla f(x_0, y_0) \neq \mathbf{0}$. Then $\nabla f(x_0, y_0)$ is normal to the level curve of $f$ through $(x_0, y_0)$.*

When we examine a contour map, we instinctively regard the distance between adjacent contours to be measured in a normal direction. If the contours correspond to equally spaced values of $f$, then the closer together the contours appear to be, the more rapidly the values of $f$ will be changing in that normal direction. It follows from Theorems 13.6.5 and 13.6.6 that this rate of change of $f$ is given by $\|\nabla f(x, y)\|$. Thus, the closer together the contours appear to be, the greater the length of the gradient of $f$.

▶ **Example 5**   A contour plot of a function $f$ is given in Figure 13.6.6$a$. Sketch the directions of the gradient of $f$ at the points $P$, $Q$, and $R$. At which of these three points does the gradient vector have maximum length? Minimum length?

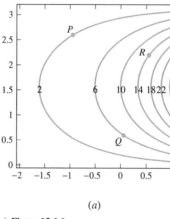

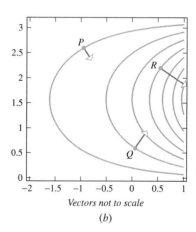

*Vectors not to scale*

(a)                           (b)

▲ **Figure 13.6.6**

***Solution.***   It follows from Theorems 13.6.5 and 13.6.6 that the directions of the gradient vectors will be as given in Figure 13.6.6$b$. Based on the density of the contour lines, we would guess that the gradient of $f$ has maximum length at $R$ and minimum length at $P$, with the length at $Q$ somewhere in between. ◀

**REMARK**

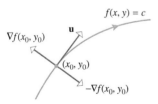

▲ **Figure 13.6.7**

If $(x_0, y_0)$ is a point on the level curve $f(x, y) = c$, then the slope of the surface $z = f(x, y)$ at that point in the direction of **u** is

$$D_{\mathbf{u}} f(x_0, y_0) = \nabla f(x_0, y_0) \cdot \mathbf{u}$$

If **u** is tangent to the level curve at $(x_0, y_0)$, then $f(x, y)$ is neither increasing nor decreasing in that direction, so $D_{\mathbf{u}} f(x_0, y_0) = 0$. Thus, $\nabla f(x_0, y_0)$, $-\nabla f(x_0, y_0)$, and the tangent vector **u** mark the directions of maximum slope, minimum slope, and zero slope at a point $(x_0, y_0)$ on a level curve (Figure 13.6.7). Good skiers use these facts intuitively to control their speed by zigzagging down ski slopes—they ski across the slope with their skis tangential to a level curve to stop their downhill motion, and they point their skis down the slope and normal to the level curve to obtain the most rapid descent.

■ **AN APPLICATION OF GRADIENTS**

There are numerous applications in which the motion of an object must be controlled so that it moves toward a heat source. For example, in medical applications the operation of certain diagnostic equipment is designed to locate heat sources generated by tumors or infections, and in military applications the trajectories of heat-seeking missiles are controlled to seek and destroy enemy aircraft. The following example illustrates how gradients are used to solve such problems.

*Heat-seeking missiles such as "Stinger" and "Sidewinder" use infrared sensors to measure gradients.*

▶ **Example 6**   A heat-seeking particle is located at the point $(2, 3)$ on a flat metal plate whose temperature at a point $(x, y)$ is

$$T(x, y) = 10 - 8x^2 - 2y^2$$

Find an equation for the trajectory of the particle if it moves continuously in the direction of maximum temperature increase.

*Solution.*    Assume that the trajectory is represented parametrically by the equations

$$x = x(t), \quad y = y(t)$$

where the particle is at the point (2, 3) at time $t = 0$. Because the particle moves in the direction of maximum temperature increase, its direction of motion at time $t$ is in the direction of the gradient of $T(x, y)$, and hence its velocity vector $\mathbf{v}(t)$ at time $t$ points in the direction of the gradient. Thus, there is a scalar $k$ that depends on $t$ such that

$$\mathbf{v}(t) = k\nabla T(x, y)$$

from which we obtain

$$\frac{dx}{dt}\mathbf{i} + \frac{dy}{dt}\mathbf{j} = k(-16x\mathbf{i} - 4y\mathbf{j})$$

Equating components yields

$$\frac{dx}{dt} = -16kx, \quad \frac{dy}{dt} = -4ky$$

and dividing to eliminate $k$ yields

$$\frac{dy}{dx} = \frac{-4ky}{-16kx} = \frac{y}{4x}$$

Thus, we can obtain the trajectory by solving the initial-value problem

$$\frac{dy}{dx} - \frac{y}{4x} = 0, \quad y(2) = 3$$

The differential equation is a separable first-order equation and hence can be solved by the method of separation of variables discussed in Section 8.2. We leave it for you to show that the solution of the initial-value problem is

$$y = \frac{3}{\sqrt[4]{2}}x^{1/4}$$

The graph of the trajectory and a contour plot of the temperature function are shown in Figure 13.6.8. ◄

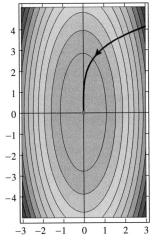

▲ **Figure 13.6.8**

---

✔ **QUICK CHECK EXERCISES 13.6**    *(See page 971 for answers.)*

1. The gradient of $f(x, y, z) = xy^2z^3$ at the point $(1, 1, 1)$ is _____.

2. Suppose that the differentiable function $f(x, y)$ has the property that

$$f\left(2 + \frac{s\sqrt{3}}{2}, 1 + \frac{s}{2}\right) = 3se^s$$

The directional derivative of $f$ in the direction of

$$\mathbf{u} = \frac{\sqrt{3}}{2}\mathbf{i} + \frac{1}{2}\mathbf{j}$$

at $(2, 1)$ is _____.

3. If the gradient of $f(x, y)$ at the origin is $6\mathbf{i} + 8\mathbf{j}$, then the directional derivative of $f$ in the direction of $\mathbf{a} = 3\mathbf{i} + 4\mathbf{j}$ at the origin is _____. The slope of the tangent line to the level curve of $f$ through the origin at $(0, 0)$ is _____.

4. If the gradient of $f(x, y, z)$ at $(1, 2, 3)$ is $2\mathbf{i} - 2\mathbf{j} + \mathbf{k}$, then the maximum value for a directional derivative of $f$ at $(1, 2, 3)$ is _____ and the minimum value for a directional derivative at this point is _____.

**EXERCISE SET 13.6** ⌁ Graphing Utility [c] CAS

**1–8** Find $D_{\mathbf{u}} f$ at $P$. ▪

**1.** $f(x, y) = (1 + xy)^{3/2}$; $P(3, 1)$; $\mathbf{u} = \dfrac{1}{\sqrt{2}}\mathbf{i} + \dfrac{1}{\sqrt{2}}\mathbf{j}$

**2.** $f(x, y) = \sin(5x - 3y)$; $P(3, 5)$; $\mathbf{u} = \frac{3}{5}\mathbf{i} - \frac{4}{5}\mathbf{j}$

**3.** $f(x, y) = \ln(1 + x^2 + y)$; $P(0, 0)$;
$\mathbf{u} = -\dfrac{1}{\sqrt{10}}\mathbf{i} - \dfrac{3}{\sqrt{10}}\mathbf{j}$

**4.** $f(x, y) = \dfrac{cx + dy}{x - y}$; $P(3, 4)$; $\mathbf{u} = \frac{4}{5}\mathbf{i} + \frac{3}{5}\mathbf{j}$

**5.** $f(x, y, z) = 4x^5 y^2 z^3$; $P(2, -1, 1)$; $\mathbf{u} = \frac{1}{3}\mathbf{i} + \frac{2}{3}\mathbf{j} - \frac{2}{3}\mathbf{k}$

**6.** $f(x, y, z) = ye^{xz} + z^2$; $P(0, 2, 3)$; $\mathbf{u} = \frac{2}{7}\mathbf{i} - \frac{3}{7}\mathbf{j} + \frac{6}{7}\mathbf{k}$

**7.** $f(x, y, z) = \ln(x^2 + 2y^2 + 3z^2)$; $P(-1, 2, 4)$;
$\mathbf{u} = -\frac{3}{13}\mathbf{i} - \frac{4}{13}\mathbf{j} - \frac{12}{13}\mathbf{k}$

**8.** $f(x, y, z) = \sin xyz$; $P\left(\frac{1}{2}, \frac{1}{3}, \pi\right)$;
$\mathbf{u} = \dfrac{1}{\sqrt{3}}\mathbf{i} - \dfrac{1}{\sqrt{3}}\mathbf{j} + \dfrac{1}{\sqrt{3}}\mathbf{k}$

**9–18** Find the directional derivative of $f$ at $P$ in the direction of $\mathbf{a}$. ▪

**9.** $f(x, y) = 4x^3 y^2$; $P(2, 1)$; $\mathbf{a} = 4\mathbf{i} - 3\mathbf{j}$

**10.** $f(x, y) = 9x^3 - 2y^3$; $P(1, 0)$; $\mathbf{a} = \mathbf{i} - \mathbf{j}$

**11.** $f(x, y) = y^2 \ln x$; $P(1, 4)$; $\mathbf{a} = -3\mathbf{i} + 3\mathbf{j}$

**12.** $f(x, y) = e^x \cos y$; $P(0, \pi/4)$; $\mathbf{a} = 5\mathbf{i} - 2\mathbf{j}$

**13.** $f(x, y) = \tan^{-1}(y/x)$; $P(-2, 2)$; $\mathbf{a} = -\mathbf{i} - \mathbf{j}$

**14.** $f(x, y) = xe^y - ye^x$; $P(0, 0)$; $\mathbf{a} = 5\mathbf{i} - 2\mathbf{j}$

**15.** $f(x, y, z) = xy + z^2$; $P(-3, 0, 4)$; $\mathbf{a} = \mathbf{i} + \mathbf{j} + \mathbf{k}$

**16.** $f(x, y, z) = y - \sqrt{x^2 + z^2}$; $P(-3, 1, 4)$;
$\mathbf{a} = 2\mathbf{i} - 2\mathbf{j} - \mathbf{k}$

**17.** $f(x, y, z) = \dfrac{z - x}{z + y}$; $P(1, 0, -3)$; $\mathbf{a} = -6\mathbf{i} + 3\mathbf{j} - 2\mathbf{k}$

**18.** $f(x, y, z) = e^{x+y+3z}$; $P(-2, 2, -1)$; $\mathbf{a} = 20\mathbf{i} - 4\mathbf{j} + 5\mathbf{k}$

**19–22** Find the directional derivative of $f$ at $P$ in the direction of a vector making the counterclockwise angle $\theta$ with the positive $x$-axis. ▪

**19.** $f(x, y) = \sqrt{xy}$; $P(1, 4)$; $\theta = \pi/3$

**20.** $f(x, y) = \dfrac{x - y}{x + y}$; $P(-1, -2)$; $\theta = \pi/2$

**21.** $f(x, y) = \tan(2x + y)$; $P(\pi/6, \pi/3)$; $\theta = 7\pi/4$

**22.** $f(x, y) = \sinh x \cosh y$; $P(0, 0)$; $\theta = \pi$

**23.** Find the directional derivative of
$$f(x, y) = \frac{x}{x + y}$$
at $P(1, 0)$ in the direction of $Q(-1, -1)$.

**24.** Find the directional derivative of $f(x, y) = e^{-x} \sec y$ at $P(0, \pi/4)$ in the direction of the origin.

**25.** Find the directional derivative of $f(x, y) = \sqrt{xy}e^y$ at $P(1, 1)$ in the direction of the negative $y$-axis.

**26.** Let
$$f(x, y) = \frac{y}{x + y}$$
Find a unit vector $\mathbf{u}$ for which $D_{\mathbf{u}} f(2, 3) = 0$.

**27.** Find the directional derivative of
$$f(x, y, z) = \frac{y}{x + z}$$
at $P(2, 1, -1)$ in the direction from $P$ to $Q(-1, 2, 0)$.

**28.** Find the directional derivative of the function
$$f(x, y, z) = x^3 y^2 z^5 - 2xz + yz + 3x$$
at $P(-1, -2, 1)$ in the direction of the negative $z$-axis.

**FOCUS ON CONCEPTS**

**29.** Suppose that $D_{\mathbf{u}} f(1, 2) = -5$ and $D_{\mathbf{v}} f(1, 2) = 10$, where $\mathbf{u} = \frac{3}{5}\mathbf{i} - \frac{4}{5}\mathbf{j}$ and $\mathbf{v} = \frac{4}{5}\mathbf{i} + \frac{3}{5}\mathbf{j}$. Find
(a) $f_x(1, 2)$      (b) $f_y(1, 2)$
(c) the directional derivative of $f$ at $(1, 2)$ in the direction of the origin.

**30.** Given that $f_x(-5, 1) = -3$ and $f_y(-5, 1) = 2$, find the directional derivative of $f$ at $P(-5, 1)$ in the direction of the vector from $P$ to $Q(-4, 3)$.

**31.** The accompanying figure shows some level curves of an unspecified function $f(x, y)$. Which of the three vectors shown in the figure is most likely to be $\nabla f$? Explain.

**32.** The accompanying figure shows some level curves of an unspecified function $f(x, y)$. Of the gradients at $P$ and $Q$, which probably has the greater length? Explain.

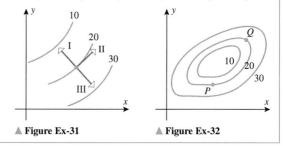

▲ Figure Ex-31          ▲ Figure Ex-32

**33–40** Find $\nabla z$ or $\nabla w$. ▪

**33.** $z = \sin(7y^2 - 7xy)$

**34.** $z = 7\sin(6x/y)$

**35.** $z = \dfrac{6x + 7y}{6x - 7y}$

**36.** $z = \dfrac{6xe^{3y}}{x + 8y}$

**37.** $w = -x^9 - y^3 + z^{12}$

**38.** $w = xe^{8y} \sin 6z$

**39.** $w = \ln\sqrt{x^2 + y^2 + z^2}$

**40.** $w = e^{-5x} \sec x^2 yz$

**41–46** Find the gradient of $f$ at the indicated point. ▪

**41.** $f(x, y) = 5x^2 + y^4$; $(4, 2)$

**42.** $f(x, y) = 5\sin x^2 + \cos 3y$; $(\sqrt{\pi}/2, 0)$

**43.** $f(x, y) = (x^2 + xy)^3$; $(-1, -1)$

**44.** $f(x, y) = (x^2 + y^2)^{-1/2}$; $(3, 4)$

**45.** $f(x, y, z) = y \ln(x + y + z);\ (-3, 4, 0)$

**46.** $f(x, y, z) = y^2 z \tan^3 x;\ (\pi/4, -3, 1)$

**47–50** Sketch the level curve of $f(x, y)$ that passes through $P$ and draw the gradient vector at $P$. ▪

**47.** $f(x, y) = 4x - 2y + 3;\ P(1, 2)$

**48.** $f(x, y) = y/x^2;\ P(-2, 2)$

**49.** $f(x, y) = x^2 + 4y^2;\ P(-2, 0)$

**50.** $f(x, y) = x^2 - y^2;\ P(2, -1)$

**51.** Find a unit vector **u** that is normal at $P(1, -2)$ to the level curve of $f(x, y) = 4x^2 y$ through $P$.

**52.** Find a unit vector **u** that is normal at $P(2, -3)$ to the level curve of $f(x, y) = 3x^2 y - xy$ through $P$.

**53–60** Find a unit vector in the direction in which $f$ increases most rapidly at $P$, and find the rate of change of $f$ at $P$ in that direction. ▪

**53.** $f(x, y) = 4x^3 y^2;\ P(-1, 1)$

**54.** $f(x, y) = 3x - \ln y;\ P(2, 4)$

**55.** $f(x, y) = \sqrt{x^2 + y^2};\ P(4, -3)$

**56.** $f(x, y) = \dfrac{x}{x + y};\ P(0, 2)$

**57.** $f(x, y, z) = x^3 z^2 + y^3 z + z - 1;\ P(1, 1, -1)$

**58.** $f(x, y, z) = \sqrt{x - 3y + 4z};\ P(0, -3, 0)$

**59.** $f(x, y, z) = \dfrac{x}{z} + \dfrac{z}{y^2};\ P(1, 2, -2)$

**60.** $f(x, y, z) = \tan^{-1}\left(\dfrac{x}{y + z}\right);\ P(4, 2, 2)$

**61–66** Find a unit vector in the direction in which $f$ decreases most rapidly at $P$, and find the rate of change of $f$ at $P$ in that direction. ▪

**61.** $f(x, y) = 20 - x^2 - y^2;\ P(-1, -3)$

**62.** $f(x, y) = e^{xy};\ P(2, 3)$

**63.** $f(x, y) = \cos(3x - y);\ P(\pi/6, \pi/4)$

**64.** $f(x, y) = \sqrt{\dfrac{x - y}{x + y}};\ P(3, 1)$

**65.** $f(x, y, z) = \dfrac{x + z}{z - y};\ P(5, 7, 6)$

**66.** $f(x, y, z) = 4e^{xy} \cos z;\ P(0, 1, \pi/4)$

**67–70 True–False** Determine whether the statement is true or false. Explain your answer. In each exercise, assume that $f$ denotes a differentiable function of two variables whose domain is the $xy$-plane. ▪

**67.** If $\mathbf{v} = 2\mathbf{u}$, then the directional derivative of $f$ in the direction of $\mathbf{v}$ at a point $(x_0, y_0)$ is twice the directional derivative of $f$ in the direction of $\mathbf{u}$ at the point $(x_0, y_0)$.

**68.** If $y = x^2$ is a contour of $f$, then $f_x(0, 0) = 0$.

**69.** If **u** is a fixed unit vector and $D_\mathbf{u} f(x, y) = 0$ for all points $(x, y)$, then $f$ is a constant function.

**70.** If the displacement vector from $(x_0, y_0)$ to $(x_1, y_1)$ is a positive multiple of $\nabla f(x_0, y_0)$, then $f(x_0, y_0) \le f(x_1, y_1)$.

**FOCUS ON CONCEPTS**

**71.** Given that $\nabla f(4, -5) = 2\mathbf{i} - \mathbf{j}$, find the directional derivative of the function $f$ at the point $(4, -5)$ in the direction of $\mathbf{a} = 5\mathbf{i} + 2\mathbf{j}$.

**72.** Given that $\nabla f(x_0, y_0) = \mathbf{i} - 2\mathbf{j}$ and $D_\mathbf{u} f(x_0, y_0) = -2$, find **u** (two answers).

**73.** The accompanying figure shows some level curves of an unspecified function $f(x, y)$.
(a) Use the available information to approximate the length of the vector $\nabla f(1, 2)$, and sketch the approximation. Explain how you approximated the length and determined the direction of the vector.
(b) Sketch an approximation of the vector $-\nabla f(4, 4)$.

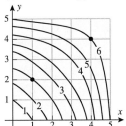

◀ **Figure Ex-73**

**74.** The accompanying figure shows a topographic map of a hill and a point $P$ at the bottom of the hill. Suppose that you want to climb from the point $P$ toward the top of the hill in such a way that you are always ascending in the direction of steepest slope. Sketch the projection of your path on the contour map. This is called the ***path of steepest ascent***. Explain how you determined the path.

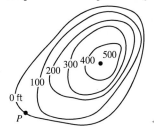

◀ **Figure Ex-74**

**75.** Let $z = 3x^2 - y^2$. Find all points at which $\|\nabla z\| = 6$.

**76.** Given that $z = 3x + y^2$, find $\nabla \|\nabla z\|$ at the point $(5, 2)$.

**77.** A particle moves along a path $C$ given by the equations $x = t$ and $y = -t^2$. If $z = x^2 + y^2$, find $dz/ds$ along $C$ at the instant when the particle is at the point $(2, -4)$.

**78.** The temperature (in degrees Celsius) at a point $(x, y)$ on a metal plate in the $xy$-plane is

$$T(x, y) = \frac{xy}{1 + x^2 + y^2}$$

*(cont.)*

(a) Find the rate of change of temperature at $(1, 1)$ in the direction of $\mathbf{a} = 2\mathbf{i} - \mathbf{j}$.

(b) An ant at $(1, 1)$ wants to walk in the direction in which the temperature drops most rapidly. Find a unit vector in that direction.

**79.** If the electric potential at a point $(x, y)$ in the $xy$-plane is $V(x, y)$, then the *electric intensity vector* at the point $(x, y)$ is $\mathbf{E} = -\nabla V(x, y)$. Suppose that $V(x, y) = e^{-2x} \cos 2y$.

(a) Find the electric intensity vector at $(\pi/4, 0)$.

(b) Show that at each point in the plane, the electric potential decreases most rapidly in the direction of the vector $\mathbf{E}$.

**80.** On a certain mountain, the elevation $z$ above a point $(x, y)$ in an $xy$-plane at sea level is $z = 2000 - 0.02x^2 - 0.04y^2$, where $x$, $y$, and $z$ are in meters. The positive $x$-axis points east, and the positive $y$-axis north. A climber is at the point $(-20, 5, 1991)$.

(a) If the climber uses a compass reading to walk due west, will she begin to ascend or descend?

(b) If the climber uses a compass reading to walk northeast, will she ascend or descend? At what rate?

(c) In what compass direction should the climber begin walking to travel a level path (two answers)?

**81.** Given that the directional derivative of $f(x, y, z)$ at the point $(3, -2, 1)$ in the direction of $\mathbf{a} = 2\mathbf{i} - \mathbf{j} - 2\mathbf{k}$ is $-5$ and that $\|\nabla f(3, -2, 1)\| = 5$, find $\nabla f(3, -2, 1)$.

**82.** The temperature (in degrees Celsius) at a point $(x, y, z)$ in a metal solid is

$$T(x, y, z) = \frac{xyz}{1 + x^2 + y^2 + z^2}$$

(a) Find the rate of change of temperature with respect to distance at $(1, 1, 1)$ in the direction of the origin.

(b) Find the direction in which the temperature rises most rapidly at the point $(1, 1, 1)$. (Express your answer as a unit vector.)

(c) Find the rate at which the temperature rises moving from $(1, 1, 1)$ in the direction obtained in part (b).

**83.** Let $r = \sqrt{x^2 + y^2}$.

(a) Show that $\nabla r = \dfrac{\mathbf{r}}{r}$, where $\mathbf{r} = x\mathbf{i} + y\mathbf{j}$.

(b) Show that $\nabla f(r) = f'(r) \nabla r = \dfrac{f'(r)}{r} \mathbf{r}$.

**84.** Use the formula in part (b) of Exercise 83 to find

(a) $\nabla f(r)$ if $f(r) = re^{-3r}$

(b) $f(r)$ if $\nabla f(r) = 3r^2 \mathbf{r}$ and $f(2) = 1$.

**85.** Let $\mathbf{u}_r$ be a unit vector whose counterclockwise angle from the positive $x$-axis is $\theta$, and let $\mathbf{u}_\theta$ be a unit vector $90°$ counterclockwise from $\mathbf{u}_r$. Show that if $z = f(x, y)$, $x = r \cos \theta$, and $y = r \sin \theta$, then

$$\nabla z = \frac{\partial z}{\partial r} \mathbf{u}_r + \frac{1}{r} \frac{\partial z}{\partial \theta} \mathbf{u}_\theta$$

[*Hint:* Use part (c) of Exercise 57, Section 13.5.]

**86.** Prove: If $f$ and $g$ are differentiable, then

(a) $\nabla(f + g) = \nabla f + \nabla g$

(b) $\nabla(cf) = c\nabla f$ ($c$ constant)

(c) $\nabla(fg) = f\nabla g + g\nabla f$

(d) $\nabla\left(\dfrac{f}{g}\right) = \dfrac{g\nabla f - f\nabla g}{g^2}$

(e) $\nabla(f^n) = nf^{n-1} \nabla f$.

**87–88** A heat-seeking particle is located at the point $P$ on a flat metal plate whose temperature at a point $(x, y)$ is $T(x, y)$. Find parametric equations for the trajectory of the particle if it moves continuously in the direction of maximum temperature increase.

**87.** $T(x, y) = 5 - 4x^2 - y^2$; $P(1, 4)$

**88.** $T(x, y) = 100 - x^2 - 2y^2$; $P(5, 3)$

**89.** Use a graphing utility to generate the trajectory of the particle together with some representative level curves of the temperature function in Exercise 87.

**90.** Use a graphing utility to generate the trajectory of the particle together with some representative level curves of the temperature function in Exercise 88.

**91.** (a) Use a CAS to graph $f(x, y) = (x^2 + 3y^2)e^{-(x^2+y^2)}$.

(b) At how many points do you think it is true that $D_{\mathbf{u}} f(x, y) = 0$ for all unit vectors $\mathbf{u}$?

(c) Use a CAS to find $\nabla f$.

(d) Use a CAS to solve the equation $\nabla f(x, y) = 0$ for $x$ and $y$.

(e) Use the result in part (d) together with Theorem 13.6.5 to check your conjecture in part (b).

**92.** Prove: If $x = x(t)$ and $y = y(t)$ are differentiable at $t$, and if $z = f(x, y)$ is differentiable at the point $(x(t), y(t))$, then

$$\frac{dz}{dt} = \nabla z \cdot \mathbf{r}'(t)$$

where $\mathbf{r}(t) = x(t)\mathbf{i} + y(t)\mathbf{j}$.

**93.** Prove: If $f$, $f_x$, and $f_y$ are continuous on a circular region, and if $\nabla f(x, y) = \mathbf{0}$ throughout the region, then $f(x, y)$ is constant on the region. [*Hint:* See Exercise 69, Section 13.5.]

**94.** Prove: If the function $f$ is differentiable at the point $(x, y)$ and if $D_{\mathbf{u}} f(x, y) = 0$ in two nonparallel directions, then $D_{\mathbf{u}} f(x, y) = 0$ in all directions.

**95.** Given that the functions $u = u(x, y, z)$, $v = v(x, y, z)$, $w = w(x, y, z)$, and $f(u, v, w)$ are all differentiable, show that

$$\nabla f(u, v, w) = \frac{\partial f}{\partial u} \nabla u + \frac{\partial f}{\partial v} \nabla v + \frac{\partial f}{\partial w} \nabla w$$

**96.** Writing Let $f$ denote a differentiable function of two variables. Write a short paragraph that discusses the connections between directional derivatives of $f$ and slopes of tangent lines to the graph of $f$.

**97.** Writing Let $f$ denote a differentiable function of two variables. Although we have defined what it means to say that $f$ is differentiable, we have not defined the "derivative" of $f$. Write a short paragraph that discusses the merits of defining the derivative of $f$ to be the gradient $\nabla f$.

## 13.7    TANGENT PLANES AND NORMAL VECTORS

*In this section we will discuss tangent planes to surfaces in three-dimensional space. We will be concerned with three main questions: What is a tangent plane? When do tangent planes exist? How do we find equations of tangent planes?*

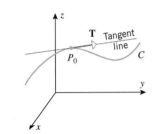

▲ Figure 13.7.1

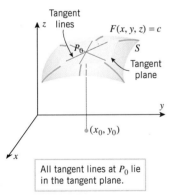

All tangent lines at $P_0$ lie in the tangent plane.

▲ Figure 13.7.2

■ **TANGENT PLANES AND NORMAL VECTORS TO LEVEL SURFACES $F(x, y, z) = c$**

We begin by considering the problem of finding tangent planes to level surfaces of a function $F(x, y, z)$. These surfaces are represented by equations of the form $F(x, y, z) = c$. We will assume that $F$ has continuous first-order partial derivatives, since this has an important geometric consequence. Fix $c$, and suppose that $P_0(x_0, y_0, z_0)$ satisfies the equation $F(x, y, z) = c$. In advanced courses it is proved that if $F$ has continuous first-order partial derivatives, and if $\nabla F(x_0, y_0, z_0) \neq \mathbf{0}$, then near $P_0$ the graph of $F(x, y, z) = c$ is indeed a "surface" rather than some possibly exotic-looking set of points in 3-space.

We will base our concept of a tangent plane to a level surface $S: F(x, y, z) = c$ on the more elementary notion of a tangent line to a curve $C$ in 3-space (Figure 13.7.1). Intuitively, we would expect a tangent plane to $S$ at a point $P_0$ to be composed of the tangent lines at $P_0$ of all curves on $S$ that pass through $P_0$ (Figure 13.7.2). Suppose $C$ is a curve on $S$ through $P_0$ that is parametrized by $x = x(t)$, $y = y(t)$, $z = z(t)$ with $x_0 = x(t_0)$, $y_0 = y(t_0)$, and $z_0 = z(t_0)$. The tangent line $l$ to $C$ through $P_0$ is then parallel to the vector

$$\mathbf{r}' = x'(t_0)\mathbf{i} + y'(t_0)\mathbf{j} + z'(t_0)\mathbf{k}$$

where we assume that $\mathbf{r}' \neq \mathbf{0}$ (Definition 12.2.7). Since $C$ is on the surface $F(x, y, z) = c$, we have

$$c = F(x(t), y(t), z(t)) \tag{1}$$

Computing the derivative at $t_0$ of both sides of (1), we have by the chain rule that

$$0 = F_x(x_0, y_0, z_0)x'(t_0) + F_y(x_0, y_0, z_0)y'(t_0) + F_z(x_0, y_0, z_0)z'(t_0)$$

We can write this equation in vector form as

$$0 = (F_x(x_0, y_0, z_0)\mathbf{i} + F_y(x_0, y_0, z_0)\mathbf{j} + F_z(x_0, y_0, z_0)\mathbf{k}) \cdot (x'(t_0)\mathbf{i} + y'(t_0)\mathbf{j} + z'(t_0)\mathbf{k})$$

or

$$0 = \nabla F(x_0, y_0, z_0) \cdot \mathbf{r}' \tag{2}$$

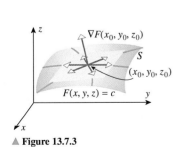

▲ Figure 13.7.3

It follows that if $\nabla F(x_0, y_0, z_0) \neq \mathbf{0}$, then $\nabla F(x_0, y_0, z_0)$ is normal to line $l$. Therefore, the tangent line $l$ to $C$ at $P_0$ is contained in the plane through $P_0$ with normal vector $\nabla F(x_0, y_0, z_0)$. Since $C$ was *arbitrary*, we conclude that the same is true for any curve on $S$ through $P_0$ (Figure 13.7.3). Thus, it makes sense to define the tangent plane to $S$ at $P_0$ to be the plane through $P_0$ whose normal vector is

$$\mathbf{n} = \nabla F(x_0, y_0, z_0) = \langle F_x(x_0, y_0, z_0), F_y(x_0, y_0, z_0), F_z(x_0, y_0, z_0) \rangle$$

Using the point-normal form [see Formula (3) in Section 11.6], we have the following definition.

Definition 13.7.1 can be viewed as an extension of Theorem 13.6.6 from curves to surfaces.

**13.7.1 DEFINITION** Assume that $F(x, y, z)$ has continuous first-order partial derivatives and that $P_0(x_0, y_0, z_0)$ is a point on the level surface $S: F(x, y, z) = c$. If $\nabla F(x_0, y_0, z_0) \neq \mathbf{0}$, then $\mathbf{n} = \nabla F(x_0, y_0, z_0)$ is a **normal vector** to $S$ at $P_0$ and the **tangent plane** to $S$ at $P_0$ is the plane with equation

$$F_x(x_0, y_0, z_0)(x - x_0) + F_y(x_0, y_0, z_0)(y - y_0) + F_z(x_0, y_0, z_0)(z - z_0) = 0 \quad (3)$$

The line through the point $P_0$ parallel to the normal vector $\mathbf{n}$ is perpendicular to the tangent plane (3). We will call this the **normal line**, or sometimes more simply the **normal** to the surface $F(x, y, z) = c$ at $P_0$. It follows that this line can be expressed parametrically as

$$x = x_0 + F_x(x_0, y_0, z_0)t, \quad y = y_0 + F_y(x_0, y_0, z_0)t, \quad z = z_0 + F_z(x_0, y_0, z_0)t \quad (4)$$

▶ **Example 1** Consider the ellipsoid $x^2 + 4y^2 + z^2 = 18$.

(a) Find an equation of the tangent plane to the ellipsoid at the point $(1, 2, 1)$.

(b) Find parametric equations of the line that is normal to the ellipsoid at the point $(1, 2, 1)$.

(c) Find the acute angle that the tangent plane at the point $(1, 2, 1)$ makes with the $xy$-plane.

**Solution (a).** We apply Definition 13.7.1 with $F(x, y, z) = x^2 + 4y^2 + z^2$ and $(x_0, y_0, z_0) = (1, 2, 1)$. Since

$$\nabla F(x, y, z) = \langle F_x(x, y, z), F_y(x, y, z), F_z(x, y, z) \rangle = \langle 2x, 8y, 2z \rangle$$

we have

$$\mathbf{n} = \nabla F(1, 2, 1) = \langle 2, 16, 2 \rangle$$

Hence, from (3) the equation of the tangent plane is

$$2(x - 1) + 16(y - 2) + 2(z - 1) = 0 \quad \text{or} \quad x + 8y + z = 18$$

**Solution (b).** Since $\mathbf{n} = \langle 2, 16, 2 \rangle$ at the point $(1, 2, 1)$, it follows from (4) that parametric equations for the normal line to the ellipsoid at the point $(1, 2, 1)$ are

$$x = 1 + 2t, \quad y = 2 + 16t, \quad z = 1 + 2t$$

**Solution (c).** To find the acute angle $\theta$ between the tangent plane and the $xy$-plane, we will apply Formula (9) of Section 11.6 with $\mathbf{n}_1 = \mathbf{n} = \langle 2, 16, 2 \rangle$ and $\mathbf{n}_2 = \langle 0, 0, 1 \rangle$. This yields

$$\cos \theta = \frac{|\langle 2, 16, 2 \rangle \cdot \langle 0, 0, 1 \rangle|}{\|\langle 2, 16, 2 \rangle\| \, \|\langle 0, 0, 1 \rangle\|} = \frac{2}{(2\sqrt{66})(1)} = \frac{1}{\sqrt{66}}$$

Thus,

$$\theta = \cos^{-1}\left(\frac{1}{\sqrt{66}}\right) \approx 83°$$

(Figure 13.7.4). ◀

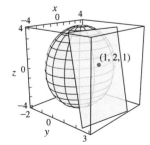

▲ **Figure 13.7.4**

### TANGENT PLANES TO SURFACES OF THE FORM $z = f(x, y)$

To find a tangent plane to a surface of the form $z = f(x, y)$, we can use Equation (3) with the function $F(x, y, z) = z - f(x, y)$.

▶ **Example 2** Find an equation for the tangent plane and parametric equations for the normal line to the surface $z = x^2 y$ at the point $(2, 1, 4)$.

***Solution.*** Let $F(x, y, z) = z - x^2 y$. Then $F(x, y, z) = 0$ on the surface, so we can find the find the gradient of $F$ at the point $(2, 1, 4)$:

$$\nabla F(x, y, z) = -2xy\mathbf{i} - x^2\mathbf{j} + \mathbf{k}$$
$$\nabla F(2, 1, 4) = -4\mathbf{i} - 4\mathbf{j} + \mathbf{k}$$

From (3) the tangent plane has equation

$$-4(x - 2) - 4(y - 1) + 1(z - 4) = 0 \quad \text{or} \quad -4x - 4y + z = -8$$

and the normal line has equations

$$x = 2 - 4t, \qquad y = 1 - 4t, \qquad z = 4 + t \quad ◄$$

Suppose that $f(x, y)$ is differentiable at a point $(x_0, y_0)$ and that $z_0 = f(x_0, y_0)$. It can be shown that the procedure of Example 2 can be used to find the tangent plane to the surface $z = f(x, y)$ at the point $(x_0, y_0, z_0)$. This yields an alternative equation for a tangent plane to the graph of a differentiable function.

---

**13.7.2** **THEOREM** *If $f(x, y)$ is differentiable at the point $(x_0, y_0)$, then the tangent plane to the surface $z = f(x, y)$ at the point $P_0(x_0, y_0, f(x_0, y_0))$ [or $(x_0, y_0)$] is the plane*

$$z = f(x_0, y_0) + f_x(x_0, y_0)(x - x_0) + f_y(x_0, y_0)(y - y_0) \qquad (5)$$

---

**PROOF** Consider the function $F(x, y, z) = z - f(x, y)$. Since $F(x, y, z) = 0$ on the surface, we will apply (3) to this function. The partial derivatives of $F$ are

$$F_x(x, y, z) = -f_x(x, y), \quad F_y(x, y, z) = -f_y(x, y), \quad F_z(x, y, z) = 1$$

Since the point at which we evaluate these derivatives lies on the surface, it will have the form $(x_0, y_0, f(x_0, y_0))$. Thus, (3) gives

$$0 = F_x(x_0, y_0, z_0)(x - x_0) + F_y(x_0, y_0, z_0)(y - y_0) + F_z(x_0, y_0, z_0)(z - f(x_0, y_0))$$
$$= -f_x(x_0, y_0)(x - x_0) - f_y(x_0, y_0)(y - y_0) + 1(z - f(x_0, y_0))$$

which is equivalent to (5). ■

Recall from Section 13.4 that if a function $f(x, y)$ is differentiable at a point $(x_0, y_0)$, then the local linear approximation $L(x, y)$ to $f$ at $(x_0, y_0)$ has the equation

$$L(x, y) = f(x_0, y_0) + f_x(x_0, y_0)(x - x_0) + f_y(x_0, y_0)(y - y_0)$$

Notice that the equation $z = L(x, y)$ is identical to that of the tangent plane to $f(x, y)$ at the point $(x_0, y_0)$. Thus, the graph of the local linear approximation to $f(x, y)$ at the point $(x_0, y_0)$ is the tangent plane to the surface $z = f(x, y)$ at the point $(x_0, y_0)$.

## TANGENT PLANES AND TOTAL DIFFERENTIALS

Recall that for a function $z = f(x, y)$ of two variables, the approximation by differentials is

$$\Delta z = \Delta f = f(x, y) - f(x_0, y_0) \approx dz = f_x(x_0, y_0)(x - x_0) + f_y(x_0, y_0)(y - y_0)$$

Note that the tangent plane in Figure 13.7.5 is analogous to the tangent line in Figure 13.4.2.

The tangent plane provides a geometric interpretation of this approximation. We see in Figure 13.7.5 that $\Delta z$ is the change in $z$ *along the surface* $z = f(x, y)$ from the point $P_0(x_0, y_0, f(x_0, y_0))$ to the point $P(x, y, f(x, y))$, and $dz$ is the change in $z$ *along the tangent plane* from $P_0$ to $Q(x, y, L(x, y))$. The small vertical displacement at $(x, y)$ between the surface and the plane represents the error in the local linear approximation to $f$ at $(x_0, y_0)$. We have seen that near $(x_0, y_0)$ this error term has magnitude much smaller than the distance between $(x, y)$ and $(x_0, y_0)$.

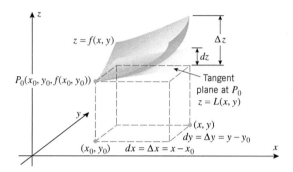

▶ **Figure 13.7.5**

**USING GRADIENTS TO FIND TANGENT LINES TO INTERSECTIONS OF SURFACES**

In general, the intersection of two surfaces $F(x, y, z) = 0$ and $G(x, y, z) = 0$ will be a curve in 3-space. If $(x_0, y_0, z_0)$ is a point on this curve, then $\nabla F(x_0, y_0, z_0)$ will be normal to the surface $F(x, y, z) = 0$ at $(x_0, y_0, z_0)$ and $\nabla G(x_0, y_0, z_0)$ will be normal to the surface $G(x, y, z) = 0$ at $(x_0, y_0, z_0)$. Thus, if the curve of intersection can be smoothly parametrized, then its unit tangent vector $\mathbf{T}$ at $(x_0, y_0, z_0)$ will be orthogonal to both $\nabla F(x_0, y_0, z_0)$ and $\nabla G(x_0, y_0, z_0)$ (Figure 13.7.6). Consequently, if

$$\nabla F(x_0, y_0, z_0) \times \nabla G(x_0, y_0, z_0) \neq \mathbf{0}$$

then this cross product will be parallel to $\mathbf{T}$ and hence will be tangent to the curve of intersection. This tangent vector can be used to determine the direction of the tangent line to the curve of intersection at the point $(x_0, y_0, z_0)$.

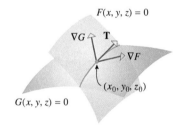

▲ **Figure 13.7.6**

▶ **Example 3**   Find parametric equations of the tangent line to the curve of intersection of the paraboloid $z = x^2 + y^2$ and the ellipsoid $3x^2 + 2y^2 + z^2 = 9$ at the point $(1, 1, 2)$ (Figure 13.7.7).

*Solution.*   We begin by rewriting the equations of the surfaces as

$$x^2 + y^2 - z = 0 \quad \text{and} \quad 3x^2 + 2y^2 + z^2 - 9 = 0$$

and we take

$$F(x, y, z) = x^2 + y^2 - z \quad \text{and} \quad G(x, y, z) = 3x^2 + 2y^2 + z^2 - 9$$

We will need the gradients of these functions at the point $(1, 1, 2)$. The computations are

$$\nabla F(x, y, z) = 2x\mathbf{i} + 2y\mathbf{j} - \mathbf{k}, \quad \nabla G(x, y, z) = 6x\mathbf{i} + 4y\mathbf{j} + 2z\mathbf{k}$$
$$\nabla F(1, 1, 2) = 2\mathbf{i} + 2\mathbf{j} - \mathbf{k}, \quad \nabla G(1, 1, 2) = 6\mathbf{i} + 4\mathbf{j} + 4\mathbf{k}$$

Thus, a tangent vector at $(1, 1, 2)$ to the curve of intersection is

$$\nabla F(1, 1, 2) \times \nabla G(1, 1, 2) = \begin{vmatrix} \mathbf{i} & \mathbf{j} & \mathbf{k} \\ 2 & 2 & -1 \\ 6 & 4 & 4 \end{vmatrix} = 12\mathbf{i} - 14\mathbf{j} - 4\mathbf{k}$$

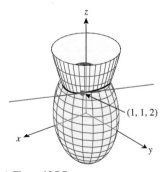

▲ **Figure 13.7.7**

Since any scalar multiple of this vector will do just as well, we can multiply by $\frac{1}{2}$ to reduce the size of the coefficients and use the vector of $6\mathbf{i} - 7\mathbf{j} - 2\mathbf{k}$ to determine the direction of the tangent line. This vector and the point $(1, 1, 2)$ yield the parametric equations

$$x = 1 + 6t, \quad y = 1 - 7t, \quad z = 2 - 2t \blacktriangleleft$$

✓ **QUICK CHECK EXERCISES 13.7**    *(See page 977 for answers.)*

1. Suppose that $f(1, 0, -1) = 2$, and $f(x, y, z)$ is differentiable at $(1, 0, -1)$ with $\nabla f(1, 0, -1) = \langle 2, 1, 1 \rangle$. An equation for the tangent plane to the level surface $f(x, y, z) = 2$ at the point $(1, 0, -1)$ is _____, and parametric equations for the normal line to the level surface through the point $(1, 0, -1)$ are

   $$x = \text{\_\_\_\_}, \quad y = \text{\_\_\_\_}, \quad z = \text{\_\_\_\_}$$

2. Suppose that $f(x, y)$ is differentiable at the point $(3, 1)$ with $f(3, 1) = 4$, $f_x(3, 1) = 2$, and $f_y(3, 1) = -3$. An equation for the tangent plane to the graph of $f$ at the point $(3, 1, 4)$ is _____, and parametric equations for the normal line to the graph of $f$ through the point $(3, 1, 4)$ are

   $$x = \text{\_\_\_\_}, \quad y = \text{\_\_\_\_}, \quad z = \text{\_\_\_\_}$$

3. An equation for the tangent plane to the graph of $z = x^2 \sqrt{y}$ at the point $(2, 4, 8)$ is _____, and parametric equations for the normal line to the graph of $z = x^2 \sqrt{y}$ through the point $(2, 4, 8)$ are

   $$x = \text{\_\_\_\_}, \quad y = \text{\_\_\_\_}, \quad z = \text{\_\_\_\_}$$

4. The sphere $x^2 + y^2 + z^2 = 9$ and the plane $x + y + z = 5$ intersect in a circle that passes through the point $(2, 1, 2)$. Parametric equations for the tangent line to this circle at $(2, 1, 2)$ are

   $$x = \text{\_\_\_\_}, \quad y = \text{\_\_\_\_}, \quad z = \text{\_\_\_\_}$$

**EXERCISE SET 13.7**    <u>C</u> CAS

1. Consider the ellipsoid $x^2 + y^2 + 4z^2 = 12$.
   (a) Find an equation of the tangent plane to the ellipsoid at the point $(2, 2, 1)$.
   (b) Find parametric equations of the line that is normal to the ellipsoid at the point $(2, 2, 1)$.
   (c) Find the acute angle that the tangent plane at the point $(2, 2, 1)$ makes with the $xy$-plane.

2. Consider the surface $xz - yz^3 + yz^2 = 2$.
   (a) Find an equation of the tangent plane to the surface at the point $(2, -1, 1)$.
   (b) Find parametric equations of the line that is normal to the surface at the point $(2, -1, 1)$.
   (c) Find the acute angle that the tangent plane at the point $(2, -1, 1)$ makes with the $xy$-plane.

**3–12** Find an equation for the tangent plane and parametric equations for the normal line to the surface at the point $P$. ▪

3. $x^2 + y^2 + z^2 = 25$; $P(-3, 0, 4)$
4. $x^2 y - 4z^2 = -7$; $P(-3, 1, -2)$
5. $x^2 - xyz = 56$; $P(-4, 5, 2)$
6. $z = x^2 + y^2$; $P(2, -3, 13)$
7. $z = 4x^3 y^2 + 2y$; $P(1, -2, 12)$
8. $z = \frac{1}{2} x^7 y^{-2}$; $P(2, 4, 4)$
9. $z = xe^{-y}$; $P(1, 0, 1)$
10. $z = \ln \sqrt{x^2 + y^2}$; $P(-1, 0, 0)$
11. $z = e^{3y} \sin 3x$; $P(\pi/6, 0, 1)$
12. $z = x^{1/2} + y^{1/2}$; $P(4, 9, 5)$

**FOCUS ON CONCEPTS**

13. Find all points on the surface at which the tangent plane is horizontal.
    (a) $z = x^3 y^2$
    (b) $z = x^2 - xy + y^2 - 2x + 4y$

14. Find a point on the surface $z = 3x^2 - y^2$ at which the tangent plane is parallel to the plane $6x + 4y - z = 5$.

15. Find a point on the surface $z = 8 - 3x^2 - 2y^2$ at which the tangent plane is perpendicular to the line $x = 2 - 3t$, $y = 7 + 8t$, $z = 5 - t$.

16. Show that the surfaces

    $$z = \sqrt{x^2 + y^2} \quad \text{and} \quad z = \frac{1}{10}(x^2 + y^2) + \frac{5}{2}$$

    intersect at $(3, 4, 5)$ and have a common tangent plane at that point.

17. (a) Find all points of intersection of the line

    $$x = -1 + t, \quad y = 2 + t, \quad z = 2t + 7$$

    and the surface

    $$z = x^2 + y^2$$

    (b) At each point of intersection, find the cosine of the acute angle between the given line and the line normal to the surface.

18. Show that if $f$ is differentiable and $z = xf(x/y)$, then all tangent planes to the graph of this equation pass through the origin.

**19–22 True–False** Determine whether the statement is true or false. Explain your answer. ■

**19.** If the tangent plane to the level surface of $F(x, y, z)$ at the point $P_0(x_0, y_0, z_0)$ is also tangent to a level surface of $G(x, y, z)$ at $P_0$, then $\nabla F(x_0, y_0, z_0) = \nabla G(x_0, y_0, z_0)$.

**20.** If the tangent plane to the graph of $z = f(x, y)$ at the point $(1, 1, 2)$ has equation $x - y + 2z = 4$, then $f_x(1, 1) = 1$ and $f_y(1, 1) = -1$.

**21.** If the tangent plane to the graph of $z = f(x, y)$ at the point $(1, 2, 1)$ has equation $2x + y - z = 3$, then the local linear approximation to $f$ at $(1, 2)$ is given by the function $L(x, y) = 1 + 2(x - 1) + (y - 2)$.

**22.** The normal line to the surface $z = f(x, y)$ at the point $P_0(x_0, y_0, f(x_0, y_0))$ has a direction vector given by $f_x(x_0, y_0)\mathbf{i} + f_y(x_0, y_0)\mathbf{j} - \mathbf{k}$.

**23–24** Find two unit vectors that are normal to the given surface at the point $P$. ■

**23.** $\sqrt{\dfrac{z+x}{y-1}} = z^2;\ \ P(3, 5, 1)$

**24.** $\sin xz - 4\cos yz = 4;\ \ P(\pi, \pi, 1)$

**25.** Show that every line that is normal to the sphere

$$x^2 + y^2 + z^2 = 1$$

passes through the origin.

**26.** Find all points on the ellipsoid $2x^2 + 3y^2 + 4z^2 = 9$ at which the plane tangent to the ellipsoid is parallel to the plane $x - 2y + 3z = 5$.

**27.** Find all points on the surface $x^2 + y^2 - z^2 = 1$ at which the normal line is parallel to the line through $P(1, -2, 1)$ and $Q(4, 0, -1)$.

**28.** Show that the ellipsoid $2x^2 + 3y^2 + z^2 = 9$ and the sphere

$$x^2 + y^2 + z^2 - 6x - 8y - 8z + 24 = 0$$

have a common tangent plane at the point $(1, 1, 2)$.

**29.** Find parametric equations for the tangent line to the curve of intersection of the paraboloid $z = x^2 + y^2$ and the ellipsoid $x^2 + 4y^2 + z^2 = 9$ at the point $(1, -1, 2)$.

**30.** Find parametric equations for the tangent line to the curve of intersection of the cone $z = \sqrt{x^2 + y^2}$ and the plane $x + 2y + 2z = 20$ at the point $(4, 3, 5)$.

**31.** Find parametric equations for the tangent line to the curve of intersection of the cylinders $x^2 + z^2 = 25$ and $y^2 + z^2 = 25$ at the point $(3, -3, 4)$.

**c** **32.** The accompanying figure shows the intersection of the surfaces $z = 8 - x^2 - y^2$ and $4x + 2y - z = 0$.
  (a) Find parametric equations for the tangent line to the curve of intersection at the point $(0, 2, 4)$.
  (b) Use a CAS to generate a reasonable facsimile of the figure. You need not generate the colors, but try to obtain a similar viewpoint.

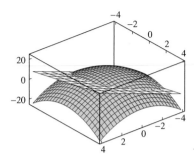

◀ **Figure Ex-32**

**33.** Show that the equation of the plane that is tangent to the ellipsoid

$$\frac{x^2}{a^2} + \frac{y^2}{b^2} + \frac{z^2}{c^2} = 1$$

at $(x_0, y_0, z_0)$ can be written in the form

$$\frac{x_0 x}{a^2} + \frac{y_0 y}{b^2} + \frac{z_0 z}{c^2} = 1$$

**34.** Show that the equation of the plane that is tangent to the paraboloid

$$z = \frac{x^2}{a^2} + \frac{y^2}{b^2}$$

at $(x_0, y_0, z_0)$ can be written in the form

$$z + z_0 = \frac{2x_0 x}{a^2} + \frac{2y_0 y}{b^2}$$

**35.** Prove: If the surfaces $z = f(x, y)$ and $z = g(x, y)$ intersect at $P(x_0, y_0, z_0)$, and if $f$ and $g$ are differentiable at $(x_0, y_0)$, then the normal lines at $P$ are perpendicular if and only if

$$f_x(x_0, y_0)g_x(x_0, y_0) + f_y(x_0, y_0)g_y(x_0, y_0) = -1$$

**36.** Use the result in Exercise 35 to show that the normal lines to the cones $z = \sqrt{x^2 + y^2}$ and $z = -\sqrt{x^2 + y^2}$ are perpendicular to the normal lines to the sphere $x^2 + y^2 + z^2 = a^2$ at every point of intersection (see Figure Ex-38).

**37.** Two surfaces $f(x, y, z) = 0$ and $g(x, y, z) = 0$ are said to be **orthogonal** at a point $P$ of intersection if $\nabla f$ and $\nabla g$ are nonzero at $P$ and the normal lines to the surfaces are perpendicular at $P$. Show that if $\nabla f(x_0, y_0, z_0) \neq \mathbf{0}$ and $\nabla g(x_0, y_0, z_0) \neq \mathbf{0}$, then the surfaces $f(x, y, z) = 0$ and $g(x, y, z) = 0$ are orthogonal at the point $(x_0, y_0, z_0)$ if and only if

$$f_x g_x + f_y g_y + f_z g_z = 0$$

at this point. [*Note:* This is a more general version of the result in Exercise 35.]

**38.** Use the result of Exercise 37 to show that the sphere $x^2 + y^2 + z^2 = a^2$ and the cone $z^2 = x^2 + y^2$ are orthogonal at every point of intersection (see the accompanying figure).

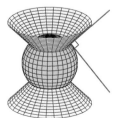

◀ **Figure Ex-38**

**39.** Show that the volume of the solid bounded by the coordinate planes and a plane tangent to the portion of the surface $xyz = k$, $k > 0$, in the first octant does not depend on the point of tangency.

**40.** Writing Discuss the role of the chain rule in defining a tangent plane to a level surface.

**41.** Writing Discuss the relationship between tangent planes and local linear approximations for functions of two variables.

✔ **QUICK CHECK ANSWERS 13.7**

**1.** $2(x - 1) + y + (z + 1) = 0$; $x = 1 + 2t$; $y = t$; $z = -1 + t$
**2.** $z = 4 + 2(x - 3) - 3(y - 1)$; $x = 3 + 2t$; $y = 1 - 3t$; $z = 4 - t$
**3.** $z = 8 + 8(x - 2) + (y - 4)$; $x = 2 + 8t$; $y = 4 + t$; $z = 8 - t$    **4.** $x = 2 + t$; $y = 1$; $z = 2 - t$

## 13.8 MAXIMA AND MINIMA OF FUNCTIONS OF TWO VARIABLES

*Earlier in this text we learned how to find maximum and minimum values of a function of one variable. In this section we will develop similar techniques for functions of two variables.*

**■ EXTREMA**

If we imagine the graph of a function $f$ of two variables to be a mountain range (Figure 13.8.1), then the mountaintops, which are the high points in their immediate vicinity, are called *relative maxima* of $f$, and the valley bottoms, which are the low points in their immediate vicinity, are called *relative minima* of $f$.

Just as a geologist might be interested in finding the highest mountain and deepest valley in an entire mountain range, so a mathematician might be interested in finding the largest and smallest values of $f(x, y)$ over the *entire* domain of $f$. These are called the *absolute maximum* and *absolute minimum values* of $f$. The following definitions make these informal ideas precise.

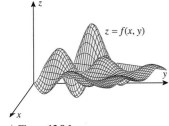
▲ **Figure 13.8.1**

> **13.8.1 DEFINITION** A function $f$ of two variables is said to have a ***relative maximum*** at a point $(x_0, y_0)$ if there is a disk centered at $(x_0, y_0)$ such that $f(x_0, y_0) \geq f(x, y)$ for all points $(x, y)$ that lie inside the disk, and $f$ is said to have an ***absolute maximum*** at $(x_0, y_0)$ if $f(x_0, y_0) \geq f(x, y)$ for all points $(x, y)$ in the domain of $f$.

> **13.8.2 DEFINITION** A function $f$ of two variables is said to have a ***relative minimum*** at a point $(x_0, y_0)$ if there is a disk centered at $(x_0, y_0)$ such that $f(x_0, y_0) \leq f(x, y)$ for all points $(x, y)$ that lie inside the disk, and $f$ is said to have an ***absolute minimum*** at $(x_0, y_0)$ if $f(x_0, y_0) \leq f(x, y)$ for all points $(x, y)$ in the domain of $f$.

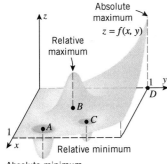
▲ **Figure 13.8.2**

If $f$ has a relative maximum or a relative minimum at $(x_0, y_0)$, then we say that $f$ has a ***relative extremum*** at $(x_0, y_0)$, and if $f$ has an absolute maximum or absolute minimum at $(x_0, y_0)$, then we say that $f$ has an ***absolute extremum*** at $(x_0, y_0)$.

Figure 13.8.2 shows the graph of a function $f$ whose domain is the square region in the $xy$-plane whose points satisfy the inequalities $0 \leq x \leq 1$, $0 \leq y \leq 1$. The function $f$ has relative minima at the points $A$ and $C$ and a relative maximum at $B$. There is an absolute minimum at $A$ and an absolute maximum at $D$.

For functions of two variables we will be concerned with two important questions:

- Are there any relative or absolute extrema?
- If so, where are they located?

### BOUNDED SETS

Just as we distinguished between finite intervals and infinite intervals on the real line, so we will want to distinguish between regions of "finite extent" and regions of "infinite extent" in 2-space and 3-space. A set of points in 2-space is called **bounded** if the entire set can be contained within some rectangle, and is called **unbounded** if there is no rectangle that contains all the points of the set. Similarly, a set of points in 3-space is **bounded** if the entire set can be contained within some box, and is unbounded otherwise (Figure 13.8.3).

Explain why any subset of a bounded set is also bounded.

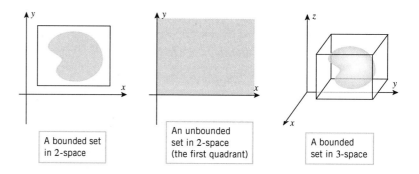

A bounded set in 2-space

An unbounded set in 2-space (the first quadrant)

A bounded set in 3-space

▶ **Figure 13.8.3**

### THE EXTREME-VALUE THEOREM

For functions of one variable that are continuous on a closed interval, the Extreme-Value Theorem (Theorem 4.4.2) answered the existence question for absolute extrema. The following theorem, which we state without proof, is the corresponding result for functions of two variables.

> **13.8.3** THEOREM (*Extreme-Value Theorem*) *If $f(x, y)$ is continuous on a closed and bounded set $R$, then $f$ has both an absolute maximum and an absolute minimum on $R$.*

▶ **Example 1** The square region $R$ whose points satisfy the inequalities

$$0 \le x \le 1 \quad \text{and} \quad 0 \le y \le 1$$

is a closed and bounded set in the $xy$-plane. The function $f$ whose graph is shown in Figure 13.8.2 is continuous on $R$; thus, it is guaranteed to have an absolute maximum and minimum on $R$ by the last theorem. These occur at points $D$ and $A$ that are shown in the figure. ◀

**REMARK** | If any of the conditions in the Extreme-Value Theorem fail to hold, then there is no guarantee that an absolute maximum or absolute minimum exists on the region $R$. Thus, a discontinuous function on a closed and bounded set need not have any absolute extrema, and a continuous function on a set that is not closed and bounded also need not have any absolute extrema.

■ **FINDING RELATIVE EXTREMA**

Recall that if a function $g$ of one variable has a relative extremum at a point $x_0$ where $g$ is differentiable, then $g'(x_0) = 0$. To obtain the analog of this result for functions of two variables, suppose that $f(x, y)$ has a relative maximum at a point $(x_0, y_0)$ and that the partial derivatives of $f$ exist at $(x_0, y_0)$. It seems plausible geometrically that the traces of the surface $z = f(x, y)$ on the planes $x = x_0$ and $y = y_0$ have horizontal tangent lines at $(x_0, y_0)$ (Figure 13.8.4), so

$$f_x(x_0, y_0) = 0 \quad \text{and} \quad f_y(x_0, y_0) = 0$$

The same conclusion holds if $f$ has a relative minimum at $(x_0, y_0)$, all of which suggests the following result, which we state without formal proof.

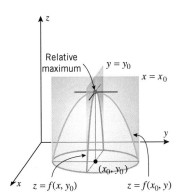

Relative maximum

$y = y_0$

$x = x_0$

$(x_0, y_0)$

$z = f(x, y_0)$ $z = f(x_0, y)$

▲ **Figure 13.8.4**

---

**13.8.4 THEOREM** *If $f$ has a relative extremum at a point $(x_0, y_0)$, and if the first-order partial derivatives of $f$ exist at this point, then*

$$f_x(x_0, y_0) = 0 \quad \text{and} \quad f_y(x_0, y_0) = 0$$

---

Recall that the *critical points* of a function $f$ of one variable are those values of $x$ in the domain of $f$ at which $f'(x) = 0$ or $f$ is not differentiable. The following definition is the analog for functions of two variables.

**Explain why**

$$D_{\mathbf{u}} f(x_0, y_0) = 0$$

**for all $\mathbf{u}$ if $(x_0, y_0)$ is a critical point of $f$ and $f$ is differentiable at $(x_0, y_0)$.**

---

**13.8.5 DEFINITION** A point $(x_0, y_0)$ in the domain of a function $f(x, y)$ is called a ***critical point*** of the function if $f_x(x_0, y_0) = 0$ and $f_y(x_0, y_0) = 0$ or if one or both partial derivatives do not exist at $(x_0, y_0)$.

---

It follows from this definition and Theorem 13.8.4 that relative extrema occur at critical points, just as for a function of one variable. However, recall that for a function of one variable a relative extremum need not occur at *every* critical point. For example, the function might have an inflection point with a horizontal tangent line at the critical point (see Figure 4.2.6). Similarly, a function of two variables need not have a relative extremum at every critical point. For example, consider the function

$$f(x, y) = y^2 - x^2$$

This function, whose graph is the hyperbolic paraboloid shown in Figure 13.8.5, has a critical point at $(0, 0)$, since

$$f_x(x, y) = -2x \quad \text{and} \quad f_y(x, y) = 2y$$

from which it follows that

$$f_x(0, 0) = 0 \quad \text{and} \quad f_y(0, 0) = 0$$

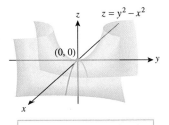

$z$ $z = y^2 - x^2$

$(0, 0)$

$y$

$x$

The function $f(x, y) = y^2 - x^2$ has neither a relative maximum nor a relative minimum at the critical point $(0, 0)$.

▲ **Figure 13.8.5**

However, the function $f$ has neither a relative maximum nor a relative minimum at $(0, 0)$. For obvious reasons, the point $(0, 0)$ is called a *saddle point* of $f$. In general, we will say that a surface $z = f(x, y)$ has a ***saddle point*** at $(x_0, y_0)$ if there are two distinct vertical planes through this point such that the trace of the surface in one of the planes has a relative maximum at $(x_0, y_0)$ and the trace in the other has a relative minimum at $(x_0, y_0)$.

▶ **Example 2** The three functions graphed in Figure 13.8.6 all have critical points at $(0, 0)$. For the paraboloids, the partial derivatives at the origin are zero. You can check this algebraically by evaluating the partial derivatives at $(0, 0)$, but you can see it geometrically by observing that the traces in the $xz$-plane and $yz$-plane have horizontal tangent lines at $(0, 0)$. For the cone neither partial derivative exists at the origin because the traces in the $xz$-plane and the $yz$-plane have corners there. The paraboloid in part $(a)$ and the cone in part $(c)$ have a relative minimum and absolute minimum at the origin, and the paraboloid in part $(b)$ has a relative maximum and an absolute maximum at the origin. ◄

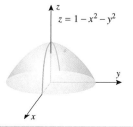

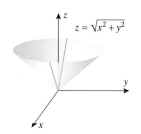

$f_x(0, 0) = f_y(0, 0) = 0$
relative and absolute min at $(0, 0)$

$(a)$

$f_x(0, 0) = f_y(0, 0) = 0$
relative and absolute max at $(0, 0)$

$(b)$

$f_x(0, 0)$ and $f_y(0, 0)$ do not exist
relative and absolute min at $(0, 0)$

$(c)$

▲ Figure 13.8.6

**THE SECOND PARTIALS TEST**

For functions of one variable the second derivative test (Theorem 4.2.4) was used to determine the behavior of a function at a critical point. The following theorem, which is usually proved in advanced calculus, is the analog of that theorem for functions of two variables.

With the notation of Theorem 13.8.6, show that if $D > 0$, then $f_{xx}(x_0, y_0)$ and $f_{yy}(x_0, y_0)$ have the same sign. Thus, we can replace $f_{xx}(x_0, y_0)$ by $f_{yy}(x_0, y_0)$ in parts $(a)$ and $(b)$ of the theorem.

**13.8.6  THEOREM** (*The Second Partials Test*)  *Let $f$ be a function of two variables with continuous second-order partial derivatives in some disk centered at a critical point $(x_0, y_0)$, and let*

$$D = f_{xx}(x_0, y_0) f_{yy}(x_0, y_0) - f_{xy}^2(x_0, y_0)$$

$(a)$  *If $D > 0$ and $f_{xx}(x_0, y_0) > 0$, then $f$ has a relative minimum at $(x_0, y_0)$.*

$(b)$  *If $D > 0$ and $f_{xx}(x_0, y_0) < 0$, then $f$ has a relative maximum at $(x_0, y_0)$.*

$(c)$  *If $D < 0$, then $f$ has a saddle point at $(x_0, y_0)$.*

$(d)$  *If $D = 0$, then no conclusion can be drawn.*

▶ **Example 3**  Locate all relative extrema and saddle points of

$$f(x, y) = 3x^2 - 2xy + y^2 - 8y$$

**Solution.**  Since $f_x(x, y) = 6x - 2y$ and $f_y(x, y) = -2x + 2y - 8$, the critical points of $f$ satisfy the equations

$$6x - 2y = 0$$
$$-2x + 2y - 8 = 0$$

Solving these for $x$ and $y$ yields $x = 2$, $y = 6$ (verify), so $(2, 6)$ is the only critical point. To apply Theorem 13.8.6 we need the second-order partial derivatives

$$f_{xx}(x, y) = 6, \quad f_{yy}(x, y) = 2, \quad f_{xy}(x, y) = -2$$

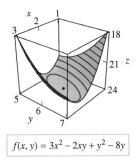

$$f(x, y) = 3x^2 - 2xy + y^2 - 8y$$

▲ Figure 13.8.7

At the point $(2, 6)$ we have

$$D = f_{xx}(2, 6) f_{yy}(2, 6) - f_{xy}^2(2, 6) = (6)(2) - (-2)^2 = 8 > 0$$

and

$$f_{xx}(2, 6) = 6 > 0$$

so $f$ has a relative minimum at $(2, 6)$ by part $(a)$ of the second partials test. Figure 13.8.7 shows a graph of $f$ in the vicinity of the relative minimum. ◄

▶ **Example 4**    Locate all relative extrema and saddle points of

$$f(x, y) = 4xy - x^4 - y^4$$

*Solution.*    Since

$$f_x(x, y) = 4y - 4x^3$$
$$f_y(x, y) = 4x - 4y^3 \tag{1}$$

the critical points of $f$ have coordinates satisfying the equations

$$4y - 4x^3 = 0 \quad \text{or} \quad \begin{matrix} y = x^3 \\ x = y^3 \end{matrix} \tag{2}$$
$$4x - 4y^3 = 0$$

Substituting the top equation in the bottom yields $x = (x^3)^3$ or, equivalently, $x^9 - x = 0$ or $x(x^8 - 1) = 0$, which has solutions $x = 0, x = 1, x = -1$. Substituting these values in the top equation of (2), we obtain the corresponding $y$-values $y = 0, y = 1, y = -1$. Thus, the critical points of $f$ are $(0, 0)$, $(1, 1)$, and $(-1, -1)$.

From (1),

$$f_{xx}(x, y) = -12x^2, \quad f_{yy}(x, y) = -12y^2, \quad f_{xy}(x, y) = 4$$

which yields the following table:

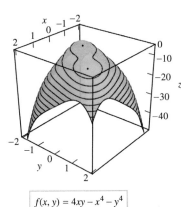

$$f(x, y) = 4xy - x^4 - y^4$$

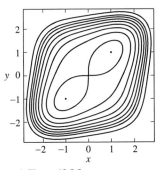

▲ Figure 13.8.8

| CRITICAL POINT $(x_0, y_0)$ | $f_{xx}(x_0, y_0)$ | $f_{yy}(x_0, y_0)$ | $f_{xy}(x_0, y_0)$ | $D = f_{xx}f_{yy} - f_{xy}^2$ |
|---|---|---|---|---|
| $(0, 0)$ | 0 | 0 | 4 | $-16$ |
| $(1, 1)$ | $-12$ | $-12$ | 4 | 128 |
| $(-1, -1)$ | $-12$ | $-12$ | 4 | 128 |

At the points $(1, 1)$ and $(-1, -1)$, we have $D > 0$ and $f_{xx} < 0$, so relative maxima occur at these critical points. At $(0, 0)$ there is a saddle point since $D < 0$. The surface and a contour plot are shown in Figure 13.8.8. ◄

The following theorem, which is the analog for functions of two variables of Theorem 4.4.3, will lead to an important method for finding absolute extrema.

The "figure eight" pattern at $(0, 0)$ in the contour plot for the surface in Figure 13.8.8 is typical for level curves that pass through a saddle point. If a bug starts at the point $(0, 0, 0)$ on the surface, in how many directions can it walk and remain in the $xy$-plane?

**13.8.7    THEOREM**    *If a function f of two variables has an absolute extremum (either an absolute maximum or an absolute minimum) at an interior point of its domain, then this extremum occurs at a critical point.*

PROOF   If $f$ has an absolute maximum at the point $(x_0, y_0)$ in the interior of the domain of $f$, then $f$ has a relative maximum at $(x_0, y_0)$. If both partial derivatives exist at $(x_0, y_0)$, then

$$f_x(x_0, y_0) = 0 \quad \text{and} \quad f_y(x_0, y_0) = 0$$

by Theorem 13.8.4, so $(x_0, y_0)$ is a critical point of $f$. If either partial derivative does not exist, then again $(x_0, y_0)$ is a critical point, so $(x_0, y_0)$ is a critical point in all cases. The proof for an absolute minimum is similar. ■

## FINDING ABSOLUTE EXTREMA ON CLOSED AND BOUNDED SETS

If $f(x, y)$ is continuous on a closed and bounded set $R$, then the Extreme-Value Theorem (Theorem 13.8.3) guarantees the existence of an absolute maximum and an absolute minimum of $f$ on $R$. These absolute extrema can occur either on the boundary of $R$ or in the interior of $R$, but if an absolute extremum occurs in the interior, then it occurs at a critical point by Theorem 13.8.7. Thus, we are led to the following procedure for finding absolute extrema:

Compare this procedure with that in Section 4.4 for finding the extreme values of $f(x)$ on a closed interval.

***How to Find the Absolute Extrema of a Continuous Function $f$ of Two Variables on a Closed and Bounded Set $R$***

**Step 1.** Find the critical points of $f$ that lie in the interior of $R$.

**Step 2.** Find all boundary points at which the absolute extrema can occur.

**Step 3.** Evaluate $f(x, y)$ at the points obtained in the preceding steps. The largest of these values is the absolute maximum and the smallest the absolute minimum.

▶ **Example 5**   Find the absolute maximum and minimum values of

$$f(x, y) = 3xy - 6x - 3y + 7 \tag{3}$$

on the closed triangular region $R$ with vertices $(0, 0)$, $(3, 0)$, and $(0, 5)$.

*Solution.*   The region $R$ is shown in Figure 13.8.9. We have

$$\frac{\partial f}{\partial x} = 3y - 6 \quad \text{and} \quad \frac{\partial f}{\partial y} = 3x - 3$$

so all critical points occur where

$$3y - 6 = 0 \quad \text{and} \quad 3x - 3 = 0$$

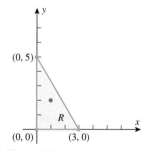

▲ Figure 13.8.9

Solving these equations yields $x = 1$ and $y = 2$, so $(1, 2)$ is the only critical point. As shown in Figure 13.8.9, this critical point is in the interior of $R$.

Next we want to determine the locations of the points on the boundary of $R$ at which the absolute extrema might occur. The boundary of $R$ consists of three line segments, each of which we will treat separately:

*The line segment between $(0, 0)$ and $(3, 0)$:* On this line segment we have $y = 0$, so (3) simplifies to a function of the single variable $x$,

$$u(x) = f(x, 0) = -6x + 7, \quad 0 \le x \le 3$$

This function has no critical points because $u'(x) = -6$ is nonzero for all $x$. Thus the extreme values of $u(x)$ occur at the endpoints $x = 0$ and $x = 3$, which correspond to the points $(0, 0)$ and $(3, 0)$ of $R$.

*The line segment between* $(0, 0)$ *and* $(0, 5)$: On this line segment we have $x = 0$, so (3) simplifies to a function of the single variable $y$,

$$v(y) = f(0, y) = -3y + 7, \quad 0 \le y \le 5$$

This function has no critical points because $v'(y) = -3$ is nonzero for all $y$. Thus, the extreme values of $v(y)$ occur at the endpoints $y = 0$ and $y = 5$, which correspond to the points $(0, 0)$ and $(0, 5)$ of $R$.

*The line segment between* $(3, 0)$ *and* $(0, 5)$: In the $xy$-plane, an equation for this line segment is

$$y = -\tfrac{5}{3}x + 5, \quad 0 \le x \le 3 \tag{4}$$

so (3) simplifies to a function of the single variable $x$,

$$w(x) = f\left(x, -\tfrac{5}{3}x + 5\right) = 3x\left(-\tfrac{5}{3}x + 5\right) - 6x - 3\left(-\tfrac{5}{3}x + 5\right) + 7$$
$$= -5x^2 + 14x - 8, \quad 0 \le x \le 3$$

Since $w'(x) = -10x + 14$, the equation $w'(x) = 0$ yields $x = \tfrac{7}{5}$ as the only critical point of $w$. Thus, the extreme values of $w$ occur either at the critical point $x = \tfrac{7}{5}$ or at the endpoints $x = 0$ and $x = 3$. The endpoints correspond to the points $(0, 5)$ and $(3, 0)$ of $R$, and from (4) the critical point corresponds to $\left(\tfrac{7}{5}, \tfrac{8}{3}\right)$.

Finally, Table 13.8.1 lists the values of $f(x, y)$ at the interior critical point and at the points on the boundary where an absolute extremum can occur. From the table we conclude that the absolute maximum value of $f$ is $f(0, 0) = 7$ and the absolute minimum value is $f(3, 0) = -11$. ◄

**Table 13.8.1**

| $(x, y)$ | $(0, 0)$ | $(3, 0)$ | $(0, 5)$ | $\left(\tfrac{7}{5}, \tfrac{8}{3}\right)$ | $(1, 2)$ |
|---|---|---|---|---|---|
| $f(x, y)$ | 7 | −11 | −8 | $\tfrac{9}{5}$ | 1 |

---

► **Example 6**   Determine the dimensions of a rectangular box, open at the top, having a volume of 32 ft³, and requiring the least amount of material for its construction.

*Solution.*   Let

$$x = \text{length of the box (in feet)}$$
$$y = \text{width of the box (in feet)}$$
$$z = \text{height of the box (in feet)}$$
$$S = \text{surface area of the box (in square feet)}$$

We may reasonably assume that the box with least surface area requires the least amount of material, so our objective is to minimize the surface area

$$S = xy + 2xz + 2yz \tag{5}$$

(Figure 13.8.10) subject to the volume requirement

$$xyz = 32 \tag{6}$$

From (6) we obtain $z = 32/xy$, so (5) can be rewritten as

$$S = xy + \frac{64}{y} + \frac{64}{x} \tag{7}$$

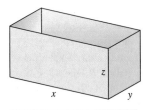

Two sides each have area $xz$.
Two sides each have area $yz$.
The base has area $xy$.

▲ **Figure 13.8.10**

which expresses $S$ as a function of two variables. The dimensions $x$ and $y$ in this formula must be positive, but otherwise have no limitation, so our problem reduces to finding the absolute minimum value of $S$ over the open first quadrant: $x > 0$, $y > 0$. Because this region is neither closed nor bounded, we have no mathematical guarantee at this stage that an absolute minimum exists. However, if $S$ has an absolute minimum value in the open first quadrant, then it must occur at a critical point of $S$. Thus, our next step is to find the critical points of $S$.

Differentiating (7) we obtain

$$\frac{\partial S}{\partial x} = y - \frac{64}{x^2}, \quad \frac{\partial S}{\partial y} = x - \frac{64}{y^2} \tag{8}$$

so the coordinates of the critical points of $S$ satisfy

$$y - \frac{64}{x^2} = 0, \quad x - \frac{64}{y^2} = 0$$

Solving the first equation for $y$ yields

$$y = \frac{64}{x^2} \tag{9}$$

and substituting this expression in the second equation yields

$$x - \frac{64}{(64/x^2)^2} = 0$$

which can be rewritten as

$$x \left( 1 - \frac{x^3}{64} \right) = 0$$

The solutions of this equation are $x = 0$ and $x = 4$. Since we require $x > 0$, the only solution of significance is $x = 4$. Substituting this value into (9) yields $y = 4$. We conclude that the point $(x, y) = (4, 4)$ is the only critical point of $S$ in the first quadrant. Since $S = 48$ if $x = y = 4$, this suggests we try to show that the minimum value of $S$ on the open first quadrant is 48.

It immediately follows from Equation (7) that $48 < S$ at any point in the first quadrant for which at least one of the inequalities

$$xy > 48, \quad \frac{64}{y} > 48, \quad \frac{64}{x} > 48$$

is satisfied. Therefore, to prove that $48 \leq S$, we can restrict attention to the set of points in the first quadrant that satisfy the three inequalities

$$xy \leq 48, \quad \frac{64}{y} \leq 48, \quad \frac{64}{x} \leq 48$$

These inequalities can be rewritten as

$$xy \leq 48, \quad y \geq \frac{4}{3}, \quad x \geq \frac{4}{3}$$

and they define a closed and bounded region $R$ within the first quadrant (Figure 13.8.11). The function $S$ is continuous on $R$, so Theorem 13.8.3 guarantees that $S$ has an absolute minimum value somewhere on $R$. Since the point $(4, 4)$ lies within $R$, and $48 < S$ on the boundary of $R$ (why?), the minimum value of $S$ on $R$ must occur at an interior point. It then follows from Theorem 13.8.7 that the mimimum value of $S$ on $R$ must occur at a critical point of $S$. Hence, the absolute minimum of $S$ on $R$ (and therefore on the entire open first quadrant) is $S = 48$ at the point $(4, 4)$. Substituting $x = 4$ and $y = 4$ into (6) yields $z = 2$, so the box using the least material has a height of 2 ft and a square base whose edges are 4 ft long. ◄

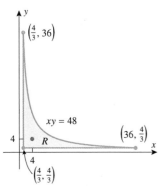

▲ Figure 13.8.11

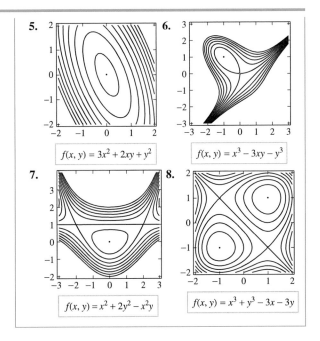

**REMARK**  Fortunately, in our solution to Example 6 we were able to prove the existence of an absolute minimum of $S$ in the first quadrant. The general problem of finding the absolute extrema of a function on an unbounded region, or on a region that is not closed, can be difficult and will not be considered in this text. However, in applied problems we can sometimes use physical considerations to deduce that an absolute extremum has been found. For example, the graph of Equation (7) in Figure 13.8.12 strongly suggests that the relative minimum at $x = 4$ and $y = 4$ is also an absolute minimum.

▲ **Figure 13.8.12**

---

✔ **QUICK CHECK EXERCISES 13.8**    *(See page 989 for answers.)*

1. The critical points of the function $f(x, y) = x^3 + xy + y^2$ are _____.

2. Suppose that $f(x, y)$ has continuous second-order partial derivatives everywhere and that the origin is a critical point for $f$. State what information (if any) is provided by the second partials test if
   (a) $f_{xx}(0, 0) = 2$, $f_{xy}(0, 0) = 2$, $f_{yy}(0, 0) = 2$
   (b) $f_{xx}(0, 0) = -2$, $f_{xy}(0, 0) = 2$, $f_{yy}(0, 0) = 2$
   (c) $f_{xx}(0, 0) = 3$, $f_{xy}(0, 0) = 2$, $f_{yy}(0, 0) = 2$

   (d) $f_{xx}(0, 0) = -3$, $f_{xy}(0, 0) = 2$, $f_{yy}(0, 0) = -2$.

3. For the function $f(x, y) = x^3 - 3xy + y^3$, state what information (if any) is provided by the second partials test at the point
   (a) $(0, 0)$        (b) $(-1, -1)$        (c) $(1, 1)$.

4. A rectangular box has total surface area of 2 ft². Express the volume of the box as a function of the dimensions $x$ and $y$ of the base of the box.

---

**EXERCISE SET 13.8**    ⊠ Graphing Utility    © CAS

1–2  Locate all absolute maxima and minima, if any, by inspection. Then check your answers using calculus. ▨

1. (a) $f(x, y) = (x - 2)^2 + (y + 1)^2$
   (b) $f(x, y) = 1 - x^2 - y^2$
   (c) $f(x, y) = x + 2y - 5$

2. (a) $f(x, y) = 1 - (x + 1)^2 - (y - 5)^2$
   (b) $f(x, y) = e^{xy}$
   (c) $f(x, y) = x^2 - y^2$

3–4  Complete the squares and locate all absolute maxima and minima, if any, by inspection. Then check your answers using calculus. ▨

3. $f(x, y) = 13 - 6x + x^2 + 4y + y^2$

4. $f(x, y) = 1 - 2x - x^2 + 4y - 2y^2$

**FOCUS ON CONCEPTS**

5–8  The contour plots show all significant features of the function. Make a conjecture about the number and the location of all relative extrema and saddle points, and then use calculus to check your conjecture. ▨

5.

$f(x, y) = 3x^2 + 2xy + y^2$

6.

$f(x, y) = x^3 - 3xy - y^3$

7.

$f(x, y) = x^2 + 2y^2 - x^2 y$

8.

$f(x, y) = x^3 + y^3 - 3x - 3y$

**9–20** Locate all relative maxima, relative minima, and saddle points, if any. ■

**9.** $f(x, y) = y^2 + xy + 3y + 2x + 3$

**10.** $f(x, y) = x^2 + xy - 2y - 2x + 1$

**11.** $f(x, y) = x^2 + xy + y^2 - 3x$

**12.** $f(x, y) = xy - x^3 - y^2$   **13.** $f(x, y) = x^2 + y^2 + \dfrac{2}{xy}$

**14.** $f(x, y) = xe^y$   **15.** $f(x, y) = x^2 + y - e^y$

**16.** $f(x, y) = xy + \dfrac{2}{x} + \dfrac{4}{y}$   **17.** $f(x, y) = e^x \sin y$

**18.** $f(x, y) = y \sin x$   **19.** $f(x, y) = e^{-(x^2+y^2+2x)}$

**20.** $f(x, y) = xy + \dfrac{a^3}{x} + \dfrac{b^3}{y}$   $(a \neq 0, b \neq 0)$

**C** **21.** Use a CAS to generate a contour plot of
$$f(x, y) = 2x^2 - 4xy + y^4 + 2$$
for $-2 \leq x \leq 2$ and $-2 \leq y \leq 2$, and use the plot to approximate the locations of all relative extrema and saddle points in the region. Check your answer using calculus, and identify the relative extrema as relative maxima or minima.

**C** **22.** Use a CAS to generate a contour plot of
$$f(x, y) = 2y^2x - yx^2 + 4xy$$
for $-5 \leq x \leq 5$ and $-5 \leq y \leq 5$, and use the plot to approximate the locations of all relative extrema and saddle points in the region. Check your answer using calculus, and identify the relative extrema as relative maxima or minima.

**23–26 True–False** Determine whether the statement is true or false. Explain your answer. In these exercises, assume that $f(x, y)$ has continuous second-order partial derivatives and that
$$D(x, y) = f_{xx}(x, y) f_{yy}(x, y) - f_{xy}^2(x, y) \quad ■$$

**23.** If the function $f$ is defined on the disk $x^2 + y^2 \leq 1$, then $f$ has a critical point somewhere on this disk.

**24.** If the function $f$ is defined on the disk $x^2 + y^2 \leq 1$, and if $f$ is not a constant function, then $f$ has a finite number of critical points on this disk.

**25.** If $P(x_0, y_0)$ is a critical point of $f$, and if $f$ is defined on a disk centered at $P$ with $D(x_0, y_0) > 0$, then $f$ has a relative extremum at $P$.

**26.** If $P(x_0, y_0)$ is a critical point of $f$ with $f(x_0, y_0) = 0$, and if $f$ is defined on a disk centered at $P$ with $D(x_0, y_0) < 0$, then $f$ has both positive and negative values on this disk.

**FOCUS ON CONCEPTS**

**27.** (a) Show that the second partials test provides no information about the critical points of the function $f(x, y) = x^4 + y^4$.
(b) Classify all critical points of $f$ as relative maxima, relative minima, or saddle points.

**28.** (a) Show that the second partials test provides no information about the critical points of the function $f(x, y) = x^4 - y^4$.

(b) Classify all critical points of $f$ as relative maxima, relative minima, or saddle points.

**29.** Recall from Theorem 4.4.4 that if a continuous function of one variable has exactly one relative extremum on an interval, then that relative extremum is an absolute extremum on the interval. This exercise shows that this result does not extend to functions of two variables.
(a) Show that $f(x, y) = 3xe^y - x^3 - e^{3y}$ has only one critical point and that a relative maximum occurs there. (See the accompanying figure.)
(b) Show that $f$ does not have an absolute maximum.

***Source:*** This exercise is based on the article "The Only Critical Point in Town Test" by Ira Rosenholtz and Lowell Smylie, *Mathematics Magazine*, Vol. 58, No. 3, May 1985, pp. 149–150.

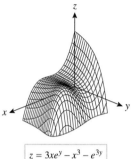

$z = 3xe^y - x^3 - e^{3y}$   ◀ **Figure Ex-29**

**30.** If $f$ is a continuous function of one variable with two relative maxima on an interval, then there must be a relative minimum between the relative maxima. (Convince yourself of this by drawing some pictures.) The purpose of this exercise is to show that this result does not extend to functions of two variables. Show that $f(x, y) = 4x^2e^y - 2x^4 - e^{4y}$ has two relative maxima but no other critical points (see Figure Ex-30).

***Source:*** This exercise is based on the problem "Two Mountains Without a Valley" proposed and solved by Ira Rosenholtz, *Mathematics Magazine*, Vol. 60, No. 1, February 1987, p. 48.

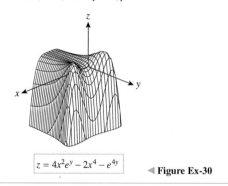

$z = 4x^2e^y - 2x^4 - e^{4y}$   ◀ **Figure Ex-30**

**31–36** Find the absolute extrema of the given function on the indicated closed and bounded set $R$. ■

**31.** $f(x, y) = xy - x - 3y$; $R$ is the triangular region with vertices $(0, 0)$, $(0, 4)$, and $(5, 0)$.

**32.** $f(x, y) = xy - 2x$; $R$ is the triangular region with vertices $(0, 0)$, $(0, 4)$, and $(4, 0)$.

**33.** $f(x, y) = x^2 - 3y^2 - 2x + 6y$; $R$ is the region bounded by the square with vertices $(0, 0)$, $(0, 2)$, $(2, 2)$, and $(2, 0)$.

**34.** $f(x, y) = xe^y - x^2 - e^y$; $R$ is the rectangular region with vertices $(0, 0)$, $(0, 1)$, $(2, 1)$, and $(2, 0)$.

**35.** $f(x, y) = x^2 + 2y^2 - x$; $R$ is the disk $x^2 + y^2 \leq 4$.

**36.** $f(x, y) = xy^2$; $R$ is the region that satisfies the inequalities $x \geq 0$, $y \geq 0$, and $x^2 + y^2 \leq 1$.

**37.** Find three positive numbers whose sum is 48 and such that their product is as large as possible.

**38.** Find three positive numbers whose sum is 27 and such that the sum of their squares is as small as possible.

**39.** Find all points on the portion of the plane $x + y + z = 5$ in the first octant at which $f(x, y, z) = xy^2z^2$ has a maximum value.

**40.** Find the points on the surface $x^2 - yz = 5$ that are closest to the origin.

**41.** Find the dimensions of the rectangular box of maximum volume that can be inscribed in a sphere of radius $a$.

**42.** An international airline has a regulation that each passenger can carry a suitcase having the sum of its width, length, and height less than or equal to 129 cm. Find the dimensions of the suitcase of maximum volume that a passenger can carry under this regulation.

**43.** A closed rectangular box with a volume of 16 ft³ is made from two kinds of materials. The top and bottom are made of material costing 10¢ per square foot and the sides from material costing 5¢ per square foot. Find the dimensions of the box so that the cost of materials is minimized.

**44.** A manufacturer makes two models of an item, standard and deluxe. It costs $40 to manufacture the standard model and $60 for the deluxe. A market research firm estimates that if the standard model is priced at $x$ dollars and the deluxe at $y$ dollars, then the manufacturer will sell $500(y - x)$ of the standard items and $45{,}000 + 500(x - 2y)$ of the deluxe each year. How should the items be priced to maximize the profit?

**45.** Consider the function
$$f(x, y) = 4x^2 - 3y^2 + 2xy$$
over the unit square $0 \leq x \leq 1, 0 \leq y \leq 1$.
(a) Find the maximum and minimum values of $f$ on each edge of the square.
(b) Find the maximum and minimum values of $f$ on each diagonal of the square.
(c) Find the maximum and minimum values of $f$ on the entire square.

**46.** Show that among all parallelograms with perimeter $l$, a square with sides of length $l/4$ has maximum area. [*Hint:* The area of a parallelogram is given by the formula $A = ab \sin \alpha$, where $a$ and $b$ are the lengths of two adjacent sides and $\alpha$ is the angle between them.]

**47.** Determine the dimensions of a rectangular box, open at the top, having volume $V$, and requiring the least amount of material for its construction.

**48.** A length of sheet metal 27 inches wide is to be made into a water trough by bending up two sides as shown in the accompanying figure. Find $x$ and $\phi$ so that the trapezoid-shaped cross section has a maximum area.

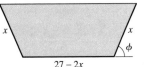

$27 - 2x$          ◀ **Figure Ex-48**

**49–50** A common problem in experimental work is to obtain a mathematical relationship $y = f(x)$ between two variables $x$ and $y$ by "fitting" a curve to points in the plane that correspond to experimentally determined values of $x$ and $y$, say
$$(x_1, y_1), (x_2, y_2), \ldots, (x_n, y_n)$$
The curve $y = f(x)$ is called a **mathematical model** of the data. The general form of the function $f$ is commonly determined by some underlying physical principle, but sometimes it is just determined by the pattern of the data. We are concerned with fitting a straight line $y = mx + b$ to data. Usually, the data will not lie on a line (possibly due to experimental error or variations in experimental conditions), so the problem is to find a line that fits the data "best" according to some criterion. One criterion for selecting the line of best fit is to choose $m$ and $b$ to minimize the function
$$g(m, b) = \sum_{i=1}^{n} (mx_i + b - y_i)^2$$
This is called the **method of least squares**, and the resulting line is called the **regression line** or the **least squares line of best fit**. Geometrically, $|mx_i + b - y_i|$ is the vertical distance between the data point $(x_i, y_i)$ and the line $y = mx + b$.

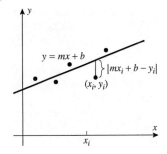

These vertical distances are called the **residuals** of the data points, so the effect of minimizing $g(m, b)$ is to minimize the sum of the squares of the residuals. In these exercises, we will derive a formula for the regression line. ■

**49.** The purpose of this exercise is to find the values of $m$ and $b$ that produce the regression line.
(a) To minimize $g(m, b)$, we start by finding values of $m$ and $b$ such that $\partial g/\partial m = 0$ and $\partial g/\partial b = 0$. Show

that these equations are satisfied if $m$ and $b$ satisfy the conditions

$$\left(\sum_{i=1}^{n} x_i^2\right) m + \left(\sum_{i=1}^{n} x_i\right) b = \sum_{i=1}^{n} x_i y_i$$

$$\left(\sum_{i=1}^{n} x_i\right) m + nb = \sum_{i=1}^{n} y_i$$

(b) Let $\bar{x} = (x_1 + x_2 + \cdots + x_n)/n$ denote the arithmetic average of $x_1, x_2, \ldots, x_n$. Use the fact that

$$\sum_{i=1}^{n} (x_i - \bar{x})^2 \geq 0$$

to show that

$$n\left(\sum_{i=1}^{n} x_i^2\right) - \left(\sum_{i=1}^{n} x_i\right)^2 \geq 0$$

with equality if and only if all the $x_i$'s are the same.

(c) Assuming that not all the $x_i$'s are the same, prove that the equations in part (a) have the unique solution

$$m = \frac{n\sum_{i=1}^{n} x_i y_i - \sum_{i=1}^{n} x_i \sum_{i=1}^{n} y_i}{n\sum_{i=1}^{n} x_i^2 - \left(\sum_{i=1}^{n} x_i\right)^2}$$

$$b = \frac{1}{n}\left(\sum_{i=1}^{n} y_i - m\sum_{i=1}^{n} x_i\right)$$

[*Note:* We have shown that $g$ has a critical point at these values of $m$ and $b$. In the next exercise we will show that $g$ has an absolute minimum at this critical point. Accepting this to be so, we have shown that the line $y = mx + b$ is the regression line for these values of $m$ and $b$.]

**50.** Assume that not all the $x_i$'s are the same, so that $g(m, b)$ has a unique critical point at the values of $m$ and $b$ obtained in Exercise 49(c). The purpose of this exercise is to show that $g$ has an absolute minimum value at this point.

(a) Find the partial derivatives $g_{mm}(m, b)$, $g_{bb}(m, b)$, and $g_{mb}(m, b)$, and then apply the second partials test to show that $g$ has a relative minimum at the critical point obtained in Exercise 49.

(b) Show that the graph of the equation $z = g(m, b)$ is a quadric surface. [*Hint:* See Formula (4) of Section 11.7.]

(c) It can be proved that the graph of $z = g(m, b)$ is an elliptic paraboloid. Accepting this to be so, show that this paraboloid opens in the positive $z$-direction, and explain how this shows that $g$ has an absolute minimum at the critical point obtained in Exercise 49.

**51–54** Use the formulas obtained in Exercise 49 to find and draw the regression line. If you have a calculating utility that can calculate regression lines, use it to check your work. ■

**51.**

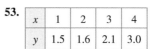

**52.**

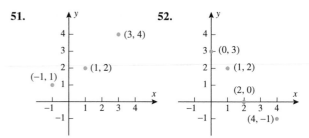

**53.**

| $x$ | 1 | 2 | 3 | 4 |
|-----|-----|-----|-----|-----|
| $y$ | 1.5 | 1.6 | 2.1 | 3.0 |

**54.**

| $x$ | 1 | 2 | 3 | 4 | 5 |
|-----|-----|-----|-----|-----|-----|
| $y$ | 4.2 | 3.5 | 3.0 | 2.4 | 2.0 |

**55.** The following table shows the life expectancy by year of birth of females in the United States:

| YEAR OF BIRTH | 2000 | 2001 | 2002 | 2003 | 2004 | 2005 | 2006 | 2007 |
|---|---|---|---|---|---|---|---|---|
| LIFE EXPECTANCY | 79.3 | 79.4 | 79.5 | 79.6 | 79.9 | 79.9 | 80.2 | 80.4 |

*Source:* Data from *The 2011 Statistical Abstract*, the U.S. Census Bureau.

(a) Take $t = 0$ to be the year 1930, and let $y$ be the life expectancy for birth year $t$. Use the regression capability of a calculating utility to find the regression line of $y$ as a function of $t$.

(b) Use a graphing utility to make a graph that shows the data points and the regression line.

(c) Use the regression line to make a conjecture about the life expectancy of females born in the year 2015.

**56.** A company manager wants to establish a relationship between the sales of a certain product and the price. The company research department provides the following data:

| PRICE ($x$) IN DOLLARS | $35.00 | $40.00 | $45.00 | $48.00 | $50.00 |
|---|---|---|---|---|---|
| DAILY SALES VOLUME ($y$) IN UNITS | 80 | 75 | 68 | 66 | 63 |

(a) Use a calculating utility to find the regression line of $y$ as a function of $x$.

(b) Use a graphing utility to make a graph that shows the data points and the regression line.

(c) Use the regression line to make a conjecture about the number of units that would be sold at a price of $60.00.

**57.** If a gas is cooled with its volume held constant, then it follows from the **ideal gas law** in physics that its pressure drops proportionally to the drop in temperature. The temperature that, in theory, corresponds to a pressure of zero is called **absolute zero**. Suppose that an experiment produces the following data for pressure $P$ versus temperature $T$ with the volume held constant: *(cont.)*

| P (KILOPASCALS) | 134 | 142 | 155 | 160 | 171 | 184 |
|---|---|---|---|---|---|---|
| T (°CELSIUS) | 0 | 20 | 40 | 60 | 80 | 100 |

(a) Use a calculating utility to find the regression line of $P$ as a function of $T$.

(b) Use a graphing utility to make a graph that shows the data points and the regression line.

(c) Use the regression line to estimate the value of absolute zero in degrees Celsius.

**58.** Find

(a) a continuous function $f(x, y)$ that is defined on the entire $xy$-plane and has no absolute extrema on the $xy$-plane;

(b) a function $f(x, y)$ that is defined everywhere on the rectangle $0 \le x \le 1, 0 \le y \le 1$ and has no absolute extrema on the rectangle.

**59.** Show that if $f$ has a relative maximum at $(x_0, y_0)$, then $G(x) = f(x, y_0)$ has a relative maximum at $x = x_0$ and $H(y) = f(x_0, y)$ has a relative maximum at $y = y_0$.

**60.** Writing Explain how to determine the location of relative extrema or saddle points of $f(x, y)$ by examining the contours of $f$.

**61.** Writing Suppose that the second partials test gives no information about a certain critical point $(x_0, y_0)$ because $D(x_0, y_0) = 0$. Discuss what other steps you might take to determine whether there is a relative extremum at that critical point.

✔ **QUICK CHECK ANSWERS 13.8**

**1.** $(0, 0)$ and $\left(\frac{1}{6}, -\frac{1}{12}\right)$ **2.** (a) no information (b) a saddle point at $(0, 0)$ (c) a relative minimum at $(0, 0)$
(d) a relative maximum at $(0, 0)$ **3.** (a) a saddle point at $(0, 0)$ (b) no information, since $(-1, -1)$ is not a critical point
(c) a relative minimum at $(1, 1)$ **4.** $V = \dfrac{xy(1 - xy)}{x + y}$

---

## 13.9 LAGRANGE MULTIPLIERS

*In this section we will study a powerful new method for maximizing or minimizing a function subject to constraints on the variables. This method will help us to solve certain optimization problems that are difficult or impossible to solve using the methods studied in the last section.*

■ **EXTREMUM PROBLEMS WITH CONSTRAINTS**

In Example 6 of the last section, we solved the problem of minimizing

$$S = xy + 2xz + 2yz \tag{1}$$

subject to the constraint

$$xyz - 32 = 0 \tag{2}$$

This is a special case of the following general problem:

**13.9.1 Three-Variable Extremum Problem with One Constraint**
Maximize or minimize the function $f(x, y, z)$ subject to the constraint $g(x, y, z) = 0$.

We will also be interested in the following two-variable version of this problem:

**13.9.2 Two-Variable Extremum Problem with One Constraint**
Maximize or minimize the function $f(x, y)$ subject to the constraint $g(x, y) = 0$.

### LAGRANGE MULTIPLIERS

One way to attack problems of these types is to solve the constraint equation for one of the variables in terms of the others and substitute the result into $f$. This produces a new function of one or two variables that incorporates the constraint and can be maximized or minimized by applying standard methods. For example, to solve the problem in Example 6 of the last section we substituted (2) into (1) to obtain

$$S = xy + \frac{64}{y} + \frac{64}{x}$$

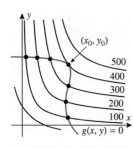

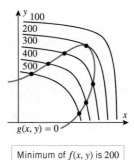

Maximum of $f(x, y)$ is 400

(a)

Minimum of $f(x, y)$ is 200

(b)

**▲ Figure 13.9.1**

which we then minimized by finding the critical points and applying the second partials test. However, this approach hinges on our ability to solve the constraint equation for one of the variables in terms of the others. If this cannot be done, then other methods must be used. One such method, called the *method of Lagrange multipliers*, will be discussed in this section.

To motivate the method of Lagrange multipliers, suppose that we are trying to maximize a function $f(x, y)$ subject to the constraint $g(x, y) = 0$. Geometrically, this means that we are looking for a point $(x_0, y_0)$ on the graph of the constraint curve at which $f(x, y)$ is as large as possible. To help locate such a point, let us construct a contour plot of $f(x, y)$ in the same coordinate system as the graph of $g(x, y) = 0$. For example, Figure 13.9.1a shows some typical level curves of $f(x, y) = c$, which we have labeled $c = 100, 200, 300, 400$, and 500 for purposes of illustration. In this figure, each point of intersection of $g(x, y) = 0$ with a level curve is a candidate for a solution, since these points lie on the constraint curve. Among the seven such intersections shown in the figure, the maximum value of $f(x, y)$ occurs at the intersection $(x_0, y_0)$ where $f(x, y)$ has a value of 400. Note that at $(x_0, y_0)$ the constraint curve and the level curve just touch and thus have a *common* tangent line at this point. Since $\nabla f(x_0, y_0)$ is normal to the level curve $f(x, y) = 400$ at $(x_0, y_0)$, and since $\nabla g(x_0, y_0)$ is normal to the constraint curve $g(x, y) = 0$ at $(x_0, y_0)$, we conclude that the vectors $\nabla f(x_0, y_0)$ and $\nabla g(x_0, y_0)$ must be parallel. That is,

$$\nabla f(x_0, y_0) = \lambda \nabla g(x_0, y_0) \tag{3}$$

for some scalar $\lambda$. The same condition holds at points on the constraint curve where $f(x, y)$ has a minimum. For example, if the level curves are as shown in Figure 13.9.1b, then the minimum value of $f(x, y)$ occurs where the constraint curve just touches a level curve.

**Joseph Louis Lagrange (1736–1813)** French–Italian mathematician and astronomer. Lagrange, the son of a public official, was born in Turin, Italy. (Baptismal records list his name as Giuseppe Lodovico Lagrangia.) Although his father wanted him to be a lawyer, Lagrange was attracted to mathematics and astronomy after reading a memoir by the astronomer Halley. At age 16 he began to study mathematics on his own and by age 19 was appointed to a professorship at the Royal Artillery School in Turin. The following year Lagrange sent Euler solutions to some famous problems using new methods that eventually blossomed into a branch of mathematics called calculus of variations. These methods and Lagrange's applications of them to problems in celestial mechanics were so monumental that by age 25 he was regarded by many of his contemporaries as the greatest living mathematician.

In 1776, on the recommendations of Euler, he was chosen to succeed Euler as the director of the Berlin Academy. During his stay in Berlin, Lagrange distinguished himself not only in celestial me-

chanics, but also in algebraic equations and the theory of numbers. After twenty years in Berlin, he moved to Paris at the invitation of Louis XVI. He was given apartments in the Louvre and treated with great honor, even during the revolution.

Napoleon was a great admirer of Lagrange and showered him with honors—count, senator, and Legion of Honor. The years Lagrange spent in Paris were devoted primarily to didactic treatises summarizing his mathematical conceptions. One of Lagrange's most famous works is a memoir, *Mécanique Analytique*, in which he reduced the theory of mechanics to a few general formulas from which all other necessary equations could be derived.

It is an interesting historical fact that Lagrange's father speculated unsuccessfully in several financial ventures, so his family was forced to live quite modestly. Lagrange himself stated that if his family had money, he would not have made mathematics his vocation. In spite of his fame, Lagrange was always a shy and modest man. On his death, he was buried with honor in the Pantheon.

*[Image: http://commons.wikimedia.org/wiki/File:Joseph_Louis_Lagrange.jpg]*

Thus, to find the maximum or minimum of $f(x, y)$ subject to the constraint $g(x, y) = 0$, we look for points at which (3) holds—this is the method of Lagrange multipliers.

Our next objective in this section is to make the preceding intuitive argument more precise. For this purpose it will help to begin with some terminology about the problem of maximizing or minimizing a function $f(x, y)$ subject to a constraint $g(x, y) = 0$. As with other kinds of maximization and minimization problems, we need to distinguish between relative and absolute extrema. We will say that $f$ has a *constrained absolute maximum* (*minimum*) at $(x_0, y_0)$ if $f(x_0, y_0)$ is the largest (smallest) value of $f$ on the constraint curve, and we will say that $f$ has a *constrained relative maximum* (*minimum*) at $(x_0, y_0)$ if $f(x_0, y_0)$ is the largest (smallest) value of $f$ on some segment of the constraint curve that extends on both sides of the point $(x_0, y_0)$ (Figure 13.9.2).

Let us assume that a constrained relative maximum or minimum occurs at the point $(x_0, y_0)$, and for simplicity let us further assume that the equation $g(x, y) = 0$ can be smoothly parametrized as
$$x = x(s), \quad y = y(s)$$
where $s$ is an arc length parameter with reference point $(x_0, y_0)$ at $s = 0$. Thus, the quantity
$$z = f(x(s), y(s))$$
has a relative maximum or minimum at $s = 0$, and this implies that $dz/ds = 0$ at that point. From the chain rule, this equation can be expressed as
$$\frac{dz}{ds} = \frac{\partial f}{\partial x}\frac{dx}{ds} + \frac{\partial f}{\partial y}\frac{dy}{ds} = \left(\frac{\partial f}{\partial x}\mathbf{i} + \frac{\partial f}{\partial y}\mathbf{j}\right) \cdot \left(\frac{dx}{ds}\mathbf{i} + \frac{dy}{ds}\mathbf{j}\right) = 0$$
where the derivatives are all evaluated at $s = 0$. However, the first factor in the dot product is the gradient of $f$, and the second factor is the unit tangent vector to the constraint curve. Since the point $(x_0, y_0)$ corresponds to $s = 0$, it follows from this equation that
$$\nabla f(x_0, y_0) \cdot \mathbf{T}(0) = 0$$
which implies that the gradient is either $\mathbf{0}$ or is normal to the constraint curve at a constrained relative extremum. However, the constraint curve $g(x, y) = 0$ is a level curve for the function $g(x, y)$, so that if $\nabla g(x_0, y_0) \neq \mathbf{0}$, then $\nabla g(x_0, y_0)$ is normal to this curve at $(x_0, y_0)$. It then follows that there is some scalar $\lambda$ such that
$$\nabla f(x_0, y_0) = \lambda \nabla g(x_0, y_0) \tag{4}$$

This scalar is called a ***Lagrange multiplier***. Thus, the ***method of Lagrange multipliers*** for finding constrained relative extrema is to look for points on the constraint curve $g(x, y) = 0$ at which Equation (4) is satisfied for some scalar $\lambda$.

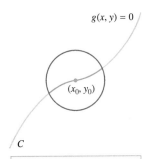

$g(x, y) = 0$

$(x_0, y_0)$

$C$

A constrained relative maximum occurs at $(x_0, y_0)$ if $f(x_0, y_0) \geq f(x, y)$ on some segment of $C$ that extends on both sides of $(x_0, y_0)$.

▲ **Figure 13.9.2**

---

**13.9.3 THEOREM** *(Constrained-Extremum Principle for Two Variables and One Constraint) Let f and g be functions of two variables with continuous first partial derivatives on some open set containing the constraint curve $g(x, y) = 0$, and assume that $\nabla g \neq \mathbf{0}$ at any point on this curve. If f has a constrained relative extremum, then this extremum occurs at a point $(x_0, y_0)$ on the constraint curve at which the gradient vectors $\nabla f(x_0, y_0)$ and $\nabla g(x_0, y_0)$ are parallel; that is, there is some number $\lambda$ such that*
$$\nabla f(x_0, y_0) = \lambda \nabla g(x_0, y_0)$$

---

▶ **Example 1** At what point or points on the circle $x^2 + y^2 = 1$ does $f(x, y) = xy$ have an absolute maximum, and what is that maximum?

***Solution.***   The circle $x^2 + y^2 = 1$ is a closed and bounded set and $f(x, y) = xy$ is a continuous function, so it follows from the Extreme-Value Theorem (Theorem 13.8.3) that $f$ has an absolute maximum and an absolute minimum on the circle. To find these extrema, we will use Lagrange multipliers to find the constrained relative extrema, and then we will evaluate $f$ at those relative extrema to find the absolute extrema.

We want to maximize $f(x, y) = xy$ subject to the constraint

$$g(x, y) = x^2 + y^2 - 1 = 0 \qquad (5)$$

First we will look for constrained *relative* extrema. For this purpose we will need the gradients

$$\nabla f = y\mathbf{i} + x\mathbf{j} \quad \text{and} \quad \nabla g = 2x\mathbf{i} + 2y\mathbf{j}$$

From the formula for $\nabla g$ we see that $\nabla g = \mathbf{0}$ if and only if $x = 0$ and $y = 0$, so $\nabla g \neq \mathbf{0}$ at any point on the circle $x^2 + y^2 = 1$. Thus, at a constrained relative extremum we must have

$$\nabla f = \lambda \nabla g \quad \text{or} \quad y\mathbf{i} + x\mathbf{j} = \lambda(2x\mathbf{i} + 2y\mathbf{j})$$

which is equivalent to the pair of equations

$$y = 2x\lambda \quad \text{and} \quad x = 2y\lambda$$

It follows from these equations that if $x = 0$, then $y = 0$, and if $y = 0$, then $x = 0$. In either case we have $x^2 + y^2 = 0$, so the constraint equation $x^2 + y^2 = 1$ is not satisfied. Thus, we can assume that $x$ and $y$ are nonzero, and we can rewrite the equations as

$$\lambda = \frac{y}{2x} \quad \text{and} \quad \lambda = \frac{x}{2y}$$

from which we obtain

$$\frac{y}{2x} = \frac{x}{2y}$$

or

$$y^2 = x^2 \qquad (6)$$

Substituting this in (5) yields

$$2x^2 - 1 = 0$$

from which we obtain $x = \pm 1/\sqrt{2}$. Each of these values, when substituted in Equation (6), produces $y$-values of $y = \pm 1/\sqrt{2}$. Thus, constrained relative extrema occur at the points $(1/\sqrt{2}, 1/\sqrt{2})$, $(1/\sqrt{2}, -1/\sqrt{2})$, $(-1/\sqrt{2}, 1/\sqrt{2})$, and $(-1/\sqrt{2}, -1/\sqrt{2})$. The values of $xy$ at these points are as follows:

| $(x, y)$ | $(1/\sqrt{2}, 1/\sqrt{2})$ | $(1/\sqrt{2}, -1/\sqrt{2})$ | $(-1/\sqrt{2}, 1/\sqrt{2})$ | $(-1/\sqrt{2}, -1/\sqrt{2})$ |
|---|---|---|---|---|
| $xy$ | $1/2$ | $-1/2$ | $-1/2$ | $1/2$ |

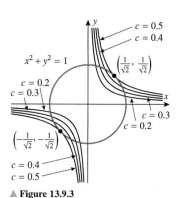

▲ **Figure 13.9.3**

Thus, the function $f(x, y) = xy$ has an absolute maximum of $\frac{1}{2}$ occurring at the two points $(1/\sqrt{2}, 1/\sqrt{2})$ and $(-1/\sqrt{2}, -1/\sqrt{2})$. Although it was not asked for, we can also see that $f$ has an absolute minimum of $-\frac{1}{2}$ occurring at the points $(1/\sqrt{2}, -1/\sqrt{2})$ and $(-1/\sqrt{2}, 1/\sqrt{2})$. Figure 13.9.3 shows some level curves $xy = c$ and the constraint curve in the vicinity of the maxima. A similar figure for the minima can be obtained using negative values of $c$ for the level curves $xy = c$. ◄

Give another solution to Example 1 using the parametrization

$$x = \cos\theta, \quad y = \sin\theta$$

and the identity

$$\sin 2\theta = 2 \sin\theta \cos\theta$$

**REMARK**    If $c$ is a constant, then the functions $g(x, y)$ and $g(x, y) - c$ have the same gradient since the constant $c$ drops out when we differentiate. Consequently, it is *not* essential to rewrite a constraint of the form $g(x, y) = c$ as $g(x, y) - c = 0$ in order to apply the constrained-extremum principle. Thus, in the last example, we could have kept the constraint in the form $x^2 + y^2 = 1$ and then taken $g(x, y) = x^2 + y^2$ rather than $g(x, y) = x^2 + y^2 - 1$.

▶ **Example 2**   Use the method of Lagrange multipliers to find the dimensions of a rectangle with perimeter $p$ and maximum area.

*Solution.*   Let

$x = $ length of the rectangle,     $y = $ width of the rectangle,     $A = $ area of the rectangle

We want to maximize $A = xy$ on the line segment

$$2x + 2y = p, \quad 0 \le x, y \tag{7}$$

that corresponds to the perimeter constraint. This segment is a closed and bounded set, and since $f(x, y) = xy$ is a continuous function, it follows from the Extreme-Value Theorem (Theorem 13.8.3) that $f$ has an absolute maximum on this segment. This absolute maximum must also be a constrained relative maximum since $f$ is 0 at the endpoints of the segment and positive elsewhere on the segment. If $g(x, y) = 2x + 2y$, then we have

$$\nabla f = y\mathbf{i} + x\mathbf{j} \quad \text{and} \quad \nabla g = 2\mathbf{i} + 2\mathbf{j}$$

Noting that $\nabla g \ne \mathbf{0}$, it follows from (4) that

$$y\mathbf{i} + x\mathbf{j} = \lambda(2\mathbf{i} + 2\mathbf{j})$$

at a constrained relative maximum. This is equivalent to the two equations

$$y = 2\lambda \quad \text{and} \quad x = 2\lambda$$

Eliminating $\lambda$ from these equations we obtain $x = y$, which shows that the rectangle is actually a square. Using this condition and constraint (7), we obtain $x = p/4$, $y = p/4$. ◀

■ **THREE VARIABLES AND ONE CONSTRAINT**

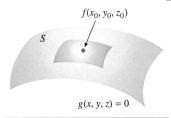

$f(x_0, y_0, z_0)$

$S$

$g(x, y, z) = 0$

A constrained relative maximum occurs at $(x_0, y_0, z_0)$ if $f(x_0, y_0, z_0) \ge f(x, y, z)$ at all points of $S$ near $(x_0, y_0, z_0)$.

▲ **Figure 13.9.4**

The method of Lagrange multipliers can also be used to maximize or minimize a function of three variables $f(x, y, z)$ subject to a constraint $g(x, y, z) = 0$. As a rule, the graph of $g(x, y, z) = 0$ will be some surface $S$ in 3-space. Thus, from a geometric viewpoint, the problem is to maximize or minimize $f(x, y, z)$ as $(x, y, z)$ varies over the surface $S$ (Figure 13.9.4). As usual, we distinguish between relative and absolute extrema. We will say that $f$ has a ***constrained absolute maximum (minimum)*** at $(x_0, y_0, z_0)$ if $f(x_0, y_0, z_0)$ is the largest (smallest) value of $f(x, y, z)$ on $S$, and we will say that $f$ has a ***constrained relative maximum (minimum)*** at $(x_0, y_0, z_0)$ if $f(x_0, y_0, z_0)$ is the largest (smallest) value of $f(x, y, z)$ at all points of $S$ "near" $(x_0, y_0, z_0)$.

The following theorem, which we state without proof, is the three-variable analog of Theorem 13.9.3.

---

**13.9.4**   **THEOREM** (*Constrained-Extremum Principle for Three Variables and One Constraint*)   *Let $f$ and $g$ be functions of three variables with continuous first partial derivatives on some open set containing the constraint surface $g(x, y, z) = 0$, and assume that $\nabla g \ne \mathbf{0}$ at any point on this surface. If $f$ has a constrained relative extremum, then this extremum occurs at a point $(x_0, y_0, z_0)$ on the constraint surface at which the gradient vectors $\nabla f(x_0, y_0, z_0)$ and $\nabla g(x_0, y_0, z_0)$ are parallel; that is, there is some number $\lambda$ such that*

$$\nabla f(x_0, y_0, z_0) = \lambda \nabla g(x_0, y_0, z_0)$$

---

▶ **Example 3**   Find the points on the sphere $x^2 + y^2 + z^2 = 36$ that are closest to and farthest from the point $(1, 2, 2)$.

***Solution.***   To avoid radicals, we will find points on the sphere that minimize and maximize the *square* of the distance to $(1, 2, 2)$. Thus, we want to find the relative extrema of

$$f(x, y, z) = (x - 1)^2 + (y - 2)^2 + (z - 2)^2$$

subject to the constraint

$$x^2 + y^2 + z^2 = 36 \tag{8}$$

If we let $g(x, y, z) = x^2 + y^2 + z^2$, then $\nabla g = 2x\mathbf{i} + 2y\mathbf{j} + 2z\mathbf{k}$. Thus, $\nabla g = \mathbf{0}$ if and only if $x = y = z = 0$. It follows that $\nabla g \neq \mathbf{0}$ at any point of the sphere (8), and hence the constrained relative extrema must occur at points where

$$\nabla f(x, y, z) = \lambda \nabla g(x, y, z)$$

That is,

$$2(x - 1)\mathbf{i} + 2(y - 2)\mathbf{j} + 2(z - 2)\mathbf{k} = \lambda(2x\mathbf{i} + 2y\mathbf{j} + 2z\mathbf{k})$$

which leads to the equations

$$2(x - 1) = 2x\lambda, \quad 2(y - 2) = 2y\lambda, \quad 2(z - 2) = 2z\lambda \tag{9}$$

We may assume that $x$, $y$, and $z$ are nonzero since $x = 0$ does not satisfy the first equation, $y = 0$ does not satisfy the second, and $z = 0$ does not satisfy the third. Thus, we can rewrite (9) as

$$\frac{x - 1}{x} = \lambda, \quad \frac{y - 2}{y} = \lambda, \quad \frac{z - 2}{z} = \lambda$$

The first two equations imply that

$$\frac{x - 1}{x} = \frac{y - 2}{y}$$

from which it follows that

$$y = 2x \tag{10}$$

Similarly, the first and third equations imply that

$$z = 2x \tag{11}$$

Substituting (10) and (11) in the constraint equation (8), we obtain

$$9x^2 = 36 \quad \text{or} \quad x = \pm 2$$

Substituting these values in (10) and (11) yields two points:

$$(2, 4, 4) \quad \text{and} \quad (-2, -4, -4)$$

Since $f(2, 4, 4) = 9$ and $f(-2, -4, -4) = 81$, it follows that $(2, 4, 4)$ is the point on the sphere closest to $(1, 2, 2)$, and $(-2, -4, -4)$ is the point that is farthest (Figure 13.9.5). ◄

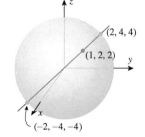

(2, 4, 4)

(1, 2, 2)

(−2, −4, −4)

▲ **Figure 13.9.5**

**REMARK**   Solving nonlinear systems such as (9) usually involves trial and error. A technique that sometimes works is demonstrated in Example 3. In that example the equations were solved for a common variable ($\lambda$), and we then derived relationships between the remaining variables ($x$, $y$, and $z$). Substituting those relationships in the constraint equation led to the value of one of the variables, and the values of the other variables were then computed.

Next we will use Lagrange multipliers to solve the problem of Example 6 in the last section.

▶ **Example 4**   Use Lagrange multipliers to determine the dimensions of a rectangular box, open at the top, having a volume of 32 ft³, and requiring the least amount of material for its construction.

*Solution.*    With the notation introduced in Example 6 of the last section, the problem is to minimize the surface area

$$S = xy + 2xz + 2yz$$

subject to the volume constraint

$$xyz = 32 \tag{12}$$

If we let $f(x, y, z) = xy + 2xz + 2yz$ and $g(x, y, z) = xyz$, then

$$\nabla f = (y + 2z)\mathbf{i} + (x + 2z)\mathbf{j} + (2x + 2y)\mathbf{k} \quad \text{and} \quad \nabla g = yz\mathbf{i} + xz\mathbf{j} + xy\mathbf{k}$$

It follows that $\nabla g \neq \mathbf{0}$ at any point on the surface $xyz = 32$, since $x$, $y$, and $z$ are all nonzero on this surface. Thus, at a constrained relative extremum we must have $\nabla f = \lambda \nabla g$, that is,

$$(y + 2z)\mathbf{i} + (x + 2z)\mathbf{j} + (2x + 2y)\mathbf{k} = \lambda(yz\mathbf{i} + xz\mathbf{j} + xy\mathbf{k})$$

This condition yields the three equations

$$y + 2z = \lambda yz, \quad x + 2z = \lambda xz, \quad 2x + 2y = \lambda xy$$

Because $x$, $y$, and $z$ are nonzero, these equations can be rewritten as

$$\frac{1}{z} + \frac{2}{y} = \lambda, \quad \frac{1}{z} + \frac{2}{x} = \lambda, \quad \frac{2}{y} + \frac{2}{x} = \lambda$$

From the first two equations,

$$y = x \tag{13}$$

and from the first and third equations,

$$z = \tfrac{1}{2}x \tag{14}$$

Substituting (13) and (14) in the volume constraint (12) yields

$$\tfrac{1}{2}x^3 = 32$$

This equation, together with (13) and (14), yields

$$x = 4, \quad y = 4, \quad z = 2$$

which agrees with the result that was obtained in Example 6 of the last section. ◄

There are variations in the method of Lagrange multipliers that can be used to solve problems with two or more constraints. However, we will not discuss that topic here.

---

✔**QUICK CHECK EXERCISES 13.9**    *(See page 997 for answers.)*

1. (a) Suppose that $f(x, y)$ and $g(x, y)$ are differentiable at the origin and have nonzero gradients there, and that $g(0, 0) = 0$. If the maximum value of $f(x, y)$ subject to the constraint $g(x, y) = 0$ occurs at the origin, how is the tangent line to the graph of $g(x, y) = 0$ related to the tangent line at the origin to the level curve of $f$ through $(0, 0)$?

   (b) Suppose that $f(x, y, z)$ and $g(x, y, z)$ are differentiable at the origin and have nonzero gradients there, and that $g(0, 0, 0) = 0$. If the maximum value of $f(x, y, z)$ subject to the constraint $g(x, y, z) = 0$ occurs at the origin,

   how is the tangent plane to the graph of the constraint $g(x, y, z) = 0$ related to the tangent plane at the origin to the level surface of $f$ through $(0, 0, 0)$?

2. The maximum value of $x + y$ subject to the constraint $x^2 + y^2 = 1$ is _____.

3. The maximum value of $x + y + z$ subject to the constraint $x^2 + y^2 + z^2 = 1$ is _____.

4. The maximum and minimum values of $2x + 3y$ subject to the constraint $x + y = 1$, where $0 \leq x, 0 \leq y$, are _____ and _____, respectively.

**EXERCISE SET 13.9**  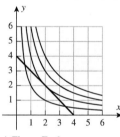 Graphing Utility  [C] CAS

---

**FOCUS ON CONCEPTS**

1. The accompanying figure shows graphs of the line $x + y = 4$ and the level curves of height $c = 2, 4, 6$, and 8 for the function $f(x, y) = xy$.
   (a) Use the figure to find the maximum value of the function $f(x, y) = xy$ subject to $x + y = 4$, and explain your reasoning.
   (b) How can you tell from the figure that your answer to part (a) is not the minimum value of $f$ subject to the constraint?
   (c) Use Lagrange multipliers to check your work.

2. The accompanying figure shows the graphs of the line $3x + 4y = 25$ and the level curves of height $c = 9, 16, 25, 36$, and 49 for the function $f(x, y) = x^2 + y^2$.
   (a) Use the accompanying figure to find the minimum value of the function $f(x, y) = x^2 + y^2$ subject to $3x + 4y = 25$, and explain your reasoning.
   (b) How can you tell from the accompanying figure that your answer to part (a) is not the maximum value of $f$ subject to the constraint?
   (c) Use Lagrange multipliers to check your work.

 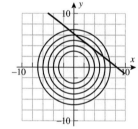

▲ **Figure Ex-1** ▲ **Figure Ex-2**

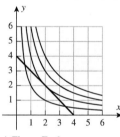 3. (a) On a graphing utility, graph the circle $x^2 + y^2 = 25$ and two distinct level curves of $f(x, y) = x^2 - y$ that just touch the circle in a single point.
   (b) Use the results you obtained in part (a) to approximate the maximum and minimum values of $f$ subject to the constraint $x^2 + y^2 = 25$.
   (c) Check your approximations in part (b) using Lagrange multipliers.

[C] 4. (a) If you have a CAS with implicit plotting capability, use it to graph the circle $(x - 4)^2 + (y - 4)^2 = 4$ and two level curves of $f(x, y) = x^3 + y^3 - 3xy$ that just touch the circle.
   (b) Use the result you obtained in part (a) to approximate the minimum value of $f$ subject to the constraint $(x - 4)^2 + (y - 4)^2 = 4$.
   (c) Confirm graphically that you have found a minimum and not a maximum.
   (d) Check your approximation using Lagrange multipliers and solving the required equations numerically.

5–12 Use Lagrange multipliers to find the maximum and minimum values of $f$ subject to the given constraint. Also, find the points at which these extreme values occur. ■

5. $f(x, y) = xy;\ 4x^2 + 8y^2 = 16$
6. $f(x, y) = x^2 - y^2;\ x^2 + y^2 = 25$
7. $f(x, y) = 4x^3 + y^2;\ 2x^2 + y^2 = 1$
8. $f(x, y) = x - 3y - 1;\ x^2 + 3y^2 = 16$
9. $f(x, y, z) = 2x + y - 2z;\ x^2 + y^2 + z^2 = 4$
10. $f(x, y, z) = 3x + 6y + 2z;\ 2x^2 + 4y^2 + z^2 = 70$
11. $f(x, y, z) = xyz;\ x^2 + y^2 + z^2 = 1$
12. $f(x, y, z) = x^4 + y^4 + z^4;\ x^2 + y^2 + z^2 = 1$

13–16 True–False Determine whether the statement is true or false. Explain your answer. ■

13. A "Lagrange multiplier" is a special type of gradient vector.

14. The extrema of $f(x, y)$ subject to the constraint $g(x, y) = 0$ occur at those points for which $\nabla f = \nabla g$.

15. In the method of Lagrange multipliers it is necessary to solve a constraint equation $g(x, y) = 0$ for $y$ in terms of $x$.

16. The extrema of $f(x, y)$ subject to the constraint $g(x, y) = 0$ occur at those points at which a contour of $f$ is tangent to the constraint curve $g(x, y) = 0$.

17–24 Solve using Lagrange multipliers. ■

17. Find the point on the line $2x - 4y = 3$ that is closest to the origin.

18. Find the point on the line $y = 2x + 3$ that is closest to $(4, 2)$.

19. Find the point on the plane $x + 2y + z = 1$ that is closest to the origin.

20. Find the point on the plane $4x + 3y + z = 2$ that is closest to $(1, -1, 1)$.

21. Find the points on the circle $x^2 + y^2 = 45$ that are closest to and farthest from $(1, 2)$.

22. Find the points on the surface $xy - z^2 = 1$ that are closest to the origin.

23. Find a vector in 3-space whose length is 5 and whose components have the largest possible sum.

24. Suppose that the temperature at a point $(x, y)$ on a metal plate is $T(x, y) = 4x^2 - 4xy + y^2$. An ant, walking on the plate, traverses a circle of radius 5 centered at the origin. What are the highest and lowest temperatures encountered by the ant?

25–32 Use Lagrange multipliers to solve the indicated exercises from Section 13.8. ■

25. Exercise 38
26. Exercise 39

**27.** Exercise 40

**28.** Exercise 41

**29.** Exercise 43

**30.** Exercises 45(a) and (b)

**31.** Exercise 46

**32.** Exercise 47

c **33.** Let $\alpha$, $\beta$, and $\gamma$ be the angles of a triangle.
 (a) Use Lagrange multipliers to find the maximum value of $f(\alpha, \beta, \gamma) = \cos \alpha \cos \beta \cos \gamma$, and determine the angles for which the maximum occurs.
 (b) Express $f(\alpha, \beta, \gamma)$ as a function of $\alpha$ and $\beta$ alone, and use a CAS to graph this function of two variables. Confirm that the result obtained in part (a) is consistent with the graph.

**34.** The accompanying figure shows the intersection of the elliptic paraboloid $z = x^2 + 4y^2$ and the right circular cylinder $x^2 + y^2 = 1$. Use Lagrange multipliers to find the highest and lowest points on the curve of intersection.

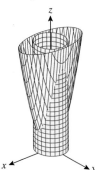

◀ **Figure Ex-34**

**35.** Writing  List a sequence of steps for solving a two-variable extremum problem with one constraint using the method of Lagrange multipliers. Interpret each step geometrically.

**36.** Writing  Redo Example 2 using the methods of Section 4.5, and compare your solution with that of Example 2. For example, how is the perimeter constraint used in each approach?

---

✔ **QUICK CHECK ANSWERS 13.9**

---

**1.** (a) They are the same line. (b) They are the same plane.  **2.** $\sqrt{2}$  **3.** $\sqrt{3}$  **4.** 3; 2

---

**CHAPTER 13 REVIEW EXERCISES**  ◺ Graphing Utility

---

**1.** Let $f(x, y) = e^x \ln y$. Find
 (a) $f(\ln y, e^x)$   (b) $f(r + s, rs)$.

**2.** Sketch the domain of $f$ using solid lines for portions of the boundary included in the domain and dashed lines for portions not included.
 (a) $f(x, y) = \ln(xy - 1)$   (b) $f(x, y) = (\sin^{-1} x)/e^y$

**3.** Show that the level curves of the cone $z = \sqrt{x^2 + y^2}$ and the paraboloid $z = x^2 + y^2$ are circles, and make a sketch that illustrates the difference between the contour plots of the two functions.

**4.** (a) In words, describe the level surfaces of the function $f(x, y, z) = a^2 x^2 + a^2 y^2 + z^2$, where $a > 0$.
 (b) Find a function $f(x, y, z)$ whose level surfaces form a family of circular paraboloids that open in the positive $z$-direction.

**5–6** (a) Find the limit of $f(x, y)$ as $(x, y) \to (0, 0)$ if it exists, and (b) determine whether $f$ is continuous at $(0, 0)$. ■

**5.** $f(x, y) = \dfrac{x^4 - x + y - x^3 y}{x - y}$

**6.** $f(x, y) = \begin{cases} \dfrac{x^4 - y^4}{x^2 + y^2} & \text{if } (x, y) \neq (0, 0) \\ 0 & \text{if } (x, y) = (0, 0) \end{cases}$

**7.** (a) A company manufactures two types of computer monitors: standard monitors and high resolution monitors. Suppose that $P(x, y)$ is the profit that results from producing and selling $x$ standard monitors and $y$ high-resolution monitors. What do the two partial derivatives $\partial P/\partial x$ and $\partial P/\partial y$ represent?
 (b) Suppose that the temperature at time $t$ at a point $(x, y)$ on the surface of a lake is $T(x, y, t)$. What do the partial derivatives $\partial T/\partial x$, $\partial T/\partial y$, and $\partial T/\partial t$ represent?

**8.** Let $z = f(x, y)$.
 (a) Express $\partial z/\partial x$ and $\partial z/\partial y$ as limits.
 (b) In words, what do the derivatives $f_x(x_0, y_0)$ and $f_y(x_0, y_0)$ tell you about the surface $z = f(x, y)$?
 (c) In words, what do the derivatives $\partial z/\partial x(x_0, y_0)$ and $\partial z/\partial y(x_0, y_0)$ tell you about the rates of change of $z$ with respect to $x$ and $y$?

**9.** The pressure in newtons per square meter (N/m²) of a gas in a cylinder is given by $P = 10T/V$ with $T$ in kelvins (K) and $V$ in cubic meters (m³).
 (a) If $T$ is increasing at a rate of 3 K/min with $V$ held fixed at 2.5 m³, find the rate at which the pressure is changing when $T = 50$ K.
 (b) If $T$ is held fixed at 50 K while $V$ is decreasing at the rate of 3 m³/min, find the rate at which the pressure is changing when $V = 2.5$ m³.

**10.** Find the slope of the tangent line at the point $(1, -2, -3)$ on the curve of intersection of the surface $z = 5 - 4x^2 - y^2$ with

(a) the plane $x = 1$  (b) the plane $y = -2$.

**11–14** Verify the assertion. ■

**11.** If $w = \tan(x^2 + y^2) + x\sqrt{y}$, then $w_{xy} = w_{yx}$.

**12.** If $w = \ln(3x - 3y) + \cos(x + y)$, then $\partial^2 w/\partial x^2 = \partial^2 w/\partial y^2$.

**13.** If $F(x, y, z) = 2z^3 - 3(x^2 + y^2)z$, then $F$ satisfies the equation $F_{xx} + F_{yy} + F_{zz} = 0$.

**14.** If $f(x, y, z) = xyz + x^2 + \ln(y/z)$, then $f_{xyzx} = f_{zxxy}$.

**15.** What do $\Delta f$ and $df$ represent, and how are they related?

**16.** If $w = x^2 y - 2xy + y^2 x$, find the increment $\Delta w$ and the differential $dw$ if $(x, y)$ varies from $(1, 0)$ to $(1.1, -0.1)$.

**17.** Use differentials to estimate the change in the volume $V = \frac{1}{3}x^2 h$ of a pyramid with a square base when its height $h$ is increased from 2 to 2.2 m and its base dimension $x$ is decreased from 1 to 0.9 m. Compare this to $\Delta V$.

**18.** Find the local linear approximation of $f(x, y) = \sin(xy)$ at $\left(\frac{1}{3}, \pi\right)$.

**19.** Suppose that $z$ is a differentiable function of $x$ and $y$ with

$$\frac{\partial z}{\partial x}(1, 2) = 4 \quad \text{and} \quad \frac{\partial z}{\partial y}(1, 2) = 2$$

If $x = x(t)$ and $y = y(t)$ are differentiable functions of $t$ with $x(0) = 1$, $y(0) = 2$, $x'(0) = -\frac{1}{2}$, and (under composition) $z'(0) = 2$, find $y'(0)$.

**20.** In each part, use Theorem 13.5.3 to find $dy/dx$.

(a) $3x^2 - 5xy + \tan xy = 0$

(b) $x \ln y + \sin(x - y) = \pi$

**21.** Given that $f(x, y) = 0$, use Theorem 13.5.3 to express $d^2y/dx^2$ in terms of partial derivatives of $f$.

**22.** Let $z = f(x, y)$, where $x = g(t)$ and $y = h(t)$.

(a) Show that

$$\frac{d}{dt}\left(\frac{\partial z}{\partial x}\right) = \frac{\partial^2 z}{\partial x^2}\frac{dx}{dt} + \frac{\partial^2 z}{\partial y \partial x}\frac{dy}{dt}$$

and

$$\frac{d}{dt}\left(\frac{\partial z}{\partial y}\right) = \frac{\partial^2 z}{\partial x \partial y}\frac{dx}{dt} + \frac{\partial^2 z}{\partial y^2}\frac{dy}{dt}$$

(b) Use the formulas in part (a) to help find a formula for $d^2z/dt^2$.

**23.** (a) How are the directional derivative and the gradient of a function related?

(b) Under what conditions is the directional derivative of a differentiable function 0?

(c) In what direction does the directional derivative of a differentiable function have its maximum value? Its minimum value?

**24.** In words, what does the derivative $D_{\mathbf{u}} f(x_0, y_0)$ tell you about the surface $z = f(x, y)$?

**25.** Find $D_{\mathbf{u}} f(-3, 5)$ for $f(x, y) = y \ln(x + y)$ if $\mathbf{u} = \frac{3}{5}\mathbf{i} + \frac{4}{5}\mathbf{j}$.

**26.** Suppose that $\nabla f(0, 0) = 2\mathbf{i} + \frac{3}{2}\mathbf{j}$.

(a) Find a unit vector $\mathbf{u}$ such that $D_{\mathbf{u}} f(0, 0)$ is a maximum. What is this maximum value?

(b) Find a unit vector $\mathbf{u}$ such that $D_{\mathbf{u}} f(0, 0)$ is a minimum. What is this minimum value?

**27.** At the point $(1, 2)$, the directional derivative $D_{\mathbf{u}} f$ is $2\sqrt{2}$ toward $P_1(2, 3)$ and $-3$ toward $P_2(1, 0)$. Find $D_{\mathbf{u}} f(1, 2)$ toward the origin.

**28.** Find equations for the tangent plane and normal line to the given surface at $P_0$.

(a) $z = x^2 e^{2y}$; $P_0(1, \ln 2, 4)$

(b) $x^2 y^3 z^4 + xyz = 2$; $P_0(2, 1, -1)$

**29.** Find all points $P_0$ on the surface $z = 2 - xy$ at which the normal line passes through the origin.

**30.** Show that for all tangent planes to the surface

$$x^{2/3} + y^{2/3} + z^{2/3} = 1$$

the sum of the squares of the $x$-, $y$-, and $z$-intercepts is 1.

**31.** Find all points on the paraboloid $z = 9x^2 + 4y^2$ at which the normal line is parallel to the line through the points $P(4, -2, 5)$ and $Q(-2, -6, 4)$.

**32.** Suppose the equations of motion of a particle are $x = t - 1$, $y = 4e^{-t}$, $z = 2 - \sqrt{t}$, where $t > 0$. Find, to the nearest tenth of a degree, the acute angle between the velocity vector and the normal line to the surface $(x^2/4) + y^2 + z^2 = 1$ at the points where the particle collides with the surface. Use a calculating utility with a root-finding capability where needed.

**33–36** Locate all relative minima, relative maxima, and saddle points. ■

**33.** $f(x, y) = x^2 + 3xy + 3y^2 - 6x + 3y$

**34.** $f(x, y) = x^2 y - 6y^2 - 3x^2$

**35.** $f(x, y) = x^3 - 3xy + \frac{1}{2}y^2$

**36.** $f(x, y) = 4x^2 - 12xy + 9y^2$

**37–39** Solve these exercises two ways:

(a) Use the constraint to eliminate a variable.

(b) Use Lagrange multipliers. ■

**37.** Find all relative extrema of $x^2 y^2$ subject to the constraint $4x^2 + y^2 = 8$.

**38.** Find the dimensions of the rectangular box of maximum volume that can be inscribed in the ellipsoid

$$(x/a)^2 + (y/b)^2 + (z/c)^2 = 1$$

**39.** As illustrated in the accompanying figure on the next page, suppose that a current $I$ branches into currents $I_1$, $I_2$, and $I_3$ through resistors $R_1$, $R_2$, and $R_3$ in such a way that the total power dissipated in the three resistors is a minimum. Find the ratios $I_1 : I_2 : I_3$ if the power dissipated in $R_i$ is $I_i^2 R_i$ $(i = 1, 2, 3)$ and $I_1 + I_2 + I_3 = I$.

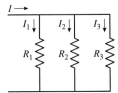

◀ **Figure Ex-39**

**40–42** In economics, a ***production model*** is a mathematical relationship between the output of a company or a country and the labor and capital equipment required to produce that output. Much of the pioneering work in the field of production models occurred in the 1920s when Paul Douglas of the University of Chicago and his collaborator Charles Cobb proposed that the output $P$ can be expressed in terms of the labor $L$ and the capital equipment $K$ by an equation of the form

$$P = cL^\alpha K^\beta$$

where $c$ is a constant of proportionality and $\alpha$ and $\beta$ are constants such that $0 < \alpha < 1$ and $0 < \beta < 1$. This is called the ***Cobb–Douglas production model***. Typically, $P$, $L$, and $K$ are all expressed in terms of their equivalent monetary values. These exercises explore properties of this model. ■

**40.** (a) Consider the Cobb–Douglas production model given by the formula $P = L^{0.75}K^{0.25}$. Sketch the level curves $P(L, K) = 1$, $P(L, K) = 2$, and $P(L, K) = 3$ in an $LK$-coordinate system ($L$ horizontal and $K$ vertical). Your sketch need not be accurate numerically, but it should show the general shape of the curves and their relative positions.

(b) Use a graphing utility to make a more extensive contour plot of the model.

**41.** (a) Find $\partial P/\partial L$ and $\partial P/\partial K$ for the Cobb–Douglas production model $P = cL^\alpha K^\beta$.

(b) The derivative $\partial P/\partial L$ is called the ***marginal productivity of labor***, and the derivative $\partial P/\partial K$ is called the ***marginal productivity of capital***. Explain what these quantities mean in practical terms.

(c) Show that if $\beta = 1 - \alpha$, then $P$ satisfies the partial differential equation

$$K\frac{\partial P}{\partial K} + L\frac{\partial P}{\partial L} = P$$

**42.** Consider the Cobb–Douglas production model

$$P = 1000L^{0.6}K^{0.4}$$

(a) Find the maximum output value of $P$ if labor costs $50.00 per unit, capital costs $100.00 per unit, and the total cost of labor and capital is set at $200,000.

(b) How should the $200,000 be allocated between labor and capital to achieve the maximum?

## CHAPTER 13 MAKING CONNECTIONS

**1.** Suppose that a function $z = f(x, y)$ is expressed in polar form by making the substitutions $x = r\cos\theta$ and $y = r\sin\theta$. Show that

$$r\frac{\partial z}{\partial r} = x\frac{\partial z}{\partial x} + y\frac{\partial z}{\partial y}$$

$$\frac{\partial z}{\partial \theta} = -y\frac{\partial z}{\partial x} + x\frac{\partial z}{\partial y}$$

**2.** A function $f(x, y)$ is said to be ***homogeneous of degree $n$*** if $f(tx, ty) = t^n f(x, y)$ for $t > 0$. In each part, show that the function is homogeneous, and find its degree.

(a) $f(x, y) = 3x^2 + y^2$      (b) $f(x, y) = \sqrt{x^2 + y^2}$

(c) $f(x, y) = x^2y - 2y^3$      (d) $f(x, y) = \dfrac{5}{(x^2 + 2y^2)^2}$

**3.** Suppose that a function $f(x, y)$ is defined for all points $(x, y) \neq (0, 0)$. Prove that $f$ is homogeneous of degree $n$ if and only if there exists a function $g(\theta)$ that is $2\pi$ periodic such that in polar form the equation $z = f(x, y)$ becomes

$$z = r^n g(\theta)$$

for $r > 0$ and $-\infty < \theta < +\infty$.

**4.** (a) Use the chain rule to show that if $f(x, y)$ is a homogeneous function of degree $n$, then

$$x\frac{\partial f}{\partial x} + y\frac{\partial f}{\partial y} = nf$$

[*Hint:* Let $u = tx$ and $v = ty$ in $f(tx, ty)$, and differentiate both sides of $f(u, v) = t^n f(x, y)$ with respect to $t$.]

(b) Use the results of Exercises 1 and 3 to give another derivation of the equation in part (a).

(c) Confirm that the functions in Exercise 2 satisfy the equation in part (a).

**5.** Suppose that a function $f(x, y)$ is defined for all points $(x, y) \neq (0, 0)$ and satisfies

$$x\frac{\partial f}{\partial x} + y\frac{\partial f}{\partial y} = nf$$

Prove that $f$ is homogeneous of degree $n$. [*Hint:* Express the function $z = f(x, y)$ in polar form and use Exercise 1 to conclude that

$$r\frac{\partial z}{\partial r} - nz = 0$$

Divide both sides of this equation by $r^{n+1}$ and interpret the left-hand side of the resulting equation as the partial derivative with respect to $r$ of a product of two functions.]

# 14

# MULTIPLE INTEGRALS

Stone/Getty Images

*Finding the areas of complex surfaces such as those used in the design of the Denver International Airport require integration methods studied in this chapter.*

In this chapter we will extend the concept of a definite integral to functions of two and three variables. Whereas functions of one variable are usually integrated over intervals, functions of two variables are usually integrated over regions in 2-space and functions of three variables over regions in 3-space. Calculating such integrals will require some new techniques that will be a central focus in this chapter. Once we have developed the basic methods for integrating functions of two and three variables, we will show how such integrals can be used to calculate surface areas and volumes of solids; and we will also show how they can be used to find masses and centers of gravity of flat plates and three-dimensional solids. In addition to our study of integration, we will generalize the concept of a parametric curve in 2-space to a parametric surface in 3-space. This will allow us to work with a wider variety of surfaces than previously possible and will provide a powerful tool for generating surfaces using computers and other graphing utilities.

## 14.1 DOUBLE INTEGRALS

*The notion of a definite integral can be extended to functions of two or more variables. In this section we will discuss the double integral, which is the extension to functions of two variables.*

### ■ VOLUME

Recall that the definite integral of a function of one variable

$$\int_a^b f(x)\,dx = \lim_{\max \Delta x_k \to 0} \sum_{k=1}^n f(x_k^*)\Delta x_k = \lim_{n \to +\infty} \sum_{k=1}^n f(x_k^*)\Delta x_k \tag{1}$$

arose from the problem of finding areas under curves. [In the rightmost expression in (1), we use the "limit as $n \to +\infty$" to encapsulate the process by which we increase the number of subintervals of $[a, b]$ in such a way that the lengths of the subintervals approach zero.] Integrals of functions of two variables arise from the problem of finding volumes under surfaces.

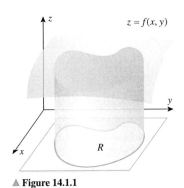

▲ **Figure 14.1.1**

$z = f(x, y)$

---

**14.1.1**  **THE VOLUME PROBLEM**  Given a function $f$ of two variables that is continuous and nonnegative on a region $R$ in the $xy$-plane, find the volume of the solid enclosed between the surface $z = f(x, y)$ and the region $R$ (Figure 14.1.1).

---

Later, we will place more restrictions on the region $R$, but for now we will just assume that the entire region can be enclosed within some suitably large rectangle with sides parallel to the coordinate axes. This ensures that $R$ does not extend indefinitely in any direction.

The procedure for finding the volume $V$ of the solid in Figure 14.1.1 will be similar to the limiting process used for finding areas, except that now the approximating elements will be rectangular parallelepipeds rather than rectangles. We proceed as follows:

- Using lines parallel to the coordinate axes, divide the rectangle enclosing the region $R$ into subrectangles, and exclude from consideration all those subrectangles that contain any points outside of $R$. This leaves only rectangles that are subsets of $R$ (Figure 14.1.2). Assume that there are $n$ such rectangles, and denote the area of the $k$th such rectangle by $\Delta A_k$.

- Choose any arbitrary point in each subrectangle, and denote the point in the $k$th subrectangle by $(x_k^*, y_k^*)$. As shown in Figure 14.1.3, the product $f(x_k^*, y_k^*)\Delta A_k$ is the volume of a rectangular parallelepiped with base area $\Delta A_k$ and height $f(x_k^*, y_k^*)$, so the sum

$$\sum_{k=1}^{n} f(x_k^*, y_k^*)\Delta A_k$$

can be viewed as an approximation to the volume $V$ of the entire solid.

- There are two sources of error in the approximation: first, the parallelepipeds have flat tops, whereas the surface $z = f(x, y)$ may be curved; second, the rectangles that form the bases of the parallelepipeds may not completely cover the region $R$. However, if we repeat the above process with more and more subdivisions in such a way that both the lengths and the widths of the subrectangles approach zero, then it is plausible that the errors of both types approach zero, and the exact volume of the solid will be

$$V = \lim_{n \to +\infty} \sum_{k=1}^{n} f(x_k^*, y_k^*)\Delta A_k$$

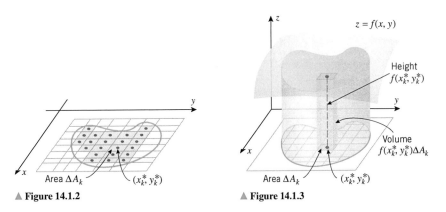

▲ **Figure 14.1.2**        ▲ **Figure 14.1.3**

This suggests the following definition.

Definition 14.1.2 is satisfactory for our present purposes, but some issues would have to be resolved before it could be regarded as rigorous. For example, we would have to prove that the limit actually exists and that its value does not depend on how the points $(x_1^*, y_1^*), (x_2^*, y_2^*), \ldots, (x_n^*, y_n^*)$ are chosen. These facts are true if the region $R$ is not too "complicated" and if $f$ is continuous on $R$. The details are beyond the scope of this text.

**14.1.2   DEFINITION (*Volume Under a Surface*)**   If $f$ is a function of two variables that is continuous and nonnegative on a region $R$ in the $xy$-plane, then the volume of the solid enclosed between the surface $z = f(x, y)$ and the region $R$ is defined by

$$V = \lim_{n \to +\infty} \sum_{k=1}^{n} f(x_k^*, y_k^*) \Delta A_k \tag{2}$$

Here, $n \to +\infty$ indicates the process of increasing the number of subrectangles of the rectangle enclosing $R$ in such a way that both the lengths and the widths of the subrectangles approach zero.

It is assumed in Definition 14.1.2 that $f$ is nonnegative on the region $R$. If $f$ is continuous on $R$ and has both positive and negative values, then the limit

$$\lim_{n \to +\infty} \sum_{k=1}^{n} f(x_k^*, y_k^*) \Delta A_k \tag{3}$$

no longer represents the volume between $R$ and the surface $z = f(x, y)$; rather, it represents a *difference* of volumes—the volume between $R$ and the portion of the surface that is above the $xy$-plane minus the volume between $R$ and the portion of the surface below the $xy$-plane. We call this the ***net signed volume*** between the region $R$ and the surface $z = f(x, y)$.

### DEFINITION OF A DOUBLE INTEGRAL

As in Definition 14.1.2, the notation $n \to +\infty$ in (3) encapsulates a process in which the enclosing rectangle for $R$ is repeatedly subdivided in such a way that both the lengths and the widths of the subrectangles approach zero. Note that subdividing so that the subrectangle lengths approach zero forces the mesh of the partition of the length of the enclosing rectangle for $R$ to approach zero. Similarly, subdividing so that the subrectangle widths approach zero forces the mesh of the partition of the width of the enclosing rectangle for $R$ to approach zero. Thus, we have extended the notion conveyed by Formula (1) where the definite integral of a one-variable function is expressed as a limit of Riemann sums. By extension, the sums in (3) are also called ***Riemann sums***, and the limit of the Riemann sums is denoted by

$$\iint\limits_{R} f(x, y) \, dA = \lim_{n \to +\infty} \sum_{k=1}^{n} f(x_k^*, y_k^*) \Delta A_k \tag{4}$$

which is called the ***double integral*** of $f(x, y)$ over $R$.

If $f$ is continuous and nonnegative on the region $R$, then the volume formula in (2) can be expressed as

$$V = \iint\limits_{R} f(x, y) \, dA \tag{5}$$

If $f$ has both positive and negative values on $R$, then a positive value for the double integral of $f$ over $R$ means that there is more volume above $R$ than below, a negative value for the double integral means that there is more volume below $R$ than above, and a value of zero means that the volume above $R$ is the same as the volume below $R$.

### EVALUATING DOUBLE INTEGRALS

Except in the simplest cases, it is impractical to obtain the value of a double integral from the limit in (4). However, we will now show how to evaluate double integrals by calculating two successive single integrals. For the rest of this section we will limit our discussion to the case where $R$ is a rectangle; in the next section we will consider double integrals over more complicated regions.

The partial derivatives of a function $f(x, y)$ are calculated by holding one of the variables fixed and differentiating with respect to the other variable. Let us consider the reverse of this process, *partial integration*. The symbols

$$\int_a^b f(x, y)\, dx \quad \text{and} \quad \int_c^d f(x, y)\, dy$$

denote *partial definite integrals*; the first integral, called the *partial definite integral with respect to x*, is evaluated by holding $y$ fixed and integrating with respect to $x$, and the second integral, called the *partial definite integral with respect to y*, is evaluated by holding $x$ fixed and integrating with respect to $y$. As the following example shows, the partial definite integral with respect to $x$ is a function of $y$, and the partial definite integral with respect to $y$ is a function of $x$.

▶ **Example 1**

$$\int_0^1 xy^2\, dx = y^2 \int_0^1 x\, dx = \left. \frac{y^2 x^2}{2} \right]_{x=0}^1 = \frac{y^2}{2}$$

$$\int_0^1 xy^2\, dy = x \int_0^1 y^2\, dy = \left. \frac{xy^3}{3} \right]_{y=0}^1 = \frac{x}{3} \quad ◀$$

A partial definite integral with respect to $x$ is a function of $y$ and hence can be integrated with respect to $y$; similarly, a partial definite integral with respect to $y$ can be integrated with respect to $x$. This two-stage integration process is called *iterated* (or *repeated*) *integration*. We introduce the following notation:

$$\int_c^d \int_a^b f(x, y)\, dx\, dy = \int_c^d \left[ \int_a^b f(x, y)\, dx \right] dy \tag{6}$$

$$\int_a^b \int_c^d f(x, y)\, dy\, dx = \int_a^b \left[ \int_c^d f(x, y)\, dy \right] dx \tag{7}$$

These integrals are called *iterated integrals*.

▶ **Example 2**    Evaluate

(a) $\displaystyle\int_1^3 \int_2^4 (40 - 2xy)\, dy\, dx$    (b) $\displaystyle\int_2^4 \int_1^3 (40 - 2xy)\, dx\, dy$

*Solution (a).*

$$\int_1^3 \int_2^4 (40 - 2xy)\, dy\, dx = \int_1^3 \left[ \int_2^4 (40 - 2xy)\, dy \right] dx$$

$$= \int_1^3 (40y - xy^2)\big]_{y=2}^4\, dx$$

$$= \int_1^3 [(160 - 16x) - (80 - 4x)]\, dx$$

$$= \int_1^3 (80 - 12x)\, dx$$

$$= (80x - 6x^2)\big]_1^3 = 112$$

*Solution (b).*

$$\int_2^4 \int_1^3 (40 - 2xy)\,dx\,dy = \int_2^4 \left[ \int_1^3 (40 - 2xy)\,dx \right] dy$$

$$= \int_2^4 (40x - x^2 y)\Big]_{x=1}^3 \, dy$$

$$= \int_2^4 [(120 - 9y) - (40 - y)]\,dy$$

$$= \int_2^4 (80 - 8y)\,dy$$

$$= (80y - 4y^2)\Big]_2^4 = 112 \ \blacktriangleleft$$

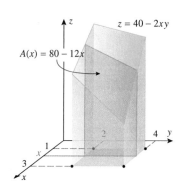

**▲ Figure 14.1.4**

It is no accident that both parts of Example 2 produced the same answer. Consider the solid $S$ bounded above by the surface $z = 40 - 2xy$ and below by the rectangle $R$ defined by $1 \le x \le 3$ and $2 \le y \le 4$. By the method of slicing discussed in Section 6.2, the volume of $S$ is given by

$$V = \int_1^3 A(x)\,dx$$

where $A(x)$ is the area of a vertical cross section of $S$ taken perpendicular to the $x$-axis (Figure 14.1.4). For a fixed value of $x$, $1 \le x \le 3$, $z = 40 - 2xy$ is a function of $y$, so the integral

$$A(x) = \int_2^4 (40 - 2xy)\,dy$$

represents the area under the graph of this function of $y$. Thus,

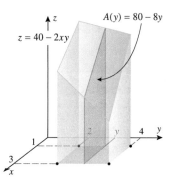

**▲ Figure 14.1.5**

$$V = \int_1^3 \left[ \int_2^4 (40 - 2xy)\,dy \right] dx = \int_1^3 \int_2^4 (40 - 2xy)\,dy\,dx$$

is the volume of $S$. Similarly, by the method of slicing with cross sections of $S$ taken perpendicular to the $y$-axis, the volume of $S$ is given by

$$V = \int_2^4 A(y)\,dy = \int_2^4 \left[ \int_1^3 (40 - 2xy)\,dx \right] dy = \int_2^4 \int_1^3 (40 - 2xy)\,dx\,dy$$

(Figure 14.1.5). Thus, the iterated integrals in parts (a) and (b) of Example 2 both measure the volume of $S$, which by Formula (5) is the double integral of $z = 40 - 2xy$ over $R$. That is,

$$\int_1^3 \int_2^4 (40 - 2xy)\,dy\,dx = \iint_R (40 - 2xy)\,dA = \int_2^4 \int_1^3 (40 - 2xy)\,dx\,dy$$

We will often denote the rectangle

$$\{(x, y) : a \le x \le b, c \le y \le d\}$$

as $[a, b] \times [c, d]$ for simplicity.

The geometric argument above applies to any continuous function $f(x, y)$ that is nonnegative on a rectangle $R = [a, b] \times [c, d]$, as is the case for $f(x, y) = 40 - 2xy$ on $[1, 3] \times [2, 4]$. The conclusion that the double integral of $f(x, y)$ over $R$ has the same value as either of the two possible iterated integrals is true even when $f$ is negative at some points in $R$. We state this result in the following theorem and omit a formal proof.

---

**14.1.3   THEOREM (*Fubini's Theorem*)**   *Let $R$ be the rectangle defined by the inequalities*

$$a \le x \le b, \quad c \le y \le d$$

*If $f(x, y)$ is continuous on this rectangle, then*

$$\iint_R f(x, y)\,dA = \int_c^d \int_a^b f(x, y)\,dx\,dy = \int_a^b \int_c^d f(x, y)\,dy\,dx$$

Theorem 14.1.3 allows us to evaluate a double integral over a rectangle by converting it to an iterated integral. This can be done in two ways, both of which produce the value of the double integral.

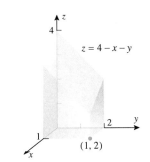

$z = 4 - x - y$

$(1, 2)$

▲ Figure 14.1.6

▶ **Example 3** Use a double integral to find the volume of the solid that is bounded above by the plane $z = 4 - x - y$ and below by the rectangle $R = [0, 1] \times [0, 2]$ (Figure 14.1.6).

*Solution.* The volume is the double integral of $z = 4 - x - y$ over $R$. Using Theorem 14.1.3, this can be obtained from either of the iterated integrals

$$\int_0^2 \int_0^1 (4 - x - y)\, dx\, dy \quad \text{or} \quad \int_0^1 \int_0^2 (4 - x - y)\, dy\, dx \qquad (8)$$

Using the first of these, we obtain

$$V = \iint\limits_R (4 - x - y)\, dA = \int_0^2 \int_0^1 (4 - x - y)\, dx\, dy$$

$$= \int_0^2 \left[ 4x - \frac{x^2}{2} - xy \right]_{x=0}^1 dy = \int_0^2 \left( \frac{7}{2} - y \right) dy$$

$$= \left[ \frac{7}{2} y - \frac{y^2}{2} \right]_0^2 = 5$$

You can check this result by evaluating the second integral in (8). ◀

**TECHNOLOGY MASTERY**

If you have a CAS with a built-in capability for computing iterated double integrals, use it to check Example 3.

Theorem 14.1.3 guarantees that the double integral in Example 4 can also be evaluated by integrating first with respect to $y$ and then with respect to $x$. Verify this.

▶ **Example 4** Evaluate the double integral

$$\iint\limits_R y^2 x\, dA$$

over the rectangle $R = \{(x, y) : -3 \le x \le 2, 0 \le y \le 1\}$.

*Solution.* In view of Theorem 14.1.3, the value of the double integral can be obtained by evaluating one of two possible iterated double integrals. We choose to integrate first with

Guido Fubini (**1879–1943**) Italian mathematician. Fubini, the son of a mathematician, showed brilliance in mathematics as a young pupil in Venice. He entered college at the Scuola Normale Superiore di Pisa in 1896 and presented his doctoral thesis on the subject of elliptic geometry in 1900 at the young age of 20. He subsequently had teaching positions at various universities, finally settling at the University of Turin where he remained for several decades. His mathematical work was diverse, and he made major contributions to many branches of mathematics. At the outbreak of World War I he shifted his attention to the accuracy of artillery fire, and following the war he worked on other applied subjects such as electrical circuits and acoustics. In 1939, as he neared age 60 and retirement, Benito Mussolini's Fascists adopted Hitler's anti-Jewish policies, so Fubini, who was Jewish, accepted a position at Princeton University, where he stayed until his death four years later. Fubini was well liked by his colleagues at Princeton and stories about him abound. He once gave a lecture on ballistics in which he showed that if you fired a projectile of a certain shape, then under the right conditions it could double back on itself and hit your own troops. Then, tongue in cheek, he suggested that one could fool the enemy by aiming this "Fubini Gun" at one's own troops and hit the unsuspecting enemy after the projectile reversed direction.

Fubini was exceptionally short, which occasionally caused problems. The story goes that one day his worried landlady called his friends to report that he had not come home. After searching everywhere, including the area near the local lake, it was discovered that Fubini was trapped in a stalled elevator and was unable to reach any of the buttons. Fubini celebrated his rescue with a party and later left a sign in his room that said, "To my landlady: When I am not home at 6:30 at night, please check the elevator. . . ."

[*Image: Wendy Wray*] ·

respect to $x$ and then with respect to $y$.

$$\iint\limits_{R} y^2 x \, dA = \int_0^1 \int_{-3}^2 y^2 x \, dx \, dy = \int_0^1 \left[ \frac{1}{2} y^2 x^2 \right]_{x=-3}^2 dy$$

$$= \int_0^1 \left( -\frac{5}{2} y^2 \right) dy = -\frac{5}{6} y^3 \Big]_0^1 = -\frac{5}{6} \blacktriangleleft$$

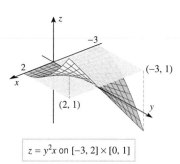

$z = y^2 x$ on $[-3, 2] \times [0, 1]$

▲ **Figure 14.1.7**

The integral in Example 4 can be interpreted as the net signed volume between the rectangle $[-3, 2] \times [0, 1]$ and the surface $z = y^2 x$. That is, it is the volume below $z = y^2 x$ and above $[0, 2] \times [0, 1]$ minus the volume above $z = y^2 x$ and below $[-3, 0] \times [0, 1]$ (Figure 14.1.7).

■ **PROPERTIES OF DOUBLE INTEGRALS**

To distinguish between double integrals of functions of two variables and definite integrals of functions of one variable, we will refer to the latter as *single integrals*. Because double integrals, like single integrals, are defined as limits, they inherit many of the properties of limits. The following results, which we state without proof, are analogs of those in Theorem 5.5.4.

$$\iint\limits_{R} cf(x, y) \, dA = c \iint\limits_{R} f(x, y) \, dA \quad (c \text{ a constant}) \tag{9}$$

$$\iint\limits_{R} [f(x, y) + g(x, y)] \, dA = \iint\limits_{R} f(x, y) \, dA + \iint\limits_{R} g(x, y) \, dA \tag{10}$$

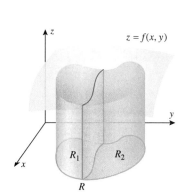

The volume of the entire solid is the sum of the volumes of the solids above $R_1$ and $R_2$.

▲ **Figure 14.1.8**

$$\iint\limits_{R} [f(x, y) - g(x, y)] \, dA = \iint\limits_{R} f(x, y) \, dA - \iint\limits_{R} g(x, y) \, dA \tag{11}$$

It is evident intuitively that if $f(x, y)$ is nonnegative on a region $R$, then subdividing $R$ into two regions $R_1$ and $R_2$ has the effect of subdividing the solid between $R$ and $z = f(x, y)$ into two solids, the sum of whose volumes is the volume of the entire solid (Figure 14.1.8). This suggests the following result, which holds even if $f$ has negative values:

$$\iint\limits_{R} f(x, y) \, dA = \iint\limits_{R_1} f(x, y) \, dA + \iint\limits_{R_2} f(x, y) \, dA \tag{12}$$

The proof of this result will be omitted.

✔ **QUICK CHECK EXERCISES 14.1**   *(See page 1008 for answers.)*

1. The double integral is defined as a limit of Riemann sums by

$$\iint\limits_{R} f(x, y) \, dA = \underline{\hspace{2cm}}$$

2. The iterated integral

$$\int_1^5 \int_2^4 f(x, y) \, dx \, dy$$

integrates $f$ over the rectangle defined by

$$\underline{\hspace{1cm}} \le x \le \underline{\hspace{1cm}}, \quad \underline{\hspace{1cm}} \le y \le \underline{\hspace{1cm}}$$

3. Supply the missing integrand and limits of integration.

$$\int_1^5 \int_2^4 (3x^2 - 2xy + y^2) \, dx \, dy = \int_\square^\square \underline{\hspace{1.5cm}} dy$$

4. The volume of the solid enclosed by the surface $z = x/y$ and the rectangle $0 \le x \le 4$, $1 \le y \le e^2$ in the $xy$-plane is

$$\underline{\hspace{2cm}}.$$

**EXERCISE SET 14.1**    ☐c CAS

**1–12** Evaluate the iterated integrals. ▨

**1.** $\displaystyle\int_0^1 \int_0^2 (x+3)\, dy\, dx$

**2.** $\displaystyle\int_1^3 \int_{-1}^1 (2x-4y)\, dy\, dx$

**3.** $\displaystyle\int_2^4 \int_0^1 x^2 y\, dx\, dy$

**4.** $\displaystyle\int_{-2}^0 \int_{-1}^2 (x^2+y^2)\, dx\, dy$

**5.** $\displaystyle\int_0^{\ln 3} \int_0^{\ln 2} e^{x+y}\, dy\, dx$

**6.** $\displaystyle\int_0^2 \int_0^1 y\sin x\, dy\, dx$

**7.** $\displaystyle\int_{-1}^0 \int_2^5 dx\, dy$

**8.** $\displaystyle\int_4^6 \int_{-3}^7 dy\, dx$

**9.** $\displaystyle\int_0^1 \int_0^1 \frac{x}{(xy+1)^2}\, dy\, dx$

**10.** $\displaystyle\int_{\pi/2}^\pi \int_1^2 x\cos xy\, dy\, dx$

**11.** $\displaystyle\int_0^{\ln 2} \int_0^1 xye^{y^2x}\, dy\, dx$

**12.** $\displaystyle\int_3^4 \int_1^2 \frac{1}{(x+y)^2}\, dy\, dx$

**13–16** Evaluate the double integral over the rectangular region $R$. ▨

**13.** $\displaystyle\iint_R 4xy^3\, dA;\ \ R=\{(x,y): -1\le x\le 1, -2\le y\le 2\}$

**14.** $\displaystyle\iint_R \frac{xy}{\sqrt{x^2+y^2+1}}\, dA;$

$R=\{(x,y): 0\le x\le 1, 0\le y\le 1\}$

**15.** $\displaystyle\iint_R x\sqrt{1-x^2}\, dA;\ \ R=\{(x,y): 0\le x\le 1, 2\le y\le 3\}$

**16.** $\displaystyle\iint_R (x\sin y - y\sin x)\, dA;$

$R=\{(x,y): 0\le x\le \pi/2, 0\le y\le \pi/3\}$

---

**FOCUS ON CONCEPTS**

**17.** (a) Let $f(x,y)=x^2+y$, and as shown in the accompanying figure, let the rectangle $R=[0,2]\times[0,2]$ be subdivided into 16 subrectangles. Take $(x_k^*, y_k^*)$ to be the center of the $k$th rectangle, and approximate the double integral of $f$ over $R$ by the resulting Riemann sum.

(b) Compare the result in part (a) to the exact value of the integral.

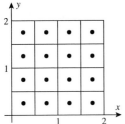
◄ **Figure Ex-17**

**18.** (a) Let $f(x,y)=x-2y$, and as shown in Exercise 17, let the rectangle $R=[0,2]\times[0,2]$ be subdivided into 16 subrectangles. Take $(x_k^*, y_k^*)$ to be the center of the $k$th rectangle, and approximate the double integral of $f$ over $R$ by the resulting Riemann sum.

(b) Compare the result in part (a) to the exact value of the integral.

**19–20** Each iterated integral represents the volume of a solid. Make a sketch of the solid. Use geometry to find the volume of the solid, and then evaluate the iterated integral. ▨

**19.** $\displaystyle\int_0^5 \int_1^2 4\, dx\, dy$

**20.** $\displaystyle\int_0^1 \int_0^1 (2-x-y)\, dx\, dy$

**21–22** Each iterated integral represents the volume of a solid. Make a sketch of the solid. (You do *not* have to find the volume.) ▨

**21.** $\displaystyle\int_0^3 \int_0^4 \sqrt{25-x^2-y^2}\, dy\, dx$

**22.** $\displaystyle\int_{-2}^2 \int_{-2}^2 (x^2+y^2)\, dx\, dy$

**23–26 True–False** Determine whether the statement is true or false. Explain your answer. ▨

**23.** In the definition of a double integral

$$\iint_R f(x,y)\, dA = \lim_{n\to+\infty} \sum_{k=1}^n f(x_k^*, y_k^*)\Delta A_k$$

the symbol $\Delta A_k$ represents a rectangular region within $R$ from which the point $(x_k^*, y_k^*)$ is taken.

**24.** If $R$ is the rectangle $\{(x,y): 1\le x\le 4, 0\le y\le 3\}$ and $\int_0^3 f(x,y)\, dy = 2x$, then

$$\iint_R f(x,y)\, dA = 15$$

**25.** If $R$ is the rectangle $\{(x,y): 1\le x\le 5, 2\le y\le 4\}$, then

$$\iint_R f(x,y)\, dA = \int_1^5 \int_2^4 f(x,y)\, dx\, dy$$

**26.** Suppose that for some region $R$ in the $xy$-plane

$$\iint_R f(x,y)\, dA = 0$$

If $R$ is subdivided into two regions $R_1$ and $R_2$, then

$$\iint_{R_1} f(x,y)\, dA = -\iint_{R_2} f(x,y)\, dA$$

**27.** In this exercise, suppose that $f(x,y)=g(x)h(y)$ and $R=\{(x,y): a\le x\le b, c\le y\le d\}$. Show that

$$\iint_R f(x,y)\, dA = \left[\int_a^b g(x)\, dx\right]\left[\int_c^d h(y)\, dy\right]$$

**28.** Use the result in Exercise 27 to evaluate the integral

$$\int_0^{\ln 2} \int_{-1}^{1} \sqrt{e^y + 1} \tan x \, dx \, dy$$

by inspection. Explain your reasoning.

**29–32** Use a double integral to find the volume. ▪

**29.** The volume under the plane $z = 2x + y$ and over the rectangle $R = \{(x, y) : 3 \le x \le 5, 1 \le y \le 2\}$.

**30.** The volume under the surface $z = 3x^3 + 3x^2 y$ and over the rectangle $R = \{(x, y) : 1 \le x \le 3, 0 \le y \le 2\}$.

**31.** The volume of the solid enclosed by the surface $z = x^2$ and the planes $x = 0$, $x = 2$, $y = 3$, $y = 0$, and $z = 0$.

**32.** The volume in the first octant bounded by the coordinate planes, the plane $y = 4$, and the plane $(x/3) + (z/5) = 1$.

**33.** Evaluate the integral by choosing a convenient order of integration:

$$\iint_R x \cos(xy) \cos^2 \pi x \, dA; \ R = \left[0, \tfrac{1}{2}\right] \times [0, \pi]$$

**34.** (a) Sketch the solid in the first octant that is enclosed by the planes $x = 0$, $z = 0$, $x = 5$, $z - y = 0$, and $z = -2y + 6$.
(b) Find the volume of the solid by breaking it into two parts.

**35–40** The *average value* or *mean value* of a continuous function $f(x, y)$ over a rectangle $R = [a, b] \times [c, d]$ is defined as

$$f_{ave} = \frac{1}{A(R)} \iint_R f(x, y) \, dA$$

where $A(R) = (b - a)(d - c)$ is the area of the rectangle $R$ (compare to Definition 5.8.1). Use this definition in these exercises. ▪

**35.** Find the average value of $f(x, y) = xy^2$ over the rectangle $[0, 8] \times [0, 6]$.

**36.** Find the average value of $f(x, y) = x^2 + 7y$ over the rectangle $[0, 3] \times [0, 6]$.

**37.** Find the average value of $f(x, y) = y \sin xy$ over the rectangle $[0, 1] \times [0, \pi/2]$.

**38.** Find the average value of $f(x, y) = x(x^2 + y)^{1/2}$ over the rectangle $[0, 1] \times [0, 3]$.

**39.** Suppose that the temperature in degrees Celsius at a point $(x, y)$ on a flat metal plate is $T(x, y) = 10 - 8x^2 - 2y^2$, where $x$ and $y$ are in meters. Find the average temperature of the rectangular portion of the plate for which $0 \le x \le 1$ and $0 \le y \le 2$.

**40.** Show that if $f(x, y)$ is constant on the rectangle $R = [a, b] \times [c, d]$, say $f(x, y) = k$, then $f_{ave} = k$ over $R$.

**41–42** Most computer algebra systems have commands for approximating double integrals numerically. Read the relevant documentation and use a CAS to find a numerical approximation of the double integral in these exercises. ▪

C **41.** $\displaystyle \int_0^2 \int_0^1 \sin \sqrt{x^3 + y^3} \, dx \, dy$

C **42.** $\displaystyle \int_{-1}^1 \int_{-1}^1 e^{-(x^2 + y^2)} \, dx \, dy$

C **43.** Use a CAS to evaluate the iterated integrals

$$\int_0^1 \int_0^1 \frac{y - x}{(x + y)^3} \, dx \, dy \quad \text{and} \quad \int_0^1 \int_0^1 \frac{y - x}{(x + y)^3} \, dy \, dx$$

Does this contradict Theorem 14.1.3? Explain.

C **44.** Use a CAS to show that the volume $V$ under the surface $z = xy^3 \sin xy$ over the rectangle shown in the accompanying figure is $V = 3/\pi$.

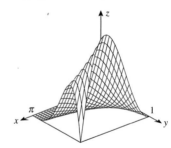

◀ **Figure Ex-44**

**45.** Writing Discuss how computing a volume using an iterated double integral corresponds to the method of computing a volume by slicing (Section 6.2).

**46.** Writing Discuss how the double integral property given in Formula (12) generalizes the single integral property in Theorem 5.5.5.

✔ **QUICK CHECK ANSWERS 14.1**

**1.** $\displaystyle \lim_{n \to +\infty} \sum_{k=1}^{n} f(x_k^*, y_k^*) \Delta A_k$    **2.** $2 \le x \le 4, \ 1 \le y \le 5$    **3.** $\displaystyle \int_1^5 (56 - 12y + 2y^2) \, dy$    **4.** 16

## 14.2  DOUBLE INTEGRALS OVER NONRECTANGULAR REGIONS

*In this section we will show how to evaluate double integrals over regions other than rectangles.*

### ITERATED INTEGRALS WITH NONCONSTANT LIMITS OF INTEGRATION

Later in this section we will see that double integrals over nonrectangular regions can often be evaluated as iterated integrals of the following types:

Note that in (1) and (2) the limits of integration in the outer integral are constants. This is consistent with the fact that the value of each iterated integral is a number that represents a net signed volume.

$$\int_a^b \int_{g_1(x)}^{g_2(x)} f(x, y) \, dy \, dx = \int_a^b \left[ \int_{g_1(x)}^{g_2(x)} f(x, y) \, dy \right] dx \tag{1}$$

$$\int_c^d \int_{h_1(y)}^{h_2(y)} f(x, y) \, dx \, dy = \int_c^d \left[ \int_{h_1(y)}^{h_2(y)} f(x, y) \, dx \right] dy \tag{2}$$

We begin with an example that illustrates how to evaluate such integrals.

▶ **Example 1**   Evaluate

(a) $\displaystyle\int_0^1 \int_{-x}^{x^2} y^2 x \, dy \, dx$      (b) $\displaystyle\int_0^{\pi/3} \int_0^{\cos y} x \sin y \, dx \, dy$

*Solution (a).*

$$\int_0^1 \int_{-x}^{x^2} y^2 x \, dy \, dx = \int_0^1 \left[ \int_{-x}^{x^2} y^2 x \, dy \right] dx = \int_0^1 \frac{y^3 x}{3} \bigg]_{y=-x}^{x^2} dx$$

$$= \int_0^1 \left[ \frac{x^7}{3} + \frac{x^4}{3} \right] dx = \left( \frac{x^8}{24} + \frac{x^5}{15} \right) \bigg]_0^1 = \frac{13}{120}$$

*Solution (b).*

$$\int_0^{\pi/3} \int_0^{\cos y} x \sin y \, dx \, dy = \int_0^{\pi/3} \left[ \int_0^{\cos y} x \sin y \, dx \right] dy = \int_0^{\pi/3} \frac{x^2}{2} \sin y \bigg]_{x=0}^{\cos y} dy$$

$$= \int_0^{\pi/3} \left[ \frac{1}{2} \cos^2 y \sin y \right] dy = -\frac{1}{6} \cos^3 y \bigg]_0^{\pi/3} = \frac{7}{48} \blacktriangleleft$$

### DOUBLE INTEGRALS OVER NONRECTANGULAR REGIONS

Plane regions can be extremely complex, and the theory of double integrals over very general regions is a topic for advanced courses in mathematics. We will limit our study of double integrals to two basic types of regions, which we will call *type I* and *type II*; they are defined as follows.

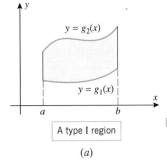

A type I region

(a)

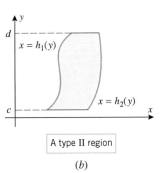

A type II region

(b)

▲ **Figure 14.2.1**

---

**14.2.1**   DEFINITION

(a)   A *type I region* is bounded on the left and right by vertical lines $x = a$ and $x = b$ and is bounded below and above by continuous curves $y = g_1(x)$ and $y = g_2(x)$, where $g_1(x) \le g_2(x)$ for $a \le x \le b$ (Figure 14.2.1a).

(b)   A *type II region* is bounded below and above by horizontal lines $y = c$ and $y = d$ and is bounded on the left and right by continuous curves $x = h_1(y)$ and $x = h_2(y)$ satisfying $h_1(y) \le h_2(y)$ for $c \le y \le d$ (Figure 14.2.1b).

The following theorem will enable us to evaluate double integrals over type I and type II regions using iterated integrals.

---

**14.2.2** THEOREM

(a) *If R is a type I region on which $f(x, y)$ is continuous, then*

$$\iint\limits_{R} f(x, y)\, dA = \int_a^b \int_{g_1(x)}^{g_2(x)} f(x, y)\, dy\, dx \tag{3}$$

(b) *If R is a type II region on which $f(x, y)$ is continuous, then*

$$\iint\limits_{R} f(x, y)\, dA = \int_c^d \int_{h_1(y)}^{h_2(y)} f(x, y)\, dx\, dy \tag{4}$$

---

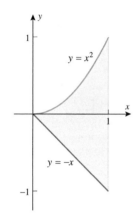

▲ **Figure 14.2.2**

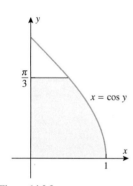

▲ **Figure 14.2.3**

▶ **Example 2** Each of the iterated integrals in Example 1 is equal to a double integral over a region $R$. Identify the region $R$ in each case.

*Solution.* Using Theorem 14.2.2, the integral in Example 1(a) is the double integral of the function $f(x, y) = y^2 x$ over the type I region $R$ bounded on the left and right by the vertical lines $x = 0$ and $x = 1$ and bounded below and above by the curves $y = -x$ and $y = x^2$ (Figure 14.2.2). The integral in Example 1(b) is the double integral of the function $f(x, y) = x \sin y$ over the type II region $R$ bounded below and above by the horizontal lines $y = 0$ and $y = \pi/3$ and bounded on the left and right by the curves $x = 0$ and $x = \cos y$ (Figure 14.2.3). ◀

We will not prove Theorem 14.2.2, but for the case where $f(x, y)$ is nonnegative on the region $R$, it can be made plausible by a geometric argument that is similar to that given for Theorem 14.1.3. Since $f(x, y)$ is nonnegative, the double integral can be interpreted as the volume of the solid $S$ that is bounded above by the surface $z = f(x, y)$ and below by the region $R$, so it suffices to show that the iterated integrals also represent this volume. Consider the iterated integral in (3), for example. For a fixed value of $x$, the function $f(x, y)$ is a function of $y$, and hence the integral

$$A(x) = \int_{g_1(x)}^{g_2(x)} f(x, y)\, dy$$

represents the area under the graph of this function of $y$ between $y = g_1(x)$ and $y = g_2(x)$. This area, shown in yellow in Figure 14.2.4, is the cross-sectional area at $x$ of the solid $S$, and hence by the method of slicing, the volume $V$ of the solid $S$ is

$$V = \int_a^b \int_{g_1(x)}^{g_2(x)} f(x, y)\, dy\, dx$$

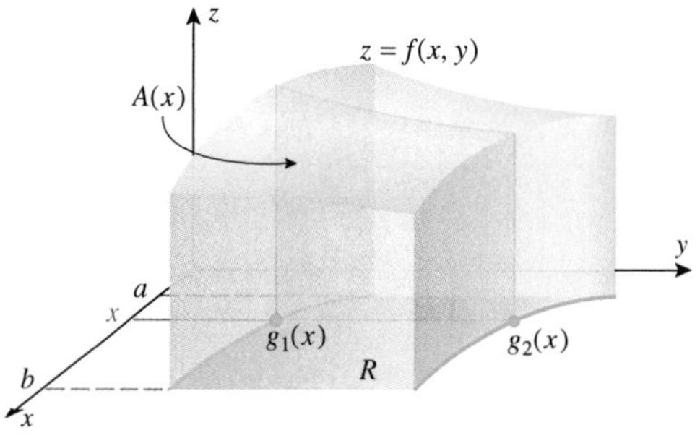

▶ **Figure 14.2.4**

which shows that in (3) the iterated integral is equal to the double integral. Similarly, the iterated integral in (4) is equal to the corresponding double integral.

■ **SETTING UP LIMITS OF INTEGRATION FOR EVALUATING DOUBLE INTEGRALS**

To apply Theorem 14.2.2, it is helpful to start with a two-dimensional sketch of the region $R$. [It is not necessary to graph $f(x, y)$.] For a type I region, the limits of integration in Formula (3) can be obtained as follows:

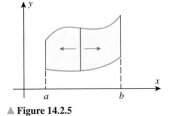

*Determining Limits of Integration: Type I Region*

**Step 1.** Since $x$ is held fixed for the first integration, we draw a vertical line through the region $R$ at an arbitrary fixed value $x$ (Figure 14.2.5). This line crosses the boundary of $R$ twice. The lower point of intersection is on the curve $y = g_1(x)$ and the higher point is on the curve $y = g_2(x)$. These two intersections determine the lower and upper $y$-limits of integration in Formula (3).

**Step 2.** Imagine moving the line drawn in Step 1 first to the left and then to the right (Figure 14.2.5). The leftmost position where the line intersects the region $R$ is $x = a$, and the rightmost position where the line intersects the region $R$ is $x = b$. This yields the limits for the $x$-integration in Formula (3).

▲ **Figure 14.2.5**

▶ **Example 3**    Evaluate

$$\iint\limits_{R} xy \, dA$$

over the region $R$ enclosed between $y = \frac{1}{2}x$, $y = \sqrt{x}$, $x = 2$, and $x = 4$.

*Solution.*    We view $R$ as a type I region. The region $R$ and a vertical line corresponding to a fixed $x$ are shown in Figure 14.2.6. This line meets the region $R$ at the lower boundary $y = \frac{1}{2}x$ and the upper boundary $y = \sqrt{x}$. These are the $y$-limits of integration. Moving this line first left and then right yields the $x$-limits of integration, $x = 2$ and $x = 4$. Thus,

$$\iint\limits_{R} xy \, dA = \int_{2}^{4} \int_{x/2}^{\sqrt{x}} xy \, dy \, dx = \int_{2}^{4} \left[ \frac{xy^2}{2} \right]_{y=x/2}^{\sqrt{x}} dx = \int_{2}^{4} \left( \frac{x^2}{2} - \frac{x^3}{8} \right) dx$$

$$= \left[ \frac{x^3}{6} - \frac{x^4}{32} \right]_{2}^{4} = \left( \frac{64}{6} - \frac{256}{32} \right) - \left( \frac{8}{6} - \frac{16}{32} \right) = \frac{11}{6} \quad ◀$$

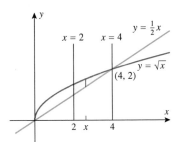

▲ **Figure 14.2.6**

If $R$ is a type II region, then the limits of integration in Formula (4) can be obtained as follows:

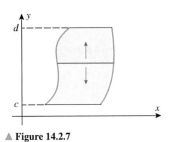

*Determining Limits of Integration: Type II Region*

**Step 1.** Since $y$ is held fixed for the first integration, we draw a horizontal line through the region $R$ at a fixed value $y$ (Figure 14.2.7). This line crosses the boundary of $R$ twice. The leftmost point of intersection is on the curve $x = h_1(y)$ and the rightmost point is on the curve $x = h_2(y)$. These intersections determine the $x$-limits of integration in (4).

**Step 2.** Imagine moving the line drawn in Step 1 first down and then up (Figure 14.2.7). The lowest position where the line intersects the region $R$ is $y = c$, and the highest position where the line intersects the region $R$ is $y = d$. This yields the $y$-limits of integration in (4).

▲ **Figure 14.2.7**

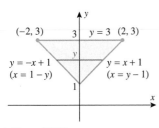

▲ **Figure 14.2.8**

To integrate over a type II region, the left- and right-hand boundaries must be expressed in the form $x = h_1(y)$ and $x = h_2(y)$. This is why we rewrote the boundary equations

$$y = -x + 1 \quad \text{and} \quad y = x + 1$$

as

$$x = 1 - y \quad \text{and} \quad x = y - 1$$

in Example 4.

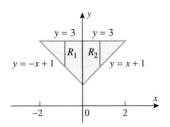

▲ **Figure 14.2.9**

▶ **Example 4** Evaluate

$$\iint\limits_R (2x - y^2)\, dA$$

over the triangular region $R$ enclosed between the lines $y = -x + 1$, $y = x + 1$, and $y = 3$.

*Solution.* We view $R$ as a type II region. The region $R$ and a horizontal line corresponding to a fixed $y$ are shown in Figure 14.2.8. This line meets the region $R$ at its left-hand boundary $x = 1 - y$ and its right-hand boundary $x = y - 1$. These are the $x$-limits of integration. Moving this line first down and then up yields the $y$-limits, $y = 1$ and $y = 3$. Thus,

$$\iint\limits_R (2x - y^2)\, dA = \int_1^3 \int_{1-y}^{y-1} (2x - y^2)\, dx\, dy = \int_1^3 \left[ x^2 - y^2 x \right]_{x=1-y}^{y-1} dy$$

$$= \int_1^3 [(1 - 2y + 2y^2 - y^3) - (1 - 2y + y^3)]\, dy$$

$$= \int_1^3 (2y^2 - 2y^3)\, dy = \left[ \frac{2y^3}{3} - \frac{y^4}{2} \right]_1^3 = -\frac{68}{3} \quad ◀$$

In Example 4 we could have treated $R$ as a type I region, but with an added complication. Viewed as a type I region, the upper boundary of $R$ is the line $y = 3$ (Figure 14.2.9) and the lower boundary consists of two parts, the line $y = -x + 1$ to the left of the $y$-axis and the line $y = x + 1$ to the right of the $y$-axis. To carry out the integration it is necessary to decompose the region $R$ into two parts, $R_1$ and $R_2$, as shown in Figure 14.2.9, and write

$$\iint\limits_R (2x - y^2)\, dA = \iint\limits_{R_1} (2x - y^2)\, dA + \iint\limits_{R_2} (2x - y^2)\, dA$$

$$= \int_{-2}^0 \int_{-x+1}^3 (2x - y^2)\, dy\, dx + \int_0^2 \int_{x+1}^3 (2x - y^2)\, dy\, dx$$

This will yield the same result that was obtained in Example 4. (Verify.)

▶ **Example 5** Use a double integral to find the volume of the tetrahedron bounded by the coordinate planes and the plane $z = 4 - 4x - 2y$.

*Solution.* The tetrahedron in question is bounded above by the plane

$$z = 4 - 4x - 2y \tag{5}$$

and below by the triangular region $R$ shown in Figure 14.2.10. Thus, the volume is given by

$$V = \iint\limits_R (4 - 4x - 2y)\, dA$$

The region $R$ is bounded by the $x$-axis, the $y$-axis, and the line $y = 2 - 2x$ [set $z = 0$ in (5)], so that treating $R$ as a type I region yields

$$V = \iint\limits_R (4 - 4x - 2y)\, dA = \int_0^1 \int_0^{2-2x} (4 - 4x - 2y)\, dy\, dx$$

$$= \int_0^1 \left[ 4y - 4xy - y^2 \right]_{y=0}^{2-2x} dx = \int_0^1 (4 - 8x + 4x^2)\, dx = \frac{4}{3} \quad ◀$$

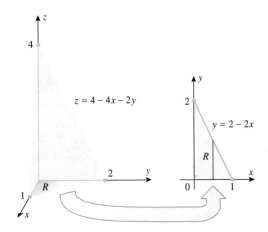

▶ **Figure 14.2.10**

---

▶ **Example 6**  Find the volume of the solid bounded by the cylinder $x^2 + y^2 = 4$ and the planes $y + z = 4$ and $z = 0$.

*Solution.*  The solid shown in Figure 14.2.11 is bounded above by the plane $z = 4 - y$ and below by the region $R$ within the circle $x^2 + y^2 = 4$. The volume is given by

$$V = \iint\limits_R (4 - y)\, dA$$

Treating $R$ as a type I region we obtain

$$V = \int_{-2}^{2} \int_{-\sqrt{4-x^2}}^{\sqrt{4-x^2}} (4 - y)\, dy\, dx = \int_{-2}^{2} \left[ 4y - \frac{1}{2}y^2 \right]_{y=-\sqrt{4-x^2}}^{\sqrt{4-x^2}} dx$$

$$= \int_{-2}^{2} 8\sqrt{4 - x^2}\, dx = 8(2\pi) = 16\pi \qquad \boxed{\text{See Formula (3) of Section 7.4.}} \quad ◀$$

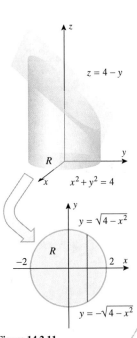

▲ **Figure 14.2.11**

■ **REVERSING THE ORDER OF INTEGRATION**
Sometimes the evaluation of an iterated integral can be simplified by reversing the order of integration. The next example illustrates how this is done.

▶ **Example 7**  Since there is no elementary antiderivative of $e^{x^2}$, the integral

$$\int_0^2 \int_{y/2}^1 e^{x^2}\, dx\, dy$$

cannot be evaluated by performing the $x$-integration first. Evaluate this integral by expressing it as an equivalent iterated integral with the order of integration reversed.

*Solution.*  For the inside integration, $y$ is fixed and $x$ varies from the line $x = y/2$ to the line $x = 1$ (Figure 14.2.12). For the outside integration, $y$ varies from 0 to 2, so the given iterated integral is equal to a double integral over the triangular region $R$ in Figure 14.2.12.

To reverse the order of integration, we treat $R$ as a type I region, which enables us to write the given integral as

$$\int_0^2 \int_{y/2}^1 e^{x^2}\, dx\, dy = \iint\limits_R e^{x^2}\, dA = \int_0^1 \int_0^{2x} e^{x^2}\, dy\, dx = \int_0^1 \left[ e^{x^2} y \right]_{y=0}^{2x} dx$$

$$= \int_0^1 2x e^{x^2}\, dx = e^{x^2} \Big]_0^1 = e - 1 \quad ◀$$

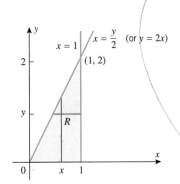

▲ **Figure 14.2.12**

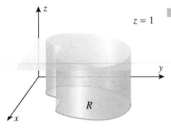

Cylinder with base $R$ and height 1

▲ **Figure 14.2.13**

Formula (7) can be confusing because it equates an area and a volume; the formula is intended to equate only the *numerical values* of the area and volume and not the units, which must, of course, be different.

### ■ AREA CALCULATED AS A DOUBLE INTEGRAL

Although double integrals arose in the context of calculating volumes, they can also be used to calculate areas. To see why this is so, recall that a *right cylinder* is a solid that is generated when a plane region is translated along a line that is perpendicular to the region. In Formula (2) of Section 6.2 we stated that the volume $V$ of a right cylinder with cross-sectional area $A$ and height $h$ is

$$V = A \cdot h \tag{6}$$

Now suppose that we are interested in finding the area $A$ of a region $R$ in the $xy$-plane. If we translate the region $R$ upward 1 unit, then the resulting solid will be a right cylinder that has cross-sectional area $A$, base $R$, and the plane $z = 1$ as its top (Figure 14.2.13). Thus, it follows from (6) that

$$\iint_R 1\,dA = (\text{area of } R) \cdot 1$$

which we can rewrite as

$$\text{area of } R = \iint_R 1\,dA = \iint_R dA \tag{7}$$

▶ **Example 8**   Use a double integral to find the area of the region $R$ enclosed between the parabola $y = \frac{1}{2}x^2$ and the line $y = 2x$.

*Solution.*   The region $R$ may be treated equally well as type I (Figure 14.2.14$a$) or type II (Figure 14.2.14$b$). Treating $R$ as type I yields

$$\text{area of } R = \iint_R dA = \int_0^4 \int_{x^2/2}^{2x} dy\,dx = \int_0^4 \big[y\big]_{y=x^2/2}^{2x} dx$$

$$= \int_0^4 \left(2x - \frac{1}{2}x^2\right) dx = \left[x^2 - \frac{x^3}{6}\right]_0^4 = \frac{16}{3}$$

Treating $R$ as type II yields

$$\text{area of } R = \iint_R dA = \int_0^8 \int_{y/2}^{\sqrt{2y}} dx\,dy = \int_0^8 \big[x\big]_{x=y/2}^{\sqrt{2y}} dy$$

$$= \int_0^8 \left(\sqrt{2y} - \frac{1}{2}y\right) dy = \left[\frac{2\sqrt{2}}{3}y^{3/2} - \frac{y^2}{4}\right]_0^8 = \frac{16}{3} \; ◀$$

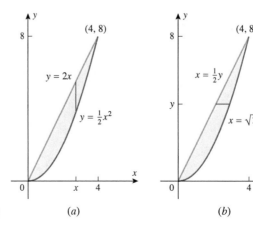

▶ **Figure 14.2.14**   $(a)$   $(b)$

✔ **QUICK CHECK EXERCISES 14.2**    *(See page 1018 for answers.)*

1. Supply the missing integrand and limits of integration.

   (a) $\displaystyle\int_1^5 \int_2^{y/2} 6x^2 y\,dx\,dy = \int_0^{\square} \underline{\hspace{1.5cm}}\,dy$

   (b) $\displaystyle\int_1^5 \int_2^{x/2} 6x^2 y\,dy\,dx = \int_{\square}^{\square} \underline{\hspace{1.5cm}}\,dx$

2. Let $R$ be the triangular region in the $xy$-plane with vertices $(0, 0)$, $(3, 0)$, and $(0, 4)$. Supply the missing portions of the integrals.

   (a) Treating $R$ as a type I region,
   $$\iint_R f(x, y)\,dA = \int_{\square}^{\square} \int_{\square}^{\square} f(x, y)\,\underline{\hspace{1cm}}$$

3. Let $R$ be the triangular region in the $xy$-plane with vertices $(0, 0)$, $(3, 3)$, and $(0, 4)$. Expressed as an iterated double integral, the area of $R$ is $A(R) = \underline{\hspace{1.5cm}}$.

   (b) Treating $R$ as a type II region,
   $$\iint_R f(x, y)\,dA = \int_{\square}^{\square} \int_{\square}^{\square} f(x, y)\,\underline{\hspace{1cm}}$$

4. The line $y = 2 - x$ and the parabola $y = x^2$ intersect at the points $(-2, 4)$ and $(1, 1)$. If $R$ is the region enclosed by $y = 2 - x$ and $y = x^2$, then
   $$\iint_R (1 + 2y)\,dA = \underline{\hspace{1.5cm}}$$

**EXERCISE SET 14.2**    ◨ Graphing Utility    C CAS

**1–8** Evaluate the iterated integral. ▪

1. $\displaystyle\int_0^1 \int_{x^2}^x xy^2\,dy\,dx$

2. $\displaystyle\int_1^{3/2} \int_y^{3-y} y\,dx\,dy$

3. $\displaystyle\int_0^3 \int_0^{\sqrt{9-y^2}} y\,dx\,dy$

4. $\displaystyle\int_{1/4}^1 \int_{x^2}^x \sqrt{\frac{x}{y}}\,dy\,dx$

5. $\displaystyle\int_{\sqrt{\pi}}^{\sqrt{2\pi}} \int_0^{x^3} \sin\frac{y}{x}\,dy\,dx$

6. $\displaystyle\int_{-1}^1 \int_{-x^2}^{x^2} (x^2 - y)\,dy\,dx$

7. $\displaystyle\int_0^1 \int_0^x y\sqrt{x^2 - y^2}\,dy\,dx$

8. $\displaystyle\int_1^2 \int_0^{y^2} e^{x/y^2}\,dx\,dy$

**FOCUS ON CONCEPTS**

9. Let $R$ be the region shown in the accompanying figure. Fill in the missing limits of integration.

   (a) $\displaystyle\iint_R f(x, y)\,dA = \int_{\square}^{\square} \int_{\square}^{\square} f(x, y)\,dy\,dx$

   (b) $\displaystyle\iint_R f(x, y)\,dA = \int_{\square}^{\square} \int_{\square}^{\square} f(x, y)\,dx\,dy$

10. Let $R$ be the region shown in the accompanying figure. Fill in the missing limits of integration.

    (a) $\displaystyle\iint_R f(x, y)\,dA = \int_{\square}^{\square} \int_{\square}^{\square} f(x, y)\,dy\,dx$

    (b) $\displaystyle\iint_R f(x, y)\,dA = \int_{\square}^{\square} \int_{\square}^{\square} f(x, y)\,dx\,dy$

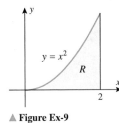

▲ **Figure Ex-9**

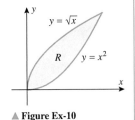

▲ **Figure Ex-10**

11. Let $R$ be the region shown in the accompanying figure. Fill in the missing limits of integration.

    (a) $\displaystyle\iint_R f(x, y)\,dA = \int_1^2 \int_{\square}^{\square} f(x, y)\,dy\,dx$
    $$+ \int_2^4 \int_{\square}^{\square} f(x, y)\,dy\,dx$$
    $$+ \int_4^5 \int_{\square}^{\square} f(x, y)\,dy\,dx$$

    (b) $\displaystyle\iint_R f(x, y)\,dA = \int_{\square}^{\square} \int_{\square}^{\square} f(x, y)\,dx\,dy$

12. Let $R$ be the region shown in the accompanying figure. Fill in the missing limits of integration.

    (a) $\displaystyle\iint_R f(x, y)\,dA = \int_{\square}^{\square} \int_{\square}^{\square} f(x, y)\,dy\,dx$

    (b) $\displaystyle\iint_R f(x, y)\,dA = \int_{\square}^{\square} \int_{\square}^{\square} f(x, y)\,dx\,dy$

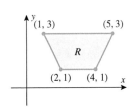

▲ **Figure Ex-11**

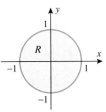

▲ **Figure Ex-12**

13. Evaluate $\displaystyle\iint_R xy\,dA$, where $R$ is the region in

    (a) Exercise 9

    (b) Exercise 11.

**14.** Evaluate $\displaystyle\iint\limits_{R} (x + y)\, dA$, where $R$ is the region in

    (a) Exercise 10              (b) Exercise 12.

**15–18** Evaluate the double integral in two ways using iterated integrals: (a) viewing $R$ as a type I region, and (b) viewing $R$ as a type II region. ■

**15.** $\displaystyle\iint\limits_{R} x^2\, dA$; $R$ is the region bounded by $y = 16/x$, $y = x$, and $x = 8$.

**16.** $\displaystyle\iint\limits_{R} xy^2\, dA$; $R$ is the region enclosed by $y = 1$, $y = 2$, $x = 0$, and $y = x$.

**17.** $\displaystyle\iint\limits_{R} (3x - 2y)\, dA$; $R$ is the region enclosed by the circle $x^2 + y^2 = 1$.

**18.** $\displaystyle\iint\limits_{R} y\, dA$; $R$ is the region in the first quadrant enclosed between the circle $x^2 + y^2 = 25$ and the line $x + y = 5$.

**19–24** Evaluate the double integral. ■

**19.** $\displaystyle\iint\limits_{R} x(1 + y^2)^{-1/2}\, dA$; $R$ is the region in the first quadrant enclosed by $y = x^2$, $y = 4$, and $x = 0$.

**20.** $\displaystyle\iint\limits_{R} x \cos y\, dA$; $R$ is the triangular region bounded by the lines $y = x$, $y = 0$, and $x = \pi$.

**21.** $\displaystyle\iint\limits_{R} xy\, dA$; $R$ is the region enclosed by $y = \sqrt{x}$, $y = 6 - x$, and $y = 0$.

**22.** $\displaystyle\iint\limits_{R} x\, dA$; $R$ is the region enclosed by $y = \sin^{-1} x$, $x = 1/\sqrt{2}$, and $y = 0$.

**23.** $\displaystyle\iint\limits_{R} (x - 1)\, dA$; $R$ is the region in the first quadrant enclosed between $y = x$ and $y = x^3$.

**24.** $\displaystyle\iint\limits_{R} x^2\, dA$; $R$ is the region in the first quadrant enclosed by $xy = 1$, $y = x$, and $y = 2x$.

**25.** Evaluate $\displaystyle\iint\limits_{R} \sin(y^3)\, dA$, where $R$ is the region bounded by $y = \sqrt{x}$, $y = 2$, and $x = 0$. [*Hint:* Choose the order of integration carefully.]

**26.** Evaluate $\displaystyle\iint\limits_{R} x\, dA$, where $R$ is the region bounded by $x = \ln y$, $x = 0$, and $y = e$.

**27.** (a) By hand or with the help of a graphing utility, make a sketch of the region $R$ enclosed between the curves $y = x + 2$ and $y = e^x$.

    (b) Estimate the intersections of the curves in part (a).

    (c) Viewing $R$ as a type I region, estimate $\displaystyle\iint\limits_{R} x\, dA$.

    (d) Viewing $R$ as a type II region, estimate $\displaystyle\iint\limits_{R} x\, dA$.

**28.** (a) By hand or with the help of a graphing utility, make a sketch of the region $R$ enclosed between the curves $y = 4x^3 - x^4$ and $y = 3 - 4x + 4x^2$.

    (b) Find the intersections of the curves in part (a).

    (c) Find $\displaystyle\iint\limits_{R} x\, dA$.

**29–32** Use double integration to find the area of the plane region enclosed by the given curves. ■

**29.** $y = \sin x$ and $y = \cos x$, for $0 \le x \le \pi/4$.

**30.** $y^2 = -x$ and $3y - x = 4$.

**31.** $y^2 = 9 - x$ and $y^2 = 9 - 9x$.

**32.** $y = \cosh x$, $y = \sinh x$, $x = 0$, and $x = 1$.

**33–36 True–False** Determine whether the statement is true or false. Explain your answer. ■

**33.** $\displaystyle\int_{0}^{1} \int_{x^2}^{2x} f(x, y)\, dy\, dx = \int_{x^2}^{2x} \int_{0}^{1} f(x, y)\, dx\, dy$

**34.** If a region $R$ is bounded below by $y = g_1(x)$ and above by $y = g_2(x)$ for $a \le x \le b$, then

$$\iint\limits_{R} f(x, y)\, dA = \int_{a}^{b} \int_{g_1(x)}^{g_2(x)} f(x, y)\, dy\, dx$$

**35.** If $R$ is the region in the $xy$-plane enclosed by $y = x^2$ and $y = 1$, then

$$\iint\limits_{R} f(x, y)\, dA = 2 \int_{0}^{1} \int_{x^2}^{1} f(x, y)\, dy\, dx$$

**36.** The area of a region $R$ in the $xy$-plane is given by $\displaystyle\iint\limits_{R} xy\, dA$.

**37–38** Use double integration to find the volume of the solid. ■

**37.**                     **38.**

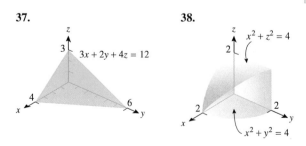

**39–44** Use double integration to find the volume of each solid. ■

**39.** The solid bounded by the cylinder $x^2 + y^2 = 9$ and the planes $z = 0$ and $z = 3 - x$.

**40.** The solid in the first octant bounded above by the paraboloid $z = x^2 + 3y^2$, below by the plane $z = 0$, and laterally by $y = x^2$ and $y = x$.

**41.** The solid bounded above by the paraboloid $z = 9x^2 + y^2$, below by the plane $z = 0$, and laterally by the planes $x = 0$, $y = 0$, $x = 3$, and $y = 2$.

**42.** The solid enclosed by $y^2 = x$, $z = 0$, and $x + z = 1$.

**43.** The wedge cut from the cylinder $4x^2 + y^2 = 9$ by the planes $z = 0$ and $z = y + 3$.

**44.** The solid in the first octant bounded above by $z = 9 - x^2$, below by $z = 0$, and laterally by $y^2 = 3x$.

C **45–46** Use a double integral and a CAS to find the volume of the solid. ■

**45.** The solid bounded above by the paraboloid $z = 1 - x^2 - y^2$ and below by the $xy$-plane.

**46.** The solid in the first octant that is bounded by the paraboloid $z = x^2 + y^2$, the cylinder $x^2 + y^2 = 4$, and the coordinate planes.

**47–52** Express the integral as an equivalent integral with the order of integration reversed. ■

**47.** $\int_0^2 \int_0^{\sqrt{x}} f(x, y) \, dy \, dx$ 　 **48.** $\int_0^4 \int_{2y}^8 f(x, y) \, dx \, dy$

**49.** $\int_0^2 \int_1^{e^y} f(x, y) \, dx \, dy$ 　 **50.** $\int_1^e \int_0^{\ln x} f(x, y) \, dy \, dx$

**51.** $\int_0^1 \int_{\sin^{-1} y}^{\pi/2} f(x, y) \, dx \, dy$ 　 **52.** $\int_0^1 \int_{y^2}^{\sqrt{y}} f(x, y) \, dx \, dy$

**53–56** Evaluate the integral by first reversing the order of integration. ■

**53.** $\int_0^1 \int_{4x}^4 e^{-y^2} \, dy \, dx$ 　 **54.** $\int_0^2 \int_{y/2}^1 \cos(x^2) \, dx \, dy$

**55.** $\int_0^4 \int_{\sqrt{y}}^2 e^{x^3} \, dx \, dy$ 　 **56.** $\int_1^3 \int_0^{\ln x} x \, dy \, dx$

C **57.** Try to evaluate the integral with a CAS using the stated order of integration, and then by reversing the order of integration.

(a) $\int_0^4 \int_{\sqrt{x}}^2 \sin \pi y^3 \, dy \, dx$

(b) $\int_0^1 \int_{\sin^{-1} y}^{\pi/2} \sec^2(\cos x) \, dx \, dy$

**58.** Use the appropriate Wallis formula (see Exercise Set 7.3) to find the volume of the solid enclosed between the circular paraboloid $z = x^2 + y^2$, the right circular cylinder $x^2 + y^2 = 4$, and the $xy$-plane (see the accompanying figure for cut view).

**59.** Evaluate $\iint_R xy^2 \, dA$ over the region $R$ shown in the accompanying figure.

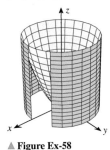

▲ **Figure Ex-58**

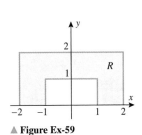

▲ **Figure Ex-59**

**60.** Give a geometric argument to show that

$$\int_0^1 \int_0^{\sqrt{1-y^2}} \sqrt{1 - x^2 - y^2} \, dx \, dy = \frac{\pi}{6}$$

**61–62** The *average value* or *mean value* of a continuous function $f(x, y)$ over a region $R$ in the $xy$-plane is defined as

$$f_{\text{ave}} = \frac{1}{A(R)} \iint_R f(x, y) \, dA$$

where $A(R)$ is the area of the region $R$ (compare to the definition preceding Exercise 35 in Section 14.1). Use this definition in these exercises. ■

**61.** Find the average value of $1/(1 + x^2)$ over the triangular region with vertices $(0, 0)$, $(1, 1)$, and $(0, 1)$.

**62.** Find the average value of $f(x, y) = x^2 - xy$ over the region enclosed by $y = x$ and $y = 3x - x^2$.

**63.** Suppose that the temperature in degrees Celsius at a point $(x, y)$ on a flat metal plate is $T(x, y) = 5xy + x^2$, where $x$ and $y$ are in meters. Find the average temperature of the diamond-shaped portion of the plate for which $|2x + y| \le 4$ and $|2x - y| \le 4$.

**64.** A circular lens of radius 2 inches has thickness $1 - (r^2/4)$ inches at all points $r$ inches from the center of the lens. Find the average thickness of the lens.

C **65.** Use a CAS to approximate the intersections of the curves $y = \sin x$ and $y = x/2$, and then approximate the volume of the solid in the first octant that is below the surface $z = \sqrt{1 + x + y}$ and above the region in the $xy$-plane that is enclosed by the curves.

**66.** Writing Describe the steps you would follow to find the limits of integration that express a double integral over a nonrectangular region as an iterated double integral. Illustrate your discussion with an example.

**67.** Writing Describe the steps you would follow to reverse the order of integration in an iterated double integral. Illustrate your discussion with an example.

1. (a) $\int_1^5 \left( \frac{1}{4} y^4 - 16y \right) dy$ (b) $\int_1^5 \left( \frac{3}{4} x^4 - 12x^2 \right) dx$   2. (a) $\int_0^3 \int_0^{-\frac{4}{3}x+4} f(x, y)\, dy\, dx$ (b) $\int_0^4 \int_0^{-\frac{3}{4}y+3} f(x, y)\, dx\, dy$

3. $\int_0^3 \int_x^{-\frac{1}{3}x+4} dy\, dx$   4. $\int_{-2}^1 \int_{x^2}^{2-x} (1 + 2y)\, dy\, dx = 18.9$

---

## 14.3 DOUBLE INTEGRALS IN POLAR COORDINATES

*In this section we will study double integrals in which the integrand and the region of integration are expressed in polar coordinates. Such integrals are important for two reasons: first, they arise naturally in many applications, and second, many double integrals in rectangular coordinates can be evaluated more easily if they are converted to polar coordinates.*

---

### ■ SIMPLE POLAR REGIONS

Some double integrals are easier to evaluate if the region of integration is expressed in polar coordinates. This is usually true if the region is bounded by a cardioid, a rose curve, a spiral, or, more generally, by any curve whose equation is simpler in polar coordinates than in rectangular coordinates. For example, the quarter-disk in Figure 14.3.1 is described in rectangular coordinates by

$$0 \le y \le \sqrt{4 - x^2}, \quad 0 \le x \le 2$$

However, in polar coordinates the region is described more simply by

$$0 \le r \le 2, \quad 0 \le \theta \le \pi/2$$

Moreover, double integrals whose integrands involve $x^2 + y^2$ also tend to be easier to evaluate in polar coordinates because this sum simplifies to $r^2$ when the conversion formulas $x = r \cos\theta$ and $y = r \sin\theta$ are applied.

Figure 14.3.2a shows a region $R$ in a polar coordinate system that is enclosed between two rays, $\theta = \alpha$ and $\theta = \beta$, and two polar curves, $r = r_1(\theta)$ and $r = r_2(\theta)$. If, as shown in the figure, the functions $r_1(\theta)$ and $r_2(\theta)$ are continuous and their graphs do not cross, then the region $R$ is called a *simple polar region*. If $r_1(\theta)$ is identically zero, then the boundary $r = r_1(\theta)$ reduces to a point (the origin), and the region has the general shape shown in Figure 14.3.2b. If, in addition, $\beta = \alpha + 2\pi$, then the rays coincide, and the region has the

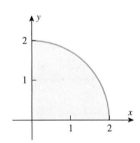

▶ **Figure 14.3.1**

An overview of polar coordinates can be found in Section 10.2.

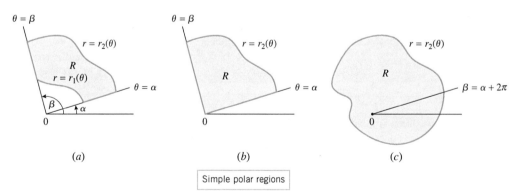

(a)  (b)  (c)

Simple polar regions

▲ **Figure 14.3.2**

general shape shown in Figure 14.3.2c. The following definition expresses these geometric ideas algebraically.

---

**14.3.1**  DEFINITION  A *simple polar region* in a polar coordinate system is a region that is enclosed between two rays, $\theta = \alpha$ and $\theta = \beta$, and two continuous polar curves, $r = r_1(\theta)$ and $r = r_2(\theta)$, where the equations of the rays and the polar curves satisfy the following conditions:

(i) $\alpha \leq \beta$      (ii) $\beta - \alpha \leq 2\pi$      (iii) $0 \leq r_1(\theta) \leq r_2(\theta)$

---

REMARK  Conditions (i) and (ii) together imply that the ray $\theta = \beta$ can be obtained by rotating the ray $\theta = \alpha$ counterclockwise through an angle that is at most $2\pi$ radians. This is consistent with Figure 14.3.2. Condition (iii) implies that the boundary curves $r = r_1(\theta)$ and $r = r_2(\theta)$ can touch but cannot actually cross over one another (why?). Thus, in keeping with Figure 14.3.2, it is appropriate to describe $r = r_1(\theta)$ as the *inner boundary* of the region and $r = r_2(\theta)$ as the *outer boundary*.

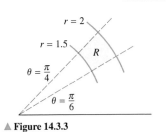

▲ **Figure 14.3.3**

A *polar rectangle* is a simple polar region for which the bounding polar curves are circular arcs. For example, Figure 14.3.3 shows the polar rectangle $R$ given by

$$1.5 \leq r \leq 2, \quad \frac{\pi}{6} \leq \theta \leq \frac{\pi}{4}$$

### DOUBLE INTEGRALS IN POLAR COORDINATES

Next we will consider the polar version of Problem 14.1.1.

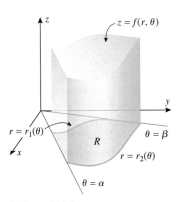

▲ **Figure 14.3.4**

---

**14.3.2**  THE VOLUME PROBLEM IN POLAR COORDINATES  Given a function $f(r, \theta)$ that is continuous and nonnegative on a simple polar region $R$, find the volume of the solid that is enclosed between the region $R$ and the surface whose equation in cylindrical coordinates is $z = f(r, \theta)$ (Figure 14.3.4).

---

To motivate a formula for the volume $V$ of the solid in Figure 14.3.4, we will use a limit process similar to that used to obtain Formula (2) of Section 14.1, except that here we will use circular arcs and rays to subdivide the region $R$ into polar rectangles. As shown in Figure 14.3.5, we will exclude from consideration all polar rectangles that contain any points outside of $R$, leaving only polar rectangles that are subsets of $R$. Assume that there are $n$ such polar rectangles, and denote the area of the $k$th polar rectangle by $\Delta A_k$. Let $(r_k^*, \theta_k^*)$ be any point in this polar rectangle. As shown in Figure 14.3.6, the product $f(r_k^*, \theta_k^*)\Delta A_k$ is the volume of a solid with base area $\Delta A_k$ and height $f(r_k^*, \theta_k^*)$, so the sum

$$\sum_{k=1}^{n} f(r_k^*, \theta_k^*)\Delta A_k$$

can be viewed as an approximation to the volume $V$ of the entire solid.

If we now increase the number of subdivisions in such a way that the dimensions of the polar rectangles approach zero, then it seems plausible that the errors in the approximations approach zero, and the exact volume of the solid is

$$V = \lim_{n \to +\infty} \sum_{k=1}^{n} f(r_k^*, \theta_k^*)\Delta A_k \tag{1}$$

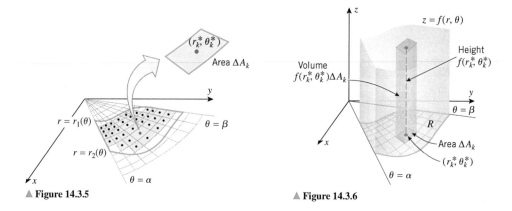

▲ **Figure 14.3.5**    ▲ **Figure 14.3.6**

If $f(r, \theta)$ is continuous on $R$ and has both positive and negative values, then the limit

$$\lim_{n \to +\infty} \sum_{k=1}^{n} f(r_k^*, \theta_k^*) \Delta A_k \tag{2}$$

represents the net signed volume between the region $R$ and the surface $z = f(r, \theta)$ (as with double integrals in rectangular coordinates). The sums in (2) are called ***polar Riemann sums***, and the limit of the polar Riemann sums is denoted by

$$\iint\limits_{R} f(r, \theta) \, dA = \lim_{n \to +\infty} \sum_{k=1}^{n} f(r_k^*, \theta_k^*) \Delta A_k \tag{3}$$

which is called the ***polar double integral*** of $f(r, \theta)$ over $R$. If $f(r, \theta)$ is continuous and nonnegative on $R$, then the volume formula (1) can be expressed as

$$V = \iint\limits_{R} f(r, \theta) \, dA \tag{4}$$

Polar double integrals are also called *double integrals in polar coordinates* to distinguish them from double integrals over regions in the $xy$-plane; the latter are called *double integrals in rectangular coordinates*. Double integrals in polar coordinates have the usual integral properties, such as those stated in Formulas (9), (10), and (11) of Section 14.1.

■ **EVALUATING POLAR DOUBLE INTEGRALS**

In Sections 14.1 and 14.2 we evaluated double integrals in rectangular coordinates by expressing them as iterated integrals. Polar double integrals are evaluated the same way. To motivate the formula that expresses a double polar integral as an iterated integral, we will assume that $f(r, \theta)$ is nonnegative so that we can interpret (3) as a volume. However, the results that we will obtain will also be applicable if $f$ has negative values. To begin, let us choose the arbitrary point $(r_k^*, \theta_k^*)$ in (3) to be at the "center" of the $k$th polar rectangle as shown in Figure 14.3.7. Suppose also that this polar rectangle has a central angle $\Delta \theta_k$ and a "radial thickness" $\Delta r_k$. Thus, the inner radius of this polar rectangle is $r_k^* - \frac{1}{2} \Delta r_k$ and the outer radius is $r_k^* + \frac{1}{2} \Delta r_k$. Treating the area $\Delta A_k$ of this polar rectangle as the difference in area of two sectors, we obtain

$$\Delta A_k = \tfrac{1}{2} \left( r_k^* + \tfrac{1}{2} \Delta r_k \right)^2 \Delta \theta_k - \tfrac{1}{2} \left( r_k^* - \tfrac{1}{2} \Delta r_k \right)^2 \Delta \theta_k$$

which simplifies to

$$\Delta A_k = r_k^* \Delta r_k \Delta \theta_k \tag{5}$$

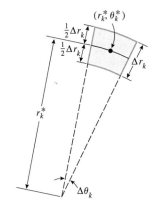

▲ **Figure 14.3.7**

Thus, from (3) and (4)

$$V = \iint\limits_{R} f(r, \theta) \, dA = \lim_{n \to +\infty} \sum_{k=1}^{n} f(r_k^*, \theta_k^*) r_k^* \Delta r_k \Delta \theta_k$$

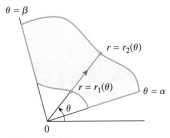

**▲ Figure 14.3.8**

which suggests that the volume $V$ can be expressed as the iterated integral

$$V = \iint\limits_{R} f(r, \theta)\, dA = \int_{\alpha}^{\beta} \int_{r_1(\theta)}^{r_2(\theta)} f(r, \theta)r\, dr\, d\theta \qquad (6)$$

in which the limits of integration are chosen to cover the region $R$; that is, with $\theta$ fixed between $\alpha$ and $\beta$, the value of $r$ varies from $r_1(\theta)$ to $r_2(\theta)$ (Figure 14.3.8).

Although we assumed $f(r, \theta)$ to be nonnegative in deriving Formula (6), it can be proved that the relationship between the polar double integral and the iterated integral in this formula also holds if $f$ has negative values. Accepting this to be so, we obtain the following theorem, which we state without formal proof.

Note the extra factor of $r$ that appears in the integrand when expressing a polar double integral as an iterated integral in polar coordinates.

---

**14.3.3  THEOREM**  *If $R$ is a simple polar region whose boundaries are the rays $\theta = \alpha$ and $\theta = \beta$ and the curves $r = r_1(\theta)$ and $r = r_2(\theta)$ shown in Figure 14.3.8, and if $f(r, \theta)$ is continuous on $R$, then*

$$\iint\limits_{R} f(r, \theta)\, dA = \int_{\alpha}^{\beta} \int_{r_1(\theta)}^{r_2(\theta)} f(r, \theta)r\, dr\, d\theta \qquad (7)$$

---

To apply this theorem you will need to be able to find the rays and the curves that form the boundary of the region $R$, since these determine the limits of integration in the iterated integral. This can be done as follows:

### Determining Limits of Integration for a Polar Double Integral: Simple Polar Region

**Step 1.** Since $\theta$ is held fixed for the first integration, draw a radial line from the origin through the region $R$ at a fixed angle $\theta$ (Figure 14.3.9a). This line crosses the boundary of $R$ at most twice. The innermost point of intersection is on the inner boundary curve $r = r_1(\theta)$ and the outermost point is on the outer boundary curve $r = r_2(\theta)$. These intersections determine the $r$-limits of integration in (7).

**Step 2.** Imagine rotating the radial line from Step 1 about the origin, thus sweeping out the region $R$. The least angle at which the radial line intersects the region $R$ is $\theta = \alpha$ and the greatest angle is $\theta = \beta$ (Figure 14.3.9b). This determines the $\theta$-limits of integration.

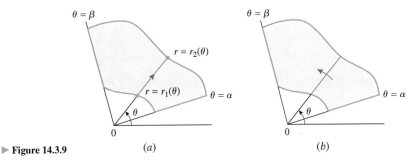

**▶ Figure 14.3.9**                    (a)                                (b)

▶ **Example 1** Evaluate

$$\iint\limits_{R} \sin\theta \, dA$$

where $R$ is the region in the first quadrant that is outside the circle $r = 2$ and inside the cardioid $r = 2(1 + \cos\theta)$.

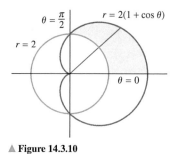

▲ **Figure 14.3.10**

**Solution.** The region $R$ is sketched in Figure 14.3.10. Following the two steps outlined above we obtain

$$\iint\limits_{R} \sin\theta \, dA = \int_{0}^{\pi/2} \int_{2}^{2(1+\cos\theta)} (\sin\theta) r \, dr \, d\theta$$

$$= \int_{0}^{\pi/2} \left[ \frac{1}{2} r^2 \sin\theta \right]_{r=2}^{2(1+\cos\theta)} d\theta$$

$$= 2 \int_{0}^{\pi/2} [(1 + \cos\theta)^2 \sin\theta - \sin\theta] \, d\theta$$

$$= 2 \left[ -\frac{1}{3}(1 + \cos\theta)^3 + \cos\theta \right]_{0}^{\pi/2}$$

$$= 2 \left[ -\frac{1}{3} - \left( -\frac{5}{3} \right) \right] = \frac{8}{3} \quad \blacktriangleleft$$

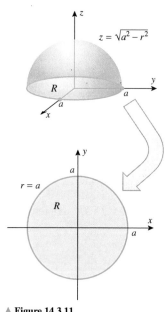

▲ **Figure 14.3.11**

▶ **Example 2** The sphere of radius $a$ centered at the origin is expressed in rectangular coordinates as $x^2 + y^2 + z^2 = a^2$, and hence its equation in cylindrical coordinates is $r^2 + z^2 = a^2$. Use this equation and a polar double integral to find the volume of the sphere.

**Solution.** In cylindrical coordinates the upper hemisphere is given by the equation

$$z = \sqrt{a^2 - r^2}$$

so the volume enclosed by the entire sphere is

$$V = 2 \iint\limits_{R} \sqrt{a^2 - r^2} \, dA$$

where $R$ is the circular region shown in Figure 14.3.11. Thus,

$$V = 2 \iint\limits_{R} \sqrt{a^2 - r^2} \, dA = \int_{0}^{2\pi} \int_{0}^{a} \sqrt{a^2 - r^2}(2r) \, dr \, d\theta$$

$$= \int_{0}^{2\pi} \left[ -\frac{2}{3}(a^2 - r^2)^{3/2} \right]_{r=0}^{a} d\theta = \int_{0}^{2\pi} \frac{2}{3} a^3 \, d\theta$$

$$= \left[ \frac{2}{3} a^3 \theta \right]_{0}^{2\pi} = \frac{4}{3} \pi a^3 \quad \blacktriangleleft$$

■ **FINDING AREAS USING POLAR DOUBLE INTEGRALS**

Recall from Formula (7) of Section 14.2 that the area of a region $R$ in the $xy$-plane can be expressed as

$$\text{area of } R = \iint\limits_{R} 1 \, dA = \iint\limits_{R} dA \tag{8}$$

The argument used to derive this result can also be used to show that the formula applies to polar double integrals over regions in polar coordinates.

▶ **Example 3**    Use a polar double integral to find the area enclosed by the three-petaled rose $r = \sin 3\theta$.

*Solution.*    The rose is sketched in Figure 14.3.12. We will use Formula (8) to calculate the area of the petal $R$ in the first quadrant and multiply by three.

$$A = 3 \iint\limits_{R} dA = 3 \int_0^{\pi/3} \int_0^{\sin 3\theta} r \, dr \, d\theta$$

$$= \frac{3}{2} \int_0^{\pi/3} \sin^2 3\theta \, d\theta = \frac{3}{4} \int_0^{\pi/3} (1 - \cos 6\theta) \, d\theta$$

$$= \frac{3}{4} \left[ \theta - \frac{\sin 6\theta}{6} \right]_0^{\pi/3} = \frac{1}{4}\pi \blacktriangleleft$$

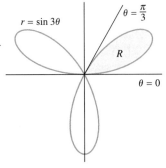

$r = \sin 3\theta$

$\theta = \frac{\pi}{3}$

$R$

$\theta = 0$

▲ **Figure 14.3.12**

■ **CONVERTING DOUBLE INTEGRALS FROM RECTANGULAR TO POLAR COORDINATES**
Sometimes a double integral that is difficult to evaluate in rectangular coordinates can be evaluated more easily in polar coordinates by making the substitution $x = r \cos\theta$, $y = r \sin\theta$ and expressing the region of integration in polar form; that is, we rewrite the double integral in rectangular coordinates as

$$\iint\limits_{R} f(x, y) \, dA = \iint\limits_{R} f(r \cos\theta, r \sin\theta) \, dA = \iint\limits_{\substack{\text{appropriate} \\ \text{limits}}} f(r \cos\theta, r \sin\theta) r \, dr \, d\theta \quad (9)$$

▶ **Example 4**    Use polar coordinates to evaluate $\displaystyle\int_{-1}^{1} \int_0^{\sqrt{1-x^2}} (x^2 + y^2)^{3/2} \, dy \, dx$.

*Solution.*    In this problem we are starting with an iterated integral in rectangular coordinates rather than a double integral, so before we can make the conversion to polar coordinates we will have to identify the region of integration. To do this, we observe that for fixed $x$ the $y$-integration runs from $y = 0$ to $y = \sqrt{1 - x^2}$, which tells us that the lower boundary of the region is the $x$-axis and the upper boundary is a semicircle of radius 1 centered at the origin. From the $x$-integration we see that $x$ varies from $-1$ to 1, so we conclude that the region of integration is as shown in Figure 14.3.13. In polar coordinates, this is the region swept out as $r$ varies between 0 and 1 and $\theta$ varies between 0 and $\pi$. Thus,

$$\int_{-1}^{1} \int_0^{\sqrt{1-x^2}} (x^2 + y^2)^{3/2} \, dy \, dx = \iint\limits_{R} (x^2 + y^2)^{3/2} \, dA$$

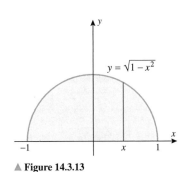

$y$

$y = \sqrt{1 - x^2}$

$-1$    $x$    $1$

$x$

▲ **Figure 14.3.13**

$$= \int_0^{\pi} \int_0^1 (r^3) r \, dr \, d\theta = \int_0^{\pi} \frac{1}{5} \, d\theta = \frac{\pi}{5} \blacktriangleleft$$

**REMARK**    The reason the conversion to polar coordinates worked so nicely in Example 4 is that the substitution $x = r \cos\theta$, $y = r \sin\theta$ collapsed the sum $x^2 + y^2$ into the single term $r^2$, thereby simplifying the integrand. Whenever you see an expression involving $x^2 + y^2$ in the integrand, you should consider the possibility of converting to polar coordinates.

✔️ **QUICK CHECK EXERCISES 14.3**  *(See page 1025 for answers.)*

**1.** The polar region inside the circle $r = 2 \sin \theta$ and outside the circle $r = 1$ is a simple polar region given by the inequalities

_____ $\leq r \leq$ _____,  _____ $\leq \theta \leq$ _____

**2.** Let $R$ be the region in the first quadrant enclosed between the circles $x^2 + y^2 = 9$ and $x^2 + y^2 = 100$. Supply the missing limits of integration.

$$\iint\limits_{R} f(r, \theta)\, dA = \int_{\square}^{\square} \int_{\square}^{\square} f(r, \theta) r\, dr\, d\theta$$

**3.** Let $V$ be the volume of the solid bounded above by the hemisphere $z = \sqrt{1 - r^2}$ and bounded below by the disk enclosed within the circle $r = \sin \theta$. Expressed as a double integral in polar coordinates, $V = $ _____.

**4.** Express the iterated integral as a double integral in polar coordinates.

$$\int_{1/\sqrt{2}}^{1} \int_{\sqrt{1-x^2}}^{x} \left( \frac{1}{x^2 + y^2} \right) dy\, dx = \underline{\qquad}$$

## EXERCISE SET 14.3

**1–6** Evaluate the iterated integral. ▪

**1.** $\displaystyle\int_0^{\pi/2} \int_0^{\sin \theta} r \cos \theta\, dr\, d\theta$

**2.** $\displaystyle\int_0^{\pi} \int_0^{1+\cos \theta} r\, dr\, d\theta$

**3.** $\displaystyle\int_0^{\pi/2} \int_0^{a \sin \theta} r^2\, dr\, d\theta$

**4.** $\displaystyle\int_0^{\pi/6} \int_0^{\cos 3\theta} r\, dr\, d\theta$

**5.** $\displaystyle\int_0^{\pi} \int_0^{1-\sin \theta} r^2 \cos \theta\, dr\, d\theta$

**6.** $\displaystyle\int_0^{\pi/2} \int_0^{\cos \theta} r^3\, dr\, d\theta$

**7–10** Use a double integral in polar coordinates to find the area of the region described. ▪

**7.** The region enclosed by the cardioid $r = 1 - \cos \theta$.

**8.** The region enclosed by the rose $r = \sin 2\theta$.

**9.** The region in the first quadrant bounded by $r = 1$ and $r = \sin 2\theta$, with $\pi/4 \leq \theta \leq \pi/2$.

**10.** The region inside the circle $x^2 + y^2 = 4$ and to the right of the line $x = 1$.

**FOCUS ON CONCEPTS**

**11–12** Let $R$ be the region described. Sketch the region $R$ and fill in the missing limits of integration.

$$\iint\limits_{R} f(r, \theta)\, dA = \int_{\square}^{\square} \int_{\square}^{\square} f(r, \theta) r\, dr\, d\theta \ \blacksquare$$

**11.** The region inside the circle $r = 4 \sin \theta$ and outside the circle $r = 2$.

**12.** The region inside the circle $r = 1$ and outside the cardioid $r = 1 + \cos \theta$.

**13–16** Express the volume of the solid described as a double integral in polar coordinates. ▪

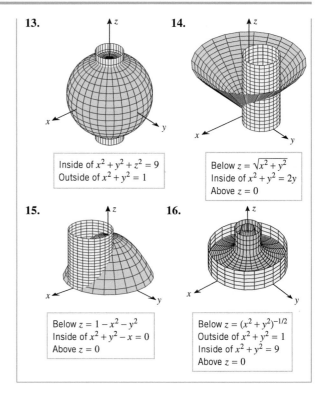

**13.**

Inside of $x^2 + y^2 + z^2 = 9$
Outside of $x^2 + y^2 = 1$

**14.**

Below $z = \sqrt{x^2 + y^2}$
Inside of $x^2 + y^2 = 2y$
Above $z = 0$

**15.**

Below $z = 1 - x^2 - y^2$
Inside of $x^2 + y^2 - x = 0$
Above $z = 0$

**16.**

Below $z = (x^2 + y^2)^{-1/2}$
Outside of $x^2 + y^2 = 1$
Inside of $x^2 + y^2 = 9$
Above $z = 0$

**17–20** Find the volume of the solid described in the indicated exercise. ▪

**17.** Exercise 13  **18.** Exercise 14

**19.** Exercise 15  **20.** Exercise 16

**21.** Find the volume of the solid in the first octant bounded above by the surface $z = r \sin \theta$, below by the $xy$-plane, and laterally by the plane $x = 0$ and the surface $r = 3 \sin \theta$.

**22.** Find the volume of the solid inside the surface $r^2 + z^2 = 4$ and outside the surface $r = 2 \cos \theta$.

**23–26** Use polar coordinates to evaluate the double integral. ▪

**23.** $\displaystyle\iint\limits_{R} \sin(x^2 + y^2)\, dA$, where $R$ is the region enclosed by the circle $x^2 + y^2 = 9$.

**24.** $\displaystyle\iint\limits_{R} \sqrt{9 - x^2 - y^2}\, dA$, where $R$ is the region in the first quadrant within the circle $x^2 + y^2 = 9$.

**25.** $\displaystyle\iint\limits_{R} \frac{1}{1 + x^2 + y^2}\, dA$, where $R$ is the sector in the first quadrant bounded by $y = 0$, $y = x$, and $x^2 + y^2 = 4$.

**26.** $\displaystyle\iint\limits_{R} 2y\, dA$, where $R$ is the region in the first quadrant bounded above by the circle $(x - 1)^2 + y^2 = 1$ and below by the line $y = x$.

**27–34** Evaluate the iterated integral by converting to polar coordinates. ■

**27.** $\displaystyle\int_{0}^{1} \int_{0}^{\sqrt{1-x^2}} (x^2 + y^2)\, dy\, dx$

**28.** $\displaystyle\int_{-2}^{2} \int_{-\sqrt{4-y^2}}^{\sqrt{4-y^2}} e^{-(x^2+y^2)}\, dx\, dy$

**29.** $\displaystyle\int_{0}^{2} \int_{0}^{\sqrt{2x-x^2}} \sqrt{x^2 + y^2}\, dy\, dx$

**30.** $\displaystyle\int_{0}^{1} \int_{0}^{\sqrt{1-y^2}} \cos(x^2 + y^2)\, dx\, dy$

**31.** $\displaystyle\int_{0}^{a} \int_{0}^{\sqrt{a^2-x^2}} \frac{dy\, dx}{(1 + x^2 + y^2)^{3/2}} \quad (a > 0)$

**32.** $\displaystyle\int_{0}^{1} \int_{y}^{\sqrt{y}} \sqrt{x^2 + y^2}\, dx\, dy$

**33.** $\displaystyle\int_{0}^{\sqrt{2}} \int_{y}^{\sqrt{4-y^2}} \frac{1}{\sqrt{1 + x^2 + y^2}}\, dx\, dy$

**34.** $\displaystyle\int_{-4}^{0} \int_{-\sqrt{16-x^2}}^{\sqrt{16-x^2}} 3x\, dy\, dx$

**35–38 True–False** Determine whether the statement is true or false. Explain your answer. ■

**35.** The disk of radius 2 that is centered at the origin is a polar rectangle.

**36.** If $f$ is continuous and nonnegative on a simple polar region $R$, then the volume of the solid enclosed between $R$ and the surface $z = f(r, \theta)$ is expressed as
$$\iint\limits_{R} f(r, \theta)r\, dA$$

**37.** If $R$ is the region in the first quadrant between the circles $r = 1$ and $r = 2$, and if $f$ is continuous on $R$, then
$$\iint\limits_{R} f(r, \theta)\, dA = \int_{0}^{\pi/2} \int_{1}^{2} f(r, \theta)\, dr\, d\theta$$

**38.** The area enclosed by the circle $r = \sin\theta$ is given by
$$A = \int_{0}^{2\pi} \int_{0}^{\sin\theta} r\, dr\, d\theta$$

**39.** Use a double integral in polar coordinates to find the volume of a cylinder of radius $a$ and height $h$.

**40.** Suppose that a geyser, centered at the origin of a polar coordinate system, sprays water in a circular pattern in such a way that the depth $D$ of water that reaches a point at a distance of $r$ feet from the origin in 1 hour is $D = ke^{-r}$. Find the total volume of water that the geyser sprays inside a circle of radius $R$ centered at the origin.

**41.** Evaluate $\displaystyle\iint\limits_{R} x^2\, dA$ over the region $R$ shown in the accompanying figure.

**42.** Show that the shaded area in the accompanying figure is $a^2\phi - \frac{1}{2}a^2 \sin 2\phi$.

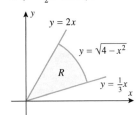

▲ **Figure Ex-41**          ▲ **Figure Ex-42**

**43.** (a) Use a double integral in polar coordinates to find the volume of the oblate spheroid
$$\frac{x^2}{a^2} + \frac{y^2}{a^2} + \frac{z^2}{c^2} = 1 \quad (0 < c < a)$$
  (b) Use the result in part (a) and the World Geodetic System of 1984 (WGS-84) discussed in Exercise 54 of Section 11.7 to find the volume of the Earth in cubic meters.

**44.** Use polar coordinates to find the volume of the solid that is above the $xy$-plane, inside the cylinder $x^2 + y^2 - ay = 0$, and inside the ellipsoid
$$\frac{x^2}{a^2} + \frac{y^2}{a^2} + \frac{z^2}{c^2} = 1$$

**45.** Find the area of the region enclosed by the lemniscate $r^2 = 2a^2 \cos 2\theta$.

**46.** Find the area in the first quadrant that is inside the circle $r = 4 \sin\theta$ and outside the lemniscate $r^2 = 8 \cos 2\theta$.

✔ **QUICK CHECK ANSWERS 14.3**

**1.** $1 \le r \le 2\sin\theta$, $\pi/6 \le \theta \le 5\pi/6$    **2.** $\displaystyle\int_{0}^{\pi/2} \int_{3}^{10} f(r, \theta)r\, dr\, d\theta$    **3.** $\displaystyle\int_{0}^{\pi} \int_{0}^{\sin\theta} r\sqrt{1 - r^2}\, dr\, d\theta$    **4.** $\displaystyle\int_{0}^{\pi/4} \int_{1}^{\sec\theta} \frac{1}{r}\, dr\, d\theta$

## 14.4 SURFACE AREA; PARAMETRIC SURFACES

*Earlier we showed how to find the surface area of a surface of revolution. In this section we will derive area formulas for surfaces with equations of the form $z = f(x, y)$ and for surfaces that are represented by parametric equations.*

■ **SURFACE AREA FOR SURFACES OF THE FORM $z = f(x, y)$**
Earlier we showed that the expression

$$\int_a^b 2\pi f(x)\sqrt{1 + [f'(x)]^2}\, dx$$

gives the area of the surface that is generated by revolving the portion of the curve $y = f(x)$ over the interval $[a, b]$ about the $x$-axis, assuming that $f$ is smooth and nonnegative on the interval. We now obtain a formula for the surface area $S$ of a surface of the form $z = f(x, y)$.

Consider a surface $\sigma$ of the form $z = f(x, y)$ defined over a region $R$ in the $xy$-plane (Figure 14.4.1a). We will assume that $f$ has continuous first partial derivatives at the interior points of $R$. (Geometrically, this means that the surface will have a nonvertical tangent plane at each interior point of $R$.) We begin by subdividing $R$ into rectangular regions by lines parallel to the $x$- and $y$-axes and by discarding any nonrectangular portions that contain points on the boundary of $R$. Assume that what remains are $n$ rectangles labeled $R_1, R_2, \ldots, R_n$.

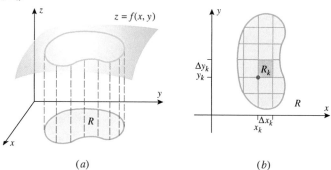

▶ **Figure 14.4.1**            (*a*)                              (*b*)

Let $(x_k, y_k)$ be the lower left corner of the $k$th rectangle $R_k$, and assume that $R_k$ has area $\Delta A_k = \Delta x_k \Delta y_k$, where $\Delta x_k$ and $\Delta y_k$ are the dimensions of $R_k$ (Figure 14.4.1b). The portion of $\sigma$ that lies over $R_k$ will be some *curvilinear patch* on the surface that has a corner at $P_k(x_k, y_k, f(x_k, y_k))$; denote the area of this patch by $\Delta S_k$ (Figure 14.4.2a). To obtain an approximation of $\Delta S_k$, we will replace $\sigma$ by the tangent plane to $\sigma$ at $P_k$. The equation of this tangent plane is

$$z = f(x_k, y_k) + f_x(x_k, y_k)(x - x_k) + f_y(x_k, y_k)(y - y_k)$$

(see Theorem 13.7.2). The portion of the tangent plane that lies over $R_k$ will be a parallelogram $\tau_k$. This parallelogram will have a vertex at $P_k$ and adjacent sides determined by the

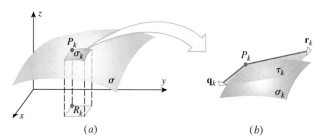

▶ **Figure 14.4.2**            (*a*)                              (*b*)

vectors

$$\mathbf{q}_k = \left\langle \Delta x_k, 0, \frac{\partial z}{\partial x} \Delta x_k \right\rangle \quad \text{and} \quad \mathbf{r}_k = \left\langle 0, \Delta y_k, \frac{\partial z}{\partial y} \Delta y_k \right\rangle$$

as illustrated in Figure 14.4.2*b*. [Here we use $\partial z/\partial x$ to represent $f_x(x_k, y_k)$ and $\partial z/\partial y$ to represent $f_y(x_k, y_k)$.]

If the dimensions of $R_k$ are small, then $\tau_k$ should provide a good approximation to the curvilinear patch $\sigma_k$. By Theorem 11.4.5(*b*), the area of the parallelogram $\tau_k$ is the length of the cross product of $\mathbf{q}_k$ and $\mathbf{r}_k$. Thus, we expect the approximation

$$\Delta S_k \approx \text{area } \tau_k = \| \mathbf{q}_k \times \mathbf{r}_k \|$$

to be good when $\Delta x_k$ and $\Delta y_k$ are close to 0. Computing the cross product yields

$$\| \mathbf{q}_k \times \mathbf{r}_k \| = \begin{Vmatrix} \mathbf{i} & \mathbf{j} & \mathbf{k} \\ \Delta x_k & 0 & \dfrac{\partial z}{\partial x} \Delta x_k \\ 0 & \Delta y_k & \dfrac{\partial z}{\partial y} \Delta y_k \end{Vmatrix} = \left( -\frac{\partial z}{\partial x} \mathbf{i} - \frac{\partial z}{\partial y} \mathbf{j} + \mathbf{k} \right) \Delta x_k \Delta y_k$$

so

$$\Delta S_k \approx \left\| \left( -\frac{\partial z}{\partial x} \mathbf{i} - \frac{\partial z}{\partial y} \mathbf{j} + \mathbf{k} \right) \Delta x_k \Delta y_k \right\| = \left\| -\frac{\partial z}{\partial x} \mathbf{i} - \frac{\partial z}{\partial y} \mathbf{j} + \mathbf{k} \right\| \Delta x_k \Delta y_k$$

$$= \sqrt{\left( \frac{\partial z}{\partial x} \right)^2 + \left( \frac{\partial z}{\partial y} \right)^2 + 1} \, \Delta A_k \tag{1}$$

It follows that the surface area of the entire surface can be approximated as

$$S \approx \sum_{k=1}^{n} \sqrt{\left( \frac{\partial z}{\partial x} \right)^2 + \left( \frac{\partial z}{\partial y} \right)^2 + 1} \, \Delta A_k$$

If we assume that the errors in the approximations approach zero as $n$ increases in such a way that the dimensions of the rectangles approach zero, then it is plausible that the exact value of $S$ is

$$S = \lim_{n \to +\infty} \sum_{k=1}^{n} \sqrt{\left( \frac{\partial z}{\partial x} \right)^2 + \left( \frac{\partial z}{\partial y} \right)^2 + 1} \, \Delta A_k$$

or, equivalently,

$$S = \iint_R \sqrt{\left( \frac{\partial z}{\partial x} \right)^2 + \left( \frac{\partial z}{\partial y} \right)^2 + 1} \, dA \tag{2}$$

▶ **Example 1** Find the surface area of that portion of the surface $z = \sqrt{4 - x^2}$ that lies above the rectangle $R$ in the $xy$-plane whose coordinates satisfy $0 \le x \le 1$ and $0 \le y \le 4$.

*Solution.* As shown in Figure 14.4.3, the surface is a portion of the cylinder $x^2 + z^2 = 4$. It follows from (2) that the surface area is

$$S = \iint_R \sqrt{\left( \frac{\partial z}{\partial x} \right)^2 + \left( \frac{\partial z}{\partial y} \right)^2 + 1} \, dA$$

$$= \iint_R \sqrt{\left( -\frac{x}{\sqrt{4 - x^2}} \right)^2 + 0 + 1} \, dA = \int_0^4 \int_0^1 \frac{2}{\sqrt{4 - x^2}} \, dx \, dy$$

$$= 2 \int_0^4 \left[ \sin^{-1} \left( \frac{1}{2} x \right) \right]_{x=0}^{1} \, dy = 2 \int_0^4 \frac{\pi}{6} \, dy = \frac{4}{3} \pi \quad ◀$$

Formula 21 of Section 7.1

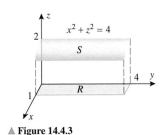

▲ **Figure 14.4.3**

▶ **Example 2**    Find the surface area of the portion of the paraboloid $z = x^2 + y^2$ below the plane $z = 1$.

*Solution.*    The surface $z = x^2 + y^2$ is the circular paraboloid shown in Figure 14.4.4. The trace of the paraboloid in the plane $z = 1$ projects onto the circle $x^2 + y^2 = 1$ in the *xy*-plane, and the portion of the paraboloid that lies below the plane $z = 1$ projects onto the region $R$ that is enclosed by this circle. Thus, it follows from (2) that the surface area is

$$S = \iint_R \sqrt{4x^2 + 4y^2 + 1}\, dA$$

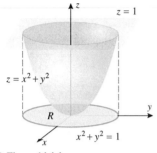

▲ **Figure 14.4.4**

The expression $4x^2 + 4y^2 + 1 = 4(x^2 + y^2) + 1$ in the integrand suggests that we evaluate the integral in polar coordinates. In accordance with Formula (9) of Section 14.3, we substitute $x = r\cos\theta$ and $y = r\sin\theta$ in the integrand, replace $dA$ by $r\, dr\, d\theta$, and find the limits of integration by expressing the region $R$ in polar coordinates. This yields

$$S = \int_0^{2\pi} \int_0^1 \sqrt{4r^2 + 1}\, r\, dr\, d\theta = \int_0^{2\pi} \left[ \frac{1}{12}(4r^2 + 1)^{3/2} \right]_{r=0}^1 d\theta$$

$$= \int_0^{2\pi} \frac{1}{12}(5\sqrt{5} - 1)\, d\theta = \frac{1}{6}\pi(5\sqrt{5} - 1) \quad \blacktriangleleft$$

Some surfaces can't be described conveniently in terms of a function $z = f(x, y)$. For such surfaces, a parametric description may provide a simpler approach. We pause for a discussion of surfaces represented parametrically, with the ultimate goal of deriving a formula for the area of a parametric surface.

■ **PARAMETRIC REPRESENTATION OF SURFACES**
We have seen that curves in 3-space can be represented by three equations involving one parameter, say

$$x = x(t), \quad y = y(t), \quad z = z(t)$$

Surfaces in 3-space can be represented parametrically by three equations involving two parameters, say

$$x = x(u, v), \quad y = y(u, v), \quad z = z(u, v) \tag{3}$$

To visualize why such equations represent a surface, think of $(u, v)$ as a point that varies over some region in a $uv$-plane. If $u$ is held constant, then $v$ is the only varying parameter in (3), and hence these equations represent a curve in 3-space. We call this a ***constant u-curve*** (Figure 14.4.5). Similarly, if $v$ is held constant, then $u$ is the only varying parameter in (3), so again these equations represent a curve in 3-space. We call this a ***constant v-curve***. By varying the constants we generate a family of $u$-curves and a family of $v$-curves that together form a surface.

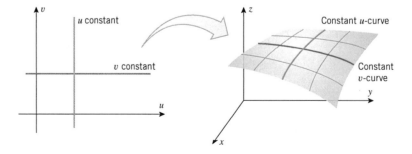

▶ **Figure 14.4.5**

▶ **Example 3**   Consider the paraboloid $z = 4 - x^2 - y^2$. One way to parametrize this surface is to take $x = u$ and $y = v$ as the parameters, in which case the surface is represented by the parametric equations

$$x = u, \quad y = v, \quad z = 4 - u^2 - v^2 \tag{4}$$

Figure 14.4.6*a* shows a computer-generated graph of this surface. The constant $u$-curves correspond to constant $x$-values and hence appear on the surface as traces parallel to the $yz$-plane. Similarly, the constant $v$-curves correspond to constant $y$-values and hence appear on the surface as traces parallel to the $xz$-plane. ◀

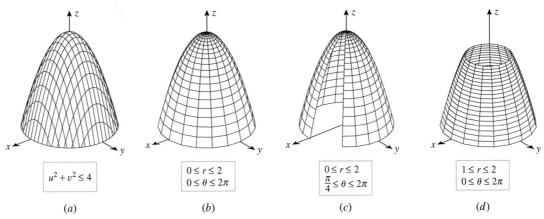

$$u^2 + v^2 \leq 4$$

(a)

$$0 \leq r \leq 2$$
$$0 \leq \theta \leq 2\pi$$

(b)

$$0 \leq r \leq 2$$
$$\frac{\pi}{4} \leq \theta \leq 2\pi$$

(c)

$$1 \leq r \leq 2$$
$$0 \leq \theta \leq 2\pi$$

(d)

▲ **Figure 14.4.6**

**TECHNOLOGY MASTERY**

If you have a graphing utility that can generate parametric surfaces, consult the relevant documentation and then try to generate the surfaces in Figure 14.4.6.

▶ **Example 4**   The paraboloid $z = 4 - x^2 - y^2$ that was considered in Example 3 can also be parametrized by first expressing the equation in cylindrical coordinates. For this purpose, we make the substitution $x = r \cos\theta$, $y = r \sin\theta$, which yields $z = 4 - r^2$. Thus, the paraboloid can be represented parametrically in terms of $r$ and $\theta$ as

$$x = r \cos\theta, \quad y = r \sin\theta, \quad z = 4 - r^2 \tag{5}$$

A computer-generated graph of this surface for $0 \leq r \leq 2$ and $0 \leq \theta \leq 2\pi$ is shown in Figure 14.4.6*b*. The constant $r$-curves correspond to constant $z$-values and hence appear on the surface as traces parallel to the $xy$-plane. The constant $\theta$-curves appear on the surface as traces from vertical planes through the origin at varying angles with the $x$-axis. Parts (*c*) and (*d*) of Figure 14.4.6 show the effect of restrictions on the parameters $r$ and $\theta$. ◀

▶ **Example 5**   One way to generate the sphere $x^2 + y^2 + z^2 = 1$ with a graphing utility is to graph the upper and lower hemispheres

$$z = \sqrt{1 - x^2 - y^2} \quad \text{and} \quad z = -\sqrt{1 - x^2 - y^2}$$

on the same screen. However, this sometimes produces a fragmented sphere (Figure 14.4.7*a*) because roundoff error sporadically produces negative values inside the radical when $1 - x^2 - y^2$ is near zero. A better graph can be generated by first expressing the sphere in spherical coordinates as $\rho = 1$ and then using the spherical-to-rectangular conversion formulas in Table 11.8.1 to obtain the parametric equations

$$x = \sin\phi \cos\theta, \quad y = \sin\phi \sin\theta, \quad z = \cos\phi$$

with parameters $\theta$ and $\phi$. Figure 14.4.7*b* shows the graph of this parametric surface for

$0 \le \theta \le 2\pi$ and $0 \le \phi \le \pi$. In the language of cartographers, the constant $\phi$-curves are the *lines of latitude* and the constant $\theta$-curves are the *lines of longitude*. ◄

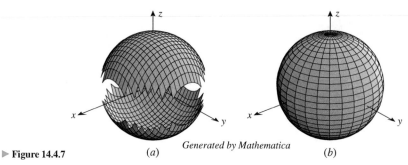

▶ **Figure 14.4.7**        (*a*)     *Generated by Mathematica*      (*b*)

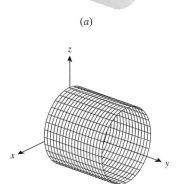

(*a*)

(*b*)

▲ **Figure 14.4.8**

▶ **Example 6**   Find parametric equations for the portion of the right circular cylinder

$$x^2 + z^2 = 9 \quad \text{for which} \quad 0 \le y \le 5$$

in terms of the parameters $u$ and $v$ shown in Figure 14.4.8*a*. The parameter $u$ is the $y$-coordinate of a point $P(x, y, z)$ on the surface, and $v$ is the angle shown in the figure.

***Solution.***   The radius of the cylinder is 3, so it is evident from the figure that $y = u$, $x = 3\cos v$, and $z = 3\sin v$. Thus, the surface can be represented parametrically as

$$x = 3\cos v, \quad y = u, \quad z = 3\sin v$$

To obtain the portion of the surface from $y = 0$ to $y = 5$, we let the parameter $u$ vary over the interval $0 \le u \le 5$, and to ensure that the entire lateral surface is covered, we let the parameter $v$ vary over the interval $0 \le v \le 2\pi$. Figure 14.4.8*b* shows a computer-generated graph of the surface in which $u$ and $v$ vary over these intervals. Constant $u$-curves appear as circular traces parallel to the $xz$-plane, and constant $v$-curves appear as lines parallel to the $y$-axis. ◄

■ **REPRESENTING SURFACES OF REVOLUTION PARAMETRICALLY**
The basic idea of Example 6 can be adapted to obtain parametric equations for surfaces of revolution. For example, suppose that we want to find parametric equations for the surface generated by revolving the plane curve $y = f(x)$ about the $x$-axis. Figure 14.4.9 suggests that the surface can be represented parametrically as

$$x = u, \quad y = f(u)\cos v, \quad z = f(u)\sin v \tag{6}$$

In the exercises we will discuss formulas analogous to (6) for surfaces of revolution about other axes.

where $v$ is the angle shown.

▶ **Example 7**   Find parametric equations for the surface generated by revolving the curve $y = 1/x$ about the $x$-axis.

***Solution.***   From (6) this surface can be represented parametrically as

A general principle for representing surfaces of revolution parametrically is to let the variable about whose axis the curve is revolving be equal to $u$ and let the other variables be $f(u)\cos v$ and $f(u)\sin v$.

$$x = u, \quad y = \frac{1}{u}\cos v, \quad z = \frac{1}{u}\sin v$$

Figure 14.4.10 shows a computer-generated graph of the surface in which $0.7 \le u \le 5$ and $0 \le v \le 2\pi$. This surface is a portion of Gabriel's horn, which was discussed in Exercise 55 of Section 7.8. ◄

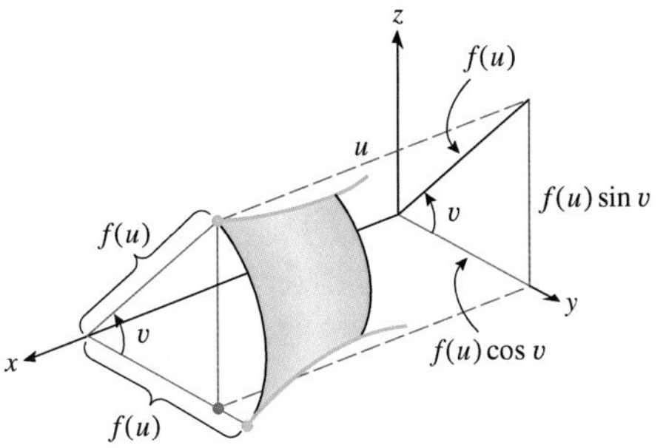

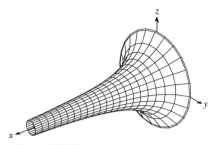

▲ Figure 14.4.9

▲ Figure 14.4.10

### VECTOR-VALUED FUNCTIONS OF TWO VARIABLES

Recall that the parametric equations

$$x = x(t), \quad y = y(t), \quad z = z(t)$$

can be expressed in vector form as

$$\mathbf{r} = x(t)\mathbf{i} + y(t)\mathbf{j} + z(t)\mathbf{k}$$

where $\mathbf{r} = x\mathbf{i} + y\mathbf{j} + z\mathbf{k}$ is the radius vector and $\mathbf{r}(t) = x(t)\mathbf{i} + y(t)\mathbf{j} + z(t)\mathbf{k}$ is a vector-valued function of one variable. Similarly, the parametric equations

$$x = x(u, v), \quad y = y(u, v), \quad z = z(u, v)$$

can be expressed in vector form as

$$\mathbf{r} = x(u, v)\mathbf{i} + y(u, v)\mathbf{j} + z(u, v)\mathbf{k}$$

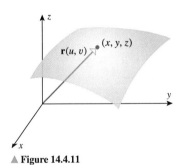

▲ Figure 14.4.11

Here the function $\mathbf{r}(u, v) = x(u, v)\mathbf{i} + y(u, v)\mathbf{j} + z(u, v)\mathbf{k}$ is a ***vector-valued function of two variables***. We define the ***graph*** of $\mathbf{r}(u, v)$ to be the graph of the corresponding parametric equations. Geometrically, we can view $\mathbf{r}$ as a vector from the origin to a point $(x, y, z)$ that moves over the surface $\mathbf{r} = \mathbf{r}(u, v)$ as $u$ and $v$ vary (Figure 14.4.11). As with vector-valued functions of one variable, we say that $\mathbf{r}(u, v)$ is ***continuous*** if each component is continuous.

---

▶ **Example 8**   The paraboloid in Example 3 was expressed parametrically as

$$x = u, \quad y = v, \quad z = 4 - u^2 - v^2$$

These equations can be expressed in vector form as

$$\mathbf{r} = u\mathbf{i} + v\mathbf{j} + (4 - u^2 - v^2)\mathbf{k} \quad \blacktriangleleft$$

---

### PARTIAL DERIVATIVES OF VECTOR-VALUED FUNCTIONS

Partial derivatives of vector-valued functions of two variables are obtained by taking partial derivatives of the components. For example, if

$$\mathbf{r}(u, v) = x(u, v)\mathbf{i} + y(u, v)\mathbf{j} + z(u, v)\mathbf{k}$$

then

$$\frac{\partial \mathbf{r}}{\partial u} = \frac{\partial x}{\partial u}\mathbf{i} + \frac{\partial y}{\partial u}\mathbf{j} + \frac{\partial z}{\partial u}\mathbf{k}$$

$$\frac{\partial \mathbf{r}}{\partial v} = \frac{\partial x}{\partial v}\mathbf{i} + \frac{\partial y}{\partial v}\mathbf{j} + \frac{\partial z}{\partial v}\mathbf{k}$$

These derivatives can also be written as $\mathbf{r}_u$ and $\mathbf{r}_v$ or $\mathbf{r}_u(u, v)$ and $\mathbf{r}_v(u, v)$ and can be expressed as the limits

$$\frac{\partial \mathbf{r}}{\partial u} = \lim_{\Delta u \to 0} \frac{\mathbf{r}(u + \Delta u, v) - \mathbf{r}(u, v)}{\Delta u} = \lim_{w \to u} \frac{\mathbf{r}(w, v) - \mathbf{r}(u, v)}{w - u} \tag{7}$$

$$\frac{\partial \mathbf{r}}{\partial v} = \lim_{\Delta v \to 0} \frac{\mathbf{r}(u, v + \Delta v) - \mathbf{r}(u, v)}{\Delta v} = \lim_{w \to v} \frac{\mathbf{r}(u, w) - \mathbf{r}(u, v)}{w - v} \tag{8}$$

▶ **Example 9**   Find the partial derivatives of the vector-valued function $\mathbf{r}$ in Example 8.

*Solution.*

$$\frac{\partial \mathbf{r}}{\partial u} = \frac{\partial}{\partial u}[u\mathbf{i} + v\mathbf{j} + (4 - u^2 - v^2)\mathbf{k}] = \mathbf{i} - 2u\mathbf{k}$$

$$\frac{\partial \mathbf{r}}{\partial v} = \frac{\partial}{\partial v}[u\mathbf{i} + v\mathbf{j} + (4 - u^2 - v^2)\mathbf{k}] = \mathbf{j} - 2v\mathbf{k} \blacktriangleleft$$

### ▪ TANGENT PLANES TO PARAMETRIC SURFACES

Our next objective is to show how to find tangent planes to parametric surfaces. Let $\sigma$ denote a parametric surface in 3-space, with $P_0$ a point on $\sigma$. We will say that a plane is *tangent* to $\sigma$ at $P_0$ provided a line through $P_0$ lies in the plane if and only if it is a tangent line at $P_0$ to a curve on $\sigma$. We showed in Section 13.7 that if $z = f(x, y)$, then the graph of $f$ has a tangent plane at a point if $f$ is differentiable at that point. It is beyond the scope of this text to obtain precise conditions under which a parametric surface has a tangent plane at a point, so we will simply assume the existence of tangent planes at points of interest and focus on finding their equations.

Suppose that the parametric surface $\sigma$ is the graph of the vector-valued function $\mathbf{r}(u, v)$ and that we are interested in the tangent plane at the point $(x_0, y_0, z_0)$ on the surface that corresponds to the parameter values $u = u_0$ and $v = v_0$; that is,

$$\mathbf{r}(u_0, v_0) = x_0\mathbf{i} + y_0\mathbf{j} + z_0\mathbf{k}$$

If $v = v_0$ is kept fixed and $u$ is allowed to vary, then $\mathbf{r}(u, v_0)$ is a vector-valued function of one variable whose graph is the constant $v$-curve through the point $(u_0, v_0)$; similarly, if $u = u_0$ is kept fixed and $v$ is allowed to vary, then $\mathbf{r}(u_0, v)$ is a vector-valued function of one variable whose graph is the constant $u$-curve through the point $(u_0, v_0)$. Moreover, it follows from the geometric interpretation of the derivative developed in Section 12.2 that if $\partial \mathbf{r}/\partial u \neq \mathbf{0}$ at $(u_0, v_0)$, then this vector is tangent to the constant $v$-curve through $(u_0, v_0)$; and if $\partial \mathbf{r}/\partial v \neq \mathbf{0}$ at $(u_0, v_0)$, then this vector is tangent to the constant $u$-curve through $(u_0, v_0)$ (Figure 14.4.12). Thus, if $\partial \mathbf{r}/\partial u \times \partial \mathbf{r}/\partial v \neq \mathbf{0}$ at $(u_0, v_0)$, then the vector

$$\frac{\partial \mathbf{r}}{\partial u} \times \frac{\partial \mathbf{r}}{\partial v} = \begin{vmatrix} \mathbf{i} & \mathbf{j} & \mathbf{k} \\ \dfrac{\partial x}{\partial u} & \dfrac{\partial y}{\partial u} & \dfrac{\partial z}{\partial u} \\ \dfrac{\partial x}{\partial v} & \dfrac{\partial y}{\partial v} & \dfrac{\partial z}{\partial v} \end{vmatrix} \tag{9}$$

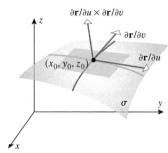

▲ **Figure 14.4.12**

is orthogonal to both tangent vectors at the point $(u_0, v_0)$ and hence is normal to the tangent plane and the surface at this point (Figure 14.4.12). Accordingly, we make the following definition.

**14.4.1** DEFINITION If a parametric surface $\sigma$ is the graph of $\mathbf{r} = \mathbf{r}(u, v)$, and if $\partial \mathbf{r}/\partial u \times \partial \mathbf{r}/\partial v \neq \mathbf{0}$ at a point on the surface, then the *principal unit normal vector* to the surface at that point is denoted by $\mathbf{n}$ or $\mathbf{n}(u, v)$ and is defined as

$$\mathbf{n} = \frac{\dfrac{\partial \mathbf{r}}{\partial u} \times \dfrac{\partial \mathbf{r}}{\partial v}}{\left\| \dfrac{\partial \mathbf{r}}{\partial u} \times \dfrac{\partial \mathbf{r}}{\partial v} \right\|} \tag{10}$$

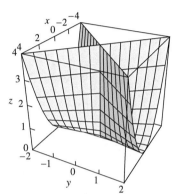

▲ **Figure 14.4.13**

▶ **Example 10** Find an equation of the tangent plane to the parametric surface

$$x = uv, \quad y = u, \quad z = v^2$$

at the point where $u = 2$ and $v = -1$. This surface, called *Whitney's umbrella*, is an example of a self-intersecting parametric surface (Figure 14.4.13).

*Solution.* We start by writing the equations in the vector form

$$\mathbf{r} = uv\mathbf{i} + u\mathbf{j} + v^2\mathbf{k}$$

The partial derivatives of $\mathbf{r}$ are

$$\frac{\partial \mathbf{r}}{\partial u}(u, v) = v\mathbf{i} + \mathbf{j}$$

$$\frac{\partial \mathbf{r}}{\partial v}(u, v) = u\mathbf{i} + 2v\mathbf{k}$$

and at $u = 2$ and $v = -1$ these partial derivatives are

$$\frac{\partial \mathbf{r}}{\partial u}(2, -1) = -\mathbf{i} + \mathbf{j}$$

$$\frac{\partial \mathbf{r}}{\partial v}(2, -1) = 2\mathbf{i} - 2\mathbf{k}$$

Thus, from (9) and (10) a normal to the surface at this point is

$$\frac{\partial \mathbf{r}}{\partial u}(2, -1) \times \frac{\partial \mathbf{r}}{\partial v}(2, -1) = \begin{vmatrix} \mathbf{i} & \mathbf{j} & \mathbf{k} \\ -1 & 1 & 0 \\ 2 & 0 & -2 \end{vmatrix} = -2\mathbf{i} - 2\mathbf{j} - 2\mathbf{k}$$

Convince yourself that the result obtained in Example 10 is consistent with Figure 14.4.13.

Since any normal will suffice to find the tangent plane, it makes sense to multiply this vector by $-\frac{1}{2}$ and use the simpler normal $\mathbf{i} + \mathbf{j} + \mathbf{k}$. It follows from the given parametric equations that the point on the surface corresponding to $u = 2$ and $v = -1$ is $(-2, 2, 1)$, so the tangent plane at this point can be expressed in point-normal form as

$$(x + 2) + (y - 2) + (z - 1) = 0 \quad \text{or} \quad x + y + z = 1 \quad \blacktriangleleft$$

▶ **Example 11** The sphere $x^2 + y^2 + z^2 = a^2$ can be expressed in spherical coordinates as $\rho = a$, and the spherical-to-rectangular conversion formulas in Table 11.8.1 can then be used to express the sphere as the graph of the vector-valued function

$$\mathbf{r}(\phi, \theta) = a \sin \phi \cos \theta \mathbf{i} + a \sin \phi \sin \theta \mathbf{j} + a \cos \phi \mathbf{k}$$

where $0 \leq \phi \leq \pi$ and $0 \leq \theta \leq 2\pi$ (verify). Use this function to show that the radius vector is normal to the tangent plane at each point on the sphere.

*Solution.*   We will show that at each point of the sphere the unit normal vector $\mathbf{n}$ is a scalar multiple of $\mathbf{r}$ (and hence is parallel to $\mathbf{r}$). We have

$$\frac{\partial \mathbf{r}}{\partial \phi} \times \frac{\partial \mathbf{r}}{\partial \theta} = \begin{vmatrix} \mathbf{i} & \mathbf{j} & \mathbf{k} \\ \dfrac{\partial x}{\partial \phi} & \dfrac{\partial y}{\partial \phi} & \dfrac{\partial z}{\partial \phi} \\ \dfrac{\partial x}{\partial \theta} & \dfrac{\partial y}{\partial \theta} & \dfrac{\partial z}{\partial \theta} \end{vmatrix} = \begin{vmatrix} \mathbf{i} & \mathbf{j} & \mathbf{k} \\ a\cos\phi\cos\theta & a\cos\phi\sin\theta & -a\sin\phi \\ -a\sin\phi\sin\theta & a\sin\phi\cos\theta & 0 \end{vmatrix}$$

$$= a^2 \sin^2\phi\cos\theta\,\mathbf{i} + a^2 \sin^2\phi\sin\theta\,\mathbf{j} + a^2 \sin\phi\cos\phi\,\mathbf{k}$$

and hence

$$\left\| \frac{\partial \mathbf{r}}{\partial \phi} \times \frac{\partial \mathbf{r}}{\partial \theta} \right\| = \sqrt{a^4 \sin^4\phi\cos^2\theta + a^4 \sin^4\phi\sin^2\theta + a^4 \sin^2\phi\cos^2\phi}$$

$$= \sqrt{a^4 \sin^4\phi + a^4 \sin^2\phi\cos^2\phi}$$

$$= a^2 \sqrt{\sin^2\phi} = a^2|\sin\phi| = a^2\sin\phi$$

For $\phi \neq 0$ or $\pi$, it follows from (10) that

$$\mathbf{n} = \sin\phi\cos\theta\,\mathbf{i} + \sin\phi\sin\theta\,\mathbf{j} + \cos\phi\,\mathbf{k} = \frac{1}{a}\mathbf{r}$$

Furthermore, the tangent planes at $\phi = 0$ or $\pi$ are horizontal, to which $\mathbf{r} = \pm a\mathbf{k}$ is clearly normal.  ◄

### ▪ SURFACE AREA OF PARAMETRIC SURFACES

We now obtain a formula for the surface area $S$ of a parametric surface $\sigma$. Let $\sigma$ be a parametric surface whose vector equation is

$$\mathbf{r} = x(u,v)\mathbf{i} + y(u,v)\mathbf{j} + z(u,v)\mathbf{k}$$

Our discussion will be analogous to the case for surfaces of the form $z = f(x, y)$. Here, $R$ will be a region in the $uv$-plane that we subdivide into $n$ rectangular regions as shown in Figure 14.4.14*a*. Let $R_k$ be the $k$th rectangular region, and denote its area by $\Delta A_k$. The patch $\sigma_k$ is the image of $R_k$ on $\sigma$. The patch will have a corner at $\mathbf{r}(u_k, v_k)$; denote the area of $\sigma_k$ by $\Delta S_k$ (Figure 14.4.14*b*).

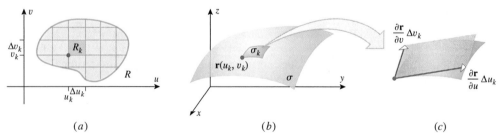

*(a)*  *(b)*  *(c)*

▲ **Figure 14.4.14**

Recall that in the case of $z = f(x, y)$ we used the area of a parallelogram in a tangent plane to the surface to approximate the area of the patch. In the parametric case, the desired parallelogram is spanned by the tangent vectors

$$\frac{\partial \mathbf{r}}{\partial u}\Delta u_k \quad \text{and} \quad \frac{\partial \mathbf{r}}{\partial v}\Delta v_k$$

where the partial derivatives are evaluated at $(u_k, v_k)$ (Figure 14.4.14c). Thus,

$$\Delta S_k \approx \left\| \frac{\partial \mathbf{r}}{\partial u} \Delta u_k \times \frac{\partial \mathbf{r}}{\partial v} \Delta v_k \right\| = \left\| \frac{\partial \mathbf{r}}{\partial u} \times \frac{\partial \mathbf{r}}{\partial v} \right\| \Delta u_k \Delta v_k = \left\| \frac{\partial \mathbf{r}}{\partial u} \times \frac{\partial \mathbf{r}}{\partial v} \right\| \Delta A_k \qquad (11)$$

The surface area of the entire surface is the sum of the areas $\Delta S_k$. If we assume that the errors in the approximations in (11) approach zero as $n$ increases in such a way that the dimensions of the rectangles $R_k$ approach zero, then it is plausible that the exact value of $S$ is

$$S = \lim_{n \to +\infty} \sum_{k=1}^{n} \left\| \frac{\partial \mathbf{r}}{\partial u} \times \frac{\partial \mathbf{r}}{\partial v} \right\| \Delta A_k$$

or, equivalently,

$$S = \iint_R \left\| \frac{\partial \mathbf{r}}{\partial u} \times \frac{\partial \mathbf{r}}{\partial v} \right\| dA \qquad (12)$$

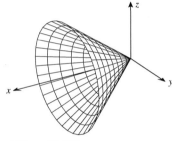
▲ **Figure 14.4.15**

▶ **Example 12**   It follows from (6) that the parametric equations

$$x = u, \quad y = u \cos v, \quad z = u \sin v$$

represent the cone that results when the line $y = x$ in the $xy$-plane is revolved about the $x$-axis. Use Formula (12) to find the surface area of that portion of the cone for which $0 \le u \le 2$ and $0 \le v \le 2\pi$ (Figure 14.4.15).

***Solution.***   The surface can be expressed in vector form as

$$\mathbf{r} = u\mathbf{i} + u \cos v \mathbf{j} + u \sin v \mathbf{k} \quad (0 \le u \le 2, \ 0 \le v \le 2\pi)$$

Thus,

$$\frac{\partial \mathbf{r}}{\partial u} = \mathbf{i} + \cos v \mathbf{j} + \sin v \mathbf{k}$$

$$\frac{\partial \mathbf{r}}{\partial v} = -u \sin v \mathbf{j} + u \cos v \mathbf{k}$$

$$\frac{\partial \mathbf{r}}{\partial u} \times \frac{\partial \mathbf{r}}{\partial v} = \begin{vmatrix} \mathbf{i} & \mathbf{j} & \mathbf{k} \\ 1 & \cos v & \sin v \\ 0 & -u \sin v & u \cos v \end{vmatrix} = u\mathbf{i} - u \cos v \mathbf{j} - u \sin v \mathbf{k}$$

$$\left\| \frac{\partial \mathbf{r}}{\partial u} \times \frac{\partial \mathbf{r}}{\partial v} \right\| = \sqrt{u^2 + (-u \cos v)^2 + (-u \sin v)^2} = |u|\sqrt{2} = u\sqrt{2}$$

Thus, from (12)

$$S = \iint_R \left\| \frac{\partial \mathbf{r}}{\partial u} \times \frac{\partial \mathbf{r}}{\partial v} \right\| dA = \int_0^{2\pi} \int_0^2 \sqrt{2}u \, du \, dv = 2\sqrt{2} \int_0^{2\pi} dv = 4\pi\sqrt{2} \blacktriangleleft$$

✔ **QUICK CHECK EXERCISES 14.4**   *(See page 1039 for answers.)*

1. The surface area of a surface of the form $z = f(x, y)$ over a region $R$ in the $xy$-plane is given by

$$S = \iint_R \underline{\hspace{1.5cm}} dA$$

2. Consider the surface represented parametrically by

$$x = 1 - u$$
$$y = (1 - u) \cos v \qquad (0 \le u \le 1, 0 \le v \le 2\pi)$$
$$z = (1 - u) \sin v$$

   (a) Describe the constant $u$-curves.
   (b) Describe the constant $v$-curves.

**3.** If

$$\mathbf{r}(u, v) = (1 - u)\mathbf{i} + [(1 - u)\cos v]\mathbf{j} + [(1 - u)\sin v]\mathbf{k}$$

then

$$\frac{\partial \mathbf{r}}{\partial u} = \underline{\hspace{1cm}} \quad \text{and} \quad \frac{\partial \mathbf{r}}{\partial v} = \underline{\hspace{1cm}}.$$

**4.** If

$$\mathbf{r}(u, v) = (1 - u)\mathbf{i} + [(1 - u)\cos v]\mathbf{j} + [(1 - u)\sin v]\mathbf{k}$$

the principal unit normal to the graph of $\mathbf{r}$ at the point where $u = 1/2$ and $v = \pi/6$ is given by _____.

**5.** Suppose $\sigma$ is a parametric surface with vector equation

$$\mathbf{r}(u, v) = x(u, v)\mathbf{i} + y(u, v)\mathbf{j} + z(u, v)\mathbf{k}$$

If $\sigma$ has no self-intersections and $\sigma$ is smooth on a region $R$ in the $uv$-plane, then the surface area of $\sigma$ is given by

$$S = \iint_R \underline{\hspace{1cm}} \, dA$$

---

**EXERCISE SET 14.4**  Graphing Utility  CAS

**1–4** Express the area of the given surface as an iterated double integral, and then find the surface area. ▨

**1.** The portion of the cylinder $y^2 + z^2 = 9$ that is above the rectangle $R = \{(x, y) : 0 \le x \le 2, -3 \le y \le 3\}$.

**2.** The portion of the plane $2x + 2y + z = 8$ in the first octant.

**3.** The portion of the cone $z^2 = 4x^2 + 4y^2$ that is above the region in the first quadrant bounded by the line $y = x$ and the parabola $y = x^2$.

**4.** The portion of the surface $z = 2x + y^2$ that is above the triangular region with vertices $(0, 0)$, $(0, 1)$, and $(1, 1)$.

**5–10** Express the area of the given surface as an iterated double integral in polar coordinates, and then find the surface area. ▨

**5.** The portion of the cone $z = \sqrt{x^2 + y^2}$ that lies inside the cylinder $x^2 + y^2 = 2x$.

**6.** The portion of the paraboloid $z = 1 - x^2 - y^2$ that is above the $xy$-plane.

**7.** The portion of the surface $z = xy$ that is above the sector in the first quadrant bounded by the lines $y = x/\sqrt{3}$, $y = 0$, and the circle $x^2 + y^2 = 9$.

**8.** The portion of the paraboloid $2z = x^2 + y^2$ that is inside the cylinder $x^2 + y^2 = 8$.

**9.** The portion of the sphere $x^2 + y^2 + z^2 = 16$ between the planes $z = 1$ and $z = 2$.

**10.** The portion of the sphere $x^2 + y^2 + z^2 = 8$ that is inside the cone $z = \sqrt{x^2 + y^2}$.

**11–12** Sketch the parametric surface. ▨

**11.** (a) $x = u$, $y = v$, $z = \sqrt{u^2 + v^2}$
   (b) $x = u$, $y = \sqrt{u^2 + v^2}$, $z = v$
   (c) $x = \sqrt{u^2 + v^2}$, $y = u$, $z = v$

**12.** (a) $x = u$, $y = v$, $z = u^2 + v^2$
   (b) $x = u$, $y = u^2 + v^2$, $z = v$
   (c) $x = u^2 + v^2$, $y = u$, $z = v$

**13–14** Find a parametric representation of the surface in terms of the parameters $u = x$ and $v = y$. ▨

**13.** (a) $2z - 3x + 4y = 5$      (b) $z = x^2$

**14.** (a) $z + zx^2 - y = 0$      (b) $y^2 - 3z = 5$

**15.** (a) Find parametric equations for the portion of the cylinder $x^2 + y^2 = 5$ that extends between the planes $z = 0$ and $z = 1$.
   (b) Find parametric equations for the portion of the cylinder $x^2 + z^2 = 4$ that extends between the planes $y = 1$ and $y = 3$.

**16.** (a) Find parametric equations for the portion of the plane $x + y = 1$ that extends between the planes $z = -1$ and $z = 1$.
   (b) Find parametric equations for the portion of the plane $y - 2z = 5$ that extends between the planes $x = 0$ and $x = 3$.

**17.** Find parametric equations for the surface generated by revolving the curve $y = \sin x$ about the $x$-axis.

**18.** Find parametric equations for the surface generated by revolving the curve $y - e^x = 0$ about the $x$-axis.

**19–24** Find a parametric representation of the surface in terms of the parameters $r$ and $\theta$, where $(r, \theta, z)$ are the cylindrical coordinates of a point on the surface. ▨

**19.** $z = \dfrac{1}{1 + x^2 + y^2}$      **20.** $z = e^{-(x^2 + y^2)}$

**21.** $z = 2xy$      **22.** $z = x^2 - y^2$

**23.** The portion of the sphere $x^2 + y^2 + z^2 = 9$ on or above the plane $z = 2$.

**24.** The portion of the cone $z = \sqrt{x^2 + y^2}$ on or below the plane $z = 3$.

**25.** Find a parametric representation of the cone

$$z = \sqrt{3x^2 + 3y^2}$$

in terms of parameters $\rho$ and $\theta$, where $(\rho, \theta, \phi)$ are spherical coordinates of a point on the surface.

**26.** Describe the cylinder $x^2 + y^2 = 9$ in terms of parameters $\theta$ and $\phi$, where $(\rho, \theta, \phi)$ are spherical coordinates of a point on the surface.

**27–32** Eliminate the parameters to obtain an equation in rectangular coordinates, and describe the surface. ▨

**27.** $x = 2u + v$, $y = u - v$, $z = 3v$ for $-\infty < u < +\infty$ and $-\infty < v < +\infty$.

**28.** $x = u \cos v$, $y = u^2$, $z = u \sin v$ for $0 \le u \le 2$ and $0 \le v < 2\pi$.

**29.** $x = 3 \sin u$, $y = 2 \cos u$, $z = 2v$ for $0 \le u < 2\pi$ and $1 \le v \le 2$.

**30.** $x = \sqrt{u} \cos v$, $y = \sqrt{u} \sin v$, $z = u$ for $0 \le u \le 4$ and $0 \le v < 2\pi$.

**31.** $\mathbf{r}(u, v) = 3u \cos v \mathbf{i} + 4u \sin v \mathbf{j} + u \mathbf{k}$ for $0 \le u \le 1$ and $0 \le v < 2\pi$.

**32.** $\mathbf{r}(u, v) = \sin u \cos v \mathbf{i} + 2 \sin u \sin v \mathbf{j} + 3 \cos u \mathbf{k}$ for $0 \le u \le \pi$ and $0 \le v < 2\pi$.

**33.** The accompanying figure shows the graphs of two parametric representations of the cone $z = \sqrt{x^2 + y^2}$ for $0 \le z \le 2$.
  (a) Find parametric equations that produce reasonable facsimiles of these surfaces.
  (b) Use a graphing utility to check your answer in part (a).

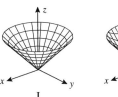

I        II    ◀ **Figure Ex-33**

**34.** The accompanying figure shows the graphs of two parametric representations of the paraboloid $z = x^2 + y^2$ for $0 \le z \le 2$.
  (a) Find parametric equations that produce reasonable facsimiles of these surfaces.
  (b) Use a graphing utility to check your answer in part (a).

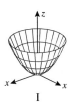

I        II    ◀ **Figure Ex-34**

**35.** In each part, the figure shows a portion of the parametric surface $x = 3 \cos v$, $y = u$, $z = 3 \sin v$. Find restrictions on $u$ and $v$ that produce the surface, and check your answer with a graphing utility.

(a) 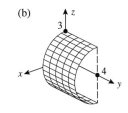    (b)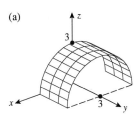

**36.** In each part, the figure shows a portion of the parametric surface $x = 3 \cos v$, $y = 3 \sin v$, $z = u$. Find restrictions on $u$ and $v$ that produce the surface, and check your answer with a graphing utility.

(a) 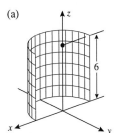    (b)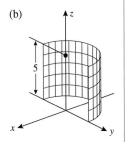

**37.** In each part, the figure shows a hemisphere that is a portion of the sphere $x = \sin \phi \cos \theta$, $y = \sin \phi \sin \theta$, $z = \cos \phi$. Find restrictions on $\phi$ and $\theta$ that produce the hemisphere, and check your answer with a graphing utility.

(a) 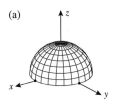    (b)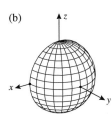

**38.** In each part, the figure shows a portion of the sphere $x = \sin \phi \cos \theta$, $y = \sin \phi \sin \theta$, $z = \cos \phi$. Find restrictions on $\phi$ and $\theta$ that produce the surface, and check your answer with a graphing utility.

(a) 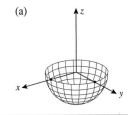    (b)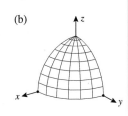

**39–44** Find an equation of the tangent plane to the parametric surface at the stated point. ▪

**39.** $x = u, y = v, z = u^2 + v^2$;  $(1, 2, 5)$

**40.** $x = u^2, y = v^2, z = u + v$;  $(1, 4, 3)$

**41.** $x = 3v \sin u, y = 2v \cos u, z = u^2$;  $(0, 2, 0)$

**42.** $\mathbf{r} = uv\mathbf{i} + (u - v)\mathbf{j} + (u + v)\mathbf{k}$;  $u = 1, v = 2$

**43.** $\mathbf{r} = u \cos v\mathbf{i} + u \sin v\mathbf{j} + v\mathbf{k}$;  $u = 1/2, v = \pi/4$

**44.** $\mathbf{r} = uv\mathbf{i} + ue^v\mathbf{j} + ve^u\mathbf{k}$;  $u = \ln 2, v = 0$

**45–46** Find the area of the given surface. ▪

**45.** The portion of the paraboloid

$$\mathbf{r}(u, v) = u \cos v\mathbf{i} + u \sin v\mathbf{j} + u^2\mathbf{k}$$

for which $1 \leq u \leq 2, 0 \leq v \leq 2\pi$.

**46.** The portion of the cone

$$\mathbf{r}(u, v) = u \cos v\mathbf{i} + u \sin v\mathbf{j} + u\mathbf{k}$$

for which $0 \leq u \leq 2v, 0 \leq v \leq \pi/2$.

**47–50 True–False** Determine whether the statement is true or false. Explain your answer. ▪

**47.** If $f$ has continuous first partial derivatives in the interior of a region $R$ in the $xy$-plane, then the surface area of the surface $z = f(x, y)$ over $R$ is

$$\iint\limits_{R} \sqrt{[f(x, y)]^2 + 1} \, dA$$

**48.** Suppose that $z = f(x, y)$ has continuous first partial derivatives in the interior of a region $R$ in the $xy$-plane, and set $\mathbf{q} = \langle 1, 0, \partial z/\partial x \rangle$ and $\mathbf{r} = \langle 0, 1, \partial z/\partial y \rangle$. Then the surface area of the surface $z = f(x, y)$ over $R$ is

$$\iint\limits_{R} \|\mathbf{q} \times \mathbf{r}\| \, dA$$

**49.** If $\mathbf{r}(u, v) = x(u, v)\mathbf{i} + y(u, v)\mathbf{j} + z(u, v)\mathbf{k}$ such that $\partial\mathbf{r}/\partial u$ and $\partial\mathbf{r}/\partial v$ are nonzero vectors at $(u_0, v_0)$, then

$$\frac{\partial\mathbf{r}}{\partial u} \times \frac{\partial\mathbf{r}}{\partial v}$$

is normal to the graph of $\mathbf{r} = \mathbf{r}(u, v)$ at $(u_0, v_0)$.

**50.** For the function $f(x, y) = ax + by$, the area of the surface $z = f(x, y)$ over a rectangle $R$ in the $xy$-plane is the product of $\|\langle 1, 0, a \rangle \times \langle 0, 1, b \rangle\|$ and the area of $R$.

**51.** Use parametric equations to derive the formula for the surface area of a sphere of radius $a$.

**52.** Use parametric equations to derive the formula for the lateral surface area of a right circular cylinder of radius $r$ and height $h$.

**53.** The portion of the surface

$$z = \frac{h}{a}\sqrt{x^2 + y^2} \quad (a, h > 0)$$

between the $xy$-plane and the plane $z = h$ is a right circular

cone of height $h$ and radius $a$. Use a double integral to show that the lateral surface area of this cone is $S = \pi a\sqrt{a^2 + h^2}$.

**54.** The accompanying figure shows the *torus* that is generated by revolving the circle

$$(x - a)^2 + z^2 = b^2 \quad (0 < b < a)$$

in the $xz$-plane about the $z$-axis.

(a) Show that this torus can be expressed parametrically as

$$x = (a + b \cos v) \cos u$$
$$y = (a + b \cos v) \sin u$$
$$z = b \sin v$$

where $u$ and $v$ are the parameters shown in the figure and $0 \leq u \leq 2\pi, 0 \leq v \leq 2\pi$.

(b) Use a graphing utility to generate a torus.

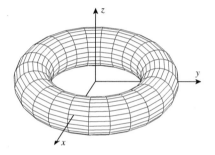

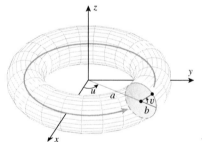

◀ **Figure Ex-54**

**55.** Find the surface area of the torus in Exercise 54(a).

**56.** Use a CAS to graph the *helicoid*

$$x = u \cos v, \quad y = u \sin v, \quad z = v$$

for $0 \leq u \leq 5$ and $0 \leq v \leq 4\pi$ (see the accompanying figure on the next page), and then use the numerical double integration operation of the CAS to approximate the surface area.

**57.** Use a CAS to graph the *pseudosphere*

$$x = \cos u \sin v$$
$$y = \sin u \sin v$$
$$z = \cos v + \ln\left(\tan\frac{v}{2}\right)$$

for $0 \leq u \leq 2\pi, 0 < v < \pi$ (see the accompanying figure on the next page), and then use the numerical double integration operation of the CAS to approximate the surface area between the planes $z = -1$ and $z = 1$.

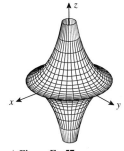

▲ **Figure Ex-56**          ▲ **Figure Ex-57**

58. (a) Find parametric equations for the surface of revolution that is generated by revolving the curve $z = f(x)$ in the $xz$-plane about the $z$-axis.
    (b) Use the result obtained in part (a) to find parametric equations for the surface of revolution that is generated by revolving the curve $z = 1/x^2$ in the $xz$-plane about the $z$-axis.
    (c) Use a graphing utility to check your work by graphing the parametric surface.

**59–61** The parametric equations in these exercises represent a quadric surface for positive values of $a$, $b$, and $c$. Identify the type of surface by eliminating the parameters $u$ and $v$. Check your conclusion by choosing specific values for the constants and generating the surface with a graphing utility.

59. $x = a \cos u \cos v$, $y = b \sin u \cos v$, $z = c \sin v$

60. $x = a \cos u \cosh v$, $y = b \sin u \cosh v$, $z = c \sinh v$

61. $x = a \sinh v$, $y = b \sinh u \cosh v$, $z = c \cosh u \cosh v$

62. **Writing** An early popular approach to defining surface area was to take a limit of surface areas of inscribed polyhedra, but an example in which this approach fails was published in 1890 by H. A. Schwartz. Frieda Zames discusses Schwartz's example in her article "Surface Area and the Cylinder Area Paradox," *The Two-Year College Mathematics Journal*, Vol. 8, No. 4, September 1977, pp. 207–211. Read the article and write a short summary.

✔ **QUICK CHECK ANSWERS 14.4**

1. $\sqrt{\left(\dfrac{\partial z}{\partial x}\right)^2 + \left(\dfrac{\partial z}{\partial y}\right)^2 + 1}$    2. (a) The constant $u$-curves are circles of radius $1 - u$ centered at $(1 - u, 0, 0)$ and parallel to the $yz$-plane. (b) The constant $v$-curves are line segments joining the points $(1, \cos v, \sin v)$ and $(0, 0, 0)$.
3. $\dfrac{\partial \mathbf{r}}{\partial u} = -\mathbf{i} - (\cos v)\mathbf{j} - (\sin v)\mathbf{k}$; $\dfrac{\partial \mathbf{r}}{\partial v} = -[(1 - u)\sin v]\mathbf{j} + [(1 - u)\cos v]\mathbf{k}$    4. $\dfrac{1}{\sqrt{8}}(-2\mathbf{i} + \sqrt{3}\mathbf{j} + \mathbf{k})$    5. $\left\| \dfrac{\partial \mathbf{r}}{\partial u} \times \dfrac{\partial \mathbf{r}}{\partial v} \right\|$

## 14.5 TRIPLE INTEGRALS

*In the preceding sections we defined and discussed properties of double integrals for functions of two variables. In this section we will define triple integrals for functions of three variables.*

### ■ DEFINITION OF A TRIPLE INTEGRAL

A single integral of a function $f(x)$ is defined over a finite closed interval on the $x$-axis, and a double integral of a function $f(x, y)$ is defined over a finite closed region $R$ in the $xy$-plane. Our first goal in this section is to define what is meant by a *triple integral* of $f(x, y, z)$ over a closed solid region $G$ in an $xyz$-coordinate system. To ensure that $G$ does not extend indefinitely in some direction, we will assume that it can be enclosed in a suitably large box whose sides are parallel to the coordinate planes (Figure 14.5.1). In this case we say that $G$ is a *finite solid*.

To define the triple integral of $f(x, y, z)$ over $G$, we first divide the box into $n$ "subboxes" by planes parallel to the coordinate planes. We then discard those subboxes that contain any points outside of $G$ and choose an arbitrary point in each of the remaining subboxes. As shown in Figure 14.5.1, we denote the volume of the $k$th remaining subbox by $\Delta V_k$ and the point selected in the $k$th subbox by $(x_k^*, y_k^*, z_k^*)$. Next we form the product

$$f(x_k^*, y_k^*, z_k^*)\,\Delta V_k$$

Volume = $\Delta V_k$

$(x_k^*, y_k^*, z_k^*)$

▲ **Figure 14.5.1**

for each subbox, then add the products for all of the subboxes to obtain the ***Riemann sum***

$$\sum_{k=1}^{n} f(x_k^*, y_k^*, z_k^*)\Delta V_k$$

Finally, we repeat this process with more and more subdivisions in such a way that the length, width, and height of each subbox approach zero, and $n$ approaches $+\infty$. The limit

$$\iiint\limits_{G} f(x, y, z)\, dV = \lim_{n \to +\infty} \sum_{k=1}^{n} f(x_k^*, y_k^*, z_k^*)\Delta V_k \tag{1}$$

is called the ***triple integral*** of $f(x, y, z)$ over the region $G$. Conditions under which the triple integral exists are studied in advanced calculus. However, for our purposes it suffices to say that existence is ensured when $f$ is continuous on $G$ and the region $G$ is not too "complicated."

### ■ PROPERTIES OF TRIPLE INTEGRALS
Triple integrals enjoy many properties of single and double integrals:

$$\iiint\limits_{G} cf(x, y, z)\, dV = c \iiint\limits_{G} f(x, y, z)\, dV \quad (c \text{ a constant})$$

$$\iiint\limits_{G} [f(x, y, z) + g(x, y, z)]\, dV = \iiint\limits_{G} f(x, y, z)\, dV + \iiint\limits_{G} g(x, y, z)\, dV$$

$$\iiint\limits_{G} [f(x, y, z) - g(x, y, z)]\, dV = \iiint\limits_{G} f(x, y, z)\, dV - \iiint\limits_{G} g(x, y, z)\, dV$$

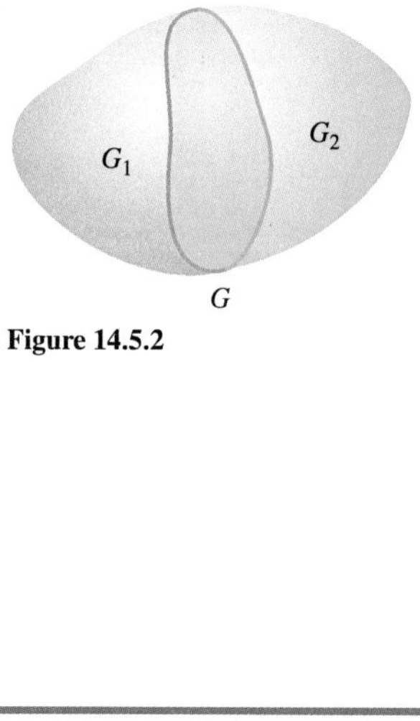

Moreover, if the region $G$ is subdivided into two subregions $G_1$ and $G_2$ (Figure 14.5.2), then

$$\iiint\limits_{G} f(x, y, z)\, dV = \iiint\limits_{G_1} f(x, y, z)\, dV + \iiint\limits_{G_2} f(x, y, z)\, dV$$

$G_1$  $G_2$

$G$

▲ **Figure 14.5.2**

We omit the proofs.

### ■ EVALUATING TRIPLE INTEGRALS OVER RECTANGULAR BOXES
Just as a double integral can be evaluated by two successive single integrations, so a triple integral can be evaluated by three successive integrations. The following theorem, which we state without proof, is the analog of Theorem 14.1.3.

There are two possible orders of integration for the iterated integrals in Theorem 14.1.3:

$$dx\, dy, \quad dy\, dx$$

Six orders of integration are possible for the iterated integral in Theorem 14.5.1:

$$dx\, dy\, dz, \quad dy\, dz\, dx, \quad dz\, dx\, dy$$
$$dx\, dz\, dy, \quad dz\, dy\, dx, \quad dy\, dx\, dz$$

**14.5.1**  THEOREM (***Fubini's Theorem***[*])  *Let $G$ be the rectangular box defined by the inequalities*
$$a \le x \le b, \quad c \le y \le d, \quad k \le z \le l$$

*If $f$ is continuous on the region $G$, then*

$$\iiint\limits_{G} f(x, y, z)\, dV = \int_a^b \int_c^d \int_k^l f(x, y, z)\, dz\, dy\, dx \tag{2}$$

*Moreover, the iterated integral on the right can be replaced with any of the five other iterated integrals that result by altering the order of integration.*

---

[*]See the Fubini biography on p. 1005.

► **Example 1**   Evaluate the triple integral

$$\iiint\limits_{G} 12xy^2z^3 \, dV$$

over the rectangular box $G$ defined by the inequalities $-1 \leq x \leq 2, 0 \leq y \leq 3, 0 \leq z \leq 2$.

*Solution.*   Of the six possible iterated integrals we might use, we will choose the one in (2). Thus, we will first integrate with respect to $z$, holding $x$ and $y$ fixed, then with respect to $y$, holding $x$ fixed, and finally with respect to $x$.

$$\iiint\limits_{G} 12xy^2z^3 \, dV = \int_{-1}^{2} \int_{0}^{3} \int_{0}^{2} 12xy^2z^3 \, dz \, dy \, dx$$

$$= \int_{-1}^{2} \int_{0}^{3} \left[3xy^2z^4\right]_{z=0}^{2} dy \, dx = \int_{-1}^{2} \int_{0}^{3} 48xy^2 \, dy \, dx$$

$$= \int_{-1}^{2} \left[16xy^3\right]_{y=0}^{3} dx = \int_{-1}^{2} 432x \, dx$$

$$= 216x^2 \Big]_{-1}^{2} = 648 \quad ◄$$

### EVALUATING TRIPLE INTEGRALS OVER MORE GENERAL REGIONS

Next we will consider how triple integrals can be evaluated over solids that are not rectangular boxes. For the moment we will limit our discussion to solids of the type shown in Figure 14.5.3. Specifically, we will assume that the solid $G$ is bounded above by a surface $z = g_2(x, y)$ and below by a surface $z = g_1(x, y)$ and that the projection of the solid on the $xy$-plane is a type I or type II region $R$ (see Definition 14.2.1). In addition, we will assume that $g_1(x, y)$ and $g_2(x, y)$ are continuous on $R$ and that $g_1(x, y) \leq g_2(x, y)$ on $R$. Geometrically, this means that the surfaces may touch but cannot cross. We call a solid of this type a **simple $xy$-solid**.

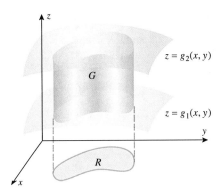

► **Figure 14.5.3**

The following theorem, which we state without proof, will enable us to evaluate triple integrals over simple $xy$-solids.

---

**14.5.2**   **THEOREM**   *Let $G$ be a simple $xy$-solid with upper surface $z = g_2(x, y)$ and lower surface $z = g_1(x, y)$, and let $R$ be the projection of $G$ on the $xy$-plane. If $f(x, y, z)$ is continuous on $G$, then*

$$\iiint\limits_{G} f(x, y, z) \, dV = \iint\limits_{R} \left[\int_{g_1(x,y)}^{g_2(x,y)} f(x, y, z) \, dz\right] dA \qquad (3)$$

---

In (3), the first integration is with respect to $z$, after which a function of $x$ and $y$ remains. This function of $x$ and $y$ is then integrated over the region $R$ in the $xy$-plane. To apply (3), it is helpful to begin with a three-dimensional sketch of the solid $G$. The limits of integration can be obtained from the sketch as follows:

*Determining Limits of Integration: Simple xy-Solid*

**Step 1.** Find an equation $z = g_2(x, y)$ for the upper surface and an equation $z = g_1(x, y)$ for the lower surface of $G$. The functions $g_1(x, y)$ and $g_2(x, y)$ determine the lower and upper $z$-limits of integration.

**Step 2.** Make a two-dimensional sketch of the projection $R$ of the solid on the $xy$-plane. From this sketch determine the limits of integration for the double integral over $R$ in (3).

▶ **Example 2**    Let $G$ be the wedge in the first octant that is cut from the cylindrical solid $y^2 + z^2 \le 1$ by the planes $y = x$ and $x = 0$. Evaluate

$$\iiint_G z\, dV$$

*Solution.*    The solid $G$ and its projection $R$ on the $xy$-plane are shown in Figure 14.5.4. The upper surface of the solid is formed by the cylinder and the lower surface by the $xy$-plane. Since the portion of the cylinder $y^2 + z^2 = 1$ that lies above the $xy$-plane has the equation $z = \sqrt{1 - y^2}$, and the $xy$-plane has the equation $z = 0$, it follows from (3) that

$$\iiint_G z\, dV = \iint_R \left[ \int_0^{\sqrt{1-y^2}} z\, dz \right] dA \qquad (4)$$

For the double integral over $R$, the $x$- and $y$-integrations can be performed in either order, since $R$ is both a type I and type II region. We will integrate with respect to $x$ first. With this choice, (4) yields

$$\iiint_G z\, dV = \int_0^1 \int_0^y \int_0^{\sqrt{1-y^2}} z\, dz\, dx\, dy = \int_0^1 \int_0^y \frac{1}{2} z^2 \Big]_{z=0}^{\sqrt{1-y^2}} dx\, dy$$

$$= \int_0^1 \int_0^y \frac{1}{2}(1 - y^2)\, dx\, dy = \frac{1}{2} \int_0^1 (1 - y^2)x \Big]_{x=0}^{y} dy$$

$$= \frac{1}{2} \int_0^1 (y - y^3)\, dy = \frac{1}{2} \left[ \frac{1}{2}y^2 - \frac{1}{4}y^4 \right]_0^1 = \frac{1}{8} \blacktriangleleft$$

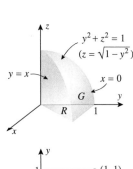

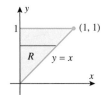

▲ **Figure 14.5.4**

**TECHNOLOGY MASTERY**

Most computer algebra systems have a built-in capability for computing iterated triple integrals. If you have a CAS, consult the relevant documentation and use the CAS to check Examples 1 and 2.

■ **VOLUME CALCULATED AS A TRIPLE INTEGRAL**
Triple integrals have many physical interpretations, some of which we will consider in Section 14.8. However, in the special case where $f(x, y, z) = 1$, Formula (1) yields

$$\iiint_G dV = \lim_{n \to +\infty} \sum_{k=1}^n \Delta V_k$$

which Figure 14.5.1 suggests is the volume of $G$; that is,

$$\text{volume of } G = \iiint\limits_G dV \tag{5}$$

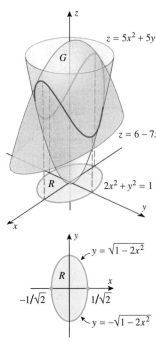

▲ Figure 14.5.5

▶ **Example 3**   Use a triple integral to find the volume of the solid within the cylinder $x^2 + y^2 = 9$ and between the planes $z = 1$ and $x + z = 5$.

*Solution.*   The solid $G$ and its projection $R$ on the $xy$-plane are shown in Figure 14.5.5. The lower surface of the solid is the plane $z = 1$ and the upper surface is the plane $x + z = 5$ or, equivalently, $z = 5 - x$. Thus, from (3) and (5)

$$\text{volume of } G = \iiint\limits_G dV = \iint\limits_R \left[ \int_1^{5-x} dz \right] dA \tag{6}$$

For the double integral over $R$, we will integrate with respect to $y$ first. Thus, (6) yields

$$\text{volume of } G = \int_{-3}^{3} \int_{-\sqrt{9-x^2}}^{\sqrt{9-x^2}} \int_1^{5-x} dz \, dy \, dx = \int_{-3}^{3} \int_{-\sqrt{9-x^2}}^{\sqrt{9-x^2}} z \Big]_{z=1}^{5-x} dy \, dx$$

$$= \int_{-3}^{3} \int_{-\sqrt{9-x^2}}^{\sqrt{9-x^2}} (4 - x) \, dy \, dx = \int_{-3}^{3} (8 - 2x)\sqrt{9 - x^2} \, dx$$

$$= 8 \int_{-3}^{3} \sqrt{9 - x^2} \, dx - \int_{-3}^{3} 2x\sqrt{9 - x^2} \, dx \qquad \boxed{\begin{array}{l}\text{For the first integral, see}\\ \text{Formula (3) of Section 7.4.}\end{array}}$$

$$= 8 \left( \frac{9}{2}\pi \right) - \int_{-3}^{3} 2x\sqrt{9 - x^2} \, dx \qquad \boxed{\begin{array}{l}\text{The second integral is 0 because}\\ \text{the integrand is an odd function.}\end{array}}$$

$$= 8 \left( \frac{9}{2}\pi \right) - 0 = 36\pi \quad ◀$$

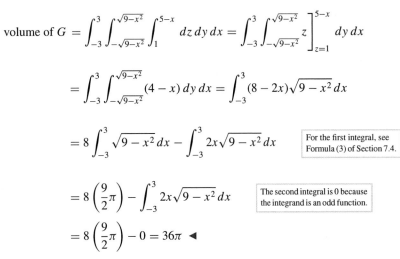

▲ Figure 14.5.6

▶ **Example 4**   Find the volume of the solid enclosed between the paraboloids

$$z = 5x^2 + 5y^2 \quad \text{and} \quad z = 6 - 7x^2 - y^2$$

*Solution.*   The solid $G$ and its projection $R$ on the $xy$-plane are shown in Figure 14.5.6. The projection $R$ is obtained by solving the given equations simultaneously to determine where the paraboloids intersect. We obtain

$$5x^2 + 5y^2 = 6 - 7x^2 - y^2$$

or

$$2x^2 + y^2 = 1 \tag{7}$$

which tells us that the paraboloids intersect in a curve on the elliptic cylinder given by (7).

The projection of this intersection on the $xy$-plane is an ellipse with this same equation. Therefore,

$$\text{volume of } G = \iiint\limits_{G} dV = \iint\limits_{R} \left[ \int_{5x^2+5y^2}^{6-7x^2-y^2} dz \right] dA$$

$$= \int_{-1/\sqrt{2}}^{1/\sqrt{2}} \int_{-\sqrt{1-2x^2}}^{\sqrt{1-2x^2}} \int_{5x^2+5y^2}^{6-7x^2-y^2} dz\, dy\, dx$$

$$= \int_{-1/\sqrt{2}}^{1/\sqrt{2}} \int_{-\sqrt{1-2x^2}}^{\sqrt{1-2x^2}} (6 - 12x^2 - 6y^2)\, dy\, dx$$

$$= \int_{-1/\sqrt{2}}^{1/\sqrt{2}} \left[ 6(1-2x^2)y - 2y^3 \right]_{y=-\sqrt{1-2x^2}}^{\sqrt{1-2x^2}} dx$$

$$= 8 \int_{-1/\sqrt{2}}^{1/\sqrt{2}} (1-2x^2)^{3/2}\, dx = \frac{8}{\sqrt{2}} \int_{-\pi/2}^{\pi/2} \cos^4 \theta\, d\theta = \frac{3\pi}{\sqrt{2}} \blacktriangleleft$$

$$\underbrace{\phantom{xxxxxx}}_{\text{Let } x = \dfrac{1}{\sqrt{2}} \sin\theta.} \qquad \underbrace{\phantom{xxxxxx}}_{\substack{\text{Use the Wallis cosine formula} \\ \text{in Exercise 70 of Section 7.3.}}}$$

### ▦ INTEGRATION IN OTHER ORDERS

In Formula (3) for integrating over a simple $xy$-solid, the $z$-integration was performed first. However, there are situations in which it is preferable to integrate in a different order. For example, Figure 14.5.7a shows a **simple xz-solid**, and Figure 14.5.7b shows a **simple yz-solid**. For a simple $xz$-solid it is usually best to integrate with respect to $y$ first, and for a simple $yz$-solid it is usually best to integrate with respect to $x$ first:

$$\iiint\limits_{\substack{G \\ \text{simple } xz\text{-solid}}} f(x, y, z)\, dV = \iint\limits_{R} \left[ \int_{g_1(x,z)}^{g_2(x,z)} f(x, y, z)\, dy \right] dA \tag{8}$$

$$\iiint\limits_{\substack{G \\ \text{simple } yz\text{-solid}}} f(x, y, z)\, dV = \iint\limits_{R} \left[ \int_{g_1(y,z)}^{g_2(y,z)} f(x, y, z)\, dx \right] dA \tag{9}$$

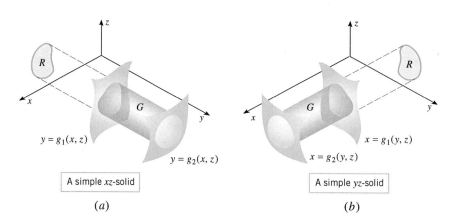

$y = g_1(x, z)$

$y = g_2(x, z)$

A simple $xz$-solid

$x = g_1(y, z)$

$x = g_2(y, z)$

A simple $yz$-solid

▶ **Figure 14.5.7**   $(a)$   $(b)$

Sometimes a solid $G$ can be viewed as a simple $xy$-solid, a simple $xz$-solid, and a simple $yz$-solid, in which case the order of integration can be chosen to simplify the computations.

▶ **Example 5** In Example 2 we evaluated

$$\iiint_G z\, dV$$

over the wedge in Figure 14.5.4 by integrating first with respect to $z$. Evaluate this integral by integrating first with respect to $x$.

*Solution.* The solid is bounded in the back by the plane $x = 0$ and in the front by the plane $x = y$, so

$$\iiint_G z\, dV = \iint_R \left[ \int_0^y z\, dx \right] dA$$

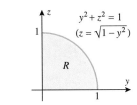

$y^2 + z^2 = 1$
$(z = \sqrt{1 - y^2})$

$R$

▲ **Figure 14.5.8**

where $R$ is the projection of $G$ on the $yz$-plane (Figure 14.5.8). The integration over $R$ can be performed first with respect to $z$ and then $y$ or vice versa. Performing the $z$-integration first yields

$$\iiint_G z\, dV = \int_0^1 \int_0^{\sqrt{1-y^2}} \int_0^y z\, dx\, dz\, dy = \int_0^1 \int_0^{\sqrt{1-y^2}} zx \Big]_{x=0}^{y} dz\, dy$$

$$= \int_0^1 \int_0^{\sqrt{1-y^2}} zy\, dz\, dy = \int_0^1 \frac{1}{2}z^2 y \Big]_{z=0}^{\sqrt{1-y^2}} dy = \int_0^1 \frac{1}{2}(1 - y^2)y\, dy = \frac{1}{8}$$

which agrees with the result in Example 2. ◀

---

✔ **QUICK CHECK EXERCISES 14.5**    *(See page 1048 for answers.)*

1. The iterated integral

$$\int_1^5 \int_2^4 \int_3^6 f(x, y, z)\, dx\, dz\, dy$$

integrates $f$ over the rectangular box defined by

_____ $\le x \le$ _____,    _____ $\le y \le$ _____,

_____ $\le z \le$ _____

2. Let $G$ be the solid in the first octant bounded below by the surface $z = y + x^2$ and bounded above by the plane $z = 4$. Supply the missing limits of integration.

(a) $\displaystyle\iiint_G f(x, y, z)\, dA = \int_{\square}^{\square} \int_{\square}^{\square} \int_{y+x^2}^{4} f(x, y, z)\, dz\, dx\, dy$

(b) $\displaystyle\iiint_G f(x, y, z)\, dA = \int_{\square}^{\square} \int_{\square}^{\square} \int_{y+x^2}^{4} f(x, y, z)\, dz\, dy\, dx$

(c) $\displaystyle\iiint_G f(x, y, z)\, dA = \int_{\square}^{\square} \int_{\square}^{\square} \int_{\square}^{\square} f(x, y, z)\, dy\, dz\, dx$

3. The volume of the solid $G$ in Quick Check Exercise 2 is _____.

---

**EXERCISE SET 14.5**    ⒸCAS

**1–8** Evaluate the iterated integral. ▨

1. $\displaystyle\int_{-1}^{1} \int_0^2 \int_0^1 (x^2 + y^2 + z^2)\, dx\, dy\, dz$

2. $\displaystyle\int_{1/3}^{1/2} \int_0^{\pi} \int_0^1 zx \sin xy\, dz\, dy\, dx$

3. $\displaystyle\int_0^2 \int_{-1}^{y^2} \int_{-1}^{z} yz\, dx\, dz\, dy$

4. $\displaystyle\int_0^{\pi/4} \int_0^1 \int_0^{x^2} x \cos y\, dz\, dx\, dy$

5. $\displaystyle\int_0^3 \int_0^{\sqrt{9-z^2}} \int_0^x xy\, dy\, dx\, dz$

6. $\displaystyle\int_1^3 \int_x^{x^2} \int_0^{\ln z} xe^y\, dy\, dz\, dx$

7. $\displaystyle\int_0^2 \int_0^{\sqrt{4-x^2}} \int_{-5+x^2+y^2}^{3-x^2-y^2} x\, dz\, dy\, dx$

8. $\displaystyle\int_1^2 \int_z^2 \int_0^{\sqrt{3}y} \frac{y}{x^2 + y^2}\, dx\, dy\, dz$

**9–12** Evaluate the triple integral.

**9.** $\iiint\limits_{G} xy \sin yz \, dV$, where $G$ is the rectangular box defined by the inequalities $0 \leq x \leq \pi$, $0 \leq y \leq 1$, $0 \leq z \leq \pi/6$.

**10.** $\iiint\limits_{G} y \, dV$, where $G$ is the solid enclosed by the plane $z = y$, the $xy$-plane, and the parabolic cylinder $y = 1 - x^2$.

**11.** $\iiint\limits_{G} xyz \, dV$, where $G$ is the solid in the first octant that is bounded by the parabolic cylinder $z = 2 - x^2$ and the planes $z = 0$, $y = x$, and $y = 0$.

**12.** $\iiint\limits_{G} \cos(z/y) \, dV$, where $G$ is the solid defined by the inequalities $\pi/6 \leq y \leq \pi/2$, $y \leq x \leq \pi/2$, $0 \leq z \leq xy$.

**C** **13.** Use the numerical triple integral operation of a CAS to approximate
$$\iiint\limits_{G} \frac{\sqrt{x + z^2}}{y} \, dV$$
where $G$ is the rectangular box defined by the inequalities $0 \leq x \leq 3$, $1 \leq y \leq 2$, $-2 \leq z \leq 1$.

**C** **14.** Use the numerical triple integral operation of a CAS to approximate
$$\iiint\limits_{G} e^{-x^2 - y^2 - z^2} \, dV$$
where $G$ is the spherical region $x^2 + y^2 + z^2 \leq 1$.

**15–18** Use a triple integral to find the volume of the solid.

**15.** The solid in the first octant bounded by the coordinate planes and the plane $3x + 6y + 4z = 12$.

**16.** The solid bounded by the surface $z = \sqrt{y}$ and the planes $x + y = 1$, $x = 0$, and $z = 0$.

**17.** The solid bounded by the surface $y = x^2$ and the planes $y + z = 4$ and $z = 0$.

**18.** The wedge in the first octant that is cut from the solid cylinder $y^2 + z^2 \leq 1$ by the planes $y = x$ and $x = 0$.

**FOCUS ON CONCEPTS**

**19.** Let $G$ be the solid enclosed by the surfaces in the accompanying figure. Fill in the missing limits of integration.

(a) $\iiint\limits_{G} f(x, y, z) \, dV$
$$= \int_{\square}^{\square} \int_{\square}^{\square} \int_{\square}^{\square} f(x, y, z) \, dz \, dy \, dx$$

(b) $\iiint\limits_{G} f(x, y, z) \, dV$
$$= \int_{\square}^{\square} \int_{\square}^{\square} \int_{\square}^{\square} f(x, y, z) \, dz \, dx \, dy$$

**20.** Let $G$ be the solid enclosed by the surfaces in the accompanying figure. Fill in the missing limits of integration.

(a) $\iiint\limits_{G} f(x, y, z) \, dV$
$$= \int_{\square}^{\square} \int_{\square}^{\square} \int_{\square}^{\square} f(x, y, z) \, dz \, dy \, dx$$

(b) $\iiint\limits_{G} f(x, y, z) \, dV$
$$= \int_{\square}^{\square} \int_{\square}^{\square} \int_{\square}^{\square} f(x, y, z) \, dz \, dx \, dy$$

$z = 4x^2 + y^2$
$z = 4 - 3y^2$

▲ **Figure Ex-19**

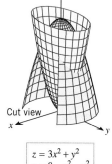

Cut view

$z = 3x^2 + y^2$
$z = 8 - x^2 - y^2$

▲ **Figure Ex-20**

**21–24** Set up (but do not evaluate) an iterated triple integral for the volume of the solid enclosed between the given surfaces.

**21.** The surfaces in Exercise 19.

**22.** The surfaces in Exercise 20.

**23.** The elliptic cylinder $x^2 + 9y^2 = 9$ and the planes $z = 0$ and $z = x + 3$.

**24.** The cylinders $x^2 + y^2 = 1$ and $x^2 + z^2 = 1$.

**25–26** In each part, sketch the solid whose volume is given by the integral.

**25.** (a) $\int_{-1}^{1} \int_{-\sqrt{1-x^2}}^{\sqrt{1-x^2}} \int_{0}^{y+1} dz \, dy \, dx$

(b) $\int_{0}^{9} \int_{0}^{y/3} \int_{0}^{\sqrt{y^2-9x^2}} dz \, dx \, dy$

(c) $\int_{0}^{1} \int_{0}^{\sqrt{1-x^2}} \int_{0}^{2} dy \, dz \, dx$

**26.** (a) $\int_{0}^{3} \int_{x^2}^{9} \int_{0}^{2} dz \, dy \, dx$

(b) $\int_{0}^{2} \int_{0}^{2-y} \int_{0}^{2-x-y} dz \, dx \, dy$

(c) $\int_{-2}^{2} \int_{0}^{4-y^2} \int_{0}^{2} dx \, dz \, dy$

**27–30 True–False** Determine whether the statement is true or false. Explain your answer.

**27.** If $G$ is the rectangular solid that is defined by $1 \leq x \leq 3$, $2 \leq y \leq 5$, $-1 \leq z \leq 1$, and if $f(x, y, z)$ is continuous on $G$, then

$$\iiint_G f(x, y, z)\, dV = \int_1^3 \int_{-1}^1 \int_2^5 f(x, y, z)\, dy\, dz\, dx$$

**28.** If $G$ is a simple $xy$-solid and $f(x, y, z)$ is continuous on $G$, then the triple integral of $f$ over $G$ can be expressed as an iterated integral whose outermost integration is performed with respect to $z$.

**29.** If $G$ is the portion of the unit ball in the first octant, then

$$\iiint_G f(x, y, z)\, dV = \int_0^1 \int_0^1 \int_0^{\sqrt{1-x^2-y^2}} f(x, y, z)\, dz\, dy\, dx$$

**30.** If $G$ is a simple $xy$-solid and

$$\text{volume of } G = \iiint_G f(x, y, z)\, dV$$

then $f(x, y, z) = 1$ at every point in $G$.

**31.** Let $G$ be the rectangular box defined by the inequalities $a \leq x \leq b, c \leq y \leq d, k \leq z \leq l$. Show that

$$\iiint_G f(x)g(y)h(z)\, dV$$

$$= \left[ \int_a^b f(x)\, dx \right]\left[ \int_c^d g(y)\, dy \right]\left[ \int_k^l h(z)\, dz \right]$$

**32.** Use the result of Exercise 31 to evaluate

(a) $\displaystyle\iiint_G xy^2 \sin z\, dV$, where $G$ is the set of points satisfying $-1 \leq x \leq 1, 0 \leq y \leq 1, 0 \leq z \leq \pi/2$;

(b) $\displaystyle\iiint_G e^{2x+y-z}\, dV$, where $G$ is the set of points satisfying $0 \leq x \leq 1, 0 \leq y \leq \ln 3, 0 \leq z \leq \ln 2$.

**33–36** The **average value** or **mean value** of a continuous function $f(x, y, z)$ over a solid $G$ is defined as

$$f_{\text{ave}} = \frac{1}{V(G)} \iiint_G f(x, y, z)\, dV$$

where $V(G)$ is the volume of the solid $G$ (compare to the definition preceding Exercise 61 of Section 14.2). Use this definition in these exercises. ■

**33.** Find the average value of $f(x, y, z) = x + y + z$ over the tetrahedron shown in the accompanying figure.

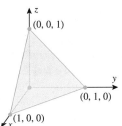

◀ **Figure Ex-33**

**34.** Find the average value of $f(x, y, z) = xyz$ over the spherical region $x^2 + y^2 + z^2 \leq 1$.

**C 35.** Use the numerical triple integral operation of a CAS to approximate the average distance from the origin to a point in the solid of Example 4.

**C 36.** Let $d(x, y, z)$ be the distance from the point $(z, z, z)$ to the point $(x, y, 0)$. Use the numerical triple integral operation of a CAS to approximate the average value of $d$ for $0 \leq x \leq 1, 0 \leq y \leq 1$, and $0 \leq z \leq 1$. Write a short explanation as to why this value may be considered to be the average distance between a point on the diagonal from $(0, 0, 0)$ to $(1, 1, 1)$ and a point on the face in the $xy$-plane for the unit cube $0 \leq x \leq 1, 0 \leq y \leq 1$, and $0 \leq z \leq 1$.

**37.** Let $G$ be the tetrahedron in the first octant bounded by the coordinate planes and the plane

$$\frac{x}{a} + \frac{y}{b} + \frac{z}{c} = 1 \quad (a > 0, b > 0, c > 0)$$

(a) List six different iterated integrals that represent the volume of $G$.

(b) Evaluate any one of the six to show that the volume of $G$ is $\frac{1}{6}abc$.

**38.** Use a triple integral to derive the formula for the volume of the ellipsoid

$$\frac{x^2}{a^2} + \frac{y^2}{b^2} + \frac{z^2}{c^2} = 1$$

**FOCUS ON CONCEPTS**

**39–40** Express each integral as an equivalent integral in which the $z$-integration is performed first, the $y$-integration second, and the $x$-integration last. ■

**39.** (a) $\displaystyle\int_0^5 \int_0^2 \int_0^{\sqrt{4-y^2}} f(x, y, z)\, dx\, dy\, dz$

(b) $\displaystyle\int_0^9 \int_0^{3-\sqrt{x}} \int_0^z f(x, y, z)\, dy\, dz\, dx$

(c) $\displaystyle\int_0^4 \int_y^{8-y} \int_0^{\sqrt{4-y}} f(x, y, z)\, dx\, dz\, dy$

**40.** (a) $\displaystyle\int_0^3 \int_0^{\sqrt{9-z^2}} \int_0^{\sqrt{9-y^2-z^2}} f(x, y, z)\, dx\, dy\, dz$

(b) $\displaystyle\int_0^4 \int_0^2 \int_0^{x/2} f(x, y, z)\, dy\, dz\, dx$

(c) $\displaystyle\int_0^4 \int_0^{4-y} \int_0^{\sqrt{z}} f(x, y, z)\, dx\, dz\, dy$

**41.** **Writing** The following initial steps can be used to express a triple integral over a solid $G$ as an iterated triple integral: First project $G$ onto one of the coordinate planes to obtain a region $R$, and then project $R$ onto one of the coordinate axes. Describe how you would use these steps to find the limits of integration. Illustrate your discussion with an example.

✔ QUICK CHECK ANSWERS 14.5

1. $3 \le x \le 6,\ 1 \le y \le 5,\ 2 \le z \le 4$  2. (a) $\displaystyle\int_0^4 \int_0^{\sqrt{4-y}} \int_{y+x^2}^4 f(x, y, z)\, dz\, dx\, dy$  (b) $\displaystyle\int_0^2 \int_0^{4-x^2} \int_{y+x^2}^4 f(x, y, z)\, dz\, dy\, dx$

(c) $\displaystyle\int_0^2 \int_{x^2}^4 \int_0^{z-x^2} f(x, y, z)\, dy\, dz\, dx$  3. $\dfrac{128}{15}$

## 14.6  TRIPLE INTEGRALS IN CYLINDRICAL AND SPHERICAL COORDINATES

*In Section 14.3 we saw that some double integrals are easier to evaluate in polar coordinates than in rectangular coordinates. Similarly, some triple integrals are easier to evaluate in cylindrical or spherical coordinates than in rectangular coordinates. In this section we will study triple integrals in these coordinate systems.*

### ■ TRIPLE INTEGRALS IN CYLINDRICAL COORDINATES

Recall that in rectangular coordinates the triple integral of a continuous function $f$ over a solid region $G$ is defined as

$$\iiint\limits_G f(x, y, z)\, dV = \lim_{n \to +\infty} \sum_{k=1}^n f(x_k^*, y_k^*, z_k^*)\, \Delta V_k$$

where $\Delta V_k$ denotes the volume of a rectangular parallelepiped interior to $G$ and $(x_k^*, y_k^*, z_k^*)$ is a point in this parallelepiped (see Figure 14.5.1). Triple integrals in cylindrical and spherical coordinates are defined similarly, except that the region $G$ is divided not into rectangular parallelepipeds but into regions more appropriate to these coordinate systems.

In cylindrical coordinates, the simplest equations are of the form

$$r = \text{constant}, \quad \theta = \text{constant}, \quad z = \text{constant}$$

The first equation represents a right circular cylinder centered on the $z$-axis, the second a vertical half-plane hinged on the $z$-axis, and the third a horizontal plane. (See Figure 11.8.3.) These surfaces can be paired up to determine solids called **cylindrical wedges** or **cylindrical elements of volume**. To be precise, a cylindrical wedge is a solid enclosed between six surfaces of the following form:

| | | |
|---|---|---|
| two cylinders (blue) | $r = r_1, \quad r = r_2$ | $(r_1 < r_2)$ |
| two vertical half-planes (yellow) | $\theta = \theta_1, \quad \theta = \theta_2$ | $(\theta_1 < \theta_2)$ |
| two horizontal planes (gray) | $z = z_1, \quad z = z_2$ | $(z_1 < z_2)$ |

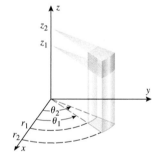

▲ Figure 14.6.1

(Figure 14.6.1). The dimensions $\theta_2 - \theta_1$, $r_2 - r_1$, and $z_2 - z_1$ are called the **central angle**, **thickness**, and **height** of the wedge.

To define the triple integral over $G$ of a function $f(r, \theta, z)$ in cylindrical coordinates we proceed as follows:

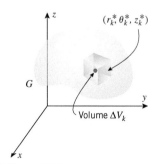

▲ Figure 14.6.2

• Subdivide $G$ into pieces by a three-dimensional grid consisting of concentric circular cylinders centered on the $z$-axis, half-planes hinged on the $z$-axis, and horizontal planes. Exclude from consideration all pieces that contain any points outside of $G$, thereby leaving only cylindrical wedges that are subsets of $G$.

• Assume that there are $n$ such cylindrical wedges, and denote the volume of the $k$th cylindrical wedge by $\Delta V_k$. As indicated in Figure 14.6.2, let $(r_k^*, \theta_k^*, z_k^*)$ be any point in the $k$th cylindrical wedge.

- Repeat this process with more and more subdivisions so that as $n$ increases, the height, thickness, and central angle of the cylindrical wedges approach zero. Define

$$\iiint\limits_{G} f(r, \theta, z)\, dV = \lim_{n \to +\infty} \sum_{k=1}^{n} f(r_k^*, \theta_k^*, z_k^*)\Delta V_k \tag{1}$$

For computational purposes, it will be helpful to express (1) as an iterated integral. Toward this end we note that the volume $\Delta V_k$ of the $k$th cylindrical wedge can be expressed as

$$\Delta V_k = [\text{area of base}] \cdot [\text{height}] \tag{2}$$

If we denote the thickness, central angle, and height of this wedge by $\Delta r_k$, $\Delta\theta_k$, and $\Delta z_k$, and if we choose the arbitrary point $(r_k^*, \theta_k^*, z_k^*)$ to lie above the "center" of the base (Figures 14.3.6 and 14.6.3), then it follows from (5) of Section 14.3 that the base has area $\Delta A_k = r_k^* \Delta r_k \Delta\theta_k$. Thus, (2) can be written as

$$\Delta V_k = r_k^* \Delta r_k \Delta\theta_k \Delta z_k = r_k^* \Delta z_k \Delta r_k \Delta\theta_k$$

Substituting this expression in (1) yields

$$\iiint\limits_{G} f(r, \theta, z)\, dV = \lim_{n \to +\infty} \sum_{k=1}^{n} f(r_k^*, \theta_k^*, z_k^*) r_k^* \Delta z_k \Delta r_k \Delta\theta_k$$

which suggests that a triple integral in cylindrical coordinates can be evaluated as an iterated integral of the form

$$\iiint\limits_{G} f(r, \theta, z)\, dV = \iiint\limits_{\substack{\text{appropriate}\\ \text{limits}}} f(r, \theta, z)\, r\, dz\, dr\, d\theta \tag{3}$$

In this formula the integration with respect to $z$ is done first, then with respect to $r$, and then with respect to $\theta$, but any order of integration is allowable.

The following theorem, which we state without proof, makes the preceding ideas more precise.

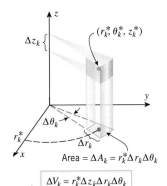

▲ **Figure 14.6.3**

Note the extra factor of $r$ that appears in the integrand on converting a triple integral to an iterated integral in cylindrical coordinates.

---

**14.6.1    THEOREM**  *Let $G$ be a solid region whose upper surface has the equation $z = g_2(r, \theta)$ and whose lower surface has the equation $z = g_1(r, \theta)$ in cylindrical coordinates. If the projection of the solid on the xy-plane is a simple polar region $R$, and if $f(r, \theta, z)$ is continuous on $G$, then*

$$\iiint\limits_{G} f(r, \theta, z)\, dV = \iint\limits_{R} \left[ \int_{g_1(r,\theta)}^{g_2(r,\theta)} f(r, \theta, z)\, dz \right] dA \tag{4}$$

*where the double integral over $R$ is evaluated in polar coordinates. In particular, if the projection $R$ is as shown in Figure 14.6.4, then (4) can be written as*

$$\iiint\limits_{G} f(r, \theta, z)\, dV = \int_{\theta_1}^{\theta_2} \int_{r_1(\theta)}^{r_2(\theta)} \int_{g_1(r,\theta)}^{g_2(r,\theta)} f(r, \theta, z)\, r\, dz\, dr\, d\theta \tag{5}$$

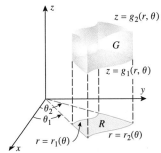

▲ **Figure 14.6.4**

The type of solid to which Formula (5) applies is illustrated in Figure 14.6.4. To apply (4) and (5) it is best to begin with a three-dimensional sketch of the solid $G$, from which the limits of integration can be obtained as follows:

*Determining Limits of Integration: Cylindrical Coordinates*

**Step 1.** Identify the upper surface $z = g_2(r, \theta)$ and the lower surface $z = g_1(r, \theta)$ of the solid. The functions $g_1(r, \theta)$ and $g_2(r, \theta)$ determine the $z$-limits of integration. (If the upper and lower surfaces are given in rectangular coordinates, convert them to cylindrical coordinates.)

**Step 2.** Make a two-dimensional sketch of the projection $R$ of the solid on the $xy$-plane. From this sketch the $r$- and $\theta$-limits of integration may be obtained exactly as with double integrals in polar coordinates.

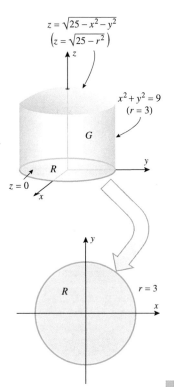

▶ **Example 1** Use triple integration in cylindrical coordinates to find the volume of the solid $G$ that is bounded above by the hemisphere $z = \sqrt{25 - x^2 - y^2}$, below by the $xy$-plane, and laterally by the cylinder $x^2 + y^2 = 9$.

*Solution.* The solid $G$ and its projection $R$ on the $xy$-plane are shown in Figure 14.6.5. In cylindrical coordinates, the upper surface of $G$ is the hemisphere $z = \sqrt{25 - r^2}$ and the lower surface is the plane $z = 0$. Thus, from (4), the volume of $G$ is

$$V = \iiint\limits_{G} dV = \iint\limits_{R} \left[ \int_0^{\sqrt{25-r^2}} dz \right] dA$$

For the double integral over $R$, we use polar coordinates:

$$V = \int_0^{2\pi} \int_0^3 \int_0^{\sqrt{25-r^2}} r\, dz\, dr\, d\theta = \int_0^{2\pi} \int_0^3 \left[ rz \right]_{z=0}^{\sqrt{25-r^2}} dr\, d\theta$$

$$= \int_0^{2\pi} \int_0^3 r\sqrt{25 - r^2}\, dr\, d\theta = \int_0^{2\pi} \left[ -\frac{1}{3}(25 - r^2)^{3/2} \right]_{r=0}^{3} d\theta$$

$$= \int_0^{2\pi} \frac{61}{3}\, d\theta = \frac{122}{3}\pi \blacktriangleleft$$

$$\boxed{\begin{array}{l} u = 25 - r^2 \\ du = -2r\, dr \end{array}}$$

▲ **Figure 14.6.5**

■ **CONVERTING TRIPLE INTEGRALS FROM RECTANGULAR TO CYLINDRICAL COORDINATES**
Sometimes a triple integral that is difficult to integrate in rectangular coordinates can be evaluated more easily by making the substitution $x = r\cos\theta$, $y = r\sin\theta$, $z = z$ to convert it to an integral in cylindrical coordinates. Under such a substitution, a rectangular triple integral can be expressed as an iterated integral in cylindrical coordinates as

$$\iiint\limits_{G} f(x, y, z)\, dV = \iiint\limits_{\substack{\text{appropriate}\\\text{limits}}} f(r\cos\theta, r\sin\theta, z)r\, dz\, dr\, d\theta \qquad (6)$$

The order of integration on the right side of (6) can be changed, provided the limits of integration are adjusted accordingly.

▶ **Example 2** Use cylindrical coordinates to evaluate

$$\int_{-3}^{3} \int_{-\sqrt{9-x^2}}^{\sqrt{9-x^2}} \int_0^{9-x^2-y^2} x^2\, dz\, dy\, dx$$

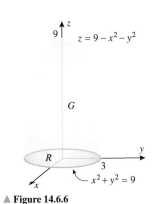

▲ **Figure 14.6.6**

***Solution.*** In problems of this type, it is helpful to sketch the region of integration $G$ and its projection $R$ on the $xy$-plane. From the $z$-limits of integration, the upper surface of $G$ is the paraboloid $z = 9 - x^2 - y^2$ and the lower surface is the $xy$-plane $z = 0$. From the $x$- and $y$-limits of integration, the projection $R$ is the region in the $xy$-plane enclosed by the circle $x^2 + y^2 = 9$ (Figure 14.6.6). Thus,

$$\int_{-3}^{3} \int_{-\sqrt{9-x^2}}^{\sqrt{9-x^2}} \int_{0}^{9-x^2-y^2} x^2 \, dz \, dy \, dx = \iiint_G x^2 \, dV$$

$$= \iint_R \left[ \int_0^{9-r^2} r^2 \cos^2 \theta \, dz \right] dA = \int_0^{2\pi} \int_0^3 \int_0^{9-r^2} (r^2 \cos^2 \theta) r \, dz \, dr \, d\theta$$

$$= \int_0^{2\pi} \int_0^3 \int_0^{9-r^2} r^3 \cos^2 \theta \, dz \, dr \, d\theta = \int_0^{2\pi} \int_0^3 \left[ zr^3 \cos^2 \theta \right]_{z=0}^{9-r^2} dr \, d\theta$$

$$= \int_0^{2\pi} \int_0^3 (9r^3 - r^5) \cos^2 \theta \, dr \, d\theta = \int_0^{2\pi} \left[ \left( \frac{9r^4}{4} - \frac{r^6}{6} \right) \cos^2 \theta \right]_{r=0}^{3} d\theta$$

$$= \frac{243}{4} \int_0^{2\pi} \cos^2 \theta \, d\theta = \frac{243}{4} \int_0^{2\pi} \frac{1}{2} (1 + \cos 2\theta) \, d\theta = \frac{243\pi}{4} \quad \blacktriangleleft$$

### ▌ TRIPLE INTEGRALS IN SPHERICAL COORDINATES

In spherical coordinates, the simplest equations are of the form

$$\rho = \text{constant}, \quad \theta = \text{constant}, \quad \phi = \text{constant}$$

As indicated in Figure 11.8.4, the first equation represents a sphere centered at the origin and the second a half-plane hinged on the $z$-axis. The graph of the third equation is a right circular cone nappe with its vertex at the origin and its line of symmetry along the $z$-axis for $\phi \neq \pi/2$, and is the $xy$-plane if $\phi = \pi/2$. By a ***spherical wedge*** or ***spherical element of volume*** we mean a solid enclosed between six surfaces of the following form:

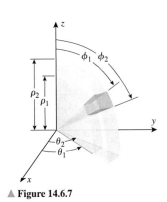

▲ **Figure 14.6.7**

| two spheres (green) | $\rho = \rho_1, \quad \rho = \rho_2 \quad (\rho_1 < \rho_2)$ |
| two vertical half-planes (yellow) | $\theta = \theta_1, \quad \theta = \theta_2 \quad (\theta_1 < \theta_2)$ |
| nappes of two circular cones (pink) | $\phi = \phi_1, \quad \phi = \phi_2 \quad (\phi_1 < \phi_2)$ |

(Figure 14.6.7). We will refer to the numbers $\rho_2 - \rho_1, \theta_2 - \theta_1$, and $\phi_2 - \phi_1$ as the ***dimensions*** of a spherical wedge.

If $G$ is a solid region in three-dimensional space, then the triple integral over $G$ of a continuous function $f(\rho, \theta, \phi)$ in spherical coordinates is similar in definition to the triple integral in cylindrical coordinates, except that the solid $G$ is partitioned into *spherical wedges* by a three-dimensional grid consisting of spheres centered at the origin, half-planes hinged on the $z$-axis, and nappes of right circular cones with vertices at the origin and lines of symmetry along the $z$-axis (Figure 14.6.8).

The defining equation of a triple integral in spherical coordinates is

$$\iiint_G f(\rho, \theta, \phi) \, dV = \lim_{n \to +\infty} \sum_{k=1}^{n} f(\rho_k^*, \theta_k^*, \phi_k^*) \Delta V_k \tag{7}$$

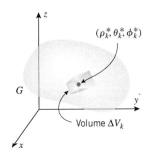

▲ **Figure 14.6.8**

where $\Delta V_k$ is the volume of the $k$th spherical wedge that is interior to $G$, $(\rho_k^*, \theta_k^*, \phi_k^*)$ is an arbitrary point in this wedge, and $n$ increases in such a way that the dimensions of each interior spherical wedge tend to zero.

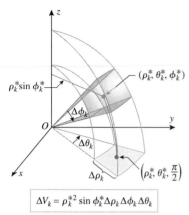

$$\Delta V_k = \rho_k^{*2} \sin \phi_k^* \, \Delta\rho_k \, \Delta\phi_k \, \Delta\theta_k$$

▲ **Figure 14.6.9**

Note the extra factor of $\rho^2 \sin \phi$ that appears in the integrand on converting a triple integral to an iterated integral in spherical coordinates. This is analogous to the extra factor of $r$ that appears in an iterated integral in cylindrical coordinates.

For computational purposes, it will be desirable to express (7) as an iterated integral. In Exercise 30 we will help you to show that if the point $(\rho_k^*, \theta_k^*, \phi_k^*)$ is suitably chosen, then the volume $\Delta V_k$ in (7) can be written as

$$\Delta V_k = \rho_k^{*2} \sin \phi_k^* \, \Delta\rho_k \, \Delta\phi_k \, \Delta\theta_k \tag{8}$$

where $\Delta\rho_k$, $\Delta\phi_k$, and $\Delta\theta_k$ are the dimensions of the wedge (Figure 14.6.9). Substituting this in (7) we obtain

$$\iiint\limits_G f(\rho, \theta, \phi) \, dV = \lim_{n \to +\infty} \sum_{k=1}^{n} f(\rho_k^*, \theta_k^*, \phi_k^*) \rho_k^{*2} \sin \phi_k^* \, \Delta\rho_k \, \Delta\phi_k \, \Delta\theta_k$$

which suggests that a triple integral in spherical coordinates can be evaluated as an iterated integral of the form

$$\iiint\limits_G f(\rho, \theta, \phi) \, dV = \iiint\limits_{\substack{\text{appropriate} \\ \text{limits}}} f(\rho, \theta, \phi) \rho^2 \sin \phi \, d\rho \, d\phi \, d\theta \tag{9}$$

The analog of Theorem 14.6.1 for triple integrals in spherical coordinates is tedious to state, so instead we will give some examples that illustrate techniques for obtaining the limits of integration. In all of our examples we will use the same order of integration—first with respect to $\rho$, then $\phi$, and then $\theta$. Once you have mastered the basic ideas, there should be no trouble using other orders of integration.

Suppose that we want to integrate $f(\rho, \theta, \phi)$ over the spherical solid $G$ enclosed by the sphere $\rho = \rho_0$. The basic idea is to choose the limits of integration so that every point of the solid is accounted for in the integration process. Figure 14.6.10 illustrates one way of doing this. Holding $\theta$ and $\phi$ fixed for the first integration, we let $\rho$ vary from 0 to $\rho_0$. This covers a radial line from the origin to the surface of the sphere. Next, keeping $\theta$ fixed, we let $\phi$ vary from 0 to $\pi$ so that the radial line sweeps out a fan-shaped region. Finally, we let $\theta$ vary from 0 to $2\pi$ so that the fan-shaped region makes a complete revolution, thereby sweeping out the entire sphere. Thus, the triple integral of $f(\rho, \theta, \phi)$ over the spherical solid $G$ can be evaluated by writing

$$\iiint\limits_G f(\rho, \theta, \phi) \, dV = \int_0^{2\pi} \int_0^{\pi} \int_0^{\rho_0} f(\rho, \theta, \phi) \rho^2 \sin \phi \, d\rho \, d\phi \, d\theta$$

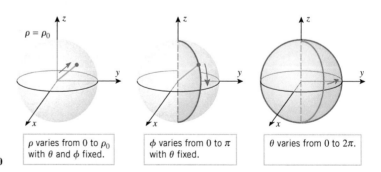

▶ **Figure 14.6.10**

$\rho$ varies from 0 to $\rho_0$ with $\theta$ and $\phi$ fixed.

$\phi$ varies from 0 to $\pi$ with $\theta$ fixed.

$\theta$ varies from 0 to $2\pi$.

Table 14.6.1 suggests how the limits of integration in spherical coordinates can be obtained for some other common solids.

**Table 14.6.1**

| DETERMINATION OF LIMITS | INTEGRAL |
|---|---|

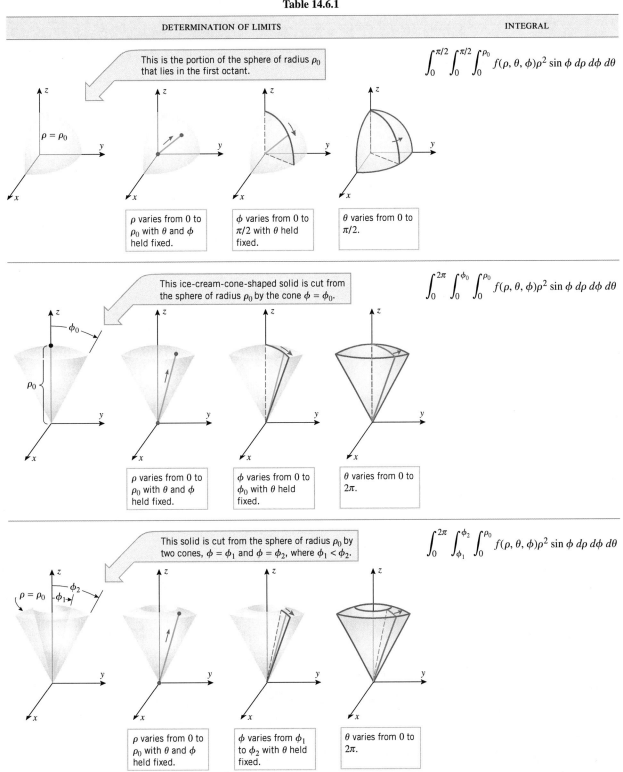

This is the portion of the sphere of radius $\rho_0$ that lies in the first octant.

$$\int_0^{\pi/2} \int_0^{\pi/2} \int_0^{\rho_0} f(\rho, \theta, \phi)\rho^2 \sin \phi \, d\rho \, d\phi \, d\theta$$

$\rho$ varies from 0 to $\rho_0$ with $\theta$ and $\phi$ held fixed.

$\phi$ varies from 0 to $\pi/2$ with $\theta$ held fixed.

$\theta$ varies from 0 to $\pi/2$.

This ice-cream-cone-shaped solid is cut from the sphere of radius $\rho_0$ by the cone $\phi = \phi_0$.

$$\int_0^{2\pi} \int_0^{\phi_0} \int_0^{\rho_0} f(\rho, \theta, \phi)\rho^2 \sin \phi \, d\rho \, d\phi \, d\theta$$

$\rho$ varies from 0 to $\rho_0$ with $\theta$ and $\phi$ held fixed.

$\phi$ varies from 0 to $\phi_0$ with $\theta$ held fixed.

$\theta$ varies from 0 to $2\pi$.

This solid is cut from the sphere of radius $\rho_0$ by two cones, $\phi = \phi_1$ and $\phi = \phi_2$, where $\phi_1 < \phi_2$.

$$\int_0^{2\pi} \int_{\phi_1}^{\phi_2} \int_0^{\rho_0} f(\rho, \theta, \phi)\rho^2 \sin \phi \, d\rho \, d\phi \, d\theta$$

$\rho$ varies from 0 to $\rho_0$ with $\theta$ and $\phi$ held fixed.

$\phi$ varies from $\phi_1$ to $\phi_2$ with $\theta$ held fixed.

$\theta$ varies from 0 to $2\pi$.

**Table 14.6.1** (*continued*)

| DETERMINATION OF LIMITS | INTEGRAL |
|---|---|

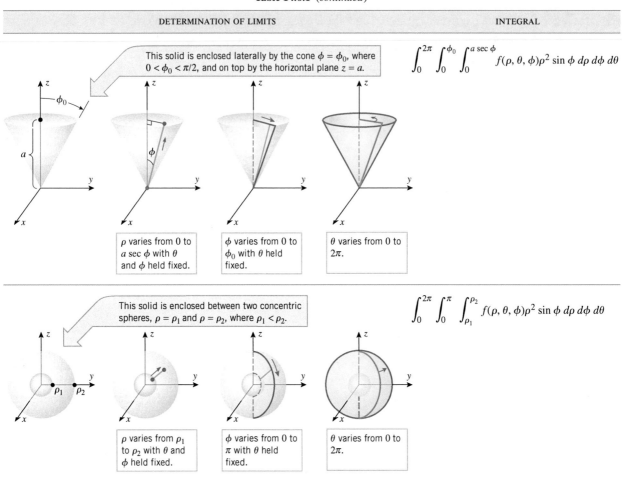

This solid is enclosed laterally by the cone $\phi = \phi_0$, where $0 < \phi_0 < \pi/2$, and on top by the horizontal plane $z = a$.

$$\int_0^{2\pi} \int_0^{\phi_0} \int_0^{a \sec \phi} f(\rho, \theta, \phi)\rho^2 \sin \phi \, d\rho \, d\phi \, d\theta$$

$\rho$ varies from 0 to $a \sec \phi$ with $\theta$ and $\phi$ held fixed.

$\phi$ varies from 0 to $\phi_0$ with $\theta$ held fixed.

$\theta$ varies from 0 to $2\pi$.

This solid is enclosed between two concentric spheres, $\rho = \rho_1$ and $\rho = \rho_2$, where $\rho_1 < \rho_2$.

$$\int_0^{2\pi} \int_0^{\pi} \int_{\rho_1}^{\rho_2} f(\rho, \theta, \phi)\rho^2 \sin \phi \, d\rho \, d\phi \, d\theta$$

$\rho$ varies from $\rho_1$ to $\rho_2$ with $\theta$ and $\phi$ held fixed.

$\phi$ varies from 0 to $\pi$ with $\theta$ held fixed.

$\theta$ varies from 0 to $2\pi$.

▶ **Example 3**   Use spherical coordinates to find the volume of the solid $G$ bounded above by the sphere $x^2 + y^2 + z^2 = 16$ and below by the cone $z = \sqrt{x^2 + y^2}$.

**Solution.**   The solid $G$ is sketched in Figure 14.6.11. In spherical coordinates, the equation of the sphere $x^2 + y^2 + z^2 = 16$ is $\rho = 4$ and the equation of the cone $z = \sqrt{x^2 + y^2}$ is

$$\rho \cos \phi = \sqrt{\rho^2 \sin^2 \phi \cos^2 \theta + \rho^2 \sin^2 \phi \sin^2 \theta}$$

which simplifies to

$$\rho \cos \phi = \rho \sin \phi$$

Dividing both sides of this equation by $\rho \cos \phi$ yields $\tan \phi = 1$, from which it follows that

$$\phi = \pi/4$$

$z \quad x^2 + y^2 + z^2 = 16$
$(\rho = 4)$

$z = \sqrt{x^2 + y^2}$
$\left(\phi = \dfrac{\pi}{4}\right)$

▲ **Figure 14.6.11**

Thus, it follows from the second entry in Table 14.6.1 that the volume of $G$ is

$$
\begin{aligned}
V = \iiint\limits_{G} dV &= \int_0^{2\pi} \int_0^{\pi/4} \int_0^4 \rho^2 \sin\phi \, d\rho \, d\phi \, d\theta \\
&= \int_0^{2\pi} \int_0^{\pi/4} \left[ \frac{\rho^3}{3} \sin\phi \right]_{\rho=0}^4 d\phi \, d\theta \\
&= \int_0^{2\pi} \int_0^{\pi/4} \frac{64}{3} \sin\phi \, d\phi \, d\theta \\
&= \frac{64}{3} \int_0^{2\pi} \left[ -\cos\phi \right]_{\phi=0}^{\pi/4} d\theta = \frac{64}{3} \int_0^{2\pi} \left( 1 - \frac{\sqrt{2}}{2} \right) d\theta \\
&= \frac{64\pi}{3} (2 - \sqrt{2}) \approx 39.26 \blacktriangleleft
\end{aligned}
$$

### CONVERTING TRIPLE INTEGRALS FROM RECTANGULAR TO SPHERICAL COORDINATES

Referring to Table 11.8.1, triple integrals can be converted from rectangular coordinates to spherical coordinates by making the substitution $x = \rho \sin\phi \cos\theta$, $y = \rho \sin\phi \sin\theta$, $z = \rho \cos\phi$. The two integrals are related by the equation

$$
\iiint\limits_{G} f(x, y, z) \, dV = \iiint\limits_{\substack{\text{appropriate} \\ \text{limits}}} f(\rho \sin\phi \cos\theta, \rho \sin\phi \sin\theta, \rho \cos\phi) \rho^2 \sin\phi \, d\rho \, d\phi \, d\theta \qquad (10)
$$

---

▶ **Example 4** Use spherical coordinates to evaluate

$$
\int_{-2}^{2} \int_{-\sqrt{4-x^2}}^{\sqrt{4-x^2}} \int_0^{\sqrt{4-x^2-y^2}} z^2 \sqrt{x^2 + y^2 + z^2} \, dz \, dy \, dx
$$

*Solution.* In problems like this, it is helpful to begin (when possible) with a sketch of the region $G$ of integration. From the $z$-limits of integration, the upper surface of $G$ is the hemisphere $z = \sqrt{4 - x^2 - y^2}$ and the lower surface is the $xy$-plane $z = 0$. From the $x$- and $y$-limits of integration, the projection of the solid $G$ on the $xy$-plane is the region enclosed by the circle $x^2 + y^2 = 4$. From this information we obtain the sketch of $G$ in Figure 14.6.12. Thus,

$$
\begin{aligned}
\int_{-2}^{2} \int_{-\sqrt{4-x^2}}^{\sqrt{4-x^2}} &\int_0^{\sqrt{4-x^2-y^2}} z^2 \sqrt{x^2 + y^2 + z^2} \, dz \, dy \, dx \\
&= \iiint\limits_{G} z^2 \sqrt{x^2 + y^2 + z^2} \, dV \\
&= \int_0^{2\pi} \int_0^{\pi/2} \int_0^2 \rho^5 \cos^2\phi \sin\phi \, d\rho \, d\phi \, d\theta \\
&= \int_0^{2\pi} \int_0^{\pi/2} \frac{32}{3} \cos^2\phi \sin\phi \, d\phi \, d\theta \\
&= \frac{32}{3} \int_0^{2\pi} \left[ -\frac{1}{3} \cos^3\phi \right]_{\phi=0}^{\pi/2} d\theta = \frac{32}{9} \int_0^{2\pi} d\theta = \frac{64}{9}\pi \blacktriangleleft
\end{aligned}
$$

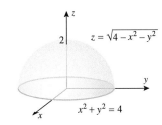

▲ **Figure 14.6.12**

$z = \sqrt{4 - x^2 - y^2}$

$x^2 + y^2 = 4$

✔**QUICK CHECK EXERCISES 14.6**    *(See page 1058 for answers.)*

---

**1.** (a) The cylindrical wedge $1 \leq r \leq 3$, $\pi/6 \leq \theta \leq \pi/2$, $0 \leq z \leq 5$ has volume $V =$ _____.
(b) The spherical wedge $1 \leq \rho \leq 3$, $\pi/6 \leq \theta \leq \pi/2$, $0 \leq \phi \leq \pi/3$ has volume $V =$ _____.

**2.** Let $G$ be the solid region inside the sphere of radius 2 centered at the origin and above the plane $z = 1$. In each part, supply the missing integrand and limits of integration for the iterated integral in cylindrical coordinates.
(a) The volume of $G$ is

$$\iiint\limits_{G} dV = \int_{\square}^{\square} \int_{\square}^{\square} \int_{\square}^{\square} \underline{\hspace{1cm}} \, dz \, dr \, d\theta$$

(b) $\iiint\limits_{G} \dfrac{z}{x^2 + y^2 + z^2} \, dV$

$$= \int_{\square}^{\square} \int_{\square}^{\square} \int_{\square}^{\square} \underline{\hspace{1cm}} \, dz \, dr \, d\theta$$

**3.** Let $G$ be the solid region described in Quick Check Exercise 2. In each part, supply the missing integrand and limits of integration for the iterated integral in spherical coordinates.
(a) The volume of $G$ is

$$\iiint\limits_{G} dV = \int_{\square}^{\square} \int_{\square}^{\square} \int_{\square}^{\square} \underline{\hspace{1cm}} \, d\rho \, d\phi \, d\theta$$

(b) $\iiint\limits_{G} \dfrac{z}{x^2 + y^2 + z^2} \, dV$

$$= \int_{\square}^{\square} \int_{\square}^{\square} \int_{\square}^{\square} \underline{\hspace{1cm}} \, d\rho \, d\phi \, d\theta$$

---

**EXERCISE SET 14.6**    ☐ CAS

---

**1–4** Evaluate the iterated integral.

**1.** $\displaystyle\int_{0}^{2\pi} \int_{0}^{1} \int_{0}^{\sqrt{1-r^2}} zr \, dz \, dr \, d\theta$

**2.** $\displaystyle\int_{0}^{\pi/2} \int_{0}^{\cos\theta} \int_{0}^{r^2} r \sin\theta \, dz \, dr \, d\theta$

**3.** $\displaystyle\int_{0}^{\pi/2} \int_{0}^{\pi/2} \int_{0}^{1} \rho^3 \sin\phi \cos\phi \, d\rho \, d\phi \, d\theta$

**4.** $\displaystyle\int_{0}^{2\pi} \int_{0}^{\pi/4} \int_{0}^{a \sec\phi} \rho^2 \sin\phi \, d\rho \, d\phi \, d\theta$    $(a > 0)$

**FOCUS ON CONCEPTS**

**5.** Sketch the region $G$ and identify the function $f$ so that

$$\iiint\limits_{G} f(r, \theta, z) \, dV$$

corresponds to the iterated integral in Exercise 1.

**6.** Sketch the region $G$ and identify the function $f$ so that

$$\iiint\limits_{G} f(r, \theta, z) \, dV$$

corresponds to the iterated integral in Exercise 2.

**7.** Sketch the region $G$ and identify the function $f$ so that

$$\iiint\limits_{G} f(\rho, \theta, \phi) \, dV$$

corresponds to the iterated integral in Exercise 3.

**8.** Sketch the region $G$ and identify the function $f$ so that

$$\iiint\limits_{G} f(\rho, \theta, \phi) \, dV$$

corresponds to the iterated integral in Exercise 4.

**9–12** Use cylindrical coordinates to find the volume of the solid.

**9.** The solid enclosed by the paraboloid $z = x^2 + y^2$ and the plane $z = 9$.

**10.** The solid that is bounded above by the sphere $x^2 + y^2 + z^2 = 1$ and below by the cone $z = \sqrt{x^2 + y^2}$.

**11.** The solid that is inside the surface $r^2 + z^2 = 20$ but not above the surface $z = r^2$.

**12.** The solid enclosed between the cone $z = (hr)/a$ and the plane $z = h$.

**13–16** Use spherical coordinates to find the volume of the solid.

**13.** The solid bounded above by the sphere $\rho = 4$ and below by the cone $\phi = \pi/3$.

**14.** The solid within the cone $\phi = \pi/4$ and between the spheres $\rho = 1$ and $\rho = 2$.

**15.** The solid enclosed by the sphere $x^2 + y^2 + z^2 = 4a^2$ and the planes $z = 0$ and $z = a$.

**16.** The solid within the sphere $x^2 + y^2 + z^2 = 9$, outside the cone $z = \sqrt{x^2 + y^2}$, and above the xy-plane.

**17–20** Use cylindrical or spherical coordinates to evaluate the integral. ■

**17.** $\displaystyle\int_0^a \int_0^{\sqrt{a^2-x^2}} \int_0^{a^2-x^2-y^2} x^2\, dz\, dy\, dx \quad (a > 0)$

**18.** $\displaystyle\int_{-1}^1 \int_0^{\sqrt{1-x^2}} \int_0^{\sqrt{1-x^2-y^2}} e^{-(x^2+y^2+z^2)^{3/2}}\, dz\, dy\, dx$

**19.** $\displaystyle\int_0^2 \int_0^{\sqrt{4-y^2}} \int_{\sqrt{x^2+y^2}}^{\sqrt{8-x^2-y^2}} z^2\, dz\, dx\, dy$

**20.** $\displaystyle\int_{-3}^3 \int_{-\sqrt{9-y^2}}^{\sqrt{9-y^2}} \int_{-\sqrt{9-x^2-y^2}}^{\sqrt{9-x^2-y^2}} \sqrt{x^2+y^2+z^2}\, dz\, dx\, dy$

**21–24 True–False** Determine whether the statement is true or false. Explain your answer. ■

**21.** A rectangular triple integral can be expressed as an iterated integral in cylindrical coordinates as

$$\iiint\limits_G f(x,y,z)\, dV = \iiint\limits_{\substack{\text{appropriate}\\ \text{limits}}} f(r\cos\theta, r\sin\theta, z)r^2\, dz\, dr\, d\theta$$

**22.** If $0 \le \rho_1 < \rho_2$, $0 \le \theta_1 < \theta_2 \le 2\pi$, and $0 \le \phi_1 < \phi_2 \le \pi$, then the volume of the spherical wedge bounded by the spheres $\rho = \rho_1$ and $\rho = \rho_2$, the half-planes $\theta = \theta_1$ and $\theta = \theta_2$, and the cones $\phi = \phi_1$ and $\phi = \phi_2$ is

$$\int_{\theta_1}^{\theta_2} \int_{\phi_1}^{\phi_2} \int_{\rho_1}^{\rho_2} \rho^2 \sin\phi\, d\rho\, d\phi\, d\theta$$

**23.** Let $G$ be the solid region in 3-space between the spheres of radius 1 and 3 centered at the origin and above the cone $z = \sqrt{x^2+y^2}$. The volume of $G$ equals

$$\int_0^{\pi/4} \int_0^{2\pi} \int_1^3 \rho^2 \sin\phi\, d\rho\, d\theta\, d\phi$$

**24.** If $G$ is the solid in Exercise 23 and $f(x,y,z)$ is continuous on $G$, then

$$\iiint\limits_G f(x,y,z)\, dV = \int_0^{\pi/4} \int_0^{2\pi} \int_1^3 F(\rho,\theta,\phi)\rho^2 \sin\phi\, d\rho\, d\theta\, d\phi$$

where $F(\rho,\theta,\phi) = f(\rho\sin\phi\sin\theta, \rho\sin\phi\cos\theta, \rho\cos\phi)$.

**C 25.** (a) Use a CAS to evaluate

$$\int_{-2}^2 \int_1^4 \int_{\pi/6}^{\pi/3} \frac{r\tan^3\theta}{\sqrt{1+z^2}}\, d\theta\, dr\, dz$$

(b) Find a function $f(x,y,z)$ and sketch a region $G$ in 3-space so that the triple integral in rectangular coordinates

$$\iiint\limits_G f(x,y,z)\, dV$$

matches the iterated integral in cylindrical coordinates given in part (a).

**C 26.** Use a CAS to evaluate

$$\int_0^{\pi/2} \int_0^{\pi/4} \int_0^{\cos\theta} \rho^{17} \cos\phi \cos^{19}\theta\, d\rho\, d\phi\, d\theta$$

**27.** Find the volume enclosed by $x^2 + y^2 + z^2 = a^2$ using
(a) cylindrical coordinates
(b) spherical coordinates.

**28.** Let $G$ be the solid in the first octant bounded by the sphere $x^2 + y^2 + z^2 = 4$ and the coordinate planes. Evaluate

$$\iiint\limits_G xyz\, dV$$

(a) using rectangular coordinates
(b) using cylindrical coordinates
(c) using spherical coordinates.

**29.** Find the volume of the solid in the first octant bounded by the sphere $\rho = 2$, the coordinate planes, and the cones $\phi = \pi/6$ and $\phi = \pi/3$.

**30.** In this exercise we will obtain a formula for the volume of the spherical wedge illustrated in Figures 14.6.7 and 14.6.9.
(a) Use a triple integral in cylindrical coordinates to show that the volume of the solid bounded above by a sphere $\rho = \rho_0$, below by a cone $\phi = \phi_0$, and on the sides by $\theta = \theta_1$ and $\theta = \theta_2$ $(\theta_1 < \theta_2)$ is

$$V = \tfrac{1}{3}\rho_0^3(1 - \cos\phi_0)(\theta_2 - \theta_1)$$

[*Hint:* In cylindrical coordinates, the sphere has the equation $r^2 + z^2 = \rho_0^2$ and the cone has the equation $z = r\cot\phi_0$. For simplicity, consider only the case $0 < \phi_0 < \pi/2$.]

(b) Subtract appropriate volumes and use the result in part (a) to deduce that the volume $\Delta V$ of the spherical wedge is

$$\Delta V = \frac{\rho_2^3 - \rho_1^3}{3}(\cos\phi_1 - \cos\phi_2)(\theta_2 - \theta_1)$$

(c) Apply the Mean-Value Theorem to the functions $\cos\phi$ and $\rho^3$ to deduce that the formula in part (b) can be written as

$$\Delta V = \rho^{*2} \sin\phi^*\, \Delta\rho\, \Delta\phi\, \Delta\theta$$

where $\rho^*$ is between $\rho_1$ and $\rho_2$, $\phi^*$ is between $\phi_1$ and $\phi_2$, and $\Delta\rho = \rho_2 - \rho_1$, $\Delta\phi = \phi_2 - \phi_1$, $\Delta\theta = \theta_2 - \theta_1$.

**31. Writing** Suppose that a triple integral is expressed in cylindrical or spherical coordinates in such a way that the outermost variable of integration is $\theta$ and none of the limits of integration involves $\theta$. Discuss what this says about the region of integration for the integral.

1. (a) $\dfrac{20}{3}\pi$ (b) $\dfrac{13}{9}\pi$    2. (a) $\displaystyle\int_0^{2\pi}\int_0^{\sqrt{3}}\int_1^{\sqrt{4-r^2}} r\,dz\,dr\,d\theta$ (b) $\displaystyle\int_0^{2\pi}\int_0^{\sqrt{3}}\int_1^{\sqrt{4-r^2}} \dfrac{rz}{r^2+z^2}\,dz\,dr\,d\theta$

3. (a) $\displaystyle\int_0^{2\pi}\int_0^{\pi/3}\int_{\sec\phi}^2 \rho^2\sin\phi\,d\rho\,d\phi\,d\theta$ (b) $\displaystyle\int_0^{2\pi}\int_0^{\pi/3}\int_{\sec\phi}^2 \rho\cos\phi\sin\phi\,d\rho\,d\phi\,d\theta$

## 14.7 CHANGE OF VARIABLES IN MULTIPLE INTEGRALS; JACOBIANS

*In this section we will discuss a general method for evaluating double and triple integrals by substitution. Most of the results in this section are very difficult to prove, so our approach will be informal and motivational. Our goal is to provide a geometric understanding of the basic principles and an exposure to computational techniques.*

### ■ CHANGE OF VARIABLE IN A SINGLE INTEGRAL

To motivate techniques for evaluating double and triple integrals by substitution, it will be helpful to consider the effect of a substitution $x = g(u)$ on a single integral over an interval $[a, b]$. If $g$ is differentiable and either increasing or decreasing, then $g$ is one-to-one and

$$\int_a^b f(x)\,dx = \int_{g^{-1}(a)}^{g^{-1}(b)} f(g(u))g'(u)\,du$$

In this relationship $f(x)$ and $dx$ are expressed in terms of $u$, and the $u$-limits of integration result from solving the equations

$$a = g(u) \quad \text{and} \quad b = g(u)$$

In the case where $g$ is decreasing we have $g^{-1}(b) < g^{-1}(a)$, which is contrary to our usual convention of writing definite integrals with the larger limit of integration at the top. We can remedy this by reversing the limits of integration and writing

$$\int_a^b f(x)\,dx = -\int_{g^{-1}(b)}^{g^{-1}(a)} f(g(u))g'(u)\,du = \int_{g^{-1}(b)}^{g^{-1}(a)} f(g(u))|g'(u)|\,du$$

where the absolute value results from the fact that $g'(u)$ is negative. Thus, regardless of whether $g$ is increasing or decreasing we can write

$$\int_a^b f(x)\,dx = \int_\alpha^\beta f(g(u))|g'(u)|\,du \tag{1}$$

where $\alpha$ and $\beta$ are the $u$-limits of integration and $\alpha < \beta$.

The expression $g'(u)$ that appears in (1) is called the ***Jacobian*** of the change of variable $x = g(u)$ in honor of C. G. J. Jacobi, who made the first serious study of change of variables in multiple integrals in the mid-1800s. Formula (1) reveals three effects of the change of variable $x = g(u)$:

- The new integrand becomes $f(g(u))$ times the absolute value of the Jacobian.
- $dx$ becomes $du$.
- The $x$-interval of integration is transformed into a $u$-interval of integration.

Our goal in this section is to show that analogous results hold for changing variables in double and triple integrals.

### ■ TRANSFORMATIONS OF THE PLANE

In earlier sections we considered parametric equations of three kinds:

$$x = x(t), \quad y = y(t) \qquad \boxed{\text{A curve in the plane}}$$

$$x = x(t), \quad y = y(t), \quad z = z(t) \qquad \boxed{\text{A curve in 3-space}}$$

$$x = x(u, v), \quad y = y(u, v), \quad z = z(u, v) \qquad \boxed{\text{A surface in 3-space}}$$

Now we will consider parametric equations of the form

$$x = x(u, v), \quad y = y(u, v) \qquad (2)$$

Parametric equations of this type associate points in the $xy$-plane with points in the $uv$-plane. These equations can be written in vector form as

$$\mathbf{r} = \mathbf{r}(u, v) = x(u, v)\mathbf{i} + y(u, v)\mathbf{j}$$

where $\mathbf{r} = x\mathbf{i} + y\mathbf{j}$ is a position vector in the $xy$-plane and $\mathbf{r}(u, v)$ is a vector-valued function of the variables $u$ and $v$.

It will also be useful in this section to think of the parametric equations in (2) in terms of inputs and outputs. If we think of the pair of numbers $(u, v)$ as an input, then the two equations, in combination, produce a unique output $(x, y)$, and hence define a function $T$ that associates points in the $xy$-plane with points in the $uv$-plane. This function is described by the formula

$$T(u, v) = (x(u, v), y(u, v))$$

We call $T$ a *transformation* from the $uv$-plane to the $xy$-plane and $(x, y)$ the *image* of $(u, v)$ under the transformation $T$. We also say that $T$ *maps* $(u, v)$ into $(x, y)$. The set $R$ of all images in the $xy$-plane of a set $S$ in the $uv$-plane is called the *image of S under T*. If distinct points in the $uv$-plane have distinct images in the $xy$-plane, then $T$ is said to be *one-to-one*. In this case the equations in (2) define $u$ and $v$ as functions of $x$ and $y$, say

$$u = u(x, y), \quad v = v(x, y)$$

These equations, which can often be obtained by solving (2) for $u$ and $v$ in terms of $x$ and $y$, define a transformation from the $xy$-plane to the $uv$-plane that maps the image of $(u, v)$ under $T$ back into $(u, v)$. This transformation is denoted by $T^{-1}$ and is called the *inverse of T* (Figure 14.7.1).

**Carl Gustav Jacob Jacobi (1804–1851)** German mathematician. Jacobi, the son of a banker, grew up in a background of wealth and culture and showed brilliance in mathematics early. He resisted studying mathematics by rote, preferring instead to learn general principles from the works of the masters, Euler and Lagrange. He entered the University of Berlin at age 16 as a student of mathematics and classical studies. However, he soon realized that he could not do both and turned fully to mathematics with a blazing intensity that he would maintain throughout his life. He received his Ph.D. in 1825 and was able to secure a position as a lecturer at the University of Berlin by giving up Judaism and becoming a Christian. However, his promotion opportunities remained limited and he moved on to the University of Königsberg. Jacobi was born to teach—he had a dynamic personality and delivered his lectures with a clarity and enthusiasm that frequently left his audience spellbound. In spite of extensive teaching commitments, he was able to publish volumes of revolutionary mathematical research that eventually made him the leading European mathematician after Gauss. His main body of research was in the area of elliptic functions, a branch of mathematics with important applications in astronomy and physics as well as in other fields of mathematics. Because of his family wealth, Jacobi was not dependent on his teaching salary in his early years. However, his comfortable world eventually collapsed. In 1840 his family went bankrupt and he was wiped out financially. In 1842 he had a nervous breakdown from overwork. In 1843 he became seriously ill with diabetes and moved to Berlin with the help of a government grant to defray his medical expenses. In 1848 he made an injudicious political speech that caused the government to withdraw the grant, eventually resulting in the loss of his home. His health continued to decline and in 1851 he finally succumbed to successive bouts of influenza and smallpox. In spite of all his problems, Jacobi was a tireless worker to the end. When a friend expressed concern about the effect of the hard work on his health, Jacobi replied, "Certainly, I have sometimes endangered my health by overwork, but what of it? Only cabbages have no nerves, no worries. And what do they get out of their perfect well-being?"

*[Image: http://commons.wikimedia.org/wiki/File:Carl_Jacobi2.jpg]*

Because there are four variables involved, a three-dimensional figure is
not very useful for describing the transformation geometrically. The idea here
is to use the two planes to get the four
dimensions needed.

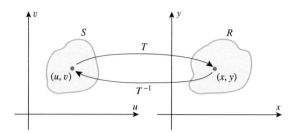

▶ **Figure 14.7.1**

One way to visualize the geometric effect of a transformation $T$ is to determine the images in the $xy$-plane of the vertical and horizontal lines in the $uv$-plane. Following the discussion in Section 14.4, sets of points in the $xy$-plane that are images of horizontal lines ($v$ constant) are called ***constant v-curves***, and sets of points that are images of vertical lines ($u$ constant) are called ***constant u-curves*** (Figure 14.7.2).

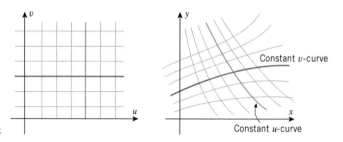

▶ **Figure 14.7.2**

---

▶ **Example 1**    Let $T$ be the transformation from the $uv$-plane to the $xy$-plane defined by the equations

$$x = \tfrac{1}{4}(u + v), \quad y = \tfrac{1}{2}(u - v) \tag{3}$$

(a) Find $T(1, 3)$.

(b) Sketch the constant $v$-curves corresponding to $v = -2, -1, 0, 1, 2$.

(c) Sketch the constant $u$-curves corresponding to $u = -2, -1, 0, 1, 2$.

(d) Sketch the image under $T$ of the square region in the $uv$-plane bounded by the lines $u = -2$, $u = 2$, $v = -2$, and $v = 2$.

*Solution (a).*    Substituting $u = 1$ and $v = 3$ in (3) yields $T(1, 3) = (1, -1)$.

*Solutions (b and c).*    In these parts it will be convenient to express the transformation equations with $u$ and $v$ as functions of $x$ and $y$. From (3)

$$4x = u + v, \quad 2y = u - v$$

Combining these equations gives

$$4x + 2y = 2u, \quad 4x - 2y = 2v$$

or

$$2x + y = u, \quad 2x - y = v$$

Thus, the constant $v$-curves corresponding to $v = -2, -1, 0, 1$, and 2 are

$$2x - y = -2, \quad 2x - y = -1, \quad 2x - y = 0, \quad 2x - y = 1, \quad 2x - y = 2$$

and the constant $u$-curves corresponding to $u = -2, -1, 0, 1$, and 2 are

$$2x + y = -2, \quad 2x + y = -1, \quad 2x + y = 0, \quad 2x + y = 1, \quad 2x + y = 2$$

In Figure 14.7.3 the constant $v$-curves are shown in purple and the constant $u$-curves in blue.

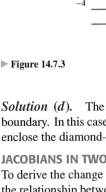

► **Figure 14.7.3**

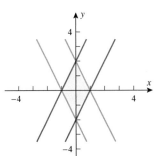

▲ **Figure 14.7.4**

*Solution (d).* The image of a region can often be found by finding the image of its boundary. In this case the images of the boundary lines $u = -2$, $u = 2$, $v = -2$, and $v = 2$ enclose the diamond-shaped region in the $xy$-plane shown in Figure 14.7.4. ◄

■ **JACOBIANS IN TWO VARIABLES**

To derive the change of variables formula for double integrals, we will need to understand the relationship between the area of a *small* rectangular region in the $uv$-plane and the area of its image in the $xy$-plane under a transformation $T$ given by the equations

$$x = x(u, v), \quad y = y(u, v)$$

For this purpose, suppose that $\Delta u$ and $\Delta v$ are positive, and consider a rectangular region $S$ in the $uv$-plane enclosed by the lines

$$u = u_0, \quad u = u_0 + \Delta u, \quad v = v_0, \quad v = v_0 + \Delta v$$

If the functions $x(u, v)$ and $y(u, v)$ are continuous, and if $\Delta u$ and $\Delta v$ are not too large, then the image of $S$ in the $xy$-plane will be a region $R$ that looks like a slightly distorted parallelogram (Figure 14.7.5). The sides of $R$ are the constant $u$-curves and $v$-curves that correspond to the sides of $S$.

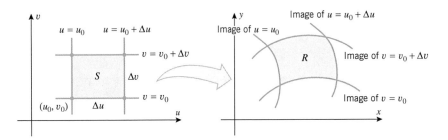

► **Figure 14.7.5**

If we let

$$\mathbf{r} = \mathbf{r}(u, v) = x(u, v)\mathbf{i} + y(u, v)\mathbf{j}$$

be the position vector of the point in the $xy$-plane that corresponds to the point $(u, v)$ in the $uv$-plane, then the constant $v$-curve corresponding to $v = v_0$ and the constant $u$-curve corresponding to $u = u_0$ can be represented in vector form as

$$\mathbf{r}(u, v_0) = x(u, v_0)\mathbf{i} + y(u, v_0)\mathbf{j} \qquad \boxed{\text{Constant } v\text{-curve}}$$

$$\mathbf{r}(u_0, v) = x(u_0, v)\mathbf{i} + y(u_0, v)\mathbf{j} \qquad \boxed{\text{Constant } u\text{-curve}}$$

Since we are assuming $\Delta u$ and $\Delta v$ to be small, the region $R$ can be approximated by a parallelogram determined by the "secant vectors"

$$\mathbf{a} = \mathbf{r}(u_0 + \Delta u, v_0) - \mathbf{r}(u_0, v_0) \tag{4}$$

$$\mathbf{b} = \mathbf{r}(u_0, v_0 + \Delta v) - \mathbf{r}(u_0, v_0) \tag{5}$$

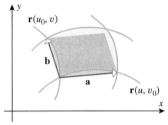

▲ Figure 14.7.6

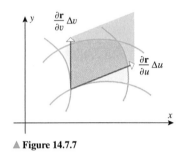

▲ Figure 14.7.7

shown in Figure 14.7.6. A more useful approximation of $R$ can be obtained by using Formulas (7) and (8) of Section 14.4 to approximate these secant vectors by tangent vectors as follows:

$$\mathbf{a} = \frac{\mathbf{r}(u_0 + \Delta u, v_0) - \mathbf{r}(u_0, v_0)}{\Delta u} \Delta u$$

$$\approx \frac{\partial \mathbf{r}}{\partial u} \Delta u = \left( \frac{\partial x}{\partial u} \mathbf{i} + \frac{\partial y}{\partial u} \mathbf{j} \right) \Delta u$$

$$\mathbf{b} = \frac{\mathbf{r}(u_0, v_0 + \Delta v) - \mathbf{r}(u_0, v_0)}{\Delta v} \Delta v$$

$$\approx \frac{\partial \mathbf{r}}{\partial v} \Delta v = \left( \frac{\partial x}{\partial v} \mathbf{i} + \frac{\partial y}{\partial v} \mathbf{j} \right) \Delta v$$

where the partial derivatives are evaluated at $(u_0, v_0)$ (Figure 14.7.7). Hence, it follows that the area of the region $R$, which we will denote by $\Delta A$, can be approximated by the area of the parallelogram determined by these vectors. Thus, from Theorem 11.4.5(*b*) we have

$$\Delta A \approx \left\| \frac{\partial \mathbf{r}}{\partial u} \Delta u \times \frac{\partial \mathbf{r}}{\partial v} \Delta v \right\| = \left\| \frac{\partial \mathbf{r}}{\partial u} \times \frac{\partial \mathbf{r}}{\partial v} \right\| \Delta u \, \Delta v \tag{6}$$

where the derivatives are evaluated at $(u_0, v_0)$. Computing the cross product, we obtain

$$\frac{\partial \mathbf{r}}{\partial u} \times \frac{\partial \mathbf{r}}{\partial v} = \begin{vmatrix} \mathbf{i} & \mathbf{j} & \mathbf{k} \\ \dfrac{\partial x}{\partial u} & \dfrac{\partial y}{\partial u} & 0 \\ \dfrac{\partial x}{\partial v} & \dfrac{\partial y}{\partial v} & 0 \end{vmatrix} = \begin{vmatrix} \dfrac{\partial x}{\partial u} & \dfrac{\partial y}{\partial u} \\ \dfrac{\partial x}{\partial v} & \dfrac{\partial y}{\partial v} \end{vmatrix} \mathbf{k} = \begin{vmatrix} \dfrac{\partial x}{\partial u} & \dfrac{\partial x}{\partial v} \\ \dfrac{\partial y}{\partial u} & \dfrac{\partial y}{\partial v} \end{vmatrix} \mathbf{k} \tag{7}$$

The determinant in (7) is sufficiently important that it has its own terminology and notation.

> **14.7.1    DEFINITION**    If $T$ is the transformation from the $uv$-plane to the $xy$-plane defined by the equations $x = x(u, v)$, $y = y(u, v)$, then the **Jacobian of $T$** is denoted by $J(u, v)$ or by $\partial(x, y)/\partial(u, v)$ and is defined by
>
> $$J(u, v) = \frac{\partial(x, y)}{\partial(u, v)} = \begin{vmatrix} \dfrac{\partial x}{\partial u} & \dfrac{\partial x}{\partial v} \\ \dfrac{\partial y}{\partial u} & \dfrac{\partial y}{\partial v} \end{vmatrix} = \frac{\partial x}{\partial u} \frac{\partial y}{\partial v} - \frac{\partial y}{\partial u} \frac{\partial x}{\partial v}$$

Using the notation in this definition, it follows from (6) and (7) that

$$\Delta A \approx \left\| \frac{\partial(x, y)}{\partial(u, v)} \mathbf{k} \right\| \Delta u \, \Delta v$$

or, since $\mathbf{k}$ is a unit vector,

$$\Delta A \approx \left| \frac{\partial(x, y)}{\partial(u, v)} \right| \Delta u \, \Delta v \tag{8}$$

At the point $(u_0, v_0)$ this important formula relates the areas of the regions $R$ and $S$ in Figure 14.7.5; it tells us that *for small values of $\Delta u$ and $\Delta v$, the area of $R$ is approximately the absolute value of the Jacobian times the area of $S$.* Moreover, it is proved in advanced calculus courses that the relative error in the approximation approaches zero as $\Delta u \to 0$ and $\Delta v \to 0$.

■ **CHANGE OF VARIABLES IN DOUBLE INTEGRALS**

Our next objective is to provide a geometric motivation for the following result.

---

**14.7.2    CHANGE OF VARIABLES FORMULA FOR DOUBLE INTEGRALS**    If the transformation $x = x(u, v)$, $y = y(u, v)$ maps the region $S$ in the $uv$-plane into the region $R$ in the $xy$-plane, and if the Jacobian $\partial(x, y)/\partial(u, v)$ is nonzero and does not change sign on $S$, then with appropriate restrictions on the transformation and the regions it follows that

$$\iint\limits_{R} f(x, y)\, dA_{xy} = \iint\limits_{S} f(x(u, v), y(u, v)) \left| \frac{\partial(x, y)}{\partial(u, v)} \right| dA_{uv} \qquad (9)$$

where we have attached subscripts to the $dA$'s to help identify the associated variables.

---

A precise statement of conditions under which Formula (9) holds is beyond the scope of this course. Suffice it to say that the formula holds if $T$ is a one-to-one transformation, $f(x, y)$ is continuous on $R$, the partial derivatives of $x(u, v)$ and $y(u, v)$ exist and are continuous on $S$, and the regions $R$ and $S$ are not complicated.

To motivate Formula (9), we proceed as follows:

- Subdivide the region $S$ in the $uv$-plane into pieces by lines parallel to the coordinate axes, and exclude from consideration any pieces that contain points outside of $S$. This leaves only rectangular regions that are subsets of $S$. Assume that there are $n$ such regions and denote the $k$th such region by $S_k$. Assume that $S_k$ has dimensions $\Delta u_k$ by $\Delta v_k$ and, as shown in Figure 14.7.8$a$, let $(u_k^*, v_k^*)$ be its "lower left corner."

- As shown in Figure 14.7.8$b$, the transformation $T$ defined by the coordinate equations $x = x(u, v)$, $y = y(u, v)$ maps $S_k$ into a curvilinear parallelogram $R_k$ in the $xy$-plane and maps the point $(u_k^*, v_k^*)$ into the point $(x_k^*, y_k^*) = (x(u_k^*, v_k^*), y(u_k^*, v_k^*))$ in $R_k$. Denote the area of $R_k$ by $\Delta A_k$.

- In rectangular coordinates the double integral of $f(x, y)$ over a region $R$ is defined as a limit of Riemann sums in which $R$ is subdivided into *rectangular* subregions. It is proved in advanced calculus courses that under appropriate conditions subdivisions into *curvilinear* parallelograms can be used instead. Accepting this to be so, we can approximate the double integral of $f(x, y)$ over $R$ as

$$\iint\limits_{R} f(x, y)\, dA_{xy} \approx \sum_{k=1}^{n} f(x_k^*, y_k^*)\, \Delta A_k$$

$$\approx \sum_{k=1}^{n} f(x(u_k^*, v_k^*), y(u_k^*, v_k^*)) \left| \frac{\partial(x, y)}{\partial(u, v)} \right| \Delta u_k\, \Delta v_k$$

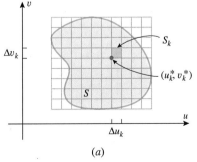
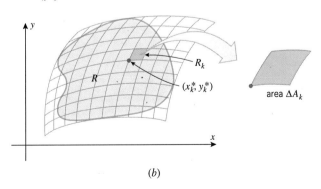

$(a)$                      $(b)$

▲ **Figure 14.7.8**

where the Jacobian is evaluated at $(u_k^*, v_k^*)$. But the last expression is a Riemann sum for the integral

$$\iint_S f(x(u, v), y(u, v)) \left| \frac{\partial(x, y)}{\partial(u, v)} \right| dA_{uv}$$

so Formula (9) follows if we assume that the errors in the approximations approach zero as $n \to +\infty$.

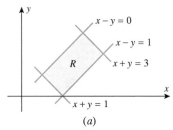

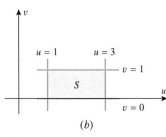

▲ **Figure 14.7.9**

▶ **Example 2**   Evaluate

$$\iint_R \frac{x - y}{x + y} dA$$

where $R$ is the region enclosed by $x - y = 0$, $x - y = 1$, $x + y = 1$, and $x + y = 3$ (Figure 14.7.9a).

*Solution.*   This integral would be tedious to evaluate directly because the region $R$ is oriented in such a way that we would have to subdivide it and integrate over each part separately. However, the occurrence of the expressions $x - y$ and $x + y$ in the equations of the boundary suggests that the transformation

$$u = x + y, \quad v = x - y \tag{10}$$

would be helpful, since with this transformation the boundary lines

$$x + y = 1, \quad x + y = 3, \quad x - y = 0, \quad x - y = 1$$

are constant $u$-curves and constant $v$-curves corresponding to the lines

$$u = 1, \quad u = 3, \quad v = 0, \quad v = 1$$

in the $uv$-plane. These lines enclose the rectangular region $S$ shown in Figure 14.7.9b. To find the Jacobian $\partial(x, y)/\partial(u, v)$ of this transformation, we first solve (10) for $x$ and $y$ in terms of $u$ and $v$. This yields

$$x = \tfrac{1}{2}(u + v), \quad y = \tfrac{1}{2}(u - v)$$

from which we obtain

$$\frac{\partial(x, y)}{\partial(u, v)} = \begin{vmatrix} \dfrac{\partial x}{\partial u} & \dfrac{\partial x}{\partial v} \\ \dfrac{\partial y}{\partial u} & \dfrac{\partial y}{\partial v} \end{vmatrix} = \begin{vmatrix} \tfrac{1}{2} & \tfrac{1}{2} \\ \tfrac{1}{2} & -\tfrac{1}{2} \end{vmatrix} = -\tfrac{1}{4} - \tfrac{1}{4} = -\tfrac{1}{2}$$

Thus, from Formula (9), but with the notation $dA$ rather than $dA_{xy}$,

$$\iint_R \frac{x - y}{x + y} dA = \iint_S \frac{v}{u} \left| \frac{\partial(x, y)}{\partial(u, v)} \right| dA_{uv}$$

$$= \iint_S \frac{v}{u} \left| -\frac{1}{2} \right| dA_{uv} = \frac{1}{2} \int_0^1 \int_1^3 \frac{v}{u} \, du \, dv$$

$$= \frac{1}{2} \int_0^1 v \ln |u| \Big]_{u=1}^3 dv$$

$$= \frac{1}{2} \ln 3 \int_0^1 v \, dv = \frac{1}{4} \ln 3 \blacktriangleleft$$

The underlying idea illustrated in Example 2 is to find a one-to-one transformation that maps a rectangle $S$ in the $uv$-plane into the region $R$ of integration, and then use that transformation as a substitution in the integral to produce an equivalent integral over $S$.

▶ **Example 3**  Evaluate

$$\iint\limits_R e^{xy}\, dA$$

where $R$ is the region enclosed by the lines $y = \frac{1}{2}x$ and $y = x$ and the hyperbolas $y = 1/x$ and $y = 2/x$ (Figure 14.7.10a).

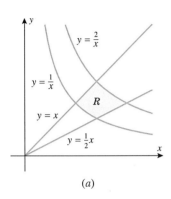

*Solution.*  As in the last example, we look for a transformation in which the boundary curves in the $xy$-plane become constant $v$-curves and constant $u$-curves. For this purpose we rewrite the four boundary curves as

$$\frac{y}{x} = \frac{1}{2}, \quad \frac{y}{x} = 1, \quad xy = 1, \quad xy = 2$$

which suggests the transformation

$$u = \frac{y}{x}, \quad v = xy \tag{11}$$

With this transformation the boundary curves in the $xy$-plane are constant $u$-curves and constant $v$-curves corresponding to the lines

$$u = \tfrac{1}{2}, \quad u = 1, \quad v = 1, \quad v = 2$$

in the $uv$-plane. These lines enclose the region $S$ shown in Figure 14.7.10b. To find the Jacobian $\partial(x, y)/\partial(u, v)$ of this transformation, we first solve (11) for $x$ and $y$ in terms of $u$ and $v$. This yields

$$x = \sqrt{v/u}, \quad y = \sqrt{uv}$$

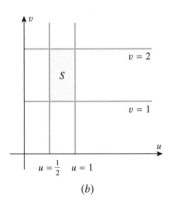

from which we obtain

$$\frac{\partial(x, y)}{\partial(u, v)} = \begin{vmatrix} \dfrac{\partial x}{\partial u} & \dfrac{\partial x}{\partial v} \\[2mm] \dfrac{\partial y}{\partial u} & \dfrac{\partial y}{\partial v} \end{vmatrix} = \begin{vmatrix} -\dfrac{1}{2u}\sqrt{\dfrac{v}{u}} & \dfrac{1}{2\sqrt{uv}} \\[3mm] \dfrac{1}{2}\sqrt{\dfrac{v}{u}} & \dfrac{1}{2}\sqrt{\dfrac{u}{v}} \end{vmatrix} = -\frac{1}{4u} - \frac{1}{4u} = -\frac{1}{2u}$$

**(a)**

**(b)**

▲ **Figure 14.7.10**

Thus, from Formula (9), but with the notation $dA$ rather than $dA_{xy}$,

$$\iint\limits_R e^{xy}\, dA = \iint\limits_S e^v \left| -\frac{1}{2u} \right| dA_{uv} = \frac{1}{2} \iint\limits_S \frac{1}{u} e^v \, dA_{uv}$$

$$= \frac{1}{2} \int_1^2 \int_{1/2}^1 \frac{1}{u} e^v \, du \, dv = \frac{1}{2} \int_1^2 e^v \ln|u| \Big]_{u=1/2}^1 \, dv$$

$$= \frac{1}{2} \ln 2 \int_1^2 e^v \, dv = \frac{1}{2}(e^2 - e) \ln 2 \quad ◀$$

■ **CHANGE OF VARIABLES IN TRIPLE INTEGRALS**
Equations of the form

$$x = x(u, v, w), \quad y = y(u, v, w), \quad z = z(u, v, w) \tag{12}$$

define a ***transformation*** $T$ from $uvw$-space to $xyz$-space. Just as a transformation $x = x(u, v)$, $y = y(u, v)$ in two variables maps small rectangles in the $uv$-plane into curvilinear parallelograms in the $xy$-plane, so (12) maps small rectangular parallelepipeds

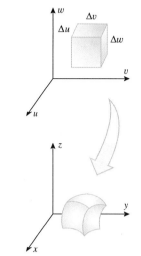

**Figure 14.7.11**

in $uvw$-space into curvilinear parallelepipeds in $xyz$-space (Figure 14.7.11). The definition of the Jacobian of (12) is similar to Definition 14.7.1.

---

**14.7.3**    DEFINITION    If $T$ is the transformation from $uvw$-space to $xyz$-space defined by the equations $x = x(u, v, w)$, $y = y(u, v, w)$, $z = z(u, v, w)$, then the ***Jacobian of*** $T$ is denoted by $J(u, v, w)$ or $\partial(x, y, z)/\partial(u, v, w)$ and is defined by

$$J(u, v, w) = \frac{\partial(x, y, z)}{\partial(u, v, w)} = \begin{vmatrix} \dfrac{\partial x}{\partial u} & \dfrac{\partial x}{\partial v} & \dfrac{\partial x}{\partial w} \\[2mm] \dfrac{\partial y}{\partial u} & \dfrac{\partial y}{\partial v} & \dfrac{\partial y}{\partial w} \\[2mm] \dfrac{\partial z}{\partial u} & \dfrac{\partial z}{\partial v} & \dfrac{\partial z}{\partial w} \end{vmatrix}$$

---

For small values of $\Delta u$, $\Delta v$, and $\Delta w$, the volume $\Delta V$ of the curvilinear parallelepiped in Figure 14.7.11 is related to the volume $\Delta u \, \Delta v \, \Delta w$ of the rectangular parallelepiped by

$$\Delta V \approx \left| \frac{\partial(x, y, z)}{\partial(u, v, w)} \right| \Delta u \, \Delta v \, \Delta w \tag{13}$$

which is the analog of Formula (8). Using this relationship and an argument similar to the one that led to Formula (9), we can obtain the following result.

---

**14.7.4**    CHANGE OF VARIABLES FORMULA FOR TRIPLE INTEGRALS    If the transformation $x = x(u, v, w)$, $y = y(u, v, w)$, $z = z(u, v, w)$ maps the region $S$ in $uvw$-space into the region $R$ in $xyz$-space, and if the Jacobian $\partial(x, y, z)/\partial(u, v, w)$ is nonzero and does not change sign on $S$, then with appropriate restrictions on the transformation and the regions it follows that

$$\iiint\limits_{R} f(x, y, z) \, dV_{xyz} = \iiint\limits_{S} f(x(u, v, w), y(u, v, w), z(u, v, w)) \left| \frac{\partial(x, y, z)}{\partial(u, v, w)} \right| dV_{uvw}$$

$$\tag{14}$$

---

▶ **Example 4**    Find the volume of the region $G$ enclosed by the ellipsoid

$$\frac{x^2}{a^2} + \frac{y^2}{b^2} + \frac{z^2}{c^2} = 1$$

*Solution.*    The volume $V$ is given by the triple integral

$$V = \iiint\limits_{G} dV$$

To evaluate this integral, we make the change of variables

$$x = au, \quad y = bv, \quad z = cw \tag{15}$$

which maps the region $S$ in $uvw$-space enclosed by a sphere of radius 1 into the region $G$ in $xyz$-space. This can be seen from (15) by noting that

$$\frac{x^2}{a^2} + \frac{y^2}{b^2} + \frac{z^2}{c^2} = 1 \quad \text{becomes} \quad u^2 + v^2 + w^2 = 1$$

The Jacobian of (15) is

$$\frac{\partial(x, y, z)}{\partial(u, v, w)} = \begin{vmatrix} \dfrac{\partial x}{\partial u} & \dfrac{\partial x}{\partial v} & \dfrac{\partial x}{\partial w} \\[2mm] \dfrac{\partial y}{\partial u} & \dfrac{\partial y}{\partial v} & \dfrac{\partial y}{\partial w} \\[2mm] \dfrac{\partial z}{\partial u} & \dfrac{\partial z}{\partial v} & \dfrac{\partial z}{\partial w} \end{vmatrix} = \begin{vmatrix} a & 0 & 0 \\ 0 & b & 0 \\ 0 & 0 & c \end{vmatrix} = abc$$

Thus, from Formula (14), but with the notation $dV$ rather than $dV_{xyz}$,

$$V = \iiint\limits_{G} dV = \iiint\limits_{S} \left| \frac{\partial(x, y, z)}{\partial(u, v, w)} \right| dV_{uvw} = abc \iiint\limits_{S} dV_{uvw}$$

The last integral is the volume enclosed by a sphere of radius 1, which we know to be $\frac{4}{3}\pi$. Thus, the volume enclosed by the ellipsoid is $V = \frac{4}{3}\pi abc$. ◄

Jacobians also arise in converting triple integrals in rectangular coordinates to iterated integrals in cylindrical and spherical coordinates. For example, we will ask you to show in Exercise 48 that the Jacobian of the transformation

$$x = r\cos\theta, \quad y = r\sin\theta, \quad z = z$$

is

$$\frac{\partial(x, y, z)}{\partial(r, \theta, z)} = r$$

and the Jacobian of the transformation

$$x = \rho\sin\phi\cos\theta, \quad y = \rho\sin\phi\sin\theta, \quad z = \rho\cos\phi$$

is

$$\frac{\partial(x, y, z)}{\partial(\rho, \phi, \theta)} = \rho^2 \sin\phi$$

Thus, Formulas (6) and (10) of Section 14.6 can be expressed in terms of Jacobians as

$$\iiint\limits_{G} f(x, y, z)\, dV = \iiint\limits_{\substack{\text{appropriate} \\ \text{limits}}} f(r\cos\theta, r\sin\theta, z) \frac{\partial(x, y, z)}{\partial(r, \theta, z)}\, dz\, dr\, d\theta \tag{16}$$

The absolute-value signs are omitted from Formulas (16) and (17) because the Jacobians are nonnegative (see the restrictions in Table 11.8.1).

$$\iiint\limits_{G} f(x, y, z)\, dV = \iiint\limits_{\substack{\text{appropriate} \\ \text{limits}}} f(\rho\sin\phi\cos\theta, \rho\sin\phi\sin\theta, \rho\cos\phi) \frac{\partial(x, y, z)}{\partial(\rho, \phi, \theta)}\, d\rho\, d\phi\, d\theta$$

$$\tag{17}$$

✔ **QUICK CHECK EXERCISES 14.7**   *(See page 1071 for answers.)*

1. Let $T$ be the transformation from the $uv$-plane to the $xy$-plane defined by the equations

$$x = u - 2v, \quad y = 3u + v$$

   (a) Sketch the image under $T$ of the rectangle $1 \le u \le 3$, $0 \le v \le 2$.
   (b) Solve for $u$ and $v$ in terms of $x$ and $y$:

$$u = \underline{\hspace{1cm}}, \quad v = \underline{\hspace{1cm}}$$

2. State the relationship between $R$ and $S$ in the change of variables formula

$$\iint\limits_{R} f(x, y)\, dA_{xy} = \iint\limits_{S} f(x(u, v), y(u, v)) \left| \frac{\partial(x, y)}{\partial(u, v)} \right| dA_{uv}$$

3. Let $T$ be the transformation in Quick Check Exercise 1.
   (a) The Jacobian $\partial(x, y)/\partial(u, v)$ of $T$ is $\underline{\hspace{1cm}}$.
   (b) Let $R$ be the region in Quick Check Exercise 1(a). Fill in the missing integrand and limits of integration for the change of variables given by $T$.

$$\iint\limits_{R} e^{x+2y}\, dA = \int_{\Box}^{\Box} \int_{\Box}^{\Box} \underline{\hspace{1cm}}\, du\, dv$$

4. The Jacobian of the transformation

$$x = uv, \quad y = vw, \quad z = 2w$$

   is

$$\frac{\partial(x, y, z)}{\partial(u, v, w)} = \underline{\hspace{1cm}}$$

**EXERCISE SET 14.7**

**1–4** Find the Jacobian $\partial(x, y)/\partial(u, v)$. ■

1. $x = u + 4v, \ y = 3u - 5v$

2. $x = u + 2v^2, \ y = 2u^2 - v$

3. $x = \sin u + \cos v, \ y = -\cos u + \sin v$

4. $x = \dfrac{2u}{u^2 + v^2}, \ y = -\dfrac{2v}{u^2 + v^2}$

**5–8** Solve for $x$ and $y$ in terms of $u$ and $v$, and then find the Jacobian $\partial(x, y)/\partial(u, v)$. ■

5. $u = 2x - 5y, \ v = x + 2y$

6. $u = e^x, \ v = ye^{-x}$

7. $u = x^2 - y^2, \ v = x^2 + y^2 \quad (x > 0, \ y > 0)$

8. $u = xy, \ v = xy^3 \quad (x > 0, \ y > 0)$

**9–12** Find the Jacobian $\partial(x, y, z)/\partial(u, v, w)$. ■

9. $x = 3u + v, \ y = u - 2w, \ z = v + w$

10. $x = u - uv, \ y = uv - uvw, \ z = uvw$

11. $u = xy, \ v = y, \ w = x + z$

12. $u = x + y + z, \ v = x + y - z, \ w = x - y + z$

**13–16 True–False** Determine whether the statement is true or false. Explain your answer. ■

13. If $\mathbf{r} = x(u, v)\mathbf{i} + y(u, v)\mathbf{j}$, then evaluating $|\partial(x, y)/\partial(u, v)|$ at a point $(u_0, v_0)$ gives the perimeter of the parallelogram generated by the vectors $\partial\mathbf{r}/\partial u$ and $\partial\mathbf{r}/\partial v$ at $(u_0, v_0)$.

14. If $\mathbf{r} = x(u, v)\mathbf{i} + y(u, v)\mathbf{j}$ maps the rectangle $0 \le u \le 2$, $1 \le v \le 5$ to a region $R$ in the $xy$-plane, then the area of $R$ is given by

$$\int_{1}^{5} \int_{0}^{2} \left| \frac{\partial(x, y)}{\partial(u, v)} \right| du\, dv$$

15. The Jacobian of the transformation $x = r\cos\theta, \ y = r\sin\theta$ is

$$\frac{\partial(x, y)}{\partial(r, \theta)} = r^2$$

16. The Jacobian of the transformation $x = \rho\sin\phi\cos\theta$, $y = \rho\sin\phi\sin\theta, \ z = \rho\cos\phi$ is

$$\frac{\partial(x, y, z)}{\partial(\rho, \phi, \theta)} = \rho^2\sin\phi$$

**FOCUS ON CONCEPTS**

**17–20** Sketch the image in the $xy$-plane of the set $S$ under the given transformation. ■

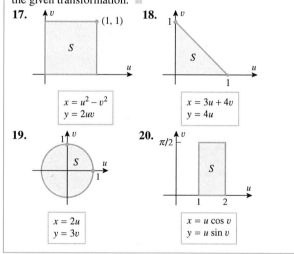

21. Use the transformation $u = x - 2y, \ v = 2x + y$ to find

$$\iint\limits_{R} \frac{x - 2y}{2x + y}\, dA \qquad \text{(cont.)}$$

where $R$ is the rectangular region enclosed by the lines $x - 2y = 1$, $x - 2y = 4$, $2x + y = 1$, $2x + y = 3$.

**22.** Use the transformation $u = x + y$, $v = x - y$ to find

$$\iint\limits_{R} (x - y)e^{x^2 - y^2}\, dA$$

over the rectangular region $R$ enclosed by the lines $x + y = 0$, $x + y = 1$, $x - y = 1$, $x - y = 4$.

**23.** Use the transformation $u = \frac{1}{2}(x + y)$, $v = \frac{1}{2}(x - y)$ to find

$$\iint\limits_{R} \sin \tfrac{1}{2}(x + y) \cos \tfrac{1}{2}(x - y)\, dA$$

over the triangular region $R$ with vertices $(0, 0)$, $(2, 0)$, $(1, 1)$.

**24.** Use the transformation $u = y/x$, $v = xy$ to find

$$\iint\limits_{R} xy^3\, dA$$

over the region $R$ in the first quadrant enclosed by $y = x$, $y = 3x$, $xy = 1$, $xy = 4$.

**25–27** The transformation $x = au$, $y = bv$ ($a > 0$, $b > 0$) can be rewritten as $x/a = u$, $y/b = v$, and hence it maps the circular region

$$u^2 + v^2 \leq 1$$

into the elliptical region

$$\frac{x^2}{a^2} + \frac{y^2}{b^2} \leq 1$$

In these exercises, perform the integration by transforming the elliptical region of integration into a circular region of integration and then evaluating the transformed integral in polar coordinates. ◼

**25.** $\displaystyle\iint\limits_{R} \sqrt{16x^2 + 9y^2}\, dA$, where $R$ is the region enclosed by the ellipse $(x^2/9) + (y^2/16) = 1$.

**26.** $\displaystyle\iint\limits_{R} e^{-(x^2 + 4y^2)}\, dA$, where $R$ is the region enclosed by the ellipse $(x^2/4) + y^2 = 1$.

**27.** $\displaystyle\iint\limits_{R} \sin(4x^2 + 9y^2)\, dA$, where $R$ is the region in the first quadrant enclosed by the ellipse $4x^2 + 9y^2 = 1$ and the coordinate axes.

**28.** Show that the area of the ellipse

$$\frac{x^2}{a^2} + \frac{y^2}{b^2} = 1$$

is $\pi ab$.

**29–30** If $a$, $b$, and $c$ are positive constants, then the transformation $x = au$, $y = bv$, $z = cw$ can be rewritten as $x/a = u$, $y/b = v$, $z/c = w$, and hence it maps the spherical region

$$u^2 + v^2 + w^2 \leq 1$$

into the ellipsoidal region

$$\frac{x^2}{a^2} + \frac{y^2}{b^2} + \frac{z^2}{c^2} \leq 1$$

In these exercises, perform the integration by transforming the ellipsoidal region of integration into a spherical region of integration and then evaluating the transformed integral in spherical coordinates. ◼

**29.** $\displaystyle\iiint\limits_{G} x^2\, dV$, where $G$ is the region enclosed by the ellipsoid $9x^2 + 4y^2 + z^2 = 36$.

**30.** $\displaystyle\iiint\limits_{G} (y^2 + z^2)\, dV$, where $G$ is the region enclosed by the ellipsoid $\dfrac{x^2}{a^2} + \dfrac{y^2}{b^2} + \dfrac{z^2}{c^2} = 1$

**FOCUS ON CONCEPTS**

**31–34** Find a transformation

$$u = f(x, y), \quad v = g(x, y)$$

that when applied to the region $R$ in the $xy$-plane has as its image the region $S$ in the $uv$-plane. ◼

**31.**

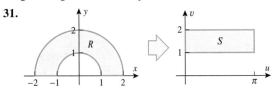

**32.**

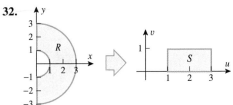

**33.**

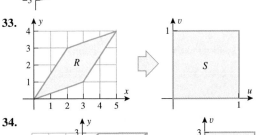

**34.**

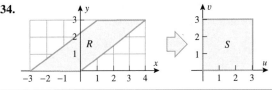

**35–38** Evaluate the integral by making an appropriate change of variables. ■

**35.** $\displaystyle\iint\limits_{R} \frac{y - 4x}{y + 4x}\, dA$, where $R$ is the region enclosed by the lines
$y = 4x$, $y = 4x + 2$, $y = 2 - 4x$, $y = 5 - 4x$.

**36.** $\displaystyle\iint\limits_{R} (x^2 - y^2)\, dA$, where $R$ is the rectangular region enclosed by the lines $y = -x$, $y = 1 - x$, $y = x$, $y = x + 2$.

**37.** $\displaystyle\iint\limits_{R} \frac{\sin(x - y)}{\cos(x + y)}\, dA$, where $R$ is the triangular region enclosed by the lines $y = 0$, $y = x$, $x + y = \pi/4$.

**38.** $\displaystyle\iint\limits_{R} e^{(y-x)/(y+x)}\, dA$, where $R$ is the region in the first quadrant enclosed by the trapezoid with vertices $(0, 1)$, $(1, 0)$, $(0, 4)$, $(4, 0)$.

**39.** Use an appropriate change of variables to find the area of the region in the first quadrant enclosed by the curves $y = x$, $y = 2x$, $x = y^2$, $x = 4y^2$.

**40.** Use an appropriate change of variables to find the volume of the solid bounded above by the plane $x + y + z = 9$, below by the $xy$-plane, and laterally by the elliptic cylinder $4x^2 + 9y^2 = 36$. [*Hint:* Express the volume as a double integral in $xy$-coordinates, then use polar coordinates to evaluate the transformed integral.]

**41.** Use the transformation $u = x$, $v = z - y$, $w = xy$ to find
$$\iiint\limits_{G} (z - y)^2 xy \, dV$$
where $G$ is the region enclosed by the surfaces $x = 1$, $x = 3$, $z = y$, $z = y + 1$, $xy = 2$, $xy = 4$.

**42.** Use the transformation $u = xy$, $v = yz$, $w = xz$ to find the volume of the region in the first octant that is enclosed by the hyperbolic cylinders $xy = 1$, $xy = 2$, $yz = 1$, $yz = 3$, $xz = 1$, $xz = 4$.

**43.** (a) Verify that
$$\begin{vmatrix} a_1 & b_1 \\ c_1 & d_1 \end{vmatrix} \begin{vmatrix} a_2 & b_2 \\ c_2 & d_2 \end{vmatrix} = \begin{vmatrix} a_1 a_2 + b_1 c_2 & a_1 b_2 + b_1 d_2 \\ c_1 a_2 + d_1 c_2 & c_1 b_2 + d_1 d_2 \end{vmatrix}$$

(b) If $x = x(u, v)$, $y = y(u, v)$ is a one-to-one transformation, then $u = u(x, y)$, $v = v(x, y)$. Assuming the necessary differentiability, use the result in part (a) and the chain rule to show that
$$\frac{\partial(x, y)}{\partial(u, v)} \cdot \frac{\partial(u, v)}{\partial(x, y)} = 1$$

**44–46** The formula obtained in part (b) of Exercise 43 is useful in integration problems where it is inconvenient or impossible to solve the transformation equations $u = f(x, y)$, $v = g(x, y)$ explicitly for $x$ and $y$ in terms of $u$ and $v$. In these exercises, use the relationship
$$\frac{\partial(x, y)}{\partial(u, v)} = \frac{1}{\partial(u, v)/\partial(x, y)}$$
to avoid solving for $x$ and $y$ in terms of $u$ and $v$. ■

**44.** Use the transformation $u = xy$, $v = xy^4$ to find
$$\iint\limits_{R} \sin(xy) \, dA$$
where $R$ is the region enclosed by the curves $xy = \pi$, $xy = 2\pi$, $xy^4 = 1$, $xy^4 = 2$.

**45.** Use the transformation $u = x^2 - y^2$, $v = x^2 + y^2$ to find
$$\iint\limits_{R} xy \, dA$$
where $R$ is the region in the first quadrant that is enclosed by the hyperbolas $x^2 - y^2 = 1$, $x^2 - y^2 = 4$ and the circles $x^2 + y^2 = 9$, $x^2 + y^2 = 16$.

**46.** Use the transformation $u = xy$, $v = x^2 - y^2$ to find
$$\iint\limits_{R} (x^4 - y^4) e^{xy} \, dA$$
where $R$ is the region in the first quadrant enclosed by the hyperbolas $xy = 1$, $xy = 3$, $x^2 - y^2 = 3$, $x^2 - y^2 = 4$.

**47.** The three-variable analog of the formula derived in part (b) of Exercise 43 is
$$\frac{\partial(x, y, z)}{\partial(u, v, w)} \cdot \frac{\partial(u, v, w)}{\partial(x, y, z)} = 1$$
Use this result to show that the volume $V$ of the oblique parallelepiped that is bounded by the planes $x + y + 2z = \pm 3$, $x - 2y + z = \pm 2$, $4x + y + z = \pm 6$ is $V = 16$.

**48.** (a) Consider the transformation
$$x = r \cos\theta, \quad y = r \sin\theta, \quad z = z$$
from cylindrical to rectangular coordinates, where $r \geq 0$. Show that
$$\frac{\partial(x, y, z)}{\partial(r, \theta, z)} = r$$

(b) Consider the transformation
$$x = \rho \sin\phi \cos\theta, \quad y = \rho \sin\phi \sin\theta, \quad z = \rho \cos\phi$$
from spherical to rectangular coordinates, where $0 \leq \phi \leq \pi$. Show that
$$\frac{\partial(x, y, z)}{\partial(\rho, \phi, \theta)} = \rho^2 \sin\phi$$

**49.** Writing For single-variable definite integrals, the technique of substitution was generally used to simplify the integrand. Discuss some motivations for using a change of variables in a multiple integral.

**50.** Writing Suppose that the boundary curves of a region $R$ in the $xy$-plane can be described as level curves of various functions. Discuss how this information can be used to choose an appropriate change of variables for a double integral over $R$. Illustrate your discussion with an example.

1. (a) The image is the region in the $xy$-plane enclosed by the parallelogram with vertices $(1, 3)$, $(-3, 5)$, $(-1, 11)$, and $(3, 9)$.
(b) $u = \frac{1}{7}(x + 2y)$, $v = \frac{1}{7}(y - 3x)$    2. $S$ is a region in the $uv$-plane and $R$ is the image of $S$ in the $xy$-plane under the transformation $x = x(u, v)$, $y = y(u, v)$.    3. (a) 7 (b) $\int_0^2 \int_1^3 7e^{7u}\, du\, dv$    4. $2vw$

## 14.8    CENTERS OF GRAVITY USING MULTIPLE INTEGRALS

*In Section 6.7 we showed how to find the mass and center of gravity of a homogeneous lamina using single integrals. In this section we will show how double and triple integrals can be used to find the mass and center of gravity of inhomogeneous laminas and three-dimensional solids.*

### DENSITY AND MASS OF AN INHOMOGENEOUS LAMINA

An idealized flat object that is thin enough to be viewed as a two-dimensional plane region is called a *lamina* (Figure 14.8.1). A lamina is called *homogeneous* if its composition is uniform throughout and *inhomogeneous* otherwise. The *density* of a *homogeneous* lamina was defined in Section 6.7 to be its mass per unit area. Thus, the density $\delta$ of a homogeneous lamina of mass $M$ and area $A$ is given by $\delta = M/A$.

For an inhomogeneous lamina the composition may vary from point to point, and hence an appropriate definition of "density" must reflect this. To motivate such a definition, suppose that the lamina is placed in an $xy$-plane. The density at a point $(x, y)$ can be specified by a function $\delta(x, y)$, called the *density function*, which can be interpreted as follows: Construct a small rectangle centered at $(x, y)$ and let $\Delta M$ and $\Delta A$ be the mass and area of the portion of the lamina enclosed by this rectangle (Figure 14.8.2). If the ratio $\Delta M/\Delta A$ approaches a limiting value as the dimensions (and hence the area) of the rectangle approach zero, then this limit is considered to be the density of the lamina at $(x, y)$. Symbolically,

$$\delta(x, y) = \lim_{\Delta A \to 0} \frac{\Delta M}{\Delta A} \tag{1}$$

From this relationship we obtain the approximation

$$\Delta M \approx \delta(x, y)\Delta A \tag{2}$$

which relates the mass and area of a small rectangular portion of the lamina centered at $(x, y)$. It is assumed that as the dimensions of the rectangle tend to zero, the error in this approximation also tends to zero.

The following result shows how to find the mass of a lamina from its density function.

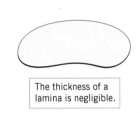

The thickness of a lamina is negligible.

▲ **Figure 14.8.1**

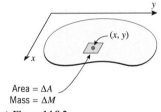

Area $= \Delta A$
Mass $= \Delta M$

▲ **Figure 14.8.2**

**14.8.1    MASS OF A LAMINA**    If a lamina with a continuous density function $\delta(x, y)$ occupies a region $R$ in the $xy$-plane, then its total mass $M$ is given by

$$M = \iint\limits_R \delta(x, y)\, dA \tag{3}$$

This formula can be motivated by a familiar limiting process that can be outlined as follows: Imagine the lamina to be subdivided into rectangular pieces using lines parallel to the

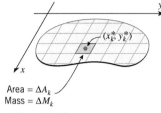

Area = $\Delta A_k$
Mass = $\Delta M_k$

▲ **Figure 14.8.3**

coordinate axes and excluding from consideration any nonrectangular parts at the boundary (Figure 14.8.3). Assume that there are $n$ such rectangular pieces, and suppose that the $k$th piece has area $\Delta A_k$. If we let $(x_k^*, y_k^*)$ denote the center of the $k$th piece, then from Formula (2), the mass $\Delta M_k$ of this piece can be approximated by

$$\Delta M_k \approx \delta(x_k^*, y_k^*)\Delta A_k \tag{4}$$

and hence the mass $M$ of the entire lamina can be approximated by

$$M \approx \sum_{k=1}^{n} \delta(x_k^*, y_k^*)\Delta A_k$$

If we now increase $n$ in such a way that the dimensions of the rectangles tend to zero, then it is plausible that the errors in our approximations will approach zero, so

$$M = \lim_{n \to +\infty} \sum_{k=1}^{n} \delta(x_k^*, y_k^*)\Delta A_k = \iint_R \delta(x, y)\, dA$$

▶ **Example 1**   A triangular lamina with vertices $(0, 0)$, $(0, 1)$, and $(1, 0)$ has density function $\delta(x, y) = xy$. Find its total mass.

*Solution.*   Referring to (3) and Figure 14.8.4, the mass $M$ of the lamina is

$$M = \iint_R \delta(x, y)\, dA = \iint_R xy\, dA = \int_0^1 \int_0^{-x+1} xy\, dy\, dx$$

$$= \int_0^1 \left[\frac{1}{2}xy^2\right]_{y=0}^{-x+1} dx = \int_0^1 \left[\frac{1}{2}x^3 - x^2 + \frac{1}{2}x\right] dx = \frac{1}{24} \text{ (unit of mass)} \blacktriangleleft$$

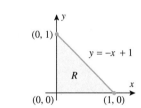

$y = -x + 1$

$R$

$(0, 0)$    $(1, 0)$

▲ **Figure 14.8.4**

### CENTER OF GRAVITY OF AN INHOMOGENEOUS LAMINA

Recall that the **center of gravity** of a lamina occupying a region $R$ in the horizontal $xy$-plane is the point $(\bar{x}, \bar{y})$ such that the effect of gravity on the lamina is "equivalent" to that of a single force acting at $(\bar{x}, \bar{y})$. If $(\bar{x}, \bar{y})$ is in $R$, then the lamina will balance horizontally on a point of support placed at $(\bar{x}, \bar{y})$. In Section 6.7 we showed how to locate the center of gravity of a homogeneous lamina. We now turn to this problem for an inhomogeneous lamina.

> **14.8.2    PROBLEM**   Suppose that a lamina with a continuous density function $\delta(x, y)$ occupies a region $R$ in a horizontal $xy$-plane. Find the coordinates $(\bar{x}, \bar{y})$ of the center of gravity.

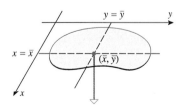

$y = \bar{y}$

$x = \bar{x}$

$(\bar{x}, \bar{y})$

▲ **Figure 14.8.5**

To motivate the solution of Problem 14.8.2, consider what happens if we try to place the lamina in Figure 14.8.5 on a knife-edge running along the line $y = \bar{y}$. Since the lamina behaves as if its entire mass is concentrated at $(\bar{x}, \bar{y})$, the lamina will be in perfect balance. Similarly, the lamina will be in perfect balance if the knife-edge runs along the line $x = \bar{x}$. To find these lines of balance we begin by reviewing some results from Section 6.7 about rotations.

Recall that if a point-mass $m$ is located at the point $(x, y)$, then the moment of $m$ about $x = a$ measures the tendency of the mass to produce a rotation about the line $x = a$, and the moment of $m$ about $y = c$ measures the tendency of the mass to produce a rotation about the line $y = c$. The moments are given by the following formulas:

$$\begin{bmatrix} \text{moment of } m \\ \text{about the} \\ \text{line } x = a \end{bmatrix} = m(x - a) \quad \text{and} \quad \begin{bmatrix} \text{moment of } m \\ \text{about the} \\ \text{line } y = c \end{bmatrix} = m(y - c) \qquad (5\text{--}6)$$

If a number of point-masses are distributed throughout the $xy$-plane, the sum of their moments about $x = a$ is a measure of the tendency of the masses to produce a rotation of the plane (viewed as a weightless sheet) about the line $x = a$. If the sum of these moments is zero, the collective masses will produce no net rotational effect about the line. (Intuitively, this means that the plane would balance on a knife-edge along the line $x = a$. Similarly, if the sum of the moments of the masses about $y = c$ is zero, the plane would balance on a knife-edge along the line $y = c$.)

We are now ready to solve Problem 14.8.2. We imagine the lamina to be subdivided into rectangular pieces using lines parallel to the coordinate axes and excluding from consideration any nonrectangular pieces at the boundary (Figure 14.8.3). We assume that there are $n$ such rectangular pieces and that the $k$th piece has area $\Delta A_k$ and mass $\Delta M_k$. We will let $(x_k^*, y_k^*)$ be the center of the $k$th piece, and we will assume that the entire mass of the $k$th piece is concentrated at its center. From (4), the mass of the $k$th piece can be approximated by

$$\Delta M_k \approx \delta(x_k^*, y_k^*)\Delta A_k$$

Since the lamina balances on the lines $x = \bar{x}$ and $y = \bar{y}$, the sum of the moments of the rectangular pieces about those lines should be close to zero; that is,

$$\sum_{k=1}^{n}(x_k^* - \bar{x})\Delta M_k = \sum_{k=1}^{n}(x_k^* - \bar{x})\delta(x_k^*, y_k^*)\Delta A_k \approx 0$$

$$\sum_{k=1}^{n}(y_k^* - \bar{y})\Delta M_k = \sum_{k=1}^{n}(y_k^* - \bar{y})\delta(x_k^*, y_k^*)\Delta A_k \approx 0$$

If we now increase $n$ in such a way that the dimensions of the rectangles tend to zero, then it is plausible that the errors in our approximations will approach zero, so that

$$\lim_{n \to +\infty} \sum_{k=1}^{n}(x_k^* - \bar{x})\delta(x_k^*, y_k^*)\Delta A_k = 0$$

$$\lim_{n \to +\infty} \sum_{k=1}^{n}(y_k^* - \bar{y})\delta(x_k^*, y_k^*)\Delta A_k = 0$$

from which we obtain

$$\iint\limits_{R}(x - \bar{x})\delta(x, y)\,dA = \iint\limits_{R}x\delta(x, y)\,dA - \bar{x}\iint\limits_{R}\delta(x, y)\,dA = 0 \qquad (7)$$

$$\iint\limits_{R}(y - \bar{y})\delta(x, y)\,dA = \iint\limits_{R}y\delta(x, y)\,dA - \bar{y}\iint\limits_{R}\delta(x, y)\,dA = 0 \qquad (8)$$

Solving (7) and (8) respectively for $\bar{x}$ and $\bar{y}$ gives formulas for the center of gravity of a lamina:

### *Center of Gravity $(\bar{x}, \bar{y})$ of a Lamina*

$$\bar{x} = \frac{\displaystyle\iint\limits_{R}x\delta(x, y)\,dA}{\displaystyle\iint\limits_{R}\delta(x, y)\,dA}, \qquad \bar{y} = \frac{\displaystyle\iint\limits_{R}y\delta(x, y)\,dA}{\displaystyle\iint\limits_{R}\delta(x, y)\,dA} \qquad (9\text{--}10)$$

In both formulas the denominator is the mass $M$ of the lamina [see (3)]. The numerator in the formula for $\bar{x}$ is denoted by $M_y$ and is called the *first moment of the lamina about the y-axis*; the numerator of the formula for $\bar{y}$ is denoted by $M_x$ and is called the *first moment of the lamina about the x-axis*. Thus, Formulas (9) and (10) can be expressed as

*Alternative Formulas for Center of Gravity($\bar{x}$, $\bar{y}$) of a Lamina*

$$\bar{x} = \frac{M_y}{M} = \frac{1}{\text{mass of } R} \iint\limits_R x\delta(x, y)\, dA \tag{11}$$

$$\bar{y} = \frac{M_x}{M} = \frac{1}{\text{mass of } R} \iint\limits_R y\delta(x, y)\, dA \tag{12}$$

▶ **Example 2**   Find the center of gravity of the triangular lamina with vertices $(0, 0)$, $(0, 1)$, and $(1, 0)$ and density function $\delta(x, y) = xy$.

*Solution.*   The lamina is shown in Figure 14.8.4. In Example 1 we found the mass of the lamina to be

$$M = \iint\limits_R \delta(x, y)\, dA = \iint\limits_R xy\, dA = \frac{1}{24}$$

The moment of the lamina about the $y$-axis is

$$M_y = \iint\limits_R x\delta(x, y)\, dA = \iint\limits_R x^2 y\, dA = \int_0^1 \int_0^{-x+1} x^2 y\, dy\, dx$$

$$= \int_0^1 \left[ \frac{1}{2}x^2 y^2 \right]_{y=0}^{-x+1} dx = \int_0^1 \left( \frac{1}{2}x^4 - x^3 + \frac{1}{2}x^2 \right) dx = \frac{1}{60}$$

and the moment about the $x$-axis is

$$M_x = \iint\limits_R y\delta(x, y)\, dA = \iint\limits_R xy^2\, dA = \int_0^1 \int_0^{-x+1} xy^2\, dy\, dx$$

$$= \int_0^1 \left[ \frac{1}{3}xy^3 \right]_{y=0}^{-x+1} dx = \int_0^1 \left( -\frac{1}{3}x^4 + x^3 - x^2 + \frac{1}{3}x \right) dx = \frac{1}{60}$$

From (11) and (12),

$$\bar{x} = \frac{M_y}{M} = \frac{1/60}{1/24} = \frac{2}{5}, \quad \bar{y} = \frac{M_x}{M} = \frac{1/60}{1/24} = \frac{2}{5}$$

so the center of gravity is $\left( \frac{2}{5}, \frac{2}{5} \right)$. ◀

Recall that the center of gravity of a *homogeneous* lamina is called the ***centroid of the lamina*** or sometimes the ***centroid of the region R***. Because the density function $\delta$ is constant for a homogeneous lamina, the factor $\delta$ may be moved through the integral signs in (9) and (10) and canceled. Thus, the centroid $(\bar{x}, \bar{y})$ is a geometric property of the region $R$ and is given by the following formulas:

### Centroid of a Region R

$$\bar{x} = \frac{\displaystyle\iint_R x\,dA}{\displaystyle\iint_R dA} = \frac{1}{\text{area of }R}\iint_R x\,dA \tag{13}$$

$$\bar{y} = \frac{\displaystyle\iint_R y\,dA}{\displaystyle\iint_R dA} = \frac{1}{\text{area of }R}\iint_R y\,dA \tag{14}$$

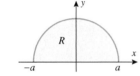

▲ **Figure 14.8.6**

▶ **Example 3** Find the centroid of the semicircular region in Figure 14.8.6.

**Solution.** By symmetry, $\bar{x} = 0$ since the $y$-axis is obviously a line of balance. From (14),

$$\bar{y} = \frac{1}{\text{area of }R}\iint_R y\,dA = \frac{1}{\frac{1}{2}\pi a^2}\iint_R y\,dA$$

$$= \frac{1}{\frac{1}{2}\pi a^2}\int_0^\pi \int_0^a (r\sin\theta)r\,dr\,d\theta \qquad \boxed{\begin{array}{l}\text{Evaluating in}\\ \text{polar coordinates}\end{array}}$$

$$= \frac{1}{\frac{1}{2}\pi a^2}\int_0^\pi \left[\frac{1}{3}r^3\sin\theta\right]_{r=0}^a d\theta$$

$$= \frac{1}{\frac{1}{2}\pi a^2}\left(\frac{1}{3}a^3\right)\int_0^\pi \sin\theta\,d\theta = \frac{1}{\frac{1}{2}\pi a^2}\left(\frac{2}{3}a^3\right) = \frac{4a}{3\pi}$$

Compare the calculation in Example 3 to that of Example 3 in Section 6.7.

so the centroid is $\left(0, \dfrac{4a}{3\pi}\right)$. ◀

### ■ CENTER OF GRAVITY AND CENTROID OF A SOLID

For a three-dimensional solid $G$, the formulas for moments, center of gravity, and centroid are similar to those for laminas. If $G$ is *homogeneous*, then its **density** is defined to be its mass per unit volume. Thus, if $G$ is a homogeneous solid of mass $M$ and volume $V$, then its density $\delta$ is given by $\delta = M/V$. If $G$ is inhomogeneous and is in an *xyz*-coordinate system, then its density at a general point $(x, y, z)$ is specified by a **density function** $\delta(x, y, z)$ whose value at a point can be viewed as a limit:

$$\delta(x, y, z) = \lim_{\Delta V \to 0}\frac{\Delta M}{\Delta V}$$

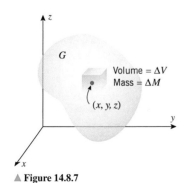

▲ **Figure 14.8.7**

where $\Delta M$ and $\Delta V$ represent the mass and volume of a rectangular parallelepiped, centered at $(x, y, z)$, whose dimensions tend to zero (Figure 14.8.7).

Using the discussion of laminas as a model, you should be able to show that the mass $M$ of a solid with a continuous density function $\delta(x, y, z)$ is

$$M = \text{mass of }G = \iiint_G \delta(x, y, z)\,dV \tag{15}$$

The formulas for center of gravity and centroid are as follows:

**Center of Gravity $(\bar{x}, \bar{y}, \bar{z})$ of a Solid $G$**      **Centroid $(\bar{x}, \bar{y}, \bar{z})$ of a Solid $G$**

$$\bar{x} = \frac{1}{M} \iiint\limits_G x\delta(x, y, z)\, dV \qquad\qquad \bar{x} = \frac{1}{V} \iiint\limits_G x\, dV$$

$$\bar{y} = \frac{1}{M} \iiint\limits_G y\delta(x, y, z)\, dV \qquad\qquad \bar{y} = \frac{1}{V} \iiint\limits_G y\, dV \qquad (16\text{–}17)$$

$$\bar{z} = \frac{1}{M} \iiint\limits_G z\delta(x, y, z)\, dV \qquad\qquad \bar{z} = \frac{1}{V} \iiint\limits_G z\, dV$$

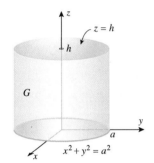

▲ **Figure 14.8.8**

▶ **Example 4** Find the mass and the center of gravity of a cylindrical solid of height $h$ and radius $a$ (Figure 14.8.8), assuming that the density at each point is proportional to the distance between the point and the base of the solid.

*Solution.* Since the density is proportional to the distance $z$ from the base, the density function has the form $\delta(x, y, z) = kz$, where $k$ is some (unknown) positive constant of proportionality. From (15) the mass of the solid is

$$M = \iiint\limits_G \delta(x, y, z)\, dV = \int_{-a}^{a} \int_{-\sqrt{a^2-x^2}}^{\sqrt{a^2-x^2}} \int_{0}^{h} kz\, dz\, dy\, dx$$

$$= k \int_{-a}^{a} \int_{-\sqrt{a^2-x^2}}^{\sqrt{a^2-x^2}} \frac{1}{2} h^2\, dy\, dx$$

$$= kh^2 \int_{-a}^{a} \sqrt{a^2 - x^2}\, dx$$

$$= \tfrac{1}{2} kh^2 \pi a^2 \qquad \boxed{\begin{array}{l}\text{Interpret the integral as}\\ \text{the area of a semicircle.}\end{array}}$$

Without additional information, the constant $k$ cannot be determined. However, as we will now see, the value of $k$ does not affect the center of gravity.

From (16),

$$\bar{z} = \frac{1}{M} \iiint\limits_G z\delta(x, y, z)\, dV = \frac{1}{\frac{1}{2} kh^2 \pi a^2} \iiint\limits_G z\delta(x, y, z)\, dV$$

$$= \frac{1}{\frac{1}{2} kh^2 \pi a^2} \int_{-a}^{a} \int_{-\sqrt{a^2-x^2}}^{\sqrt{a^2-x^2}} \int_{0}^{h} z(kz)\, dz\, dy\, dx$$

$$= \frac{k}{\frac{1}{2} kh^2 \pi a^2} \int_{-a}^{a} \int_{-\sqrt{a^2-x^2}}^{\sqrt{a^2-x^2}} \frac{1}{3} h^3\, dy\, dx$$

$$= \frac{\frac{1}{3} kh^3}{\frac{1}{2} kh^2 \pi a^2} \int_{-a}^{a} 2\sqrt{a^2 - x^2}\, dx$$

$$= \frac{\frac{1}{3} kh^3 \pi a^2}{\frac{1}{2} kh^2 \pi a^2} = \frac{2}{3} h$$

Similar calculations using (16) will yield $\bar{x} = \bar{y} = 0$. However, this is evident by inspection, since it follows from the symmetry of the solid and the form of its density function that the center of gravity is on the $z$-axis. Thus, the center of gravity is $\left(0, 0, \frac{2}{3} h\right)$. ◀

▶ **Example 5**   Find the centroid of the solid $G$ bounded below by the cone $z = \sqrt{x^2 + y^2}$ and above by the sphere $x^2 + y^2 + z^2 = 16$.

**Solution.**   The solid $G$ is sketched in Figure 14.8.9. In Example 3 of Section 14.6, spherical coordinates were used to find that the volume of $G$ is

$$V = \frac{64\pi}{3}(2 - \sqrt{2})$$

By symmetry, the centroid $(\bar{x}, \bar{y}, \bar{z})$ is on the $z$-axis, so $\bar{x} = \bar{y} = 0$. In spherical coordinates, the equation of the sphere $x^2 + y^2 + z^2 = 16$ is $\rho = 4$ and the equation of the cone $z = \sqrt{x^2 + y^2}$ is $\phi = \pi/4$, so from (17) we have

$$\bar{z} = \frac{1}{V}\iiint\limits_{G} z\, dV = \frac{1}{V}\int_0^{2\pi}\int_0^{\pi/4}\int_0^4 (\rho\cos\phi)\rho^2 \sin\phi\, d\rho\, d\phi\, d\theta$$

$$= \frac{1}{V}\int_0^{2\pi}\int_0^{\pi/4}\left[\frac{\rho^4}{4}\cos\phi\sin\phi\right]_{\rho=0}^4 d\phi\, d\theta$$

$$= \frac{64}{V}\int_0^{2\pi}\int_0^{\pi/4}\sin\phi\cos\phi\, d\phi\, d\theta = \frac{64}{V}\int_0^{2\pi}\left[\frac{1}{2}\sin^2\phi\right]_{\phi=0}^{\pi/4} d\theta$$

$$= \frac{16}{V}\int_0^{2\pi} d\theta = \frac{32\pi}{V} = \frac{3}{2(2 - \sqrt{2})}$$

The centroid of $G$ is

$$(\bar{x}, \bar{y}, \bar{z}) = \left(0, 0, \frac{3}{2(2 - \sqrt{2})}\right) \approx (0, 0, 2.561)\ ◀$$

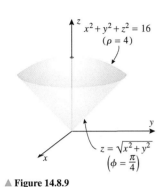

▲ **Figure 14.8.9**

✔ **QUICK CHECK EXERCISES 14.8**   *(See page 1080 for answers.)*

1. The total mass of a lamina with continuous density function $\delta(x, y)$ that occupies a region $R$ in the $xy$-plane is given by $M = $ _____.

2. Consider a lamina with mass $M$ and continuous density function $\delta(x, y)$ that occupies a region $R$ in the $xy$-plane. The $x$-coordinate of the center of gravity of the lamina is $M_y/M$, where $M_y$ is called the _____ and is given by the double integral _____.

3. Let $R$ be the region between the graphs of $y = x^2$ and $y = 2 - x$ for $0 \le x \le 1$. The area of $R$ is $\frac{7}{6}$ and the centroid of $R$ is _____.

**EXERCISE SET 14.8**   ⬚ Graphing Utility   [c] CAS

**1–4** Find the mass and center of gravity of the lamina. ▪

1. A lamina with density $\delta(x, y) = x + y$ is bounded by the $x$-axis, the line $x = 1$, and the curve $y = \sqrt{x}$.

2. A lamina with density $\delta(x, y) = y$ is bounded by $y = \sin x$, $y = 0$, $x = 0$, and $x = \pi$.

3. A lamina with density $\delta(x, y) = xy$ is in the first quadrant and is bounded by the circle $x^2 + y^2 = a^2$ and the coordinate axes.

4. A lamina with density $\delta(x, y) = x^2 + y^2$ is bounded by the $x$-axis and the upper half of the circle $x^2 + y^2 = 1$.

**FOCUS ON CONCEPTS**

**5–6** For the given density function, make a conjecture about the coordinates of the center of gravity and confirm your conjecture by integrating. ▪

5. $\delta(x, y) = |x + y - 1|$

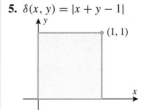

**6.** $\delta(x, y) = 1 + x^2 + y^2$

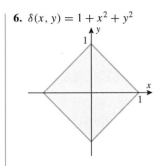

**7–8** Make a conjecture about the coordinates of the centroid of the region and confirm your conjecture by integrating. ◼

**7.**                     **8.**

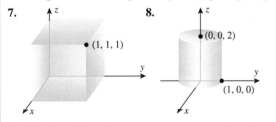

**9–12 True–False** Determine whether the statement is true or false. Explain your answer. ◼

**9.** The center of gravity of a homogeneous lamina in a plane is located at the lamina's centroid.

**10.** The mass of a two-dimensional lamina is the product of its area and the density of the lamia at its centroid.

**11.** The coordinates of the center of gravity of a two-dimensional lamina are the lamina's first moments about the $y$- and $x$-axes, respectively.

**12.** The density of a solid in 3-space is measured in units of mass per unit area.

**13.** Show that in polar coordinates the formulas for the centroid $(\bar{x}, \bar{y})$ of a region $R$ are

$$\bar{x} = \frac{1}{\text{area of } R} \iint\limits_{R} r^2 \cos\theta \, dr \, d\theta$$

$$\bar{y} = \frac{1}{\text{area of } R} \iint\limits_{R} r^2 \sin\theta \, dr \, d\theta$$

**14–17** Use the result of Exercise 13 to find the centroid $(\bar{x}, \bar{y})$ of the region. ◼

**14.** The region enclosed by the cardioid $r = a(1 + \sin\theta)$.

**15.** The petal of the rose $r = \sin 2\theta$ in the first quadrant.

**16.** The region above the $x$-axis and between the circles $x^2 + y^2 = a^2$ and $x^2 + y^2 = b^2$ $(a < b)$.

**17.** The region enclosed between the $y$-axis and the right half of the circle $x^2 + y^2 = a^2$.

**18.** Let $R$ be the rectangle bounded by the lines $x = 0$, $x = 3$, $y = 0$, and $y = 2$. By inspection, find the centroid of $R$ and use it to evaluate

$$\iint\limits_{R} x \, dA \quad \text{and} \quad \iint\limits_{R} y \, dA$$

**19–24** Find the centroid of the solid. ◼

**19.** The tetrahedron in the first octant enclosed by the coordinate planes and the plane $x + y + z = 1$.

**20.** The solid bounded by the parabolic cylinder $z = 1 - y^2$ and the planes $x + z = 1$, $x = 0$, and $z = 0$.

**21.** The solid bounded by the surface $z = y^2$ and the planes $x = 0$, $x = 1$, and $z = 1$.

**22.** The solid in the first octant bounded by the surface $z = xy$ and the planes $z = 0$, $x = 2$, and $y = 2$.

**23.** The solid in the first octant that is bounded by the sphere $x^2 + y^2 + z^2 = a^2$ and the coordinate planes.

**24.** The solid enclosed by the $xy$-plane and the hemisphere $z = \sqrt{a^2 - x^2 - y^2}$.

**25–28** Find the mass and center of gravity of the solid. ◼

**25.** The cube that has density $\delta(x, y, z) = a - x$ and is defined by the inequalities $0 \leq x \leq a$, $0 \leq y \leq a$, and $0 \leq z \leq a$.

**26.** The cylindrical solid that has density $\delta(x, y, z) = h - z$ and is enclosed by $x^2 + y^2 = a^2$, $z = 0$, and $z = h$.

**27.** The solid that has density $\delta(x, y, z) = yz$ and is enclosed by $z = 1 - y^2$ (for $y \geq 0$), $z = 0$, $y = 0$, $x = -1$, and $x = 1$.

**28.** The solid that has density $\delta(x, y, z) = xz$ and is enclosed by $y = 9 - x^2$ (for $x \geq 0$), $x = 0$, $y = 0$, $z = 0$, and $z = 1$.

**29.** Find the center of gravity of the square lamina with vertices $(0, 0)$, $(1, 0)$, $(0, 1)$, and $(1, 1)$ if
  (a) the density is proportional to the square of the distance from the origin;
  (b) the density is proportional to the distance from the $y$-axis.

**30.** Find the center of gravity of the cube that is determined by the inequalities $0 \leq x \leq 1$, $0 \leq y \leq 1$, $0 \leq z \leq 1$ if
  (a) the density is proportional to the square of the distance to the origin;
  (b) the density is proportional to the sum of the distances to the faces that lie in the coordinate planes.

**31.** Use the numerical triple integral capability of a CAS to approximate the location of the centroid of the solid that is bounded above by the surface $z = 1/(1 + x^2 + y^2)$, below by the $xy$-plane, and laterally by the plane $y = 0$ and the surface $y = \sin x$ for $0 \leq x \leq \pi$ (see the accompanying figure on the next page).

**32.** The accompanying figure on the next page shows the solid that is bounded above by the surface $z = 1/(x^2 + y^2 + 1)$, below by the $xy$-plane, and laterally by the surface $x^2 + y^2 = a^2$. *(cont.)*

(a) By symmetry, the centroid of the solid lies on the $z$-axis. Make a conjecture about the behavior of the $z$-coordinate of the centroid as $a \to 0^+$ and as $a \to +\infty$.

(b) Find the $z$-coordinate of the centroid, and check your conjecture by calculating the appropriate limits.

(c) Use a graphing utility to plot the $z$-coordinate of the centroid versus $a$, and use the graph to estimate the value of $a$ for which the centroid is $(0, 0, 0.25)$.

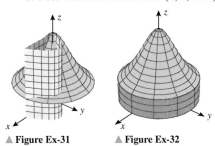

▲ **Figure Ex-31**        ▲ **Figure Ex-32**

**33–34** Use cylindrical coordinates. ■

**33.** Find the mass of the solid with density $\delta(x, y, z) = 3 - z$ that is bounded by the cone $z = \sqrt{x^2 + y^2}$ and the plane $z = 3$.

**34.** Find the mass of a right circular cylinder of radius $a$ and height $h$ if the density is proportional to the distance from the base. (Let $k$ be the constant of proportionality.)

**35–36** Use spherical coordinates. ■

**35.** Find the mass of a spherical solid of radius $a$ if the density is proportional to the distance from the center. (Let $k$ be the constant of proportionality.)

**36.** Find the mass of the solid enclosed between the spheres $x^2 + y^2 + z^2 = 1$ and $x^2 + y^2 + z^2 = 4$ if the density is $\delta(x, y, z) = (x^2 + y^2 + z^2)^{-1/2}$.

**37–38** Use cylindrical coordinates to find the centroid of the solid. ■

**37.** The solid that is bounded above by the sphere

$$x^2 + y^2 + z^2 = 2$$

and below by the paraboloid $z = x^2 + y^2$.

**38.** The solid that is bounded by the cone $z = \sqrt{x^2 + y^2}$ and the plane $z = 2$.

**39–40** Use the Wallis sine and cosine formulas:

$$\int_0^{\pi/2} \sin^n x \, dx = \frac{\pi}{2} \cdot \frac{1 \cdot 3 \cdot 5 \cdots (n-1)}{2 \cdot 4 \cdot 6 \cdots n} \quad \left(\begin{matrix} n \text{ even} \\ \text{and} \geq 2 \end{matrix}\right)$$

$$\int_0^{\pi/2} \sin^n x \, dx = \frac{2 \cdot 4 \cdot 6 \cdots (n-1)}{3 \cdot 5 \cdot 7 \cdots n} \quad \left(\begin{matrix} n \text{ odd} \\ \text{and} \geq 3 \end{matrix}\right)$$

$$\int_0^{\pi/2} \cos^n x \, dx = \frac{\pi}{2} \cdot \frac{1 \cdot 3 \cdot 5 \cdots (n-1)}{2 \cdot 4 \cdot 6 \cdots n} \quad \left(\begin{matrix} n \text{ even} \\ \text{and} \geq 2 \end{matrix}\right)$$

$$\int_0^{\pi/2} \cos^n x \, dx = \frac{2 \cdot 4 \cdot 6 \cdots (n-1)}{3 \cdot 5 \cdot 7 \cdots n} \quad \left(\begin{matrix} n \text{ odd} \\ \text{and} \geq 3 \end{matrix}\right) \quad ■$$

**39.** Find the centroid of the solid bounded above by the paraboloid $z = x^2 + y^2$, below by the plane $z = 0$, and laterally by the cylinder $(x - 1)^2 + y^2 = 1$.

**40.** Find the mass of the solid in the first octant bounded above by the paraboloid $z = 4 - x^2 - y^2$, below by the plane $z = 0$, and laterally by the cylinder $x^2 + y^2 = 2x$ and the plane $y = 0$, assuming the density to be $\delta(x, y, z) = z$.

**41–42** Use spherical coordinates to find the centroid of the solid. ■

**41.** The solid in the first octant bounded by the coordinate planes and the sphere $x^2 + y^2 + z^2 = a^2$.

**42.** The solid bounded above by the sphere $\rho = 4$ and below by the cone $\phi = \pi/3$.

**43.** Find the mass of the solid that is enclosed by the sphere $x^2 + y^2 + z^2 = 1$ and lies above the cone $z = \sqrt{x^2 + y^2}$ if the density is $\delta(x, y, z) = \sqrt{x^2 + y^2 + z^2}$.

**44.** Find the center of gravity of the solid bounded by the paraboloid $z = 1 - x^2 - y^2$ and the $xy$-plane, assuming the density to be $\delta(x, y, z) = x^2 + y^2 + z^2$.

**45.** Find the center of gravity of the solid that is bounded by the cylinder $x^2 + y^2 = 1$, the cone $z = \sqrt{x^2 + y^2}$, and the $xy$-plane if the density is $\delta(x, y, z) = z$.

**46.** Find the center of gravity of the solid hemisphere bounded by $z = \sqrt{a^2 - x^2 - y^2}$ and $z = 0$ if the density is proportional to the distance from the origin.

**47.** Find the centroid of the solid that is enclosed by the hemispheres $y = \sqrt{9 - x^2 - z^2}$, $y = \sqrt{4 - x^2 - z^2}$, and the plane $y = 0$.

**48.** Suppose that the density at a point in a gaseous spherical star is modeled by the formula

$$\delta = \delta_0 e^{-(\rho/R)^3}$$

where $\delta_0$ is a positive constant, $R$ is the radius of the star, and $\rho$ is the distance from the point to the star's center. Find the mass of the star.

**49–50** The tendency of a lamina to resist a change in rotational motion about an axis is measured by its **moment of inertia** about that axis. If a lamina occupies a region $R$ of the $xy$-plane, and if its density function $\delta(x, y)$ is continuous on $R$, then the moments of inertia about the $x$-axis, the $y$-axis, and the $z$-axis are denoted by $I_x$, $I_y$, and $I_z$, respectively, and are defined by

$$I_x = \iint_R y^2 \, \delta(x, y) \, dA, \quad I_y = \iint_R x^2 \, \delta(x, y) \, dA,$$

$$I_z = \iint_R (x^2 + y^2) \, \delta(x, y) \, dA$$

Use these definitions in Exercises 49 and 50. ■

**49.** Consider the rectangular lamina that occupies the region described by the inequalities $0 \leq x \leq a$ and $0 \leq y \leq b$. Assuming that the lamina has constant density $\delta$, show that

$$I_x = \frac{\delta ab^3}{3}, \quad I_y = \frac{\delta a^3 b}{3}, \quad I_z = \frac{\delta ab(a^2 + b^2)}{3}$$

**50.** Consider the circular lamina that occupies the region described by the inequalities $0 \le x^2 + y^2 \le a^2$. Assuming that the lamina has constant density $\delta$, show that

$$I_x = I_y = \frac{\delta \pi a^4}{4}, \quad I_z = \frac{\delta \pi a^4}{2}$$

**51–54** The tendency of a solid to resist a change in rotational motion about an axis is measured by its **moment of inertia** about that axis. If the solid occupies a region $G$ in an $xyz$-coordinate system, and if its density function $\delta(x, y, z)$ is continuous on $G$, then the moments of inertia about the $x$-axis, the $y$-axis, and the $z$-axis are denoted by $I_x$, $I_y$, and $I_z$, respectively, and are defined by

$$I_x = \iiint\limits_G (y^2 + z^2)\, \delta(x, y, z)\, dV$$

$$I_y = \iiint\limits_G (x^2 + z^2)\, \delta(x, y, z)\, dV$$

$$I_z = \iiint\limits_G (x^2 + y^2)\, \delta(x, y, z)\, dV$$

In these exercises, find the indicated moments of inertia of the solid, assuming that it has constant density $\delta$. ∎

**51.** $I_z$ for the solid cylinder $x^2 + y^2 \le a^2, 0 \le z \le h$.

**52.** $I_y$ for the solid cylinder $x^2 + y^2 \le a^2, 0 \le z \le h$.

**53.** $I_z$ for the hollow cylinder $a_1^2 \le x^2 + y^2 \le a_2^2, 0 \le z \le h$.

**54.** $I_z$ for the solid sphere $x^2 + y^2 + z^2 \le a^2$.

**55–59** These exercises reference the **Theorem of Pappus**:
*If $R$ is a bounded plane region and $L$ is a line that lies in the plane of $R$ such that $R$ is entirely on one side of $L$, then the volume of the solid formed by revolving $R$ about $L$ is given by*

$$volume = (area\ of\ R) \cdot \begin{pmatrix} distance\ traveled \\ by\ the\ centroid \end{pmatrix} \blacksquare$$

**55.** Perform the following steps to prove the Theorem of Pappus:
   (a) Introduce an $xy$-coordinate system so that $L$ is along the $y$-axis and the region $R$ is in the first quadrant. Partition $R$ into rectangular subregions in the usual way and let $R_k$ be a typical subregion of $R$ with center $(x_k^*, y_k^*)$ and area $\Delta A_k = \Delta x_k \Delta y_k$. Show that the volume generated by $R_k$ as it revolves about $L$ is

$$2\pi x_k^* \Delta x_k \Delta y_k = 2\pi x_k^* \Delta A_k$$

   (b) Show that the volume generated by $R$ as it revolves about $L$ is

$$V = \iint\limits_R 2\pi x\, dA = 2\pi \cdot \bar{x} \cdot [area\ of\ R]$$

**56.** Use the Theorem of Pappus and the result of Example 3 to find the volume of the solid generated when the region bounded by the $x$-axis and the semicircle $y = \sqrt{a^2 - x^2}$ is revolved about
   (a) the line $y = -a$        (b) the line $y = x - a$.

**57.** Use the Theorem of Pappus and the fact that the area of an ellipse with semiaxes $a$ and $b$ is $\pi ab$ to find the volume of the elliptical torus generated by revolving the ellipse

$$\frac{(x - k)^2}{a^2} + \frac{y^2}{b^2} = 1$$

about the $y$-axis. Assume that $k > a$.

**58.** Use the Theorem of Pappus to find the volume of the solid that is generated when the region enclosed by $y = x^2$ and $y = 8 - x^2$ is revolved about the $x$-axis.

**59.** Use the Theorem of Pappus to find the centroid of the triangular region with vertices $(0, 0)$, $(a, 0)$, and $(0, b)$, where $a > 0$ and $b > 0$. [*Hint:* Revolve the region about the $x$-axis to obtain $\bar{y}$ and about the $y$-axis to obtain $\bar{x}$.]

**60.** It can be proved that if a bounded plane region slides along a helix in such a way that the region is always orthogonal to the helix (i.e., orthogonal to the unit tangent vector to the helix), then the volume swept out by the region is equal to the area of the region times the distance traveled by its centroid. Use this result to find the volume of the "tube" in the accompanying figure that is swept out by sliding a circle of radius $\frac{1}{2}$ along the helix

$$x = \cos t, \quad y = \sin t, \quad z = \frac{t}{4} \quad (0 \le t \le 4\pi)$$

in such a way that the circle is always centered on the helix and lies in the plane perpendicular to the helix.

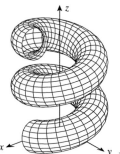
◄ **Figure Ex-60**

**61.** Writing   Give a physical interpretation of the "center of gravity" of a lamina.

---

✓**QUICK CHECK ANSWERS 14.8**

**1.** $\displaystyle\iint\limits_R \delta(x, y)\, dA$    **2.** first moment about the $y$-axis; $\displaystyle\iint\limits_R x\delta(x, y)\, dA$    **3.** $\left(\dfrac{5}{14}, \dfrac{32}{35}\right)$

## CHAPTER 14 REVIEW EXERCISES

1. The double integral over a region $R$ in the $xy$-plane is defined as

$$\iint\limits_R f(x, y)\, dA = \lim_{n \to +\infty} \sum_{k=1}^{n} f(x_k^*, y_k^*)\, \Delta A_k$$

Describe the procedure on which this definition is based.

2. The triple integral over a solid $G$ in an $xyz$-coordinate system is defined as

$$\iiint\limits_G f(x, y, z)\, dV = \lim_{n \to +\infty} \sum_{k=1}^{n} f(x_k^*, y_k^*, z_k^*)\, \Delta V_k$$

Describe the procedure on which this definition is based.

3. (a) Express the area of a region $R$ in the $xy$-plane as a double integral.
   (b) Express the volume of a region $G$ in an $xyz$-coordinate system as a triple integral.
   (c) Express the area of the portion of the surface $z = f(x, y)$ that lies above the region $R$ in the $xy$-plane as a double integral.

4. (a) Write down parametric equations for a sphere of radius $a$ centered at the origin.
   (b) Write down parametric equations for the right circular cylinder of radius $a$ and height $h$ that is centered on the $z$-axis, has its base in the $xy$-plane, and extends in the positive $z$-direction.

5. Let $R$ be the region in the accompanying figure. Fill in the missing limits of integration in the iterated integral

$$\int_\square^\square \int_\square^\square f(x, y)\, dx\, dy$$

over $R$.

6. Let $R$ be the region shown in the accompanying figure. Fill in the missing limits of integration in the sum of the iterated integrals

$$\int_0^2 \int_\square^\square f(x, y)\, dy\, dx + \int_2^3 \int_\square^\square f(x, y)\, dy\, dx$$

over $R$.

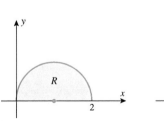

▲ Figure Ex-5        ▲ Figure Ex-6

7. (a) Find constants $a$, $b$, $c$, and $d$ such that the transformation $x = au + bv$, $y = cu + dv$ maps the region $S$ in the accompanying figure into the region $R$.
   (b) Find the area of the parallelogram $R$ by integrating over the region $S$, and check your answer using a formula from geometry.

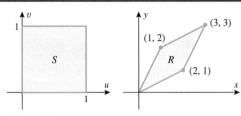

▲ Figure Ex-7

8. Give a geometric argument to show that

$$0 < \int_0^\pi \int_0^\pi \sin\sqrt{xy}\, dy\, dx < \pi^2$$

**9–10** Evaluate the iterated integral. ■

9. $\displaystyle\int_{1/2}^1 \int_0^{2x} \cos(\pi x^2)\, dy\, dx$  10. $\displaystyle\int_0^2 \int_{-y}^{2y} xe^{y^3}\, dx\, dy$

**11–12** Express the iterated integral as an equivalent integral with the order of integration reversed. ■

11. $\displaystyle\int_0^2 \int_0^{x/2} e^x e^y\, dy\, dx$  12. $\displaystyle\int_0^\pi \int_y^\pi \frac{\sin x}{x}\, dx\, dy$

**13–14** Sketch the region whose area is represented by the iterated integral. ■

13. $\displaystyle\int_0^{\pi/2} \int_{\tan(x/2)}^{\sin x} dy\, dx$

14. $\displaystyle\int_{\pi/6}^{\pi/2} \int_a^{a(1+\cos\theta)} r\, dr\, d\theta \quad (a > 0)$

**15–16** Evaluate the double integral. ■

15. $\displaystyle\iint\limits_R x^2 \sin y^2\, dA$; $R$ is the region that is bounded by $y = x^3$, $y = -x^3$, and $y = 8$.

16. $\displaystyle\iint\limits_R (4 - x^2 - y^2)\, dA$; $R$ is the sector in the first quadrant bounded by the circle $x^2 + y^2 = 4$ and the coordinate axes.

17. Convert to rectangular coordinates and evaluate:

$$\int_0^{\pi/2} \int_0^{2a\sin\theta} r\sin 2\theta\, dr\, d\theta$$

18. Convert to polar coordinates and evaluate:

$$\int_0^{\sqrt{2}} \int_x^{\sqrt{4-x^2}} 4xy\, dy\, dx$$

**19–20** Find the area of the region using a double integral. ■

19. The region bounded by $y = 2x^3$, $2x + y = 4$, and the $x$-axis.

20. The region enclosed by the rose $r = \cos 3\theta$.

21. Convert to cylindrical coordinates and evaluate:

$$\int_{-2}^2 \int_{-\sqrt{4-x^2}}^{\sqrt{4-x^2}} \int_{(x^2+y^2)^2}^{16} x^2\, dz\, dy\, dx$$

**22.** Convert to spherical coordinates and evaluate:

$$\int_0^1 \int_0^{\sqrt{1-x^2}} \int_0^{\sqrt{1-x^2-y^2}} \frac{1}{1+x^2+y^2+z^2}\, dz\, dy\, dx$$

**23.** Let $G$ be the region bounded above by the sphere $\rho = a$ and below by the cone $\phi = \pi/3$. Express

$$\iiint\limits_G (x^2 + y^2)\, dV$$

as an iterated integral in
(a) spherical coordinates      (b) cylindrical coordinates
(c) rectangular coordinates.

**24.** Let $G = \{(x, y, z) : x^2 + y^2 \leq z \leq 4x\}$. Express the volume of $G$ as an iterated integral in
(a) rectangular coordinates      (b) cylindrical coordinates.

**25–26** Find the volume of the solid using a triple integral. ▪

**25.** The solid bounded below by the cone $\phi = \pi/6$ and above by the plane $z = a$.

**26.** The solid enclosed between the surfaces $x = y^2 + z^2$ and $x = 1 - y^2$.

**27.** Find the area of the portion of the surface $z = 3y + 2x^2 + 4$ that is above the triangular region with vertices $(0, 0)$, $(1, 1)$, and $(1, -1)$.

**28.** Find the surface area of the portion of the hyperbolic paraboloid

$$\mathbf{r}(u, v) = (u + v)\mathbf{i} + (u - v)\mathbf{j} + uv\mathbf{k}$$

for which $u^2 + v^2 \leq 4$.

**29–30** Find the equation of the tangent plane to the surface at the specified point. ▪

**29.** $\mathbf{r} = u\mathbf{i} + v\mathbf{j} + (u^2 + v^2)\mathbf{k}$; $u = 1, v = 2$

**30.** $x = u \cosh v, y = u \sinh v, z = u^2$; $(-3, 0, 9)$

**31.** Suppose that you have a double integral over a region $R$ in the $xy$-plane and you want to transform that integral into an equivalent double integral over a region $S$ in the $uv$-plane. Describe the procedure you would use.

**32.** Use the transformation $u = x - 3y$, $v = 3x + y$ to find

$$\iint\limits_R \frac{x - 3y}{(3x + y)^2}\, dA$$

where $R$ is the rectangular region enclosed by the lines $x - 3y = 0$, $x - 3y = 4$, $3x + y = 1$, and $3x + y = 3$.

**33.** Let $G$ be the solid in 3-space defined by the inequalities

$$1 - e^x \leq y \leq 3 - e^x, \quad 1 - y \leq 2z \leq 2 - y, \quad y \leq e^x \leq y + 4$$

(a) Using the coordinate transformation

$$u = e^x + y, \quad v = y + 2z, \quad w = e^x - y$$

calculate the Jacobian $\partial(x, y, z)/\partial(u, v, w)$. Express your answer in terms of $u$, $v$, and $w$.
(b) Using a triple integral and the change of variables given in part (a), find the volume of $G$.

**34.** Find the average distance from a point inside a sphere of radius $a$ to the center. [See the definition preceding Exercise 33 of Section 14.5.]

**35–36** Find the centroid of the region. ▪

**35.** The region bounded by $y^2 = 4x$ and $y^2 = 8(x - 2)$.

**36.** The upper half of the ellipse $(x/a)^2 + (y/b)^2 = 1$.

**37–38** Find the centroid of the solid. ▪

**37.** The solid cone with vertex $(0, 0, h)$ and with base the disk $x^2 + y^2 \leq a^2$ in the $xy$-plane.

**38.** The solid bounded by $y = x^2$, $z = 0$, and $y + z = 4$.

## CHAPTER 14 MAKING CONNECTIONS      [C] CAS

**1.** The integral $\displaystyle\int_0^{+\infty} e^{-x^2}\, dx$, which arises in probability theory, can be evaluated using the following method. Let the value of the integral be $I$. Thus,

$$I = \int_0^{+\infty} e^{-x^2}\, dx = \int_0^{+\infty} e^{-y^2}\, dy$$

since the letter used for the variable of integration in a definite integral does not matter.
(a) Give a reasonable argument to show that

$$I^2 = \int_0^{+\infty} \int_0^{+\infty} e^{-(x^2+y^2)}\, dx\, dy$$

(b) Evaluate the iterated integral in part (a) by converting to polar coordinates.
(c) Use the result in part (b) to show that $I = \sqrt{\pi}/2$.

**2.** Show that

$$\int_0^{+\infty} \int_0^{+\infty} \frac{1}{(1 + x^2 + y^2)^2}\, dx\, dy = \frac{\pi}{4}$$

[*Hint:* See Exercise 1.]

[C] **3.** (a) Use the numerical integration capability of a CAS to approximate the value of the double integral

$$\int_{-1}^1 \int_0^{\sqrt{1-x^2}} e^{-(x^2+y^2)^2}\, dy\, dx$$

(b) Compare the approximation obtained in part (a) to the approximation that results if the integral is first converted to polar coordinates.

C **4.** (a) Find the region $G$ over which the triple integral

$$\iiint\limits_{G} (1 - x^2 - y^2 - z^2)\, dV$$

has its maximum value.

(b) Use the numerical triple integral operation of a CAS to approximate the maximum value.

(c) Find the exact maximum value.

**5–6** The accompanying figure shows the graph of an ***astroidal sphere***

$$x^{2/3} + y^{2/3} + z^{2/3} = a^{2/3}$$

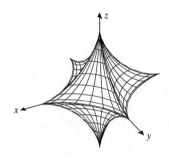

C **5.** (a) Show that the astroidal sphere can be represented parametrically as

$$x = a(\sin u \cos v)^3$$
$$y = a(\sin u \sin v)^3 \qquad (0 \le u \le \pi, \;\; 0 \le v \le 2\pi)$$
$$z = a(\cos u)^3$$

(b) Use a CAS to approximate the surface area in the case where $a = 1$.

**6.** Find the volume of the astroidal sphere using a triple integral and the transformation

$$x = \rho(\sin\phi \cos\theta)^3$$
$$y = \rho(\sin\phi \sin\theta)^3$$
$$z = \rho(\cos\phi)^3$$

for which $0 \le \rho \le a, 0 \le \phi \le \pi, 0 \le \theta \le 2\pi$.

# 15

# TOPICS IN VECTOR CALCULUS

NASA Goddard Space Flight Center (NASA/GSFC)

*Results in this chapter provide tools for analyzing and understanding the behavior of hurricanes and other fluid flows.*

The main theme of this chapter is the concept of a "flow." The body of mathematics that we will study here is concerned with analyzing flows of various types—the flow of a fluid or the flow of electricity, for example. Indeed, the early writings of Isaac Newton on calculus are replete with such nouns as "fluxion" and "fluent," which are rooted in the Latin *fluere* (to flow). We will begin this chapter by introducing the concept of a vector field, which is the mathematical description of a flow. In subsequent sections, we will introduce two new kinds of integrals that are used in a variety of applications to analyze properties of vector fields and flows. Finally, we conclude with three major theorems, Green's Theorem, the Divergence Theorem, and Stokes' Theorem. These theorems provide a deep insight into the nature of flows and are the basis for many of the most important principles in physics and engineering.

## 15.1 VECTOR FIELDS

*In this section we will consider functions that associate vectors with points in 2-space or 3-space. We will see that such functions play an important role in the study of fluid flow, gravitational force fields, electromagnetic force fields, and a wide range of other applied problems.*

▲ Figure 15.1.1

### ▦ VECTOR FIELDS

To motivate the mathematical ideas in this section, consider a *unit* point-mass located at any point in the Universe. According to Newton's Law of Universal Gravitation, the Earth exerts an attractive force on the mass that is directed toward the center of the Earth and has a magnitude that is inversely proportional to the square of the distance from the mass to the Earth's center (Figure 15.1.1). This association of force vectors with points in space is called the Earth's *gravitational field*. A similar idea arises in fluid flow. Imagine a stream in which the water flows horizontally at every level, and consider the layer of water at a specific depth. At each point of the layer, the water has a certain velocity, which we can represent by a vector at that point (Figure 15.1.2). This association of velocity vectors with points in the two-dimensional layer is called the *velocity field* at that layer. These ideas are captured in the following definition.

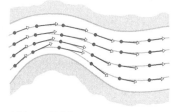

▲ **Figure 15.1.2**

---

Notice that a vector field is really just a vector-valued function. The term "vector field" is commonly used in physics and engineering.

**15.1.1** DEFINITION A ***vector field*** in a plane is a function that associates with each point $P$ in the plane a unique vector $\mathbf{F}(P)$ parallel to the plane. Similarly, a vector field in 3-space is a function that associates with each point $P$ in 3-space a unique vector $\mathbf{F}(P)$ in 3-space.

Observe that in this definition there is no reference to a coordinate system. However, for computational purposes it is usually desirable to introduce a coordinate system so that vectors can be assigned components. Specifically, if $\mathbf{F}(P)$ is a vector field in an $xy$-coordinate system, then the point $P$ will have some coordinates $(x, y)$ and the associated vector will have components that are functions of $x$ and $y$. Thus, the vector field $\mathbf{F}(P)$ can be expressed as

$$\mathbf{F}(x, y) = f(x, y)\mathbf{i} + g(x, y)\mathbf{j}$$

Similarly, in 3-space with an $xyz$-coordinate system, a vector field $\mathbf{F}(P)$ can be expressed as

$$\mathbf{F}(x, y, z) = f(x, y, z)\mathbf{i} + g(x, y, z)\mathbf{j} + h(x, y, z)\mathbf{k}$$

■ **GRAPHICAL REPRESENTATIONS OF VECTOR FIELDS**

A vector field in 2-space can be pictured geometrically by drawing representative field vectors $\mathbf{F}(x, y)$ at some well-chosen points in the $xy$-plane. But, just as it is usually not possible to describe a plane curve completely by plotting finitely many points, so it is usually not possible to describe a vector field completely by drawing finitely many vectors. Nevertheless, such graphical representations can provide useful information about the general behavior of the field if the vectors are chosen appropriately. However, graphical representations of vector fields require a substantial amount of computation, so they are usually created using computers. Figure 15.1.3 shows four computer-generated vector fields. The vector field in part (*a*) might describe the velocity of the current in a stream at various depths. At the bottom of the stream the velocity is zero, but the speed of the current increases as the depth decreases. Points at the same depth have the same speed. The vector field in part (*b*) might describe the velocity at points on a rotating wheel. At the center of the wheel the velocity is zero, but the speed increases with the distance from the center. Points at the same distance from the center have the same speed. The vector field in part (*c*) might describe the repulsive force of an electrical charge—the closer to the charge, the greater the force of repulsion. Part (*d*) shows a vector field in 3-space. Such pictures tend to be cluttered and hence are of lesser value than graphical representations of vector fields in 2-space. Note also that the

---

**TECHNOLOGY MASTERY**

If you have a graphing utility that can generate vector fields, read the relevant documentation and try to make reasonable duplicates of parts (*a*) and (*b*) of Figure 15.1.3.

---

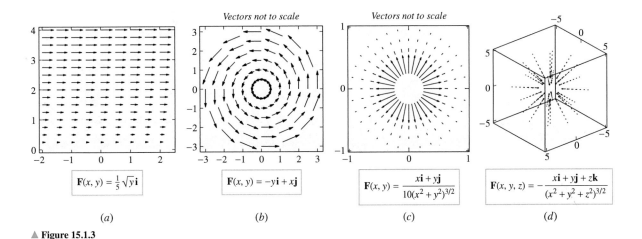

▲ **Figure 15.1.3**

vectors in parts (b) and (c) are not to scale—their lengths have been compressed for clarity. We will follow this procedure throughout this chapter.

### A COMPACT NOTATION FOR VECTOR FIELDS

Sometimes it is helpful to denote the vector fields $\mathbf{F}(x, y)$ and $\mathbf{F}(x, y, z)$ entirely in vector notation by identifying $(x, y)$ with the radius vector $\mathbf{r} = x\mathbf{i} + y\mathbf{j}$ and $(x, y, z)$ with the radius vector $\mathbf{r} = x\mathbf{i} + y\mathbf{j} + z\mathbf{k}$. With this notation a vector field in either 2-space or 3-space can be written as $\mathbf{F}(\mathbf{r})$. When no confusion is likely to arise, we will sometimes omit the $\mathbf{r}$ altogether and denote the vector field as $\mathbf{F}$.

### INVERSE-SQUARE FIELDS

According to Newton's Law of Universal Gravitation, particles with masses $m$ and $M$ attract each other with a force $\mathbf{F}$ of magnitude

$$\|\mathbf{F}\| = \frac{GmM}{r^2} \tag{1}$$

where $r$ is the distance between the particles and $G$ is a constant. If we assume that the particle of mass $M$ is located at the origin of an $xyz$-coordinate system and $\mathbf{r}$ is the radius vector to the particle of mass $m$, then $r = \|\mathbf{r}\|$, and the force $\mathbf{F}(\mathbf{r})$ exerted by the particle of mass $M$ on the particle of mass $m$ is in the direction of the unit vector $-\mathbf{r}/\|\mathbf{r}\|$. Thus, it follows from (1) that

$$\mathbf{F}(\mathbf{r}) = -\frac{GmM}{\|\mathbf{r}\|^2}\frac{\mathbf{r}}{\|\mathbf{r}\|} = -\frac{GmM}{\|\mathbf{r}\|^3}\mathbf{r} \tag{2}$$

If $m$ and $M$ are constant, and we let $c = -GmM$, then this formula can be expressed as

$$\mathbf{F}(\mathbf{r}) = \frac{c}{\|\mathbf{r}\|^3}\mathbf{r}$$

Vector fields of this form arise in electromagnetic as well as gravitational problems. Such fields are so important that they have their own terminology.

---

**15.1.2   DEFINITION**   If $\mathbf{r}$ is a radius vector in 2-space or 3-space, and if $c$ is a constant, then a vector field of the form
$$\mathbf{F}(\mathbf{r}) = \frac{c}{\|\mathbf{r}\|^3}\mathbf{r} \tag{3}$$
is called an **inverse-square field**.

---

Observe that if $c > 0$ in (3), then $\mathbf{F}(\mathbf{r})$ has the same direction as $\mathbf{r}$, so each vector in the field is directed away from the origin; and if $c < 0$, then $\mathbf{F}(\mathbf{r})$ is oppositely directed to $\mathbf{r}$, so each vector in the field is directed toward the origin. In either case the magnitude of $\mathbf{F}(\mathbf{r})$ is inversely proportional to the square of the distance from the terminal point of $\mathbf{r}$ to the origin, since

$$\|\mathbf{F}(\mathbf{r})\| = \frac{|c|}{\|\mathbf{r}\|^3}\|\mathbf{r}\| = \frac{|c|}{\|\mathbf{r}\|^2}$$

We leave it for you to verify that in 2-space Formula (3) can be written in component form as

$$\mathbf{F}(x, y) = \frac{c}{(x^2 + y^2)^{3/2}}(x\mathbf{i} + y\mathbf{j}) \tag{4}$$

and in 3-space as

$$\mathbf{F}(x, y, z) = \frac{c}{(x^2 + y^2 + z^2)^{3/2}}(x\mathbf{i} + y\mathbf{j} + z\mathbf{k}) \tag{5}$$

[see parts (c) and (d) of Figure 15.1.3].

▶ **Example 1**    *Coulomb's law* states that *the electrostatic force exerted by one charged particle on another is directly proportional to the product of the charges and inversely proportional to the square of the distance between them.* This has the same form as Newton's Law of Universal Gravitation, so the electrostatic force field exerted by a charged particle is an inverse-square field. Specifically, if a particle of charge $Q$ is at the origin of a coordinate system, and if $\mathbf{r}$ is the radius vector to a particle of charge $q$, then the force $\mathbf{F}(\mathbf{r})$ that the particle of charge $Q$ exerts on the particle of charge $q$ is of the form

$$\mathbf{F}(\mathbf{r}) = \frac{qQ}{4\pi\epsilon_0 \|\mathbf{r}\|^3}\mathbf{r}$$

where $\epsilon_0$ is a positive constant (called the ***permittivity constant***). This formula is of form (3) with $c = qQ/4\pi\epsilon_0$. ◀

■ **GRADIENT FIELDS**

An important class of vector fields arises from the process of finding gradients. Recall that if $\phi$ is a function of three variables, then the gradient of $\phi$ is defined as

$$\nabla\phi = \frac{\partial\phi}{\partial x}\mathbf{i} + \frac{\partial\phi}{\partial y}\mathbf{j} + \frac{\partial\phi}{\partial z}\mathbf{k}$$

This formula defines a vector field in 3-space called the ***gradient field of*** $\boldsymbol{\phi}$. Similarly, the gradient of a function of two variables defines a gradient field in 2-space. At each point in a gradient field where the gradient is nonzero, the vector points in the direction in which the rate of increase of $\phi$ is maximum.

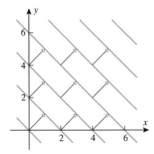

▲ **Figure 15.1.4**

▶ **Example 2**    Sketch the gradient field of $\phi(x, y) = x + y$.

***Solution.***    The gradient of $\phi$ is

$$\nabla\phi = \frac{\partial\phi}{\partial x}\mathbf{i} + \frac{\partial\phi}{\partial y}\mathbf{j} = \mathbf{i} + \mathbf{j}$$

which is constant [i.e., is the same vector at each point $(x, y)$]. A portion of the vector field is sketched in Figure 15.1.4 together with some level curves of $\phi$. Note that at each point, $\nabla\phi$ is normal to the level curve of $\phi$ through the point (Theorem 13.6.6). ◀

■ **CONSERVATIVE FIELDS AND POTENTIAL FUNCTIONS**

If $\mathbf{F}(\mathbf{r})$ is an arbitrary vector field in 2-space or 3-space, we can ask whether it is the gradient field of some function $\phi$, and if so, how we can find $\phi$. This is an important problem in various applications, and we will study it in more detail later. However, there is some terminology for such fields that we will introduce now.

---

**15.1.3**    **DEFINITION**    A vector field $\mathbf{F}$ in 2-space or 3-space is said to be ***conservative*** in a region if it is the gradient field for some function $\phi$ in that region, that is, if

$$\mathbf{F} = \nabla\phi$$

The function $\phi$ is called a ***potential function*** for $\mathbf{F}$ in the region.

▶ **Example 3**    Inverse-square fields are conservative in any region that does not contain the origin. For example, in the two-dimensional case the function

$$\phi(x, y) = -\frac{c}{(x^2 + y^2)^{1/2}} \tag{6}$$

is a potential function for (4) in any region not containing the origin, since

$$\begin{aligned}
\nabla\phi(x, y) &= \frac{\partial\phi}{\partial x}\mathbf{i} + \frac{\partial\phi}{\partial y}\mathbf{j} \\
&= \frac{cx}{(x^2 + y^2)^{3/2}}\mathbf{i} + \frac{cy}{(x^2 + y^2)^{3/2}}\mathbf{j} \\
&= \frac{c}{(x^2 + y^2)^{3/2}}(x\mathbf{i} + y\mathbf{j}) \\
&= \mathbf{F}(x, y)
\end{aligned}$$

In a later section we will discuss methods for finding potential functions for conservative vector fields. ◀

## ■ DIVERGENCE AND CURL

We will now define two important operations on vector fields in 3-space—the *divergence* and the *curl* of the field. These names originate in the study of fluid flow, in which case the divergence relates to the way in which fluid flows toward or away from a point and the curl relates to the rotational properties of the fluid at a point. We will investigate the physical interpretations of these operations in more detail later, but for now we will focus only on their computation.

---

**15.1.4  DEFINITION**    If $\mathbf{F}(x, y, z) = f(x, y, z)\mathbf{i} + g(x, y, z)\mathbf{j} + h(x, y, z)\mathbf{k}$, then we define the *divergence of* $\mathbf{F}$, written div $\mathbf{F}$, to be the function given by

$$\text{div } \mathbf{F} = \frac{\partial f}{\partial x} + \frac{\partial g}{\partial y} + \frac{\partial h}{\partial z} \tag{7}$$

---

**15.1.5  DEFINITION**    If $\mathbf{F}(x, y, z) = f(x, y, z)\mathbf{i} + g(x, y, z)\mathbf{j} + h(x, y, z)\mathbf{k}$, then we define the *curl of* $\mathbf{F}$, written curl $\mathbf{F}$, to be the vector field given by

$$\text{curl } \mathbf{F} = \left(\frac{\partial h}{\partial y} - \frac{\partial g}{\partial z}\right)\mathbf{i} + \left(\frac{\partial f}{\partial z} - \frac{\partial h}{\partial x}\right)\mathbf{j} + \left(\frac{\partial g}{\partial x} - \frac{\partial f}{\partial y}\right)\mathbf{k} \tag{8}$$

---

**REMARK**    Observe that div $\mathbf{F}$ and curl $\mathbf{F}$ depend on the point at which they are computed, and hence are more properly written as div $\mathbf{F}(x, y, z)$ and curl $\mathbf{F}(x, y, z)$. However, even though these functions are expressed in terms of $x$, $y$, and $z$, it can be proved that their values at a fixed point depend only on the point and not on the coordinate system selected. This is important in applications, since it allows physicists and engineers to compute the curl and divergence in any convenient coordinate system.

Before proceeding to some examples, we note that div $\mathbf{F}$ has scalar values, whereas curl $\mathbf{F}$ has vector values (i.e., curl $\mathbf{F}$ is itself a vector field). Moreover, for computational purposes it is useful to note that the formula for the curl can be expressed in the determinant form

$$\text{curl } \mathbf{F} = \begin{vmatrix} \mathbf{i} & \mathbf{j} & \mathbf{k} \\ \dfrac{\partial}{\partial x} & \dfrac{\partial}{\partial y} & \dfrac{\partial}{\partial z} \\ f & g & h \end{vmatrix} \qquad (9)$$

You should verify that Formula (8) results if the determinant is computed by interpreting a "product" such as $(\partial/\partial x)(g)$ to mean $\partial g/\partial x$. Keep in mind, however, that (9) is just a mnemonic device and not a true determinant, since the entries in a determinant must be numbers, not vectors and partial derivative symbols.

▶ **Example 4**   Find the divergence and the curl of the vector field

$$\mathbf{F}(x, y, z) = x^2 y \mathbf{i} + 2y^3 z \mathbf{j} + 3z \mathbf{k}$$

*Solution.*   From (7)

$$\text{div } \mathbf{F} = \frac{\partial}{\partial x}(x^2 y) + \frac{\partial}{\partial y}(2y^3 z) + \frac{\partial}{\partial z}(3z)$$

$$= 2xy + 6y^2 z + 3$$

and from (9)

$$\text{curl } \mathbf{F} = \begin{vmatrix} \mathbf{i} & \mathbf{j} & \mathbf{k} \\ \dfrac{\partial}{\partial x} & \dfrac{\partial}{\partial y} & \dfrac{\partial}{\partial z} \\ x^2 y & 2y^3 z & 3z \end{vmatrix}$$

$$= \left[ \frac{\partial}{\partial y}(3z) - \frac{\partial}{\partial z}(2y^3 z) \right] \mathbf{i} + \left[ \frac{\partial}{\partial z}(x^2 y) - \frac{\partial}{\partial x}(3z) \right] \mathbf{j} + \left[ \frac{\partial}{\partial x}(2y^3 z) - \frac{\partial}{\partial y}(x^2 y) \right] \mathbf{k}$$

$$= -2y^3 \mathbf{i} - x^2 \mathbf{k} \;\blacktriangleleft$$

▶ **Example 5**   Show that the divergence of the inverse-square field

$$\mathbf{F}(x, y, z) = \frac{c}{(x^2 + y^2 + z^2)^{3/2}}(x\mathbf{i} + y\mathbf{j} + z\mathbf{k})$$

is zero.

*Solution.*   The computations can be simplified by letting $r = (x^2 + y^2 + z^2)^{1/2}$, in which case $\mathbf{F}$ can be expressed as

$$\mathbf{F}(x, y, z) = \frac{cx\mathbf{i} + cy\mathbf{j} + cz\mathbf{k}}{r^3} = \frac{cx}{r^3}\mathbf{i} + \frac{cy}{r^3}\mathbf{j} + \frac{cz}{r^3}\mathbf{k}$$

We leave it for you to show that

$$\frac{\partial r}{\partial x} = \frac{x}{r}, \quad \frac{\partial r}{\partial y} = \frac{y}{r}, \quad \frac{\partial r}{\partial z} = \frac{z}{r}$$

Thus

$$\text{div } \mathbf{F} = c \left[ \frac{\partial}{\partial x} \left( \frac{x}{r^3} \right) + \frac{\partial}{\partial y} \left( \frac{y}{r^3} \right) + \frac{\partial}{\partial z} \left( \frac{z}{r^3} \right) \right] \qquad (10)$$

But

$$\frac{\partial}{\partial x} \left( \frac{x}{r^3} \right) = \frac{r^3 - x(3r^2)(x/r)}{(r^3)^2} = \frac{1}{r^3} - \frac{3x^2}{r^5}$$

$$\frac{\partial}{\partial y} \left( \frac{y}{r^3} \right) = \frac{1}{r^3} - \frac{3y^2}{r^5}$$

$$\frac{\partial}{\partial z} \left( \frac{z}{r^3} \right) = \frac{1}{r^3} - \frac{3z^2}{r^5}$$

Substituting these expressions in (10) yields

$$\text{div } \mathbf{F} = c \left[ \frac{3}{r^3} - \frac{3x^2 + 3y^2 + 3z^2}{r^5} \right] = c \left[ \frac{3}{r^3} - \frac{3r^2}{r^5} \right] = 0 \blacktriangleleft$$

### ■ THE ∇ OPERATOR

Thus far, the symbol $\nabla$ that appears in the gradient expression $\nabla\phi$ has not been given a meaning of its own. However, it is often convenient to view $\nabla$ as an operator

$$\nabla = \frac{\partial}{\partial x} \mathbf{i} + \frac{\partial}{\partial y} \mathbf{j} + \frac{\partial}{\partial z} \mathbf{k} \qquad (11)$$

which when applied to $\phi(x, y, z)$ produces the gradient

$$\nabla\phi = \frac{\partial\phi}{\partial x} \mathbf{i} + \frac{\partial\phi}{\partial y} \mathbf{j} + \frac{\partial\phi}{\partial z} \mathbf{k}$$

We call (11) the **del operator**. This is analogous to the derivative operator $d/dx$, which when applied to $f(x)$ produces the derivative $f'(x)$.

The del operator allows us to express the divergence of a vector field

$$\mathbf{F} = f(x, y, z)\mathbf{i} + g(x, y, z)\mathbf{j} + h(x, y, z)\mathbf{k}$$

in dot product notation as

$$\text{div } \mathbf{F} = \nabla \cdot \mathbf{F} = \frac{\partial f}{\partial x} + \frac{\partial g}{\partial y} + \frac{\partial h}{\partial z} \qquad (12)$$

and the curl of this field in cross-product notation as

$$\text{curl } \mathbf{F} = \nabla \times \mathbf{F} = \begin{vmatrix} \mathbf{i} & \mathbf{j} & \mathbf{k} \\ \dfrac{\partial}{\partial x} & \dfrac{\partial}{\partial y} & \dfrac{\partial}{\partial z} \\ f & g & h \end{vmatrix} \qquad (13)$$

### ■ THE LAPLACIAN ∇²

The operator that results by taking the dot product of the del operator with itself is denoted by $\nabla^2$ and is called the **Laplacian operator**. This operator has the form

$$\nabla^2 = \nabla \cdot \nabla = \frac{\partial^2}{\partial x^2} + \frac{\partial^2}{\partial y^2} + \frac{\partial^2}{\partial z^2} \qquad (14)$$

When applied to $\phi(x, y, z)$ the Laplacian operator produces the function

$$\nabla^2\phi = \frac{\partial^2\phi}{\partial x^2} + \frac{\partial^2\phi}{\partial y^2} + \frac{\partial^2\phi}{\partial z^2}$$

Note that $\nabla^2\phi$ can also be expressed as div $(\nabla\phi)$. The equation $\nabla^2\phi = 0$ or, equivalently,

$$\frac{\partial^2\phi}{\partial x^2} + \frac{\partial^2\phi}{\partial y^2} + \frac{\partial^2\phi}{\partial z^2} = 0$$

is known as *Laplace's equation*. This partial differential equation plays an important role in a wide variety of applications, resulting from the fact that it is satisfied by the potential function for the inverse-square field.

---

### ✔ QUICK CHECK EXERCISES 15.1    (See page 1093 for answers.)

**1.** The function $\phi(x, y, z) = xy + yz + xz$ is a potential for the vector field $\mathbf{F} = $ _____.

**2.** The vector field $\mathbf{F}(x, y, z) = $ _____, defined for $(x, y, z) \neq (0, 0, 0)$, is always directed toward the origin and is of length equal to the distance from $(x, y, z)$ to the origin.

**3.** An inverse-square field is one that can be written in the form $\mathbf{F}(\mathbf{r}) = $ _____.

**4.** The vector field

$$\mathbf{F}(x, y, z) = yz\mathbf{i} + xy^2\mathbf{j} + yz^2\mathbf{k}$$

has divergence _____ and curl _____.

---

**Pierre-Simon de Laplace (1749–1827)** French mathematician and physicist. Laplace is sometimes referred to as the French Isaac Newton because of his work in celestial mechanics. In a five-volume treatise entitled *Traité de Mécanique Céleste*, he solved extremely difficult problems involving gravitational interactions between the planets. In particular, he was able to show that our solar system is stable and not prone to catastrophic collapse as a result of these interactions. This was an issue of major concern at the time because Jupiter's orbit appeared to be shrinking and Saturn's expanding; Laplace showed that these were expected periodic anomalies. In addition to his work in celestial mechanics, he founded modern probability theory, showed with Lavoisier that respiration is a form of combustion, and developed methods that fostered many new branches of pure mathematics.

Laplace was born to moderately successful parents in Normandy, his father being a farmer and cider merchant. He matriculated in the theology program at the University of Caen at age 16 but left for Paris at age 18 with a letter of introduction to the influential mathematician d'Alembert, who eventually helped him undertake a career in mathematics. Laplace was a prolific writer, and after his election to the Academy of Sciences in 1773, the secretary wrote that the Academy had never received so many important research papers by so young a person in such a short time. Laplace had little interest in pure mathematics—he regarded mathematics merely as a tool for solving applied problems. In his impatience with mathematical detail, he frequently omitted complicated arguments with the statement, "It is easy to show that...." He admitted, however, that as time passed he often had trouble reconstructing the omitted details himself!

At the height of his fame, Laplace served on many government committees and held the posts of Minister of the Interior and Chancellor of the Senate. He barely escaped imprisonment and execution during the period of the Revolution, probably because he was able to convince each opposing party that he sided with them. Napoleon described him as a great mathematician but a poor administrator who "sought subtleties everywhere, had only doubtful ideas, and . . . carried the spirit of the infinitely small into administration." In spite of his genius, Laplace was both egotistic and insecure, attempting to ensure his place in history by conveniently failing to credit mathematicians whose work he used—an unnecessary pettiness since his own work was so brilliant. However, on the positive side he was supportive of young mathematicians, often treating them as his own children. Laplace ranks as one of the most influential mathematicians in history.

**EXERCISE SET 15.1**  ~ Graphing Utility  [c] CAS

---

**FOCUS ON CONCEPTS**

**1–2** Match the vector field $\mathbf{F}(x, y)$ with one of the plots, and explain your reasoning. ■

**1.** (a) $\mathbf{F}(x, y) = x\mathbf{i}$  (b) $\mathbf{F}(x, y) = \sin x\mathbf{i} + \mathbf{j}$

**2.** (a) $\mathbf{F}(x, y) = \mathbf{i} + \mathbf{j}$
  (b) $\mathbf{F}(x, y) = \dfrac{x}{\sqrt{x^2 + y^2}}\mathbf{i} + \dfrac{y}{\sqrt{x^2 + y^2}}\mathbf{j}$

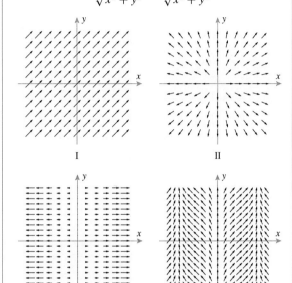

I

II

III

IV

**3–4** Determine whether the statement about the vector field $\mathbf{F}(x, y)$ is true or false. If false, explain why. ■

**3.** $\mathbf{F}(x, y) = x^2\mathbf{i} - y\mathbf{j}$.
 (a) $\|\mathbf{F}(x, y)\| \to 0$ as $(x, y) \to (0, 0)$.
 (b) If $(x, y)$ is on the positive $y$-axis, then the vector points in the negative $y$-direction.
 (c) If $(x, y)$ is in the first quadrant, then the vector points down and to the right.

**4.** $\mathbf{F}(x, y) = \dfrac{x}{\sqrt{x^2 + y^2}}\mathbf{i} - \dfrac{y}{\sqrt{x^2 + y^2}}\mathbf{j}$.
 (a) As $(x, y)$ moves away from the origin, the lengths of the vectors decrease.
 (b) If $(x, y)$ is a point on the positive $x$-axis, then the vector points up.
 (c) If $(x, y)$ is a point on the positive $y$-axis, the vector points to the right.

**5–8** Sketch the vector field by drawing some representative nonintersecting vectors. The vectors need not be drawn to scale, but they should be in reasonably correct proportion relative to each other. ■

**5.** $\mathbf{F}(x, y) = 2\mathbf{i} - \mathbf{j}$  **6.** $\mathbf{F}(x, y) = y\mathbf{j}, \quad y > 0$

**7.** $\mathbf{F}(x, y) = y\mathbf{i} - x\mathbf{j}$. [*Note:* Each vector in the field is perpendicular to the position vector $\mathbf{r} = x\mathbf{i} + y\mathbf{j}$.]

**8.** $\mathbf{F}(x, y) = \dfrac{x\mathbf{i} + y\mathbf{j}}{\sqrt{x^2 + y^2}}$. [*Note:* Each vector in the field is a unit vector in the same direction as the position vector $\mathbf{r} = x\mathbf{i} + y\mathbf{j}$.]

**~ 9–10** Use a graphing utility to generate a plot of the vector field. ■

**9.** $\mathbf{F}(x, y) = \mathbf{i} + \cos y\mathbf{j}$  **10.** $\mathbf{F}(x, y) = y\mathbf{i} - x\mathbf{j}$

**11–14 True–False** Determine whether the statement is true or false. Explain your answer. ■

**11.** The vector-valued function
$$\mathbf{F}(x, y) = y\mathbf{i} + x^2\mathbf{j} + xy\mathbf{k}$$
is an example of a vector field in the $xy$-plane.

**12.** If $\mathbf{r}$ is a radius vector in 3-space, then a vector field of the form
$$\mathbf{F}(\mathbf{r}) = \frac{1}{\|\mathbf{r}\|^2}\mathbf{r}$$
is an example of an inverse-square field.

**13.** If $\mathbf{F}$ is a vector field, then so is $\nabla \times \mathbf{F}$.

**14.** If $\mathbf{F}$ is a vector field and $\nabla \cdot \mathbf{F} = \phi$, then $\phi$ is a potential function for $\mathbf{F}$.

**15–16** Confirm that $\phi$ is a potential function for $\mathbf{F}(\mathbf{r})$ on some region, and state the region. ■

**15.** (a) $\phi(x, y) = \tan^{-1} xy$
   $\mathbf{F}(x, y) = \dfrac{y}{1 + x^2 y^2}\mathbf{i} + \dfrac{x}{1 + x^2 y^2}\mathbf{j}$
  (b) $\phi(x, y, z) = x^2 - 3y^2 + 4z^2$
   $\mathbf{F}(x, y, z) = 2x\mathbf{i} - 6y\mathbf{j} + 8z\mathbf{k}$

**16.** (a) $\phi(x, y) = 2y^2 + 3x^2 y - xy^3$
   $\mathbf{F}(x, y) = (6xy - y^3)\mathbf{i} + (4y + 3x^2 - 3xy^2)\mathbf{j}$
  (b) $\phi(x, y, z) = x \sin z + y \sin x + z \sin y$
   $\mathbf{F}(x, y, z) = (\sin z + y \cos x)\mathbf{i} + (\sin x + z \cos y)\mathbf{j}$
    $+ (\sin y + x \cos z)\mathbf{k}$

**17–22** Find div $\mathbf{F}$ and curl $\mathbf{F}$. ■

**17.** $\mathbf{F}(x, y, z) = x^2\mathbf{i} - 2\mathbf{j} + yz\mathbf{k}$

**18.** $\mathbf{F}(x, y, z) = xz^3\mathbf{i} + 2y^4 x^2\mathbf{j} + 5z^2 y\mathbf{k}$

**19.** $\mathbf{F}(x, y, z) = 7y^3 z^2\mathbf{i} - 8x^2 z^5\mathbf{j} - 3xy^4\mathbf{k}$

**20.** $\mathbf{F}(x, y, z) = e^{xy}\mathbf{i} - \cos y\mathbf{j} + \sin^2 z\mathbf{k}$

**21.** $\mathbf{F}(x, y, z) = \dfrac{1}{\sqrt{x^2 + y^2 + z^2}}(x\mathbf{i} + y\mathbf{j} + z\mathbf{k})$

**22.** $\mathbf{F}(x, y, z) = \ln x\mathbf{i} + e^{xyz}\mathbf{j} + \tan^{-1}(z/x)\mathbf{k}$

**23–24** Find $\nabla \cdot (\mathbf{F} \times \mathbf{G})$. ■

**23.** $\mathbf{F}(x, y, z) = 2x\mathbf{i} + \mathbf{j} + 4y\mathbf{k}$
   $\mathbf{G}(x, y, z) = x\mathbf{i} + y\mathbf{j} - z\mathbf{k}$

24. $\mathbf{F}(x, y, z) = yz\mathbf{i} + xz\mathbf{j} + xy\mathbf{k}$
$\mathbf{G}(x, y, z) = xy\mathbf{j} + xyz\mathbf{k}$

25–26 Find $\mathbf{\nabla} \cdot (\mathbf{\nabla} \times \mathbf{F})$. ▪

25. $\mathbf{F}(x, y, z) = \sin x\mathbf{i} + \cos(x - y)\mathbf{j} + z\mathbf{k}$

26. $\mathbf{F}(x, y, z) = e^{xz}\mathbf{i} + 3xe^y\mathbf{j} - e^{yz}\mathbf{k}$

27–28 Find $\mathbf{\nabla} \times (\mathbf{\nabla} \times \mathbf{F})$. ▪

27. $\mathbf{F}(x, y, z) = xy\mathbf{j} + xyz\mathbf{k}$

28. $\mathbf{F}(x, y, z) = y^2x\mathbf{i} - 3yz\mathbf{j} + xy\mathbf{k}$

C 29. Use a CAS to check the calculations in Exercises 23, 25, and 27.

C 30. Use a CAS to check the calculations in Exercises 24, 26, and 28.

31–38 Let $k$ be a constant, $\mathbf{F} = \mathbf{F}(x, y, z)$, $\mathbf{G} = \mathbf{G}(x, y, z)$, and $\phi = \phi(x, y, z)$. Prove the following identities, assuming that all derivatives involved exist and are continuous. ▪

31. $\text{div}(k\mathbf{F}) = k \, \text{div} \, \mathbf{F}$  32. $\text{curl}(k\mathbf{F}) = k \, \text{curl} \, \mathbf{F}$

33. $\text{div}(\mathbf{F} + \mathbf{G}) = \text{div} \, \mathbf{F} + \text{div} \, \mathbf{G}$

34. $\text{curl}(\mathbf{F} + \mathbf{G}) = \text{curl} \, \mathbf{F} + \text{curl} \, \mathbf{G}$

35. $\text{div}(\phi\mathbf{F}) = \phi \, \text{div} \, \mathbf{F} + \mathbf{\nabla}\phi \cdot \mathbf{F}$

36. $\text{curl}(\phi\mathbf{F}) = \phi \, \text{curl} \, \mathbf{F} + \mathbf{\nabla}\phi \times \mathbf{F}$

37. $\text{div}(\text{curl} \, \mathbf{F}) = 0$  38. $\text{curl}(\mathbf{\nabla}\phi) = \mathbf{0}$

39. Rewrite the identities in Exercises 31, 33, 35, and 37 in an equivalent form using the notation $\mathbf{\nabla} \cdot$ for divergence and $\mathbf{\nabla} \times$ for curl.

40. Rewrite the identities in Exercises 32, 34, 36, and 38 in an equivalent form using the notation $\mathbf{\nabla} \cdot$ for divergence and $\mathbf{\nabla} \times$ for curl.

41–42 Verify that the radius vector $\mathbf{r} = x\mathbf{i} + y\mathbf{j} + z\mathbf{k}$ has the stated property. ▪

41. (a) $\text{curl} \, \mathbf{r} = \mathbf{0}$  (b) $\mathbf{\nabla}\|\mathbf{r}\| = \dfrac{\mathbf{r}}{\|\mathbf{r}\|}$

42. (a) $\text{div} \, \mathbf{r} = 3$  (b) $\mathbf{\nabla}\dfrac{1}{\|\mathbf{r}\|} = -\dfrac{\mathbf{r}}{\|\mathbf{r}\|^3}$

43–44 Let $\mathbf{r} = x\mathbf{i} + y\mathbf{j} + z\mathbf{k}$, let $r = \|\mathbf{r}\|$, let $f$ be a differentiable function of one variable, and let $\mathbf{F}(\mathbf{r}) = f(r)\mathbf{r}$. ▪

43. (a) Use the chain rule and Exercise 41(b) to show that
$$\mathbf{\nabla}f(r) = \frac{f'(r)}{r}\mathbf{r}$$
(b) Use the result in part (a) and Exercises 35 and 42(a) to show that $\text{div} \, \mathbf{F} = 3f(r) + rf'(r)$.

44. (a) Use part (a) of Exercise 43, Exercise 36, and Exercise 41(a) to show that curl $\mathbf{F} = \mathbf{0}$.
(b) Use the result in part (a) of Exercise 43 and Exercises 35 and 42(a) to show that
$$\mathbf{\nabla}^2 f(r) = 2\frac{f'(r)}{r} + f''(r)$$

45. Use the result in Exercise 43(b) to show that the divergence of the inverse-square field $\mathbf{F} = \mathbf{r}/\|\mathbf{r}\|^3$ is zero.

46. Use the result of Exercise 43(b) to show that if $\mathbf{F}$ is a vector field of the form $\mathbf{F} = f(\|\mathbf{r}\|)\mathbf{r}$ and if div $\mathbf{F} = 0$, then $\mathbf{F}$ is an inverse-square field. [*Suggestion:* Let $r = \|\mathbf{r}\|$ and multiply $3f(r) + rf'(r) = 0$ through by $r^2$. Then write the result as a derivative of a product.]

47. A curve $C$ is called a **flow line** of a vector field $\mathbf{F}$ if $\mathbf{F}$ is a tangent vector to $C$ at each point along $C$ (see the accompanying figure).
(a) Let $C$ be a flow line for $\mathbf{F}(x, y) = -y\mathbf{i} + x\mathbf{j}$, and let $(x, y)$ be a point on $C$ for which $y \neq 0$. Show that the flow lines satisfy the differential equation
$$\frac{dy}{dx} = -\frac{x}{y}$$
(b) Solve the differential equation in part (a) by separation of variables, and show that the flow lines are concentric circles centered at the origin.

$C$
Flow lines of a vector field
◀ **Figure Ex-47**

48–50 Find a differential equation satisfied by the flow lines of $\mathbf{F}$ (see Exercise 47), and solve it to find equations for the flow lines of $\mathbf{F}$. Sketch some typical flow lines and tangent vectors. ▪

48. $\mathbf{F}(x, y) = \mathbf{i} + x\mathbf{j}$  49. $\mathbf{F}(x, y) = x\mathbf{i} + \mathbf{j}$,  $x > 0$

50. $\mathbf{F}(x, y) = x\mathbf{i} - y\mathbf{j}$,  $x > 0$ and $y > 0$

51. Writing  Discuss the similarities and differences between the concepts "vector field" and "slope field."

52. Writing  In physical applications it is often necessary to deal with vector quantities that depend not only on position in space but also on time. Give some examples and discuss how the concept of a vector field would need to be modified to apply to such situations.

✔ **QUICK CHECK ANSWERS 15.1**

1. $(y + z)\mathbf{i} + (x + z)\mathbf{j} + (x + y)\mathbf{k}$  2. $-\mathbf{r} = -x\mathbf{i} - y\mathbf{j} - z\mathbf{k}$  3. $\dfrac{c}{\|\mathbf{r}\|^3}\mathbf{r}$  4. $2xy + 2yz$; $z^2\mathbf{i} + y\mathbf{j} + (y^2 - z)\mathbf{k}$

## 15.2 LINE INTEGRALS

*In earlier chapters we considered three kinds of integrals in rectangular coordinates: single integrals over intervals, double integrals over two-dimensional regions, and triple integrals over three-dimensional regions. In this section we will discuss integrals along curves in two- or three-dimensional space.*

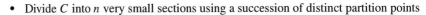

### ■ LINE INTEGRALS

The first goal of this section is to define what it means to integrate a function along a curve. To motivate the definition we will consider the problem of finding the mass of a very thin wire whose linear density function (mass per unit length) is known. We assume that we can model the wire by a smooth curve $C$ between two points $P$ and $Q$ in 3-space (Figure 15.2.1). Given any point $(x, y, z)$ on $C$, we let $f(x, y, z)$ denote the corresponding value of the density function. To compute the mass of the wire, we proceed as follows:

- Divide $C$ into $n$ very small sections using a succession of distinct partition points

$$P = P_0, P_1, P_2, \ldots, P_{n-1}, P_n = Q$$

as illustrated on the left side of Figure 15.2.2. Let $\Delta M_k$ be the mass of the $k$th section, and let $\Delta s_k$ be the length of the arc between $P_{k-1}$ and $P_k$.

▲ **Figure 15.2.1** A bent thin wire modeled by a smooth curve

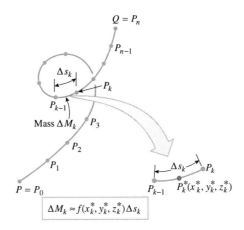

▶ **Figure 15.2.2**

- Choose an arbitrary sampling point $P_k^*(x_k^*, y_k^*, z_k^*)$ on the $k$th arc, as illustrated on the right side of Figure 15.2.2. If $\Delta s_k$ is very small, the value of $f$ will not vary much along the $k$th section and we can approximate $f$ along this section by the value $f(x_k^*, y_k^*, z_k^*)$. It follows that the mass of the $k$th section can be approximated by

$$\Delta M_k \approx f(x_k^*, y_k^*, z_k^*)\Delta s_k$$

- The mass $M$ of the entire wire can then be approximated by

$$M = \sum_{k=1}^{n} \Delta M_k \approx \sum_{k=1}^{n} f(x_k^*, y_k^*, z_k^*)\Delta s_k \tag{1}$$

- We will use the expression max $\Delta s_k \to 0$ to indicate the process of increasing $n$ in such a way that the lengths of all the sections approach 0. It is plausible that the error in (1) will approach 0 as max $\Delta s_k \to 0$ and the exact value of $M$ will be given by

$$M = \lim_{\max \Delta s_k \to 0} \sum_{k=1}^{n} f(x_k^*, y_k^*, z_k^*)\Delta s_k \tag{2}$$

The limit in (2) is similar to the limit of Riemann sums used to define the definite integral of a function over an interval (Definition 5.5.1). With this similarity in mind, we make the following definition.

---

**15.2.1 DEFINITION** If $C$ is a smooth curve in 2-space or 3-space, then the *line integral of $f$ with respect to $s$ along $C$* is

$$\int_C f(x, y)\, ds = \lim_{\max \Delta s_k \to 0} \sum_{k=1}^{n} f(x_k^*, y_k^*)\Delta s_k \qquad \boxed{\text{2-space}} \qquad (3)$$

or

$$\int_C f(x, y, z)\, ds = \lim_{\max \Delta s_k \to 0} \sum_{k=1}^{n} f(x_k^*, y_k^*, z_k^*)\Delta s_k \qquad \boxed{\text{3-space}} \qquad (4)$$

provided this limit exists and does not depend on the choice of partition or on the choice of sample points.

---

Although the term "curve integrals" is more descriptive, the integrals in Definition 15.2.1 are called "line integrals" for historical reasons.

It is usually impractical to evaluate line integrals directly from Definition 15.2.1. However, the definition is important in the application and interpretation of line integrals. For example:

- If $C$ is a curve in 3-space that models a thin wire, and if $f(x, y, z)$ is the linear density function of the wire, then it follows from (2) and Definition 15.2.1 that the mass $M$ of the wire is given by

$$M = \int_C f(x, y, z)\, ds \qquad (5)$$

That is, to obtain the mass of a thin wire, we integrate the linear density function over the smooth curve that models the wire.

- If $C$ is a smooth curve of arc length $L$, and $f$ is identically 1, then it immediately follows from Definition 15.2.1 that

$$\int_C ds = \lim_{\max \Delta s_k \to 0} \sum_{k=1}^{n} \Delta s_k = \lim_{\max \Delta s_k \to 0} L = L \qquad (6)$$

- If $C$ is a curve in the $xy$-plane and $f(x, y)$ is a nonnegative continuous function defined on $C$, then $\int_C f(x, y)\, ds$ can be interpreted as the area $A$ of the "sheet" that is swept out by a vertical line segment that extends upward from the point $(x, y)$ to a height of $f(x, y)$ and moves along $C$ from one endpoint to the other (Figure 15.2.3). To see why this is so, refer to Figure 15.2.4 in which $f(x_k^*, y_k^*)$ is the value of $f$ at an arbitrary point $P_k^*$ on the $k$th arc of the partition and note the approximation

$$\Delta A_k \approx f(x_k^*, y_k^*)\Delta s_k$$

It follows that

$$A = \sum_{k=1}^{n} \Delta A_k \approx \sum_{k=1}^{n} f(x_k^*, y_k^*)\Delta s_k$$

It is then plausible that

$$A = \lim_{\max \Delta s_k \to 0} \sum_{k=1}^{n} f(x_k^*, y_k^*)\Delta s_k = \int_C f(x, y)\, ds \qquad (7)$$

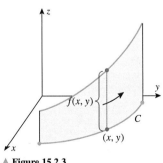

▲ Figure 15.2.3

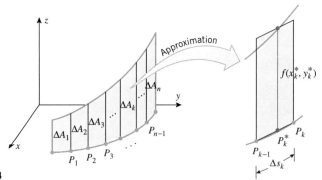

▶ **Figure 15.2.4**

Since Definition 15.2.1 is closely modeled on Definition 5.5.1, it should come as no surprise that line integrals share many of the common properties of ordinary definite integrals. For example, we have

$$\int_C [f(x, y) + g(x, y)]\, ds = \int_C f(x, y)\, ds + \int_C g(x, y)\, ds$$

provided both line integrals on the right-hand side of this equation exist. Similarly, it can be shown that if $f$ is continuous on $C$, then the line integral of $f$ with respect to $s$ along $C$ exists.

■ **EVALUATING LINE INTEGRALS**

Except in simple cases, it will not be feasible to evaluate a line integral directly from (3) or (4). However, we will now show that it is possible to express a line integral as an ordinary definite integral, so that no special methods of evaluation are required. For example, suppose that $C$ is a curve in the $xy$-plane that is smoothly parametrized by

$$\mathbf{r}(t) = x(t)\mathbf{i} + y(t)\mathbf{j} \qquad (a \le t \le b)$$

Moreover, suppose that each partition point $P_k$ of $C$ corresponds to a parameter value of $t_k$ in $[a, b]$. The arc length of $C$ between points $P_{k-1}$ and $P_k$ is then given by

$$\Delta s_k = \int_{t_{k-1}}^{t_k} \|\mathbf{r}'(t)\|\, dt \tag{8}$$

(Theorem 12.3.1). If we let $\Delta t_k = t_k - t_{k-1}$, then it follows from (8) and the Mean-Value Theorem for Integrals (Theorem 5.6.2) that there exists a point $t_k^*$ in $[t_{k-1}, t_k]$ such that

$$\Delta s_k = \int_{t_{k-1}}^{t_k} \|\mathbf{r}'(t)\|\, dt = \|\mathbf{r}'(t_k^*)\| \Delta t_k$$

We let $P_k^*(x_k^*, y_k^*) = P_k^*(x(t_k^*), y(t_k^*))$ correspond to the parameter value $t_k^*$ (Figure 15.2.5).

Since the parametrization of $C$ is smooth, it can be shown that $\max \Delta s_k \to 0$ if and only if $\max \Delta t_k \to 0$ (Exercise 57). Furthermore, the composition $f(x(t), y(t))$ is a real-valued function defined on $[a, b]$ and we have

$$\int_C f(x, y)\, ds = \lim_{\max \Delta s_k \to 0} \sum_{k=1}^{n} f(x_k^*, y_k^*)\, \Delta s_k \qquad \boxed{\text{Definition 15.2.1}}$$

$$= \lim_{\max \Delta s_k \to 0} \sum_{k=1}^{n} f(x(t_k^*), y(t_k^*)) \|\mathbf{r}'(t_k^*)\| \Delta t_k \qquad \boxed{\text{Substitution}}$$

$$= \lim_{\max \Delta t_k \to 0} \sum_{k=1}^{n} f(x(t_k^*), y(t_k^*)) \|\mathbf{r}'(t_k^*)\| \Delta t_k$$

$$= \int_a^b f(x(t), y(t)) \|\mathbf{r}'(t)\|\, dt \qquad \boxed{\text{Definition 5.5.1}}$$

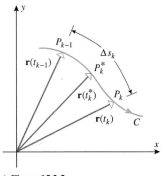

▲ **Figure 15.2.5**

Therefore, if $C$ is smoothly parametrized by

$$\mathbf{r}(t) = x(t)\mathbf{i} + y(t)\mathbf{j} \qquad (a \leq t \leq b)$$

then

$$\int_C f(x, y)\, ds = \int_a^b f(x(t), y(t)) \|\mathbf{r}'(t)\|\, dt \tag{9}$$

Similarly, if $C$ is a curve in 3-space that is smoothly parametrized by

$$\mathbf{r}(t) = x(t)\mathbf{i} + y(t)\mathbf{j} + z(t)\mathbf{k} \qquad (a \leq t \leq b)$$

then

Explain how Formulas (9) and (10)
confirm Formula (6) for arc length.

$$\int_C f(x, y, z)\, ds = \int_a^b f(x(t), y(t), z(t)) \|\mathbf{r}'(t)\|\, dt \tag{10}$$

▶ **Example 1**   Using the given parametrization, evaluate the line integral $\int_C (1 + xy^2)\, ds$.

(a)  $C : \mathbf{r}(t) = t\mathbf{i} + 2t\mathbf{j}$   $(0 \leq t \leq 1)$   (see Figure 15.2.6a)
(b)  $C : \mathbf{r}(t) = (1 - t)\mathbf{i} + (2 - 2t)\mathbf{j}$   $(0 \leq t \leq 1)$   (see Figure 15.2.6b)

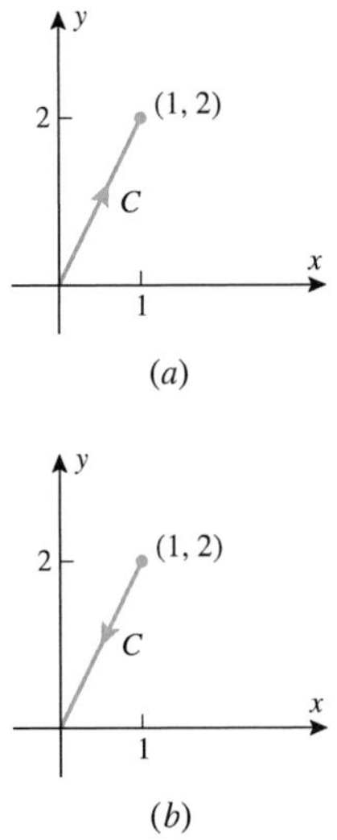

**Solution (a).**   Since $\mathbf{r}'(t) = \mathbf{i} + 2\mathbf{j}$, we have $\|\mathbf{r}'(t)\| = \sqrt{5}$ and it follows from Formula (9) that

$$\int_C (1 + xy^2)\, ds = \int_0^1 [1 + t(2t)^2]\sqrt{5}\, dt$$

$$= \int_0^1 (1 + 4t^3)\sqrt{5}\, dt$$

$$= \sqrt{5}\left[ t + t^4 \right]_0^1 = 2\sqrt{5}$$

**Solution (b).**   Since $\mathbf{r}'(t) = -\mathbf{i} - 2\mathbf{j}$, we have $\|\mathbf{r}'(t)\| = \sqrt{5}$ and it follows from Formula (9) that

$$\int_C (1 + xy^2)\, ds = \int_0^1 [1 + (1 - t)(2 - 2t)^2]\sqrt{5}\, dt$$

$$= \int_0^1 [1 + 4(1 - t)^3]\sqrt{5}\, dt$$

$$= \sqrt{5}\left[ t - (1 - t)^4 \right]_0^1 = 2\sqrt{5} \;\blacktriangleleft$$

(a)

(b)

▲ Figure 15.2.6

Note that the integrals in parts (a) and (b) of Example 1 agree, even though the corresponding parametrizations of $C$ have opposite orientations. This illustrates the important result that the value of a line integral of $f$ with respect to $s$ along $C$ *does not depend on an orientation of $C$*. (This is because $\Delta s_k$ is always positive; therefore, it does not matter in which *direction* along $C$ we list the partition points of the curve in Definition 15.2.1.) Later in this section we will discuss line integrals that are defined only for oriented curves.

Formula (9) has an alternative expression for a curve $C$ in the $xy$-plane that is given by parametric equations

$$x = x(t), \quad y = y(t) \qquad (a \leq t \leq b)$$

In this case, we write (9) in the expanded form

$$\int_C f(x, y)\, ds = \int_a^b f(x(t), y(t)) \sqrt{\left(\frac{dx}{dt}\right)^2 + \left(\frac{dy}{dt}\right)^2}\, dt \tag{11}$$

Similarly, if $C$ is a curve in 3-space that is parametrized by

$$x = x(t), \quad y = y(t), \quad z = z(t) \qquad (a \le t \le b)$$

then we write (10) in the form

$$\int_C f(x, y, z)\, ds = \int_a^b f(x(t), y(t), z(t)) \sqrt{\left(\frac{dx}{dt}\right)^2 + \left(\frac{dy}{dt}\right)^2 + \left(\frac{dz}{dt}\right)^2}\, dt \tag{12}$$

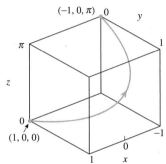

**▲ Figure 15.2.7**

▶ **Example 2**   Evaluate the line integral $\int_C (xy + z^3)\, ds$ from $(1, 0, 0)$ to $(-1, 0, \pi)$ along the helix $C$ that is represented by the parametric equations

$$x = \cos t, \quad y = \sin t, \quad z = t \qquad (0 \le t \le \pi)$$

(Figure 15.2.7).

*Solution.*   From (12)

$$\begin{aligned}
\int_C (xy + z^3)\, ds &= \int_0^\pi (\cos t \sin t + t^3) \sqrt{\left(\frac{dx}{dt}\right)^2 + \left(\frac{dy}{dt}\right)^2 + \left(\frac{dz}{dt}\right)^2}\, dt \\
&= \int_0^\pi (\cos t \sin t + t^3) \sqrt{(-\sin t)^2 + (\cos t)^2 + 1}\, dt \\
&= \sqrt{2} \int_0^\pi (\cos t \sin t + t^3)\, dt \\
&= \sqrt{2} \left[\frac{\sin^2 t}{2} + \frac{t^4}{4}\right]_0^\pi = \frac{\sqrt{2}\pi^4}{4} \quad \blacktriangleleft
\end{aligned}$$

If $\delta(x, y)$ is the linear density function of a wire that is modeled by a smooth curve $C$ in the $xy$-plane, then an argument similar to the derivation of Formula (5) shows that the mass of the wire is given by $\int_C \delta(x, y)\, ds$.

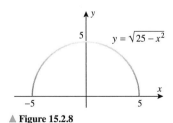

**▲ Figure 15.2.8**

▶ **Example 3**   Suppose that a semicircular wire has the equation $y = \sqrt{25 - x^2}$ and that its mass density is $\delta(x, y) = 15 - y$ (Figure 15.2.8). Physically, this means the wire has a maximum density of 15 units at the base $(y = 0)$ and that the density of the wire decreases linearly with respect to $y$ to a value of 10 units at the top $(y = 5)$. Find the mass of the wire.

*Solution.*   The mass $M$ of the wire can be expressed as the line integral

$$M = \int_C \delta(x, y)\, ds = \int_C (15 - y)\, ds$$

along the semicircle $C$. To evaluate this integral we will express $C$ parametrically as

$$x = 5 \cos t, \quad y = 5 \sin t \qquad (0 \le t \le \pi)$$

Thus, it follows from (11) that

$$M = \int_C (15 - y)\,ds = \int_0^\pi (15 - 5\sin t)\sqrt{\left(\frac{dx}{dt}\right)^2 + \left(\frac{dy}{dt}\right)^2}\,dt$$

$$= \int_0^\pi (15 - 5\sin t)\sqrt{(-5\sin t)^2 + (5\cos t)^2}\,dt$$

$$= 5\int_0^\pi (15 - 5\sin t)\,dt$$

$$= 5\left[15t + 5\cos t\right]_0^\pi$$

$$= 75\pi - 50 \approx 185.6 \text{ units of mass} \blacktriangleleft$$

In the special case where $t$ is an arc length parameter, say $t = s$, it follows from Formulas (20) and (21) in Section 12.3 that the radicals in (11) and (12) reduce to 1 and the equations simplify to

$$\int_C f(x, y)\,ds = \int_a^b f(x(s), y(s))\,ds \tag{13}$$

and

$$\int_C f(x, y, z)\,ds = \int_a^b f(x(s), y(s), z(s))\,ds \tag{14}$$

respectively.

▶ **Example 4**    Find the area of the surface extending upward from the circle $x^2 + y^2 = 1$ in the $xy$-plane to the parabolic cylinder $z = 1 - x^2$ (Figure 15.2.9).

*Solution.*    It follows from (7) that the area $A$ of the surface can be expressed as the line integral

$$A = \int_C (1 - x^2)\,ds \tag{15}$$

where $C$ is the circle $x^2 + y^2 = 1$. This circle can be parametrized in terms of arc length as

$$x = \cos s, \quad y = \sin s \qquad (0 \le s \le 2\pi)$$

Thus, it follows from (13) and (15) that

$$A = \int_C (1 - x^2)\,ds = \int_0^{2\pi} (1 - \cos^2 s)\,ds$$

$$= \int_0^{2\pi} \sin^2 s\,ds = \frac{1}{2}\int_0^{2\pi} (1 - \cos 2s)\,ds = \pi \blacktriangleleft$$

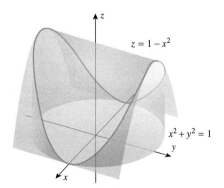

▶ Figure 15.2.9

■ **LINE INTEGRALS WITH RESPECT TO** *x*, *y*, **AND** *z*

We now describe a second type of line integral in which we replace the "*ds*" in the integral by $dx, dy,$ or $dz$. For example, suppose that $f$ is a function defined on a smooth curve $C$ in the $xy$-plane and that partition points of $C$ are denoted by $P_k(x_k, y_k)$. Letting

$$\Delta x_k = x_k - x_{k-1} \quad \text{and} \quad \Delta y_k = y_k - y_{k-1}$$

we would like to define

$$\int_C f(x, y)\, dx = \lim_{\max \Delta s_k \to 0} \sum_{k=1}^{n} f(x_k^*, y_k^*) \Delta x_k \qquad (16)$$

$$\int_C f(x, y)\, dy = \lim_{\max \Delta s_k \to 0} \sum_{k=1}^{n} f(x_k^*, y_k^*) \Delta y_k \qquad (17)$$

However, unlike $\Delta s_k$, the values of $\Delta x_k$ and $\Delta y_k$ change sign if the order of the partition points along $C$ is reversed. Therefore, in order to define the line integrals using Formulas (16) and (17), we must restrict ourselves to *oriented* curves $C$ and to partitions of $C$ in which the partition points are ordered in the direction of the curve. With this restriction, if the limit in (16) exists and does not depend on the choice of partition or sampling points, then we refer to (16) as the *line integral of f with respect to x along C*. Similarly, (17) defines the *line integral of f with respect to y along C*. If $C$ is a smooth curve in 3-space, we can have *line integrals of f with respect to x, y, and z along C*. For example,

$$\int_C f(x, y, z)\, dx = \lim_{\max \Delta s_k \to 0} \sum_{k=1}^{n} f(x_k^*, y_k^*, z_k^*) \Delta x_k$$

and so forth. As was the case with line integrals with respect to $s$, line integrals of $f$ with respect to $x$, $y$, and $z$ exist if $f$ is continuous on $C$.

The basic procedure for evaluating these line integrals is to find parametric equations for $C$, say

$$x = x(t), \quad y = y(t), \quad z = z(t) \qquad (a \le t \le b)$$

in which the orientation of $C$ is in the direction of increasing $t$, and then express the integrand in terms of $t$. For example,

$$\int_C f(x, y, z)\, dz = \int_a^b f(x(t), y(t), z(t)) z'(t)\, dt$$

[Such a formula is easy to remember—just substitute for $x$, $y$, and $z$ using the parametric equations and recall that $dz = z'(t)\, dt$.]

> Explain why Formula (16) implies that $\int_C dx = x_f - x_i$, where $x_f$ and $x_i$ are the respective $x$-coordinates of the final and initial points of $C$. What about $\int_C dy$?

> Explain why Formula (16) implies that $\int_C f(x, y)\, dx = 0$ on any oriented segment parallel to the $y$-axis. What can you say about $\int_C f(x, y)\, dy$ on any oriented segment parallel to the $x$-axis?

▶ **Example 5**    Evaluate $\int_C 3xy\, dy$, where $C$ is the line segment joining $(0, 0)$ and $(1, 2)$ with the given orientation.

(a)  Oriented from $(0, 0)$ to $(1, 2)$ as in Figure 15.2.6*a*.

(b)  Oriented from $(1, 2)$ to $(0, 0)$ as in Figure 15.2.6*b*.

*Solution (a).*    Using the parametrization

$$x = t, \quad y = 2t \qquad (0 \le t \le 1)$$

we have

$$\int_C 3xy\, dy = \int_0^1 3(t)(2t)(2)\, dt = \int_0^1 12t^2\, dt = 4t^3 \Big]_0^1 = 4$$

*Solution (b).*   Using the parametrization

$$x = 1 - t, \quad y = 2 - 2t \qquad (0 \le t \le 1)$$

we have

$$\int_C 3xy\, dy = \int_0^1 3(1-t)(2-2t)(-2)\, dt = \int_0^1 -12(1-t)^2\, dt = 4(1-t)^3 \Big]_0^1 = -4 \;\blacktriangleleft$$

In Example 5, note that reversing the orientation of the curve changed the sign of the line integral. This is because reversing the orientation of a curve changes the sign of $\Delta x_k$ in definition (16). Thus, unlike line integrals of functions with respect to $s$ along $C$, reversing the orientation of $C$ changes the sign of a line integral with respect to $x$, $y$, and $z$. If $C$ is a smooth oriented curve, we will let $-C$ denote the oriented curve consisting of the same points as $C$ but with the opposite orientation (Figure 15.2.10). We then have

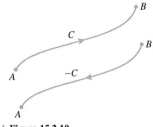

▲ Figure 15.2.10

$$\int_{-C} f(x, y)\, dx = -\int_C f(x, y)\, dx \qquad \text{and} \qquad \int_{-C} g(x, y)\, dy = -\int_C g(x, y)\, dy$$

$$(18\text{–}19)$$

while

$$\int_{-C} f(x, y)\, ds = \int_C f(x, y)\, ds \tag{20}$$

Similar identities hold for line integrals in 3-space. Unless indicated otherwise, we will assume that parametric curves are oriented in the direction of increasing parameter.

Frequently, the line integrals with respect to $x$ and $y$ occur in combination, in which case we will dispense with one of the integral signs and write

$$\int_C f(x, y)\, dx + g(x, y)\, dy = \int_C f(x, y)\, dx + \int_C g(x, y)\, dy \tag{21}$$

We will use a similar convention for combinations of line integrals with respect to $x$, $y$, and $z$ along curves in 3-space.

▶ **Example 6**   Evaluate

$$\int_C 2xy\, dx + (x^2 + y^2)\, dy$$

along the circular arc $C$ given by $x = \cos t$, $y = \sin t$ $(0 \le t \le \pi/2)$ (Figure 15.2.11).

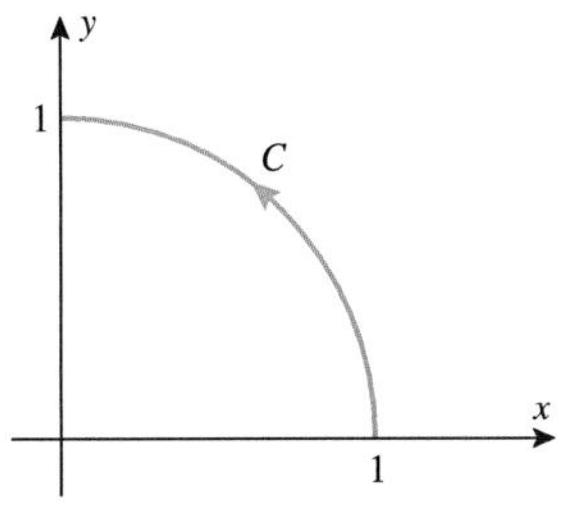

*Solution.*   We have

$$\int_C 2xy\, dx = \int_0^{\pi/2} (2\cos t \sin t)\left[\frac{d}{dt}(\cos t)\right] dt$$

$$= -2\int_0^{\pi/2} \sin^2 t \cos t\, dt = -\frac{2}{3}\sin^3 t \Big]_0^{\pi/2} = -\frac{2}{3}$$

$$\int_C (x^2 + y^2)\, dy = \int_0^{\pi/2} (\cos^2 t + \sin^2 t)\left[\frac{d}{dt}(\sin t)\right] dt$$

$$= \int_0^{\pi/2} \cos t\, dt = \sin t \Big]_0^{\pi/2} = 1$$

$x = \cos t,\ y = \sin t\ (0 \le t \le \pi/2)$

▲ Figure 15.2.11

Thus, from (21)

$$\int_C 2xy \, dx + (x^2 + y^2) \, dy = \int_C 2xy \, dx + \int_C (x^2 + y^2) \, dy$$

$$= -\frac{2}{3} + 1 = \frac{1}{3} \ \blacktriangleleft$$

It can be shown that if $f$ and $g$ are continuous functions on $C$, then combinations of line integrals with respect to $x$ and $y$ can be expressed in terms of a limit and can be evaluated together in a single step. For example, we have

$$\int_C f(x, y) \, dx + g(x, y) \, dy = \lim_{\max \Delta s_k \to 0} \sum_{k=1}^n [f(x_k^*, y_k^*) \Delta x_k + g(x_k^*, y_k^*) \, \Delta y_k] \qquad (22)$$

and

$$\int_C f(x, y) \, dx + g(x, y) \, dy = \int_a^b [f(x(t), y(t))x'(t) + g(x(t), y(t))y'(t)] \, dt \qquad (23)$$

Similar results hold for line integrals in 3-space. The evaluation of a line integral can sometimes be simplified by using Formula (23).

▶ **Example 7**   Evaluate

$$\int_C (3x^2 + y^2) \, dx + 2xy \, dy$$

along the circular arc $C$ given by $x = \cos t$, $y = \sin t$ $(0 \le t \le \pi/2)$ (Figure 15.2.11).

*Solution.*   From (23) we have

$$\int_C (3x^2 + y^2) \, dx + 2xy \, dy = \int_0^{\pi/2} [(3\cos^2 t + \sin^2 t)(-\sin t) + 2(\cos t)(\sin t)(\cos t)] \, dt$$

$$= \int_0^{\pi/2} (-3\cos^2 t \sin t - \sin^3 t + 2\cos^2 t \sin t) \, dt$$

$$= \int_0^{\pi/2} (-\cos^2 t - \sin^2 t)(\sin t) \, dt = \int_0^{\pi/2} -\sin t \, dt$$

$$= \cos t \Big]_0^{\pi/2} = -1 \ \blacktriangleleft$$

Compare the computations in Example 7 with those involved in computing

$$\int_C (3x^2 + y^2) \, dx + \int_C 2xy \, dy$$

It follows from (18) and (19) that

$$\int_{-C} f(x, y) \, dx + g(x, y) \, dy = -\int_C f(x, y) \, dx + g(x, y) \, dy \qquad (24)$$

so that reversing the orientation of $C$ changes the sign of a line integral in which $x$ and $y$ occur in combination. Similarly,

$$\int_{-C} f(x, y, z) \, dx + g(x, y, z) \, dy + h(x, y, z) \, dz$$

$$= -\int_C f(x, y, z) \, dx + g(x, y, z) \, dy + h(x, y, z) \, dz \qquad (25)$$

### ■ INTEGRATING A VECTOR FIELD ALONG A CURVE

There is an alternative notation for line integrals with respect to $x$, $y$, and $z$ that is particularly appropriate for dealing with problems involving vector fields. We will interpret $d\mathbf{r}$ as

$$d\mathbf{r} = dx\mathbf{i} + dy\mathbf{j} \quad \text{or} \quad d\mathbf{r} = dx\mathbf{i} + dy\mathbf{j} + dz\mathbf{k}$$

depending on whether $C$ is in 2-space or 3-space. For an oriented curve $C$ in 2-space and a vector field

$$\mathbf{F}(x, y) = f(x, y)\mathbf{i} + g(x, y)\mathbf{j}$$

we will write

$$\int_C \mathbf{F} \cdot d\mathbf{r} = \int_C (f(x, y)\mathbf{i} + g(x, y)\mathbf{j}) \cdot (dx\mathbf{i} + dy\mathbf{j}) = \int_C f(x, y)\,dx + g(x, y)\,dy \quad (26)$$

Similarily, for a curve $C$ in 3-space and vector field

$$\mathbf{F}(x, y, z) = f(x, y, z)\mathbf{i} + g(x, y, z)\mathbf{j} + h(x, y, z)\mathbf{k}$$

we will write

$$\int_C \mathbf{F} \cdot d\mathbf{r} = \int_C (f(x, y, z)\mathbf{i} + g(x, y, z)\mathbf{j} + h(x, y, z)\mathbf{k}) \cdot (dx\mathbf{i} + dy\mathbf{j} + dz\mathbf{k})$$
$$= \int_C f(x, y, z)\,dx + g(x, y, z)\,dy + h(x, y, z)\,dz \quad (27)$$

With these conventions, we are led to the following definition.

---

**15.2.2  DEFINITION**    If $\mathbf{F}$ is a continuous vector field and $C$ is a smooth oriented curve, then the ***line integral of $\mathbf{F}$ along $C$*** is

$$\int_C \mathbf{F} \cdot d\mathbf{r} \quad (28)$$

---

The notation in Definition 15.2.2 makes it easy to remember the formula for evaluating the line integral of $\mathbf{F}$ along $C$. For example, suppose that $C$ is an oriented curve in the plane given in vector form by

$$\mathbf{r} = \mathbf{r}(t) = x(t)\mathbf{i} + y(t)\mathbf{j} \quad (a \le t \le b)$$

If we write

$$\mathbf{F}(\mathbf{r}(t)) = f(x(t), y(t))\mathbf{i} + g(x(t), y(t))\mathbf{j}$$

then

$$\int_C \mathbf{F} \cdot d\mathbf{r} = \int_a^b \mathbf{F}(\mathbf{r}(t)) \cdot \mathbf{r}'(t)\,dt \quad (29)$$

Formula (29) is also valid for oriented curves in 3-space.

---

▶ **Example 8**    Evaluate $\int_C \mathbf{F} \cdot d\mathbf{r}$ where $\mathbf{F}(x, y) = \cos x\mathbf{i} + \sin x\mathbf{j}$ and where $C$ is the given oriented curve.

(a) $C : \mathbf{r}(t) = -\dfrac{\pi}{2}\mathbf{i} + t\mathbf{j}$   $(1 \le t \le 2)$     (see Figure 15.2.12a)

(b) $C : \mathbf{r}(t) = t\mathbf{i} + t^2\mathbf{j}$   $(-1 \le t \le 2)$     (see Figure 15.2.12b)

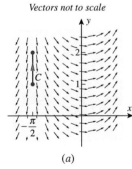

*Vectors not to scale*

(a)

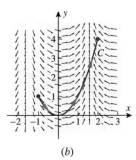

(b)

▲ **Figure 15.2.12**

*Solution (a).* Using (29) we have

$$\int_C \mathbf{F} \cdot d\mathbf{r} = \int_1^2 \mathbf{F}(\mathbf{r}(t)) \cdot \mathbf{r}'(t)\, dt = \int_1^2 (-\mathbf{j}) \cdot \mathbf{j}\, dt = \int_1^2 (-1)\, dt = -1$$

*Solution (b).* Using (29) we have

$$\int_C \mathbf{F} \cdot d\mathbf{r} = \int_{-1}^2 \mathbf{F}(\mathbf{r}(t)) \cdot \mathbf{r}'(t)\, dt = \int_{-1}^2 (\cos t\, \mathbf{i} + \sin t\, \mathbf{j}) \cdot (\mathbf{i} + 2t\mathbf{j})\, dt$$

$$= \int_{-1}^2 (\cos t + 2t \sin t)\, dt = (-2t \cos t + 3 \sin t)\Big]_{-1}^2$$

$$= -2\cos 1 - 4\cos 2 + 3(\sin 1 + \sin 2) \approx 5.83629 \blacktriangleleft$$

If we let $t$ denote an arc length parameter, say $t = s$, with $\mathbf{T} = \mathbf{r}'(s)$ the unit tangent vector field along $C$, then

$$\int_C \mathbf{F} \cdot d\mathbf{r} = \int_a^b \mathbf{F}(\mathbf{r}(s)) \cdot \mathbf{r}'(s)\, ds = \int_a^b \mathbf{F}(\mathbf{r}(s)) \cdot \mathbf{T}\, ds = \int_C \mathbf{F} \cdot \mathbf{T}\, ds$$

which shows that

$$\int_C \mathbf{F} \cdot d\mathbf{r} = \int_C \mathbf{F} \cdot \mathbf{T}\, ds \tag{30}$$

In words, the integral of a vector field along a curve has the same value as the integral of the tangential component of the vector field along the curve.

We can use (30) to interpret $\int_C \mathbf{F} \cdot d\mathbf{r}$ geometrically. If $\theta$ is the angle between $\mathbf{F}$ and $\mathbf{T}$ at a point on $C$, then at this point

$$\mathbf{F} \cdot \mathbf{T} = \|\mathbf{F}\| \|\mathbf{T}\| \cos \theta \qquad \boxed{\text{Formula (4) in Section 11.3}}$$

$$= \|\mathbf{F}\| \cos \theta \qquad \boxed{\text{Since } \|\mathbf{T}\| = 1}$$

Thus,

$$-\|\mathbf{F}\| \le \mathbf{F} \cdot \mathbf{T} \le \|\mathbf{F}\|$$

and if $\mathbf{F} \ne \mathbf{0}$, then the sign of $\mathbf{F} \cdot \mathbf{T}$ will depend on the angle between the direction of $\mathbf{F}$ and the direction of $C$ (Figure 15.2.13). That is, $\mathbf{F} \cdot \mathbf{T}$ will be positive where $\mathbf{F}$ has the same general direction as $C$, it will be 0 if $\mathbf{F}$ is normal to $C$, and it will be negative where $\mathbf{F}$ and $C$ have more or less opposite directions. The line integral of $\mathbf{F}$ along $C$ can be interpreted as the accumulated effect of the magnitude of $\mathbf{F}$ along $C$, the extent to which $\mathbf{F}$ and $C$ have the same direction, and the arc length of $C$.

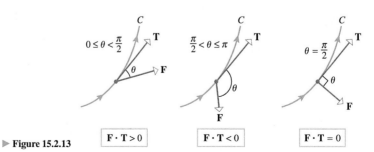

▶ **Figure 15.2.13**

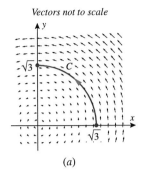

Vectors not to scale

(a)

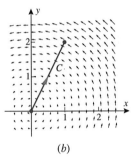

(b)

▲ Figure 15.2.14

Refer to Figure 15.2.12 and explain the sign of each line integral in Example 8 geometrically. Exercises 5 and 6 take this geometric analysis further.

▶ **Example 9**   Use (30) to evaluate $\int_C \mathbf{F} \cdot d\mathbf{r}$ where $\mathbf{F}(x, y) = -y\mathbf{i} + x\mathbf{j}$ and where $C$ is the given oriented curve.

(a)  $C : x^2 + y^2 = 3$    $(0 \le x, y;$ oriented as in Figure 15.2.14$a$)
(b)  $C : \mathbf{r}(t) = t\mathbf{i} + 2t\mathbf{j}$    $(0 \le t \le 1;$ see Figure 15.2.14$b$)

**Solution ($a$).**    At every point on $C$ the direction of $\mathbf{F}$ and the direction of $C$ are the same. (Why?) In addition, at every point on $C$

$$\|\mathbf{F}\| = \sqrt{(-y)^2 + x^2} = \sqrt{x^2 + y^2} = \sqrt{3}$$

Therefore, $\mathbf{F} \cdot \mathbf{T} = \|\mathbf{F}\| \cos(0) = \|\mathbf{F}\| = \sqrt{3}$, and

$$\int_C \mathbf{F} \cdot d\mathbf{r} = \int_C \mathbf{F} \cdot \mathbf{T}\, ds = \int_C \sqrt{3}\, ds = \sqrt{3} \int_C ds = \frac{3\pi}{2}$$

**Solution ($b$).**    The vector field $\mathbf{F}$ is normal to $C$ at every point. (Why?) Therefore,

$$\int_C \mathbf{F} \cdot d\mathbf{r} = \int_C \mathbf{F} \cdot \mathbf{T}\, ds = \int_C 0\, ds = 0 \quad ◀$$

In light of (20) and (30), you might expect that reversing the orientation of $C$ in $\int_C \mathbf{F} \cdot d\mathbf{r}$ would have no effect on the value of the line integral. However, reversing the orientation of $C$ reverses the orientation of $\mathbf{T}$ in the integrand and hence reverses the sign of the integral; that is,

$$\int_{-C} \mathbf{F} \cdot \mathbf{T}\, ds = -\int_C \mathbf{F} \cdot \mathbf{T}\, ds \tag{31}$$

$$\int_{-C} \mathbf{F} \cdot d\mathbf{r} = -\int_C \mathbf{F} \cdot d\mathbf{r} \tag{32}$$

■ **WORK AS A LINE INTEGRAL**
An important application of line integrals with respect to $x$, $y$, and $z$ is to the problem of defining the work performed by a variable force moving a particle along a curved path. In Section 6.6 we defined the work $W$ performed by a force of constant magnitude acting on an object in the direction of motion (Definition 6.6.1), and later in that section we extended the definition to allow for a force of variable magnitude acting in the direction of motion (Definition 6.6.3). In Section 11.3 we took the concept of work a step further by defining the work $W$ performed by a constant force $\mathbf{F}$ moving a particle in a straight line from point $P$ to point $Q$. We defined the work to be

$$W = \mathbf{F} \cdot \overrightarrow{PQ} \tag{33}$$

[Formula (14) in Section 11.3]. Our next goal is to define a more general concept of work —the work performed by a variable force acting on a particle that moves along a curved path in 2-space or 3-space.

In many applications variable forces arise from force fields (gravitational fields, electromagnetic fields, and so forth), so we will consider the problem of work in that context. To motivate an appropriate definition for work performed by a force field, we will use a limit process, and since the procedure is the same for 2-space and 3-space, we will discuss it in detail for 2-space only. The idea is as follows:

- Assume that a force field $\mathbf{F} = \mathbf{F}(x, y)$ moves a particle along a smooth curve $C$ from a point $P$ to a point $Q$. Divide $C$ into $n$ arcs using the partition points

$$P = P_0(x_0, y_0), P_1(x_1, y_1), P_2(x_2, y_2), \ldots, P_{n-1}(x_{n-1}, y_{n-1}), P_n(x_n, y_n) = Q$$

directed along $C$ from $P$ to $Q$, and denote the length of the $k$th arc by $\Delta s_k$. Let $(x_k^*, y_k^*)$ be any point on the $k$th arc, and let

$$\mathbf{F}_k^* = \mathbf{F}(x_k^*, y_k^*) = f(x_k^*, y_k^*)\mathbf{i} + g(x_k^*, y_k^*)\mathbf{j}$$

be the force vector at this point (Figure 15.2.15).

- If the $k$th arc is small, then the force will not vary much, so we can approximate the force by the constant value $\mathbf{F}_k^*$ on this arc. Moreover, the direction of motion will not vary much over this small arc, so we can approximate the movement of the particle by the displacement vector

$$\overrightarrow{P_{k-1}P_k} = (\Delta x_k)\mathbf{i} + (\Delta y_k)\mathbf{j}$$

where $\Delta x_k = x_k - x_{k-1}$ and $\Delta y_k = y_k - y_{k-1}$.

- Since the work done by a constant force $\mathbf{F}_k^*$ moving a particle along a straight line from $P_{k-1}$ to $P_k$ is

$$\mathbf{F}_k^* \cdot \overrightarrow{P_{k-1}P_k} = (f(x_k^*, y_k^*)\mathbf{i} + g(x_k^*, y_k^*)\mathbf{j}) \cdot ((\Delta x_k)\mathbf{i} + (\Delta y_k)\mathbf{j})$$
$$= f(x_k^*, y_k^*)\Delta x_k + g(x_k^*, y_k^*)\Delta y_k$$

[Formula (33)], the work $\Delta W_k$ performed by the force field along the $k$th arc of $C$ can be approximated by

$$\Delta W_k \approx f(x_k^*, y_k^*)\Delta x_k + g(x_k^*, y_k^*)\Delta y_k$$

The total work $W$ performed by the force moving the particle over the entire curve $C$ can then be approximated as

$$W = \sum_{k=1}^n \Delta W_k \approx \sum_{k=1}^n [f(x_k^*, y_k^*)\Delta x_k + g(x_k^*, y_k^*)\Delta y_k]$$

- As $\max \Delta s_k \to 0$, it is plausible that the error in this approximation approaches 0 and the exact work performed by the force field is

$$W = \lim_{\max \Delta s_k \to 0} \sum_{k=1}^n [f(x_k^*, y_k^*)\Delta x_k + g(x_k^*, y_k^*)\Delta y_k]$$

$$= \int_C f(x, y)\,dx + g(x, y)\,dy \qquad \boxed{\text{Formula (22)}}$$

$$= \int_C \mathbf{F} \cdot d\mathbf{r} \qquad \boxed{\text{Formula (26)}}$$

Thus, we are led to the following definition.

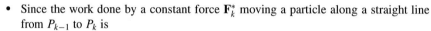

▲ Figure 15.2.15

Note from Formula (30) that the work performed by a force field on a particle moving along a smooth curve $C$ is obtained by integrating the scalar tangential component of force along $C$. This implies that the component of force orthogonal to the direction of motion of the particle has no effect on the work done.

**15.2.3 DEFINITION** Suppose that under the influence of a continuous force field $\mathbf{F}$ a particle moves along a smooth curve $C$ and that $C$ is oriented in the direction of motion of the particle. Then the **work performed by the force field** on the particle is

$$\int_C \mathbf{F} \cdot d\mathbf{r} \tag{34}$$

For example, suppose that force is measured in pounds and distance is measured in feet. It follows from part (a) of Example 9 that the work done by a force $\mathbf{F}(x, y) = -y\mathbf{i} + x\mathbf{j}$ acting on a particle moving along the circle $x^2 + y^2 = 3$ from $(\sqrt{3}, 0)$ to $(0, \sqrt{3})$ is $3\pi/2$ foot-pounds.

### ▨ LINE INTEGRALS ALONG PIECEWISE SMOOTH CURVES

Thus far, we have only considered line integrals along smooth curves. However, the notion of a line integral can be extended to curves formed from finitely many smooth curves $C_1, C_2, \ldots, C_n$ joined end to end. Such a curve is called *piecewise smooth* (Figure 15.2.16). We define a line integral along a piecewise smooth curve $C$ to be the sum of the integrals along the sections:

$$\int_C = \int_{C_1} + \int_{C_2} + \cdots + \int_{C_n}$$

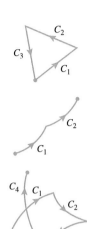

▶ **Example 10** Evaluate

$$\int_C x^2 y \, dx + x \, dy$$

where $C$ is the triangular path shown in Figure 15.2.17.

*Solution.* We will integrate over $C_1$, $C_2$, and $C_3$ separately and add the results. For each of the three integrals we must find parametric equations that trace the path of integration in the correct direction. For this purpose recall from Formula (7) of Section 12.1 that the graph of the vector-valued function

$$\mathbf{r}(t) = (1 - t)\mathbf{r}_0 + t\mathbf{r}_1 \qquad (0 \le t \le 1)$$

is the line segment joining $\mathbf{r}_0$ and $\mathbf{r}_1$, oriented in the direction from $\mathbf{r}_0$ to $\mathbf{r}_1$. Thus, the line segments $C_1$, $C_2$, and $C_3$ can be represented in vector notation as

$$C_1: \mathbf{r}(t) = (1 - t)\langle 0, 0 \rangle + t\langle 1, 0 \rangle = \langle t, 0 \rangle$$
$$C_2: \mathbf{r}(t) = (1 - t)\langle 1, 0 \rangle + t\langle 1, 2 \rangle = \langle 1, 2t \rangle$$
$$C_3: \mathbf{r}(t) = (1 - t)\langle 1, 2 \rangle + t\langle 0, 0 \rangle = \langle 1 - t, 2 - 2t \rangle$$

where $t$ varies from 0 to 1 in each case. From these equations we obtain

$$\int_{C_1} x^2 y \, dx + x \, dy = \int_{C_1} x^2 y \, dx = \int_0^1 (t^2)(0) \frac{d}{dt}[t] \, dt = 0$$

$$\int_{C_2} x^2 y \, dx + x \, dy = \int_{C_2} x \, dy = \int_0^1 (1) \frac{d}{dt}[2t] \, dt = 2$$

$$\int_{C_3} x^2 y \, dx + x \, dy = \int_0^1 (1 - t)^2 (2 - 2t) \frac{d}{dt}[1 - t] \, dt + \int_0^1 (1 - t) \frac{d}{dt}[2 - 2t] \, dt$$

$$= 2 \int_0^1 (t - 1)^3 \, dt + 2 \int_0^1 (t - 1) \, dt = -\tfrac{1}{2} - 1 = -\tfrac{3}{2}$$

Thus,

$$\int_C x^2 y \, dx + x \, dy = 0 + 2 + \left(-\tfrac{3}{2}\right) = \tfrac{1}{2} \blacktriangleleft$$

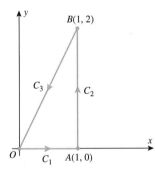

▲ **Figure 15.2.16**

▲ **Figure 15.2.17**

✔ **QUICK CHECK EXERCISES 15.2**   *(See page 1111 for answers.)*

1. The area of the surface extending upward from the line segment $y = x$ $(0 \le x \le 1)$ in the $xy$-plane to the plane $z = 2x + 1$ is _____.

2. Suppose that a wire has equation $y = 1 - x$ $(0 \le x \le 1)$ and that its mass density is $\delta(x, y) = 2 - x$. The mass of the wire is _____.

3. If $C$ is the curve represented by the equations
$$x = \sin t, \quad y = \cos t, \quad z = t \quad (0 \le t \le 2\pi)$$
then $\int_C y \, dx - x \, dy + dz = $ _____.

4. If $C$ is the unit circle $x^2 + y^2 = 1$ oriented counterclockwise and $\mathbf{F}(x, y) = x\mathbf{i} + y\mathbf{j}$, then
$$\int_C \mathbf{F} \cdot d\mathbf{r} = \underline{\hspace{2cm}}$$

---

**EXERCISE SET 15.2**    ⊠ Graphing Utility   © CAS

**FOCUS ON CONCEPTS**

1. Let $C$ be the line segment from $(0, 0)$ to $(0, 1)$. In each part, evaluate the line integral along $C$ by inspection, and explain your reasoning.

(a) $\displaystyle\int_C ds$     (b) $\displaystyle\int_C \sin xy \, dy$

2. Let $C$ be the line segment from $(0, 2)$ to $(0, 4)$. In each part, evaluate the line integral along $C$ by inspection, and explain your reasoning.

(a) $\displaystyle\int_C ds$     (b) $\displaystyle\int_C e^{xy} \, dx$

**3–4** Evaluate $\int_C \mathbf{F} \cdot d\mathbf{r}$ by inspection for the force field $\mathbf{F}(x, y) = \mathbf{i} + \mathbf{j}$ and the curve $C$ shown in the figure. Explain your reasoning. [*Note:* For clarity, the vectors in the force field are shown at less than true scale.] ▨

3.              4.

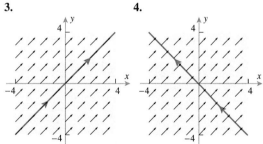

5. Use (30) to explain why the line integral in part (a) of Example 8 can be found by multiplying the length of the line segment $C$ by $-1$.

 6. (a) Use (30) to explain why the line integral in part (b) of Example 8 should be close to, but somewhat less than, the length of the parabolic curve $C$.

(b) Verify the conclusion in part (a) of this exercise by computing the length of $C$ and comparing the length with the value of the line integral.

**7–10** Evaluate $\int_C \mathbf{F} \cdot d\mathbf{r}$ along the line segment $C$ from $P$ to $Q$. ▨

7. $\mathbf{F}(x, y) = 8\mathbf{i} + 8\mathbf{j}$; $P(-4, 4)$, $Q(-4, 5)$

8. $\mathbf{F}(x, y) = 2\mathbf{i} + 5\mathbf{j}$; $P(1, -3)$, $Q(4, -3)$

9. $\mathbf{F}(x, y) = 2x\mathbf{j}$; $P(-2, 4)$, $Q(-2, 11)$

10. $\mathbf{F}(x, y) = -8x\mathbf{i} + 3y\mathbf{j}$; $P(-1, 0)$, $Q(6, 0)$

11. Let $C$ be the curve represented by the equations
$$x = 2t, \quad y = t^2 \quad (0 \le t \le 1)$$
In each part, evaluate the line integral along $C$.

(a) $\displaystyle\int_C (x - \sqrt{y}) \, ds$     (b) $\displaystyle\int_C (x - \sqrt{y}) \, dx$

(c) $\displaystyle\int_C (x - \sqrt{y}) \, dy$

12. Let $C$ be the curve represented by the equations
$$x = t, \quad y = 3t^2, \quad z = 6t^3 \quad (0 \le t \le 1)$$
In each part, evaluate the line integral along $C$.

(a) $\displaystyle\int_C xyz^2 \, ds$     (b) $\displaystyle\int_C xyz^2 \, dx$

(c) $\displaystyle\int_C xyz^2 \, dy$     (d) $\displaystyle\int_C xyz^2 \, dz$

13. In each part, evaluate the integral
$$\int_C (3x + 2y) \, dx + (2x - y) \, dy$$
along the stated curve.

(a) The line segment from $(0, 0)$ to $(1, 1)$.

(b) The parabolic arc $y = x^2$ from $(0, 0)$ to $(1, 1)$.

(c) The curve $y = \sin(\pi x/2)$ from $(0, 0)$ to $(1, 1)$.

(d) The curve $x = y^3$ from $(0, 0)$ to $(1, 1)$.

14. In each part, evaluate the integral
$$\int_C y \, dx + z \, dy - x \, dz$$
along the stated curve.

(a) The line segment from $(0, 0, 0)$ to $(1, 1, 1)$.

(b) The twisted cubic $x = t$, $y = t^2$, $z = t^3$ from $(0, 0, 0)$ to $(1, 1, 1)$.

(c) The helix $x = \cos \pi t$, $y = \sin \pi t$, $z = t$ from $(1, 0, 0)$ to $(-1, 0, 1)$.

**15–18 True–False** Determine whether the statement is true or false. Explain your answer. ▨

**15.** If $C$ is a smooth oriented curve in the $xy$-plane and $f(x, y)$ is a continuous function defined on $C$, then
$$\int_C f(x, y)\, ds = -\int_{-C} f(x, y)\, ds$$

**16.** The line integral of a continuous vector field along a smooth curve $C$ is a vector.

**17.** If $\mathbf{F}(x, y) = f(x, y)\mathbf{i} + g(x, y)\mathbf{j}$ along a smooth oriented curve $C$ in the $xy$-plane, then
$$\int_C \mathbf{F} \cdot d\mathbf{r} = \int_C f(x, y)\, dx + g(x, y)\, dy$$

**18.** If a smooth oriented curve $C$ in the $xy$-plane is a contour for a differentiable function $f(x, y)$, then
$$\int_C \nabla f \cdot d\mathbf{r} = 0$$

**19–22** Evaluate the line integral with respect to $s$ along the curve $C$. ▨

**19.** $\displaystyle\int_C \frac{1}{1+x}\, ds$

$C : \mathbf{r}(t) = t\mathbf{i} + \frac{2}{3}t^{3/2}\mathbf{j} \quad (0 \le t \le 3)$

**20.** $\displaystyle\int_C \frac{x}{1+y^2}\, ds$

$C : x = 1 + 2t, \; y = t \quad (0 \le t \le 1)$

**21.** $\displaystyle\int_C 3x^2 yz\, ds$

$C : \dot{x} = t, \; y = t^2, \; z = \frac{2}{3}t^3 \quad (0 \le t \le 1)$

**22.** $\displaystyle\int_C \frac{e^{-z}}{x^2 + y^2}\, ds$

$C : \mathbf{r}(t) = 2\cos t\mathbf{i} + 2\sin t\mathbf{j} + t\mathbf{k} \quad (0 \le t \le 2\pi)$

**23–30** Evaluate the line integral along the curve $C$. ▨

**23.** $\displaystyle\int_C (x + 2y)\, dx + (x - y)\, dy$

$C : x = 2\cos t, \; y = 4\sin t \quad (0 \le t \le \pi/4)$

**24.** $\displaystyle\int_C (x^2 - y^2)\, dx + x\, dy$

$C : x = t^{2/3}, \; y = t \quad (-1 \le t \le 1)$

**25.** $\displaystyle\int_C -y\, dx + x\, dy$

$C : y^2 = 3x$ from $(3, 3)$ to $(0, 0)$

**26.** $\displaystyle\int_C (y - x)\, dx + x^2 y\, dy$

$C : y^2 = x^3$ from $(1, -1)$ to $(1, 1)$

**27.** $\displaystyle\int_C (x^2 + y^2)\, dx - x\, dy$

$C : x^2 + y^2 = 1$, counterclockwise from $(1, 0)$ to $(0, 1)$

**28.** $\displaystyle\int_C (y - x)\, dx + xy\, dy$

$C$ : the line segment from $(3, 4)$ to $(2, 1)$

**29.** $\displaystyle\int_C yz\, dx - xz\, dy + xy\, dz$

$C : x = e^t, \; y = e^{3t}, \; z = e^{-t} \quad (0 \le t \le 1)$

**30.** $\displaystyle\int_C x^2\, dx + xy\, dy + z^2\, dz$

$C : x = \sin t, \; y = \cos t, \; z = t^2 \quad (0 \le t \le \pi/2)$

**C 31–32** Use a CAS to evaluate the line integrals along the given curves. ▨

**31.** (a) $\displaystyle\int_C (x^3 + y^3)\, ds$

$C : \mathbf{r}(t) = e^t\mathbf{i} + e^{-t}\mathbf{j} \quad (0 \le t \le \ln 2)$

(b) $\displaystyle\int_C xe^z\, dx + (x - z)\, dy + (x^2 + y^2 + z^2)\, dz$

$C : x = \sin t, \; y = \cos t, \; z = t \quad (0 \le t \le \pi/2)$

**32.** (a) $\displaystyle\int_C x^7 y^3\, ds$

$C : x = \cos^3 t, \; y = \sin^3 t \quad (0 \le t \le \pi/2)$

(b) $\displaystyle\int_C x^5 z\, dx + 7y\, dy + y^2 z\, dz$

$C : \mathbf{r}(t) = t\mathbf{i} + t^2\mathbf{j} + \ln t\mathbf{k} \quad (1 \le t \le e)$

**33–34** Evaluate $\int_C y\, dx - x\, dy$ along the curve $C$ shown in the figure. ▨

**33.** (a)
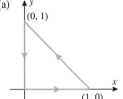

(b)
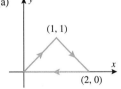

**34.** (a)
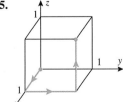

(b)
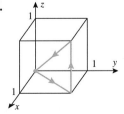

**35–36** Evaluate $\int_C x^2 z\, dx - yx^2\, dy + 3\, dz$ along the curve $C$ shown in the figure. ▨

**35.**
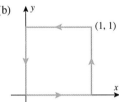

**36.**
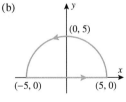

**37–40** Evaluate $\int_C \mathbf{F} \cdot d\mathbf{r}$ along the curve $C$. ■

**37.** $\mathbf{F}(x, y) = x^2\mathbf{i} + xy\mathbf{j}$
$C : \mathbf{r}(t) = 2\cos t\mathbf{i} + 2\sin t\mathbf{j} \quad (0 \leq t \leq \pi)$

**38.** $\mathbf{F}(x, y) = x^2y\mathbf{i} + 4\mathbf{j}$
$C : \mathbf{r}(t) = e^t\mathbf{i} + e^{-t}\mathbf{j} \quad (0 \leq t \leq 1)$

**39.** $\mathbf{F}(x, y) = (x^2 + y^2)^{-3/2}(x\mathbf{i} + y\mathbf{j})$
$C : \mathbf{r}(t) = e^t\sin t\mathbf{i} + e^t\cos t\mathbf{j} \quad (0 \leq t \leq 1)$

**40.** $\mathbf{F}(x, y, z) = z\mathbf{i} + x\mathbf{j} + y\mathbf{k}$
$C : \mathbf{r}(t) = \sin t\mathbf{i} + 3\sin t\mathbf{j} + \sin^2 t\mathbf{k} \quad (0 \leq t \leq \pi/2)$

**41.** Find the mass of a thin wire shaped in the form of the circular arc $y = \sqrt{9 - x^2}$ $(0 \leq x \leq 3)$ if the density function is $\delta(x, y) = x\sqrt{y}$.

**42.** Find the mass of a thin wire shaped in the form of the curve $x = e^t\cos t$, $y = e^t\sin t$ $(0 \leq t \leq 1)$ if the density function $\delta$ is proportional to the distance from the origin.

**43.** Find the mass of a thin wire shaped in the form of the helix $x = 3\cos t$, $y = 3\sin t$, $z = 4t$ $(0 \leq t \leq \pi/2)$ if the density function is $\delta = kx/(1 + y^2)$ $(k > 0)$.

**44.** Find the mass of a thin wire shaped in the form of the curve $x = 2t$, $y = \ln t$, $z = 4\sqrt{t}$ $(1 \leq t \leq 4)$ if the density function is proportional to the distance above the $xy$-plane.

**45–48** Find the work done by the force field $\mathbf{F}$ on a particle that moves along the curve $C$. ■

**45.** $\mathbf{F}(x, y) = xy\mathbf{i} + x^2\mathbf{j}$
$C : x = y^2$ from $(0, 0)$ to $(1, 1)$

**46.** $\mathbf{F}(x, y) = (x^2 + xy)\mathbf{i} + (y - x^2y)\mathbf{j}$
$C : x = t, \ y = 1/t \quad (1 \leq t \leq 3)$

**47.** $\mathbf{F}(x, y, z) = xy\mathbf{i} + yz\mathbf{j} + xz\mathbf{k}$
$C : \mathbf{r}(t) = t\mathbf{i} + t^2\mathbf{j} + t^3\mathbf{k} \quad (0 \leq t \leq 1)$

**48.** $\mathbf{F}(x, y, z) = (x + y)\mathbf{i} + xy\mathbf{j} - z^2\mathbf{k}$
$C :$ along line segments from $(0, 0, 0)$ to $(1, 3, 1)$ to $(2, -1, 4)$

**49–50** Find the work done by the force field

$$\mathbf{F}(x, y) = \frac{1}{x^2 + y^2}\mathbf{i} + \frac{4}{x^2 + y^2}\mathbf{j}$$

on a particle that moves along the curve $C$ shown in the figure. ■

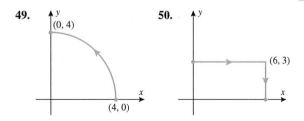

**49.** (0, 4) ... (4, 0)   **50.** (6, 3)

**51–52** Use a line integral to find the area of the surface. ■

**51.** The surface that extends upward from the parabola $y = x^2$ $(0 \leq x \leq 2)$ in the $xy$-plane to the plane $z = 3x$.

**52.** The surface that extends upward from the semicircle $y = \sqrt{4 - x^2}$ in the $xy$-plane to the surface $z = x^2y$.

**53.** As illustrated in the accompanying figure, a sinusoidal cut is made in the top of a cylindrical tin can. Suppose that the base is modeled by the parametric equations $x = \cos t$, $y = \sin t$, $z = 0$ $(0 \leq t \leq 2\pi)$, and the height of the cut as a function of $t$ is $z = 2 + 0.5\sin 3t$.
(a) Use a geometric argument to find the lateral surface area of the cut can.
(b) Write down a line integral for the surface area.
(c) Use the line integral to calculate the surface area.

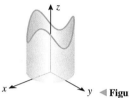

◄ **Figure Ex-53**

**54.** Evaluate the integral $\displaystyle\int_{-C} \frac{x\,dy - y\,dx}{x^2 + y^2}$, where $C$ is the circle $x^2 + y^2 = a^2$ traversed counterclockwise.

**55.** Suppose that a particle moves through the force field $\mathbf{F}(x, y) = xy\mathbf{i} + (x - y)\mathbf{j}$ from the point $(0, 0)$ to the point $(1, 0)$ along the curve $x = t$, $y = \lambda t(1 - t)$. For what value of $\lambda$ will the work done by the force field be 1?

**56.** A farmer weighing 150 lb carries a sack of grain weighing 20 lb up a circular helical staircase around a silo of radius 25 ft. As the farmer climbs, grain leaks from the sack at a rate of 1 lb per 10 ft of ascent. How much work is performed by the farmer in climbing through a vertical distance of 60 ft in exactly four revolutions? [*Hint:* Find a vector field that represents the force exerted by the farmer in lifting his own weight plus the weight of the sack upward at each point along his path.]

**57.** Suppose that a curve $C$ in the $xy$-plane is smoothly parametrized by

$$\mathbf{r}(t) = x(t)\mathbf{i} + y(t)\mathbf{j} \qquad (a \leq t \leq b)$$

In each part, refer to the notation used in the derivation of Formula (9).
(a) Let $m$ and $M$ denote the respective minimum and maximum values of $\|\mathbf{r}'(t)\|$ on $[a, b]$. Prove that

$$0 \leq m(\max \Delta t_k) \leq \max \Delta s_k \leq M(\max \Delta t_k)$$

(b) Use part (a) to prove that $\max \Delta s_k \to 0$ if and only if $\max \Delta t_k \to 0$.

**58.** Writing Discuss the similarities and differences between the definition of a definite integral over an interval (Definition 5.5.1) and the definition of the line integral with respect to arc length along a curve (Definition 15.2.1).

**59.** Writing Describe the different types of line integrals, and discuss how they are related.

1. $2\sqrt{2}$   2. $\dfrac{3\sqrt{2}}{2}$   3. $4\pi$   4. 0

## 15.3 INDEPENDENCE OF PATH; CONSERVATIVE VECTOR FIELDS

*In this section we will show that for certain kinds of vector fields* **F** *the line integral of* **F** *along a curve depends only on the endpoints of the curve and not on the curve itself. Vector fields with this property, which include gravitational and electrostatic fields, are of special importance in physics and engineering.*

### WORK INTEGRALS

We saw in the last section that if **F** is a force field in 2-space or 3-space, then the work performed by the field on a particle moving along a parametric curve $C$ from an initial point $P$ to a final point $Q$ is given by the integral

$$\int_C \mathbf{F} \cdot d\mathbf{r} \quad \text{or equivalently} \quad \int_C \mathbf{F} \cdot \mathbf{T}\, ds$$

Accordingly, we call an integral of this type a **work integral**. Recall that a work integral can also be expressed in scalar form as

$$\int_C \mathbf{F} \cdot d\mathbf{r} = \int_C f(x, y)\, dx + g(x, y)\, dy \qquad \boxed{\text{2-space}} \tag{1}$$

$$\int_C \mathbf{F} \cdot d\mathbf{r} = \int_C f(x, y, z)\, dx + g(x, y, z)\, dy + h(x, y, z)\, dz \qquad \boxed{\text{3-space}} \tag{2}$$

where $f$, $g$, and $h$ are the component functions of **F**.

### INDEPENDENCE OF PATH

The parametric curve $C$ in a work integral is called the **path of integration**. One of the important problems in applications is to determine how the path of integration affects the work performed by a force field on a particle that moves from a fixed point $P$ to a fixed point $Q$. We will show shortly that if the force field **F** is conservative (i.e., is the gradient of some potential function $\phi$), then the work that the field performs on a particle that moves from $P$ to $Q$ does not depend on the particular path $C$ that the particle follows. This is illustrated in the following example.

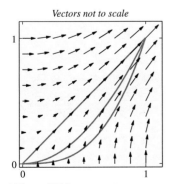

*Vectors not to scale*

▲ **Figure 15.3.1**

▶ **Example 1**   The force field $\mathbf{F}(x, y) = y\mathbf{i} + x\mathbf{j}$ is conservative since it is the gradient of $\phi(x, y) = xy$ (verify). Thus, the preceding discussion suggests that the work performed by the field on a particle that moves from the point $(0, 0)$ to the point $(1, 1)$ should be the same along different paths. Confirm that the value of the work integral

$$\int_C \mathbf{F} \cdot d\mathbf{r}$$

is the same along the following paths (Figure 15.3.1):

(a) The line segment $y = x$ from $(0, 0)$ to $(1, 1)$.

(b) The parabola $y = x^2$ from $(0, 0)$ to $(1, 1)$.

(c) The cubic $y = x^3$ from $(0, 0)$ to $(1, 1)$.

*Solution (a).*   With $x = t$ as the parameter, the path of integration is given by

$$x = t, \quad y = t \quad (0 \leq t \leq 1)$$

Thus,

$$\int_C \mathbf{F} \cdot d\mathbf{r} = \int_C (y\mathbf{i} + x\mathbf{j}) \cdot (dx\mathbf{i} + dy\mathbf{j}) = \int_C y \, dx + x \, dy$$

$$= \int_0^1 2t \, dt = 1$$

*Solution (b).*   With $x = t$ as the parameter, the path of integration is given by

$$x = t, \quad y = t^2 \quad (0 \leq t \leq 1)$$

Thus,

$$\int_C \mathbf{F} \cdot d\mathbf{r} = \int_C y \, dx + x \, dy = \int_0^1 3t^2 \, dt = 1$$

*Solution (c).*   With $x = t$ as the parameter, the path of integration is given by

$$x = t, \quad y = t^3 \quad (0 \leq t \leq 1)$$

Thus,

$$\int_C \mathbf{F} \cdot d\mathbf{r} = \int_C y \, dx + x \, dy = \int_0^1 4t^3 \, dt = 1 \blacktriangleleft$$

### THE FUNDAMENTAL THEOREM OF LINE INTEGRALS

Recall from the Fundamental Theorem of Calculus (Theorem 5.6.1) that if $F$ is an antiderivative of $f$, then

$$\int_a^b f(x) \, dx = F(b) - F(a)$$

The following result is the analog of that theorem for line integrals in 2-space.

---

**15.3.1**    **THEOREM** (*The Fundamental Theorem of Line Integrals*)    *Suppose that*

$$\mathbf{F}(x, y) = f(x, y)\mathbf{i} + g(x, y)\mathbf{j}$$

*is a conservative vector field in some open region $D$ containing the points $(x_0, y_0)$ and $(x_1, y_1)$ and that $f(x, y)$ and $g(x, y)$ are continuous in this region. If*

$$\mathbf{F}(x, y) = \nabla \phi(x, y)$$

*and if $C$ is any piecewise smooth parametric curve that starts at $(x_0, y_0)$, ends at $(x_1, y_1)$, and lies in the region $D$, then*

$$\int_C \mathbf{F}(x, y) \cdot d\mathbf{r} = \phi(x_1, y_1) - \phi(x_0, y_0) \tag{3}$$

*or, equivalently,*

$$\int_C \nabla \phi \cdot d\mathbf{r} = \phi(x_1, y_1) - \phi(x_0, y_0) \tag{4}$$

---

The value of

$$\int_C \mathbf{F} \cdot d\mathbf{r} = \int_C \mathbf{F} \cdot \mathbf{T} \, ds$$

depends on the magnitude of $\mathbf{F}$ along $C$, the alignment of $\mathbf{F}$ with the direction of $C$ at each point, and the length of $C$. If $\mathbf{F}$ is conservative, these various factors always "balance out" so that the value of $\int_C \mathbf{F} \cdot d\mathbf{r}$ depends only on the initial and final points of $C$.

PROOF   We will give the proof for a smooth curve $C$. The proof for a piecewise smooth curve, which is left as an exercise, can be obtained by applying the theorem to each individual smooth piece and adding the results. Suppose that $C$ is given parametrically by $x = x(t)$, $y = y(t)$ $(a \le t \le b)$, so that the initial and final points of the curve are

$$(x_0, y_0) = (x(a), y(a)) \quad \text{and} \quad (x_1, y_1) = (x(b), y(b))$$

Since $\mathbf{F}(x, y) = \nabla\phi$, it follows that

$$\mathbf{F}(x, y) = \frac{\partial\phi}{\partial x}\mathbf{i} + \frac{\partial\phi}{\partial y}\mathbf{j}$$

so

$$\int_C \mathbf{F}(x, y) \cdot d\mathbf{r} = \int_C \frac{\partial\phi}{\partial x}\,dx + \frac{\partial\phi}{\partial y}\,dy = \int_a^b \left[\frac{\partial\phi}{\partial x}\frac{dx}{dt} + \frac{\partial\phi}{\partial y}\frac{dy}{dt}\right] dt$$

$$= \int_a^b \frac{d}{dt}[\phi(x(t), y(t))]\,dt = \phi(x(t), y(t))\Big]_{t=a}^{b}$$

$$= \phi(x(b), y(b)) - \phi(x(a), y(a))$$

$$= \phi(x_1, y_1) - \phi(x_0, y_0) \quad \blacksquare$$

Stated informally, this theorem shows that *the value of a line integral of a conservative vector field along a piecewise smooth path is **independent of the path***; that is, the value of the integral depends on the endpoints and not on the actual path $C$. Accordingly, for line integrals of conservative vector fields, it is common to express (3) and (4) as

$$\int_{(x_0, y_0)}^{(x_1, y_1)} \mathbf{F} \cdot d\mathbf{r} = \int_{(x_0, y_0)}^{(x_1, y_1)} \nabla\phi \cdot d\mathbf{r} = \phi(x_1, y_1) - \phi(x_0, y_0) \tag{5}$$

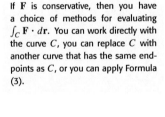

#### ▶ Example 2

(a) Confirm that the force field $\mathbf{F}(x, y) = y\mathbf{i} + x\mathbf{j}$ in Example 1 is conservative by showing that $\mathbf{F}(x, y)$ is the gradient of $\phi(x, y) = xy$.

(b) Use the Fundamental Theorem of Line Integrals to evaluate $\int_{(0,0)}^{(1,1)} \mathbf{F} \cdot d\mathbf{r}$.

*Solution (a).*

$$\nabla\phi = \frac{\partial\phi}{\partial x}\mathbf{i} + \frac{\partial\phi}{\partial y}\mathbf{j} = y\mathbf{i} + x\mathbf{j}$$

*Solution (b).*    From (5) we obtain

$$\int_{(0,0)}^{(1,1)} \mathbf{F} \cdot d\mathbf{r} = \phi(1, 1) - \phi(0, 0) = 1 - 0 = 1$$

which agrees with the results obtained in Example 1 by integrating from $(0, 0)$ to $(1, 1)$ along specific paths. ◀

If **F** is conservative, then you have a choice of methods for evaluating $\int_C \mathbf{F} \cdot d\mathbf{r}$. You can work directly with the curve $C$, you can replace $C$ with another curve that has the same endpoints as $C$, or you can apply Formula (3).

#### ▦ LINE INTEGRALS ALONG CLOSED PATHS

Parametric curves that begin and end at the same point play an important role in the study of vector fields, so there is some special terminology associated with them. A parametric curve $C$ that is represented by the vector-valued function $\mathbf{r}(t)$ for $a \le t \le b$ is said to be **closed** if the initial point $\mathbf{r}(a)$ and the terminal point $\mathbf{r}(b)$ coincide; that is, $\mathbf{r}(a) = \mathbf{r}(b)$ (Figure 15.3.2).

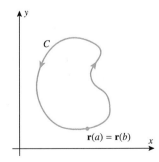

▲ **Figure 15.3.2**

It follows from (5) that the line integral of a conservative vector field along a closed path $C$ that begins and ends at $(x_0, y_0)$ is zero. This is because the point $(x_1, y_1)$ in (5) is the same as $(x_0, y_0)$ and hence

$$\int_C \mathbf{F} \cdot d\mathbf{r} = \phi(x_1, y_1) - \phi(x_0, y_0) = 0$$

Our next objective is to show that the converse of this result is also true. That is, we want to show that under appropriate conditions a vector field whose line integral is zero along *all* closed paths must be conservative. For this to be true we will need to require that the domain $D$ of the vector field be **connected**, by which we mean that any two points in $D$ can be joined by some piecewise smooth curve that lies entirely in $D$. Stated informally, $D$ is connected if it does not consist of two or more separate pieces (Figure 15.3.3).

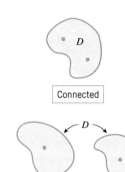

Connected

Not connected

▲ **Figure 15.3.3**

---

**15.3.2    THEOREM**    *If $f(x, y)$ and $g(x, y)$ are continuous on some open connected region $D$, then the following statements are equivalent (all true or all false):*

(*a*)   $\mathbf{F}(x, y) = f(x, y)\mathbf{i} + g(x, y)\mathbf{j}$ *is a conservative vector field on the region $D$.*

(*b*)   $\displaystyle\int_C \mathbf{F} \cdot d\mathbf{r} = 0$ *for every piecewise smooth closed curve $C$ in $D$.*

(*c*)   $\displaystyle\int_C \mathbf{F} \cdot d\mathbf{r}$ *is independent of the path from any point $P$ in $D$ to any point $Q$ in $D$ for every piecewise smooth curve $C$ in $D$.*

---

This theorem can be established by proving three implications: $(a) \Rightarrow (b)$, $(b) \Rightarrow (c)$, and $(c) \Rightarrow (a)$. Since we showed above that $(a) \Rightarrow (b)$, we need only prove the last two implications. We will prove $(c) \Rightarrow (a)$ and leave the other implication as an exercise.

**PROOF**    $(c) \Rightarrow (a)$.    We are assuming that $\int_C \mathbf{F} \cdot d\mathbf{r}$ is independent of the path for every piecewise smooth curve $C$ in the region, and we want to show that there is a function $\phi = \phi(x, y)$ such that $\nabla\phi = \mathbf{F}(x, y)$ at each point of the region; that is,

$$\frac{\partial\phi}{\partial x} = f(x, y) \quad \text{and} \quad \frac{\partial\phi}{\partial y} = g(x, y) \tag{6}$$

Now choose a fixed point $(a, b)$ in $D$, let $(x, y)$ be any point in $D$, and define

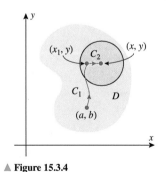

▲ **Figure 15.3.4**

$$\phi(x, y) = \int_{(a,b)}^{(x,y)} \mathbf{F} \cdot d\mathbf{r} \tag{7}$$

This is an unambiguous definition because we have assumed that the integral is independent of the path. We will show that $\nabla\phi = \mathbf{F}$. Since $D$ is open, we can find a circular disk centered at $(x, y)$ whose points lie entirely in $D$. As shown in Figure 15.3.4, choose any point $(x_1, y)$ in this disk that lies on the same horizontal line as $(x, y)$ such that $x_1 < x$. Because the integral in (7) is independent of path, we can evaluate it by first integrating from $(a, b)$ to $(x_1, y)$ along an arbitrary piecewise smooth curve $C_1$ in $D$, and then continuing along the horizontal line segment $C_2$ from $(x_1, y)$ to $(x, y)$. This yields

$$\phi(x, y) = \int_{C_1} \mathbf{F} \cdot d\mathbf{r} + \int_{C_2} \mathbf{F} \cdot d\mathbf{r} = \int_{(a,b)}^{(x_1,y)} \mathbf{F} \cdot d\mathbf{r} + \int_{C_2} \mathbf{F} \cdot d\mathbf{r}$$

Since the first term does not depend on $x$, its partial derivative with respect to $x$ is zero and hence

$$\frac{\partial \phi}{\partial x} = \frac{\partial}{\partial x} \int_{C_2} \mathbf{F} \cdot d\mathbf{r} = \frac{\partial}{\partial x} \int_{C_2} f(x, y)\, dx + g(x, y)\, dy$$

However, the line integral with respect to $y$ is zero along the horizontal line segment $C_2$, so this equation simplifies to

$$\frac{\partial \phi}{\partial x} = \frac{\partial}{\partial x} \int_{C_2} f(x, y)\, dx \qquad (8)$$

To evaluate the integral in this expression, we treat $y$ as a constant and express the line $C_2$ parametrically as

$$x = t, \quad y = y \qquad (x_1 \le t \le x)$$

At the risk of confusion, but to avoid complicating the notation, we have used $x$ both as the dependent variable in the parametric equations and as the endpoint of the line segment. With the latter interpretation of $x$, it follows that (8) can be expressed as

$$\frac{\partial \phi}{\partial x} = \frac{\partial}{\partial x} \int_{x_1}^{x} f(t, y)\, dt$$

Now we apply Part 2 of the Fundamental Theorem of Calculus (Theorem 5.6.3), treating $y$ as constant. This yields

$$\frac{\partial \phi}{\partial x} = f(x, y)$$

which proves the first part of (6). The proof that $\partial \phi/\partial y = g(x, y)$ can be obtained in a similar manner by joining $(x, y)$ to a point $(x, y_1)$ with a vertical line segment (Exercise 39). ∎

### A TEST FOR CONSERVATIVE VECTOR FIELDS

Although Theorem 15.3.2 is an important characterization of conservative vector fields, it is not an effective computational tool because it is usually not possible to evaluate the line integral over all possible piecewise smooth curves in $D$, as required in parts (b) and (c). To develop a method for determining whether a vector field is conservative, we will need to introduce some new concepts about parametric curves and connected sets. We will say that a parametric curve is *simple* if it does not intersect itself between its endpoints. A simple parametric curve may or may not be closed (Figure 15.3.5). In addition, we will say that a connected set $D$ in 2-space is *simply connected* if no simple closed curve in $D$ encloses points that are not in $D$. Stated informally, a connected set $D$ is simply connected if it has no holes; a connected set with one or more holes is said to be *multiply connected* (Figure 15.3.6).

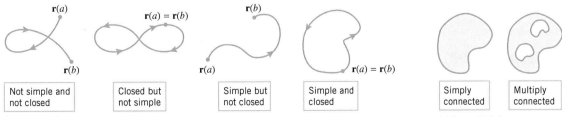

| | | | | | |
|---|---|---|---|---|---|
| Not simple and not closed | Closed but not simple | Simple but not closed | Simple and closed | Simply connected | Multiply connected |

▲ **Figure 15.3.5**                                    ▲ **Figure 15.3.6**

The following theorem is the primary tool for determining whether a vector field in 2-space is conservative.

---

**15.3.3   THEOREM (*Conservative Field Test*)**   *If $f(x, y)$ and $g(x, y)$ are continuous and have continuous first partial derivatives on some open region $D$, and if the vector field $\mathbf{F}(x, y) = f(x, y)\mathbf{i} + g(x, y)\mathbf{j}$ is conservative on $D$, then*

$$\frac{\partial f}{\partial y} = \frac{\partial g}{\partial x} \tag{9}$$

*at each point in $D$. Conversely, if $D$ is simply connected and (9) holds at each point in $D$, then $\mathbf{F}(x, y) = f(x, y)\mathbf{i} + g(x, y)\mathbf{j}$ is conservative.*

---

A complete proof of this theorem requires results from advanced calculus and will be omitted. However, it is not hard to see why (9) must hold if **F** is conservative. For this purpose suppose that $\mathbf{F} = \nabla\phi$, in which case we can express the functions $f$ and $g$ as

$$\frac{\partial \phi}{\partial x} = f \quad \text{and} \quad \frac{\partial \phi}{\partial y} = g \tag{10}$$

Thus,

$$\frac{\partial f}{\partial y} = \frac{\partial}{\partial y}\left(\frac{\partial \phi}{\partial x}\right) = \frac{\partial^2 \phi}{\partial y \partial x} \quad \text{and} \quad \frac{\partial g}{\partial x} = \frac{\partial}{\partial x}\left(\frac{\partial \phi}{\partial y}\right) = \frac{\partial^2 \phi}{\partial x \partial y}$$

But the mixed partial derivatives in these equations are equal (Theorem 13.3.2), so (9) follows.

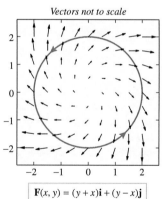

*Vectors not to scale*

$$\mathbf{F}(x, y) = (y + x)\mathbf{i} + (y - x)\mathbf{j}$$

▲ **Figure 15.3.7**

▶ **Example 3**   Use Theorem 15.3.3 to determine whether the vector field

$$\mathbf{F}(x, y) = (y + x)\mathbf{i} + (y - x)\mathbf{j}$$

is conservative on some open set.

***Solution.***   Let $f(x, y) = y + x$ and $g(x, y) = y - x$. Then

$$\frac{\partial f}{\partial y} = 1 \quad \text{and} \quad \frac{\partial g}{\partial x} = -1$$

Thus, there are no points in the $xy$-plane at which condition (9) holds, and hence **F** is not conservative on any open set. ◀

**REMARK**   Since the vector field **F** in Example 3 is not conservative, it follows from Theorem 15.3.2 that there must exist piecewise smooth closed curves in every open connected set in the $xy$-plane on which

$$\int_C \mathbf{F} \cdot d\mathbf{r} = \int_C \mathbf{F} \cdot \mathbf{T}\, ds \neq 0$$

One such curve is the oriented circle shown in Figure 15.3.7. The figure suggests that $\mathbf{F} \cdot \mathbf{T} < 0$ at each point of $C$ (why?), so $\int_C \mathbf{F} \cdot \mathbf{T}\, ds < 0$.

Once it is established that a vector field is conservative, a potential function for the field can be obtained by first integrating either of the equations in (10). This is illustrated in the following example.

▶ **Example 4**   Let $\mathbf{F}(x, y) = 2xy^3\mathbf{i} + (1 + 3x^2y^2)\mathbf{j}$.

(a) Show that $\mathbf{F}$ is a conservative vector field on the entire $xy$-plane.
(b) Find $\phi$ by first integrating $\partial\phi/\partial x$.
(c) Find $\phi$ by first integrating $\partial\phi/\partial y$.

*Solution (a).*   Since $f(x, y) = 2xy^3$ and $g(x, y) = 1 + 3x^2y^2$, we have

$$\frac{\partial f}{\partial y} = 6xy^2 = \frac{\partial g}{\partial x}$$

so (9) holds for all $(x, y)$.

*Solution (b).*   Since the field $\mathbf{F}$ is conservative, there is a potential function $\phi$ such that

$$\frac{\partial\phi}{\partial x} = 2xy^3 \quad\text{and}\quad \frac{\partial\phi}{\partial y} = 1 + 3x^2y^2 \tag{11}$$

Integrating the first of these equations with respect to $x$ (and treating $y$ as a constant) yields

$$\phi = \int 2xy^3\,dx = x^2y^3 + k(y) \tag{12}$$

where $k(y)$ represents the "constant" of integration. We are justified in treating the constant of integration as a function of $y$, since $y$ is held constant in the integration process. To find $k(y)$ we differentiate (12) with respect to $y$ and use the second equation in (11) to obtain

$$\frac{\partial\phi}{\partial y} = 3x^2y^2 + k'(y) = 1 + 3x^2y^2$$

from which it follows that $k'(y) = 1$. Thus,

$$k(y) = \int k'(y)\,dy = \int 1\,dy = y + K$$

You can also use (7) to find a potential function for a conservative vector field. For example, find a potential function for the vector field in Example 4 by evaluating (7) on the line segment

$$\mathbf{r}(t) = t(x\mathbf{i}) + t(y\mathbf{j}) \quad (0 \le t \le 1)$$

from $(0, 0)$ to $(x, y)$.

where $K$ is a (numerical) constant of integration. Substituting in (12) we obtain

$$\phi = x^2y^3 + y + K$$

The appearance of the arbitrary constant $K$ tells us that $\phi$ is not unique. As a check on the computations, you may want to verify that $\nabla\phi = \mathbf{F}$.

*Solution (c).*   Integrating the second equation in (11) with respect to $y$ (and treating $x$ as a constant) yields

$$\phi = \int (1 + 3x^2y^2)\,dy = y + x^2y^3 + k(x) \tag{13}$$

where $k(x)$ is the "constant" of integration. Differentiating (13) with respect to $x$ and using the first equation in (11) yields

$$\frac{\partial\phi}{\partial x} = 2xy^3 + k'(x) = 2xy^3$$

from which it follows that $k'(x) = 0$ and consequently that $k(x) = K$, where $K$ is a numerical constant of integration. Substituting this in (13) yields

$$\phi = y + x^2y^3 + K$$

which agrees with the solution in part (b). ◀

▶ **Example 5**    Use the potential function obtained in Example 4 to evaluate the integral

$$\int_{(1,4)}^{(3,1)} 2xy^3\, dx + (1 + 3x^2y^2)\, dy$$

*Solution.*    The integrand can be expressed as $\mathbf{F} \cdot d\mathbf{r}$, where $\mathbf{F}$ is the vector field in Example 4. Thus, using Formula (3) and the potential function $\phi = y + x^2y^3 + K$ for $\mathbf{F}$, we obtain

$$\int_{(1,4)}^{(3,1)} 2xy^3\, dx + (1 + 3x^2y^2)\, dy = \int_{(1,4)}^{(3,1)} \mathbf{F} \cdot d\mathbf{r} = \phi(3, 1) - \phi(1, 4)$$

$$= (10 + K) - (68 + K) = -58 \;\blacktriangleleft$$

In the solution to Example 5, note that the constant $K$ drops out. In future integration problems of the type in this example, we will often omit $K$ from the computations. See Exercise 7 for other ways to evaluate this integral.

▶ **Example 6**    Let $\mathbf{F}(x, y) = e^y\mathbf{i} + xe^y\mathbf{j}$ denote a force field in the $xy$-plane.

(a) Verify that the force field $\mathbf{F}$ is conservative on the entire $xy$-plane.

(b) Find the work done by the field on a particle that moves from $(1, 0)$ to $(-1, 0)$ along the semicircular path $C$ shown in Figure 15.3.8.

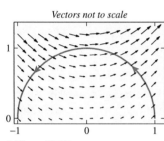

*Vectors not to scale*

▲ **Figure 15.3.8**

*Solution (a).*    For the given field we have $f(x, y) = e^y$ and $g(x, y) = xe^y$. Thus,

$$\frac{\partial}{\partial y}(e^y) = e^y = \frac{\partial}{\partial x}(xe^y)$$

so (9) holds for all $(x, y)$ and hence $\mathbf{F}$ is conservative on the entire $xy$-plane.

*Solution (b).*    From Formula (34) of Section 15.2, the work done by the field is

$$W = \int_C \mathbf{F} \cdot d\mathbf{r} = \int_C e^y\, dx + xe^y\, dy \tag{14}$$

However, the calculations involved in integrating along $C$ are tedious, so it is preferable to apply Theorem 15.3.1, taking advantage of the fact that the field is conservative and the integral is independent of path. Thus, we write (14) as

$$W = \int_{(1,0)}^{(-1,0)} e^y\, dx + xe^y\, dy = \phi(-1, 0) - \phi(1, 0) \tag{15}$$

As illustrated in Example 4, we can find $\phi$ by integrating either of the equations

$$\frac{\partial \phi}{\partial x} = e^y \quad \text{and} \quad \frac{\partial \phi}{\partial y} = xe^y \tag{16}$$

We will integrate the first. We obtain

$$\phi = \int e^y\, dx = xe^y + k(y) \tag{17}$$

Differentiating this equation with respect to $y$ and using the second equation in (16) yields

$$\frac{\partial \phi}{\partial y} = xe^y + k'(y) = xe^y$$

from which it follows that $k'(y) = 0$ or $k(y) = K$. Thus, from (17)

$$\phi = xe^y + K$$

and hence from (15)

$$W = \phi(-1, 0) - \phi(1, 0) = (-1)e^0 - 1e^0 = -2 \;\blacktriangleleft$$

### ■ CONSERVATIVE VECTOR FIELDS IN 3-SPACE

All of the results in this section have analogs in 3-space: Theorems 15.3.1 and 15.3.2 can be extended to vector fields in 3-space simply by adding a third variable and modifying the hypotheses appropriately. For example, in 3-space, Formula (3) becomes

$$\int_C \mathbf{F}(x, y, z) \cdot d\mathbf{r} = \phi(x_1, y_1, z_1) - \phi(x_0, y_0, z_0) \tag{18}$$

Theorem 15.3.3 can also be extended to vector fields in 3-space. We leave it for the exercises to show that if $\mathbf{F}(x, y, z) = f(x, y, z)\mathbf{i} + g(x, y, z)\mathbf{j} + h(x, y, z)\mathbf{k}$ is a conservative field, then

$$\frac{\partial f}{\partial y} = \frac{\partial g}{\partial x}, \quad \frac{\partial f}{\partial z} = \frac{\partial h}{\partial x}, \quad \frac{\partial g}{\partial z} = \frac{\partial h}{\partial y} \tag{19}$$

that is, curl $\mathbf{F} = \mathbf{0}$. Conversely, a vector field satisfying these conditions on a suitably restricted region is conservative on that region if $f$, $g$, and $h$ are continuous and have continuous first partial derivatives in the region. Some problems involving Formulas (18) and (19) are given in the review exercises at the end of this chapter.

### ■ CONSERVATION OF ENERGY

If $\mathbf{F}(x, y, z)$ is a conservative force field with a potential function $\phi(x, y, z)$, then we call $V(x, y, z) = -\phi(x, y, z)$ the **potential energy** of the field at the point $(x, y, z)$. Thus, it follows from the 3-space version of Theorem 15.3.1 that the work $W$ done by $\mathbf{F}$ on a particle that moves along any path $C$ from a point $(x_0, y_0, z_0)$ to a point $(x_1, y_1, z_1)$ is related to the potential energy by the equation

$$W = \int_C \mathbf{F} \cdot d\mathbf{r} = \phi(x_1, y_1, z_1) - \phi(x_0, y_0, z_0) = -[V(x_1, y_1, z_1) - V(x_0, y_0, z_0)] \tag{20}$$

That is, the work done by the field is the negative of the change in potential energy. In particular, it follows from the 3-space analog of Theorem 15.3.2 that if a particle traverses a piecewise smooth closed path in a conservative vector field, then the work done by the field is zero, and there is no change in potential energy. To take this a step further, suppose that a particle of mass $m$ moves along any piecewise smooth curve (not necessarily closed) in a conservative force field $\mathbf{F}$, starting at $(x_0, y_0, z_0)$ with speed $v_i$ and ending at $(x_1, y_1, z_1)$ with speed $v_f$. If $\mathbf{F}$ is the only force acting on the particle, then an argument similar to the derivation of Equation (6) in Section 6.6 shows that the work done on the particle by $\mathbf{F}$ is equal to the change in kinetic energy $\frac{1}{2}mv_f^2 - \frac{1}{2}mv_i^2$ of the particle. (An argument for smooth curves appears in the Making Connections exercises.) If we let $V_i$ denote the potential energy at the starting point and $V_f$ the potential energy at the final point, then it follows from (20) that

$$\tfrac{1}{2}mv_f^2 - \tfrac{1}{2}mv_i^2 = -[V_f - V_i]$$

which we can rewrite as

$$\tfrac{1}{2}mv_f^2 + V_f = \tfrac{1}{2}mv_i^2 + V_i$$

This equation states that the total energy of the particle (kinetic energy + potential energy) does not change as the particle moves along a path in a conservative vector field. This result, called the **conservation of energy principle**, explains the origin of the term "conservative vector field."

✔ **QUICK CHECK EXERCISES 15.3**   *(See page 1121 for answers.)*

**1.** If $C$ is a piecewise smooth curve from $(1, 2, 3)$ to $(4, 5, 6)$, then

$$\int_C dx + 2\, dy + 3\, dz = \underline{\hspace{2cm}}$$

**2.** If $C$ is the portion of the circle $x^2 + y^2 = 1$ where $0 \le x$, oriented counterclockwise, and $f(x, y) = ye^x$, then

$$\int_C \nabla f \cdot d\mathbf{r} = \underline{\hspace{2cm}}$$

**3.** A potential function for the vector field

$$\mathbf{F}(x, y, z) = yz\mathbf{i} + (xz + z)\mathbf{j} + (xy + y + 1)\mathbf{k}$$

is $\phi(x, y, z) = \underline{\hspace{2cm}}$.

**4.** If $a$, $b$, and $c$ are nonzero real numbers such that the vector field $x^5 y^a \mathbf{i} + x^b y^c \mathbf{j}$ is a conservative vector field, then

$$a = \underline{\hspace{1.5cm}}, \quad b = \underline{\hspace{1.5cm}}, \quad c = \underline{\hspace{1.5cm}}$$

**EXERCISE SET 15.3**   ☐ CAS

**1–6** Determine whether $\mathbf{F}$ is a conservative vector field. If so, find a potential function for it. ▪

**1.** $\mathbf{F}(x, y) = x\mathbf{i} + y\mathbf{j}$       **2.** $\mathbf{F}(x, y) = 3y^2\mathbf{i} + 6xy\mathbf{j}$

**3.** $\mathbf{F}(x, y) = x^2 y\mathbf{i} + 5xy^2\mathbf{j}$

**4.** $\mathbf{F}(x, y) = e^x \cos y\mathbf{i} - e^x \sin y\mathbf{j}$

**5.** $\mathbf{F}(x, y) = (\cos y + y \cos x)\mathbf{i} + (\sin x - x \sin y)\mathbf{j}$

**6.** $\mathbf{F}(x, y) = x \ln y\mathbf{i} + y \ln x\mathbf{j}$

**7.** In each part, evaluate $\int_C 2xy^3\, dx + (1 + 3x^2 y^2)\, dy$ over the curve $C$, and compare your answer with the result of Example 5.
  (a) $C$ is the line segment from $(1, 4)$ to $(3, 1)$.
  (b) $C$ consists of the line segment from $(1, 4)$ to $(1, 1)$, followed by the line segment from $(1, 1)$ to $(3, 1)$.

**8.** (a) Show that the line integral $\int_C y \sin x\, dx - \cos x\, dy$ is independent of the path.
  (b) Evaluate the integral in part (a) along the line segment from $(0, 1)$ to $(\pi, -1)$.
  (c) Evaluate the integral $\int_{(0,1)}^{(\pi,-1)} y \sin x\, dx - \cos x\, dy$ using Theorem 15.3.1, and confirm that the value is the same as that obtained in part (b).

**9–14** Show that the integral is independent of the path, and use Theorem 15.3.1 to find its value. ▪

**9.** $\displaystyle\int_{(1,2)}^{(4,0)} 3y\, dx + 3x\, dy$

**10.** $\displaystyle\int_{(0,0)}^{(1,\pi/2)} e^x \sin y\, dx + e^x \cos y\, dy$

**11.** $\displaystyle\int_{(0,0)}^{(3,2)} 2xe^y\, dx + x^2 e^y\, dy$

**12.** $\displaystyle\int_{(-1,2)}^{(0,1)} (3x - y + 1)\, dx - (x + 4y + 2)\, dy$

**13.** $\displaystyle\int_{(2,-2)}^{(-1,0)} 2xy^3\, dx + 3y^2 x^2\, dy$

**14.** $\displaystyle\int_{(1,1)}^{(3,3)} \left(e^x \ln y - \frac{e^y}{x}\right) dx + \left(\frac{e^x}{y} - e^y \ln x\right) dy$, where $x$ and $y$ are positive.

**15–18** Confirm that the force field $\mathbf{F}$ is conservative in some open connected region containing the points $P$ and $Q$, and then find the work done by the force field on a particle moving along an arbitrary smooth curve in the region from $P$ to $Q$. ▪

**15.** $\mathbf{F}(x, y) = xy^2\mathbf{i} + x^2 y\mathbf{j}$;  $P(1, 1)$, $Q(0, 0)$

**16.** $\mathbf{F}(x, y) = 2xy^3\mathbf{i} + 3x^2 y^2\mathbf{j}$;  $P(-3, 0)$, $Q(4, 1)$

**17.** $\mathbf{F}(x, y) = ye^{xy}\mathbf{i} + xe^{xy}\mathbf{j}$;  $P(-1, 1)$, $Q(2, 0)$

**18.** $\mathbf{F}(x, y) = e^{-y} \cos x\mathbf{i} - e^{-y} \sin x\mathbf{j}$;  $P(\pi/2, 1)$, $Q(-\pi/2, 0)$

**19–22 True–False** Determine whether the statement is true or false. Explain your answer. ▪

**19.** If $\mathbf{F}$ is a vector field and there exists a closed curve $C$ such that $\int_C \mathbf{F} \cdot d\mathbf{r} = 0$, then $\mathbf{F}$ is conservative.

**20.** If $\mathbf{F}(x, y) = a\mathbf{i} + b\mathbf{j}$ is a conservative vector field, then $a = b$.

**21.** If $\phi(x, y)$ is a potential function for a constant vector field, then the graph of $z = \phi(x, y)$ is a plane.

**22.** If $f(x, y)$ and $g(x, y)$ are differentiable functions defined on the $xy$-plane, and if $f_y(x, y) = g_x(x, y)$ for all $(x, y)$, then there exists a function $\phi(x, y)$ such that $\phi_x(x, y) = f(x, y)$ and $\phi_y(x, y) = g(x, y)$.

**23–24** Find the exact value of $\int_C \mathbf{F} \cdot d\mathbf{r}$ using any method. ▪

**23.** $\mathbf{F}(x, y) = (e^y + ye^x)\mathbf{i} + (xe^y + e^x)\mathbf{j}$
  $C : \mathbf{r}(t) = \sin(\pi t/2)\mathbf{i} + \ln t\mathbf{j}$   $(1 \le t \le 2)$

**24.** $\mathbf{F}(x, y) = 2xy\mathbf{i} + (x^2 + \cos y)\mathbf{j}$
  $C : \mathbf{r}(t) = t\mathbf{i} + t \cos(t/3)\mathbf{j}$   $(0 \le t \le \pi)$

☐ **25.** Use the numerical integration capability of a CAS or other calculating utility to approximate the value of the integral in Exercise 23 by direct integration. Confirm that the numerical approximation is consistent with the exact value.

☐ **26.** Use the numerical integration capability of a CAS or other calculating utility to approximate the value of the integral in Exercise 24 by direct integration. Confirm that the numerical approximation is consistent with the exact value.

**27–28** Is the vector field conservative? Explain.

**27.**                                 **28.**

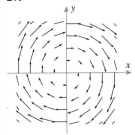

**29.** Suppose that $C$ is a circle in the domain of a conservative nonzero vector field in the $xy$-plane whose component functions are continuous. Explain why there must be at least two points on $C$ at which the vector field is normal to the circle.

**30.** Does the result in Exercise 29 remain true if the circle $C$ is replaced by a square? Explain.

**31.** Prove: If

$$\mathbf{F}(x, y, z) = f(x, y, z)\mathbf{i} + g(x, y, z)\mathbf{j} + h(x, y, z)\mathbf{k}$$

is a conservative field and $f$, $g$, and $h$ are continuous and have continuous first partial derivatives in a region, then

$$\frac{\partial f}{\partial y} = \frac{\partial g}{\partial x}, \quad \frac{\partial f}{\partial z} = \frac{\partial h}{\partial x}, \quad \frac{\partial g}{\partial z} = \frac{\partial h}{\partial y}$$

in the region.

**32.** Use the result in Exercise 31 to show that the integral

$$\int_C yz\,dx + xz\,dy + yx^2\,dz$$

is not independent of the path.

**33.** Find a nonzero function $h$ for which

$$\mathbf{F}(x, y) = h(x)[x\sin y + y\cos y]\mathbf{i}$$
$$+ h(x)[x\cos y - y\sin y]\mathbf{j}$$

is conservative.

**34.** (a)  In Example 3 of Section 15.1 we showed that

$$\phi(x, y) = -\frac{c}{(x^2 + y^2)^{1/2}}$$

is a potential function for the two-dimensional inverse-square field

$$\mathbf{F}(x, y) = \frac{c}{(x^2 + y^2)^{3/2}}(x\mathbf{i} + y\mathbf{j})$$

but we did not explain how the potential function $\phi(x, y)$ was obtained. Use Theorem 15.3.3 to show

that the two-dimensional inverse-square field is conservative everywhere except at the origin, and then use the method of Example 4 to derive the formula for $\phi(x, y)$.

(b)  Use an appropriate generalization of the method of Example 4 to derive the potential function

$$\phi(x, y, z) = -\frac{c}{(x^2 + y^2 + z^2)^{1/2}}$$

for the three-dimensional inverse-square field given by Formula (5) of Section 15.1.

**35–36** Use the result in Exercise 34(b).

**35.** In each part, find the work done by the three-dimensional inverse-square field

$$\mathbf{F}(\mathbf{r}) = \frac{1}{\|\mathbf{r}\|^3}\mathbf{r}$$

on a particle that moves along the curve $C$.

(a)  $C$ is the line segment from $P(1, 1, 2)$ to $Q(3, 2, 1)$.

(b)  $C$ is the curve

$$\mathbf{r}(t) = (2t^2 + 1)\mathbf{i} + (t^3 + 1)\mathbf{j} + (2 - \sqrt{t})\mathbf{k}$$

where $0 \le t \le 1$.

(c)  $C$ is the circle in the $xy$-plane of radius 1 centered at $(2, 0, 0)$ traversed counterclockwise.

**36.** Let $\mathbf{F}(x, y) = \dfrac{y}{x^2 + y^2}\mathbf{i} - \dfrac{x}{x^2 + y^2}\mathbf{j}$.

(a)  Show that

$$\int_{C_1} \mathbf{F} \cdot d\mathbf{r} \ne \int_{C_2} \mathbf{F} \cdot d\mathbf{r}$$

if $C_1$ and $C_2$ are the semicircular paths from $(1, 0)$ to $(-1, 0)$ given by

$$C_1 : x = \cos t, \quad y = \sin t \qquad (0 \le t \le \pi)$$
$$C_2 : x = \cos t, \quad y = -\sin t \qquad (0 \le t \le \pi)$$

(b)  Show that the components of $\mathbf{F}$ satisfy Formula (9).

(c)  Do the results in parts (a) and (b) contradict Theorem 15.3.3? Explain.

**37.** Prove Theorem 15.3.1 if $C$ is a piecewise smooth curve composed of smooth curves $C_1, C_2, \ldots, C_n$.

**38.** Prove that $(b)$ implies $(c)$ in Theorem 15.3.2. [*Hint:* Consider any two piecewise smooth oriented curves $C_1$ and $C_2$ in the region from a point $P$ to a point $Q$, and integrate around the closed curve consisting of $C_1$ and $-C_2$.]

**39.** Complete the proof of Theorem 15.3.2 by showing that $\partial\phi/\partial y = g(x, y)$, where $\phi(x, y)$ is the function in (7).

**40.** Writing  Describe the different methods available for evaluating the integral of a conservative vector field over a smooth curve.

**41.** Writing  Discuss some of the ways that you can show a vector field is *not* conservative.

**✓ QUICK CHECK ANSWERS 15.3**

**1.** 18    **2.** 2    **3.** $xyz + yz + z$    **4.** 6, 6, 5

## 15.4 GREEN'S THEOREM

*In this section we will discuss a remarkable and beautiful theorem that expresses a double integral over a plane region in terms of a line integral around its boundary.*

### GREEN'S THEOREM

**15.4.1 THEOREM (*Green's Theorem*)** *Let R be a simply connected plane region whose boundary is a simple, closed, piecewise smooth curve C oriented counterclockwise. If $f(x, y)$ and $g(x, y)$ are continuous and have continuous first partial derivatives on some open set containing R, then*

$$\int_C f(x, y)\, dx + g(x, y)\, dy = \iint_R \left( \frac{\partial g}{\partial x} - \frac{\partial f}{\partial y} \right) dA \tag{1}$$

**PROOF** For simplicity, we will prove the theorem for regions that are simultaneously type I and type II (see Definition 14.2.1). Such a region is shown in Figure 15.4.1. The crux of the proof is to show that

$$\int_C f(x, y)\, dx = -\iint_R \frac{\partial f}{\partial y}\, dA \quad \text{and} \quad \int_C g(x, y)\, dy = \iint_R \frac{\partial g}{\partial x}\, dA \tag{2-3}$$

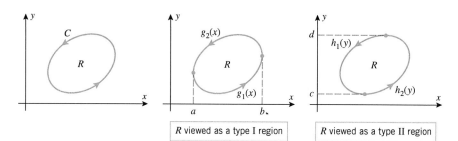

▶ **Figure 15.4.1**

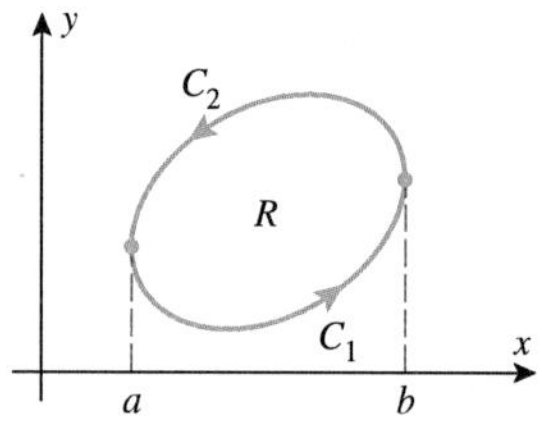

R viewed as a type I region    R viewed as a type II region

▲ **Figure 15.4.2**

To prove (2), view $R$ as a type I region and let $C_1$ and $C_2$ be the lower and upper boundary curves, oriented as in Figure 15.4.2. Then

$$\int_C f(x, y)\, dx = \int_{C_1} f(x, y)\, dx + \int_{C_2} f(x, y)\, dx$$

or, equivalently,

$$\int_C f(x, y)\, dx = \int_{C_1} f(x, y)\, dx - \int_{-C_2} f(x, y)\, dx \tag{4}$$

(This step will help simplify our calculations since $C_1$ and $-C_2$ are then both oriented left to right.) The curves $C_1$ and $-C_2$ can be expressed parametrically as

$$C_1: x = t, \quad y = g_1(t) \qquad (a \le t \le b)$$
$$-C_2: x = t, \quad y = g_2(t) \qquad (a \le t \le b)$$

Thus, we can rewrite (4) as

$$\int_C f(x, y)\, dx = \int_a^b f(t, g_1(t)) x'(t)\, dt - \int_a^b f(t, g_2(t)) x'(t)\, dt$$

$$= \int_a^b f(t, g_1(t))\, dt - \int_a^b f(t, g_2(t))\, dt$$

$$= -\int_a^b [f(t, g_2(t)) - f(t, g_1(t))]\, dt$$

$$= -\int_a^b \left[ f(t, y) \right]_{y=g_1(t)}^{y=g_2(t)} dt = -\int_a^b \left[ \int_{g_1(t)}^{g_2(t)} \frac{\partial f}{\partial y}\, dy \right] dt$$

$$= -\int_a^b \int_{g_1(x)}^{g_2(x)} \frac{\partial f}{\partial y}\, dy\, dx = -\iint_R \frac{\partial f}{\partial y}\, dA$$

Since $x = t$

The proof of (3) is obtained similarly by treating $R$ as a type II region. We omit the details. ■

Supply the details for the proof of (3).

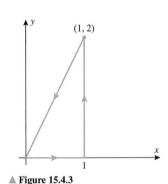

▲ **Figure 15.4.3**

▶ **Example 1**    Use Green's Theorem to evaluate

$$\int_C x^2 y\, dx + x\, dy$$

along the triangular path shown in Figure 15.4.3.

***Solution.***    Since $f(x, y) = x^2 y$ and $g(x, y) = x$, it follows from (1) that

$$\int_C x^2 y\, dx + x\, dy = \iint_R \left[ \frac{\partial}{\partial x}(x) - \frac{\partial}{\partial y}(x^2 y) \right] dA = \int_0^1 \int_0^{2x} (1 - x^2)\, dy\, dx$$

$$= \int_0^1 (2x - 2x^3)\, dx = \left[ x^2 - \frac{x^4}{2} \right]_0^1 = \frac{1}{2}$$

This agrees with the result obtained in Example 10 of Section 15.2, where we evaluated the line integral directly. Note how much simpler this solution is. ◀

George Green (**1793–1841**) English mathematician and physicist. Green left school at an early age to work in his father's bakery and consequently had little early formal education. When his father opened a mill, the boy used the top room as a study in which he taught himself physics and mathematics from library books. In 1828 Green published his most important work, *An Essay on the Application of Mathematical Analysis to the Theories of Electricity and Magnetism.* Although Green's Theorem appeared in that paper, the result went virtually unnoticed because of the small pressrun and local distribution. Following the death of his father in 1829, Green was urged by friends to seek a college education. In 1833, after four years of self-study to close the gaps in his elementary education, Green was admitted to Caius College, Cambridge. He graduated four years later, but with a disappointing performance on his final examinations—possibly because he was more interested in his own research. After a succession of works on light and sound, he was named to be Perse Fellow at Caius College. Two years later he died. In 1845, four years after his death, his paper of 1828 was published and the theories developed therein by this obscure, self-taught baker's son helped pave the way to the modern theories of electricity and magnetism.

### A NOTATION FOR LINE INTEGRALS AROUND SIMPLE CLOSED CURVES

It is common practice to denote a line integral around a simple closed curve by an integral sign with a superimposed circle. With this notation Formula (1) would be written as

$$\oint_C f(x, y)\, dx + g(x, y)\, dy = \iint_R \left( \frac{\partial g}{\partial x} - \frac{\partial f}{\partial y} \right) dA$$

Sometimes a direction arrow is added to the circle to indicate whether the integration is clockwise or counterclockwise. Thus, if we wanted to emphasize the counterclockwise direction of integration required by Theorem 15.4.1, we could express (1) as

$$\oint_C f(x, y)\, dx + g(x, y)\, dy = \iint_R \left( \frac{\partial g}{\partial x} - \frac{\partial f}{\partial y} \right) dA \tag{5}$$

### FINDING WORK USING GREEN'S THEOREM

It follows from Formula (26) of Section 15.2 that the integral on the left side of (5) is the work performed by the force field $\mathbf{F}(x, y) = f(x, y)\mathbf{i} + g(x, y)\mathbf{j}$ on a particle moving counterclockwise around the simple closed curve $C$. In the case where this vector field is conservative, it follows from Theorem 15.3.2 that the integrand in the double integral on the right side of (5) is zero, so the work performed by the field is zero, as expected. For vector fields that are not conservative, it is often more efficient to calculate the work around simple closed curves by using Green's Theorem than by parametrizing the curve.

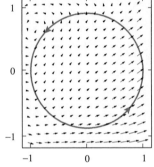

▲ **Figure 15.4.4**

▶ **Example 2**   Find the work done by the force field

$$\mathbf{F}(x, y) = (e^x - y^3)\mathbf{i} + (\cos y + x^3)\mathbf{j}$$

on a particle that travels once around the unit circle $x^2 + y^2 = 1$ in the counterclockwise direction (Figure 15.4.4).

*Solution.*   The work $W$ performed by the field is

$$W = \oint_C \mathbf{F} \cdot d\mathbf{r} = \oint_C (e^x - y^3)\, dx + (\cos y + x^3)\, dy$$

$$= \iint_R \left[ \frac{\partial}{\partial x}(\cos y + x^3) - \frac{\partial}{\partial y}(e^x - y^3) \right] dA \qquad \boxed{\text{Green's Theorem}}$$

$$= \iint_R (3x^2 + 3y^2)\, dA = 3 \iint_R (x^2 + y^2)\, dA$$

$$= 3 \int_0^{2\pi} \int_0^1 (r^2)r\, dr\, d\theta = \frac{3}{4} \int_0^{2\pi} d\theta = \frac{3\pi}{2} \blacktriangleleft$$

> We converted to polar coordinates.

### FINDING AREAS USING GREEN'S THEOREM

Green's Theorem leads to some useful new formulas for the area $A$ of a region $R$ that satisfies the conditions of the theorem. Two such formulas can be obtained as follows:

$$A = \iint_R dA = \oint_C x\, dy \quad \text{and} \quad A = \iint_R dA = \oint_C (-y)\, dx$$

> Set $f(x, y) = 0$ and $g(x, y) = x$ in (1).

> Set $f(x, y) = -y$ and $g(x, y) = 0$ in (1).

A third formula can be obtained by adding these two equations together. Thus, we have the following three formulas that express the area $A$ of a region $R$ in terms of line integrals around the boundary:

$$A = \oint_C x \, dy = -\oint_C y \, dx = \frac{1}{2} \oint_C -y \, dx + x \, dy \tag{6}$$

Although the third formula in (6) looks more complicated than the other two, it often leads to simpler integrations. Each has advantages in certain situations.

► **Example 3**    Use a line integral to find the area enclosed by the ellipse

$$\frac{x^2}{a^2} + \frac{y^2}{b^2} = 1$$

*Solution.*    The ellipse, with counterclockwise orientation, can be represented parametrically by

$$x = a \cos t, \quad y = b \sin t \quad (0 \le t \le 2\pi)$$

If we denote this curve by $C$, then from the third formula in (6) the area $A$ enclosed by the ellipse is

$$A = \frac{1}{2} \oint_C -y \, dx + x \, dy$$

$$= \frac{1}{2} \int_0^{2\pi} [(-b \sin t)(-a \sin t) + (a \cos t)(b \cos t)] \, dt$$

$$= \frac{1}{2} ab \int_0^{2\pi} (\sin^2 t + \cos^2 t) \, dt = \frac{1}{2} ab \int_0^{2\pi} dt = \pi ab \quad ◄$$

■ **GREEN'S THEOREM FOR MULTIPLY CONNECTED REGIONS**

Recall that a plane region is said to be simply connected if it has no holes and is said to be multiply connected if it has one or more holes (see Figure 15.3.6). At the beginning of this section we stated Green's Theorem for a counterclockwise integration around the boundary of a simply connected region $R$ (Theorem 15.4.1). Our next goal is to extend this theorem to multiply connected regions. To make this extension we will need to assume that *the region lies on the left when any portion of the boundary is traversed in the direction of its orientation.* This implies that the outer boundary curve of the region is oriented counterclockwise and the boundary curves that enclose holes have clockwise orientation (Figure 15.4.5$a$). If all portions of the boundary of a multiply connected region $R$ are oriented in this way, then we say that the boundary of $R$ has **positive orientation**.

We will now derive a version of Green's Theorem that applies to multiply connected regions with positively oriented boundaries. For simplicity, we will consider a multiply connected region $R$ with one hole, and we will assume that $f(x, y)$ and $g(x, y)$ have continuous first partial derivatives on some open set containing $R$. As shown in Figure 15.4.5$b$, let us divide $R$ into two regions $R'$ and $R''$ by introducing two "cuts" in $R$. The cuts are shown as line segments, but any piecewise smooth curves will suffice. If we assume that $f$ and $g$ satisfy the hypotheses of Green's Theorem on $R$ (and hence on $R'$ and $R''$), then we can apply this theorem to both $R'$ and $R''$ to obtain

$$\iint\limits_R \left( \frac{\partial g}{\partial x} - \frac{\partial f}{\partial y} \right) dA = \iint\limits_{R'} \left( \frac{\partial g}{\partial x} - \frac{\partial f}{\partial y} \right) dA + \iint\limits_{R''} \left( \frac{\partial g}{\partial x} - \frac{\partial f}{\partial y} \right) dA$$

$$= \underset{\substack{\text{Boundary} \\ \text{of } R'}}{\oint} f(x, y) \, dx + g(x, y) \, dy + \underset{\substack{\text{Boundary} \\ \text{of } R''}}{\oint} f(x, y) \, dx + g(x, y) \, dy$$

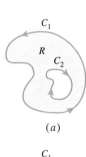

(a)

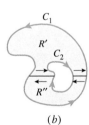

(b)

▲ **Figure 15.4.5**

However, the two line integrals are taken in opposite directions along the cuts, and hence cancel there, leaving only the contributions along $C_1$ and $C_2$. Thus,

$$\iint\limits_R \left( \frac{\partial g}{\partial x} - \frac{\partial f}{\partial y} \right) dA = \oint_{C_1} f(x, y)\,dx + g(x, y)\,dy + \oint_{C_2} f(x, y)\,dx + g(x, y)\,dy \qquad (7)$$

which is an extension of Green's Theorem to a multiply connected region with one hole. Observe that the integral around the outer boundary is taken counterclockwise and the integral around the hole is taken clockwise. More generally, if $R$ is a multiply connected region with $n$ holes, then the analog of (7) involves a sum of $n + 1$ integrals, one taken counterclockwise around the outer boundary of $R$ and the rest taken clockwise around the holes.

▶ **Example 4** Evaluate the integral

$$\oint_C \frac{-y\,dx + x\,dy}{x^2 + y^2}$$

if $C$ is a piecewise smooth simple closed curve oriented counterclockwise such that (a) $C$ does not enclose the origin and (b) $C$ encloses the origin.

*Solution (a).* Let

$$f(x, y) = -\frac{y}{x^2 + y^2}, \qquad g(x, y) = \frac{x}{x^2 + y^2} \qquad (8)$$

so that

$$\frac{\partial g}{\partial x} = \frac{y^2 - x^2}{(x^2 + y^2)^2} = \frac{\partial f}{\partial y}$$

if $x$ and $y$ are not both zero. Thus, if $C$ does not enclose the origin, we have

$$\frac{\partial g}{\partial x} - \frac{\partial f}{\partial y} = 0 \qquad (9)$$

on the simply connected region enclosed by $C$, and hence the given integral is zero by Green's Theorem.

*Solution (b).* Unlike the situation in part (a), we cannot apply Green's Theorem directly because the functions $f(x, y)$ and $g(x, y)$ in (8) are discontinuous at the origin. Our problems are further compounded by the fact that we do not have a specific curve $C$ that we can parametrize to evaluate the integral. Our strategy for circumventing these problems will be to replace $C$ with a specific curve that produces the same value for the integral and then use that curve for the evaluation. To obtain such a curve, we will apply Green's Theorem for multiply connected regions to a region that does not contain the origin. For this purpose we construct a circle $C_a$ with *clockwise* orientation, centered at the origin, and with sufficiently small radius $a$ that it lies inside the region enclosed by $C$ (Figure 15.4.6). This creates a multiply connected region $R$ whose boundary curves $C$ and $C_a$ have the orientations required by Formula (7) and such that within $R$ the functions $f(x, y)$ and $g(x, y)$ in (8) satisfy the hypotheses of Green's Theorem (the origin does not belong to $R$). Thus, it follows from (7) and (9) that

$$\oint_C \frac{-y\,dx + x\,dy}{x^2 + y^2} + \oint_{C_a} \frac{-y\,dx + x\,dy}{x^2 + y^2} = \iint\limits_R 0\,dA = 0$$

It follows from this equation that

$$\oint_C \frac{-y\,dx + x\,dy}{x^2 + y^2} = -\oint_{C_a} \frac{-y\,dx + x\,dy}{x^2 + y^2}$$

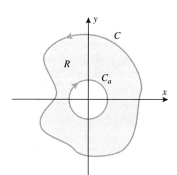

▲ **Figure 15.4.6**

which we can rewrite as

$$\oint_C \frac{-y\,dx + x\,dy}{x^2 + y^2} = \oint_{-C_a} \frac{-y\,dx + x\,dy}{x^2 + y^2}$$

> Reversing the orientation of $C_a$ reverses the sign of the integral.

But $C_a$ has clockwise orientation, so $-C_a$ has counterclockwise orientation. Thus, we have shown that the original integral can be evaluated by integrating counterclockwise around a circle of radius $a$ that is centered at the origin and lies within the region enclosed by $C$. Such a circle can be expressed parametrically as $x = a\cos t$, $y = a\sin t$ $(0 \le t \le 2\pi)$; and hence

$$\oint_C \frac{-y\,dx + x\,dy}{x^2 + y^2} = \int_0^{2\pi} \frac{(-a\sin t)(-a\sin t)\,dt + (a\cos t)(a\cos t)\,dt}{(a\cos t)^2 + (a\sin t)^2}$$

$$= \int_0^{2\pi} 1\,dt = 2\pi \blacktriangleleft$$

✔ **QUICK CHECK EXERCISES 15.4**    *(See page 1129 for answers.)*

**1.** If $C$ is the square with vertices $(\pm1, \pm1)$ oriented counterclockwise, then

$$\int_C -y\,dx + x\,dy = \underline{\hspace{2cm}}$$

**2.** If $C$ is the triangle with vertices $(0, 0)$, $(1, 0)$, and $(1, 1)$ oriented counterclockwise, then

$$\int_C 2xy\,dx + (x^2 + x)\,dy = \underline{\hspace{2cm}}$$

**3.** If $C$ is the unit circle centered at the origin and oriented counterclockwise, then

$$\int_C (y^3 - y - x)\,dx + (x^3 + x + y)\,dy = \underline{\hspace{2cm}}$$

**4.** What region $R$ and choice of functions $f(x, y)$ and $g(x, y)$ allow us to use Formula (1) of Theorem 15.4.1 to claim that

$$\int_0^1 \int_0^{\sqrt{1-x^2}} (2x + 2y)\,dy\,dx = \int_0^{\pi/2} (\sin^3 t + \cos^3 t)\,dt?$$

**EXERCISE SET 15.4**    [C] CAS

**1–2** Evaluate the line integral using Green's Theorem and check the answer by evaluating it directly. ▪

**1.** $\oint_C y^2\,dx + x^2\,dy$, where $C$ is the square with vertices $(0, 0)$, $(1, 0)$, $(1, 1)$, and $(0, 1)$ oriented counterclockwise.

**2.** $\oint_C y\,dx + x\,dy$, where $C$ is the unit circle oriented counterclockwise.

**3–13** Use Green's Theorem to evaluate the integral. In each exercise, assume that the curve $C$ is oriented counterclockwise. ▪

**3.** $\oint_C 3xy\,dx + 2xy\,dy$, where $C$ is the rectangle bounded by $x = -2$, $x = 4$, $y = 1$, and $y = 2$.

**4.** $\oint_C (x^2 - y^2)\,dx + x\,dy$, where $C$ is the circle $x^2 + y^2 = 9$.

**5.** $\oint_C x\cos y\,dx - y\sin x\,dy$, where $C$ is the square with vertices $(0, 0)$, $(\pi/2, 0)$, $(\pi/2, \pi/2)$, and $(0, \pi/2)$.

**6.** $\oint_C y\tan^2 x\,dx + \tan x\,dy$, where $C$ is the circle $x^2 + (y + 1)^2 = 1$.

**7.** $\oint_C (x^2 - y)\,dx + x\,dy$, where $C$ is the circle $x^2 + y^2 = 4$.

**8.** $\oint_C (e^x + y^2)\,dx + (e^y + x^2)\,dy$, where $C$ is the boundary of the region between $y = x^2$ and $y = x$.

**9.** $\oint_C \ln(1 + y)\,dx - \frac{xy}{1 + y}\,dy$, where $C$ is the triangle with vertices $(0, 0)$, $(2, 0)$, and $(0, 4)$.

**10.** $\oint_C x^2 y\,dx - y^2 x\,dy$, where $C$ is the boundary of the region in the first quadrant, enclosed between the coordinate axes and the circle $x^2 + y^2 = 16$.

**11.** $\oint_C \tan^{-1} y\,dx - \frac{y^2 x}{1 + y^2}\,dy$, where $C$ is the square with vertices $(0, 0)$, $(1, 0)$, $(1, 1)$, and $(0, 1)$.

**12.** $\oint_C \cos x \sin y \, dx + \sin x \cos y \, dy$, where $C$ is the triangle with vertices $(0, 0)$, $(3, 3)$, and $(0, 3)$.

**13.** $\oint_C x^2 y \, dx + (y + xy^2) \, dy$, where $C$ is the boundary of the region enclosed by $y = x^2$ and $x = y^2$.

**14.** Let $C$ be the boundary of the region enclosed between $y = x^2$ and $y = 2x$. Assuming that $C$ is oriented counterclockwise, evaluate the following integrals by Green's Theorem:

(a) $\oint_C (6xy - y^2) \, dx$      (b) $\oint_C (6xy - y^2) \, dy$.

**15–18 True–False** Determine whether the statement is true or false. Explain your answer. (In Exercises 16–18, assume that $C$ is a simple, smooth, closed curve, oriented counterclockwise.)

**15.** Green's Theorem allows us to replace any line integral by a double integral.

**16.** If

$$\int_C f(x, y) \, dx + g(x, y) \, dy = 0$$

then $\partial g / \partial x = \partial f / \partial y$ at all points in the region bounded by $C$.

**17.** It must be the case that

$$\int_C x \, dy > 0$$

**18.** It must be the case that

$$\int_C e^{x^2} \, dx + \sin y^3 \, dy = 0$$

**c 19.** Use a CAS to check Green's Theorem by evaluating both integrals in the equation

$$\oint_C e^y \, dx + ye^x \, dy = \iint_R \left[ \frac{\partial}{\partial x} (ye^x) - \frac{\partial}{\partial y} (e^y) \right] dA$$

where
(a) $C$ is the circle $x^2 + y^2 = 1$
(b) $C$ is the boundary of the region enclosed by $y = x^2$ and $x = y^2$.

**20.** In Example 3, we used Green's Theorem to obtain the area of an ellipse. Obtain this area using the first and then the second formula in (6).

**21.** Use a line integral to find the area of the region enclosed by the astroid

$$x = a \cos^3 \phi, \quad y = a \sin^3 \phi \quad (0 \le \phi \le 2\pi)$$

**22.** Use a line integral to find the area of the triangle with vertices $(0, 0)$, $(a, 0)$, and $(0, b)$, where $a > 0$ and $b > 0$.

**23.** Use the formula

$$A = \frac{1}{2} \oint_C -y \, dx + x \, dy$$

to find the area of the region swept out by the line from the origin to the ellipse $x = a \cos t$, $y = b \sin t$ if $t$ varies from $t = 0$ to $t = t_0$ $(0 \le t_0 \le 2\pi)$.

**24.** Use the formula

$$A = \frac{1}{2} \oint_C -y \, dx + x \, dy$$

to find the area of the region swept out by the line from the origin to the hyperbola $x = a \cosh t$, $y = b \sinh t$ if $t$ varies from $t = 0$ to $t = t_0$ $(t_0 \ge 0)$.

**25.** Suppose that $\mathbf{F}(x, y) = f(x, y)\mathbf{i} + g(x, y)\mathbf{j}$ is a vector field whose component functions $f$ and $g$ have continuous first partial derivatives. Let $C$ denote a simple, closed, piecewise smooth curve oriented counterclockwise that bounds a region $R$ contained in the domain of $\mathbf{F}$. We can think of $\mathbf{F}$ as a vector field in 3-space by writing it as

$$\mathbf{F}(x, y, z) = f(x, y)\mathbf{i} + g(x, y)\mathbf{j} + 0\mathbf{k}$$

With this convention, explain why

$$\int_C \mathbf{F} \cdot d\mathbf{r} = \iint_R \text{curl } \mathbf{F} \cdot \mathbf{k} \, dA$$

**26.** Suppose that $\mathbf{F}(x, y) = f(x, y)\mathbf{i} + g(x, y)\mathbf{j}$ is a vector field on the $xy$-plane and that $f$ and $g$ have continuous first partial derivatives with $f_y = g_x$ everywhere. Use Green's Theorem to explain why

$$\int_{C_1} \mathbf{F} \cdot d\mathbf{r} = \int_{C_2} \mathbf{F} \cdot d\mathbf{r}$$

where $C_1$ and $C_2$ are the oriented curves in the accompanying figure. [*Note:* Compare this result with Theorems 15.3.2 and 15.3.3.]

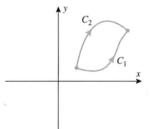

◄ **Figure Ex-26**

**27.** Suppose that $f(x)$ and $g(x)$ are continuous functions with $g(x) \le f(x)$. Let $R$ denote the region bounded by the graph of $f$, the graph of $g$, and the vertical lines $x = a$ and $x = b$. Let $C$ denote the boundary of $R$ oriented counterclockwise. What familiar formula results from applying Green's Theorem to $\int_C (-y) \, dx$?

**28.** In the accompanying figure on the next page, $C$ is a smooth oriented curve from $P(x_0, y_0)$ to $Q(x_1, y_1)$ that is contained inside the rectangle with corners at the origin and $Q$ and outside the rectangle with corners at the origin and $P$.
(a) What region in the figure has area $\int_C x \, dy$?
(b) What region in the figure has area $\int_C y \, dx$?
(c) Express $\int_C x \, dy + \int_C y \, dx$ in terms of the coordinates of $P$ and $Q$.
*(cont.)*

(d) Interpret the result of part (c) in terms of the Fundamental Theorem of Line Integrals.

(e) Interpret the result in part (c) in terms of integration by parts.

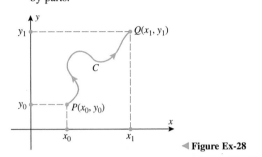

◀ **Figure Ex-28**

**29–30** Use Green's Theorem to find the work done by the force field **F** on a particle that moves along the stated path. ▦

**29.** $\mathbf{F}(x, y) = xy\mathbf{i} + \left(\frac{1}{2}x^2 + xy\right)\mathbf{j}$; the particle starts at $(5, 0)$, traverses the upper semicircle $x^2 + y^2 = 25$, and returns to its starting point along the $x$-axis.

**30.** $\mathbf{F}(x, y) = \sqrt{y}\,\mathbf{i} + \sqrt{x}\,\mathbf{j}$; the particle moves counterclockwise one time around the closed curve given by the equations $y = 0$, $x = 2$, and $y = x^3/4$.

**31.** Evaluate $\oint_C y\,dx - x\,dy$, where $C$ is the cardioid

$$r = a(1 + \cos\theta) \quad (0 \le \theta \le 2\pi)$$

**32.** Let $R$ be a plane region with area $A$ whose boundary is a piecewise smooth, simple, closed curve $C$. Use Green's Theorem to prove that the centroid $(\bar{x}, \bar{y})$ of $R$ is given by

$$\bar{x} = \frac{1}{2A}\oint_C x^2\,dy, \quad \bar{y} = -\frac{1}{2A}\oint_C y^2\,dx$$

**33–36** Use the result in Exercise 32 to find the centroid of the region. ▦

**33.**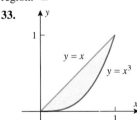

**34.**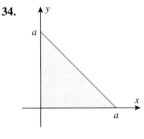

**35.**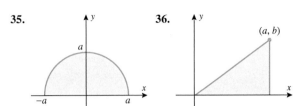

**36.**

**37.** Find a simple closed curve $C$ with counterclockwise orientation that maximizes the value of

$$\oint_C \tfrac{1}{3}y^3\,dx + \left(x - \tfrac{1}{3}x^3\right)\,dy$$

and explain your reasoning.

**38.** (a) Let $C$ be the line segment from a point $(a, b)$ to a point $(c, d)$. Show that

$$\int_C -y\,dx + x\,dy = ad - bc$$

(b) Use the result in part (a) to show that the area $A$ of a triangle with successive vertices $(x_1, y_1)$, $(x_2, y_2)$, and $(x_3, y_3)$ going counterclockwise is

$$A = \tfrac{1}{2}[(x_1 y_2 - x_2 y_1) \\ + (x_2 y_3 - x_3 y_2) + (x_3 y_1 - x_1 y_3)]$$

(c) Find a formula for the area of a polygon with successive vertices $(x_1, y_1)$, $(x_2, y_2)$, ..., $(x_n, y_n)$ going counterclockwise.

(d) Use the result in part (c) to find the area of a quadrilateral with vertices $(0, 0)$, $(3, 4)$, $(-2, 2)$, $(-1, 0)$.

**39–40** Evaluate the integral $\int_C \mathbf{F} \cdot d\mathbf{r}$, where $C$ is the boundary of the region $R$ and $C$ is oriented so that the region is on the left when the boundary is traversed in the direction of its orientation. ▦

**39.** $\mathbf{F}(x, y) = (x^2 + y)\mathbf{i} + (4x - \cos y)\mathbf{j}$; $C$ is the boundary of the region $R$ that is inside the square with vertices $(0, 0)$, $(5, 0)$, $(5, 5)$, $(0, 5)$ but is outside the rectangle with vertices $(1, 1)$, $(3, 1)$, $(3, 2)$, $(1, 2)$.

**40.** $\mathbf{F}(x, y) = (e^{-x} + 3y)\mathbf{i} + x\mathbf{j}$; $C$ is the boundary of the region $R$ inside the circle $x^2 + y^2 = 16$ and outside the circle $x^2 - 2x + y^2 = 3$.

**41.** Writing Discuss the role of the Fundamental Theorem of Calculus in the proof of Green's Theorem.

**42.** Writing Use the Internet or other sources to find information about "planimeters," and then write a paragraph that describes the relationship between these devices and Green's Theorem.

✔ **QUICK CHECK ANSWERS 15.4**

**1.** 8   **2.** $\frac{1}{2}$   **3.** $2\pi$   **4.** $R$ is the region $x^2 + y^2 \le 1$ $(0 \le x, 0 \le y)$ and $f(x, y) = -y^2$, $g(x, y) = x^2$.

## 15.5  SURFACE INTEGRALS

*In previous sections we considered four kinds of integrals—integrals over intervals, double integrals over two-dimensional regions, triple integrals over three-dimensional solids, and line integrals along curves in two- or three-dimensional space. In this section we will discuss integrals over surfaces in three-dimensional space. Such integrals occur in problems involving fluid and heat flow, electricity, magnetism, mass, and center of gravity.*

■ **DEFINITION OF A SURFACE INTEGRAL**

In this section we will define what it means to integrate a function $f(x, y, z)$ over a smooth parametric surface $\sigma$. To motivate the definition we will consider the problem of finding the mass of a curved lamina whose density function (mass per unit area) is known. Recall that in Section 6.7 we defined a *lamina* to be an idealized flat object that is thin enough to be viewed as a plane region. Analogously, a **curved lamina** is an idealized object that is thin enough to be viewed as a surface in 3-space. A curved lamina may look like a bent plate, as in Figure 15.5.1, or it may enclose a region in 3-space, like the shell of an egg. We will model the lamina by a smooth parametric surface $\sigma$. Given any point $(x, y, z)$ on $\sigma$, we let $f(x, y, z)$ denote the corresponding value of the density function. To compute the mass of the lamina, we proceed as follows:

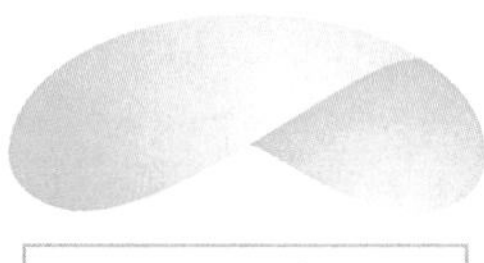

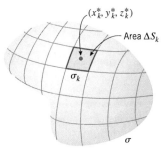

The thickness of a curved lamina is negligible.

▲ **Figure 15.5.1**

- As shown in Figure 15.5.2, we divide $\sigma$ into $n$ very small patches $\sigma_1, \sigma_2, \ldots, \sigma_n$ with areas $\Delta S_1, \Delta S_2, \ldots, \Delta S_n$, respectively. Let $(x_k^*, y_k^*, z_k^*)$ be a sample point in the $k$th patch with $\Delta M_k$ the mass of the corresponding section.

- If the dimensions of $\sigma_k$ are very small, the value of $f$ will not vary much along the $k$th section and we can approximate $f$ along this section by the value $f(x_k^*, y_k^*, z_k^*)$. It follows that the mass of the $k$th section can be approximated by

$$\Delta M_k \approx f(x_k^*, y_k^*, z_k^*)\Delta S_k$$

- The mass $M$ of the entire lamina can then be approximated by

$$M = \sum_{k=1}^{n} \Delta M_k \approx \sum_{k=1}^{n} f(x_k^*, y_k^*, z_k^*)\Delta S_k \tag{1}$$

▲ **Figure 15.5.2**

- We will use the expression $n \to \infty$ to indicate the process of increasing $n$ in such a way that the maximum dimension of each patch approaches 0. It is plausible that the error in (1) will approach 0 as $n \to \infty$ and the exact value of $M$ will be given by

$$M = \lim_{n \to \infty} \sum_{k=1}^{n} f(x_k^*, y_k^*, z_k^*)\Delta S_k \tag{2}$$

The limit in (2) is very similar to the limit used to find the mass of a thin wire [Formula (2) in Section 15.2]. By analogy to Definition 15.2.1, we make the following definition.

**15.5.1  DEFINITION**  If $\sigma$ is a smooth parametric surface, then the **surface integral** of $f(x, y, z)$ over $\sigma$ is

$$\iint\limits_{\sigma} f(x, y, z)\, dS = \lim_{n \to \infty} \sum_{k=1}^{n} f(x_k^*, y_k^*, z_k^*)\Delta S_k \tag{3}$$

provided this limit exists and does not depend on the way the subdivisions of $\sigma$ are made or how the sample points $(x_k^*, y_k^*, z_k^*)$ are chosen.

It can be shown that the integral of $f$ over $\sigma$ exists if $f$ is continuous on $\sigma$.

We see from (2) and Definition 15.5.1 that if $\sigma$ models a lamina and if $f(x, y, z)$ is the density function of the lamina, then the mass $M$ of the lamina is given by

$$M = \iint_\sigma f(x, y, z)\, dS \tag{4}$$

That is, to obtain the mass of a lamina, we integrate the density function over the smooth surface that models the lamina.

Note that if $\sigma$ is a smooth surface of surface area $S$, and $f$ is identically 1, then it immediately follows from Definition 15.5.1 that

$$\iint_\sigma dS = \lim_{n \to \infty} \sum_{k=1}^{n} \Delta S_k = \lim_{n \to \infty} S = S \tag{5}$$

■ **EVALUATING SURFACE INTEGRALS**

There are various procedures for evaluating surface integrals that depend on how the surface $\sigma$ is represented. The following theorem provides a method for evaluating a surface integral when $\sigma$ is represented parametrically.

---

**15.5.2    THEOREM**    *Let $\sigma$ be a smooth parametric surface whose vector equation is*

$$\mathbf{r} = x(u, v)\mathbf{i} + y(u, v)\mathbf{j} + z(u, v)\mathbf{k}$$

*where $(u, v)$ varies over a region $R$ in the uv-plane. If $f(x, y, z)$ is continuous on $\sigma$, then*

$$\iint_\sigma f(x, y, z)\, dS = \iint_R f(x(u, v), y(u, v), z(u, v)) \left\| \frac{\partial \mathbf{r}}{\partial u} \times \frac{\partial \mathbf{r}}{\partial v} \right\| dA \tag{6}$$

---

Explain how to use Formula (6) to confirm Formula (5).

To motivate this result, suppose that the parameter domain $R$ is subdivided as in Figure 14.4.14, and suppose that the point $(x_k^*, y_k^*, z_k^*)$ in (3) corresponds to parameter values of $u_k^*$ and $v_k^*$. If we use Formula (11) of Section 14.4 to approximate $\Delta S_k$, and if we assume that the errors in the approximations approach zero as $n \to +\infty$, then it follows from (3) that

$$\iint_\sigma f(x, y, z)\, dS = \lim_{n \to +\infty} \sum_{k=1}^{n} f(x(u_k^*, v_k^*), y(u_k^*, v_k^*), z(u_k^*, v_k^*)) \left\| \frac{\partial \mathbf{r}}{\partial u} \times \frac{\partial \mathbf{r}}{\partial v} \right\| \Delta A_k$$

which suggests Formula (6).

Although Theorem 15.5.2 is stated for *smooth* parametric surfaces, Formula (6) remains valid even if $\partial \mathbf{r}/\partial u \times \partial \mathbf{r}/\partial v$ is allowed to equal $\mathbf{0}$ on the boundary of $R$.

▶ **Example 1**   Evaluate the surface integral $\displaystyle\iint\limits_{\sigma} x^2\, dS$ over the sphere $x^2 + y^2 + z^2 = 1$.

*Solution.*   As in Example 11 of Section 14.4 (with $a = 1$), the sphere is the graph of the vector-valued function

$$\mathbf{r}(\phi, \theta) = \sin\phi\cos\theta\,\mathbf{i} + \sin\phi\sin\theta\,\mathbf{j} + \cos\phi\,\mathbf{k} \quad (0 \le \phi \le \pi,\ 0 \le \theta \le 2\pi) \qquad (7)$$

and

$$\left\| \frac{\partial\mathbf{r}}{\partial\phi} \times \frac{\partial\mathbf{r}}{\partial\theta} \right\| = \sin\phi$$

---

Explain why the function $\mathbf{r}(\phi, \theta)$ given in (7) fails to be smooth on its domain.

---

From the $\mathbf{i}$-component of $\mathbf{r}$, the integrand in the surface integral can be expressed in terms of $\phi$ and $\theta$ as $x^2 = \sin^2\phi\cos^2\theta$. Thus, it follows from (6) with $\phi$ and $\theta$ in place of $u$ and $v$ and $R$ as the rectangular region in the $\phi\theta$-plane determined by the inequalities in (7) that

$$
\begin{aligned}
\iint\limits_{\sigma} x^2\, dS &= \iint\limits_{R} (\sin^2\phi\cos^2\theta) \left\| \frac{\partial\mathbf{r}}{\partial\phi} \times \frac{\partial\mathbf{r}}{\partial\theta} \right\| dA \\[2mm]
&= \int_0^{2\pi}\int_0^{\pi} \sin^3\phi\cos^2\theta\, d\phi\, d\theta \\[2mm]
&= \int_0^{2\pi} \left[\int_0^{\pi} \sin^3\phi\, d\phi\right] \cos^2\theta\, d\theta \\[2mm]
&= \int_0^{2\pi} \left[\frac{1}{3}\cos^3\phi - \cos\phi\right]_0^{\pi} \cos^2\theta\, d\theta \qquad \boxed{\begin{array}{l}\text{Formula (11),}\\ \text{Section 7.3}\end{array}} \\[2mm]
&= \frac{4}{3}\int_0^{2\pi} \cos^2\theta\, d\theta \\[2mm]
&= \frac{4}{3}\left[\frac{1}{2}\theta + \frac{1}{4}\sin 2\theta\right]_0^{2\pi} = \frac{4\pi}{3} \qquad \boxed{\begin{array}{l}\text{Formula (8),}\\ \text{Section 7.3}\end{array}} \ \blacktriangleleft
\end{aligned}
$$

---

■ **SURFACE INTEGRALS OVER** $z = g(x, y)$, $y = g(x, z)$, **AND** $x = g(y, z)$

In the case where $\sigma$ is a surface of the form $z = g(x, y)$, we can take $x = u$ and $y = v$ as parameters and express the equation of the surface as

$$\mathbf{r} = u\mathbf{i} + v\mathbf{j} + g(u, v)\mathbf{k}$$

in which case we obtain

$$\left\| \frac{\partial\mathbf{r}}{\partial u} \times \frac{\partial\mathbf{r}}{\partial v} \right\| = \sqrt{\left(\frac{\partial z}{\partial x}\right)^2 + \left(\frac{\partial z}{\partial y}\right)^2 + 1}$$

(verify). Thus, it follows from (6) that

$$\iint\limits_{\sigma} f(x, y, z)\, dS = \iint\limits_{R} f(x, y, g(x, y))\sqrt{\left(\frac{\partial z}{\partial x}\right)^2 + \left(\frac{\partial z}{\partial y}\right)^2 + 1}\, dA$$

Note that in this formula the region $R$ lies in the $xy$-plane because the parameters are $x$ and $y$. Geometrically, this region is the projection of $\sigma$ on the $xy$-plane. The following theorem summarizes this result and gives analogous formulas for surface integrals over surfaces of the form $y = g(x, z)$ and $x = g(y, z)$.

**15.5.3    THEOREM**

(a)  *Let $\sigma$ be a surface with equation $z = g(x, y)$ and let $R$ be its projection on the xy-plane. If $g$ has continuous first partial derivatives on $R$ and $f(x, y, z)$ is continuous on $\sigma$, then*

$$\iint_{\sigma} f(x, y, z)\, dS = \iint_{R} f(x, y, g(x, y)) \sqrt{\left(\frac{\partial z}{\partial x}\right)^2 + \left(\frac{\partial z}{\partial y}\right)^2 + 1}\, dA \qquad (8)$$

(b)  *Let $\sigma$ be a surface with equation $y = g(x, z)$ and let $R$ be its projection on the xz-plane. If $g$ has continuous first partial derivatives on $R$ and $f(x, y, z)$ is continuous on $\sigma$, then*

$$\iint_{\sigma} f(x, y, z)\, dS = \iint_{R} f(x, g(x, z), z) \sqrt{\left(\frac{\partial y}{\partial x}\right)^2 + \left(\frac{\partial y}{\partial z}\right)^2 + 1}\, dA \qquad (9)$$

(c)  *Let $\sigma$ be a surface with equation $x = g(y, z)$ and let $R$ be its projection on the yz-plane. If $g$ has continuous first partial derivatives on $R$ and $f(x, y, z)$ is continuous on $\sigma$, then*

$$\iint_{\sigma} f(x, y, z)\, dS = \iint_{R} f(g(y, z), y, z) \sqrt{\left(\frac{\partial x}{\partial y}\right)^2 + \left(\frac{\partial x}{\partial z}\right)^2 + 1}\, dA \qquad (10)$$

Formulas (9) and (10) can be recovered from Formula (8). Explain how.

▶ **Example 2**    Evaluate the surface integral

$$\iint_{\sigma} xz\, dS$$

where $\sigma$ is the part of the plane $x + y + z = 1$ that lies in the first octant.

*Solution.*    The equation of the plane can be written as

$$z = 1 - x - y$$

Consequently, we can apply Formula (8) with $z = g(x, y) = 1 - x - y$ and $f(x, y, z) = xz$. We have

$$\frac{\partial z}{\partial x} = -1 \quad \text{and} \quad \frac{\partial z}{\partial y} = -1$$

so (8) becomes

$$\iint_{\sigma} xz\, dS = \iint_{R} x(1 - x - y)\sqrt{(-1)^2 + (-1)^2 + 1}\, dA \qquad (11)$$

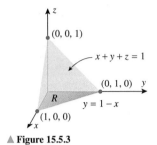

▲ **Figure 15.5.3**

where $R$ is the projection of $\sigma$ on the $xy$-plane (Figure 15.5.3). Rewriting the double integral in (11) as an iterated integral yields

$$\iint_{\sigma} xz \, dS = \sqrt{3} \int_0^1 \int_0^{1-x} (x - x^2 - xy) \, dy \, dx$$

$$= \sqrt{3} \int_0^1 \left[ xy - x^2 y - \frac{xy^2}{2} \right]_{y=0}^{1-x} dx$$

$$= \sqrt{3} \int_0^1 \left( \frac{x}{2} - x^2 + \frac{x^3}{2} \right) dx$$

$$= \sqrt{3} \left[ \frac{x^2}{4} - \frac{x^3}{3} + \frac{x^4}{8} \right]_0^1 = \frac{\sqrt{3}}{24} \quad \blacktriangleleft$$

▶ **Example 3** Evaluate the surface integral

$$\iint_{\sigma} y^2 z^2 \, dS$$

where $\sigma$ is the part of the cone $z = \sqrt{x^2 + y^2}$ that lies between the planes $z = 1$ and $z = 2$ (Figure 15.5.4).

*Solution.* We will apply Formula (8) with

$$z = g(x, y) = \sqrt{x^2 + y^2} \quad \text{and} \quad f(x, y, z) = y^2 z^2$$

Thus,

$$\frac{\partial z}{\partial x} = \frac{x}{\sqrt{x^2 + y^2}} \quad \text{and} \quad \frac{\partial z}{\partial y} = \frac{y}{\sqrt{x^2 + y^2}}$$

so

$$\sqrt{\left( \frac{\partial z}{\partial x} \right)^2 + \left( \frac{\partial z}{\partial y} \right)^2 + 1} = \sqrt{2}$$

(verify), and (8) yields

$$\iint_{\sigma} y^2 z^2 \, dS = \iint_R y^2 \left( \sqrt{x^2 + y^2} \right)^2 \sqrt{2} \, dA = \sqrt{2} \iint_R y^2 (x^2 + y^2) \, dA$$

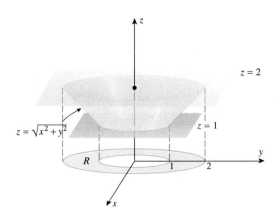

▶ **Figure 15.5.4**

where $R$ is the annulus enclosed between $x^2 + y^2 = 1$ and $x^2 + y^2 = 4$ (Figure 15.5.4). Using polar coordinates to evaluate this double integral over the annulus $R$ yields

$$\iint_\sigma y^2 z^2 \, dS = \sqrt{2} \int_0^{2\pi} \int_1^2 (r \sin\theta)^2 (r^2) r \, dr \, d\theta$$

$$= \sqrt{2} \int_0^{2\pi} \int_1^2 r^5 \sin^2\theta \, dr \, d\theta$$

$$= \sqrt{2} \int_0^{2\pi} \left[ \frac{r^6}{6} \sin^2\theta \right]_{r=1}^2 d\theta = \frac{21}{\sqrt{2}} \int_0^{2\pi} \sin^2\theta \, d\theta$$

$$= \frac{21}{\sqrt{2}} \left[ \frac{1}{2}\theta - \frac{1}{4}\sin 2\theta \right]_0^{2\pi} = \frac{21\pi}{\sqrt{2}} \qquad \boxed{\text{Formula (7), Section 7.3}} \blacktriangleleft$$

Evaluate the integral in Example 3 with the help of Formula (6) and the parametrization

$$\mathbf{r} = \langle r\cos\theta, r\sin\theta, r \rangle$$
$$(1 \le r \le 2, 0 \le \theta \le 2\pi)$$

▶ **Example 4**  Suppose that a curved lamina $\sigma$ with constant density $\delta(x, y, z) = \delta_0$ is the portion of the paraboloid $z = x^2 + y^2$ below the plane $z = 1$ (Figure 15.5.5). Find the mass of the lamina.

*Solution.*  Since $z = g(x, y) = x^2 + y^2$, it follows that

$$\frac{\partial z}{\partial x} = 2x \quad \text{and} \quad \frac{\partial z}{\partial y} = 2y$$

Therefore,

$$M = \iint_\sigma \delta_0 \, dS = \iint_R \delta_0 \sqrt{(2x)^2 + (2y)^2 + 1} \, dA = \delta_0 \iint_R \sqrt{4x^2 + 4y^2 + 1} \, dA \quad (12)$$

where $R$ is the circular region enclosed by $x^2 + y^2 = 1$. To evaluate (12) we use polar coordinates:

$$M = \delta_0 \int_0^{2\pi} \int_0^1 \sqrt{4r^2 + 1} \, r \, dr \, d\theta = \frac{\delta_0}{12} \int_0^{2\pi} (4r^2 + 1)^{3/2} \Big]_{r=0}^1 d\theta$$

$$= \frac{\delta_0}{12} \int_0^{2\pi} (5^{3/2} - 1) \, d\theta = \frac{\pi\delta_0}{6}(5\sqrt{5} - 1) \blacktriangleleft$$

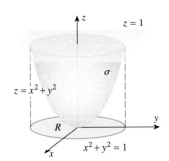
▲ **Figure 15.5.5**

---

### ✔ QUICK CHECK EXERCISES 15.5    (See page 1138 for answers.)

1. Consider the surface integral $\iint_\sigma f(x, y, z) \, dS$.
   (a) If $\sigma$ is a parametric surface whose vector equation is
   $$\mathbf{r} = x(u, v)\mathbf{i} + y(u, v)\mathbf{j} + z(u, v)\mathbf{k}$$
   to evaluate the integral replace $dS$ by _____.
   (b) If $\sigma$ is the graph of a function $z = g(x, y)$ with continuous first partial derivatives, to evaluate the integral replace $dS$ by _____.

2. If $\sigma$ is the triangular region with vertices $(1, 0, 0)$, $(0, 1, 0)$, and $(0, 0, 1)$, then
   $$\iint_\sigma (x + y + z) \, dS = \underline{\qquad}$$

3. If $\sigma$ is the sphere of radius 2 centered at the origin, then
   $$\iint_\sigma (x^2 + y^2 + z^2) \, dS = \underline{\qquad}$$

4. If $f(x, y, z)$ is the mass density function of a curved lamina $\sigma$, then the mass of $\sigma$ is given by the integral _____.

**EXERCISE SET 15.5**   |C| CAS

**1–8** Evaluate the surface integral

$$\iint_\sigma f(x, y, z)\, dS$$

1. $f(x, y, z) = z^2$; $\sigma$ is the portion of the cone $z = \sqrt{x^2 + y^2}$ between the planes $z = 1$ and $z = 2$.

2. $f(x, y, z) = xy$; $\sigma$ is the portion of the plane $x + y + z = 1$ lying in the first octant.

3. $f(x, y, z) = x^2 y$; $\sigma$ is the portion of the cylinder $x^2 + z^2 = 1$ between the planes $y = 0$, $y = 1$, and above the $xy$-plane.

4. $f(x, y, z) = (x^2 + y^2)z$; $\sigma$ is the portion of the sphere $x^2 + y^2 + z^2 = 4$ above the plane $z = 1$.

5. $f(x, y, z) = x - y - z$; $\sigma$ is the portion of the plane $x + y = 1$ in the first octant between $z = 0$ and $z = 1$.

6. $f(x, y, z) = x + y$; $\sigma$ is the portion of the plane $z = 6 - 2x - 3y$ in the first octant.

7. $f(x, y, z) = x + y + z$; $\sigma$ is the surface of the cube defined by the inequalities $0 \le x \le 1, 0 \le y \le 1, 0 \le z \le 1$. [*Hint:* Integrate over each face separately.]

8. $f(x, y, z) = x^2 + y^2$; $\sigma$ is the surface of the sphere $x^2 + y^2 + z^2 = a^2$.

**9–12 True–False** Determine whether the statement is true or false. Explain your answer.

9. If $f(x, y, z) \ge 0$ on $\sigma$, then

$$\iint_\sigma f(x, y, z)\, dS \ge 0$$

10. If $\sigma$ has surface area $S$, and if

$$\iint_\sigma f(x, y, z)\, dS = S$$

then $f(x, y, z)$ is equal to 1 identically on $\sigma$.

11. If $\sigma$ models a curved lamina, and if $f(x, y, z)$ is the density function of the lamina, then

$$\iint_\sigma f(x, y, z)\, dS$$

represents the total density of the lamina.

12. If $\sigma$ is the portion of a plane $z = c$ over a region $R$ in the $xy$-plane, then

$$\iint_\sigma f(x, y, z)\, dS = \iint_R f(x, y, c)\, dA$$

for every continuous function $f$ on $\sigma$.

**13–14** Sometimes evaluating a surface integral results in an improper integral. When this happens, one can either attempt to determine the value of the integral using an appropriate limit or one can try another method. These exercises explore both approaches.

13. Consider the integral of $f(x, y, z) = z + 1$ over the upper hemisphere $\sigma\colon z = \sqrt{1 - x^2 - y^2}$ ($0 \le x^2 + y^2 \le 1$).
    (a) Explain why evaluating this surface integral using (8) results in an improper integral.
    (b) Use (8) to evaluate the integral of $f$ over the surface $\sigma_r : z = \sqrt{1 - x^2 - y^2}$ ($0 \le x^2 + y^2 \le r^2 < 1$). Take the limit of this result as $r \to 1^-$ to determine the integral of $f$ over $\sigma$.
    (c) Parametrize $\sigma$ using spherical coordinates and evaluate the integral of $f$ over $\sigma$ using (6). Verify that your answer agrees with the result in part (b).

14. Consider the integral of $f(x, y, z) = \sqrt{x^2 + y^2 + z^2}$ over the cone $\sigma : z = \sqrt{x^2 + y^2}$ ($0 \le z \le 1$).
    (a) Explain why evaluating this surface integral using (8) results in an improper integral.
    (b) Use (8) to evaluate the integral of $f$ over the surface $\sigma_r : z = \sqrt{x^2 + y^2}$ ($0 < r^2 \le x^2 + y^2 \le 1$). Take the limit of this result as $r \to 0^+$ to determine the integral of $f$ over $\sigma$.
    (c) Parametrize $\sigma$ using spherical coordinates and evaluate the integral of $f$ over $\sigma$ using (6). Verify that your answer agrees with the result in part (b).

**FOCUS ON CONCEPTS**

**15–18** In some cases it is possible to use Definition 15.5.1 along with symmetry considerations to evaluate a surface integral without reference to a parametrization of the surface. In these exercises, $\sigma$ denotes the unit sphere centered at the origin.

15. (a) Explain why it is possible to subdivide $\sigma$ into patches and choose corresponding sample points $(x_k^*, y_k^*, z_k^*)$ such that (i) the dimensions of each patch are as small as desired and (ii) for each sample point $(x_k^*, y_k^*, z_k^*)$, there exists a sample point $(x_j^*, y_j^*, z_j^*)$ with

$$x_k = -x_j, \quad y_k = y_j, \quad z_k = z_j$$

and with $\Delta S_k = \Delta S_j$.
    (b) Use Definition 15.5.1, the result in part (a), and the fact that surface integrals exist for continuous functions to prove that $\iint_\sigma x^n\, dS = 0$ for $n$ an odd positive integer.

16. Use the argument in Exercise 15 to prove that if $f(x)$ is a continuous odd function of $x$, and if $g(y, z)$ is a continuous function, then

$$\iint_\sigma f(x)g(y, z)\, dS = 0$$

17. (a) Explain why

$$\iint_\sigma x^2\, dS = \iint_\sigma y^2\, dS = \iint_\sigma z^2\, dS \quad \text{(cont.)}$$

(b) Conclude from part (a) that

$$\iint\limits_{\sigma} x^2 \, dS = \frac{1}{3} \left[ \iint\limits_{\sigma} x^2 \, dS + \iint\limits_{\sigma} y^2 \, dS + \iint\limits_{\sigma} y^2 \, dS \right]$$

(c) Use part (b) to evaluate

$$\iint\limits_{\sigma} x^2 \, dS$$

without performing an integration.

**18.** Use the results of Exercises 16 and 17 to evaluate

$$\iint\limits_{\sigma} (x - y)^2 \, dS$$

without performing an integration.

**19–20** Set up, but do not evaluate, an iterated integral equal to the given surface integral by projecting $\sigma$ on (a) the $xy$-plane, (b) the $yz$-plane, and (c) the $xz$-plane. ▪

**19.** $\displaystyle\iint\limits_{\sigma} xyz \, dS$, where $\sigma$ is the portion of the plane

$2x + 3y + 4z = 12$ in the first octant.

**20.** $\displaystyle\iint\limits_{\sigma} xz \, dS$, where $\sigma$ is the portion of the sphere

$x^2 + y^2 + z^2 = a^2$ in the first octant.

**C** **21.** Use a CAS to confirm that the three integrals you obtained in Exercise 19 are equal, and find the exact value of the surface integral.

**C** **22.** Try to confirm with a CAS that the three integrals you obtained in Exercise 20 are equal. If you did not succeed, what was the difficulty?

**23–24** Set up, but do not evaluate, two different iterated integrals equal to the given integral. ▪

**23.** $\displaystyle\iint\limits_{\sigma} xyz \, dS$, where $\sigma$ is the portion of the surface $y^2 = x$

between the planes $z = 0$, $z = 4$, $y = 1$, and $y = 2$.

**24.** $\displaystyle\iint\limits_{\sigma} x^2 y \, dS$, where $\sigma$ is the portion of the cylinder

$y^2 + z^2 = a^2$ in the first octant between the planes $x = 0$, $x = 9$, $z = y$, and $z = 2y$.

**C** **25.** Use a CAS to confirm that the two integrals you obtained in Exercise 23 are equal, and find the exact value of the surface integral.

**C** **26.** Use a CAS to find the value of the surface integral

$$\iint\limits_{\sigma} x^2 yz \, dS$$

where the surface $\sigma$ is the portion of the elliptic paraboloid $z = 5 - 3x^2 - 2y^2$ that lies above the $xy$-plane.

**27–28** Find the mass of the lamina with constant density $\delta_0$. ▪

**27.** The lamina that is the portion of the circular cylinder $x^2 + z^2 = 4$ that lies directly above the rectangle $R = \{(x, y) : 0 \le x \le 1, 0 \le y \le 4\}$ in the $xy$-plane.

**28.** The lamina that is the portion of the paraboloid $2z = x^2 + y^2$ inside the cylinder $x^2 + y^2 = 8$.

**29.** Find the mass of the lamina that is the portion of the surface $y^2 = 4 - z$ between the planes $x = 0$, $x = 3$, $y = 0$, and $y = 3$ if the density is $\delta(x, y, z) = y$.

**30.** Find the mass of the lamina that is the portion of the cone $z = \sqrt{x^2 + y^2}$ between $z = 1$ and $z = 4$ if the density is $\delta(x, y, z) = x^2 z$.

**31.** If a curved lamina has constant density $\delta_0$, what relationship must exist between its mass and surface area? Explain your reasoning.

**32.** Show that if the density of the lamina $x^2 + y^2 + z^2 = a^2$ at each point is equal to the distance between that point and the $xy$-plane, then the mass of the lamina is $2\pi a^3$.

**33–34** The centroid of a surface $\sigma$ is defined by

$$\bar{x} = \frac{\displaystyle\iint\limits_{\sigma} x \, dS}{\text{area of } \sigma}, \quad \bar{y} = \frac{\displaystyle\iint\limits_{\sigma} y \, dS}{\text{area of } \sigma}, \quad \bar{z} = \frac{\displaystyle\iint\limits_{\sigma} z \, dS}{\text{area of } \sigma}$$

Find the centroid of the surface. ▪

**33.** The portion of the paraboloid $z = \frac{1}{2}(x^2 + y^2)$ below the plane $z = 4$.

**34.** The portion of the sphere $x^2 + y^2 + z^2 = 4$ above the plane $z = 1$.

**35–38** Evaluate the integral $\iint_{\sigma} f(x, y, z) \, dS$ over the surface $\sigma$ represented by the vector-valued function $\mathbf{r}(u, v)$. ▪

**35.** $f(x, y, z) = xyz$; $\mathbf{r}(u, v) = u \cos v \mathbf{i} + u \sin v \mathbf{j} + 3u \mathbf{k}$
$(1 \le u \le 2, \ 0 \le v \le \pi/2)$

**36.** $f(x, y, z) = \dfrac{x^2 + z^2}{y}$; $\mathbf{r}(u, v) = 2 \cos v \mathbf{i} + u \mathbf{j} + 2 \sin v \mathbf{k}$
$(1 \le u \le 3, \ 0 \le v \le 2\pi)$

**37.** $f(x, y, z) = \dfrac{1}{\sqrt{1 + 4x^2 + 4y^2}}$;
$\mathbf{r}(u, v) = u \cos v \mathbf{i} + u \sin v \mathbf{j} + u^2 \mathbf{k}$
$(0 \le u \le \sin v, \ 0 \le v \le \pi)$

**38.** $f(x, y, z) = e^{-z}$;
$\mathbf{r}(u, v) = 2 \sin u \cos v \mathbf{i} + 2 \sin u \sin v \mathbf{j} + 2 \cos u \mathbf{k}$
$(0 \le u \le \pi/2, 0 \le v \le 2\pi)$

**C** **39.** Use a CAS to approximate the mass of the curved lamina $z = e^{-x^2 - y^2}$ that lies above the region in the $xy$-plane enclosed by $x^2 + y^2 = 9$ given that the density function is $\delta(x, y, z) = \sqrt{x^2 + y^2}$.

**c 40.** The surface $\sigma$ shown in the accompanying figure, called a *Möbius strip*, is represented by the parametric equations

$$x = (5 + u\cos(v/2))\cos v$$
$$y = (5 + u\cos(v/2))\sin v$$
$$z = u\sin(v/2)$$

where $-1 \le u \le 1$ and $0 \le v \le 2\pi$.

(a) Use a CAS to generate a reasonable facsimile of this surface.

(b) Use a CAS to approximate the location of the centroid of $\sigma$ (see the definition preceding Exercise 33).

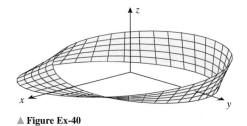

▲ **Figure Ex-40**

**41. Writing** Discuss the similarities and differences between the definition of a surface integral and the definition of a double integral.

**42. Writing** Suppose that a surface $\sigma$ in 3-space and a function $f(x, y, z)$ are described geometrically. For example, $\sigma$ might be the sphere of radius 1 centered at the origin and $f(x, y, z)$ might be the distance from the point $(x, y, z)$ to the $z$-axis. How would you explain to a classmate a procedure for evaluating the surface integral of $f$ over $\sigma$?

✔ **QUICK CHECK ANSWERS 15.5**

1. (a) $\left\| \dfrac{\partial \mathbf{r}}{\partial u} \times \dfrac{\partial \mathbf{r}}{\partial v} \right\| dA$  (b) $\sqrt{\left(\dfrac{\partial z}{\partial x}\right)^2 + \left(\dfrac{\partial z}{\partial y}\right)^2 + 1}\, dA$  2. $\dfrac{\sqrt{3}}{2}$  3. $64\pi$  4. $\displaystyle\iint_\sigma f(x, y, z)\, dS$

---

## 15.6 APPLICATIONS OF SURFACE INTEGRALS; FLUX

*In this section we will discuss applications of surface integrals to vector fields associated with fluid flow and electrostatic forces. However, the ideas that we will develop will be general in nature and applicable to other kinds of vector fields as well.*

### ◼ FLOW FIELDS

We will be concerned in this section with vector fields in 3-space that involve some type of "flow"—the flow of a fluid or the flow of charged particles in an electrostatic field, for example. In the case of fluid flow, the vector field $\mathbf{F}(x, y, z)$ represents the velocity of a fluid particle at the point $(x, y, z)$, and the fluid particles flow along "streamlines" that are tangential to the velocity vectors (Figure 15.6.1a). In the case of an electrostatic field, $\mathbf{F}(x, y, z)$ is the force that the field exerts on a small unit of positive charge at the point $(x, y, z)$, and such charges have acceleration in the directions of "electric lines" that are tangential to the force vectors (Figures 15.6.1b and 15.6.1c).

### ◼ ORIENTED SURFACES

Our main goal in this section is to study flows of vector fields through permeable surfaces placed in the field. For this purpose we will need to consider some basic ideas about surfaces. Most surfaces that we encounter in applications have two sides—a sphere has an inside and an outside, and an infinite horizontal plane has a top side and a bottom side, for example. However, there exist mathematical surfaces with only one side. For example, Figure 15.6.2a shows the construction of a surface called a *Möbius strip* [in honor of the German mathematician August Möbius (1790–1868)]. The Möbius strip has only one side in the sense that a bug can traverse the *entire* surface without crossing an edge (Figure 15.6.2b). In contrast,

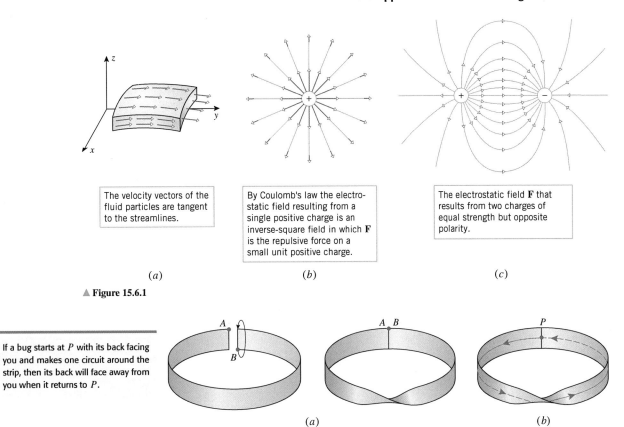

The velocity vectors of the fluid particles are tangent to the streamlines.

*(a)*

By Coulomb's law the electrostatic field resulting from a single positive charge is an inverse-square field in which **F** is the repulsive force on a small unit positive charge.

*(b)*

The electrostatic field **F** that results from two charges of equal strength but opposite polarity.

*(c)*

▲ **Figure 15.6.1**

If a bug starts at $P$ with its back facing you and makes one circuit around the strip, then its back will face away from you when it returns to $P$.

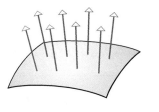

*(a)*

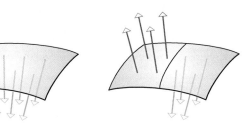

*(b)*

▲ **Figure 15.6.2**

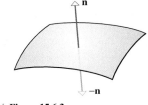

▲ **Figure 15.6.3**

a sphere is two-sided in the sense that a bug walking on the sphere can traverse the inside surface or the outside surface but cannot traverse both without somehow passing through the sphere. A two-sided surface is said to be ***orientable***, and a one-sided surface is said to be ***nonorientable***. In the rest of this text we will only be concerned with orientable surfaces.

In applications, it is important to have some way of distinguishing between the two sides of an orientable surface. For this purpose let us suppose that $\sigma$ is an orientable surface that has a unit normal vector **n** at each point. As illustrated in Figure 15.6.3, the vectors **n** and $-$**n** point to opposite sides of the surface and hence serve to distinguish between the two sides. It can be proved that if $\sigma$ is a smooth orientable surface, then it is always possible to choose the direction of **n** at each point so that $\mathbf{n} = \mathbf{n}(x, y, z)$ varies continuously over the surface. These unit vectors are then said to form an ***orientation*** of the surface. It can also be proved that a smooth orientable surface has only two possible orientations. For example, the surface in Figure 15.6.4 is oriented up by the purple vectors and down by the green vectors. However, we cannot create a third orientation by mixing the two since this

▲ **Figure 15.6.4**

produces points on the surface at which there is an abrupt change in direction (across the black curve in the figure, for example).

### ORIENTATION OF A SMOOTH PARAMETRIC SURFACE

When a surface is expressed parametrically, the parametric equations create a natural orientation of the surface. To see why this is so, recall from Section 14.4 that if a smooth parametric surface $\sigma$ is given by the vector equation

$$\mathbf{r} = x(u, v)\mathbf{i} + y(u, v)\mathbf{j} + z(u, v)\mathbf{k}$$

then the unit normal

$$\mathbf{n} = \mathbf{n}(u, v) = \frac{\dfrac{\partial \mathbf{r}}{\partial u} \times \dfrac{\partial \mathbf{r}}{\partial v}}{\left\| \dfrac{\partial \mathbf{r}}{\partial u} \times \dfrac{\partial \mathbf{r}}{\partial v} \right\|} \tag{1}$$

is a continuous vector-valued function of $u$ and $v$. Thus, Formula (1) defines an orientation of the surface; we call this the *positive orientation* of the parametric surface and we say that $\mathbf{n}$ points in the *positive direction* from the surface. The orientation determined by $-\mathbf{n}$ is called the *negative orientation* of the surface and we say that $-\mathbf{n}$ points in the *negative direction* from the surface. For example, consider the cylinder that is represented parametrically by the vector equation

$$\mathbf{r}(u, v) = \cos u\,\mathbf{i} + v\,\mathbf{j} - \sin u\,\mathbf{k} \qquad (0 \le u \le 2\pi, \ 0 \le v \le 3)$$

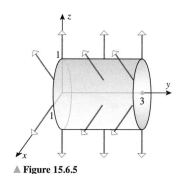

▲ Figure 15.6.5

Then

$$\frac{\partial \mathbf{r}}{\partial u} \times \frac{\partial \mathbf{r}}{\partial v} = \cos u\,\mathbf{i} - \sin u\,\mathbf{k}$$

has unit length, so that Formula (1) becomes

$$\mathbf{n} = \frac{\partial \mathbf{r}}{\partial u} \times \frac{\partial \mathbf{r}}{\partial v} = \cos u\,\mathbf{i} - \sin u\,\mathbf{k}$$

Since $\mathbf{n}$ has the same $\mathbf{i}$- and $\mathbf{k}$-components as $\mathbf{r}$, the positive orientation of the cylinder is *outward* and the negative orientation is *inward* (Figure 15.6.5).

See if you can find a parametrization of the cylinder in which the positive direction is inward.

### FLUX

In physics, the term *fluid* is used to describe both liquids and gases. Liquids are usually regarded to be *incompressible*, meaning that the liquid has a uniform density (mass per unit volume) that cannot be altered by compressive forces. Gases are regarded to be *compressible*, meaning that the density may vary from point to point and can be altered by compressive forces. In this text we will be concerned primarily with incompressible fluids. Moreover, we will assume that the velocity of the fluid at a fixed point does not vary with time. Fluid flows with this property are said to be in a *steady state*.

Our next goal in this section is to define a fundamental concept of physics known as *flux* (from the Latin word *fluxus*, meaning "flowing"). This concept is applicable to any vector field, but we will motivate it in the context of steady-state incompressible fluid flow. Imagine that fluid is flowing freely through a permeable surface, from one side of the surface to the other. In this context, you can think of flux as:

*The volume of fluid that passes through the surface in one unit of time.*

This idea is illustrated in Figure 15.6.6, which suggests that the volume of fluid that flows through a portion of the surface depends on three factors:

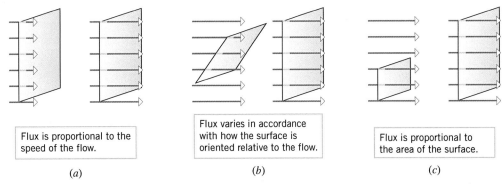

Flux is proportional to the speed of the flow.

(a)

Flux varies in accordance with how the surface is oriented relative to the flow.

(b)

Flux is proportional to the area of the surface.

(c)

▲ Figure 15.6.6

- The speed of the fluid; the greater the speed, the greater the volume (Figure 15.6.6*a*).
- How the surface is oriented relative to the flow; the more nearly orthogonal the flow is to the surface, the greater the volume (Figure 15.6.6*b*).
- The area of the portion of the surface; the greater the area, the greater the volume (Figure 15.6.6*c*).

These ideas lead us to the following problem.

---

**15.6.1   PROBLEM**   Suppose that an oriented surface $\sigma$ is immersed in an incompressible, steady-state fluid flow and that the surface is permeable so that the fluid can flow through it freely in either direction. Find the net volume of fluid $\Phi$ that passes through the surface per unit of time, where the net volume is interpreted to mean the volume that passes through the surface in the positive direction minus the volume that passes through the surface in the negative direction.

---

To solve this problem, suppose that the velocity of the fluid at a point $(x, y, z)$ on the surface $\sigma$ is given by

$$\mathbf{F}(x, y, z) = f(x, y, z)\mathbf{i} + g(x, y, z)\mathbf{j} + h(x, y, z)\mathbf{k}$$

Let $\mathbf{n}$ be the unit normal toward the positive side of $\sigma$ at the point $(x, y, z)$. As illustrated in Figure 15.6.7, the velocity vector $\mathbf{F}$ can be resolved into two orthogonal components—a component $(\mathbf{F} \cdot \mathbf{n})\mathbf{n}$ that is perpendicular to the surface $\sigma$ and a second component that is along the "face" of $\sigma$. The component of velocity along the face of the surface does not contribute to the flow through $\sigma$ and hence can be ignored in our computations. Moreover, observe that the sign of $\mathbf{F} \cdot \mathbf{n}$ determines the direction of flow—a positive value means the flow is in the direction of $\mathbf{n}$ and a negative value means that it is opposite to $\mathbf{n}$.

To solve Problem 15.6.1, we subdivide $\sigma$ into $n$ patches $\sigma_1, \sigma_2, \ldots, \sigma_n$ with areas

$$\Delta S_1, \Delta S_2, \ldots, \Delta S_n$$

If the patches are small and the flow is not too erratic, it is reasonable to assume that the velocity does not vary much on each patch. Thus, if $(x_k^*, y_k^*, z_k^*)$ is any point in the $k$th patch, we can assume that $\mathbf{F}(x, y, z)$ is constant and equal to $\mathbf{F}(x_k^*, y_k^*, z_k^*)$ throughout the patch and that the component of velocity across the surface $\sigma_k$ is

$$\mathbf{F}(x_k^*, y_k^*, z_k^*) \cdot \mathbf{n}(x_k^*, y_k^*, z_k^*) \tag{2}$$

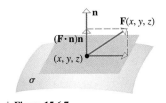

▲ Figure 15.6.7

(Figure 15.6.8). Thus, we can interpret

$$\mathbf{F}(x_k^*, y_k^*, z_k^*) \cdot \mathbf{n}(x_k^*, y_k^*, z_k^*)\Delta S_k$$

as the approximate volume of fluid crossing the patch $\sigma_k$ in the direction of $\mathbf{n}$ per unit of time (Figure 15.6.9). For example, if the component of velocity in the direction of $\mathbf{n}$ is $\mathbf{F}(x_k^*, y_k^*, z_k^*) \cdot \mathbf{n} = 25$ cm/s, and the area of the patch is $\Delta S_k = 2$ cm$^2$, then the volume of fluid $\Delta V_k$ crossing the patch in the direction of $\mathbf{n}$ per unit of time is approximately

$$\Delta V_k \approx \mathbf{F}(x_k^*, y_k^*, z_k^*) \cdot \mathbf{n}(x_k^*, y_k^*, z_k^*)\Delta S_k = 25 \text{ cm/s} \cdot 2 \text{ cm}^2 = 50 \text{ cm}^3/\text{s}$$

In the case where the velocity component $\mathbf{F}(x_k^*, y_k^*, z_k^*) \cdot \mathbf{n}(x_k^*, y_k^*, z_k^*)$ is negative, the flow is in the direction opposite to $\mathbf{n}$, so that $-\mathbf{F}(x_k^*, y_k^*, z_k^*) \cdot \mathbf{n}(x_k^*, y_k^*, z_k^*)\Delta S_k$ is the approximate volume of fluid crossing the patch $\sigma_k$ in the direction opposite to $\mathbf{n}$ per unit time. Thus, the sum

$$\sum_{k=1}^{n} \mathbf{F}(x_k^*, y_k^*, z_k^*) \cdot \mathbf{n}(x_k^*, y_k^*, z_k^*)\Delta S_k$$

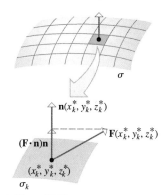

▲ Figure 15.6.8

measures the approximate net volume of fluid that crosses the surface $\sigma$ in the direction of its orientation $\mathbf{n}$ per unit of time.

If we now increase $n$ in such a way that the maximum dimension of each patch approaches zero, then it is plausible that the errors in the approximations approach zero, and the limit

$$\Phi = \lim_{n \to +\infty} \sum_{k=1}^{n} \mathbf{F}(x_k^*, y_k^*, z_k^*) \cdot \mathbf{n}(x_k^*, y_k^*, z_k^*)\Delta S_k \tag{3}$$

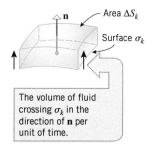

The volume of fluid crossing $\sigma_k$ in the direction of $\mathbf{n}$ per unit of time.

▲ Figure 15.6.9

represents the exact net volume of fluid that crosses the surface $\sigma$ in the direction of its orientation $\mathbf{n}$ per unit of time. The quantity $\Phi$ defined by Equation (3) is called the **flux of F across** $\sigma$. The flux can also be expressed as the surface integral

$$\Phi = \iint_\sigma \mathbf{F}(x, y, z) \cdot \mathbf{n}(x, y, z)\, dS \tag{4}$$

If the fluid has mass density $\delta$, then $\Phi\delta$ (volume/time $\times$ density) represents the net mass of fluid that passes through $\sigma$ per unit of time.

A positive flux means that in one unit of time a greater volume of fluid passes through $\sigma$ in the positive direction than in the negative direction, a negative flux means that a greater volume passes through the surface in the negative direction than in the positive direction, and a zero flux means that the same volume passes through the surface in each direction. Integrals of form (4) arise in other contexts as well and are called **flux integrals**.

■ **EVALUATING FLUX INTEGRALS**

An effective formula for evaluating flux integrals can be obtained by applying Theorem 15.5.2 and using Formula (1) for $\mathbf{n}$. This yields

$$\iint_\sigma \mathbf{F} \cdot \mathbf{n}\, dS = \iint_R \mathbf{F} \cdot \mathbf{n} \left\| \frac{\partial \mathbf{r}}{\partial u} \times \frac{\partial \mathbf{r}}{\partial v} \right\| dA$$

$$= \iint_R \mathbf{F} \cdot \frac{\dfrac{\partial \mathbf{r}}{\partial u} \times \dfrac{\partial \mathbf{r}}{\partial v}}{\left\| \dfrac{\partial \mathbf{r}}{\partial u} \times \dfrac{\partial \mathbf{r}}{\partial v} \right\|} \left\| \frac{\partial \mathbf{r}}{\partial u} \times \frac{\partial \mathbf{r}}{\partial v} \right\| dA$$

$$= \iint_R \mathbf{F} \cdot \left( \frac{\partial \mathbf{r}}{\partial u} \times \frac{\partial \mathbf{r}}{\partial v} \right) dA$$

In summary, we have the following result.

---

**15.6.2    THEOREM**    *Let $\sigma$ be a smooth parametric surface represented by the vector equation $\mathbf{r} = \mathbf{r}(u, v)$ in which $(u, v)$ varies over a region $R$ in the $uv$-plane. If the component functions of the vector field $\mathbf{F}$ are continuous on $\sigma$, and if $\mathbf{n}$ determines the positive orientation of $\sigma$, then*

$$\Phi = \iint\limits_{\sigma} \mathbf{F} \cdot \mathbf{n} \, dS = \iint\limits_{R} \mathbf{F} \cdot \left( \frac{\partial \mathbf{r}}{\partial u} \times \frac{\partial \mathbf{r}}{\partial v} \right) dA \tag{5}$$

*where it is understood that the integrand on the right side of the equation is expressed in terms of $u$ and $v$.*

---

Although Theorem 15.6.2 was derived for smooth parametric surfaces, Formula (5) is valid more generally. For example, as long as $\sigma$ has a continuous normal vector field $\mathbf{n}$ and the component functions of $\mathbf{r}(u, v)$ have continuous first partial derivatives, Formula (5) can be applied whenever $\partial \mathbf{r}/\partial u \times \partial \mathbf{r}/\partial v$ is a positive multiple of $\mathbf{n}$ in the *interior* of $R$. (That is, $\partial \mathbf{r}/\partial u \times \partial \mathbf{r}/\partial v$ is allowed to equal $\mathbf{0}$ on the boundary of $R$.)

---

▶ **Example 1**    Find the flux of the vector field $\mathbf{F}(x, y, z) = z\mathbf{k}$ across the outward-oriented sphere $x^2 + y^2 + z^2 = a^2$.

*Solution.*    The sphere with outward positive orientation can be represented by the vector-valued function

$$\mathbf{r}(\phi, \theta) = a \sin \phi \cos \theta \, \mathbf{i} + a \sin \phi \sin \theta \, \mathbf{j} + a \cos \phi \, \mathbf{k} \qquad (0 \le \phi \le \pi, \ 0 \le \theta \le 2\pi)$$

From this formula we obtain (see Example 11 of Section 14.4 for the computations)

$$\frac{\partial \mathbf{r}}{\partial \phi} \times \frac{\partial \mathbf{r}}{\partial \theta} = a^2 \sin^2 \phi \cos \theta \, \mathbf{i} + a^2 \sin^2 \phi \sin \theta \, \mathbf{j} + a^2 \sin \phi \cos \phi \, \mathbf{k}$$

Moreover, for points on the sphere we have $\mathbf{F} = z\mathbf{k} = a \cos \phi \mathbf{k}$; hence,

$$\mathbf{F} \cdot \left( \frac{\partial \mathbf{r}}{\partial \phi} \times \frac{\partial \mathbf{r}}{\partial \theta} \right) = a^3 \sin \phi \cos^2 \phi$$

Solve Example 1 using symmetry: First argue that the vector fields $x\mathbf{i}$, $y\mathbf{j}$, and $z\mathbf{k}$ will have the same flux across the sphere. Then define

$$\mathbf{H} = x\mathbf{i} + y\mathbf{j} + z\mathbf{k}$$

and explain why

$$\mathbf{H} \cdot \mathbf{n} = a$$

Use this to compute $\Phi$.

Thus, it follows from (5) with the parameters $u$ and $v$ replaced by $\phi$ and $\theta$ that

$$\Phi = \iint\limits_{\sigma} \mathbf{F} \cdot \mathbf{n} \, dS$$

$$= \iint\limits_{R} \mathbf{F} \cdot \left( \frac{\partial \mathbf{r}}{\partial \phi} \times \frac{\partial \mathbf{r}}{\partial \theta} \right) dA$$

$$= \int_{0}^{2\pi} \int_{0}^{\pi} a^3 \sin \phi \cos^2 \phi \, d\phi \, d\theta$$

$$= a^3 \int_{0}^{2\pi} \left[ -\frac{\cos^3 \phi}{3} \right]_{0}^{\pi} d\theta$$

$$= \frac{2a^3}{3} \int_{0}^{2\pi} d\theta = \frac{4\pi a^3}{3} \quad ◀$$

**REMARK** | Reversing the orientation of the surface $\sigma$ in (5) reverses the sign of $\mathbf{n}$, hence the sign of $\mathbf{F} \cdot \mathbf{n}$, and hence reverses the sign of $\Phi$. This can also be seen physically by interpreting the flux integral as the volume of fluid per unit time that crosses $\sigma$ in the positive direction minus the volume per unit time that crosses in the negative direction—reversing the orientation of $\sigma$ changes the sign of the difference. Thus, in Example 1 an inward orientation of the sphere would produce a flux of $-4\pi a^3/3$.

### ORIENTATION OF NONPARAMETRIC SURFACES

Nonparametric surfaces of the form $z = g(x, y)$, $y = g(z, x)$, and $x = g(y, z)$ can be expressed parametrically using the independent variables as parameters. More precisely, these surfaces can be represented by the vector equations

$$\mathbf{r} = u\mathbf{i} + v\mathbf{j} + g(u, v)\mathbf{k}, \quad \mathbf{r} = v\mathbf{i} + g(u, v)\mathbf{j} + u\mathbf{k}, \quad \mathbf{r} = g(u, v)\mathbf{i} + u\mathbf{j} + v\mathbf{k} \quad (6\text{–}8)$$

$$\boxed{z = g(x, y)} \qquad\qquad \boxed{y = g(z, x)} \qquad\qquad \boxed{x = g(y, z)}$$

These representations impose positive and negative orientations on the surfaces in accordance with Formula (1). We leave it as an exercise to calculate $\mathbf{n}$ and $-\mathbf{n}$ in each case and to show that the positive and negative orientations are as shown in Table 15.6.1. (To assist with perspective, each graph is pictured as a portion of the surface of a small solid region.)

**Table 15.6.1**

| $z = g(x, y)$ | $y = g(z, x)$ | $x = g(y, z)$ |
|---|---|---|
| $\mathbf{n} = \dfrac{-\dfrac{\partial z}{\partial x}\mathbf{i} - \dfrac{\partial z}{\partial y}\mathbf{j} + \mathbf{k}}{\sqrt{\left(\dfrac{\partial z}{\partial x}\right)^2 + \left(\dfrac{\partial z}{\partial y}\right)^2 + 1}}$ | $\mathbf{n} = \dfrac{-\dfrac{\partial y}{\partial x}\mathbf{i} + \mathbf{j} - \dfrac{\partial y}{\partial z}\mathbf{k}}{\sqrt{\left(\dfrac{\partial y}{\partial x}\right)^2 + \left(\dfrac{\partial y}{\partial z}\right)^2 + 1}}$ | $\mathbf{n} = \dfrac{\mathbf{i} - \dfrac{\partial x}{\partial y}\mathbf{j} - \dfrac{\partial x}{\partial z}\mathbf{k}}{\sqrt{\left(\dfrac{\partial x}{\partial y}\right)^2 + \left(\dfrac{\partial x}{\partial z}\right)^2 + 1}}$ |
| Positive **k**-component — Positive orientation | Positive **j**-component — Positive orientation | Positive **i**-component — Positive orientation |
| $-\mathbf{n} = \dfrac{\dfrac{\partial z}{\partial x}\mathbf{i} + \dfrac{\partial z}{\partial y}\mathbf{j} - \mathbf{k}}{\sqrt{\left(\dfrac{\partial z}{\partial x}\right)^2 + \left(\dfrac{\partial z}{\partial y}\right)^2 + 1}}$ | $-\mathbf{n} = \dfrac{\dfrac{\partial y}{\partial x}\mathbf{i} - \mathbf{j} + \dfrac{\partial y}{\partial z}\mathbf{k}}{\sqrt{\left(\dfrac{\partial y}{\partial x}\right)^2 + \left(\dfrac{\partial y}{\partial z}\right)^2 + 1}}$ | $-\mathbf{n} = \dfrac{-\mathbf{i} + \dfrac{\partial x}{\partial y}\mathbf{j} + \dfrac{\partial x}{\partial z}\mathbf{k}}{\sqrt{\left(\dfrac{\partial x}{\partial y}\right)^2 + \left(\dfrac{\partial x}{\partial z}\right)^2 + 1}}$ |
| Negative **k**-component — Negative orientation | Negative **j**-component — Negative orientation | Negative **i**-component — Negative orientation |

The results in Table 15.6.1 can also be obtained using gradients. To see how this can be done, rewrite the equations of the surfaces as

> The dependent variable will increase as you move away from a surface
>
> $z = g(x, y), \quad y = g(z, x)$
>
> or
>
> $x = g(y, z)$
>
> in the direction of positive orientation.

$$z - g(x, y) = 0, \quad y - g(z, x) = 0, \quad x - g(y, z) = 0$$

Each of these equations has the form $G(x, y, z) = 0$ and hence can be viewed as a level surface of a function $G(x, y, z)$. Since the gradient of $G$ is normal to the level surface, it follows that the unit normal $\mathbf{n}$ is either $\nabla G/\|\nabla G\|$ or $-\nabla G/\|\nabla G\|$. However, if $G(x, y, z) = z - g(x, y)$, then $\nabla G$ has a **k**-component of 1; if $G(x, y, z) = y - g(z, x)$, then $\nabla G$ has a **j**-component of 1; and if $G(x, y, z) = x - g(y, z)$, then $\nabla G$ has an **i**-component of 1. Thus, it is evident from Table 15.6.1 that in all three cases we have

$$\mathbf{n} = \frac{\nabla G}{\|\nabla G\|} \tag{9}$$

Moreover, we leave it as an exercise to show that if the surfaces $z = g(x, y)$, $y = g(z, x)$, and $x = g(y, z)$ are expressed in vector forms (6), (7), and (8), then

$$\nabla G = \frac{\partial \mathbf{r}}{\partial u} \times \frac{\partial \mathbf{r}}{\partial v} \tag{10}$$

[compare (1) and (9)]. Thus, we are led to the following version of Theorem 15.6.2 for nonparametric surfaces.

---

**15.6.3    THEOREM**    *Let $\sigma$ be a smooth surface of the form $z = g(x, y)$, $y = g(z, x)$, or $x = g(y, z)$, and suppose that the component functions of the vector field **F** are continuous on $\sigma$. Suppose also that the equation for $\sigma$ is rewritten as $G(x, y, z) = 0$ by taking $g$ to the left side of the equation, and let $R$ be the projection of $\sigma$ on the coordinate plane determined by the independent variables of $g$. If $\sigma$ has positive orientation, then*

$$\Phi = \iint_\sigma \mathbf{F} \cdot \mathbf{n} \, dS = \iint_R \mathbf{F} \cdot \nabla G \, dA \tag{11}$$

---

Formula (11) can either be used directly for computations or to derive some more specific formulas for each of the three surface types. For example, if $z = g(x, y)$, then we have $G(x, y, z) = z - g(x, y)$, so

$$\nabla G = -\frac{\partial g}{\partial x}\mathbf{i} - \frac{\partial g}{\partial y}\mathbf{j} + \mathbf{k} = -\frac{\partial z}{\partial x}\mathbf{i} - \frac{\partial z}{\partial y}\mathbf{j} + \mathbf{k}$$

Substituting this expression for $\nabla G$ in (11) and taking $R$ to be the projection of the surface $z = g(x, y)$ on the $xy$-plane yields

$$\iint_\sigma \mathbf{F} \cdot \mathbf{n} \, dS = \iint_R \mathbf{F} \cdot \left( -\frac{\partial z}{\partial x}\mathbf{i} - \frac{\partial z}{\partial y}\mathbf{j} + \mathbf{k} \right) dA \quad \boxed{\begin{array}{l} \sigma \text{ of the form } z = g(x, y) \\ \text{and oriented up} \end{array}} \tag{12}$$

$$\iint_\sigma \mathbf{F} \cdot \mathbf{n} \, dS = \iint_R \mathbf{F} \cdot \left( \frac{\partial z}{\partial x}\mathbf{i} + \frac{\partial z}{\partial y}\mathbf{j} - \mathbf{k} \right) dA \quad \boxed{\begin{array}{l} \sigma \text{ of the form } z = g(x, y) \\ \text{and oriented down} \end{array}} \tag{13}$$

The derivations of the corresponding formulas when $y = g(z, x)$ and $x = g(y, z)$ are left as exercises.

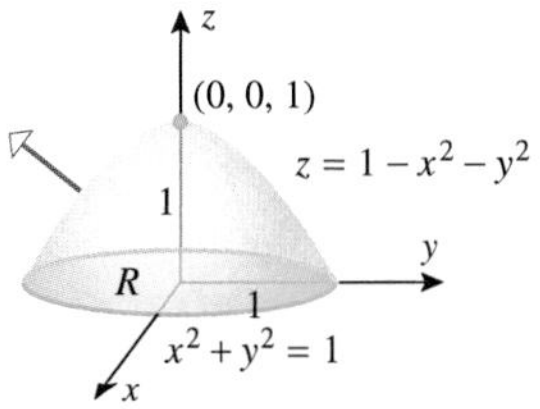

▲ **Figure 15.6.10**

---

▶ **Example 2**    Let $\sigma$ be the portion of the surface $z = 1 - x^2 - y^2$ that lies above the $xy$-plane, and suppose that $\sigma$ is oriented up, as shown in Figure 15.6.10. Find the flux of the vector field $\mathbf{F}(x, y, z) = x\mathbf{i} + y\mathbf{j} + z\mathbf{k}$ across $\sigma$.

***Solution.*** From (12) the flux $\Phi$ is given by

$$\Phi = \iint_\sigma \mathbf{F} \cdot \mathbf{n} \, dS = \iint_R \mathbf{F} \cdot \left( -\frac{\partial z}{\partial x} \mathbf{i} - \frac{\partial z}{\partial y} \mathbf{j} + \mathbf{k} \right) dA$$

$$= \iint_R (x\mathbf{i} + y\mathbf{j} + z\mathbf{k}) \cdot (2x\mathbf{i} + 2y\mathbf{j} + \mathbf{k}) \, dA$$

$$= \iint_R (x^2 + y^2 + 1) \, dA \qquad \boxed{\text{Since } z = 1 - x^2 - y^2 \text{ on the surface}}$$

$$= \int_0^{2\pi} \int_0^1 (r^2 + 1) r \, dr \, d\theta \qquad \boxed{\text{Using polar coordinates to evaluate the integral}}$$

$$= \int_0^{2\pi} \left( \frac{3}{4} \right) d\theta = \frac{3\pi}{2} \quad \blacktriangleleft$$

---

✔ **QUICK CHECK EXERCISES 15.6**  (*See page 1148 for answers.*)

In these exercises, $\mathbf{F}(x, y, z)$ denotes a vector field defined on a surface $\sigma$ oriented by a unit normal vector field $\mathbf{n}(x, y, z)$, and $\Phi$ denotes the flux of $\mathbf{F}$ across $\sigma$.

1. (a) $\Phi$ is the value of the surface integral _____.
   (b) If $\sigma$ is the unit sphere and $\mathbf{n}$ is the outward unit normal, then the flux of

   $$\mathbf{F}(x, y, z) = x\mathbf{i} + y\mathbf{j} + z\mathbf{k}$$

   across $\sigma$ is $\Phi =$ _____.

2. (a) Assume that $\sigma$ is parametrized by a vector-valued function $\mathbf{r}(u, v)$ whose domain is a region $R$ in the $uv$-plane and that $\mathbf{n}$ is a positive multiple of

   $$\frac{\partial \mathbf{r}}{\partial u} \times \frac{\partial \mathbf{r}}{\partial v}$$

   Then the double integral over $R$ whose value is $\Phi$ is _____.

   (b) Suppose that $\sigma$ is the parametric surface

   $$\mathbf{r}(u, v) = u\mathbf{i} + v\mathbf{j} + (u + v)\mathbf{k} \qquad (0 \leq u^2 + v^2 \leq 1)$$

and that $\mathbf{n}$ is a positive multiple of

$$\frac{\partial \mathbf{r}}{\partial u} \times \frac{\partial \mathbf{r}}{\partial v}$$

Then the flux of $\mathbf{F}(x, y, z) = x\mathbf{i} + y\mathbf{j} + z\mathbf{k}$ across $\sigma$ is $\Phi =$ _____.

3. (a) Assume that $\sigma$ is the graph of a function $z = g(x, y)$ over a region $R$ in the $xy$-plane and that $\mathbf{n}$ has a positive $\mathbf{k}$-component for every point on $\sigma$. Then a double integral over $R$ whose value is $\Phi$ is _____.

   (b) Suppose that $\sigma$ is the triangular region with vertices $(1, 0, 0)$, $(0, 1, 0)$, and $(0, 0, 1)$ with upward orientation. Then the flux of

   $$\mathbf{F}(x, y, z) = x\mathbf{i} + y\mathbf{j} + z\mathbf{k}$$

   across $\sigma$ is $\Phi =$ _____.

4. In the case of steady-state incompressible fluid flow, with $\mathbf{F}(x, y, z)$ the fluid velocity at $(x, y, z)$ on $\sigma$, $\Phi$ can be interpreted as _____.

---

**EXERCISE SET 15.6**  ⓒ CAS

1. Suppose that the surface $\sigma$ of the unit cube in the accompanying figure has an outward orientation. In each part, determine whether the flux of the vector field $\mathbf{F}(x, y, z) = z\mathbf{j}$ across the specified face is positive, negative, or zero.
   (a) The face $x = 1$      (b) The face $x = 0$
   (c) The face $y = 1$      (d) The face $y = 0$
   (e) The face $z = 1$      (f) The face $z = 0$

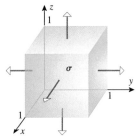

◀ **Figure Ex-1**

**2.** Find the flux of the constant vector field $\mathbf{F}(x, y, z) = 2\mathbf{i} - 2\mathbf{j} - 2\mathbf{k}$ across the entire surface $\sigma$ in Figure Ex-1. Explain your reasoning.

**3.** Find the flux of $\mathbf{F}(x, y, z) = x\mathbf{i}$ through a square of side 4 in the plane $x = -5$ oriented in the positive $x$-direction.

**4.** Find the flux of $\mathbf{F}(x, y, z) = (y + 1)\mathbf{j}$ through a square of side 5 in the $xz$-plane oriented in the negative $y$-direction.

**5.** Find the flux of $\mathbf{F}(x, y, z) = x\mathbf{i} + y\mathbf{j} + (z^2 + 4)\mathbf{k}$ through a $2 \times 3$ rectangle in the plane $z = 1$ oriented in the positive $z$-direction.

**6.** Find the flux of $\mathbf{F}(x, y, z) = 2\mathbf{i} + 3\mathbf{j}$ through a disk of radius 5 in the plane $y = 3$ oriented in the direction of increasing $y$.

**7.** Find the flux of $\mathbf{F}(x, y, z) = 9\mathbf{j} + 8\mathbf{k}$ through a disk of radius 5 in the plane $z = 2$ oriented in the upward direction.

**8.** Let $\sigma$ be the cylindrical surface that is represented by the vector-valued function $\mathbf{r}(u, v) = \cos v\mathbf{i} + \sin v\mathbf{j} + u\mathbf{k}$ with $0 \leq u \leq 1$ and $0 \leq v \leq 2\pi$.
(a) Find the unit normal $\mathbf{n} = \mathbf{n}(u, v)$ that defines the positive orientation of $\sigma$.
(b) Is the positive orientation inward or outward? Justify your answer.

**9–16** Find the flux of the vector field $\mathbf{F}$ across $\sigma$. ▤

**9.** $\mathbf{F}(x, y, z) = x\mathbf{k}$; $\sigma$ is the square $0 \leq x \leq 2, 0 \leq y \leq 2$ in the $xy$-plane, oriented in the upward direction.

**10.** $\mathbf{F}(x, y, z) = 5z\mathbf{i} + y\mathbf{j} + 2x\mathbf{k}$; $\sigma$ is the rectangle $0 \leq x \leq 2$, $0 \leq y \leq 3$ in the plane $z = 2$, oriented in the positive $z$-direction.

**11.** $\mathbf{F}(x, y, z) = x\mathbf{i} + y\mathbf{j} + 2z\mathbf{k}$; $\sigma$ is the portion of the surface $z = 1 - x^2 - y^2$ above the $xy$-plane, oriented by upward normals.

**12.** $\mathbf{F}(x, y, z) = x^2\mathbf{i} + (x + e^y)\mathbf{j} - \mathbf{k}$; $\sigma$ is the vertical rectangle $0 \leq x \leq 2, 0 \leq z \leq 4$ in the plane $y = -1$, oriented in the negative $y$-direction.

**13.** $\mathbf{F}(x, y, z) = x\mathbf{i} + y\mathbf{j} + 2z\mathbf{k}$; $\sigma$ is the portion of the cone $z^2 = x^2 + y^2$ between the planes $z = 1$ and $z = 2$, oriented by upward unit normals.

**14.** $\mathbf{F}(x, y, z) = y\mathbf{j} + \mathbf{k}$; $\sigma$ is the portion of the paraboloid $z = x^2 + y^2$ below the plane $z = 4$, oriented by downward unit normals.

**15.** $\mathbf{F}(x, y, z) = x\mathbf{k}$; the surface $\sigma$ is the portion of the paraboloid $z = x^2 + y^2$ below the plane $z = y$, oriented by downward unit normals.

**16.** $\mathbf{F}(x, y, z) = x^2\mathbf{i} + yx\mathbf{j} + zx\mathbf{k}$; $\sigma$ is the portion of the plane $6x + 3y + 2z = 6$ in the first octant, oriented by unit normals with positive components.

**17–20** Find the flux of the vector field $\mathbf{F}$ across $\sigma$ in the direction of positive orientation. ▤

**17.** $\mathbf{F}(x, y, z) = x\mathbf{i} + y\mathbf{j} + \mathbf{k}$; $\sigma$ is the portion of the paraboloid
$$\mathbf{r}(u, v) = u \cos v\mathbf{i} + u \sin v\mathbf{j} + (1 - u^2)\mathbf{k}$$
with $1 \leq u \leq 2, 0 \leq v \leq 2\pi$.

**18.** $\mathbf{F}(x, y, z) = e^{-y}\mathbf{i} - y\mathbf{j} + x \sin z\mathbf{k}$; $\sigma$ is the portion of the elliptic cylinder
$$\mathbf{r}(u, v) = 2 \cos v\mathbf{i} + \sin v\mathbf{j} + u\mathbf{k}$$
with $0 \leq u \leq 5, 0 \leq v \leq 2\pi$.

**19.** $\mathbf{F}(x, y, z) = \sqrt{x^2 + y^2}\,\mathbf{k}$; $\sigma$ is the portion of the cone
$$\mathbf{r}(u, v) = u \cos v\mathbf{i} + u \sin v\mathbf{j} + 2u\mathbf{k}$$
with $0 \leq u \leq \sin v, 0 \leq v \leq \pi$.

**20.** $\mathbf{F}(x, y, z) = x\mathbf{i} + y\mathbf{j} + z\mathbf{k}$; $\sigma$ is the portion of the sphere
$$\mathbf{r}(u, v) = 2 \sin u \cos v\mathbf{i} + 2 \sin u \sin v\mathbf{j} + 2 \cos u\mathbf{k}$$
with $0 \leq u \leq \pi/3, 0 \leq v \leq 2\pi$.

**21.** Let $\sigma$ be the surface of the cube bounded by the planes $x = \pm 1$, $y = \pm 1$, $z = \pm 1$, oriented by outward unit normals. In each part, find the flux of $\mathbf{F}$ across $\sigma$.
(a) $\mathbf{F}(x, y, z) = x\mathbf{i}$
(b) $\mathbf{F}(x, y, z) = x\mathbf{i} + y\mathbf{j} + z\mathbf{k}$
(c) $\mathbf{F}(x, y, z) = x^2\mathbf{i} + y^2\mathbf{j} + z^2\mathbf{k}$

**22.** Let $\sigma$ be the closed surface consisting of the portion of the paraboloid $z = x^2 + y^2$ for which $0 \leq z \leq 1$ and capped by the disk $x^2 + y^2 \leq 1$ in the plane $z = 1$. Find the flux of the vector field $\mathbf{F}(x, y, z) = z\mathbf{j} - y\mathbf{k}$ in the outward direction across $\sigma$.

**23–26 True–False** Determine whether the statement is true or false. Explain your answer. ▤

**23.** The Möbius strip is a surface that has two orientations.

**24.** The flux of a vector field is another vector field.

**25.** If the net volume of fluid that passes through a surface per unit time in the positive direction is zero, then the velocity of the fluid is everywhere tangent to the surface.

**26.** If a surface $\sigma$ is oriented by a unit normal vector field $\mathbf{n}$, the flux of $\mathbf{n}$ across $\sigma$ is numerically equal to the surface area of $\sigma$.

**27–28** Find the flux of $\mathbf{F}$ across the surface $\sigma$ by expressing $\sigma$ parametrically. ▤

**27.** $\mathbf{F}(x, y, z) = \mathbf{i} + \mathbf{j} + \mathbf{k}$; the surface $\sigma$ is the portion of the cone $z = \sqrt{x^2 + y^2}$ between the planes $z = 1$ and $z = 2$, oriented by downward unit normals.

**28.** $\mathbf{F}(x, y, z) = 3\mathbf{i} - 7\mathbf{j} + z\mathbf{k}$; $\sigma$ is the portion of the cylinder $x^2 + y^2 = 16$ between the planes $z = -2$ and $z = 2$, oriented by outward unit normals.

**29.** Let $x$, $y$, and $z$ be measured in meters, and suppose that $\mathbf{F}(x, y, z) = 2x\mathbf{i} - 3y\mathbf{j} + z\mathbf{k}$ is the velocity vector (in m/s) of a fluid particle at the point $(x, y, z)$ in a steady-state incompressible fluid flow.
(a) Find the net volume of fluid that passes in the upward direction through the portion of the plane $x + y + z = 1$ in the first octant in 1 s. *(cont.)*

(b) Assuming that the fluid has a mass density of 806 kg/m³, find the net mass of fluid that passes in the upward direction through the surface in part (a) in 1 s.

30. Let $x$, $y$, and $z$ be measured in meters, and suppose that $\mathbf{F}(x, y, z) = -y\mathbf{i} + z\mathbf{j} + 3x\mathbf{k}$ is the velocity vector (in m/s) of a fluid particle at the point $(x, y, z)$ in a steady-state incompressible fluid flow.
    (a) Find the net volume of fluid that passes in the upward direction through the hemisphere $z = \sqrt{9 - x^2 - y^2}$ in 1 s.
    (b) Assuming that the fluid has a mass density of 1060 kg/m³, find the net mass of fluid that passes in the upward direction through the surface in part (a) in 1 s.

31. (a) Derive the analogs of Formulas (12) and (13) for surfaces of the form $x = g(y, z)$.
    (b) Let $\sigma$ be the portion of the paraboloid $x = y^2 + z^2$ for $x \leq 1$ and $z \geq 0$ oriented by unit normals with negative $x$-components. Use the result in part (a) to find the flux of
    $$\mathbf{F}(x, y, z) = y\mathbf{i} - z\mathbf{j} + 8\mathbf{k}$$
    across $\sigma$.

32. (a) Derive the analogs of Formulas (12) and (13) for surfaces of the form $y = g(z, x)$.
    (b) Let $\sigma$ be the portion of the paraboloid $y = z^2 + x^2$ for $y \leq 1$ and $z \geq 0$ oriented by unit normals with positive $y$-components. Use the result in part (a) to find the flux of
    $$\mathbf{F}(x, y, z) = x\mathbf{i} + y\mathbf{j} + z\mathbf{k}$$
    across $\sigma$.

33. Let $\mathbf{F} = \|\mathbf{r}\|^k \mathbf{r}$, where $\mathbf{r} = x\mathbf{i} + y\mathbf{j} + z\mathbf{k}$ and $k$ is a constant. (Note that if $k = -3$, this is an inverse-square field.) Let $\sigma$ be the sphere of radius $a$ centered at the origin and oriented by the outward normal $\mathbf{n} = \mathbf{r}/\|\mathbf{r}\| = \mathbf{r}/a$.
    (a) Find the flux of $\mathbf{F}$ across $\sigma$ without performing any integrations. [*Hint:* The surface area of a sphere of radius $a$ is $4\pi a^2$.]
    (b) For what value of $k$ is the flux independent of the radius of the sphere?

C 34. Let
    $$\mathbf{F}(x, y, z) = a^2 x\mathbf{i} + (y/a)\mathbf{j} + az^2\mathbf{k}$$
    and let $\sigma$ be the sphere of radius 1 centered at the origin and oriented outward. Use a CAS to find all values of $a$ such that the flux of $\mathbf{F}$ across $\sigma$ is $3\pi$.

C 35. Let
    $$\mathbf{F}(x, y, z) = \left(\frac{6}{a} + 1\right) x\mathbf{i} - 4ay\mathbf{j} + a^2 z\mathbf{k}$$
    and let $\sigma$ be the sphere of radius $a$ centered at the origin and oriented outward. Use a CAS to find all values of $a$ such that the flux of $\mathbf{F}$ across $\sigma$ is zero.

36. **Writing** Discuss the similarities and differences between the flux of a vector field across a surface and the line integral of a vector field along a curve.

37. **Writing** Write a paragraph explaining the concept of flux to someone unfamiliar with its meaning.

✔ **QUICK CHECK ANSWERS 15.6**

1. (a) $\displaystyle\iint_\sigma \mathbf{F} \cdot \mathbf{n}\, dS$ (b) $4\pi$  2. (a) $\displaystyle\iint_R \mathbf{F} \cdot \left(\frac{\partial \mathbf{r}}{\partial u} \times \frac{\partial \mathbf{r}}{\partial v}\right) dA$ (b) $0$  3. (a) $\displaystyle\iint_R \mathbf{F} \cdot \left(-\frac{\partial z}{\partial x}\mathbf{i} - \frac{\partial z}{\partial y}\mathbf{j} + \mathbf{k}\right) dA$ (b) $\dfrac{1}{2}$

4. the net volume of fluid crossing $\sigma$ in the positive direction per unit time

---

## 15.7 THE DIVERGENCE THEOREM

*In this section we will be concerned with flux across surfaces, such as spheres, that "enclose" a region of space. We will show that the flux across such surfaces can be expressed in terms of the divergence of the vector field, and we will use this result to give a physical interpretation of the concept of divergence.*

---

■ **ORIENTATION OF PIECEWISE SMOOTH CLOSED SURFACES**

In the last section we studied flux across general surfaces. Here we will be concerned exclusively with surfaces that are boundaries of finite solids—the surface of a solid sphere, the surface of a solid box, or the surface of a solid cylinder, for example. Such surfaces are said to be *closed*. A closed surface may or may not be smooth, but most of the surfaces that arise in applications are *piecewise smooth*; that is, they consist of finitely many smooth surfaces joined together at the edges (a box, for example). We will limit our discussion to piecewise smooth surfaces that can be assigned an *inward orientation* (toward the interior of the solid) and an *outward orientation* (away from the interior). It is very difficult to make

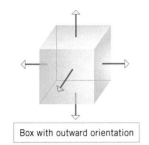

Box with outward orientation

▲ Figure 15.7.1

this concept mathematically precise, but the basic idea is that each piece of the surface is orientable, and oriented pieces fit together in such a way that the entire surface can be assigned an orientation (Figure 15.7.1).

## ■ THE DIVERGENCE THEOREM

In Section 15.1 we defined the divergence of a vector field

$$\mathbf{F}(x, y, z) = f(x, y, z)\mathbf{i} + g(x, y, z)\mathbf{j} + h(x, y, z)\mathbf{k}$$

as

$$\operatorname{div} \mathbf{F} = \frac{\partial f}{\partial x} + \frac{\partial g}{\partial y} + \frac{\partial h}{\partial z}$$

but we did not attempt to give a physical explanation of its meaning at that time. The following result, known as the *Divergence Theorem* or *Gauss's Theorem*, will provide us with a physical interpretation of divergence in the context of fluid flow.

---

**15.7.1**    THEOREM (*The Divergence Theorem*)    *Let G be a solid whose surface σ is oriented outward. If*

$$\mathbf{F}(x, y, z) = f(x, y, z)\mathbf{i} + g(x, y, z)\mathbf{j} + h(x, y, z)\mathbf{k}$$

*where f, g, and h have continuous first partial derivatives on some open set containing G, and if* **n** *is the outward unit normal on σ, then*

$$\iint\limits_{\sigma} \mathbf{F} \cdot \mathbf{n}\, dS = \iiint\limits_{G} \operatorname{div} \mathbf{F}\, dV \tag{1}$$

---

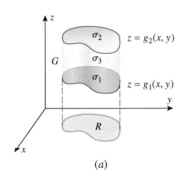

*(a)*

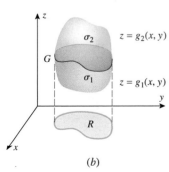

*(b)*

▲ Figure 15.7.2

The proof of this theorem for a general solid $G$ is too difficult to present here. However, we can give a proof for the special case where $G$ is simultaneously a simple $xy$-solid, a simple $yz$-solid, and a simple $zx$-solid (see Figure 14.5.3 and the related discussion for terminology).

PROOF    Formula (1) can be expressed as

$$\iint\limits_{\sigma} [f(x, y, z)\mathbf{i} + g(x, y, z)\mathbf{j} + h(x, y, z)\mathbf{k}] \cdot \mathbf{n}\, dS = \iiint\limits_{G} \left( \frac{\partial f}{\partial x} + \frac{\partial g}{\partial y} + \frac{\partial h}{\partial z} \right) dV$$

so it suffices to prove the three equalities

$$\iint\limits_{\sigma} f(x, y, z)\mathbf{i} \cdot \mathbf{n}\, dS = \iiint\limits_{G} \frac{\partial f}{\partial x}\, dV \tag{2a}$$

$$\iint\limits_{\sigma} g(x, y, z)\mathbf{j} \cdot \mathbf{n}\, dS = \iiint\limits_{G} \frac{\partial g}{\partial y}\, dV \tag{2b}$$

$$\iint\limits_{\sigma} h(x, y, z)\mathbf{k} \cdot \mathbf{n}\, dS = \iiint\limits_{G} \frac{\partial h}{\partial z}\, dV \tag{2c}$$

Since the proofs of all three equalities are similar, we will prove only the third.

Suppose that $G$ has upper surface $z = g_2(x, y)$, lower surface $z = g_1(x, y)$, and projection $R$ on the $xy$-plane. Let $\sigma_1$ denote the lower surface, $\sigma_2$ the upper surface, and $\sigma_3$ the lateral surface (Figure 15.7.2a). If the upper surface and lower surface meet as in

Figure 15.7.2*b*, then there is no lateral surface $\sigma_3$. Our proof will allow for both cases shown in those figures.

It follows from Theorem 14.5.2 that

$$\iiint\limits_{G} \frac{\partial h}{\partial z}\,dV = \iint\limits_{R} \left[ \int_{g_1(x,y)}^{g_2(x,y)} \frac{\partial h}{\partial z}\,dz \right] dA = \iint\limits_{R} \left[ h(x,y,z) \right]_{z=g_1(x,y)}^{g_2(x,y)} dA$$

so

$$\iiint\limits_{G} \frac{\partial h}{\partial z}\,dV = \iint\limits_{R} \left[ h(x,y,g_2(x,y)) - h(x,y,g_1(x,y)) \right] dA \qquad (3)$$

**Carl Friedrich Gauss (1777–1855)** German mathematician and scientist. Sometimes called the "prince of mathematicians," Gauss ranks with Newton and Archimedes as one of the three greatest mathematicians who ever lived. His father, a laborer, was an uncouth but honest man who would have liked Gauss to take up a trade such as gardening or bricklaying; but the boy's genius for mathematics was not to be denied. In the entire history of mathematics there may never have been a child so precocious as Gauss—by his own account he worked out the rudiments of arithmetic before he could talk. One day, before he was even three years old, his genius became apparent to his parents in a very dramatic way. His father was preparing the weekly payroll for the laborers under his charge while the boy watched quietly from a corner. At the end of the long and tedious calculation, Gauss informed his father that there was an error in the result and stated the answer, which he had worked out in his head. To the astonishment of his parents, a check of the computations showed Gauss to be correct!

For his elementary education Gauss was enrolled in a squalid school run by a man named Büttner whose main teaching technique was thrashing. Büttner was in the habit of assigning long addition problems which, unknown to his students, were arithmetic progressions that he could sum up using formulas. On the first day that Gauss entered the arithmetic class, the students were asked to sum the numbers from 1 to 100. But no sooner had Büttner stated the problem than Gauss turned over his slate and exclaimed in his peasant dialect, "Ligget se'." (Here it lies.) For nearly an hour Büttner glared at Gauss, who sat with folded hands while his classmates toiled away. When Büttner examined the slates at the end of the period, Gauss's slate contained a single number, 5050—the only correct solution in the class. To his credit, Büttner recognized the genius of Gauss and with the help of his assistant, John Bartels, had him brought to the attention of Karl Wilhelm Ferdinand, Duke of Brunswick. The shy and awkward boy, who was then fourteen, so captivated the Duke that he subsidized him through preparatory school, college, and the early part of his career.

From 1795 to 1798 Gauss studied mathematics at the University of Göttingen, receiving his degree in absentia from the University of Helmstadt. For his dissertation, he gave the first complete proof of the fundamental theorem of algebra, which states that every polynomial equation has as many solutions as its degree. At age 19 he solved a problem that baffled Euclid, inscribing a regular polygon of 17 sides in a circle using straightedge and compass; and in 1801, at age 24, he published his first masterpiece, *Disquisitiones*

*Arithmeticae*, considered by many to be one of the most brilliant achievements in mathematics. In that book Gauss systematized the study of number theory (properties of the integers) and formulated the basic concepts that form the foundation of that subject.

In the same year that the *Disquisitiones* was published, Gauss again applied his phenomenal computational skills in a dramatic way. The astronomer Giuseppi Piazzi had observed the asteroid Ceres for $\frac{1}{40}$ of its orbit, but lost it in the Sun. Using only three observations and the "method of least squares" that he had developed in 1795, Gauss computed the orbit with such accuracy that astronomers had no trouble relocating it the following year. This achievement brought him instant recognition as the premier mathematician in Europe, and in 1807 he was made Professor of Astronomy and head of the astronomical observatory at Göttingen.

In the years that followed, Gauss revolutionized mathematics by bringing to it standards of precision and rigor undreamed of by his predecessors. He had a passion for perfection that drove him to polish and rework his papers rather than publish less finished work in greater numbers—his favorite saying was "Pauca, sed matura" (Few, but ripe). As a result, many of his important discoveries were squirreled away in diaries that remained unpublished until years after his death.

Among his myriad achievements, Gauss discovered the Gaussian or "bell-shaped" error curve fundamental in probability, gave the first geometric interpretation of complex numbers and established their fundamental role in mathematics, developed methods of characterizing surfaces intrinsically by means of the curves that they contain, developed the theory of conformal (angle-preserving) maps, and discovered non-Euclidean geometry 30 years before the ideas were published by others. In physics he made major contributions to the theory of lenses and capillary action, and with Wilhelm Weber he did fundamental work in electromagnetism. Gauss invented the heliotrope, bifilar magnetometer, and an electrotelegraph.

Gauss was deeply religious and aristocratic in demeanor. He mastered foreign languages with ease, read extensively, and enjoyed mineralogy and botany as hobbies. He disliked teaching and was usually cool and discouraging to other mathematicians, possibly because he had already anticipated their work. It has been said that if Gauss had published all of his discoveries, the current state of mathematics would be advanced by 50 years. He was without a doubt the greatest mathematician of the modern era.

[*Image: ©SSPL/The Image Works*]

Next we will evaluate the surface integral in (2c) by integrating over each surface of $G$ separately. If there is a lateral surface $\sigma_3$, then at each point of this surface $\mathbf{k} \cdot \mathbf{n} = 0$ since $\mathbf{n}$ is horizontal and $\mathbf{k}$ is vertical. Thus,

$$\iint\limits_{\sigma_3} h(x, y, z)\mathbf{k} \cdot \mathbf{n}\, dS = 0$$

Therefore, regardless of whether $G$ has a lateral surface, we can write

$$\iint\limits_{\sigma} h(x, y, z)\mathbf{k} \cdot \mathbf{n}\, dS = \iint\limits_{\sigma_1} h(x, y, z)\mathbf{k} \cdot \mathbf{n}\, dS + \iint\limits_{\sigma_2} h(x, y, z)\mathbf{k} \cdot \mathbf{n}\, dS \tag{4}$$

On the upper surface $\sigma_2$, the outer normal is an upward normal, and on the lower surface $\sigma_1$, the outer normal is a downward normal. Thus, Formulas (12) and (13) of Section 15.6 imply that

$$\iint\limits_{\sigma_2} h(x, y, z)\mathbf{k} \cdot \mathbf{n}\, dS = \iint\limits_{R} h(x, y, g_2(x, y))\mathbf{k} \cdot \left(-\frac{\partial z}{\partial x}\mathbf{i} - \frac{\partial z}{\partial y}\mathbf{j} + \mathbf{k}\right) dA$$

$$= \iint\limits_{R} h(x, y, g_2(x, y))\, dA \tag{5}$$

and

$$\iint\limits_{\sigma_1} h(x, y, z)\mathbf{k} \cdot \mathbf{n}\, dS = \iint\limits_{R} h(x, y, g_1(x, y))\mathbf{k} \cdot \left(\frac{\partial z}{\partial x}\mathbf{i} + \frac{\partial z}{\partial y}\mathbf{j} - \mathbf{k}\right) dA$$

$$= -\iint\limits_{R} h(x, y, g_1(x, y))\, dA \tag{6}$$

Substituting (5) and (6) into (4) and combining the terms into a single integral yields

Explain how the derivation of (2c) should be modified to yield a proof of (2a) or (2b).

$$\iint\limits_{\sigma} h(x, y, z)\mathbf{k} \cdot \mathbf{n}\, dS = \iint\limits_{R} [h(x, y, g_2(x, y)) - h(x, y, g_1(x, y))]\, dA \tag{7}$$

Equation (2c) now follows from (3) and (7). ∎

The flux of a vector field across a closed surface with outward orientation is sometimes called the *outward flux* across the surface. In words, the Divergence Theorem states:

*The outward flux of a vector field across a closed surface is equal to the triple integral of the divergence over the region enclosed by the surface.*

### ■ USING THE DIVERGENCE THEOREM TO FIND FLUX

Sometimes it is easier to find the flux across a closed surface by using the Divergence Theorem than by evaluating the flux integral directly. This is illustrated in the following example.

▶ **Example 1** Use the Divergence Theorem to find the outward flux of the vector field $\mathbf{F}(x, y, z) = z\mathbf{k}$ across the sphere $x^2 + y^2 + z^2 = a^2$.

*Solution.* Let $\sigma$ denote the outward-oriented spherical surface and $G$ the region that it encloses. The divergence of the vector field is

$$\text{div } \mathbf{F} = \frac{\partial z}{\partial z} = 1$$

so from (1) the flux across $\sigma$ is

$$\Phi = \iint_{\sigma} \mathbf{F} \cdot \mathbf{n} \, dS = \iiint_{G} dV = \text{volume of } G = \frac{4\pi a^3}{3}$$

Note how much simpler this calculation is than that in Example 1 of Section 15.6. ◄

The Divergence Theorem is usually the method of choice for finding the flux across closed piecewise smooth surfaces with multiple sections, since it eliminates the need for a separate integral evaluation over each section. This is illustrated in the next three examples.

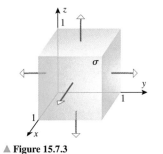

▲ **Figure 15.7.3**

▶ **Example 2**    Use the Divergence Theorem to find the outward flux of the vector field

$$\mathbf{F}(x, y, z) = 2x\mathbf{i} + 3y\mathbf{j} + z^2\mathbf{k}$$

across the unit cube in Figure 15.7.3.

*Solution.* Let $\sigma$ denote the outward-oriented surface of the cube and $G$ the region that it encloses. The divergence of the vector field is

$$\text{div } \mathbf{F} = \frac{\partial}{\partial x}(2x) + \frac{\partial}{\partial y}(3y) + \frac{\partial}{\partial z}(z^2) = 5 + 2z$$

so from (1) the flux across $\sigma$ is

$$\Phi = \iint_{\sigma} \mathbf{F} \cdot \mathbf{n} \, dS = \iiint_{G} (5 + 2z) \, dV = \int_0^1 \int_0^1 \int_0^1 (5 + 2z) \, dz \, dy \, dx$$

$$= \int_0^1 \int_0^1 \left[ 5z + z^2 \right]_{z=0}^1 \, dy \, dx = \int_0^1 \int_0^1 6 \, dy \, dx = 6 \ ◄$$

---

Let $\mathbf{F}(x, y, z)$ be the vector field in Example 2 and show that $\mathbf{F} \cdot \mathbf{n}$ is constant on each of the six faces of the cube in Figure 15.7.3. Use your computations to confirm the result in Example 2.

▶ **Example 3**    Use the Divergence Theorem to find the outward flux of the vector field

$$\mathbf{F}(x, y, z) = x^3\mathbf{i} + y^3\mathbf{j} + z^2\mathbf{k}$$

across the surface of the region that is enclosed by the circular cylinder $x^2 + y^2 = 9$ and the planes $z = 0$ and $z = 2$ (Figure 15.7.4).

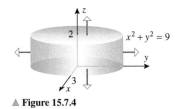

▲ **Figure 15.7.4**

*Solution.* Let $\sigma$ denote the outward-oriented surface and $G$ the region that it encloses. The divergence of the vector field is

$$\text{div } \mathbf{F} = \frac{\partial}{\partial x}(x^3) + \frac{\partial}{\partial y}(y^3) + \frac{\partial}{\partial z}(z^2) = 3x^2 + 3y^2 + 2z$$

so from (1) the flux across $\sigma$ is

$$\Phi = \iint_\sigma \mathbf{F} \cdot \mathbf{n} \, dS = \iiint_G (3x^2 + 3y^2 + 2z) \, dV$$

$$= \int_0^{2\pi} \int_0^3 \int_0^2 (3r^2 + 2z) r \, dz \, dr \, d\theta \qquad \text{Using cylindrical coordinates}$$

$$= \int_0^{2\pi} \int_0^3 \left[ 3r^3 z + z^2 r \right]_{z=0}^2 \, dr \, d\theta$$

$$= \int_0^{2\pi} \int_0^3 (6r^3 + 4r) \, dr \, d\theta$$

$$= \int_0^{2\pi} \left[ \frac{3r^4}{2} + 2r^2 \right]_0^3 \, d\theta$$

$$= \int_0^{2\pi} \frac{279}{2} \, d\theta = 279\pi \quad \blacktriangleleft$$

▶ **Example 4**  Use the Divergence Theorem to find the outward flux of the vector field

$$\mathbf{F}(x, y, z) = x^3 \mathbf{i} + y^3 \mathbf{j} + z^3 \mathbf{k}$$

across the surface of the region that is enclosed by the hemisphere $z = \sqrt{a^2 - x^2 - y^2}$ and the plane $z = 0$ (Figure 15.7.5).

*Solution.*  Let $\sigma$ denote the outward-oriented surface and $G$ the region that it encloses. The divergence of the vector field is

$$\text{div } \mathbf{F} = \frac{\partial}{\partial x}(x^3) + \frac{\partial}{\partial y}(y^3) + \frac{\partial}{\partial z}(z^3) = 3x^2 + 3y^2 + 3z^2$$

so from (1) the flux across $\sigma$ is

$$\Phi = \iint_\sigma \mathbf{F} \cdot \mathbf{n} \, dS = \iiint_G (3x^2 + 3y^2 + 3z^2) \, dV$$

$$= \int_0^{2\pi} \int_0^{\pi/2} \int_0^a (3\rho^2) \rho^2 \sin\phi \, d\rho \, d\phi \, d\theta \qquad \text{Using spherical coordinates}$$

$$= 3 \int_0^{2\pi} \int_0^{\pi/2} \int_0^a \rho^4 \sin\phi \, d\rho \, d\phi \, d\theta$$

$$= 3 \int_0^{2\pi} \int_0^{\pi/2} \left[ \frac{\rho^5}{5} \sin\phi \right]_{\rho=0}^a \, d\phi \, d\theta$$

$$= \frac{3a^5}{5} \int_0^{2\pi} \int_0^{\pi/2} \sin\phi \, d\phi \, d\theta$$

$$= \frac{3a^5}{5} \int_0^{2\pi} \left[ -\cos\phi \right]_0^{\pi/2} \, d\theta$$

$$= \frac{3a^5}{5} \int_0^{2\pi} d\theta = \frac{6\pi a^5}{5} \quad \blacktriangleleft$$

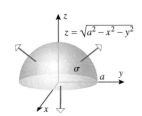

▲ **Figure 15.7.5**

### ■ DIVERGENCE VIEWED AS FLUX DENSITY

The Divergence Theorem provides a way of interpreting the divergence of a vector field **F**. Suppose that $G$ is a *small* spherical region centered at the point $P_0$ and that its surface, denoted by $\sigma(G)$, is oriented outward. Denote the volume of the region by $\text{vol}(G)$ and the flux of **F** across $\sigma(G)$ by $\Phi(G)$. If div **F** is continuous on $G$, then across the small region $G$ the value of div **F** will not vary much from its value div $\mathbf{F}(P_0)$ at the center, and we can reasonably approximate div **F** by the constant div $\mathbf{F}(P_0)$ on $G$. Thus, the Divergence Theorem implies that the flux $\Phi(G)$ of **F** across $\sigma(G)$ can be approximated by

$$\Phi(G) = \iint\limits_{\sigma(G)} \mathbf{F} \cdot \mathbf{n}\, dS = \iiint\limits_{G} \text{div } \mathbf{F}\, dV \approx \text{div } \mathbf{F}(P_0) \iiint\limits_{G} dV = \text{div } \mathbf{F}(P_0)\, \text{vol}(G)$$

from which we obtain the approximation

$$\text{div } \mathbf{F}(P_0) \approx \frac{\Phi(G)}{\text{vol}(G)} \tag{8}$$

The expression on the right side of (8) is called the ***outward flux density of F across G***. If we now let the radius of the sphere approach zero [so that $\text{vol}(G)$ approaches zero], then it is plausible that the error in this approximation will approach zero, and the divergence of **F** at the point $P_0$ will be given exactly by

$$\text{div } \mathbf{F}(P_0) = \lim_{\text{vol}(G) \to 0} \frac{\Phi(G)}{\text{vol}(G)}$$

which we can express as

Formula (9) is sometimes taken as the definition of divergence. This is a useful alternative to Definition 15.1.4 because it does not require a coordinate system.

$$\text{div } \mathbf{F}(P_0) = \lim_{\text{vol}(G) \to 0} \frac{1}{\text{vol}(G)} \iint\limits_{\sigma(G)} \mathbf{F} \cdot \mathbf{n}\, dS \tag{9}$$

This limit, which is called the ***outward flux density of F at $P_0$***, tells us that if **F** denotes the velocity field of a fluid, then *in a steady-state fluid flow* div **F** *can be interpreted as the limiting flux per unit volume at a point*. Moreover, it follows from (8) that for a small spherical region $G$ centered at a point $P_0$ in the flow, the outward flux across the surface of $G$ can be approximated by

$$\Phi(G) \approx (\text{div } \mathbf{F}(P_0))(\text{vol}(G)) \tag{10}$$

### ■ SOURCES AND SINKS

If $P_0$ is a point in an incompressible fluid at which div $\mathbf{F}(P_0) > 0$, then it follows from (8) that $\Phi(G) > 0$ for a sufficiently small sphere $G$ centered at $P_0$. Thus, there is a greater volume of fluid going out through the surface of $G$ than coming in. But this can only happen if there is some point *inside* the sphere at which fluid is entering the flow (say by condensation, melting of a solid, or a chemical reaction); otherwise the net outward flow through the surface would result in a decrease in density within the sphere, contradicting the incompressibility assumption. Similarly, if div $\mathbf{F}(P_0) < 0$, there would have to be a point *inside* the sphere at which fluid is leaving the flow (say by evaporation); otherwise the net inward flow through the surface would result in an increase in density within the sphere. In an incompressible fluid, points at which div $\mathbf{F}(P_0) > 0$ are called ***sources*** and points at which div $\mathbf{F}(P_0) < 0$ are called ***sinks***. Fluid enters the flow at a source and drains out at a sink. In an incompressible fluid without sources or sinks we must have

$$\text{div } \mathbf{F}(P) = 0$$

at every point $P$. In hydrodynamics this is called the ***continuity equation for incompressible fluids*** and is sometimes taken as the defining characteristic of an incompressible fluid.

### ■ GAUSS'S LAW FOR INVERSE-SQUARE FIELDS

The Divergence Theorem applied to inverse-square fields (see Definition 15.1.2) produces a result called ***Gauss's Law for Inverse-Square Fields***. This result is the basis for many important principles in physics.

---

**15.7.2   GAUSS'S LAW FOR INVERSE-SQUARE FIELDS   If**

$$\mathbf{F}(\mathbf{r}) = \frac{c}{\|\mathbf{r}\|^3}\mathbf{r}$$

is an inverse-square field in 3-space, and if $\sigma$ is a closed orientable surface that surrounds the origin, then the outward flux of $\mathbf{F}$ across $\sigma$ is

$$\Phi = \iint\limits_{\sigma} \mathbf{F} \cdot \mathbf{n}\, dS = 4\pi c \tag{11}$$

---

To derive this result, recall from Formula (5) of Section 15.1 that $\mathbf{F}$ can be expressed in component form as

$$\mathbf{F}(x, y, z) = \frac{c}{(x^2 + y^2 + z^2)^{3/2}}(x\mathbf{i} + y\mathbf{j} + z\mathbf{k}) \tag{12}$$

Since the components of $\mathbf{F}$ are not continuous at the origin, we cannot apply the Divergence Theorem across the solid enclosed by $\sigma$. However, we can circumvent this difficulty by constructing a sphere of radius $a$ centered at the origin, where the radius is sufficiently small that the sphere lies entirely within the region enclosed by $\sigma$ (Figure 15.7.6). We will denote the surface of this sphere by $\sigma_a$. The solid $G$ enclosed between $\sigma_a$ and $\sigma$ is an example of a three-dimensional solid with an internal "cavity." Just as we were able to extend Green's Theorem to multiply connected regions in the plane (regions with holes), so it is possible to extend the Divergence Theorem to solids in 3-space with internal cavities, provided the surface integral in the theorem is taken over the *entire* boundary with the outside boundary of the solid oriented outward and the boundaries of the cavities oriented inward. Thus, if $\mathbf{F}$ is the inverse-square field in (12), and if $\sigma_a$ is oriented inward, then the Divergence Theorem yields

$$\iiint\limits_{G} \operatorname{div} \mathbf{F}\, dV = \iint\limits_{\sigma} \mathbf{F} \cdot \mathbf{n}\, dS + \iint\limits_{\sigma_a} \mathbf{F} \cdot \mathbf{n}\, dS \tag{13}$$

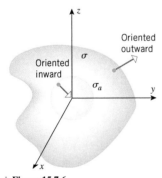

▲ **Figure 15.7.6**

But we showed in Example 5 of Section 15.1 that $\operatorname{div} \mathbf{F} = 0$, so (13) yields

$$\iint\limits_{\sigma} \mathbf{F} \cdot \mathbf{n}\, dS = -\iint\limits_{\sigma_a} \mathbf{F} \cdot \mathbf{n}\, dS \tag{14}$$

We can evaluate the surface integral over $\sigma_a$ by expressing the integrand in terms of components; however, it is easier to leave it in vector form. At each point on the sphere the unit normal $\mathbf{n}$ points inward along a radius from the origin, and hence $\mathbf{n} = -\mathbf{r}/\|\mathbf{r}\|$. Thus, (14) yields

$$\iint_{\sigma} \mathbf{F} \cdot \mathbf{n}\, dS = -\iint_{\sigma_a} \frac{c}{\|\mathbf{r}\|^3}\mathbf{r} \cdot \left(-\frac{\mathbf{r}}{\|\mathbf{r}\|}\right) dS$$

$$= \iint_{\sigma_a} \frac{c}{\|\mathbf{r}\|^4}(\mathbf{r} \cdot \mathbf{r})\, dS$$

$$= \iint_{\sigma_a} \frac{c}{\|\mathbf{r}\|^2}\, dS$$

$$= \frac{c}{a^2}\iint_{\sigma_a} dS \qquad \boxed{\|\mathbf{r}\| = a \text{ on } \sigma_a}$$

$$= \frac{c}{a^2}(4\pi a^2) \qquad \boxed{\begin{array}{l}\text{The integral is the surface}\\ \text{area of the sphere.}\end{array}}$$

$$= 4\pi c$$

which establishes (11).

### ▮ GAUSS'S LAW IN ELECTROSTATICS

It follows from Example 1 of Section 15.1 with $q = 1$ that a single charged particle of charge $Q$ located at the origin creates an inverse-square field

$$\mathbf{F}(\mathbf{r}) = \frac{Q}{4\pi\epsilon_0\|\mathbf{r}\|^3}\mathbf{r}$$

in which $\mathbf{F}(\mathbf{r})$ is the electrical force exerted by $Q$ on a unit positive charge ($q = 1$) located at the point with position vector $\mathbf{r}$. In this case Gauss's law (15.7.2) states that the outward flux $\Phi$ across any closed orientable surface $\sigma$ that surrounds $Q$ is

$$\Phi = \iint_{\sigma} \mathbf{F} \cdot \mathbf{n}\, dS = 4\pi\left(\frac{Q}{4\pi\epsilon_0}\right) = \frac{Q}{\epsilon_0}$$

This result, which is called **Gauss's Law for Electric Fields**, can be extended to more than one charge. It is one of the fundamental laws in electricity and magnetism.

---

✔ **QUICK CHECK EXERCISES 15.7**   *(See page 1158 for answers.)*

---

1. Let $G$ be a solid whose surface $\sigma$ is oriented outward by the unit normal $\mathbf{n}$, and let $\mathbf{F}(x, y, z)$ denote a vector field whose component functions have continuous first partial derivatives on some open set containing $G$. The Divergence Theorem states that the surface integral _____ and the triple integral _____ have the same value.

2. The outward flux of $\mathbf{F}(x, y, z) = x\mathbf{i} + y\mathbf{j} + z\mathbf{k}$ across any unit cube is _____.

3. If $\mathbf{F}(x, y, z)$ is the velocity vector field for a steady-state incompressible fluid flow, then a point at which div $\mathbf{F}$ is positive is called a _____ and a point at which div $\mathbf{F}$ is

negative is called a _____. The continuity equation for an incompressible fluid states that _____.

4. If

$$\mathbf{F}(\mathbf{r}) = \frac{c}{\|\mathbf{r}\|^3}\mathbf{r}$$

is an inverse-square field, and if $\sigma$ is a closed orientable surface that surrounds the origin, then Gauss's law states that the outward flux of $\mathbf{F}$ across $\sigma$ is _____. On the other hand, if $\sigma$ does not surround the origin, then it follows from the Divergence Theorem that the outward flux of $\mathbf{F}$ across $\sigma$ is _____.

**EXERCISE SET 15.7**    [c] CAS

**1–4** Verify Formula (1) in the Divergence Theorem by evaluating the surface integral and the triple integral. ▨

**1.** $\mathbf{F}(x, y, z) = x\mathbf{i} + y\mathbf{j} + z\mathbf{k}$; $\sigma$ is the surface of the cube bounded by the planes $x = 0$, $x = 1$, $y = 0$, $y = 1$, $z = 0$, $z = 1$.

**2.** $\mathbf{F}(x, y, z) = 5\mathbf{j} + 7\mathbf{k}$; $\sigma$ is the spherical surface $x^2 + y^2 + z^2 = 1$.

**3.** $\mathbf{F}(x, y, z) = 2x\mathbf{i} - yz\mathbf{j} + z^2\mathbf{k}$; the surface $\sigma$ is the paraboloid $z = x^2 + y^2$ capped by the disk $x^2 + y^2 \le 1$ in the plane $z = 1$.

**4.** $\mathbf{F}(x, y, z) = xy\mathbf{i} + yz\mathbf{j} + xz\mathbf{k}$; $\sigma$ is the surface of the cube bounded by the planes $x = 0$, $x = 2$, $y = 0$, $y = 2$, $z = 0$, $z = 2$.

**5–8 True–False** Determine whether the statement is true or false. Explain your answer. ▨

**5.** The Divergence Theorem equates a surface integral and a line integral.

**6.** If $G$ is a solid whose surface $\sigma$ is oriented outward, and if div $\mathbf{F} > 0$ at all points of $G$, then the flux of $\mathbf{F}$ across $\sigma$ is positive.

**7.** The continuity equation for incompressible fluids states that the divergence of the velocity vector field of the fluid is zero.

**8.** Since the divergence of an inverse-square field is zero, the flux of an inverse-square field across any closed orientable surface must be zero as well.

**9–19** Use the Divergence Theorem to find the flux of $\mathbf{F}$ across the surface $\sigma$ with outward orientation. ▨

**9.** $\mathbf{F}(x, y, z) = (x^2 + y)\mathbf{i} + z^2\mathbf{j} + (e^y - z)\mathbf{k}$; $\sigma$ is the surface of the rectangular solid bounded by the coordinate planes and the planes $x = 3$, $y = 1$, and $z = 2$.

**10.** $\mathbf{F}(x, y, z) = z^3\mathbf{i} - x^3\mathbf{j} + y^3\mathbf{k}$, where $\sigma$ is the sphere $x^2 + y^2 + z^2 = a^2$.

**11.** $\mathbf{F}(x, y, z) = (x - z)\mathbf{i} + (y - x)\mathbf{j} + (z - y)\mathbf{k}$; $\sigma$ is the surface of the cylindrical solid bounded by $x^2 + y^2 = a^2$, $z = 0$, and $z = 1$.

**12.** $\mathbf{F}(x, y, z) = x\mathbf{i} + y\mathbf{j} + z\mathbf{k}$; $\sigma$ is the surface of the solid bounded by the paraboloid $z = 1 - x^2 - y^2$ and the $xy$-plane.

**13.** $\mathbf{F}(x, y, z) = x^3\mathbf{i} + y^3\mathbf{j} + z^3\mathbf{k}$; $\sigma$ is the surface of the cylindrical solid bounded by $x^2 + y^2 = 4$, $z = 0$, and $z = 3$.

**14.** $\mathbf{F}(x, y, z) = (x^2 + y)\mathbf{i} + xy\mathbf{j} - (2xz + y)\mathbf{k}$; $\sigma$ is the surface of the tetrahedron in the first octant bounded by $x + y + z = 1$ and the coordinate planes.

**15.** $\mathbf{F}(x, y, z) = (x^3 - e^y)\mathbf{i} + (y^3 + \sin z)\mathbf{j} + (z^3 - xy)\mathbf{k}$, where $\sigma$ is the surface of the solid bounded above by $z = \sqrt{4 - x^2 - y^2}$ and below by the $xy$-plane. [*Hint:* Use spherical coordinates.]

**16.** $\mathbf{F}(x, y, z) = 2xz\mathbf{i} + yz\mathbf{j} + z^2\mathbf{k}$, where $\sigma$ is the surface of the solid bounded above by $z = \sqrt{a^2 - x^2 - y^2}$ and below by the $xy$-plane.

**17.** $\mathbf{F}(x, y, z) = x^2\mathbf{i} + y^2\mathbf{j} + z^2\mathbf{k}$; $\sigma$ is the surface of the conical solid bounded by $z = \sqrt{x^2 + y^2}$ and $z = 1$.

**18.** $\mathbf{F}(x, y, z) = x^2 y\mathbf{i} - xy^2\mathbf{j} + (z + 2)\mathbf{k}$; $\sigma$ is the surface of the solid bounded above by the plane $z = 2x$ and below by the paraboloid $z = x^2 + y^2$.

**19.** $\mathbf{F}(x, y, z) = x^3\mathbf{i} + x^2 y\mathbf{j} + xy\mathbf{k}$; $\sigma$ is the surface of the solid bounded by $z = 4 - x^2$, $y + z = 5$, $z = 0$, and $y = 0$.

**20.** Prove that if $\mathbf{r} = x\mathbf{i} + y\mathbf{j} + z\mathbf{k}$ and $\sigma$ is the surface of a solid $G$ oriented by outward unit normals, then

$$\text{vol}(G) = \frac{1}{3} \iint_{\sigma} \mathbf{r} \cdot \mathbf{n}\, dS$$

where vol$(G)$ is the volume of $G$.

**21.** Use the result in Exercise 20 to find the outward flux of the vector field $\mathbf{F}(x, y, z) = x\mathbf{i} + y\mathbf{j} + z\mathbf{k}$ across the surface $\sigma$ of the cylindrical solid bounded by $x^2 + 4x + y^2 = 5$, $z = -1$, and $z = 4$.

**FOCUS ON CONCEPTS**

**22.** Let $\mathbf{F}(x, y, z) = a\mathbf{i} + b\mathbf{j} + c\mathbf{k}$ be a constant vector field and let $\sigma$ be the surface of a solid $G$. Use the Divergence Theorem to show that the flux of $\mathbf{F}$ across $\sigma$ is zero. Give an informal physical explanation of this result.

**23.** Find a vector field $\mathbf{F}(x, y, z)$ that has
(a) positive divergence everywhere
(b) negative divergence everywhere.

**24.** In each part, the figure shows a horizontal layer of the vector field of a fluid flow in which the flow is parallel to the $xy$-plane at every point and is identical in each layer (i.e., is independent of $z$). For each flow, what can you say about the sign of the divergence at the origin? Explain your reasoning.

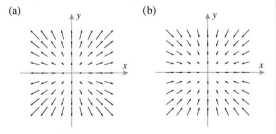

**25.** Let $\mathbf{F}(x, y, z)$ be a nonzero vector field in 3-space whose component functions have continuous first partial derivatives, and assume that div $\mathbf{F} = 0$ everywhere. If $\sigma$ is any sphere in 3-space, explain why there are infinitely many points on $\sigma$ at which $\mathbf{F}$ is tangent to the sphere.

**26.** Does the result in Exercise 25 remain true if the sphere $\sigma$ is replaced by a cube? Explain.

**27–31** Prove the identity, assuming that $\mathbf{F}$, $\sigma$, and $G$ satisfy the hypotheses of the Divergence Theorem and that all necessary differentiability requirements for the functions $f(x, y, z)$ and $g(x, y, z)$ are met. ■

**27.** $\displaystyle\iint_{\sigma} \operatorname{curl} \mathbf{F} \cdot \mathbf{n}\, dS = 0$ [*Hint:* See Exercise 37, Section 15.1.]

**28.** $\displaystyle\iint_{\sigma} \nabla f \cdot \mathbf{n}\, dS = \iiint_{G} \nabla^2 f\, dV$

$\left( \nabla^2 f = \dfrac{\partial^2 f}{\partial x^2} + \dfrac{\partial^2 f}{\partial y^2} + \dfrac{\partial^2 f}{\partial z^2} \right)$

**29.** $\displaystyle\iint_{\sigma} (f\nabla g) \cdot \mathbf{n}\, dS = \iiint_{G} (f\nabla^2 g + \nabla f \cdot \nabla g)\, dV$

**30.** $\displaystyle\iint_{\sigma} (f\nabla g - g\nabla f) \cdot \mathbf{n}\, dS = \iiint_{G} (f\nabla^2 g - g\nabla^2 f)\, dV$

[*Hint:* Interchange $f$ and $g$ in 29.]

**31.** $\displaystyle\iint_{\sigma} (f\mathbf{n}) \cdot \mathbf{v}\, dS = \iiint_{G} \nabla f \cdot \mathbf{v}\, dV$   ($\mathbf{v}$ a fixed vector)

**32.** Use the Divergence Theorem to find all positive values of $k$ such that

$$\mathbf{F}(\mathbf{r}) = \frac{\mathbf{r}}{\|\mathbf{r}\|^k}$$

satisfies the condition div $\mathbf{F} = 0$ when $\mathbf{r} \neq \mathbf{0}$.
[*Hint:* Modify the proof of (11).]

**33–36** Determine whether the vector field $\mathbf{F}(x, y, z)$ is free of sources and sinks. If it is not, locate them. ■

**33.** $\mathbf{F}(x, y, z) = (y + z)\mathbf{i} - xz^3\mathbf{j} + (x^2 \sin y)\mathbf{k}$

**34.** $\mathbf{F}(x, y, z) = xy\mathbf{i} - xy\mathbf{j} + y^2\mathbf{k}$

**35.** $\mathbf{F}(x, y, z) = x^3\mathbf{i} + y^3\mathbf{j} + z^3\mathbf{k}$

**36.** $\mathbf{F}(x, y, z) = (x^3 - x)\mathbf{i} + (y^3 - y)\mathbf{j} + (z^3 - z)\mathbf{k}$

**C 37.** Let $\sigma$ be the surface of the solid $G$ that is enclosed by the paraboloid $z = 1 - x^2 - y^2$ and the plane $z = 0$. Use a CAS to verify Formula (1) in the Divergence Theorem for the vector field

$$\mathbf{F} = (x^2 y - z^2)\mathbf{i} + (y^3 - x)\mathbf{j} + (2x + 3z - 1)\mathbf{k}$$

by evaluating the surface integral and the triple integral.

**38.** Writing  Discuss what it means to say that the divergence of a vector field is independent of a coordinate system. Explain how we know this to be true.

**39.** Writing  Describe some geometrical and physical applications of the Divergence Theorem.

---

✔ **QUICK CHECK ANSWERS 15.7**

1. $\displaystyle\iint_{\sigma} \mathbf{F} \cdot \mathbf{n}\, dS;\ \iiint_{G} \operatorname{div} \mathbf{F}\, dV$    2. 3    3. source; sink; div $\mathbf{F} = 0$    4. $4\pi c$; 0

---

**15.8  STOKES' THEOREM**

*In this section we will discuss a generalization of Green's Theorem to three dimensions that has important applications in the study of vector fields, particularly in the analysis of rotational motion of fluids. This theorem will also provide us with a physical interpretation of the curl of a vector field.*

■ **RELATIVE ORIENTATION OF CURVES AND SURFACES**

We will be concerned in this section with oriented surfaces in 3-space that are bounded by simple closed parametric curves (Figure 15.8.1a). If $\sigma$ is an oriented surface bounded by a simple closed parametric curve $C$, then there are two possible relationships between the orientations of $\sigma$ and $C$, which can be described as follows. Imagine a person walking along the curve $C$ with his or her head in the direction of the orientation of $\sigma$. The person is said to be walking in the *positive direction* of $C$ relative to the orientation of $\sigma$ if the surface is on the person's left (Figure 15.8.1b), and the person is said to be walking in the *negative direction* of $C$ relative to the orientation of $\sigma$ if the surface is on the person's right (Figure 15.8.1c). The positive direction of $C$ establishes a right-hand relationship between the orientations of $\sigma$ and $C$ in the sense that if the fingers of the right hand are curled from the direction of $C$ toward $\sigma$, then the thumb points (roughly) in the direction of the orientation of $\sigma$.

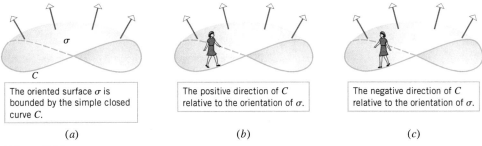

The oriented surface $\sigma$ is bounded by the simple closed curve $C$.

$(a)$

The positive direction of $C$ relative to the orientation of $\sigma$.

$(b)$

The negative direction of $C$ relative to the orientation of $\sigma$.

$(c)$

▲ **Figure 15.8.1**

### ■ STOKES' THEOREM

In Section 15.1 we defined the curl of a vector field

$$\mathbf{F}(x, y, z) = f(x, y, z)\mathbf{i} + g(x, y, z)\mathbf{j} + h(x, y, z)\mathbf{k}$$

as

$$\text{curl } \mathbf{F} = \left(\frac{\partial h}{\partial y} - \frac{\partial g}{\partial z}\right)\mathbf{i} + \left(\frac{\partial f}{\partial z} - \frac{\partial h}{\partial x}\right)\mathbf{j} + \left(\frac{\partial g}{\partial x} - \frac{\partial f}{\partial y}\right)\mathbf{k} = \begin{vmatrix} \mathbf{i} & \mathbf{j} & \mathbf{k} \\ \dfrac{\partial}{\partial x} & \dfrac{\partial}{\partial y} & \dfrac{\partial}{\partial z} \\ f & g & h \end{vmatrix} \quad (1)$$

but we did not attempt to give a physical explanation of its meaning at that time. The following result, known as **Stokes' Theorem**, will provide us with a physical interpretation of the curl in the context of fluid flow.

---

**15.8.1**    **THEOREM** (*Stokes' Theorem*)    *Let $\sigma$ be a piecewise smooth oriented surface that is bounded by a simple, closed, piecewise smooth curve $C$ with positive orientation. If the components of the vector field*

$$\mathbf{F}(x, y, z) = f(x, y, z)\mathbf{i} + g(x, y, z)\mathbf{j} + h(x, y, z)\mathbf{k}$$

*are continuous and have continuous first partial derivatives on some open set containing $\sigma$, and if $\mathbf{T}$ is the unit tangent vector to $C$, then*

$$\oint_C \mathbf{F} \cdot \mathbf{T} \, ds = \iint_\sigma (\text{curl } \mathbf{F}) \cdot \mathbf{n} \, dS \quad (2)$$

---

The proof of this theorem is beyond the scope of this text, so we will focus on its applications.

Recall from Formulas (30) and (34) in Section 15.2 that if $\mathbf{F}$ is a force field, the integral on the left side of (2) represents the work performed by the force field on a particle that traverses the curve $C$. Thus, loosely phrased, Stokes' Theorem states:

*The work performed by a force field on a particle that traverses a simple, closed, piecewise smooth curve $C$ in the positive direction can be obtained by integrating the normal component of the curl over an oriented surface $\sigma$ bounded by $C$.*

■ **USING STOKES' THEOREM TO CALCULATE WORK**

For computational purposes it is usually preferable to use Formula (30) in Section 15.2 to rewrite the formula in Stokes' Theorem as

$$\oint_C \mathbf{F} \cdot d\mathbf{r} = \iint_\sigma (\text{curl } \mathbf{F}) \cdot \mathbf{n}\, dS \tag{3}$$

Stokes' Theorem is usually the method of choice for calculating work around piecewise smooth curves with multiple sections, since it eliminates the need for a separate integral evaluation over each section. This is illustrated in the following example.

▶ **Example 1** Find the work performed by the force field

$$\mathbf{F}(x, y, z) = x^2\mathbf{i} + 4xy^3\mathbf{j} + y^2x\mathbf{k}$$

on a particle that traverses the rectangle $C$ in the plane $z = y$ shown in Figure 15.8.2.

*Solution.* The work performed by the field is

$$W = \oint_C \mathbf{F} \cdot d\mathbf{r}$$

However, to evaluate this integral directly would require four separate integrations, one over each side of the rectangle. Instead, we will use Formula (3) to express the work as the surface integral

$$W = \iint_\sigma (\text{curl } \mathbf{F}) \cdot \mathbf{n}\, dS$$

in which the plane surface $\sigma$ enclosed by $C$ is assigned a *downward* orientation to make the orientation of $C$ positive, as required by Stokes' Theorem.

Since the surface $\sigma$ has equation $z = y$ and

$$\text{curl } \mathbf{F} = \begin{vmatrix} \mathbf{i} & \mathbf{j} & \mathbf{k} \\ \dfrac{\partial}{\partial x} & \dfrac{\partial}{\partial y} & \dfrac{\partial}{\partial z} \\ x^2 & 4xy^3 & xy^2 \end{vmatrix} = 2xy\mathbf{i} - y^2\mathbf{j} + 4y^3\mathbf{k}$$

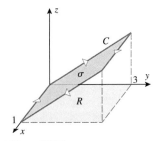

▲ **Figure 15.8.2**

George Gabriel Stokes **(1819–1903)** Irish mathematician and physicist. Born in Skreen, Ireland, Stokes came from a family deeply rooted in the Church of Ireland. His father was a rector, his mother the daughter of a rector, and three of his brothers took holy orders. He received his early education from his father and a local parish clerk. In 1837, he entered Pembroke College and after graduating with top honors accepted a fellowship at the college. In 1847 he was appointed Lucasian professor of mathematics at Cambridge, a position once held by Isaac Newton (and now held by the British physicist, Stephen Hawking), but one that had lost its esteem through the years. By virtue of his accomplishments, Stokes ultimately restored the position to the eminence it once held. Unfortunately, the position paid very little and Stokes was forced to teach at the Government School of Mines during the 1850s to supplement his income.

Stokes was one of several outstanding nineteenth century scientists who helped turn the physical sciences in a more empirical direction. He systematically studied hydrodynamics, elasticity of solids, behavior of waves in elastic solids, and diffraction of light. For Stokes, mathematics was a tool for his physical studies. He wrote classic papers on the motion of viscous fluids that laid the foundation for modern hydrodynamics; he elaborated on the wave theory of light; and he wrote papers on gravitational variation that established him as a founder of the modern science of geodesy.

Stokes was honored in his later years with degrees, medals, and memberships in foreign societies. He was knighted in 1889. Throughout his life, Stokes gave generously of his time to learned societies and readily assisted those who sought his help in solving problems. He was deeply religious and vitally concerned with the relationship between science and religion.

[*Image: http://commons.wikimedia.org/wiki/File:Stokes_George_G.jpg*]

it follows from Formula (13) of Section 15.6 with curl **F** replacing **F** that

$$W = \iint_\sigma (\text{curl } \mathbf{F}) \cdot \mathbf{n} \, dS = \iint_R (\text{curl } \mathbf{F}) \cdot \left( \frac{\partial z}{\partial x}\mathbf{i} + \frac{\partial z}{\partial y}\mathbf{j} - \mathbf{k} \right) dA$$

$$= \iint_R (2xy\mathbf{i} - y^2\mathbf{j} + 4y^3\mathbf{k}) \cdot (0\mathbf{i} + \mathbf{j} - \mathbf{k}) \, dA$$

$$= \int_0^1 \int_0^3 (-y^2 - 4y^3) \, dy \, dx$$

$$= -\int_0^1 \left[ \frac{y^3}{3} + y^4 \right]_{y=0}^3 dx$$

$$= -\int_0^1 90 \, dx = -90 \blacktriangleleft$$

Explain how the result in Example 1 shows that the given force field is not conservative.

---

▶ **Example 2**  Verify Stokes' Theorem for the vector field $\mathbf{F}(x, y, z) = 2z\mathbf{i} + 3x\mathbf{j} + 5y\mathbf{k}$, taking $\sigma$ to be the portion of the paraboloid $z = 4 - x^2 - y^2$ for which $z \geq 0$ with upward orientation, and $C$ to be the positively oriented circle $x^2 + y^2 = 4$ that forms the boundary of $\sigma$ in the $xy$-plane (Figure 15.8.3).

**Solution.**  We will verify Formula (3). Since $\sigma$ is oriented up, the positive orientation of $C$ is counterclockwise looking down the positive $z$-axis. Thus, $C$ can be represented parametrically (with positive orientation) by

$$x = 2\cos t, \quad y = 2\sin t, \quad z = 0 \qquad (0 \leq t \leq 2\pi) \tag{4}$$

Therefore,

$$\oint_C \mathbf{F} \cdot d\mathbf{r} = \oint_C 2z \, dx + 3x \, dy + 5y \, dz$$

$$= \int_0^{2\pi} [0 + (6\cos t)(2\cos t) + 0] \, dt$$

$$= \int_0^{2\pi} 12\cos^2 t \, dt = 12 \left[ \frac{1}{2}t + \frac{1}{4}\sin 2t \right]_0^{2\pi} = 12\pi$$

To evaluate the right side of (3), we start by finding curl **F**. We obtain

$$\text{curl } \mathbf{F} = \begin{vmatrix} \mathbf{i} & \mathbf{j} & \mathbf{k} \\ \dfrac{\partial}{\partial x} & \dfrac{\partial}{\partial y} & \dfrac{\partial}{\partial z} \\ 2z & 3x & 5y \end{vmatrix} = 5\mathbf{i} + 2\mathbf{j} + 3\mathbf{k}$$

Since $\sigma$ is oriented up and is expressed in the form $z = g(x, y) = 4 - x^2 - y^2$, it follows

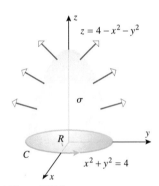

$z = 4 - x^2 - y^2$

$\sigma$

$R$

$C$

$x^2 + y^2 = 4$

▲ **Figure 15.8.3**

from Formula (12) of Section 15.6 with curl **F** replacing **F** that

$$\iint\limits_{\sigma} (\text{curl } \mathbf{F}) \cdot \mathbf{n} \, dS = \iint\limits_{R} (\text{curl } \mathbf{F}) \cdot \left( -\frac{\partial z}{\partial x}\mathbf{i} - \frac{\partial z}{\partial y}\mathbf{j} + \mathbf{k} \right) dA$$

$$= \iint\limits_{R} (5\mathbf{i} + 2\mathbf{j} + 3\mathbf{k}) \cdot (2x\mathbf{i} + 2y\mathbf{j} + \mathbf{k}) \, dA$$

$$= \iint\limits_{R} (10x + 4y + 3) \, dA$$

$$= \int_{0}^{2\pi} \int_{0}^{2} (10r\cos\theta + 4r\sin\theta + 3)r \, dr \, d\theta$$

$$= \int_{0}^{2\pi} \left[ \frac{10r^3}{3}\cos\theta + \frac{4r^3}{3}\sin\theta + \frac{3r^2}{2} \right]_{r=0}^{2} d\theta$$

$$= \int_{0}^{2\pi} \left( \frac{80}{3}\cos\theta + \frac{32}{3}\sin\theta + 6 \right) d\theta$$

$$= \left[ \frac{80}{3}\sin\theta - \frac{32}{3}\cos\theta + 6\theta \right]_{0}^{2\pi} = 12\pi$$

As guaranteed by Stokes' Theorem, the value of this surface integral is the same as the value obtained for the line integral. Note, however, that the line integral was simpler to evaluate and hence would be the method of choice in this case. ◄

**REMARK**  Observe that in Formula (3) the only relationships required between $\sigma$ and $C$ are that $C$ be the boundary of $\sigma$ and that $C$ be positively oriented relative to the orientation of $\sigma$. Thus, if $\sigma_1$ and $\sigma_2$ are *different* oriented surfaces but have the *same* positively oriented boundary curve $C$, then it follows from (3) that

$$\iint\limits_{\sigma_1} \text{curl } \mathbf{F} \cdot \mathbf{n} \, dS = \iint\limits_{\sigma_2} \text{curl } \mathbf{F} \cdot \mathbf{n} \, dS$$

For example, the parabolic surface in Example 2 has the same positively oriented boundary $C$ as the disk $R$ in Figure 15.8.3 with upper orientation. Thus, the value of the surface integral in that example would not change if $\sigma$ is replaced by $R$ (or by any other oriented surface that has the positively oriented circle $C$ as its boundary). This can be useful in computations because it is sometimes possible to circumvent a difficult integration by changing the surface of integration.

■ **RELATIONSHIP BETWEEN GREEN'S THEOREM AND STOKES' THEOREM**
It is sometimes convenient to regard a vector field

$$\mathbf{F}(x, y) = f(x, y)\mathbf{i} + g(x, y)\mathbf{j}$$

in 2-space as a vector field in 3-space by expressing it as

$$\mathbf{F}(x, y) = f(x, y)\mathbf{i} + g(x, y)\mathbf{j} + 0\mathbf{k} \tag{5}$$

If $R$ is a region in the $xy$-plane enclosed by a simple, closed, piecewise smooth curve $C$, then we can treat $R$ as a *flat* surface, and we can treat a surface integral over $R$ as an ordinary double integral over $R$. Thus, if we orient $R$ up and $C$ counterclockwise looking down the positive $z$-axis, then Formula (3) applied to (5) yields

$$\oint_{C} \mathbf{F} \cdot d\mathbf{r} = \iint\limits_{R} \text{curl } \mathbf{F} \cdot \mathbf{k} \, dA \tag{6}$$

But

$$\text{curl } \mathbf{F} = \begin{vmatrix} \mathbf{i} & \mathbf{j} & \mathbf{k} \\ \dfrac{\partial}{\partial x} & \dfrac{\partial}{\partial y} & \dfrac{\partial}{\partial z} \\ f & g & 0 \end{vmatrix} = -\frac{\partial g}{\partial z}\mathbf{i} + \frac{\partial f}{\partial z}\mathbf{j} + \left(\frac{\partial g}{\partial x} - \frac{\partial f}{\partial y}\right)\mathbf{k} = \left(\frac{\partial g}{\partial x} - \frac{\partial f}{\partial y}\right)\mathbf{k}$$

since $\partial g/\partial z = \partial f/\partial z = 0$. Substituting this expression in (6) and expressing the integrals in terms of components yields

$$\oint_C f\,dx + g\,dy = \iint\limits_R \left(\frac{\partial g}{\partial x} - \frac{\partial f}{\partial y}\right) dA$$

which is Green's Theorem [Formula (1) of Section 15.4]. Thus, we have shown that Green's Theorem can be viewed as a special case of Stokes' Theorem.

■ **CURL VIEWED AS CIRCULATION**

Stokes' Theorem provides a way of interpreting the curl of a vector field $\mathbf{F}$ in the context of fluid flow. For this purpose let $\sigma_a$ be a small oriented disk of radius $a$ centered at a point $P_0$ in a steady-state fluid flow, and let $\mathbf{n}$ be a unit normal vector at the center of the disk that points in the direction of orientation. Let us assume that the flow of liquid past the disk causes it to spin around the axis through $\mathbf{n}$, and let us try to find the direction of $\mathbf{n}$ that will produce the maximum rotation rate in the positive direction of the boundary curve $C_a$ (Figure 15.8.4). For convenience, we will denote the area of the disk $\sigma_a$ by $A(\sigma_a)$; that is, $A(\sigma_a) = \pi a^2$.

If the direction of $\mathbf{n}$ is fixed, then at each point of $C_a$ the only component of $\mathbf{F}$ that contributes to the rotation of the disk about $\mathbf{n}$ is the component $\mathbf{F} \cdot \mathbf{T}$ tangent to $C_a$ (Figure 15.8.5). Thus, for a fixed $\mathbf{n}$ the integral

$$\oint_{C_a} \mathbf{F} \cdot \mathbf{T}\,ds \tag{7}$$

can be viewed as a measure of the tendency for the fluid to flow in the positive direction around $C_a$. Accordingly, (7) is called the ***circulation of $\mathbf{F}$ around $C_a$***. For example, in the extreme case where the flow is normal to the circle at each point, the circulation around $C_a$ is zero, since $\mathbf{F} \cdot \mathbf{T} = 0$ at each point. The more closely that $\mathbf{F}$ aligns with $\mathbf{T}$ along the circle, the larger the value of $\mathbf{F} \cdot \mathbf{T}$ and the larger the value of the circulation.

To see the relationship between circulation and curl, suppose that curl $\mathbf{F}$ is continuous on $\sigma_a$, so that when $\sigma_a$ is small the value of curl $\mathbf{F}$ at any point of $\sigma_a$ will not vary much from the value of curl $\mathbf{F}(P_0)$ at the center. Thus, for a small disk $\sigma_a$ we can reasonably approximate curl $\mathbf{F}$ on $\sigma_a$ by the constant value curl $\mathbf{F}(P_0)$. Moreover, because the surface $\sigma_a$ is flat, the unit normal vectors that orient $\sigma_a$ are all equal. Thus, the vector quantity $\mathbf{n}$ in Formula (3) can be treated as a constant, and we can write

$$\oint_{C_a} \mathbf{F} \cdot \mathbf{T}\,ds = \iint\limits_{\sigma_a} (\text{curl } \mathbf{F}) \cdot \mathbf{n}\,dS \approx \text{curl } \mathbf{F}(P_0) \cdot \mathbf{n} \iint\limits_{\sigma_a} dS$$

where the line integral is taken in the positive direction of $C_a$. But the last double integral in this equation represents the surface area of $\sigma_a$, so

$$\oint_{C_a} \mathbf{F} \cdot \mathbf{T}\,ds \approx [\text{curl } \mathbf{F}(P_0) \cdot \mathbf{n}]A(\sigma_a)$$

from which we obtain

$$\text{curl } \mathbf{F}(P_0) \cdot \mathbf{n} \approx \frac{1}{A(\sigma_a)} \oint_{C_a} \mathbf{F} \cdot \mathbf{T}\,ds \tag{8}$$

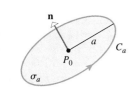

▲ Figure 15.8.4

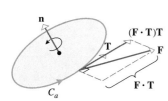

▲ Figure 15.8.5

Formula (9) is sometimes taken as a definition of curl. This is a useful alternative to Definition 15.1.5 because it does not require a coordinate system.

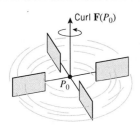

▲ **Figure 15.8.6**

The quantity on the right side of (8) is called the *circulation density of* **F** *around* $C_a$. If we now let the radius $a$ of the disk approach zero (with **n** fixed), then it is plausible that the error in this approximation will approach zero and the exact value of curl $\mathbf{F}(P_0) \cdot \mathbf{n}$ will be given by

$$\text{curl } \mathbf{F}(P_0) \cdot \mathbf{n} = \lim_{a \to 0} \frac{1}{A(\sigma_a)} \oint_{C_a} \mathbf{F} \cdot \mathbf{T}\, ds \qquad (9)$$

We call curl $\mathbf{F}(P_0) \cdot \mathbf{n}$ the *circulation density of* **F** *at* $P_0$ *in the direction of* **n**. This quantity has its maximum value when **n** is in the same direction as curl $\mathbf{F}(P_0)$; this tells us that *at each point in a steady-state fluid flow the maximum circulation density occurs in the direction of the curl*. Physically, this means that if a small paddle wheel is immersed in the fluid so that the pivot point is at $P_0$, then the paddles will turn most rapidly when the spindle is aligned with curl $\mathbf{F}(P_0)$ (Figure 15.8.6). If curl $\mathbf{F} = \mathbf{0}$ at each point of a region, then **F** is said to be *irrotational* in that region, since no circulation occurs about any point of the region.

---

✔ **QUICK CHECK EXERCISES 15.8**   *(See page 1166 for answers.)*

1. Let $\sigma$ be a piecewise smooth oriented surface that is bounded by a simple, closed, piecewise smooth curve $C$ with positive orientation. If the component functions of the vector field $\mathbf{F}(x, y, z)$ have continuous first partial derivatives on some open set containing $\sigma$, and if **T** is the unit tangent vector to $C$, then Stokes' Theorem states that the line integral _____ and the surface integral _____ are equal.

2. We showed in Example 2 that the vector field

$$\mathbf{F}(x, y, z) = 2z\mathbf{i} + 3x\mathbf{j} + 5y\mathbf{k}$$

   satisfies the equation curl $\mathbf{F} = 5\mathbf{i} + 2\mathbf{j} + 3\mathbf{k}$. It follows from Stokes' Theorem that if $C$ is any circle of radius $a$ in the $xy$-plane that is oriented counterclockwise when viewed from the positive $z$-axis, then

$$\int_C \mathbf{F} \cdot \mathbf{T}\, ds = \underline{\qquad}$$

   where **T** denotes the unit tangent vector to $C$.

3. (a) If $\sigma_1$ and $\sigma_2$ are two oriented surfaces that have the same positively oriented boundary curve $C$, and if the vector field $\mathbf{F}(x, y, z)$ has continuous first partial derivatives on some open set containing $\sigma_1$ and $\sigma_2$, then it follows from Stokes' Theorem that the surface integrals _____ and _____ are equal.

   (b) Let $\mathbf{F}(x, y, z) = 2z\mathbf{i} + 3x\mathbf{j} + 5y\mathbf{k}$, let $a$ be a positive number, and let $\sigma$ be the portion of the paraboloid $z = a^2 - x^2 - y^2$ for which $z \geq 0$ with upward orientation. Using part (a) and Quick Check Exercise 2, it follows that

$$\iint_\sigma (\text{curl } \mathbf{F}) \cdot \mathbf{n}\, dS = \underline{\qquad}$$

4. For steady-state flow, the maximum circulation density occurs in the direction of the _____ of the velocity vector field for the flow.

---

**EXERCISE SET 15.8**   [C] CAS

**1–4** Verify Formula (2) in Stokes' Theorem by evaluating the line integral and the surface integral. Assume that the surface has an upward orientation. ▪

1. $\mathbf{F}(x, y, z) = (x - y)\mathbf{i} + (y - z)\mathbf{j} + (z - x)\mathbf{k}$; $\sigma$ is the portion of the plane $x + y + z = 1$ in the first octant.

2. $\mathbf{F}(x, y, z) = x^2\mathbf{i} + y^2\mathbf{j} + z^2\mathbf{k}$; $\sigma$ is the portion of the cone $z = \sqrt{x^2 + y^2}$ below the plane $z = 1$.

3. $\mathbf{F}(x, y, z) = x\mathbf{i} + y\mathbf{j} + z\mathbf{k}$; $\sigma$ is the upper hemisphere $z = \sqrt{a^2 - x^2 - y^2}$.

4. $\mathbf{F}(x, y, z) = (z - y)\mathbf{i} + (z + x)\mathbf{j} - (x + y)\mathbf{k}$; $\sigma$ is the portion of the paraboloid $z = 9 - x^2 - y^2$ above the $xy$-plane.

**5–12** Use Stokes' Theorem to evaluate $\oint_C \mathbf{F} \cdot d\mathbf{r}$. ▪

5. $\mathbf{F}(x, y, z) = z^2\mathbf{i} + 2x\mathbf{j} - y^3\mathbf{k}$; $C$ is the circle $x^2 + y^2 = 1$ in the $xy$-plane with counterclockwise orientation looking down the positive $z$-axis.

6. $\mathbf{F}(x, y, z) = xz\mathbf{i} + 3x^2y^2\mathbf{j} + yx\mathbf{k}$; $C$ is the rectangle in the plane $z = y$ shown in Figure 15.8.2.

7. $\mathbf{F}(x, y, z) = 3z\mathbf{i} + 4x\mathbf{j} + 2y\mathbf{k}$; $C$ is the boundary of the paraboloid shown in Figure 15.8.3.

8. $\mathbf{F}(x, y, z) = -3y^2\mathbf{i} + 4z\mathbf{j} + 6x\mathbf{k}$; $C$ is the triangle in the plane $z = \frac{1}{2}y$ with vertices $(2, 0, 0)$, $(0, 2, 1)$, and $(0, 0, 0)$ with a counterclockwise orientation looking down the positive $z$-axis.

**9.** $\mathbf{F}(x, y, z) = xy\mathbf{i} + x^2\mathbf{j} + z^2\mathbf{k}$; $C$ is the intersection of the paraboloid $z = x^2 + y^2$ and the plane $z = y$ with a counterclockwise orientation looking down the positive $z$-axis.

**10.** $\mathbf{F}(x, y, z) = xy\mathbf{i} + yz\mathbf{j} + zx\mathbf{k}$; $C$ is the triangle in the plane $x + y + z = 1$ with vertices $(1, 0, 0)$, $(0, 1, 0)$, and $(0, 0, 1)$ with a counterclockwise orientation looking from the first octant toward the origin.

**11.** $\mathbf{F}(x, y, z) = (x - y)\mathbf{i} + (y - z)\mathbf{j} + (z - x)\mathbf{k}$; $C$ is the circle $x^2 + y^2 = a^2$ in the $xy$-plane with counterclockwise orientation looking down the positive $z$-axis.

**12.** $\mathbf{F}(x, y, z) = (z + \sin x)\mathbf{i} + (x + y^2)\mathbf{j} + (y + e^z)\mathbf{k}$; $C$ is the intersection of the sphere $x^2 + y^2 + z^2 = 1$ and the cone $z = \sqrt{x^2 + y^2}$ with counterclockwise orientation looking down the positive $z$-axis.

**13–16 True–False** Determine whether the statement is true or false. Explain your answer. ■

**13.** Stokes' Theorem equates a line integral and a surface integral.

**14.** Stokes' Theorem is a special case of Green's Theorem.

**15.** The circulation of a vector field $\mathbf{F}$ around a closed curve $C$ is defined to be
$$\int_C (\text{curl } \mathbf{F}) \cdot \mathbf{T} \, ds$$

**16.** If $\mathbf{F}(x, y, z)$ is defined everywhere in 3-space, and if curl $\mathbf{F}$ has no $\mathbf{k}$-component at any point in the $xy$-plane, then
$$\int_C \mathbf{F} \cdot \mathbf{T} \, ds = 0$$
for every smooth, simple, closed curve in the $xy$-plane.

**17.** Consider the vector field given by the formula
$$\mathbf{F}(x, y, z) = (x - z)\mathbf{i} + (y - x)\mathbf{j} + (z - xy)\mathbf{k}$$
(a) Use Stokes' Theorem to find the circulation around the triangle with vertices $A(1, 0, 0)$, $B(0, 2, 0)$, and $C(0, 0, 1)$ oriented counterclockwise looking from the origin toward the first octant.

(b) Find the circulation density of $\mathbf{F}$ at the origin in the direction of $\mathbf{k}$.

(c) Find the unit vector $\mathbf{n}$ such that the circulation density of $\mathbf{F}$ at the origin is maximum in the direction of $\mathbf{n}$.

**FOCUS ON CONCEPTS**

**18.** (a) Let $\sigma$ denote the surface of a solid $G$ with $\mathbf{n}$ the outward unit normal vector field to $\sigma$. Assume that $\mathbf{F}$ is a vector field with continuous first-order partial derivatives on $\sigma$. Prove that
$$\iint_\sigma (\text{curl } \mathbf{F}) \cdot \mathbf{n} \, dS = 0$$
[*Hint:* Let $C$ denote a simple closed curve on $\sigma$ that separates the surface into two subsurfaces $\sigma_1$ and $\sigma_2$ that share $C$ as their common boundary. Apply Stokes' Theorem to $\sigma_1$ and to $\sigma_2$ and add the results.]

(b) The vector field curl($\mathbf{F}$) is called the ***curl field*** of $\mathbf{F}$. In words, interpret the formula in part (a) as a statement about the flux of the curl field.

**19–20** The figures in these exercises show a horizontal layer of the vector field of a fluid flow in which the flow is parallel to the $xy$-plane at every point and is identical in each layer (i.e., is independent of $z$). For each flow, state whether you believe that the curl is nonzero at the origin, and explain your reasoning. If you believe that it is nonzero, then state whether it points in the positive or negative $z$-direction. ■

**19.** (a)             (b)

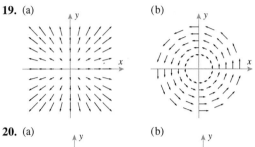

**20.** (a)             (b)

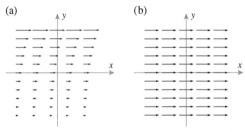

**21.** Let $\mathbf{F}(x, y, z)$ be a conservative vector field in 3-space whose component functions have continuous first partial derivatives. Explain how to use Formula (9) to prove that curl $\mathbf{F} = \mathbf{0}$.

**22.** In 1831 the physicist Michael Faraday discovered that an electric current can be produced by varying the magnetic flux through a conducting loop. His experiments showed that the electromotive force $\mathbf{E}$ is related to the magnetic induction $\mathbf{B}$ by the equation
$$\oint_C \mathbf{E} \cdot d\mathbf{r} = -\iint_\sigma \frac{\partial \mathbf{B}}{\partial t} \cdot \mathbf{n} \, dS$$
Use this result to make a conjecture about the relationship between curl $\mathbf{E}$ and $\mathbf{B}$, and explain your reasoning.

**c** **23.** Let $\sigma$ be the portion of the paraboloid $z = 1 - x^2 - y^2$ for which $z \geq 0$, and let $C$ be the circle $x^2 + y^2 = 1$ that forms the boundary of $\sigma$ in the $xy$-plane. Assuming that $\sigma$ is oriented up, use a CAS to verify Formula (2) in Stokes' Theorem for the vector field
$$\mathbf{F} = (x^2 y - z^2)\mathbf{i} + (y^3 - x)\mathbf{j} + (2x + 3z - 1)\mathbf{k}$$
by evaluating the line integral and the surface integral.

**24.** Writing Discuss what it means to say that the curl of a vector field is independent of a coordinate system. Explain how we know this to be true.

**25.** Writing Compare and contrast the Fundamental Theorem of Line Integrals, the Divergence Theorem, and Stokes' Theorem.

✔**QUICK CHECK ANSWERS 15.8**

1. $\displaystyle\int_C \mathbf{F}\cdot\mathbf{T}\,ds;$ $\displaystyle\iint_\sigma (\text{curl }\mathbf{F})\cdot\mathbf{n}\,dS$    2. $3\pi a^2$    3. (a) $\displaystyle\iint_{\sigma_1} (\text{curl }\mathbf{F})\cdot\mathbf{n}\,dS;$ $\displaystyle\iint_{\sigma_2} (\text{curl }\mathbf{F})\cdot\mathbf{n}\,dS$ (b) $3\pi a^2$    4. curl

## CHAPTER 15 REVIEW EXERCISES

1. In words, what is a vector field? Give some physical examples of vector fields.

2. (a) Give a physical example of an inverse-square field $\mathbf{F}(\mathbf{r})$ in 3-space.
   (b) Write a formula for a general inverse-square field $\mathbf{F}(\mathbf{r})$ in terms of the radius vector $\mathbf{r}$.
   (c) Write a formula for a general inverse-square field $\mathbf{F}(x, y, z)$ in 3-space using rectangular coordinates.

3. Find an explicit coordinate expression for the vector field $\mathbf{F}(x, y)$ that at every point $(x, y) \neq (1, 2)$ is the unit vector directed from $(x, y)$ to $(1, 2)$.

4. Find $\nabla\left(\dfrac{x+y}{x-y}\right)$.

5. Find $\text{curl}(z\mathbf{i} + x\mathbf{j} + y\mathbf{k})$.

6. Let
$$\mathbf{F}(x, y, z) = \frac{x}{x^2 + y^2}\mathbf{i} + \frac{y}{x^2 + y^2}\mathbf{j} + \frac{z}{x^2 + y^2}\mathbf{k}$$
   Sketch the level surface div $\mathbf{F} = 1$.

7. Assume that $C$ is the parametric curve $x = x(t)$, $y = y(t)$, where $t$ varies from $a$ to $b$. In each part, express the line integral as a definite integral with variable of integration $t$.
   (a) $\displaystyle\int_C f(x, y)\,dx + g(x, y)\,dy$    (b) $\displaystyle\int_C f(x, y)\,ds$

8. (a) Express the mass $M$ of a thin wire in 3-space as a line integral.
   (b) Express the length of a curve as a line integral.

9. Give a physical interpretation of $\int_C \mathbf{F}\cdot\mathbf{T}\,ds$.

10. State some alternative notations for $\int_C \mathbf{F}\cdot\mathbf{T}\,ds$.

**11–13** Evaluate the line integral. ■

11. $\displaystyle\int_C (x - y)\,ds;$ $C : x^2 + y^2 = 1$

12. $\displaystyle\int_C x\,dx + z\,dy - 2y^2\,dz;$

   $C : x = \cos t,\ y = \sin t,\ z = t$    $(0 \le t \le 2\pi)$

13. $\displaystyle\int_C \mathbf{F}\cdot d\mathbf{r}$ where $\mathbf{F}(x, y) = (x/y)\mathbf{i} - (y/x)\mathbf{j};$

   $\mathbf{r}(t) = t\mathbf{i} + 2t\mathbf{j}$    $(1 \le t \le 2)$

14. Find the work done by the force field
$$\mathbf{F}(x, y) = y^2\mathbf{i} + xy\mathbf{j}$$

   moving a particle from $(0, 0)$ to $(1, 1)$ along the parabola $y = x^2$.

15. State the Fundamental Theorem of Line Integrals, including all required hypotheses.

16. Evaluate $\int_C \nabla f \cdot d\mathbf{r}$ where $f(x, y, z) = xy^2z^3$ and
$$\mathbf{r}(t) = t\mathbf{i} + (t^2 + t)\mathbf{j} + \sin(3\pi t/2)\mathbf{k}    (0 \le t \le 1)$$

17. Let $\mathbf{F}(x, y) = y\mathbf{i} - 2x\mathbf{j}$.
   (a) Find a nonzero function $h(x)$ such that $h(x)\mathbf{F}(x, y)$ is a conservative vector field.
   (b) Find a nonzero function $g(y)$ such that $g(y)\mathbf{F}(x, y)$ is a conservative vector field.

18. Let $\mathbf{F}(x, y) = (ye^{xy} - 1)\mathbf{i} + xe^{xy}\mathbf{j}$.
   (a) Show that $\mathbf{F}$ is a conservative vector field.
   (b) Find a potential function for $\mathbf{F}$.
   (c) Find the work performed by the force field on a particle that moves along the sawtooth curve represented by the parametric equations
$$\begin{aligned} x &= t + \sin^{-1}(\sin t) \\ y &= (2/\pi)\sin^{-1}(\sin t) \end{aligned}    (0 \le t \le 8\pi)$$
   (see the accompanying figure).

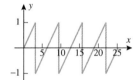

◀ **Figure Ex-18**

19. State Green's Theorem, including all of the required hypotheses.

20. Express the area of a plane region as a line integral.

21. Let $\alpha$ and $\beta$ denote angles that satisfy $0 < \beta - \alpha \le 2\pi$ and assume that $r = f(\theta)$ is a smooth polar curve with $f(\theta) > 0$ on the interval $[\alpha, \beta]$. Use the formula
$$A = \frac{1}{2}\int_C -y\,dx + x\,dy$$
   to find the area of the region $R$ enclosed by the curve $r = f(\theta)$ and the rays $\theta = \alpha$ and $\theta = \beta$.

22. (a) Use Green's Theorem to prove that
$$\int_C f(x)\,dx + g(y)\,dy = 0$$

if $f$ and $g$ are differentiable functions and $C$ is a simple, closed, piecewise smooth curve.

(b) What does this tell you about the vector field
$$\mathbf{F}(x, y) = f(x)\mathbf{i} + g(y)\mathbf{j}?$$

**23.** Assume that $\sigma$ is the parametric surface

$$\mathbf{r} = x(u, v)\mathbf{i} + y(u, v)\mathbf{j} + z(u, v)\mathbf{k}$$

where $(u, v)$ varies over a region $R$. Express the surface integral

$$\iint\limits_{\sigma} f(x, y, z)\, dS$$

as a double integral with variables of integration $u$ and $v$.

**24.** Evaluate $\iint_{\sigma} z\, dS$; $\sigma : x^2 + y^2 = 1\ (0 \le z \le 1)$.

**25.** Do you think that the surface in the accompanying figure is orientable? Explain your reasoning.

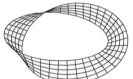

◀ **Figure Ex-25**

**26.** Give a physical interpretation of $\iint_{\sigma} \mathbf{F} \cdot \mathbf{n}\, dS$.

**27.** Find the flux of $\mathbf{F}(x, y, z) = x\mathbf{i} + y\mathbf{j} + 2z\mathbf{k}$ through the portion of the paraboloid $z = 1 - x^2 - y^2$ that is on or above the $xy$-plane, with upward orientation.

**28.** Find the flux of $\mathbf{F}(x, y, z) = x\mathbf{i} + 2y\mathbf{j} + 3z\mathbf{k}$ through the unit sphere centered at the origin with outward orientation.

**29.** State the Divergence Theorem and Stokes' Theorem, including all required hypotheses.

**30.** Let $G$ be a solid with the surface $\sigma$ oriented by outward unit normals, suppose that $\phi$ has continuous first and second partial derivatives in some open set containing $G$, and let $D_{\mathbf{n}}\phi$ be the directional derivative of $\phi$, where $\mathbf{n}$ is an outward unit normal to $\sigma$. Show that

$$\iint\limits_{\sigma} D_{\mathbf{n}}\phi\, dS = \iiint\limits_{G} \left[ \frac{\partial^2 \phi}{\partial x^2} + \frac{\partial^2 \phi}{\partial y^2} + \frac{\partial^2 \phi}{\partial z^2} \right] dV$$

**31.** Let $\sigma$ be the sphere $x^2 + y^2 + z^2 = 1$, let $\mathbf{n}$ be an inward unit normal, and let $D_{\mathbf{n}} f$ be the directional derivative of $f(x, y, z) = x^2 + y^2 + z^2$. Use the result in Exercise 30 to evaluate the surface integral

$$\iint\limits_{\sigma} D_{\mathbf{n}} f\, dS$$

**32.** Use Stokes' Theorem to evaluate $\iint_{\sigma} \text{curl}\, \mathbf{F} \cdot \mathbf{n}\, dS$ where $\mathbf{F}(x, y, z) = (z - y)\mathbf{i} + (x + z)\mathbf{j} - (x + y)\mathbf{k}$ and $\sigma$ is the portion of the paraboloid $z = 2 - x^2 - y^2$ on or above the plane $z = 1$, with upward orientation.

**33.** Let $\mathbf{F}(x, y, z) = f(x, y, z)\mathbf{i} + g(x, y, z)\mathbf{j} + h(x, y, z)\mathbf{k}$ and suppose that $f$, $g$, and $h$ are continuous and have continuous first partial derivatives in a region. It was shown in Exercise 31 of Section 15.3 that if $\mathbf{F}$ is conservative in the region, then

$$\frac{\partial f}{\partial y} = \frac{\partial g}{\partial x}, \quad \frac{\partial f}{\partial z} = \frac{\partial h}{\partial x}, \quad \frac{\partial g}{\partial z} = \frac{\partial h}{\partial y}$$

there. Use this result to show that if $\mathbf{F}$ is conservative in an open spherical region, then $\text{curl}\, \mathbf{F} = \mathbf{0}$ in that region.

**34–35** With the aid of Exercise 33, determine whether $\mathbf{F}$ is conservative. ■

**34.** (a) $\mathbf{F}(x, y, z) = z^2\mathbf{i} + e^{-y}\mathbf{j} + 2xz\mathbf{k}$
(b) $\mathbf{F}(x, y, z) = xy\mathbf{i} + x^2\mathbf{j} + \sin z\mathbf{k}$

**35.** (a) $\mathbf{F}(x, y, z) = \sin x\mathbf{i} + z\mathbf{j} + y\mathbf{k}$
(b) $\mathbf{F}(x, y, z) = z\mathbf{i} + 2yz\mathbf{j} + y^2\mathbf{k}$

**36.** As discussed in Example 1 of Section 15.1, *Coulomb's law* states that the electrostatic force $\mathbf{F}(\mathbf{r})$ that a particle of charge $Q$ exerts on a particle of charge $q$ is given by the formula

$$\mathbf{F}(\mathbf{r}) = \frac{qQ}{4\pi\epsilon_0 \|\mathbf{r}\|^3}\mathbf{r}$$

where $\mathbf{r}$ is the radius vector from $Q$ to $q$ and $\epsilon_0$ is the permittivity constant.

(a) Express the vector field $\mathbf{F}(\mathbf{r})$ in coordinate form $\mathbf{F}(x, y, z)$ with $Q$ at the origin.
(b) Find the work performed by the force field $\mathbf{F}$ on a charge $q$ that moves along a straight line from $(3, 0, 0)$ to $(3, 1, 5)$.

**CHAPTER 15 MAKING CONNECTIONS**

Assume that the motion of a particle of mass $m$ is described by a smooth vector-valued function

$$\mathbf{r}(t) = x(t)\mathbf{i} + y(t)\mathbf{j} + z(t)\mathbf{k} \quad (a \le t \le b)$$

where $t$ denotes time. Let $C$ denote the graph of the vector-valued function and let $v(t)$ and $\mathbf{a}(t)$ denote the respective speed and acceleration of the particle at time $t$.

1. We will say that the particle is moving "freely" under the influence of a force field $\mathbf{F}(x, y, z)$, provided $\mathbf{F}$ is the *only* force acting on the particle. In this case Newton's Second Law of Motion becomes

$$\mathbf{F}(x(t), y(t), z(t)) = m\mathbf{a}(t)$$

Use Theorem 12.6.2 to prove that when the particle is moving freely

$$\int_C \mathbf{F} \cdot \mathbf{T}\, ds = \int_C m\left(\frac{dv}{dt}\right) ds = m \int_a^b v(t)\left(\frac{dv}{dt}\right) dt$$

$$= m \int_a^b \frac{d}{dt}\left(\frac{1}{2}[v(t)]^2\right) dt$$

$$= \frac{1}{2}m[v(b)]^2 - \frac{1}{2}m[v(a)]^2$$

This tells us that the work performed by $\mathbf{F}$ on the particle is equal to the change in kinetic energy of the particle.

2. Suppose that the particle moves along a *prescribed* curve $C$ under the influence of a force field $\mathbf{F}(x, y, z)$. In addition to $\mathbf{F}$, the particle will experience a concurrent "support force"

$\mathbf{S}(x(t), y(t), z(t))$ from the curve. (Imagine a roller-coaster car falling without friction under the influence of the gravitational force $\mathbf{F}$. The tracks of the coaster provide the support force $\mathbf{S}$.) In this case we will say that the particle has a "constrained" motion under the influence of $\mathbf{F}$. Prove that the work performed by $\mathbf{F}$ on a particle with constrained motion is also equal to the change in kinetic energy of the particle. [*Hint:* Apply the argument of Exercise 1 to the resultant force $\mathbf{F} + \mathbf{S}$ on the particle. Use the fact that at each point on $C$, $\mathbf{S}$ will be normal to the curve.]

3. Suppose that $\mathbf{F}$ is a conservative force field. Use Exercises 1 and 2, along with the discussion in Section 15.3, to develop the conservation of energy principle for both free and constrained motion under $\mathbf{F}$.

4. As shown in the accompanying figure, a girl with mass $m$ is sliding down a smooth (frictionless) playground slide that is inclined at an angle of $\theta$ with the horizontal. If the acceleration due to gravity is $g$ and the length of the slide is $l$, prove that the speed of the child when she reaches the base of the slide is $v = \sqrt{2gl \sin \theta}$. Assume that she starts from rest at the top of the slide.

◀ **Figure Ex-4**

 **EXPANDING THE CALCULUS HORIZON**

To learn how the topics in this chapter can be used to model hurricane behavior, see the module entitled **Hurricane Modeling** at:

www.wiley.com/college/anton

# ANSWERS TO
# ODD-NUMBERED EXERCISES

▶ **Exercise Set 11.1 (Page 771)**

1. **(a)** $(0, 0, 0)$, $(3, 0, 0)$, $(3, 5, 0)$, $(0, 5, 0)$, $(0, 0, 4)$, $(3, 0, 4)$, $(3, 5, 4)$, $(0, 5, 4)$
   **(b)** $(0, 1, 0)$, $(4, 1, 0)$, $(4, 6, 0)$, $(0, 6, 0)$, $(0, 1, -2)$, $(4, 1, -2)$, $(4, 6, -2)$, $(0, 6, -2)$

3. $(4, 2, -2)$, $(4, 2, 1)$, $(4, 1, 1)$, $(4, 1, -2)$, $(-6, 1, 1)$, $(-6, 2, 1)$, $(-6, 2, -2)$, $(-6, 1, -2)$

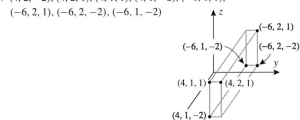

5. **(a)** point  **(b)** line parallel to the $y$-axis
   **(c)** plane parallel to the $yz$-plane

9. radius $\sqrt{74}$, center $(2, 1, -4)$  11. **(b)** $(2, 1, 6)$  **(c)** area 49

13. **(a)** $(x - 7)^2 + (y - 1)^2 + (z - 1)^2 = 16$
    **(b)** $(x - 1)^2 + y^2 + (z + 1)^2 = 16$
    **(c)** $(x + 1)^2 + (y - 3)^2 + (z - 2)^2 = 14$
    **(d)** $\left(x + \frac{1}{2}\right)^2 + (y - 2)^2 + (z - 2)^2 = \frac{5}{4}$

15. $(x - 2)^2 + (y + 1)^2 + (z + 3)^2 = r^2$;
    **(a)** $r^2 = 9$  **(b)** $r^2 = 1$  **(c)** $r^2 = 4$

Responses to True–False questions may be abridged to save space.

19. False; see Figure 11.1.6.

21. True; see Figure 11.1.3.

23. sphere, center $(-5, -2, -1)$, radius 7

25. sphere; center $\left(\frac{1}{2}, \frac{3}{4}, -\frac{5}{4}\right)$, radius $\dfrac{3\sqrt{6}}{4}$

27. no graph

29. **(a)**        **(b)**        **(c)**

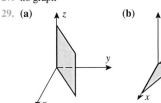

31. **(a)**        **(b)**        **(c)**

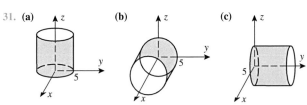

33. **(a)** $-2y + z = 0$  **(b)** $-2x + z = 0$  **(c)** $(x - 1)^2 + (y - 1)^2 = 1$
    **(d)** $(x - 1)^2 + (z - 1)^2 = 1$

35.            37.

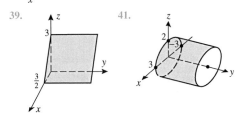

39.            41.

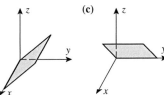

43.

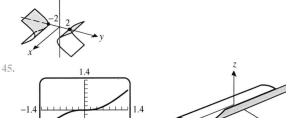

45.

47. largest distance, $3 + \sqrt{6}$; smallest distance, $3 - \sqrt{6}$

49. all points outside the circular cylinder $(y + 3)^2 + (z - 2)^2 = 16$

51. $r = (2 - \sqrt{3})R$  53. **(b)** $y^2 + z^2 = e^{2x}$

**A1**

## A2 Answers to Odd-Numbered Exercises

▶ **Exercise Set 11.2 (Page 782)**

1. (a-c)  (d-f)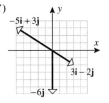

3. (a,b) 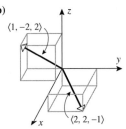 (c,d)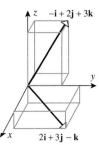

5. (a) $\langle 3, -4\rangle$ (b) $\langle -2, -3, 4\rangle$

 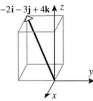

7. (a) $\langle -1, 3\rangle$ (b) $\langle -7, 2\rangle$ (c) $\langle -3, 6, 1\rangle$

9. (a) $\langle 4, -4\rangle$ (b) $\langle 8, -1, -3\rangle$

11. (a) $-\mathbf{i} + 4\mathbf{j} - 2\mathbf{k}$ (b) $18\mathbf{i} + 12\mathbf{j} - 6\mathbf{k}$ (c) $-\mathbf{i} - 5\mathbf{j} - 2\mathbf{k}$
(d) $40\mathbf{i} - 4\mathbf{j} - 4\mathbf{k}$ (e) $-2\mathbf{i} - 16\mathbf{j} - 18\mathbf{k}$ (f) $-\mathbf{i} + 13\mathbf{j} - 2\mathbf{k}$

13. (a) $\sqrt{2}$ (b) $5\sqrt{2}$ (c) $\sqrt{21}$ (d) $\sqrt{14}$

15. (a) $2\sqrt{3}$ (b) $\sqrt{14} + \sqrt{2}$ (c) $2\sqrt{14} + 2\sqrt{2}$ (d) $2\sqrt{37}$
(e) $(1/\sqrt{6})\mathbf{i} + (1/\sqrt{6})\mathbf{j} - (2/\sqrt{6})\mathbf{k}$ (f) $1$

Responses to True–False questions may be abridged to save space.
17. False; $\|\mathbf{i} + \mathbf{j}\| = \sqrt{2} \neq 1 + 1 = 2$
19. True; one in the same direction and one in the opposite direction.
21. (a) $(-1/\sqrt{17})\mathbf{i} + (4/\sqrt{17})\mathbf{j}$ (b) $(-3\mathbf{i} + 2\mathbf{j} - \mathbf{k})/\sqrt{14}$
(c) $(4\mathbf{i} + \mathbf{j} - \mathbf{k})/(3\sqrt{2})$

23. (a) $\langle -\frac{3}{2}, 2\rangle$ (b) $\dfrac{1}{\sqrt{5}}\langle 7, 0, -6\rangle$

25. (a) $\langle 3\sqrt{2}/2, 3\sqrt{2}/2\rangle$ (b) $\langle 0, 2\rangle$ (c) $\langle -5/2, 5\sqrt{3}/2\rangle$ (d) $\langle -1, 0\rangle$
27. $\langle (\sqrt{3} - \sqrt{2})/2, (1 + \sqrt{2})/2\rangle$
29. (a) $\langle -2, 5\rangle$ $-2\mathbf{i} + 5\mathbf{j}$ (b) $\langle 3, -8\rangle$

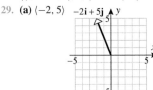 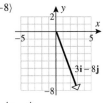

31. $\langle -\frac{2}{3}, 1\rangle$ 33. $\mathbf{u} = \frac{5}{7}\mathbf{i} + \frac{2}{7}\mathbf{j} + \frac{1}{7}\mathbf{k}$, $\mathbf{v} = \frac{8}{7}\mathbf{i} - \frac{1}{7}\mathbf{j} - \frac{4}{7}\mathbf{k}$
35. $\sqrt{5}, 3$ 37. (a) $\pm\frac{5}{3}$ (b) $3$
39. (a) $\langle 1/\sqrt{10}, 3/\sqrt{10}\rangle, \langle -1/\sqrt{10}, -3/\sqrt{10}\rangle$
(b) $\langle 1/\sqrt{2}, -1/\sqrt{2}\rangle, \langle -1/\sqrt{2}, 1/\sqrt{2}\rangle$ (c) $\pm\dfrac{1}{\sqrt{26}}\langle 5, 1\rangle$

41. (a) the circle of radius 1 about the origin
(b) the closed disk of radius 1 about the origin
(c) all points outside the closed disk of radius 1 about the origin

43. (a) the (hollow) sphere of radius 1 about the origin
(b) the closed ball of radius 1 about the origin
(c) all points outside the closed ball of radius 1 about the origin
45. magnitude $= 30\sqrt{5}$ lb, $\theta \approx 26.57°$
47. magnitude $\approx 207.06$ N, $\theta = 45°$
49. magnitude $\approx 94.995$ N, $\theta \approx 28.28°$
51. magnitude $\approx 9.165$ lb, angle $\approx -70.890°$
53. $\approx 183.02$ lb, 224.13 lb 55. $450\sqrt{2} + 150\sqrt{6}$ lb, $300 + 300\sqrt{3}$ lb
57. (a) $c_1 = -2, c_2 = 1$

▶ **Exercise Set 11.3 (Page 792)**

1. (a) $-10$; $\cos\theta = -1/\sqrt{5}$ (b) $-3$; $\cos\theta = -3/\sqrt{58}$
(c) $0$; $\cos\theta = 0$ (d) $-20$; $\cos\theta = -20/(3\sqrt{70})$
3. (a) obtuse (b) acute (c) obtuse (d) orthogonal
5. $\sqrt{2}/2, 0, -\sqrt{2}/2, -1, -\sqrt{2}/2, 0, \sqrt{2}/2$
7. (a) vertex $B$ (b) $82°, 60°, 38°$ 13. $r = 7/5$
15. (a) $\alpha = \beta \approx 55°, \gamma \approx 125°$ (b) $\alpha \approx 48°, \beta \approx 132°, \gamma \approx 71°$
19. (a) $\approx 35°$ (b) $90°$
21. $64°, 41°, 60°$ 23. $71°, 61°, 36°$
25. (a) $\left(\dfrac{2}{3}, \dfrac{4}{3}, \dfrac{4}{3}\right), \left(\dfrac{4}{3}, -\dfrac{7}{3}, \dfrac{5}{3}\right)$
(b) $\left\langle -\dfrac{74}{49}, -\dfrac{111}{49}, \dfrac{222}{49}\right\rangle, \left\langle \dfrac{270}{49}, \dfrac{62}{49}, \dfrac{121}{49}\right\rangle$
27. (a) $\langle 1, 1\rangle + \langle -4, 4\rangle$ (b) $\left\langle 0, -\dfrac{8}{5}, \dfrac{4}{5}\right\rangle + \left\langle -2, \dfrac{13}{5}, \dfrac{26}{5}\right\rangle$
(c) $\mathbf{v} = \langle 1, 4, 1\rangle$ is orthogonal to $\mathbf{b}$.
Responses to True–False questions may be abridged to save space.
29. True; $\mathbf{v} + \mathbf{w} = \mathbf{0}$ implies $0 = \mathbf{v} \cdot (\mathbf{v} + \mathbf{w}) = \|\mathbf{v}\|^2 \neq 0$,
a contradiction.
31. True; see Equation (12). 33. $\sqrt{564/29}$ 35. 169.8 N
37. 375 ft·lb 39. $-5\sqrt{3}$ J 47. (a) $40°$ (b) $x \approx -0.682328$

▶ **Exercise Set 11.4 (Page 803)**

1. (a) $-\mathbf{j} + \mathbf{k}$ 3. $\langle 7, 10, 9\rangle$ 5. $\langle -4, -6, -3\rangle$
7. (a) $\langle -20, -67, -9\rangle$ (b) $\langle -78, 52, -26\rangle$
(c) $\langle 0, -56, -392\rangle$ (d) $\langle 0, 56, 392\rangle$
9. $\dfrac{1}{\sqrt{2}}, -\dfrac{1}{\sqrt{2}}, 0$ 11. $\pm\dfrac{1}{\sqrt{6}}\langle 2, 1, 1\rangle$
Responses to True–False questions may be abridged to save space.
13. True; see Theorem 11.4.5(c).
15. False; let $\mathbf{v} = \mathbf{u} = \mathbf{i}$ and let $\mathbf{w} = 2\mathbf{i}$.
17. $\sqrt{59}$ 19. $\sqrt{374}/2$
21. 80 23. $-3$ 25. 16 27. (a) yes (b) yes (c) no
29. (a) 9 (b) $\sqrt{122}$ (c) $\sin^{-1}\left(\frac{9}{14}\right)$
31. (a) $2\sqrt{141}/29$ (b) $6/\sqrt{5}$ 33. $\frac{2}{3}$ 37. $\theta = \pi/4$
39. (a) $10\sqrt{2}$ lb·ft, direction of rotation about $P$ is counterclockwise
looking along $\overrightarrow{PQ} \times \mathbf{F} = -10\mathbf{i} + 10\mathbf{k}$ toward its initial point
(b) 10 lb·ft, direction of rotation about $P$ is counterclockwise
looking along $-10\mathbf{i}$ toward its initial point
(c) 0 lb·ft, no rotation about $P$
41. $\approx 36.19$ N·m 45. $-8\mathbf{i} - 20\mathbf{j} + 2\mathbf{k}, -8\mathbf{i} - 8\mathbf{k}$ 49. 1.887850

▶ **Exercise Set 11.5 (Page 810)**

1. (a) $L_1: x = 1, y = t, L_2: x = t, y = 1, L_3: x = t, y = t$
(b) $L_1: x = 1, y = 1, z = t, L_2: x = t, y = 1, z = 1,$
$L_3: x = 1, y = t, z = 1, L_4: x = t, y = t, z = t$
3. (a) $x = 3 + 2t, y = -2 + 3t$; line segment: $0 \le t \le 1$
(b) $x = 5 - 3t, y = -2 + 6t, z = 1 + t$; line segment: $0 \le t \le 1$

5. (a) $x = 2 + t$, $y = -3 - 4t$   (b) $x = t$, $y = -t$, $z = 1 + t$
7. (a) $P(2, -1)$, $\mathbf{v} = 4\mathbf{i} - \mathbf{j}$   (b) $P(-1, 2, 4)$, $\mathbf{v} = 5\mathbf{i} + 7\mathbf{j} - 8\mathbf{k}$
9. (a) $\langle -3, 4 \rangle + t \langle 1, 5 \rangle$; $-3\mathbf{i} + 4\mathbf{j} + t(\mathbf{i} + 5\mathbf{j})$
   (b) $\langle 2, -3, 0 \rangle + t \langle -1, 5, 1 \rangle$; $2\mathbf{i} - 3\mathbf{j} + t(-\mathbf{i} + 5\mathbf{j} + \mathbf{k})$
Responses to True–False questions may be abridged to save space.
11. False; the lines could be skew.
13. False; see part (b) of the solution to Example 3.
15. $x = -5 + 2t$, $y = 2 - 3t$   17. $x = 3 + 4t$, $y = -4 + 3t$
19. $x = -1 + 3t$, $y = 2 - 4t$, $z = 4 + t$
21. $x = -2 + 2t$, $y = -t$, $z = 5 + 2t$
23. (a) $x = 7$   (b) $y = \frac{7}{3}$   (c) $x = \dfrac{-1 \pm \sqrt{85}}{6}$, $y = \dfrac{43 \mp \sqrt{85}}{18}$
25. $(-2, 10, 0)$; $(-2, 0, -5)$;  the line does not intersect the $yz$-plane.
27. $(0, 4, -2)$, $(4, 0, 6)$   29. $(1, -1, 2)$   33. The lines are parallel.
35. The points do not lie on the same line.
39. $\langle x, y \rangle = \langle -1, 2 \rangle + t \langle 1, 1 \rangle$
41. the point $1/n$ of the way from $(-2, 0)$ to $(1, 3)$
43. the line segment joining the points $(1, 0)$ and $(-3, 6)$
45. $(5, 2)$   47. $2\sqrt{5}$   49. distance $= \sqrt{35/6}$
51. (a) $x = x_0 + (x_1 - x_0)t$, $y = y_0 + (y_1 - y_0)t$, $z = z_0 + (z_1 - z_0)t$
   (b) $x = x_1 + at$, $y = y_1 + bt$, $z = z_1 + ct$
53. (b) $\langle x, y, z \rangle = \langle 1 + 2t, -3 + 4t, 5 + t \rangle$
55. (b) $84°$   (c) $x = 7 + t$, $y = -1$, $z = -2 + t$
57. $x = t$, $y = 2 + t$, $z = 1 - t$
59. (a) $\sqrt{17}$ cm   (b) 10   (d) $\sqrt{14}/2$ cm

▶ **Exercise Set 11.6 (Page 819)**
1. $x = 3$, $y = 4$, $z = 5$   3. $x + 4y + 2z = 28$   5. $z = 0$
7. $x - y = 0$   9. $y + z = 1$   11. $2y - z = 1$
13. (a) parallel   (b) perpendicular   (c) neither
15. (a) parallel   (b) neither   (c) perpendicular
17. (a) point of intersection is $\left(\frac{5}{2}, \frac{5}{2}, \frac{5}{2}\right)$   (b) no intersection
19. $35°$
Responses to True–False questions may be abridged to save space.
21. True; each will be the negative of the other.
23. True; the direction vector of $L$ must be orthogonal to both
   normal vectors.
25. $4x - 2y + 7z = 0$   27. $4x - 13y + 21z = -14$
29. $x + y - 3z = 6$   31. $x + 5y + 3z = -6$
33. $x + 2y + 4z = \frac{29}{2}$   35. $x = 5 - 2t$, $y = 5t$, $z = -2 + 11t$
37. $7x + y + 9z = 25$   39. yes
41. $x = -\frac{11}{7} - 23t$, $y = -\frac{12}{7} + t$, $z = -7t$
43. $\frac{5}{3}$   45. $5/\sqrt{54}$   47. $25/\sqrt{126}$
49. $(x - 2)^2 + (y - 1)^2 + (z + 3)^2 = \frac{121}{14}$   51. $5/\sqrt{12}$

▶ **Exercise Set 11.7 (Page 830)**
1. (a) elliptic paraboloid, $a = 2$, $b = 3$
   (b) hyperbolic paraboloid, $a = 1$, $b = 5$
   (c) hyperboloid of one sheet, $a = b = c = 4$
   (d) circular cone, $a = b = 1$   (e) elliptic paraboloid, $a = 2$, $b = 1$
   (f) hyperboloid of two sheets, $a = b = c = 1$

3. (a) $-z = x^2 + y^2$, circular paraboloid
   opening down the negative $z$-axis

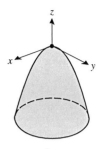

(b) $z = x^2 + y^2$, circular paraboloid,
no change
(c) $z = x^2 + y^2$, circular paraboloid,
no change
(d) $z = x^2 + y^2$, circular paraboloid,
no change

(e) $x = y^2 + z^2$,
circular paraboloid opening
along the positive $x$-axis

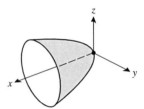

(f) $y = x^2 + z^2$,
circular paraboloid opening
along the positive $y$-axis

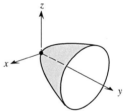

5. (a) hyperboloid of one sheet, axis is $y$-axis
   (b) hyperboloid of two sheets separated by $yz$-plane
   (c) elliptic paraboloid opening along the positive $x$-axis
   (d) elliptic cone with $x$-axis as axis
   (e) hyperbolic paraboloid straddling the $x$-axis
   (f) paraboloid opening along the negative $y$-axis

7. (a) $x = 0$: $\dfrac{y^2}{25} + \dfrac{z^2}{4} = 1$;
   $y = 0$: $\dfrac{x^2}{9} + \dfrac{z^2}{4} = 1$;
   $z = 0$: $\dfrac{x^2}{9} + \dfrac{y^2}{25} = 1$

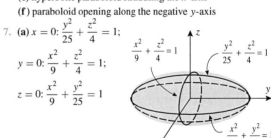

**(b)** $x = 0$: $z = 4y^2$;
$y = 0$: $z = x^2$;
$z = 0$: $x = y = 0$

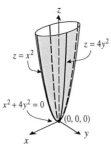

**(c)** $x = 0$: $\dfrac{y^2}{16} - \dfrac{z^2}{4} = 1$;

$y = 0$: $\dfrac{x^2}{9} - \dfrac{z^2}{4} = 1$;

$z = 0$: $\dfrac{x^2}{9} + \dfrac{y^2}{16} = 1$

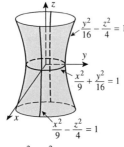

9. **(a)** $4x^2 + z^2 = 3$; ellipse   **(b)** $y^2 + z^2 = 3$; circle
   **(c)** $y^2 + z^2 = 20$; circle   **(d)** $9x^2 - y^2 = 20$; hyperbola
   **(e)** $z = 9x^2 + 16$; parabola   **(f)** $9x^2 + 4y^2 = 4$; ellipse

Responses to True–False questions may be abridged to save space.

11. False; "quadric" refers to second powers.
13. False; none of the cross sections need be circles.

15.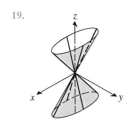

    Ellipsoid

17.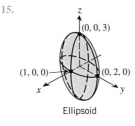

    Hyperboloid
    of one sheet

19.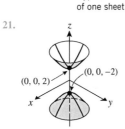

    Elliptic cone

21.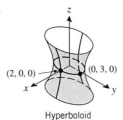

    Hyperboloid
    of two sheets

23.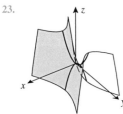

    Hyperbolic paraboloid

25.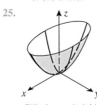

    Elliptic paraboloid

27.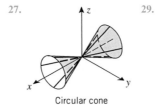

    Circular cone

29.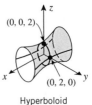

    Hyperboloid
    of one sheet

31.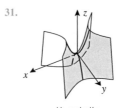

    Hyperbolic
    paraboloid

33.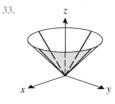

35.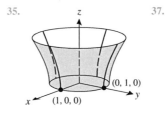

37.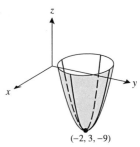

    Circular paraboloid

39.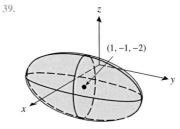

    Ellipsoid

41. **(a)** $\dfrac{x^2}{9} + \dfrac{y^2}{4} = 1$   **(b)** $6, 4$   **(c)** $(\pm\sqrt{5}, 0, \sqrt{2})$
    **(d)** The focal axis is parallel to the $x$-axis.
43. **(a)** $\dfrac{y^2}{4} - \dfrac{x^2}{4} = 1$   **(b)** $(0, \pm 2, 4)$   **(c)** $(0, \pm 2\sqrt{2}, 4)$
    **(d)** The focal axis is parallel to the $y$-axis.
45. **(a)** $z + 4 = y^2$   **(b)** $(2, 0, -4)$   **(c)** $\left(2, 0, -\dfrac{15}{4}\right)$
    **(d)** The focal axis is parallel to the $z$-axis.
47. circle of radius $\sqrt{2}$ in the plane $z = 2$, centered at $(0, 0, 2)$

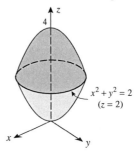

49. $y = 4(x^2 + z^2)$   51. $z = (x^2 + y^2)/4$ (circular paraboloid)

▶ Exercise Set 11.8 **(Page 837)**

1. **(a)** $(8, \pi/6, -4)$   **(b)** $(5\sqrt{2}, 3\pi/4, 6)$
   **(c)** $(2, \pi/2, 0)$   **(d)** $(8, 5\pi/3, 6)$
3. **(a)** $(2\sqrt{3}, 2, 3)$   **(b)** $(-4\sqrt{2}, 4\sqrt{2}, -2)$
   **(c)** $(5, 0, 4)$   **(d)** $(-7, 0, -9)$
5. **(a)** $(2\sqrt{2}, \pi/3, 3\pi/4)$   **(b)** $(2, 7\pi/4, \pi/4)$
   **(c)** $(6, \pi/2, \pi/3)$   **(d)** $(10, 5\pi/6, \pi/2)$
7. **(a)** $(5\sqrt{6}/4, 5\sqrt{2}/4, 5\sqrt{2}/2)$   **(b)** $(7, 0, 0)$
   **(c)** $(0, 0, 1)$   **(d)** $(0, -2, 0)$
9. **(a)** $(2\sqrt{3}, \pi/6, \pi/6)$   **(b)** $(\sqrt{2}, \pi/4, 3\pi/4)$
   **(c)** $(2, 3\pi/4, \pi/2)$   **(d)** $(4\sqrt{3}, 1, 2\pi/3)$
11. **(a)** $(5\sqrt{3}/2, \pi/4, -5/2)$   **(b)** $(0, 7\pi/6, -1)$
    **(c)** $(0, 0, 3)$   **(d)** $(4, \pi/6, 0)$

Responses to True–False questions may be abridged to save space.

15. True; see Figure 11.8.1*b*.
17. True; see Figures 11.8.3 and 11.8.4.

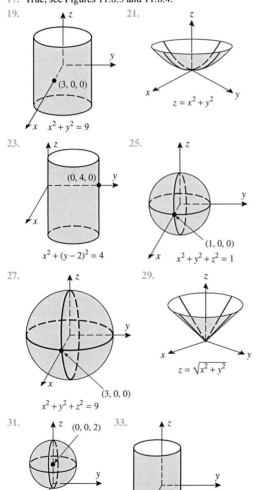

19.
21.
$z = x^2 + y^2$
23.
$(0, 4, 0)$
$x^2 + (y - 2)^2 = 4$
25.
$(1, 0, 0)$
$x^2 + y^2 + z^2 = 1$
27.
$(3, 0, 0)$
$x^2 + y^2 + z^2 = 9$
29.
$z = \sqrt{x^2 + y^2}$
31.
$(0, 0, 2)$
$x^2 + y^2 + (z - 2)^2 = 4$
33.
$(1, 0, 0)$
$(x - 1)^2 + y^2 = 1$

35. **(a)** $z = 3$   **(b)** $\rho = 3 \sec\phi$   37. **(a)** $z = 3r^2$   **(b)** $\rho = \frac{1}{3} \csc\phi \cot\phi$
39. **(a)** $r = 2$   **(b)** $\rho = 2 \csc\phi$   41. **(a)** $r^2 + z^2 = 9$   **(b)** $\rho = 3$
43. **(a)** $2r \cos\theta + 3r \sin\theta + 4z = 1$
    **(b)** $2\rho \sin\phi \cos\theta + 3\rho \sin\phi \sin\theta + 4\rho \cos\phi = 1$

45. **(a)** $r^2 \cos^2\theta = 16 - z^2$   **(b)** $\rho^2(1 - \sin^2\phi \sin^2\theta) = 16$
47. all points on or above the paraboloid $z = x^2 + y^2$ that are also on or below the plane $z = 4$
49. all points on or between concentric spheres of radii 1 and 3 centered at the origin
51. spherical: $(4000, \pi/6, \pi/6)$; rectangular: $(1000\sqrt{3}, 1000, 2000\sqrt{3})$
53. **(a)** $(10, \pi/2, 1)$   **(b)** $(0, 10, 1)$   **(c)** $(\sqrt{101}, \pi/2, \tan^{-1} 10)$

▶ Chapter 11 Review Exercises **(Page 838)**

3. **(b)** $-1/2, \pm\sqrt{3}/2$   **(d)** true
5. $(x + 3)^2 + (y - 5)^2 + (z + 4)^2 = r^2$;
   **(a)** $r^2 = 16$   **(b)** $r^2 = 25$   **(c)** $r^2 = 9$
7. $(7, 5)$
9. **(a)** $-\frac{3}{4}$   **(b)** $\frac{1}{7}$   **(c)** $(48 \pm 25\sqrt{3})/11$   **(d)** $c = \frac{4}{3}$
13. 13 ft·lb   15. **(a)** $\sqrt{26}/2$   **(b)** $\sqrt{26}/3$
17. **(a)** 29   **(b)** $\dfrac{29}{\sqrt{65}}$   19. $x = 4 + t,\ y = 1 - t,\ z = 2$
21. $x + 5y - z - 2 = 0$   23. $a_1a_2 + b_1b_2 + c_1c_2 = 0$
25. **(a)** hyperboloid of one sheet   **(b)** sphere   **(c)** circular cone
27. **(a)** $z = x^2 - y^2$   **(b)** $xz = 1$
29. **(a)**   **(b)**

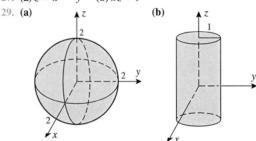

**(c)**

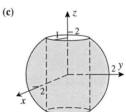

31. **(a)**   **(b)**

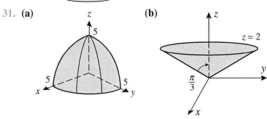

$z = 2$

**(c)**

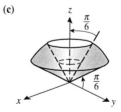

▶ Chapter 11 Making Connections **(Page 840)**

Answers are provided in the Student Solutions Manual.

## A6    Answers to Odd-Numbered Exercises

▶ **Exercise Set 12.1 (Page 845)**

1. $(-\infty, +\infty)$; $\mathbf{r}(\pi) = -\mathbf{i} - 3\pi\mathbf{j}$   3. $[2, +\infty)$; $\mathbf{r}(3) = -\mathbf{i} - \ln 3\mathbf{j} + \mathbf{k}$
5. $\mathbf{r} = 3\cos t\mathbf{i} + (t + \sin t)\mathbf{j}$    7. $x = 3t^2$, $y = -2$
9. the line in 2-space through $(3, 0)$ with direction vector $\mathbf{a} = -2\mathbf{i} + 5\mathbf{j}$
11. the line in 3-space through the point $(0, -3, 1)$ and parallel to the vector $2\mathbf{i} + 3\mathbf{k}$
13. an ellipse centered at $(0, 0, 1)$ in the plane $z = 1$
15. (a) slope $-\frac{3}{2}$   (b) $\left(\frac{5}{2}, 0, \frac{3}{2}\right)$
17. (a)                (b)

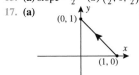

19. $\mathbf{r} = (1 - t)(3\mathbf{i} + 4\mathbf{j})$, $0 \le t \le 1$
21. $x = 2$                23. $(x - 1)^2 + (y - 3)^2 = 1$

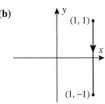

25. $x^2 - y^2 = 1, x \ge 1$   27.

29.

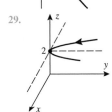

Responses to True–False questions may be abridged to save space.
31. False; the natural domain of a vector-valued function is the *intersection* of the domains of its component functions.
33. True; $\mathbf{r}(t) = (1 - t)\mathbf{r}_0 + t\mathbf{r}_1 (0 \le t \le 1)$ represents the line segment in 3-space that is traced from $\mathbf{r}_0$ to $\mathbf{r}_1$.
35. $x = t, y = t, z = 2t^2$

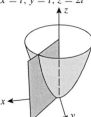

37. $\mathbf{r}(t) = t\mathbf{i} + t^2\mathbf{j} \pm \frac{1}{3}\sqrt{81 - 9t^2 - t^4}\mathbf{k}$   43. $c = 3/(2\pi)$

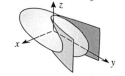

47. (a) III, since the curve is a subset of the plane $y = -x$
  (b) IV, since only $x$ is periodic in $t$ and $y$, $z$ increase without bound
  (c) II, since all three components are periodic in $t$
  (d) I, since the projection onto the $yz$-plane is a circle and the curve increases without bound in the $x$-direction
49. (a) $x = 3\cos t$, $y = 3\sin t$, $z = 9\cos^2 t$
  (b)

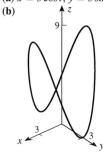

▶ **Exercise Set 12.2 (Page 856)**

1. $\left(\frac{1}{3}, 0\right)$   3. $2\mathbf{i} - 3\mathbf{j} + 4\mathbf{k}$   5. (a) continuous   (b) not continuous
7.                          9. $(\sin t)\mathbf{j}$   11. $\mathbf{r}'(2) = \langle 1, 4 \rangle$

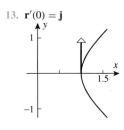 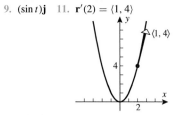

13. $\mathbf{r}'(0) = \mathbf{j}$              15. $\mathbf{r}'(\pi/2) = -2\mathbf{k}$

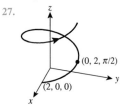 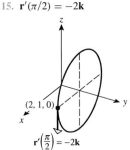

17.                        19. $x = 1 + 2t$, $y = 2 - t$
                           21. $x = 1 - \sqrt{3}\pi t$, $y = \sqrt{3} + \pi t$, $z = 1 + 3t$
                           23. $\mathbf{r} = (-\mathbf{i} + 2\mathbf{j}) + t\left(2\mathbf{i} + \frac{3}{4}\mathbf{j}\right)$
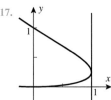      25. $\mathbf{r} = (4\mathbf{i} + \mathbf{j}) + t(-4\mathbf{i} + \mathbf{j} + 4\mathbf{k})$
                           27. (a) $\mathbf{i} - \mathbf{j} + \mathbf{k}$   (b) $-\mathbf{i} + \mathbf{k}$   (c) 0
                           29. $7t^6$; $18t^5\mathbf{i} - 10t^4\mathbf{j}$
                           31. $3t\mathbf{i} + 2t^2\mathbf{j} + \mathbf{C}$

33. $\langle te^t - e^t, t\ln t - t\rangle + \mathbf{C}$   35. $\mathbf{j}$   37. $(5\sqrt{5} - 1)/3$
39. $\frac{52}{3}\mathbf{i} + 4\mathbf{j}$
Responses to True–False questions may be abridged to save space.
41. False; for example, $\mathbf{r}(t) = \langle t, |t|\rangle$ is continuous at $t = 0$, but the specified limit doesn't exist at $t = 0$.
43. True; see the definition of $\int_a^b \mathbf{r}(t)\, dt$.
45. $(t^2 + 1)\mathbf{i} + (t^3 - 1)\mathbf{j}$
47. $y(t) = \left(\frac{1}{2}t^2 + 2\right)\mathbf{i} + (e^t - 1)\mathbf{j}$
49. (a) $(-2, 4, 6)$ and $(1, 1, -3)$   (b) $76°, 71°$   51. $68°$

▶ **Exercise Set 12.3 (Page 866)**

1. smooth   3. not smooth, $\mathbf{r}'(1) = \mathbf{0}$   5. $L = \frac{3}{2}$   7. $L = e - e^{-1}$
9. $L = 28$   11. $L = 2\pi\sqrt{10}$   13. $\mathbf{r}'(\tau) = 4\mathbf{i} + 8(4\tau + 1)\mathbf{j}$

**15.** $\mathbf{r}'(\tau) = 2\tau e^{\tau^2}\mathbf{i} - 8\tau e^{-\tau^2}\mathbf{j}$

Responses to True–False questions may be abridged to save space.

**17.** False; $\displaystyle\int_a^b \|\mathbf{r}'(t)\| \, dt$ is a scalar that represents the arc length of the curve in 2-space traced by $\mathbf{r}(t)$ from $t = a$ to $t = b$ (Theorem 12.3.1).

**19.** False; $\mathbf{r}'$ isn't defined at the point corresponding to the origin.

**21.** (a) $x = \dfrac{s}{\sqrt{2}}, y = \dfrac{s}{\sqrt{2}}$   (b) $x = y = z = \dfrac{s}{\sqrt{3}}$

**23.** (a) $x = 1 + \dfrac{s}{3}, y = 3 - \dfrac{2s}{3}, z = 4 + \dfrac{2s}{3}$   (b) $\left(\frac{28}{3}, -\frac{41}{3}, \frac{62}{3}\right)$

**25.** $x = 3 + \cos s, y = 2 + \sin s, 0 \le s \le 2\pi$

**27.** $x = \frac{1}{3}[(3s + 1)^{2/3} - 1]^{3/2}, y = \frac{1}{2}[(3s + 1)^{2/3} - 1], s \ge 0$

**29.** $x = \left(\dfrac{s}{\sqrt{2}} + 1\right)\cos\left[\ln\left(\dfrac{s}{\sqrt{2}} + 1\right)\right],$

$y = \left(\dfrac{s}{\sqrt{2}} + 1\right)\sin\left[\ln\left(\dfrac{s}{\sqrt{2}} + 1\right)\right],$

$\qquad 0 \le s \le \sqrt{2}(e^{\pi/2} - 1)$

**33.** $x = 2a \cos^{-1}[1 - s/(4a)]$
$\quad - 2a(1 - [1 - s/(4a)]^2)^{1/2}(2[1 - s/(4a)]^2 - 1),$
$y = \dfrac{s(8a - s)}{8a}$ for $0 \le s \le 8a$

**35.** (a) $9/2$   (b) $9 - 2\sqrt{6}$   **37.** (a) $\sqrt{3}(1 - e^{-2})$   (b) $4\sqrt{5}$

**39.** (a) $g(\tau) = \pi(\tau)$   (b) $g(\tau) = \pi(1 - \tau)$   **41.** 44 in

**43.** (a) $2t + \dfrac{1}{t}$   (b) $2t + \dfrac{1}{t}$   (c) $8 + \ln 3$

▶ **Exercise Set 12.4 (Page 872)**

**1.** (a) 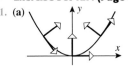   (b)

**5.** $\mathbf{T}(1) = \dfrac{2}{\sqrt{5}}\mathbf{i} + \dfrac{1}{\sqrt{5}}\mathbf{j}, \mathbf{N}(1) = \dfrac{1}{\sqrt{5}}\mathbf{i} - \dfrac{2}{\sqrt{5}}\mathbf{j}$

**7.** $\mathbf{T}\left(\dfrac{\pi}{3}\right) = -\dfrac{\sqrt{3}}{2}\mathbf{i} + \dfrac{1}{2}\mathbf{j}, \mathbf{N}\left(\dfrac{\pi}{3}\right) = -\dfrac{1}{2}\mathbf{i} - \dfrac{\sqrt{3}}{2}\mathbf{j}$

**9.** $\mathbf{T}\left(\dfrac{\pi}{2}\right) = -\dfrac{4}{\sqrt{17}}\mathbf{i} + \dfrac{1}{\sqrt{17}}\mathbf{k}, \mathbf{N}\left(\dfrac{\pi}{2}\right) = -\mathbf{j}$

**11.** $\mathbf{T}(0) = \dfrac{1}{\sqrt{3}}\mathbf{i} + \dfrac{1}{\sqrt{3}}\mathbf{j} + \dfrac{1}{\sqrt{3}}\mathbf{k}, \mathbf{N}(0) = -\dfrac{1}{\sqrt{2}}\mathbf{i} + \dfrac{1}{\sqrt{2}}\mathbf{j}$

**13.** $x = s, y = 1$   **15.** $\mathbf{B} = \frac{4}{5}\cos t\,\mathbf{i} - \frac{4}{5}\sin t\,\mathbf{j} - \frac{3}{5}\mathbf{k}$   **17.** $\mathbf{B} = -\mathbf{k}$

**19.** $\mathbf{T}\left(\dfrac{\pi}{4}\right) = \dfrac{\sqrt{2}}{2}(-\mathbf{i} + \mathbf{j}), \mathbf{N}\left(\dfrac{\pi}{4}\right) = -\dfrac{\sqrt{2}}{2}(\mathbf{i} + \mathbf{j}),$
$\mathbf{B}\left(\dfrac{\pi}{4}\right) = \mathbf{k}$; rectifying: $x + y = \sqrt{2}$; osculating: $z = 1$;
normal: $-x + y = 0$

Responses to True–False questions may be abridged to save space.

**21.** False; $\mathbf{T}(t)$ points in the direction of increasing parameter but may not be orthogonal to $\mathbf{r}(t)$. For example, if $\mathbf{r}(t) = \langle t, t \rangle$, then $\mathbf{T}(t) = \langle 1/\sqrt{2}, 1/\sqrt{2} \rangle$ is parallel to $\mathbf{r}(t)$.

**23.** True; $\mathbf{T}(s) = \mathbf{r}'(s)$, the unit tangent vector, and $\mathbf{N}(s) = \dfrac{\mathbf{r}''(s)}{\|\mathbf{r}''(s)\|}$, the unit normal vector, are orthogonal, so $\mathbf{r}'(s)$ and $\mathbf{r}''(s)$ are orthogonal.

▶ **Exercise Set 12.5 (Page 879)**

**1.** $\kappa \approx 2$   **3.** (a) I is the curvature of II.   (b) I is the curvature of II.

**5.** $\dfrac{6}{|t|(4 + 9t^2)^{3/2}}$   **7.** $\dfrac{12e^{2t}}{(9e^{6t} + e^{-2t})^{3/2}}$   **9.** $\dfrac{4}{17}$   **11.** $\dfrac{1}{2\cosh^2 t}$

**13.** $\kappa = \frac{2}{5}, \rho = \frac{5}{2}$   **15.** $\kappa = \dfrac{\sqrt{2}}{3}, \rho = \dfrac{3\sqrt{2}}{2}$   **17.** $\kappa = \frac{1}{4}$

Responses to True–False questions may be abridged to save space.

**19.** True; see Example 1: a circle of radius $a$ has constant curvature $1/a$.

**21.** False; see Definition 12.5.1: the curvature of the graph of $\mathbf{r}(s)$ is $\|\mathbf{r}''(s)\|$, the length of $\mathbf{r}''(s)$.

**25.** 1   **27.** $\dfrac{e^{-1}}{(1 + e^{-2})^{3/2}}$   **29.** $\dfrac{96}{125}$   **31.** $\dfrac{1}{\sqrt{2}}$

**33.** (a) 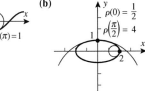   (b)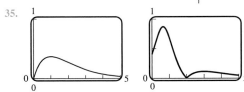

**35.**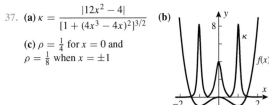

**37.** (a) $\kappa = \dfrac{|12x^2 - 4|}{[1 + (4x^3 - 4x)^2]^{3/2}}$   (b)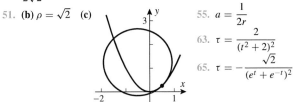
(c) $\rho = \frac{1}{4}$ for $x = 0$ and
$\rho = \frac{1}{8}$ when $x = \pm 1$

**41.** $\dfrac{3}{2\sqrt{2}}$   **43.** $\frac{2}{3}$   **45.** $\rho = 2|p|$   **47.** $(3, 0), (-3, 0)$

**51.** (b) $\rho = \sqrt{2}$   (c)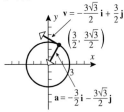

**55.** $a = \dfrac{1}{2r}$

**63.** $\tau = \dfrac{2}{(t^2 + 2)^2}$

**65.** $\tau = -\dfrac{\sqrt{2}}{(e^t + e^{-t})^2}$

▶ **Exercise Set 12.6 (Page 891)**

**1.** $\mathbf{v}(t) = -3\sin t\,\mathbf{i} + 3\cos t\,\mathbf{j}$
$\mathbf{a}(t) = -3\cos t\,\mathbf{i} - 3\sin t\,\mathbf{j}$
$\|\mathbf{v}(t)\| = 3$

**3.** $\mathbf{v}(t) = e^t\mathbf{i} - e^{-t}\mathbf{j}$
$\mathbf{a}(t) = e^t\mathbf{i} + e^{-t}\mathbf{j}$
$\|\mathbf{v}(t)\| = \sqrt{e^{2t} + e^{-2t}}$

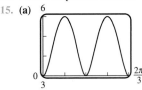

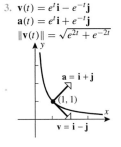

**5.** $\mathbf{v} = \mathbf{i} + \mathbf{j} + \mathbf{k}, \|\mathbf{v}\| = \sqrt{3}, \mathbf{a} = \mathbf{j} + 2\mathbf{k}$

**7.** $\mathbf{v} = -\sqrt{2}\mathbf{i} + \sqrt{2}\mathbf{j} + \mathbf{k}, \|\mathbf{v}\| = \sqrt{5}, \mathbf{a} = -\sqrt{2}\mathbf{i} - \sqrt{2}\mathbf{j}$

**13.** minimum speed $3\sqrt{2}$ when $\mathbf{r} = 24\mathbf{i} + 8\mathbf{j}$

**15.** (a) 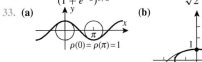   (b) maximum speed $= 6$,
minimum speed $= 3$
(d) The maximum speed first occurs when $t = \pi/6$.

**17.** $\mathbf{v}(t) = (1 - \sin t)\mathbf{i} + (\cos t - 1)\mathbf{j}$;
$\mathbf{r}(t) = (t + \cos t - 1)\mathbf{i} + (\sin t - t + 1)\mathbf{j}$

**19.** $\mathbf{v}(t) = (1 - \cos t)\mathbf{i} + \sin t\,\mathbf{j} + e^t\mathbf{k}$;
$\mathbf{r}(t) = (t - \sin t - 1)\mathbf{i} + (1 - \cos t)\mathbf{j} + e^t\mathbf{k}$

21. $15°$   23. (a) $0.7\mathbf{i} + 2.7\mathbf{j} - 3.4\mathbf{k}$   (b) $\mathbf{r}_0 = -0.7\mathbf{i} - 2.9\mathbf{j} + 4.8\mathbf{k}$

25. $\Delta\mathbf{r} = 8\mathbf{i} + \frac{26}{3}\mathbf{j}$, $s = (13\sqrt{13} - 5\sqrt{5})/3$

27. $\Delta\mathbf{r} = 2\mathbf{i} - \frac{2}{3}\mathbf{j} + \sqrt{2}\ln 3\mathbf{k}$; $s = \frac{8}{3}$

31. (a) $a_T = 0$, $a_N = \sqrt{2}$   (b) $a_T\mathbf{T} = \mathbf{0}$, $a_N\mathbf{N} = \mathbf{i} + \mathbf{j}$   (c) $1/\sqrt{2}$

33. (a) $a_T = 2\sqrt{5}$, $a_N = 2\sqrt{5}$   (b) $a_T\mathbf{T} = 2\mathbf{i} + 4\mathbf{j}$, $a_N\mathbf{N} = 4\mathbf{i} - 2\mathbf{j}$
    (c) $2/\sqrt{5}$

35. (a) $a_T = -7/\sqrt{6}$, $a_N = \sqrt{53/6}$

    (b) $a_T\mathbf{T} = -\frac{7}{6}(\mathbf{i} - 2\mathbf{j} + \mathbf{k})$, $a_N\mathbf{N} = \frac{13}{6}\mathbf{i} + \frac{5}{3}\mathbf{j} + \frac{7}{6}\mathbf{k}$   (c) $\dfrac{\sqrt{53}}{6\sqrt{6}}$

37. $a_T = -3$, $a_N = 2$, $\mathbf{T} = -\mathbf{j}$, $\mathbf{N} = \mathbf{i}$   39. $-3/2$

41. $a_N = 8.41 \times 10^{10}$ km/s$^2$

43. $a_N = 18/(1 + 4x^2)^{3/2}$   45. $a_N = 0$

Responses to True–False questions may be abridged to save space.

47. True; the velocity and unit tangent vectors have the same direction, so are parallel.

49. False; in this case the velocity and acceleration vectors will be parallel, but they may have opposite direction.

53. $\approx 257.20$ N

55. $40\sqrt{3}$ ft   57. 800 ft/s   59. $15°$ or $75°$   61. (c) $\approx 14.942$ ft

63. (a) $\rho \approx 176.78$ m   (b) $\frac{125}{4}$ m

65. (b) $R$ is maximum when $\alpha = 45°$, maximum value $v_0^2/g$

67. (a) 2.62 s   (b) 181.5 ft

69. (a) $v_0 \approx 83$ ft/s, $\alpha \approx 8°$   (b) 268.76 ft

▶ Exercise Set 12.7 **(Page 901)**

7. 7.75 km/s   9. 10.88 km/s

11. (a) minimum distance = 220,680 mi,
    maximum distance = 246,960 mi   (b) 27.5 days

13. (a) 17,224 mi/h   (b) $e \approx 0.071$, apogee altitude = 819 mi

▶ Chapter 12 Review Exercises **(Page 902)**

3. the circle of radius 3 in the $xy$-plane, with center at the origin

5. a parabola in the plane $x = -2$, vertex at $(-2, 0, -1)$, opening upward

11. $x = 1 + t$, $y = -t$, $z = t$   13. $(\sin t)\mathbf{i} - (\cos t)\mathbf{j} + \mathbf{C}$

15. $y(t) = \left(\frac{1}{3}t^3 + 1\right)\mathbf{i} + (t^2 + 1)\mathbf{j}$   17. 15/4

19. $\mathbf{r}(s) = \dfrac{s - 3}{3}\mathbf{i} + \dfrac{12 - 2s}{3}\mathbf{j} + \dfrac{9 + 2s}{3}\mathbf{k}$   25. 3/5   27. 0

29. (a) speed   (b) distance traveled
    (c) distance of the particle from the origin

33. (a) $\mathbf{r}(t) = \left(\frac{1}{6}t^4 + t\right)\mathbf{i} + \left(\frac{1}{2}t^2 + 2t\right)\mathbf{j} - \left(\frac{1}{4}\cos 2t + t - \frac{1}{4}\right)\mathbf{k}$
    (b) 3.475   35. 10.65 km/s   37. 24.78 ft

▶ Chapter 12 Making Connections **(Page 904)**

Where correct answers to a Making Connections exercise may vary, no answer is listed. Sample answers for these questions are available on the Book Companion Site.

1. (c) (i) $\mathbf{N} = \frac{1}{\sqrt{5}}\mathbf{i} - \frac{2}{\sqrt{5}}\mathbf{j}$   (ii) $\mathbf{N} = -\mathbf{j}$

2. (b) (i) $\mathbf{N} = -\sin t\mathbf{i} - \cos t\mathbf{j}$

    (ii) $\mathbf{N} = \dfrac{-(4t + 18t^3)\mathbf{i} + (2 - 18t^4)\mathbf{j} + (6t + 12t^3)\mathbf{k}}{2\sqrt{81t^8 + 117t^6 + 54t^4 + 13t^2 + 1}}$

3. (c) $\kappa(s) \to +\infty$, so the spiral winds ever tighter.

4. semicircle: 53.479 ft; quarter-circle: 60.976 ft; point: 64.001 ft

▶ Exercise Set 13.1 **(Page 914)**

1. (a) 5   (b) 3   (c) 1   (d) $-2$   (e) $9a^3 + 1$   (f) $a^3b^2 - a^2b^3 + 1$

3. (a) $x^2 - y^2 + 3$   (b) $3x^3y^4 + 3$   5. $x^3e^{x^3(3y+1)}$

7. (a) $t^2 + 3t^{10}$   (b) 0   (c) 3076

9. (a) 2.5 mg/L   (b) $C(100, t) = 20(e^{-0.2t} - e^{-t})$
   (c) $C(x, 1) = 0.2x(e^{-0.2} - e^{-1}) \approx 0.09x$

11. (a) WCI $= 17.8°$F   (b) WCI $= 22.6°$F   13. (a) $30°$F   (b) $22.5°$F

15. (a) 66%   (b) 73.5%   (c) 60.6%

17. (a) 19   (b) $-9$   (c) 3   (d) $a^6 + 3$   (e) $-t^8 + 3$   (f) $(a + b)(a - b)^2b^3 + 3$

19. $(y + 1)e^{x^2(y+1)z^2}$   21. (a) $80\sqrt{\pi}$   (b) $n(n + 1)/2$

23. 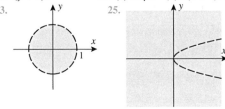   25.

27. (a) all points above or on the line $y = -2$   (b) all points on or within the sphere $x^2 + y^2 + z^2 = 25$   (c) all points in 3-space

Responses to True–False questions may be abridged to save space.

29. True; the interval $[0, 1]$ is the intersection of the domains of $\sin^{-1} t$ and $\sqrt{t}$.

31. False; the natural domain is an infinite solid cylinder.

33. 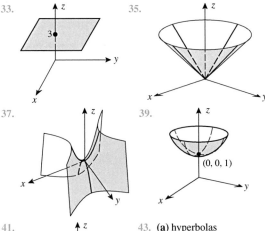   35.

37. 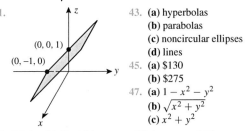   39.
    $(0, 0, 1)$

41.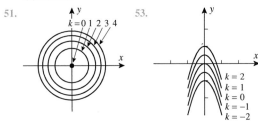
    $(0, 0, 1)$
    $(0, -1, 0)$

43. (a) hyperbolas
    (b) parabolas
    (c) noncircular ellipses
    (d) lines

45. (a) \$130
    (b) \$275

47. (a) $1 - x^2 - y^2$
    (b) $\sqrt{x^2 + y^2}$
    (c) $x^2 + y^2$

49. (a) $A$   (b) $B$   (c) increase   (d) decrease   (e) increase
    (f) decrease

51.   $k = 0\ 1\ 2\ 3\ 4$   53.
    $k = 2$
    $k = 1$
    $k = 0$
    $k = -1$
    $k = -2$

55.

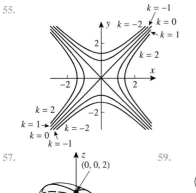

57.

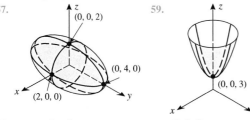

59.

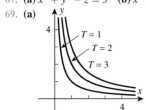

61. concentric spheres, common center at $(2, 0, 0)$
63. concentric cylinders, common axis the $y$-axis
65. (a) $x^2 - 2x^3 + 3xy = 0$  (b) $x^2 - 2x^3 + 3xy = 0$
    (c) $x^2 - 2x^3 + 3xy = -18$
67. (a) $x^2 + y^2 - z = 5$  (b) $x^2 + y^2 - z = -2$  (c) $x^2 + y^2 - z = 0$
69. (a)                              (b) the path $xy = 4$

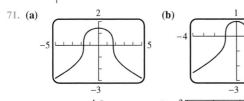

71. (a)                    (b)

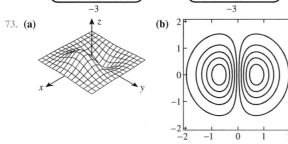

73. (a)                    (b)

75. (a) The graph of $g$ is the graph of $f$ shifted one unit in the positive
    $x$-direction.
    (b) The graph of $g$ is the graph of $f$ shifted one unit up the $z$-axis.
    (c) The graph of $g$ is the graph of $f$ shifted one unit down the $y$-axis
    and then inverted with respect to the plane $z = 0$.

▶ **Exercise Set 13.2 (Page 925)**
1. 35   3. $-8$   5. 0
7. (a) along $x = 0$ limit does not exist
   (b) along $x = 0$ limit does not exist
9. 1   11. 0   13. 0   15. limit does not exist   17. $\frac{8}{3}$   19. 0
21. limit does not exist   23. 0   25. 0   27. 0

Responses to True–False questions may be abridged to save space.
29. True; by the definition of open set.
31. False; let $f(x, y) = \begin{cases} 1, & x \le 0 \\ -1, & x > 0 \end{cases}$ and let $g(x, y) = -f(x, y)$.
33. (a) no   (d) no; yes   37. $-\pi/2$   39. no
41.                              43.

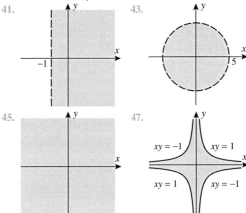

45.                              47.

49. all of 3-space   51. all points not on the cylinder $x^2 + z^2 = 1$

▶ **Exercise Set 13.3 (Page 936)**
1. (a) $9x^2y^2$ (b) $6x^3y$ (c) $9y^2$ (d) $9x^2$ (e) $6y$ (f) $6x^3$ (g) 36 (h) 12
3. $18xy - 15x^4y$, $9x^2 - 3x^5$
5. $(16x + 40)(x^2 + 5x - 2y)^7$, $-16(x^2 + 5x - 2y)^7$
7. $-\dfrac{7}{q}e^{-7p/q}$, $\dfrac{7p}{q^2}e^{-7p/q}$
9. $(15x^2y + 7y^2)\cos(5x^3y + 7xy^2)$, $(5x^3 + 14xy)\cos(5x^3y + 7xy^2)$
11. (a) $\frac{3}{8}$ (b) $\frac{1}{4}$   13. (a) $-4\cos 7$ (b) $2\cos 7$
15. $\partial z/\partial x = -4$; $\partial z/\partial y = \frac{1}{2}$   17. (a) 4.9 (b) 1.2
19. $z = f(x, y)$ has II as its graph, $f_x$ has I as its graph, and $f_y$ has III as
    its graph.
Responses to True–False questions may be abridged to save space.
21. True; on $y = 2$, $f(x, 2) = c$ is a constant function of $x$.
23. True; $z$ must be a linear function of $x$ and $y$.
25. $8xy^3e^{x^2y^3}$, $12x^2y^2e^{x^2y^3}$
27. $x^3/(y^{3/5} + x) + 3x^2\ln(1 + xy^{-3/5})$, $-\frac{3}{5}x^4/(y^{8/5} + xy)$
29. $-\dfrac{y(x^2 - y^2)}{(x^2 + y^2)^2}$, $\dfrac{x(x^2 - y^2)}{(x^2 + y^2)^2}$
31. $(3/2)x^2y(5x^2 - 7)(3x^5y - 7x^3y)^{-1/2}$
    $(1/2)x^3(3x^2 - 7)(3x^5y - 7x^3y)^{-1/2}$
33. $\dfrac{y^{-1/2}}{y^2 + x^2}$, $-\dfrac{xy^{-3/2}}{y^2 + x^2} - \dfrac{3}{2}y^{-5/2}\tan^{-1}\left(\dfrac{x}{y}\right)$
35. $-\frac{4}{3}y^2\sec^2 x(y^2\tan x)^{-7/3}$, $-\frac{8}{3}y\tan x(y^2\tan x)^{-7/3}$
37. $-6, -21$   39. $1/\sqrt{17}, 8/\sqrt{17}$
41. (a) $2xy^4z^3 + y$  (b) $4x^2y^3z^3 + x$  (c) $3x^2y^4z^2 + 2z$
    (d) $2y^4z^3 + y$  (e) $32z^3 + 1$  (f) 438
43. $2z/x$, $z/y$, $\ln(x^2y\cos z) - z\tan z$
45. $-y^2z^3/(1 + x^2y^4z^6)$, $-2xyz^3/(1 + x^2y^4z^6)$, $-3xy^2z^2/(1 + x^2y^4z^6)$
47. $yze^z\cos(xz)$, $e^z\sin(xz)$, $ye^z(\sin(xz) + x\cos(xz))$
49. $x/\sqrt{x^2 + y^2 + z^2}$, $y/\sqrt{x^2 + y^2 + z^2}$, $z/\sqrt{x^2 + y^2 + z^2}$
51. (a) $e$  (b) $2e$  (c) $e$
53. (a)                    (b)                    55. 4
                                                  57. $-2$

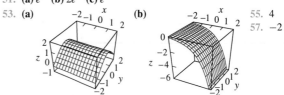

59. (a) $\partial V/\partial r = 2\pi rh$  (b) $\partial V/\partial h = \pi r^2$  (c) $48\pi$  (d) $64\pi$

61. (a) $\dfrac{1}{5}\dfrac{\text{lb}}{\text{in}^2\cdot\text{K}}$  (b) $-\dfrac{25}{8}\dfrac{\text{in}^5}{\text{lb}}$

63. (a) $\dfrac{\partial V}{\partial l} = 6$  (b) $\dfrac{\partial V}{\partial w} = 15$  (c) $\dfrac{\partial V}{\partial h} = 10$

67. (a) $\pm\sqrt{6}/4$  69. $-x/z,\ -y/z$

71. $-\dfrac{2x + yz^2\cos(xyz)}{xyz\cos(xyz) + \sin(xyz)};\ -\dfrac{xz^2\cos(xyz)}{xyz\cos(xyz) + \sin(xyz)}$

73. $-x/w,\ -y/w,\ -z/w$

75. $-\dfrac{yzw\cos(xyz)}{2w + \sin(xyz)},\ -\dfrac{xzw\cos(xyz)}{2w + \sin(xyz)},\ -\dfrac{xyw\cos(xyz)}{2w + \sin(xyz)}$

77. $e^{x^2},\ -e^{y^2}$

79. $f_x(x, y) = 2xy^3\sin(x^6y^9),\ f_y(x, y) = 3x^2y^2\sin(x^6y^9)$

81. (a) $\dfrac{\cos y}{4\sqrt{x^3}}$  (b) $-\sqrt{x}\cos y$  (c) $-\dfrac{1}{2\sqrt{x}}\sin y$  (d) $-\dfrac{1}{2\sqrt{x}}\sin y$

83. (a) $6\cos(3x^2 + 6y^2) - 36x^2\sin(3x^2 + 6y^2)$
    (b) $12\cos(3x^2 + 6y^2) - 144y^2\sin(3x^2 + 6y^2)$
    (c) $-72xy\sin(3x^2 + 6y^2)$  (d) $-72xy\sin(3x^2 + 6y^2)$

85. $-32y^3$  87. $-e^x\sin y$  89. $\dfrac{20}{(4x - 5y)^2}$  91. $\dfrac{2(x - y)}{(x + y)^3}$

93. (a) $\dfrac{\partial^3 f}{\partial x^3}$  (b) $\dfrac{\partial^3 f}{\partial y^2\partial x}$  (c) $\dfrac{\partial^4 f}{\partial x^2\partial y^2}$  (d) $\dfrac{\partial^4 f}{\partial y^3\partial x}$

95. (a) $30xy^4 - 4$  (b) $60x^2y^3$  (c) $60x^3y^2$

97. (a) $-30$  (b) $-125$  (c) $150$

99. (a) $15x^2y^4z^7 + 2y$  (b) $35x^3y^4z^6 + 3y^2$  (c) $21x^2y^5z^6$
    (d) $42x^3y^5z^5$  (e) $140x^3y^3z^6 + 6y$  (f) $30xy^4z^7$  (g) $105x^2y^4z^6$
    (h) $210xy^4z^6$

107. $\dfrac{\partial f}{\partial v} = 8vw^3x^4y^5,\ \dfrac{\partial f}{\partial w} = 12v^2w^2x^4y^5,\ \dfrac{\partial f}{\partial x} = 16v^2w^3x^3y^5,$

$\dfrac{\partial f}{\partial y} = 20v^2w^3x^4y^4$

109. $\dfrac{\partial f}{\partial v_1} = \dfrac{2v_1}{v_3^2 + v_4^2},\ \dfrac{\partial f}{\partial v_2} = \dfrac{-2v_2}{v_3^2 + v_4^2},\ \dfrac{\partial f}{\partial v_3} = \dfrac{-2v_3(v_1^2 - v_2^2)}{(v_3^2 + v_4^2)^2},$

$\dfrac{\partial f}{\partial v_4} = \dfrac{-2v_4(v_1^2 - v_2^2)}{(v_3^2 + v_4^2)^2}$

111. (a) 0  (b) 0  (c) 0  (d) 0  (e) $2(1 + yw)e^{yw}\sin z\cos z$
    (f) $2xw(2 + yw)e^{yw}\sin z\cos z$

113. $-i\sin(x_1 + 2x_2 + \cdots + nx_n)$

115. (a) $xy$-plane, $12x^2 + 6x$  (b) $y \neq 0,\ -3x^2/y^2$

117. $f_x(2, -1) = 11,\ f_y(2, -1) = -8$

119. (b) does not exist if $y \neq 0$ and $x = -y$

▶ **Exercise Set 13.4 (Page 947)**

1. 5.04  3. 4.14  9. $dz = 7\,dx - 2\,dy$  11. $dz = 3x^2y^2\,dx + 2x^3y\,dy$

13. $dz = \dfrac{y}{1 + x^2y^2}\,dx + \dfrac{x}{1 + x^2y^2}\,dy$  15. $dw = 8\,dx - 3\,dy + 4\,dz$

17. $dw = 3x^2y^2z\,dx + 2x^3yz\,dy + x^3y^2\,dz$

19. $dw = \dfrac{yz}{1 + x^2y^2z^2}\,dx + \dfrac{xz}{1 + x^2y^2z^2}\,dy + \dfrac{xy}{1 + x^2y^2z^2}\,dz$

21. $df = 0.10,\ \Delta f = 0.1009$  23. $df = 0.03,\ \Delta f \approx 0.029412$

25. $df = 0.96,\ \Delta f \approx 0.97929$

Responses to True–False questions may be abridged to save space.

27. False; see the discussion at the beginning of this section.

29. True; see Theorems 13.4.3 and 13.4.4.

31. The increase in the area of the rectangle is given by the sum of the areas of the three small rectangles, and the total differential is given by the sum of the areas of the upper left and lower right rectangles.

33. (a) $L = \frac{1}{5} - \frac{4}{125}(x - 4) - \frac{3}{125}(y - 3)$  (b) 0.000176603

35. (a) $L = 0$  (b) 0.0024

37. (a) $L = 6 + 6(x - 1) + 3(y - 2) + 2(z - 3)$  (b) $-0.00481$

39. (a) $L = e + e(x - 1) - e(y + 1) - e(z + 1)$  (b) 0.01554

45. 0.5  47. $1, 1, -1, 2$  49. $(-1, 1)$  51. $(1, 0, 1)$  53. 8%

55. $r\%$  57. 0.3%

59. (a) $(r + s)\%$  (b) $(r + s)\%$  (c) $(2r + 3s)\%$  (d) $\left(3r + \dfrac{s}{2}\right)\%$

61. $\approx 39\ \text{ft}^2$

▶ **Exercise Set 13.5 (Page 956)**

1. $42t^{13}$  3. $3t^{-2}\sin(1/t)$  5. $-\frac{10}{3}t^{7/3}e^{1 - t^{10/3}}$  7. $\dfrac{dw}{dt} = 165t^{32}$

9. $-2t\cos t^2$  11. 3264  13. 0

17. $24u^2v^2 - 16uv^3 - 2v + 3,\ 16u^3v - 24u^2v^2 - 2u - 3$

19. $-\dfrac{2\sin u}{3\sin v},\ -\dfrac{2\cos u\cos v}{3\sin^2 v}$  21. $e^u, 0$

23. $3r^2\sin\theta\cos^2\theta - 4r^3\sin^3\theta\cos\theta,$
    $-2r^3\sin^2\theta\cos\theta + r^4\sin^4\theta + r^3\cos^3\theta - 3r^4\sin^2\theta\cos^2\theta$

25. $\dfrac{x^2 + y^2}{4x^2y^3},\ \dfrac{y^2 - 3x^2}{4xy^4}$  27. $\dfrac{\partial z}{\partial r} = \dfrac{2r\cos^2\theta}{r^2\cos^2\theta + 1},\ \dfrac{\partial z}{\partial\theta} = \dfrac{-2r^2\cos\theta\sin\theta}{r^2\cos^2\theta + 1}$

29. $\dfrac{dw}{d\rho} = 2\rho(4\sin^2\phi + \cos^2\phi),\ \dfrac{\partial w}{\partial\phi} = 6\rho^2\sin\phi\cos\phi,\ \dfrac{dw}{d\theta} = 0$

31. $-\pi$  33. $\sqrt{3}e^{\sqrt{3}}, (2 - 4\sqrt{3})e^{\sqrt{3}}$  35. $-0.779\ \text{rad/s}$

Responses to True–False questions may be abridged to save space.

37. False; the symbols $\partial z$ and $\partial x$ have no individual meaning.

39. False; consider $z = xy, x = t, y = t$.

41. $-\dfrac{2xy^3}{3x^2y^2 - \sin y}$

43. $-\dfrac{ye^{xy}}{xe^{xy} + ye^y + e^y}$  45. $\dfrac{2x + yz}{6yz - xy},\ \dfrac{xz - 3z^2}{6yz - xy}$

47. $\dfrac{ye^x}{15\cos 3z + 3},\ \dfrac{e^x}{15\cos 3z + 3}$

61. $\dfrac{\partial w}{\partial\rho} = (\sin\phi\cos\theta)\dfrac{\partial w}{\partial x} + (\sin\phi\sin\theta)\dfrac{\partial w}{\partial y} + (\cos\phi)\dfrac{\partial w}{\partial z},$

$\dfrac{\partial w}{\partial\phi} = (\rho\cos\phi\cos\theta)\dfrac{\partial w}{\partial x} + (\rho\cos\phi\sin\theta)\dfrac{\partial w}{\partial y} - (\rho\sin\phi)\dfrac{\partial w}{\partial z},$

$\dfrac{\partial w}{\partial\theta} = -(\rho\sin\phi\sin\theta)\dfrac{\partial w}{\partial x} + (\rho\sin\phi\cos\theta)\dfrac{\partial w}{\partial y}$

65. (a) $\dfrac{dw}{dt} = \sum_{i=1}^{4}\dfrac{\partial w}{\partial x_i}\dfrac{dx_i}{dt}$  (b) $\dfrac{\partial w}{\partial v_j} = \sum_{i=1}^{4}\dfrac{\partial w}{\partial x_i}\dfrac{\partial x_i}{\partial v_j},\ j = 1, 2, 3$

▶ **Exercise Set 13.6 (Page 968)**

1. $6\sqrt{2}$  3. $-3/\sqrt{10}$  5. $-320$  7. $-314/741$  9. 0  11. $-8\sqrt{2}$

13. $\sqrt{2}/4$  15. $5/\sqrt{3}$  17. $-8/63$  19. $1/2 + \sqrt{3}/8$  21. $2\sqrt{2}$

23. $1/\sqrt{5}$  25. $-\frac{3}{2}e$  27. $3/\sqrt{11}$  29. (a) 5  (b) 10  (c) $-5\sqrt{5}$

31. III  33. $\cos(7y^2 - 7xy)(-7y\mathbf{i} + (14y - 7x)\mathbf{j})$

35. $\left(\dfrac{-84y}{(6x - 7y)^2}\right)\mathbf{i} + \left(\dfrac{84x}{(6x - 7y)^2}\right)\mathbf{j}$  37. $-9x^8\mathbf{i} - 3y^2\mathbf{j} + 12z^{11}\mathbf{k}$

39. $\nabla w = \dfrac{x}{x^2 + y^2 + z^2}\mathbf{i} + \dfrac{y}{x^2 + y^2 + z^2}\mathbf{j} + \dfrac{z}{x^2 + y^2 + z^2}\mathbf{k}$

41. $40\mathbf{i} + 32\mathbf{j}$  43. $-36\mathbf{i} - 12\mathbf{j}$  45. $4(\mathbf{i} + \mathbf{j} + \mathbf{k})$

47.

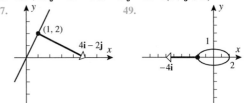

51. $\pm(-4\mathbf{i} + \mathbf{j})/\sqrt{17}$  53. $\mathbf{u} = (3\mathbf{i} - 2\mathbf{j})/\sqrt{13},\ \|\nabla f(-1, 1)\| = 4\sqrt{13}$

55. $\mathbf{u} = (4\mathbf{i} - 3\mathbf{j})/5,\ \|\nabla f(4, -3)\| = 1$  57. $\dfrac{1}{\sqrt{2}}(\mathbf{i} - \mathbf{j}), 3\sqrt{2}$

59. $\dfrac{1}{\sqrt{2}}(-\mathbf{i} + \mathbf{j}),\ \dfrac{1}{\sqrt{2}}$

61. $\mathbf{u} = -(\mathbf{i} + 3\mathbf{j})/\sqrt{10},\ -\|\nabla f(-1, -3)\| = -2\sqrt{10}$

63. $\mathbf{u} = (3\mathbf{i} - \mathbf{j})/\sqrt{10},\ -\|\nabla f(\pi/6, \pi/4)\| = -\sqrt{5}$

65. $(\mathbf{i} - 11\mathbf{j} + 12\mathbf{k})/\sqrt{266},\ -\sqrt{266}$

Responses to True–False questions may be abridged to save space.

67. False; they are equal.    69. False; let $\mathbf{u} = \mathbf{i}$ and let $f(x, y) = y$.

71. $8/\sqrt{29}$

73. **(a)** $\approx 1/\sqrt{2}$

**(b)**
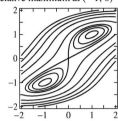
$-\nabla f(4, 4)$

75. $9x^2 + y^2 = 9$

77. $36/\sqrt{17}$

79. **(a)** $2e^{-\pi/2}\mathbf{i}$

81. $-\frac{5}{3}(2\mathbf{i} - \mathbf{j} - 2\mathbf{k})$

87. $x(t) = e^{-8t}$, $y(t) = 4e^{-2t}$

89.
$C = -10$
$C = -5$
$C = 0$
$C = -15$

91. **(a)**

**(c)** $\nabla f = [2x - 2x(x^2 + 3y^2)]e^{-(x^2+y^2)}\mathbf{i}$
$+ [6y - 2y(x^2 + 3y^2)]e^{-(x^2+y^2)}\mathbf{j}$

**(d)** $x = y = 0$ or $x = 0$, $y = \pm 1$ or
$x = \pm 1$, $y = 0$

▶ **Exercise Set 13.7 (Page 975)**

1. **(a)** $x + y + 2z = 6$    **(b)** $x = 2 + t$, $y = 2 + t$, $z = 1 + 2t$
**(c)** $35.26°$

3. tangent plane: $3x - 4z = -25$;
normal line: $x = -3 + (3t/4)$, $y = 0$, $z = 4 - t$

5. tangent plane: $9x - 4y - 10z = -76$;
normal line: $x = -4 + 9t$, $y = 5 - 4t$, $z = 2 - 10t$

7. tangent plane: $48x - 14y - z = 64$;
normal line: $x = 1 + 48t$, $y = -2 - 14t$, $z = 12 - t$

9. tangent plane: $x - y - z = 0$;
normal line: $x = 1 + t$, $y = -t$, $z = 1 - t$

11. tangent plane: $3y - z = -1$;
normal line: $x = \pi/6$, $y = 3t$, $z = 1 - t$

13. **(a)** all points on the $x$-axis or $y$-axis    **(b)** $(0, -2, -4)$

15. $\left(\frac{1}{2}, -2, -\frac{3}{4}\right)$    17. **(a)** $(-2, 1, 5)$, $(0, 3, 9)$    **(b)** $\dfrac{4}{3\sqrt{14}}$, $\dfrac{4}{\sqrt{222}}$

Responses to True–False questions may be abridged to save space.

19. False; they need only be parallel.

21. True; see Formula (15) of Section 13.4.

23. $\pm\dfrac{1}{\sqrt{227}}(\mathbf{i} - \mathbf{j} - 15\mathbf{k})$    27. $(1, 2/3, 2/3)$, $(-1, -2/3, -2/3)$

29. $x = 1 + 8t$, $y = -1 + 5t$, $z = 2 + 6t$

31. $x = 3 + 4t$, $y = -3 - 4t$, $z = 4 - 3t$

▶ **Exercise Set 13.8 (Page 985)**

1. **(a)** minimum at $(2, -1)$, no maxima
**(b)** maximum at $(0, 0)$, no minima    **(c)** no maxima or minima

3. minimum at $(3, -2)$, no maxima    5. relative minimum at $(0, 0)$

7. relative minimum at $(0, 0)$; saddle points at $(\pm 2, 1)$

9. saddle point at $(1, -2)$    11. relative minimum at $(2, -1)$

13. relative minima at $(-1, -1)$ and $(1, 1)$    15. saddle point at $(0, 0)$

17. no critical points    19. relative maximum at $(-1, 0)$

21. saddle point at $(0, 0)$;
relative minima at $(1, 1)$
and $(-1, -1)$

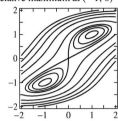

Responses to True–False questions may be abridged to save space.

23. False; let $f(x, y) = y$.

25. True; this follows from Theorem 13.8.6.

27. **(b)** relative minimum at $(0, 0)$

31. absolute maximum 0,
absolute minimum $-12$

33. absolute maximum 3,
absolute minimum $-1$

35. absolute maximum $\frac{33}{4}$,
absolute minimum $-\frac{1}{4}$

37. $16, 16, 16$

39. maximum at $(1, 2, 2)$

41. $2a/\sqrt{3}, 2a/\sqrt{3}, 2a/\sqrt{3}$

43. length and width 2 ft, height 4 ft

45. **(a)** $x = 0$: minimum $-3$, maximum 0;
$x = 1$: minimum 3, maximum 13/3;
$y = 0$: minimum 0, maximum 4;
$y = 1$: minimum $-3$, maximum 3
**(b)** $y = x$: minimum 0, maximum 3;
$y = 1 - x$: maximum 4, minimum $-3$
**(c)** minimum $-3$, maximum 13/3

47. length and width $\sqrt[3]{2V}$, height $\sqrt[3]{2V}/2$    51. $y = \frac{3}{4}x + \frac{19}{12}$

53. $y = 0.5x + 0.8$

55. **(a)** $y = 79.22 + 0.1571t$    **(b)**
**(c)** about 81.6 years

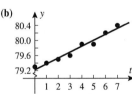

57. **(a)** $P = \dfrac{2798}{21} + \dfrac{171}{350}T$    **(b)** 190
**(c)** $T \approx -272.7096°C$

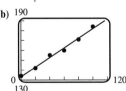

▶ **Exercise Set 13.9 (Page 996)**

1. **(a)** 4    3. **(a)**

**(c)** maximum $\frac{101}{4}$,
minimum $-5$

5. maximum $\sqrt{2}$ at $(-\sqrt{2}, -1)$ and $(\sqrt{2}, 1)$,
minimum $-\sqrt{2}$ at $(-\sqrt{2}, 1)$ and $(\sqrt{2}, -1)$

7. maximum $\sqrt{2}$ at $(1/\sqrt{2}, 0)$, minimum $-\sqrt{2}$ at $(-1/\sqrt{2}, 0)$

9. maximum 6 at $\left(\frac{4}{3}, \frac{2}{3}, -\frac{4}{3}\right)$, minimum $-6$ at $\left(-\frac{4}{3}, -\frac{2}{3}, \frac{4}{3}\right)$

11. maximum is $1/(3\sqrt{3})$ at $(1/\sqrt{3}, 1/\sqrt{3}, 1/\sqrt{3})$, $(1/\sqrt{3}, -1/\sqrt{3}, -1/\sqrt{3})$, $(-1/\sqrt{3}, 1/\sqrt{3}, -1/\sqrt{3})$, and $(-1/\sqrt{3}, -1/\sqrt{3}, 1/\sqrt{3})$; minimum is $-1/(3\sqrt{3})$ at $(1/\sqrt{3}, 1/\sqrt{3}, -1/\sqrt{3})$, $(1/\sqrt{3}, -1/\sqrt{3}, 1/\sqrt{3})$, $(-1/\sqrt{3}, 1/\sqrt{3}, 1/\sqrt{3})$, and $(-1/\sqrt{3}, -1/\sqrt{3}, -1/\sqrt{3})$

Responses to True–False questions may be abridged to save space.

13. False; a Lagrange multiplier is a scalar.

15. False; we must solve three equations in three unknowns.

17. $\left(\frac{3}{10}, -\frac{3}{5}\right)$   19. $\left(\frac{1}{6}, \frac{1}{3}, \frac{1}{6}\right)$

21. $(3, 6)$ is closest and $(-3, -6)$ is farthest   23. $5(\mathbf{i} + \mathbf{j} + \mathbf{k})/\sqrt{3}$

25. $9, 9, 9$   27. $(\pm\sqrt{5}, 0, 0)$   29. length and width 2 ft, height 4 ft

33. (a) $\alpha = \beta = \gamma = \pi/3$, maximum $1/8$

(b)

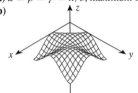

▶ **Chapter 13 Review Exercises (Page 997)**

1. (a) $xy$   (b) $e^{r+s} \ln(rs)$

5. (a) not defined on line $y = x$   (b) not continuous

9. (a) 12 Pa/min   (b) 240 Pa/min

15. $df$ (the differential of $f$) is an approximation for $\Delta f$ (the change in $f$)

17. $dV = -0.06667$ m$^3$; $\Delta V = -0.07267$ m$^3$   19. 2

21. $\dfrac{-f_y^2 f_{xx} + 2 f_x f_y f_{xy} - f_x^2 f_{yy}}{f_y^3}$   25. $\dfrac{7}{2} + \dfrac{4}{5} \ln 2$   27. $-7/\sqrt{5}$

29. $(0, 0, 2)$, $(1, 1, 1)$, $(-1, -1, 1)$   31. $\left(-\frac{1}{3}, -\frac{1}{2}, 2\right)$

33. relative minimum at $(15, -8)$

35. saddle point at $(0, 0)$, relative minimum at $(3, 9)$

37. absolute maximum of 4 at $(\pm 1, \pm 2)$, absolute minimum of 0 at $(\pm\sqrt{2}, 0)$ and $(0, \pm 2\sqrt{2})$

39. $I_1 : I_2 : I_3 = \dfrac{1}{R_1} : \dfrac{1}{R_2} : \dfrac{1}{R_3}$

41. (a) $\partial P/\partial L = c\alpha L^{\alpha-1} K^{\beta}$, $\partial P/\partial K = c\beta L^{\alpha} K^{\beta-1}$

▶ **Chapter 13 Making Connections (Page 999)**

Answers are provided in the Student Solutions Manual.

▶ **Exercise Set 14.1 (Page 1007)**

1. 7   3. 2   5. 2   7. 3   9. $1 - \ln 2$   11. $\dfrac{1 - \ln 2}{2}$   13. 0   15. $\frac{1}{3}$

17. (a) $37/4$   (b) exact value $= 28/3$; differ by $1/12$

19. (1, 0, 4)   21.

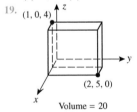

Volume = 20

Responses to True–False questions may be abridged to save space.

23. False; $\Delta A_k$ is the area of such a rectangular region.

25. False; $\displaystyle\iint_R f(x, y) \, dA = \int_1^5 \int_2^4 f(x, y) \, dy \, dx$.

29. 19   31. 8   33. $\dfrac{1}{3\pi}$   35. 48   37. $1 - \dfrac{2}{\pi}$   39. $\frac{14}{3}$ °C

41. 1.381737122   43. first integral equals $\frac{1}{2}$, second equals $-\frac{1}{2}$; no

▶ **Exercise Set 14.2 (Page 1015)**

1. $\frac{1}{40}$   3. 9   5. $\dfrac{\pi}{2}$   7. $\frac{1}{12}$

9. (a) $\displaystyle\int_0^2 \int_0^{x^2} f(x, y) \, dy \, dx$   (b) $\displaystyle\int_0^4 \int_{\sqrt{y}}^2 f(x, y) \, dx \, dy$

11. (a) $\displaystyle\int_1^2 \int_{-2x+5}^3 f(x, y) \, dy \, dx + \int_2^4 \int_1^3 f(x, y) \, dy \, dx + \int_4^5 \int_{2x-7}^3 f(x, y) \, dy \, dx$   (b) $\displaystyle\int_1^3 \int_{(5-y)/2}^{(y+7)/2} f(x, y) \, dx \, dy$

13. (a) $\frac{16}{3}$   (b) 38   15. 576   17. 0   19. $\dfrac{\sqrt{17} - 1}{2}$   21. $\frac{50}{3}$

23. $-\frac{7}{60}$   25. $\dfrac{1 - \cos 8}{3}$

27. (a)

(b) $(-1.8414, 0.1586)$, $(1.1462, 3.1462)$
(c) $-0.4044$
(d) $-0.4044$

29. $\sqrt{2} - 1$   31. 32

Responses to True–False questions may be abridged to save space.

33. False; $\displaystyle\int_0^1 \int_{x^2}^{2x} f(x, y) \, dy \, dx$ integrates $f(x, y)$ over the region between the graphs of $y = x^2$ and $y = 2x$ for $0 \le x \le 1$ and results in a number, but $\displaystyle\int_{x^2}^{2x} \int_0^1 f(x, y) \, dx \, dy$ produces an expression involving $x$.

35. False; although $R$ is symmetric across the $x$-axis, the integrand may not be.

37. 12   39. $27\pi$   41. 170   43. $\dfrac{27\pi}{2}$   45. $\dfrac{\pi}{2}$

47. $\displaystyle\int_0^{\sqrt{2}} \int_{y^2}^2 f(x, y) \, dx \, dy$   49. $\displaystyle\int_1^{e^2} \int_{\ln x}^2 f(x, y) \, dy \, dx$

51. $\displaystyle\int_0^{\pi/2} \int_0^{\sin x} f(x, y) \, dy \, dx$   53. $\dfrac{1 - e^{-16}}{8}$   55. $\dfrac{e^8 - 1}{3}$

57. (a) 0   (b) $\tan 1$   59. 0   61. $\dfrac{\pi}{2} - \ln 2$   63. $\frac{2}{3}$ °C   65. 0.676089

▶ **Exercise Set 14.3 (Page 1024)**

1. $\frac{1}{6}$   3. $\frac{2}{9} a^3$   5. 0   7. $\dfrac{3\pi}{2}$   9. $\dfrac{\pi}{16}$   11. $\displaystyle\int_{\pi/6}^{5\pi/6} \int_2^{4\sin\theta} f(r, \theta) r \, dr \, d\theta$

13. $8 \displaystyle\int_0^{\pi/2} \int_1^3 r\sqrt{9 - r^2} \, dr \, d\theta$   15. $2 \displaystyle\int_0^{\pi/2} \int_0^{\cos\theta} (1 - r^2) r \, dr \, d\theta$

17. $\dfrac{64\sqrt{2}}{3} \pi$   19. $\dfrac{5\pi}{32}$   21. $\dfrac{27\pi}{16}$   23. $(1 - \cos 9)\pi$   25. $\dfrac{\pi}{8} \ln 5$   27. $\dfrac{\pi}{8}$

29. $\frac{16}{9}$   31. $\dfrac{\pi}{2} \left(1 - \dfrac{1}{\sqrt{1 + a^2}}\right)$   33. $\dfrac{\pi}{4}(\sqrt{5} - 1)$

Responses to True–False questions may be abridged to save space.

35. True; the disk is given in polar coordinates by $0 \le r \le 2$, $0 \le \theta \le 2\pi$.

37. False; the integrand is missing a factor of $r$:
$$\iint_R f(r, \theta) \, dA = \int_0^{\pi/2} \int_1^2 f(r, \theta) r \, dr \, d\theta.$$

39. $\pi a^2 h$   41. $\dfrac{1}{5} + \dfrac{\pi}{2}$

43. (a) $\dfrac{4}{3} \pi a^2 c$   (b) $\approx 1.0831682 \times 10^{21}$ m$^3$   45. $2a^2$

▶

1. $6\pi$   3. $\dfrac{\sqrt{5}}{6}$   5. $\sqrt{2}\pi$   7. $\dfrac{(10\sqrt{10}-1)\pi}{18}$   9. $8\pi$

11. **(a)** 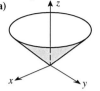   **(b)**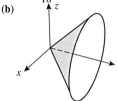

**(c)**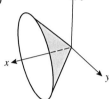

13. **(a)** $x=u,\ y=v,\ z=\frac{5}{2}+\frac{3}{2}u-2v$   **(b)** $x=u,\ y=v,\ z=u^2$

15. **(a)** $x=\sqrt{5}\cos u,\ y=\sqrt{5}\sin u,\ z=v;\ 0\le u\le 2\pi, 0\le v\le 1$
    **(b)** $x=2\cos u,\ y=v,\ z=2\sin u;\ 0\le u\le 2\pi,\ 1\le v\le 3$

17. $x=u,\ y=\sin u\cos v,\ z=\sin u\sin v$

19. $x=r\cos\theta,\ y=r\sin\theta,\ z=\dfrac{1}{1+r^2}$

21. $x=r\cos\theta,\ y=r\sin\theta,\ z=2r^2\cos\theta\sin\theta$

23. $x=r\cos\theta,\ y=r\sin\theta,\ z=\sqrt{9-r^2};\ r\le\sqrt{5}$

25. $x=\dfrac{1}{2}\rho\cos\theta,\ y=\dfrac{1}{2}\rho\sin\theta,\ z=\dfrac{\sqrt{3}}{2}\rho$   27. $z=x-2y$; a plane

29. $(x/3)^2+(y/2)^2=1;\ 2\le z\le 4$; part of an elliptic cylinder

31. $(x/3)^2+(y/4)^2=z^2;\ 0\le z\le 1$; part of an elliptic cone

33. **(a)** $x=r\cos\theta,\ y=r\sin\theta,\ z=r,\ 0\le r\le 2;$
    $x=u,\ y=v,\ z=\sqrt{u^2+v^2},\ 0\le u^2+v^2\le 4$

35. **(a)** $0\le u\le 3, 0\le v\le \pi$   **(b)** $0\le u\le 4,\ -\pi/2\le v\le\pi/2$

37. **(a)** $0\le\phi\le\pi/2, 0\le\theta\le 2\pi$   **(b)** $0\le\phi\le\pi,0\le\theta\le\pi$

39. $2x+4y-z=5$   41. $z=0$   43. $x-y+\dfrac{\sqrt{2}}{2}z=\dfrac{\pi\sqrt{2}}{8}$

45. $\dfrac{(17\sqrt{17}-5\sqrt{5})\pi}{6}$

Responses to True–False questions may be abridged to save space.

47. False; the surface area is $S=\displaystyle\iint\limits_{R}\sqrt{[f_x(x,y)]^2+[f_y(x,y)]^2+1}\,dA$.

49. True; see the discussion preceding Definition 14.4.1.

51. $4\pi a^2$   55. $4\pi^2 ab$   57. $9.099$

59. $(x/a)^2+(y/b)^2+(z/c)^2=1$; ellipsoid

61. $(x/a)^2+(y/b)^2-(z/c)^2=-1$; hyperboloid of two sheets

▶

1. $8$   3. $\frac{47}{3}$   5. $\frac{81}{5}$   7. $\frac{128}{15}$   9. $\pi(\pi-3)/2$   11. $\frac{1}{6}$   13. $9.425$

15. $4$   17. $\frac{256}{15}$

19. **(a)** $\displaystyle\int_{-1}^{1}\int_{-\sqrt{1-x^2}}^{\sqrt{1-x^2}}\int_{4x^2+y^2}^{4-3y^2} f(x,y,z)\,dz\,dy\,dx$

**(b)** $\displaystyle\int_{-1}^{1}\int_{-\sqrt{1-y^2}}^{\sqrt{1-y^2}}\int_{4x^2+y^2}^{4-3y^2} f(x,y,z)\,dz\,dx\,dy$

21. $4\displaystyle\int_{0}^{1}\int_{0}^{\sqrt{1-x^2}}\int_{4x^2+y^2}^{4-3y^2} dz\,dy\,dx$

23. $2\displaystyle\int_{-3}^{3}\int_{0}^{\frac{1}{3}\sqrt{9-x^2}}\int_{0}^{x+3} dz\,dy\,dx$

25. **(a)** 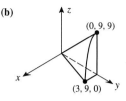   **(b)**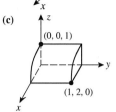

**(c)**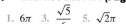

Responses to True–False questions may be abridged to save space.

27. True; apply Fubini's Theorem (Theorem 14.5.1).

29. False;

$$\iiint\limits_{G} f(x,y,z)\,dV=\int_{0}^{1}\int_{0}^{\sqrt{1-x^2}}\int_{0}^{\sqrt{1-x^2-y^2}} f(x,y,z)\,dz\,dy\,dx.$$

33. $\frac{3}{4}$   35. $3.291$

37. **(a)** $\displaystyle\int_{0}^{a}\int_{0}^{b(1-x/a)}\int_{0}^{c(1-x/a-y/b)} dz\,dy\,dx$ is one example.

39. **(a)** $\displaystyle\int_{0}^{2}\int_{0}^{\sqrt{4-x^2}}\int_{0}^{5} f(x,y,z)\,dz\,dy\,dx$

**(b)** $\displaystyle\int_{0}^{9}\int_{0}^{3-\sqrt{x}}\int_{y}^{3-\sqrt{x}} f(x,y,z)\,dz\,dy\,dx$

**(c)** $\displaystyle\int_{0}^{2}\int_{0}^{4-x^2}\int_{y}^{8-y} f(x,y,z)\,dz\,dy\,dx$

▶

1. $\dfrac{\pi}{4}$   3. $\dfrac{\pi}{16}$

5. The region is bounded by the $xy$-plane and the upper half of a sphere of radius 1 centered at the origin; $f(r,\theta,z)=z$.

7. The region is the portion of the first octant inside a sphere of radius 1 centered at the origin; $f(\rho,\theta,\phi)=\rho\cos\phi$.

9. $\dfrac{81\pi}{2}$   11. $\frac{152}{3}\pi$   13. $\dfrac{64\pi}{3}$   15. $\dfrac{11\pi a^3}{3}$   17. $\dfrac{\pi a^6}{48}$

19. $\dfrac{32(2\sqrt{2}-1)\pi}{15}$

Responses to True–False questions may be abridged to save space.

21. False; the factor $r^2$ should be $r$ [Formula (6)]:

$$\iiint\limits_{G} f(x,y,z)\,dV=\iiint\limits_{\substack{\text{appropriate}\\\text{limits}}} f(r\cos\theta,r\sin\theta,z)r\,dz\,dr\,d\theta.$$

23. True; $G$ is the spherical wedge bounded by the spheres $\rho=1$ and $\rho=3$, the half-planes $\theta=0$ and $\theta=2\pi$, and above the cone $\phi=\pi/4$, so

$$(\text{volume of }G)=\iiint\limits_{G} dV=\int_{0}^{\pi/4}\int_{0}^{2\pi}\int_{1}^{3}\rho^2\sin\phi\,d\rho\,d\theta\,d\phi.$$

25. **(a)** $\frac{5}{2}(-8+3\ln 3)\ln(\sqrt{5}-2)$   **(b)** $f(x,y,z)=\dfrac{y^3}{x^3\sqrt{1+z^2}}$;
    $G$ is the cylindrical wedge $1\le r\le 4,\ \dfrac{\pi}{6}\le\theta\le\dfrac{\pi}{3},\ -2\le z\le 2$

27. $\dfrac{4\pi a^3}{3}$   29. $\dfrac{2(\sqrt{3}-1)\pi}{3}$

▶

1. $-17$   3. $\cos(u-v)$   5. $x=\frac{2}{9}u+\frac{5}{9}v,\ y=-\frac{1}{9}u+\frac{2}{9}v;\ \frac{1}{9}$

7. $x=\dfrac{\sqrt{u+v}}{\sqrt{2}},\ y=\dfrac{\sqrt{v-u}}{\sqrt{2}};\ \dfrac{1}{4\sqrt{v^2-u^2}}$   9. $5$   11. $\dfrac{1}{v}$

Responses to True–False questions may be abridged to save space.

13. False; $|\partial(x,y)/\partial(u,v)| = \|\partial \mathbf{r}/\partial u \times \partial \mathbf{r}/\partial v\|$; evaluating this at $(u_0, v_0)$ gives the area of the indicated parallelogram.

15. False; $\partial(x,y)/\partial(r,\theta) = r$.

17. 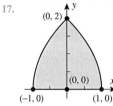     19.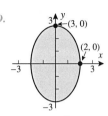

21. $\frac{3}{2}\ln 3$   23. $1 - \frac{1}{2}\sin 2$   25. $96\pi$   27. $\frac{\pi}{24}(1-\cos 1)$   29. $\frac{192}{5}\pi$

31. $u = \begin{cases} \cot^{-1}(x/y), & y \neq 0 \\ 0, & y = 0 \text{ and } x > 0 \\ \pi, & y = 0 \text{ and } x < 0 \end{cases}$

$v = \sqrt{x^2 + y^2}$; other answers possible

33. $u = (3/7)x - (2/7)y$, $v = (-1/7)x + (3/7)y$; other answers possible

35. $\frac{1}{4}\ln \frac{5}{2}$

37. $\frac{1}{2}\left[\ln(\sqrt{2}+1) - \frac{\pi}{4}\right]$   39. $\frac{35}{256}$   41. $2\ln 3$   45. $21/8$

▶ **Exercise Set 14.8 (Page 1077)**

1. $M = \frac{13}{20}$, center of gravity $\left(\frac{190}{273}, \frac{6}{13}\right)$

3. $M = a^4/8$, center of gravity $(8a/15, 8a/15)$

5. $\left(\frac{1}{2}, \frac{1}{2}\right)$   7. $\left(\frac{1}{2}, \frac{1}{2}, \frac{1}{2}\right)$

Responses to True–False questions may be abridged to save space.

9. True; recall this from Section 6.7.

11. False; the center of gravity of the lamina is $(\bar{x}, \bar{y}) = (M_y/M, M_x/M)$, where $M_y$ and $M_x$ are the lamina's first moments about the $y$- and $x$-axes, respectively, and $M$ is the mass of the lamina.

15. $\left(\dfrac{128}{105\pi}, \dfrac{128}{105\pi}\right)$   17. $\left(\dfrac{4a}{3\pi}, 0\right)$   19. $\left(\frac{1}{4}, \frac{1}{4}, \frac{1}{4}\right)$   21. $\left(\frac{1}{2}, 0, \frac{3}{5}\right)$

23. $(3a/8, 3a/8, 3a/8)$

25. $M = a^4/2$, center of gravity $(a/3, a/2, a/2)$

27. $M = \frac{1}{6}$, center of gravity $\left(0, \frac{16}{35}, \frac{1}{2}\right)$   29. (a) $\left(\frac{5}{8}, \frac{5}{8}\right)$   (b) $\left(\frac{2}{3}, \frac{1}{2}\right)$

31. $(1.177406, 0.353554, 0.231557)$

33. $\frac{27\pi}{4}$   35. $\pi k a^4$   37. $\left(0, 0, \frac{7}{16\sqrt{2}-14}\right)$   39. $\left(\frac{4}{3}, 0, \frac{10}{9}\right)$

41. $(3a/8, 3a/8, 3a/8)$   43. $(2-\sqrt{2})\pi/4$   45. $(0,0,8/15)$

47. $(0, 195/152, 0)$   51. $\frac{1}{2}\delta\pi a^4 h$   53. $\frac{1}{2}\delta\pi h(a_2^4 - a_1^4)$   57. $2\pi^2 abk$

59. $(a/3, b/3)$

▶ **Chapter 14 Review Exercises (Page 1081)**

3. (a) $\displaystyle\iint_R dA$   (b) $\displaystyle\iiint_G dV$   (c) $\displaystyle\iint_R \sqrt{1 + \left(\frac{\partial z}{\partial x}\right)^2 + \left(\frac{\partial z}{\partial y}\right)^2}\, dA$

5. $\displaystyle\int_0^1 \int_{1-\sqrt{1-y^2}}^{1+\sqrt{1-y^2}} f(x,y)\, dx\, dy$

7. (a) $a = 2, b = 1, c = 1, d = 2$ or $a = 1, b = 2, c = 2, d = 1$   (b) 3

9. $-\dfrac{1}{\sqrt{2}\pi}$

11. $\displaystyle\int_0^1 \int_{2y}^2 e^x e^y\, dx\, dy$

13.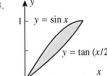
$y = \sin x$
$y = \tan (x/2)$

15. $\frac{1}{3}(1 - \cos 64)$
17. $a^2$
19. $\frac{3}{2}$
21. $32\pi$

23. (a) $\displaystyle\int_0^{2\pi}\int_0^{\pi/3}\int_0^a \rho^4 \sin^3\phi\, d\rho\, d\phi\, d\theta$

(b) $\displaystyle\int_0^{2\pi}\int_0^{\sqrt{3}a/2}\int_{r/\sqrt{3}}^{\sqrt{a^2-r^2}} r^3\, dz\, dr\, d\theta$

(c) $\displaystyle\int_{-\sqrt{3}a/2}^{\sqrt{3}a/2}\int_{-\sqrt{(3a^2/4)-x^2}}^{\sqrt{(3a^2/4)-x^2}}\int_{\sqrt{x^2+y^2}/\sqrt{3}}^{\sqrt{a^2-x^2-y^2}} (x^2 + y^2)\, dz\, dy\, dx$

25. $\dfrac{\pi a^3}{9}$   27. $\dfrac{1}{24}(26^{3/2} - 10^{3/2}) \approx 4.20632$   29. $2x + 4y - z = 5$

33. (a) $\dfrac{1}{2(u+w)}$   (b) $\frac{1}{2}(7\ln 7 - 5\ln 5 - 3\ln 3)$   35. $\left(\frac{8}{5}, 0\right)$

37. $(0, 0, h/4)$

▶ **Chapter 14 Making Connections (Page 1082)**

Where correct answers to a Making Connections exercise may vary, no answer is listed. Sample answers for these questions are available on the Book Companion Site.

1. (b) $\dfrac{\pi}{4}$   3. (a) $1.173108605$   (b) $1.173108605$

4. (a) the sphere $0 \leq x^2 + y^2 + z^2 \leq 1$   (b) $4.934802202$   (c) $\pi^2/2$

5. (b) $4.4506$   6. $\frac{4}{35}\pi a^3$

▶ **Exercise Set 15.1 (Page 1092)**

1. (a) III   (b) IV   3. (a) true   (b) true   (c) true

5. 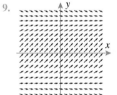   7.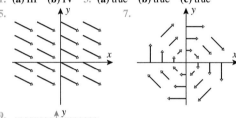

9.

Responses to True–False questions may be abridged to save space.

11. False; the vector field has a nonzero $\mathbf{k}$-component.

13. True; this is the curl of $\mathbf{F}$.

15. (a) all $x, y$   (b) all $x, y$   17. div $\mathbf{F} = 2x + y$, curl $\mathbf{F} = z\mathbf{i}$

19. div $\mathbf{F} = 0$, curl $\mathbf{F} = (40x^2 z^4 - 12xy^3)\mathbf{i} + (14y^3 z + 3y^4)\mathbf{j} - (16xz^5 + 21y^2 z^2)\mathbf{k}$

21. div $\mathbf{F} = \dfrac{2}{\sqrt{x^2 + y^2 + z^2}}$, curl $\mathbf{F} = 0$   23. $4x$   25. $0$

27. $(1 + y)\mathbf{i} + x\mathbf{j}$

39. $\nabla \cdot (k\mathbf{F}) = k\nabla \cdot \mathbf{F}, \nabla \cdot (\mathbf{F} + \mathbf{G}) = \nabla \cdot \mathbf{F} + \nabla \cdot \mathbf{G}, \nabla \cdot (\phi\mathbf{F}) = \phi\nabla \cdot \mathbf{F} + \nabla\phi \cdot \mathbf{F}, \nabla \cdot (\nabla \times \mathbf{F}) = 0$   47. (b) $x^2 + y^2 = K$

49. $\dfrac{dy}{dx} = \dfrac{1}{x}, y = \ln x + K$

▶ **Exercise Set 15.2 (Page 1108)**

1. (a) 1   (b) 0   3. 16   7. 8   9. $-28$

11. (a) $\frac{4\sqrt{2}-2}{3}$   (b) 1   (c) $\frac{2}{3}$

13. (a) 3   (b) 3   (c) 3   (d) 3

Responses to True–False questions may be abridged to save space.

15. False; line integrals of functions are independent of the orientation of the curve.   17. True; this is Equation (26).

19. 2   21. $\frac{13}{20}$   23. $1 - \pi$   25. 3   27. $-1 - (\pi/4)$   29. $1 - e^3$

**31.** (a) $\dfrac{63\sqrt{17}}{64} + \dfrac{1}{4}\ln(4+\sqrt{17}) - \dfrac{1}{8}\ln\dfrac{\sqrt{17}+1}{\sqrt{17}-1} - \dfrac{1}{4}\ln(\sqrt{2}+1) +$
$\dfrac{1}{8}\ln\dfrac{\sqrt{2}+1}{\sqrt{2}-1}$  (b) $\dfrac{\pi^3}{24} + \dfrac{e^{\pi/2}}{5} + \dfrac{\pi}{4} + \dfrac{6}{5}$
**33.** (a) $-1$  (b) $-2$  **35.** $\frac{5}{2}$  **37.** $0$  **39.** $1 - e^{-1}$  **41.** $6\sqrt{3}$
**43.** $5k\tan^{-1}3$  **45.** $\frac{3}{5}$  **47.** $\frac{27}{28}$  **49.** $\frac{3}{4}$  **51.** $\dfrac{17\sqrt{17}-1}{4}$
**53.** (b) $S = \displaystyle\int_C z(t)\,dt$  (c) $4\pi$  **55.** $\lambda = -12$

▶ **Exercise Set 15.3 (Page 1120)**

**1.** conservative, $\phi = \dfrac{x^2}{2} + \dfrac{y^2}{2} + K$  **3.** not conservative
**5.** conservative, $\phi = x\cos y + y\sin x + K$
**9.** $-6$  **11.** $9e^2$  **13.** $32$  **15.** $W = -\frac{1}{2}$  **17.** $W = 1 - e^{-1}$
Responses to True–False questions may be abridged to save space.
**19.** False; the integral must be 0 for *all* closed curves $C$.
**21.** True; if $\nabla\phi$ is constant, then $\phi$ must be a linear function.
**23.** $\ln 2 - 1$  **25.** $\approx -0.307$  **27.** no  **33.** $h(x) = Ce^x$
**35.** (a) $W = -\dfrac{1}{\sqrt{14}} + \dfrac{1}{\sqrt{6}}$  (b) $W = -\dfrac{1}{\sqrt{14}} + \dfrac{1}{\sqrt{6}}$  (c) $W = 0$

▶ **Exercise Set 15.4 (Page 1127)**

**1.** $0$  **3.** $0$  **5.** $0$  **7.** $8\pi$  **9.** $-4$  **11.** $-1$  **13.** $0$
Responses to True–False questions may be abridged to save space.
**15.** False; Green's Theorem applies to closed curves.
**17.** True; the integral is the area of the region bounded by $C$.
**19.** (a) $\approx -3.550999378$  (b) $\approx -0.269616482$  **21.** $\frac{3}{8}a^2\pi$  **23.** $\frac{1}{2}abt_0$
**27.** Formula (1) of Section 6.1  **29.** $\frac{250}{3}$  **31.** $-3\pi a^2$  **33.** $\left(\frac{8}{15}, \frac{8}{21}\right)$
**35.** $\left(0, \dfrac{4a}{3\pi}\right)$  **37.** the circle $x^2 + y^2 = 1$  **39.** $69$

▶ **Exercise Set 15.5 (Page 1136)**

**1.** $\dfrac{15}{2}\pi\sqrt{2}$  **3.** $\dfrac{\pi}{4}$  **5.** $-\dfrac{\sqrt{2}}{2}$  **7.** $9$
Responses to True–False questions may be abridged to save space.
**9.** True; this follows from the definition.
**11.** False; the integral is the total mass of the lamina.
**13.** (b) $2\pi\left[1 - \sqrt{1-r^2} + \dfrac{r^2}{2}\right] \to 3\pi$ as $r \to 1^-$
 (c) $\mathbf{r}(\phi, \theta) = \sin\phi\cos\theta\,\mathbf{i} + \sin\phi\sin\theta\,\mathbf{j} + \cos\phi\,\mathbf{k}$,
 $0 \le \theta \le 2\pi, 0 \le \phi \le \pi/2$;
 $\displaystyle\iint (1+z)\,dS = \int_0^{2\pi}\int_0^{\pi/2} (1+\cos\phi)\sin\phi\,d\phi\,d\theta = 3\pi$
**17.** (c) $4\pi/3$
**19.** (a) $\dfrac{\sqrt{29}}{16}\displaystyle\int_0^6\int_0^{(12-2x)/3} xy(12-2x-3y)\,dy\,dx$
 (b) $\dfrac{\sqrt{29}}{4}\displaystyle\int_0^3\int_0^{(12-4z)/3} yz(12-3y-4z)\,dy\,dz$
 (c) $\dfrac{\sqrt{29}}{9}\displaystyle\int_0^3\int_0^{6-2z} xz(12-2x-4z)\,dx\,dz$
**21.** $\dfrac{18\sqrt{29}}{5}$
**23.** $\displaystyle\int_0^4\int_1^2 y^3z\sqrt{4y^2+1}\,dy\,dz; \dfrac{1}{2}\int_0^4\int_1^4 xz\sqrt{1+4x}\,dx\,dz$

**25.** $\dfrac{391\sqrt{17}}{15} - \dfrac{5\sqrt{5}}{3}$  **27.** $\frac{4}{3}\pi\delta_0$  **29.** $\frac{1}{4}(37\sqrt{37}-1)$  **31.** $M = \delta_0 S$
**33.** $(0, 0, 149/65)$  **35.** $\dfrac{93}{\sqrt{10}}$  **37.** $\dfrac{\pi}{4}$  **39.** $57.895751$

▶ **Exercise Set 15.6 (Page 1146)**

**1.** (a) zero  (b) zero  (c) positive  (d) negative  (e) zero  (f) zero
**3.** $-80$  **5.** $30$  **7.** $200\pi$  **9.** $4$  **11.** $2\pi$  **13.** $\dfrac{14\pi}{3}$  **15.** $0$
**17.** $18\pi$  **19.** $\frac{4}{9}$  **21.** (a) $8$  (b) $24$  (c) $0$
Responses to True–False questions may be abridged to save space.
**23.** False; the Möbius strip has no orientation.
**25.** False; the net volume can be zero because as much fluid passes
 through the surface in the negative direction as in the positive
 direction.
**27.** $-3\pi$  **29.** (a) $0\,\text{m}^3/\text{s}$  (b) $0\,\text{kg/s}$  **31.** (b) $32/3$
**33.** (a) $4\pi a^{k+3}$  (b) $k = -3$  **35.** $a = 2, 3$

▶ **Exercise Set 15.7 (Page 1157)**

**1.** $3$  **3.** $\dfrac{4\pi}{3}$
Responses to True–False questions may be abridged to save space.
**5.** False; it equates a surface integral and a triple integral.
**7.** True; see subsection entitled Sources and Sinks.
**9.** $12$  **11.** $3\pi a^2$  **13.** $180\pi$  **15.** $\dfrac{192\pi}{5}$  **17.** $\dfrac{\pi}{2}$  **19.** $\dfrac{4608}{35}$
**21.** $135\pi$  **23.** (a) $\mathbf{F} = x\mathbf{i} + y\mathbf{j} + z\mathbf{k}$  (b) $\mathbf{F} = -x\mathbf{i} - y\mathbf{j} - z\mathbf{k}$
**33.** no sources or sinks
**35.** sources at all points except the origin, no sinks  **37.** $\dfrac{7\pi}{4}$

▶ **Exercise Set 15.8 (Page 1164)**

**1.** $\frac{3}{2}$  **3.** $0$  **5.** $2\pi$  **7.** $16\pi$  **9.** $0$  **11.** $\pi a^2$
Responses to True–False questions may be abridged to save space.
**13.** True; see Theorem 15.8.1.  **15.** False; the circulation is $\int_C \mathbf{F}\cdot\mathbf{T}\,ds$.
**17.** (a) $\frac{3}{2}$  (b) $-1$  (c) $-\dfrac{1}{\sqrt{2}}\mathbf{j} - \dfrac{1}{\sqrt{2}}\mathbf{k}$  **23.** $-\dfrac{5\pi}{4}$

▶ **Chapter 15 Review Exercises (Page 1166)**

**3.** $\dfrac{1-x}{\sqrt{(1-x)^2 + (2-y)^2}}\mathbf{i} + \dfrac{2-y}{\sqrt{(1-x)^2 + (2-y)^2}}\mathbf{j}$  **5.** $\mathbf{i}+\mathbf{j}+\mathbf{k}$
**7.** (a) $\displaystyle\int_a^b\left[ f(x(t), y(t))\dfrac{dx}{dt} + g(x(t), y(t))\dfrac{dy}{dt}\right]dt$
 (b) $\displaystyle\int_a^b f(x(t), y(t))\sqrt{x'(t)^2 + y'(t)^2}\,dt$
**11.** $0$  **13.** $-7/2$  **17.** (a) $h(x) = Cx^{-3/2}$  (b) $g(y) = C/y^3$
**21.** $A = \dfrac{1}{2}\displaystyle\int_\alpha^\beta r^2\,d\theta$
**23.** $\displaystyle\iint_R f(x(u,v), y(u,v), z(u,v))\|r_u \times r_v\|\,du\,dv$  **25.** yes  **27.** $2\pi$
**31.** $-8\pi$  **35.** (a) conservative  (b) not conservative

▶ **Chapter 15 Making Connections (Page 1168)**

Answers are provided in the Student Solutions Manual.

# INDEX